THINKING QUANTITATIVELY COMMUNICATING WITH NUMBERS UPDATE

Eric Gaze

Bowdoin College

PEARSON

Boston Columbus Indianapolis New York San Francisco
Amsterdam Cape Town Dubai London Madrid Milan Munich Paris Montreal Toronto
Delhi Mexico City São Paulo Sydney Hong Kong Seoul Singapore Taipei Tokyo

Reproduced by Pearson from electronic files supplied by the author.

Publishing as Pearson, 501 Boylston Street, Boston, MA 02116.

ISBN-13: 978-0-13-454050-4
ISBN-10: 0-13-454050-6

1 16

www.pearsonhighered.com

Contents

Definitions

A Note from the Author to the Instructor

The purpose of this Quantitative Reasoning (QR) course is to provide a comprehensive overview of the quantitative skills required to cope with the practical demands of daily life, as well as preparing students for a deeper understanding of information presented in mathematical terms. Critical thinking and problem solving are an emphasis. The application of quantitative skills to decision making, requiring reasoning from evidence, enhances your students' personal, civic, and business lives. These reasoning capabilities are based upon the ability to communicate with numbers effectively, so developing quantitative literacy is a key focus.

What Is Quantitative Reasoning?

Quantitative Reasoning is the **skill set** necessary to process quantitative information and the **capacity** to critique, reflect upon, and apply such information in making decisions. Also called *numeracy*, it encompasses not just mathematical ability but also a disposition to engage quantitative information in a reflective and systematic way and use it to support valid inferences.[1] Derek Bok, in his book *Our Underachieving Colleges* (p. 68), provides a useful list of qualities of mind and habits of thought related to critical thinking that we will attempt to cultivate in this course.

The ability to:

- Recognize and define problems clearly
- Ask pertinent questions
- Identify arguments/issues on all sides
- Gather relevant facts . . . appreciate their relevance
- Perceive as many plausible solutions as possible
- Exercise good judgment in choosing solutions
- Use inference/analogy/logic to test the cogency of arguments

[1]Peters, E., Västfjäll, D., Slovic, P., Mertz, C. K., Mazzocco, K., & Dickert, S. Numeracy and decision making. *Psychological Science* 17, 407–413 (2006).

The Approach

The quantitative skill set will be built around the unifying theme of ratios and proportional reasoning, providing students with a coherent framework to connect the different topics covered. This approach is backed by research on how people learn, with spaced repetition of key ideas a fundamental learning principle.[2] We will use the spreadsheet program Excel to help develop students' quantitative reasoning, thus providing students with valuable computer skills. It is not necessary for you or the students to have expertise in using Excel. Everything you need will be taught as the course unfolds. The input/output interface of Excel is a terrific way to deepen algebraic reasoning skills as students explore the relationships between quantities. Spreadsheets are built to work with data, so Excel will facilitate the introduction of statistics in the ***Spotlight on Statistics*** sections found at the end of most chapters. In addition, financial applications are most easily studied using the power of spreadsheets, so financial literacy will be systematically developed through applications and examples throughout the course. Intermixing topics in these different but related contexts is another key learning principle that helps students to master concepts.

The text *Mathematics and Democracy*[3] gives the following justification for mastering the above-mentioned skills:

> Quantitatively literate citizens need to **know more than formulas and equations**. They need a predisposition to look at the world through mathematical eyes, to see the benefits (and risks) of thinking quantitatively about commonplace issues, and to **approach complex problems with confidence** in the value of careful reasoning. Quantitative literacy **empowers people** by giving them tools to **think for themselves**, to ask intelligent questions of experts, and to confront authority confidently. These are **skills required to thrive in the modern world**.

The Course

So, how do we cultivate these aspects of critical thinking in this course?

The chapters in the course are, for the most part, laid out in a linear fashion. I start with the fundamental concepts related to proportional reasoning, ratios, rates, units, conversions, scales, and percentages. Proportionality provides the fundamental example of a functional relationship, and we discuss total change and percent change to quantify the change in these relationships. This naturally leads to linear growth and exponential growth. Correlation

[2]Brown, P., et al., *Make It Stick: The Science of Successful Learning*, Harvard University Press, 2014.
[3]http://www.maa.org/ql/001-22.pdf

provides a nice application to linear functions, and then we finish with financial applications with logic functions used for random simulations, leading to the final chapter on probability. It is possible to cover all 11 chapters in a semester, but some may wish to go much slower and cover just Chapters 1–5, with Chapters 6–11 providing material for a second semester of QR. Many other options are possible, as well. Chapters 1–5 form the core, and from there you could cover 6 and 7, or skip these and choose any or all of the application chapters, 8, 9, 10, and 11.

The program is fully digital, which I find really exciting. Students are required to engage in the course every step of the way by reading the eText, watching the videos, and working through problems. The text was designed to be digital from the outset, so the eText steps through the content in very manageable chunks on each screen. Green boxed notes emphasize or more fully explain content as you might when teaching, providing structure for students as they work through the examples. Caution notes are interspersed throughout the chapters to prevent students from making common mistakes.

The Guided Worksheets are a key element to successfully teaching this course. They contain stepped-out problems to help students grapple with big concepts, process what they have read, and tie concepts together. These worksheets are downloadable within the course or available as a printed booklet that can be packaged with the code. The Guided Worksheets are a great way to introduce new material; I usually have students work in small groups on the first couple of problems, then stop and have a discussion about the content. The worksheets provide a way to engage students with the material before being taught the correct procedures. It primes them for the instructor's explanations, leads to more engaging classes, and strengthens their memory of concepts by confronting them with what they don't know (an important part of the learning process). Once you explain the concept to the students, they can then continue to work through the worksheet, testing their understanding and allowing for meaningful class discussions.

Every chapter of the eText contains videos in which I walk through examples emphasizing fundamental concepts. The videos allow me to go a bit deeper into the examples, assisting students in the analysis and synthesis of the material, and making connections so that students have more durable knowledge beyond the initial exposure. You can use the videos to "flip" your classroom, assigning students a section in the eText to read, with the videos providing lecture-style support of the content. Then in class you can use the worksheets as a discovery-based learning tool, and a way to engage students in the material to facilitate meaningful discussion.

In addition to the conceptual and example-based videos, throughout the eText you'll find Spreadsheet Tutorial videos that provide a just-in-time review of basic Excel skills. These are short videos focused solely on particular skills. You'll see these highlighted at the bottom of various slides where that skill comes into play. These videos are also available in the multimedia library. In addition to these tutorial videos, the Appendix offers a complete Introduction to Excel so both you and your students can feel fully confident with the Excel used in this course.

Gradable online homework problems in MyMathLab reinforce all of the content, including both skill exercises important for solidifying students' foundational skill set, and more involved problems requiring students to apply their critical thinking skills. In addition, there are Excel problems available that are a perfect way to reinforce students' understanding of the concepts explored in the chapters. These spreadsheets come prepared as blank templates, with all relevant data in place, and space provided for student answers to make grading as easy as possible. Full solution templates are provided for instructors, and the problems range from straightforward questions, to more involved applications that could serve as mini-projects if so desired. Real world problems require real world data, and these Excel spreadsheets provide the perfect tool to develop students' quantitative, statistical, financial, and algebraic literacies. Projects are provided that ask students to make connections and apply the course material in novel domains. All of this repeated practice of knowledge retrieval and application leads to deep, meaningful understanding.

In addition, all of these assignments taken individually are low-stakes; the emphasis is on students doing homework and projects, not studying for a high-stakes midterm worth 40% of their grade. Homework consists of a combination of skill practice and Excel work. I quiz my students weekly on the material so they have an opportunity to practice knowledge retrieval, an important part of making their learning durable and long lasting. I do give a midterm and final but weight them only 10% each so the emphasis is on the homework, projects and quizzes. For the midterm, I first give a practice exam that is very similar in layout and content to the actual midterm. This alleviates much of the math/test-taking anxiety and allows students to focus on mastering foundational material. Samples of my quizzes, reading assignments, midterms, and projects can be found in the Instructor's Resource Guide.

It is important to note that although Excel is a major component of the course it is <u>not necessary to teach in a computer classroom</u>. I use the worksheets with screen shots of Excel to discuss how spreadsheets can be used. This method provides students with a way to take notes on how to use Excel, which is difficult for them to do if they are actually logged on to a computer in a computer classroom. I have found that students are eager to learn Excel and are more than happy to put in the extra effort outside class to master this valuable skill. Despite the course being a non-STEM, general education course, I regularly have economics majors requesting to take this course so they can learn Excel and deepen their understanding of how to work with data. The Spotlights on Statistics provide a meaningful foundation for students in data analysis, and the financial applications are eye-opening for most of my students, many of whom have no idea how credit cards work or how to invest for retirement.

Resources

Thinking Quantitatively is different from anything you've probably encountered and understandably may seem daunting, so it is important to know that many resources are available for you to draw upon as you teach. I believe strongly in this course, and this method of teaching, so I want to provide as much support as I can to help you develop your own amazing courses.

Instructor Tutorial Videos

Providing a holistic view of the entire course, the video solutions are selected homework problems that encompass the entire course and tie together all the math concepts with Excel. In addition to the homework problems, five project videos detail projects that will cover the expanse of the course, including such wide-ranging topics as modeling, Excel basics, financial literacy, percent change, statistics, real world data, and much more! The video solutions can be hidden from students in the MyMathLab course and used for instructor's eyes only or made fully visible to students as well as instructors.

Instructor's Resource Guide (download only)

This guide will help you develop your course with projects, tips, ideas for structuring lessons, additional resources about using Excel, sample assessments, suggestions, and guidance for teaching a quantitative reasoning course using *Thinking Quantitatively*. Additionally, alternatives for using the Guided Worksheets along with more detailed suggestions on how to flip your classroom are provided.

Thinking Quantitatively blog

http://thinkingquantitatively.wordpress.com/

I thoroughly enjoy talking about quantitative reasoning and aim to create a forum in which I can provide ideas and offer support but in which you, too, can have input, offer suggestions, give feedback, propose new ideas, support your fellow instructors, boast of a particularly effective class, or share students' "a-ha" moments. The *Thinking Quantitatively* blog will be a place where I can support you but we can all support each other in helping to develop stronger quantitative reasoning courses and to spread our mission of a more mathematically literate society.

RSS Feeds

Quantitative reasoning involves thinking about real life issues, so in Instructors Resources you'll see an RSS Feed link. Organized by topics covered in the course, these feeds will provide news as available. You can use these feeds to develop additional examples for your class, group project ideas, extra credit problems, or whatever you can think up to enhance your course! These links will also be provided to students in Tools for Success so they, too, have a place to go for project ideas or just to practice their newly developed quantitative reasoning skills by reading current articles.

Webinars

Throughout the life of the edition, I will be presenting webinars on various topics related to teaching *Thinking Quantitatively* as well as quantitative reasoning in general. These webinars will be open to anyone interested, but I am also happy to provide one-on-one webinar training to support you in developing and enhancing your course. Please contact my editor, Marnie Greenhut, at marnie.greenhut@pearson.com to discuss setting up these one-on-one trainings. I am still teaching myself but promise I will do my best to accommodate you!

In Conclusion

In the preface to the students I include an example illustrating how to approach problems in this course, which may be of interest. The following three math faux pas[4] should be discussed with the class:

1. Students expect and often ask to be told the procedure to solve problems.
2. Students ask for help on problems without first making a serious effort to solve them on their own.
3. Students are reluctant to ask questions about the motivation for the content presented and the reasoning behind their teacher's and classmates' assertions.

It is important that students participate fully in this course, and the structure and resources have been designed to help make this happen. My experience in teaching this course is that this is the first time for many students that mathematics makes sense. This is a profound experience for both the students and the instructor. I hope you enjoy teaching this course as much as I have.

Best of luck!

Eric Gaze

[4]Harel, G., & Rabin, J. Teaching practices associated with the authoritative proof scheme. *Journal for Research in Mathematics Education*, 41(1), 16 (2010).

A Note from the Author to the Student

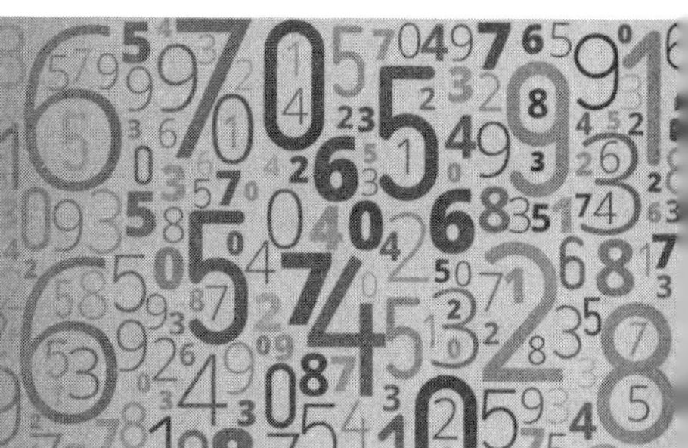

The purpose of this Quantitative Reasoning (QR) course is to provide a comprehensive overview of the quantitative skills required to cope with the practical demands of daily life, as well as preparing you for a deeper understanding of information presented in mathematical terms. Critical thinking and problem solving are an emphasis. The application of quantitative skills to decision making, requiring reasoning from evidence, will enhance your personal, civic, and business lives. These reasoning capabilities are based upon the ability to communicate with numbers effectively, so developing your quantitative literacy is a key focus.

What Is Quantitative Reasoning?

Quantitative Reasoning is the **skill set** necessary to process quantitative information and the **capacity** to critique, reflect upon, and apply such information in making decisions. Also called *numeracy*, it encompasses not just mathematical ability but also a disposition to engage quantitative information in a reflective and systematic way and use it to support valid inferences.[1] Derek Bok, in his book *Our Underachieving Colleges* (p. 68), provides a useful list of qualities of mind and habits of thought related to critical thinking that we will attempt to cultivate in this course.

The ability to:

- Recognize and define problems clearly
- Ask pertinent questions
- Identify arguments/issues on all sides
- Gather relevant facts . . . appreciate their relevance
- Perceive as many plausible solutions as possible
- Exercise good judgment in choosing solutions
- Use inference/analogy/logic to test the cogency of arguments

[1] Peters, E., Västfjäll, D., Slovic, P., Mertz, C. K., Mazzocco, K., & Dickert, S. Numeracy and decision making. *Psychological Science* 17, 407–413 (2006).

The Approach

The quantitative skill set will be built around the unifying theme of ratios and proportional reasoning, providing you with a coherent framework to connect the different topics covered. Ratios and proportions are mathematical concepts you learned starting in middle school. We will break down problems that appear complex and see how at their root they are based on the familiar concepts of ratio and proportion. This should help relieve any mathematical anxiety you may have about this course, and instill in you a confidence in approaching problems that are quantitative in nature. Recognizing that most problems encountered in daily life require just a few fundamental solution techniques rooted in proportional reasoning will help you see problems in a new light. We will use the spreadsheet program Excel to help develop your quantitative reasoning abilities, thus providing you with valuable computer skills to carry you throughout your college career and personal and professional lives. No more wondering "when am I ever going to use this?" that is so common in traditional math courses! The utility of the mathematical concepts encountered in this course are front and center, with applications providing context for all of the content.

The input/output interface of Excel is a terrific way to deepen your algebraic reasoning skills as you explore the relationships between quantities. Spreadsheets are built to work with data, so Excel will facilitate our introduction of statistics in the ***Spotlight on Statistics*** sections found at the end of most chapters. In addition, financial applications are most easily studied using the power of spreadsheets, so your financial literacy will be systematically developed through applications and examples throughout the course.

The text *Mathematics and Democracy*[2] gives the following justification for mastering the above-mentioned skills:

Quantitatively literate citizens need to **know more than formulas and equations**. They need a predisposition to look at the world through mathematical eyes, to see the benefits (and risks) of thinking quantitatively about commonplace issues, and to **approach complex problems with confidence** in the value of careful reasoning. Quantitative literacy **empowers people** by giving them tools to **think for themselves**, to ask intelligent questions of experts, and to confront authority confidently. These are **skills required to thrive in the modern world**.

The Course

Why should you take this course? To "thrive in the modern world" requires a fundamental literacy with quantitative information. One hundred years ago it was critical to be able to read

[2] http://www.maa.org/ql/001-22.pdf

and write to participate fully in all aspects of our society. Today the same holds true for being quantitatively literate. It is not just that many careers are requiring more and more quantitative reasoning skills, as our economy becomes increasingly driven by data and computation; but all aspects of your life require more QR, from personal finance, to health-related decisions, to voting on public policy issues. Data truly exist everywhere in the 21st century, and organization and analysis of data start with a basic facility with spreadsheets. You will leave this course confident in your ability to use Excel and in your ability to have meaningful discussions involving quantitative information.

This course will probably be unlike any other math course you've taken. You will not be asked to plug and chug numbers. You will not be asked to factor a quadratic polynomial. You will not be asked to memorize formulas. You will not be asked to do rote, boring homework. You will be asked to look at problems from a new perspective. You will be asked to think and question and think again. You will be asked to think deeply about quantitative problems, and share your insights through effective communication. If my students are any indication, this will be one of the most rewarding and beneficial math classes you've taken. Throw out your preconceived notions of a math class and get ready to really dig in, explore, develop your reasoning ability, and have fun!

The single biggest obstacle to success in anything (not just this math course) is how willing you are to participate and persist in the endeavor. Your mere presence in the classroom, while necessary, is far from sufficient for success (the plants in my office don't seem to have learned much over the years). You must learn to be Present with a capital P. Boredom, dislike, and fear are all states of mind that can be changed! The following five states of mind (AEIOU) should be cultivated, and all negative thoughts about this course and its possible outcomes should be banished. To get the most out of this course requires full participation. Your overall enjoyment and success are not dependent on your instructor but on how you engage with the material.

1. **Be Active** in all parts of the learning process from the classroom to homework.
2. **Be Engaged** in what others are saying and in what you are doing.
3. **Be Interested**, as it is so much more fun than being bored.
4. **Be Observant** and reflect on what you see, and ask questions as much as possible.
5. **Be Uplifting** toward others and yourself.

Resources

Guided Worksheets

ISBN-10: 0-13-454044-1 ISBN-13: 978-0-13-454044-3

The Guided Worksheets are a key element to truly grasping the content. These worksheets are downloadable within the course or available as a printed booklet. If your instructor did not order the Guided Worksheet booklet and you'd rather have the booklet than download the pages, you can purchase it from the Purchase Options tab in the left-hand navigation bar of your course. Use the worksheets to take notes, jot down questions or ideas, and work through the example problems. Class sessions will be more interesting if you take full advantage of the Guided Worksheets.

Flashcards (online only)

In Tools for Success you'll find a link to an engaging flashcard application to help you learn the vocabulary from the course. Some chapters do have a lot of vocabulary, and the better and sooner you learn it, the easier it will be to understand the explanations.

Thinking Quantitatively blog

http://thinkingquantitativelystudents.wordpress.com/

I thoroughly enjoy talking about quantitative reasoning and aim to create a forum in which you can participate in the discussion. Quantitative reasoning involves thinking about real life issues so we can share news and discuss the findings in news reports. You can share what you're doing in your class and learn what students at other colleges are doing in their courses. I think you're going to really enjoy this course, and the *Thinking Quantitatively* blog will be a place where you can share that enthusiasm.

RSS Feeds

In Tools for Success you'll see an RSS Feed link. This is organized by topics covered in the course and will provide news on a daily basis. Use these feeds for ideas for projects or test yourself to analyze articles and real data to see how much you've learned and how you've begun to think differently!

Some Practical Advice!

Here is some final practical advice on how to go about succeeding in this course. Critical thinking requires a certain tolerance for ambiguity that some students are uncomfortable with, especially in a math class. When confronted with a real world problem, often it is not clear what action to take or what relevant information is needed for the solution. The following three questions can magically clear away the "fog of ambiguity" and set you on a constructive path to the solution. Therefore, don't despair if you ever experience a problem in which your first reaction is, "What in the world is going on?" Ask these three questions instead!

1. What information is given?

2. What are they looking for?

3. How can I use the given information to find this?

Let's use an example from the course to illustrate the power of these three magic questions.

Example: Your car averages 27 miles per gallon (mpg), and you drive approximately 15,000 miles in a year. Assuming the cost of gas is \$3.40 a gallon, how much can you anticipate spending on gas in a given year?

1. What information is given?
   a. 27 mpg
   b. 15,000 miles in a year
   c. \$3.40 per gallon
2. What are they looking for?
   a. They are asking for the total money spent on gas in a year, so a dollar amount.
3. How can I use the given information to find this?
   a. They are looking for a dollar amount, so we need to use the \$3.40 per gallon. If we know the number of gallons used in a year we can multiply \$3.40 by the number of gallons to get the total amount spent on gas (total expenditure):

$$\text{Cost}(\$) = \frac{\$3.40}{1\text{ gal}} \cdot x\text{ gal}$$

   Alternatively, we could think of this as a proportion:

$$\frac{\text{Cost }(\$)}{x\text{ gal}} = \frac{\$3.40}{1\text{ gal}}$$

   b. We are not given the number of gallons used in a year, but we are given the number of miles driven in a year: 15,000. Maybe we can use this somehow to find gallons.

   c. We have not used the 27 mpg yet. This is telling us we can drive 27 miles per 1 gallon of gas. So we use 2 gallons for 54 miles and 10 gallons for 270 miles, hmmm . . . maybe we can set up a proportion using 27 miles per 1 gallon and the 15,000 miles:

$$\frac{27\text{ miles}}{1\text{ gal}} = \frac{15{,}000\text{ miles}}{x\text{ gal}}$$

   Cross multiplying gives us:

$$27 \cdot x = 1 \cdot 15{,}000$$

$$x = \frac{15{,}000}{27} = 555.56\text{ gal}$$

d. Great! Now we know the gallons used in a year, so we can plug this number into the equation from part **a** (or use the proportion), and solve for cost:

$$\text{Cost (\$)} = \frac{\$3.40}{1 \text{ gal}} \cdot 555.56 \text{ gal} = \$1{,}888.90$$

That's a lot of money! In addition to maintenance and insurance, the additional cost of gas makes owning a car expensive. This is the sort of calculation that a quantitatively literate person is comfortable carrying out when confronted with a real world decision like buying a car.

I hope this example illustrates what is meant by quantitative reasoning, and how proportional reasoning (setting up a proportion and solving) underlies much of the mathematics we carry out on a day-to-day basis. The three questions provide concrete action items to work on, so we don't get stuck wallowing in a fog of numbers. This course will teach you how to confidently carry out calculations such as the ones in this example, and empower you to embrace numbers in all aspects of your life.

Best of luck!

Eric Gaze

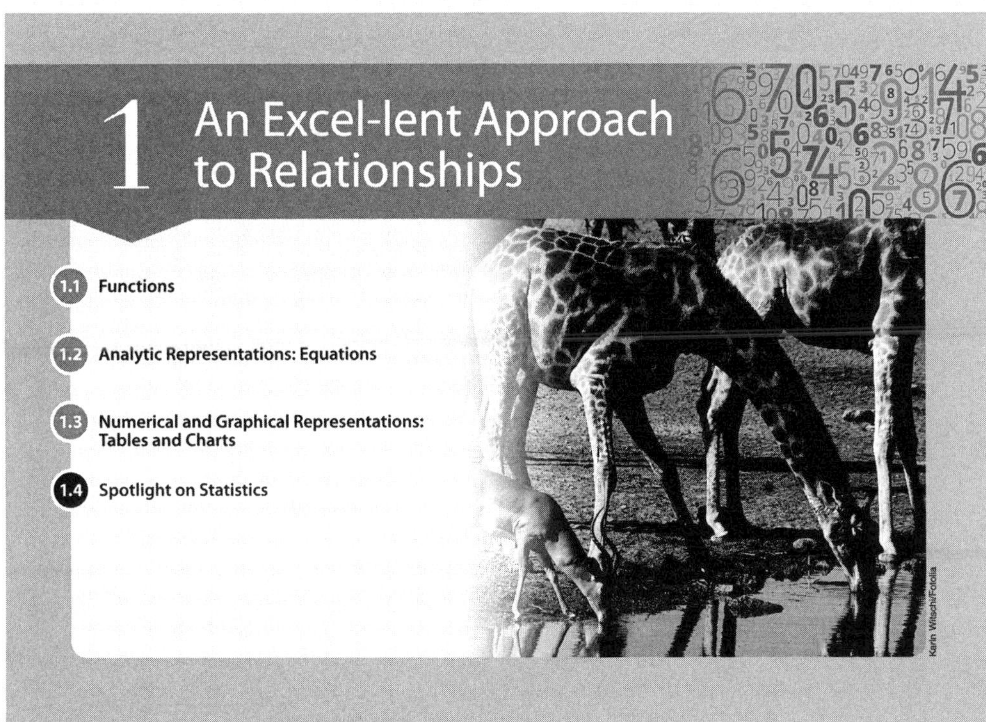

1
An Excel-lent Approach to Relationships
1.1 Functions
1.2 Analytic Representations: Equations
1.3 Numerical and Graphical Representations: Tables and Charts
1.4 Spotlight on Statistics
Karin Wisch/Fotolia

01-1

2 / 30

1.1 Functions

OBJECTIVE 1 **Learn Function Basics**

OBJECTIVE 2 **Explore Financial Functions**

OBJECTIVE 1 Learn Function Basics

The approach to developing your quantitative literacy in this text is to systematically build the skill set a numerate person possesses around the unifying theme of ratios. A ratio is the most basic form of a relationship, simply comparing the relative sizes of two quantities. In mathematics we study a special type of relationship between **inputs** and **outputs**, called a function.

DEFINITION

A **function** is a relationship between quantities referred to as *inputs* and *outputs*, in which every input is paired up with one and only one output.

01-2

TABLE 1.1
Function Examples

VIDEO
Function Definition

Inputs	Outputs	Function?
Senators	States	Yes
States	Senators	No: two outputs per input
Senators	Country of residence	Yes: *constant* function, same output for every input
People	Birthdays	Yes: everyone born on one and only one day
Birthdays	People	No: many people born on the same day
Social Security number	U.S. citizens	Yes: *one-to-one* function, no two inputs have same output

We have already seen two types of special functions. A **function** is **constant** if the output is the same, or constant, for all inputs: *All senators have the same country of residence.*

A function is **one-to-one**, or 1-1, if every output is paired with one and only one input (kind of the opposite of a constant function, because different inputs have different outputs): *Every citizen has a distinct Social Security number and vice versa.*

The set, or collection, of all valid inputs is called the **domain**; this is the realm in which the function operates: *The collection of senators is the domain of the function that maps senators to the states they represent.*

The set, or collection, of all outputs is called the **range**, since these are the values over which the function ranges: *The collection of states is the range of the function that maps senators to the states they represent.*

The inputs and outputs are referred to as **variables**, since they *vary* over their domain and range. The inputs are referred to as the **independent variables** since they are *independently* chosen. They are typically represented with the letter x: *We can choose any senator we like for an input.*

The outputs are referred to as the **dependent variables** since they depend on the inputs. They are typically represented with the letter y: *The state a chosen senator represents is completely determined by the senator chosen.*

OBJECTIVE 2 Explore Financial Functions

We are now going to explore some financial functions and develop our financial literacy at the same time. The following examples will introduce you to loans and their associated ***payments***.

Using a credit card is a type of loan. The credit card company is lending you money, called the **principal**, to buy something.

Example 1 Compute a Credit Card Balance

You buy a flat screen TV for $1,000 at Best Buy, using a store credit card that has no monthly payments due for the first year. You will be charged interest each month, however, at an **annual percentage rate (APR)** of 12%. Let's create a spreadsheet to determine what you will owe at the end of 1 year, assuming that you make no payments.

SOLUTION First, summarize the key information from the problem and use it to create the spreadsheet shown in **Figure 1.1**.

- **Principal:** \$1,000
- **APR:** 12%
- **Period:** monthly
- **Periodic rate:** 12%/12 = 1%

VIDEO *Flat Screen TV Loan*

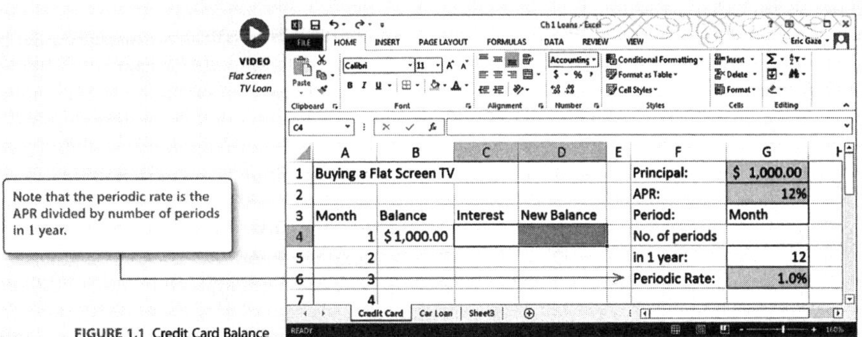

FIGURE 1.1 Credit Card Balance

SPREADSHEET TUTORIALS Entering Data by Range | Entering Numbers | Formatting Cells with the Percent Style | Formatting Financial Numbers

We are ready to compute the interest charged in the first month in cell **C4**, which is a function of the balance and the periodic rate. Be sure to use cell references for the balance in cell **B4** and the periodic rate in cell **G6**.

Interest = Periodic Rate*Balance
C4 = G6*B4

VIDEO *TV Loan: Interest*

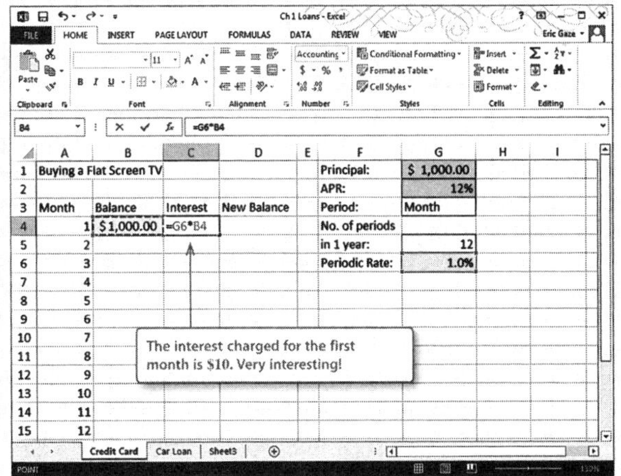

FIGURE 1.2 Computing Interest for Credit Card Balance

SPREADSHEET TUTORIALS Formatting Financial Numbers | Using Arithmetic Operators

The new balance in cell **D4** is a **function** of the original **balance** plus **interest**:

D4 = B4 + C4

This new balance becomes the starting balance for month 2.

CAUTION This is an important step. You must link the starting balance of month 2 to the ending balance of month 1 before you can fill the formulas: **B5 = D4** •

VIDEO *TV Loan: New Balance*

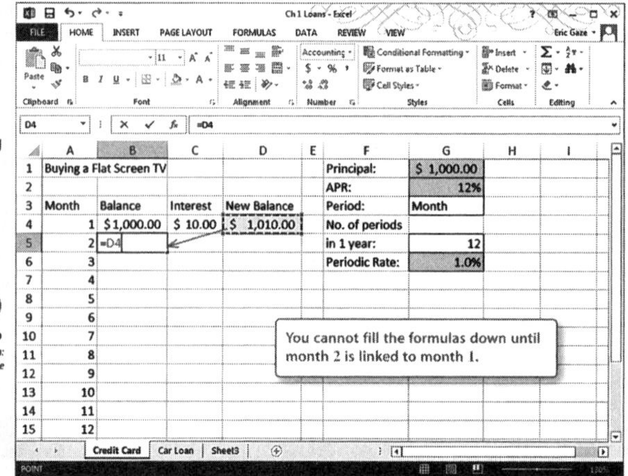

FIGURE 1.3 Linking Month 2 and Month 1 for Credit Card Balance

We are now almost ready to fill down the interest formula. When we fill down, the cell references will change their row numbers:

C4 = G6*B4
C5 = **G7*B5**

CAUTION We do not want the cell reference for the periodic rate in cell **G6** to change when we fill down. •

SPREADSHEET TUTORIALS Formatting Financial Numbers Using Arithmetic Operators

We need to make **G6** an **absolute cell reference** by putting in dollar signs: **$G$6**. This will fix the reference to cell **G6** when we fill. We will continue to use a **relative cell reference** for the balance in cell **B4**:

C4 = $G$6*B4
C5 = **$G$6*B5**

VIDEO *TV Loan: Filling Formulas*

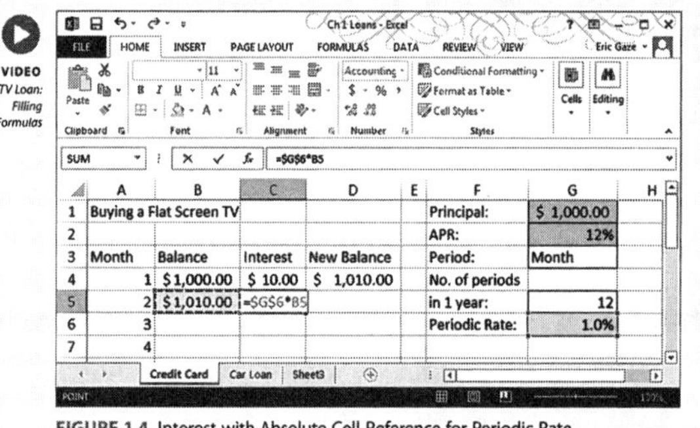

Filling down changes the row numbers of relative cell references. The absolute cell reference, $G$6, does not change.

FIGURE 1.4 Interest with Absolute Cell Reference for Periodic Rate

SPREADSHEET TUTORIAL Copying Formulas Containing Absolute Cell References

Next we can fill down the new balance formula in cell **D4** to complete the entries for month 2:

$$\begin{aligned} D4 &= B4 + C4 \\ \downarrow\ D5 &= B5 + C5 \end{aligned}$$

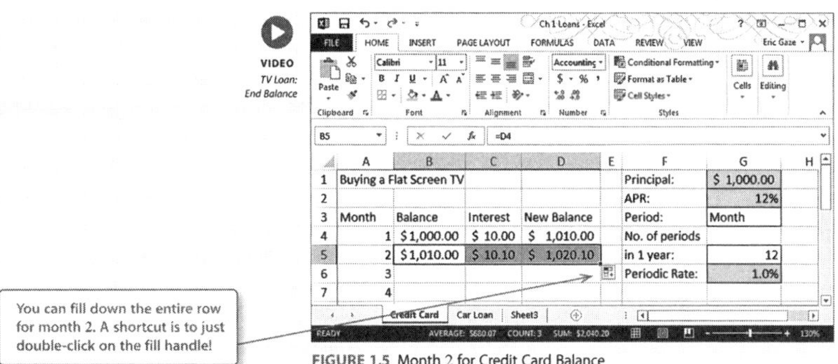
VIDEO
TV Loan: End Balance
You can fill down the entire row for month 2. A shortcut is to just double-click on the fill handle!
B5
=D4

	A	B	C	D	E	F	G
1	Buying a Flat Screen TV					Principal:	$ 1,000.00
2						APR:	12%
3	Month	Balance	Interest	New Balance		Period:	Month
4	1	$1,000.00	$ 10.00	$ 1,010.00		No. of periods	
5	2	$1,010.00	$ 10.10	$ 1,020.10		in 1 year:	12
6	3					Periodic Rate:	1.0%
7	4						

FIGURE 1.5 Month 2 for Credit Card Balance

We are finally ready to fill down all the formulas in the row for month 2. We can do this all at once by highlighting the entire row and filling down:

FIGURE 1.6 Full Year Filled in for Credit Card Balance

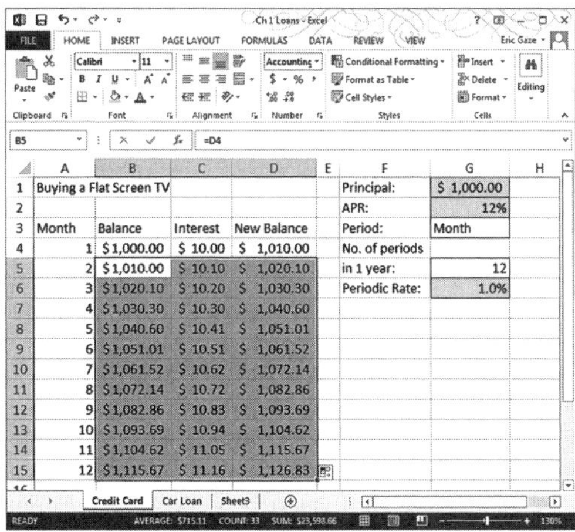
B5
=D4

	A	B	C	D	E	F	G
1	Buying a Flat Screen TV					Principal:	$ 1,000.00
2						APR:	12%
3	Month	Balance	Interest	New Balance		Period:	Month
4	1	$1,000.00	$ 10.00	$ 1,010.00		No. of periods	
5	2	$1,010.00	$ 10.10	$ 1,020.10		in 1 year:	12
6	3	$1,020.10	$ 10.20	$ 1,030.30		Periodic Rate:	1.0%
7	4	$1,030.30	$ 10.30	$ 1,040.60			
8	5	$1,040.60	$ 10.41	$ 1,051.01			
9	6	$1,051.01	$ 10.51	$ 1,061.52			
10	7	$1,061.52	$ 10.62	$ 1,072.14			
11	8	$1,072.14	$ 10.72	$ 1,082.86			
12	9	$1,082.86	$ 10.83	$ 1,093.69			
13	10	$1,093.69	$ 10.94	$ 1,104.62			
14	11	$1,104.62	$ 11.05	$ 1,115.67			
15	12	$1,115.67	$ 11.16	$ 1,126.83			

SPREADSHEET TUTORIAL Copying a Formula Using the Fill Handle

Notice how the formula for interest in cell **C15 = $G$6*B15** is still referencing the fixed periodic rate in cell **G6**. That is, **C15** is 1% of **B15**.

FIGURE 1.7 Full-Year Credit Card Balance

VIDEO *TV Loan: APY*

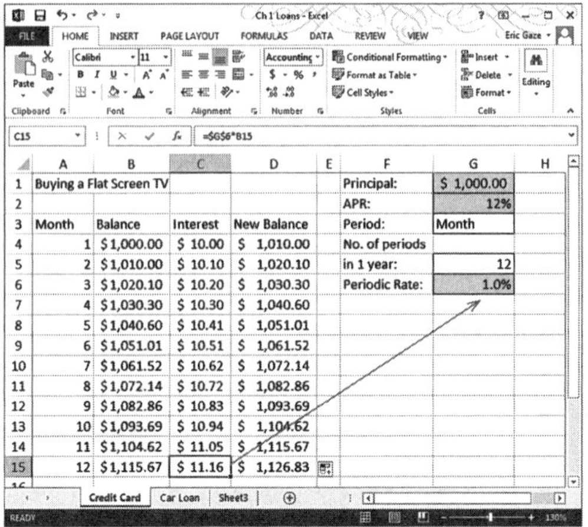

We can see from **Figure 1.7** that **we will owe $1,126.83 after 12 months**. This means we are being charged $126.83 in total interest for the year. This is more than 12% (**APR**) of the original $1,000 we borrowed and gives us the **annual percentage yield (APY)**:

The APR of 12% yields an *effective interest rate* of 12.863% for the year. This new rate is called the APY.

$$\frac{126.83}{1{,}000} = \frac{12.683}{100} = 12.683\%$$

SPREADSHEET TUTORIAL Copying Formulas Containing Absolute Cell References

1.2 Analytic Representations: Equations

OBJECTIVE 1 Understand Order of Operations

OBJECTIVE 2 Evaluate Payment Function

OBJECTIVE 1 Understand Order of Operations

Our next example looks at a different type of loan, called an **amortized loan**, meaning the monthly payments are fixed. Credit cards do not have fixed monthly payments, but car loans do.

The monthly payment for a car loan is a function of four inputs: the **principal** (P), **APR**, number of **periods** (months) in 1 year (n), and **term** (t). This **function** can be represented by a complicated formula that requires care when evaluating a payment, especially in Excel.

Typing this formula into Excel requires us to understand the order of operations. The formula below is formatted as a fraction so it is clear what the numerator and denominator are, and the exponent is superscripted; however, in Excel we have to enter a formula as a string of text, all on a single line and in a single font.

$$\text{PMT} = \frac{P \times \frac{\text{APR}}{n}}{\left(1 - \left(1 + \frac{\text{APR}}{n}\right)^{-nt}\right)}$$

As mentioned, in order to enter the formula for the monthly car payment into Excel, we need to use the **order of operations**. This procedure tells us in what order to perform calculations.

1. ***Parentheses:*** Everything entered in parentheses will be computed first. When in doubt, use parentheses, especially for the numerator and denominator of a fraction.
2. ***Exponents:*** Exponents are next; use the ^ symbol by pressing Shift and the 6 key. Complicated exponents need parentheses: = 2^(1/3).
3. ***Multiplication and division:*** These have the same rank; Excel will compute from left to right.
4. ***Addition and subtraction:*** These are also of equal rank and will be computed from left to right.

The following examples illustrate the need for order of operations:

- = 3*5 − 2 = 13 (not 9)
- = 3*(5 − 2) = 9 (not 13)
- = 5 + 2*3 = 11 (not 21)
- PMT = (P*(APR/n))/(1 − (1 + (APR/n))^(−n*t))

Note how different these equations look! These are just two different ways of writing the same equation.

$$\text{PMT} = \frac{P \times \frac{\text{APR}}{n}}{\left(1 - \left(1 + \frac{\text{APR}}{n}\right)^{-nt}\right)}$$

OBJECTIVE 2 Evaluate Payment Function

Example 2 Compute a Monthly Car Loan Payment

You are buying a new VW Jetta for $17,254.38. You make a down payment of $2,254.38, so you need to borrow $15,000. You secure a loan for 5 years at 6%. What is your monthly payment?

- **Principal:** $P = \$15{,}000$
- **APR:** 6%
- **No. of periods (months) in 1 year:** $n = 12$
- **Term:** $t = 5$

Your monthly car payment is a function of the principal, APR, number of periods in a year, and length of the loan. $\text{PMT} = f(P, \text{APR}, n, t)$

SOLUTION The monthly payment (PMT) is a **function** of the four different inputs listed above and can be computed using the formula:

$$\text{PMT} = \frac{P \times \frac{\text{APR}}{n}}{\left(1 - \left(1 + \frac{\text{APR}}{n}\right)^{-nt}\right)}$$

Re-create the spreadsheet below, paying special attention to the monthly payment in cell **E2**, which is a **function** of the **principal** borrowed (P), **APR**, number of **periods** in 1 year (n), and the **term** (t). Be sure to use cell references for all the inputs (the cell reference for P is **A2**, for APR is **B2**, for n is **C2**, and for t is **D2**).

$$\text{PMT} = \frac{P \times \frac{\text{APR}}{n}}{\left(1 - \left(1 + \frac{\text{APR}}{n}\right)^{-nt}\right)}$$

$$\text{PMT} = (P*(\text{APR}/n))/(1 - (1 + (\text{APR}/n))\text{^}(-n*t))$$

VIDEO
Car Loan: Order of Operations

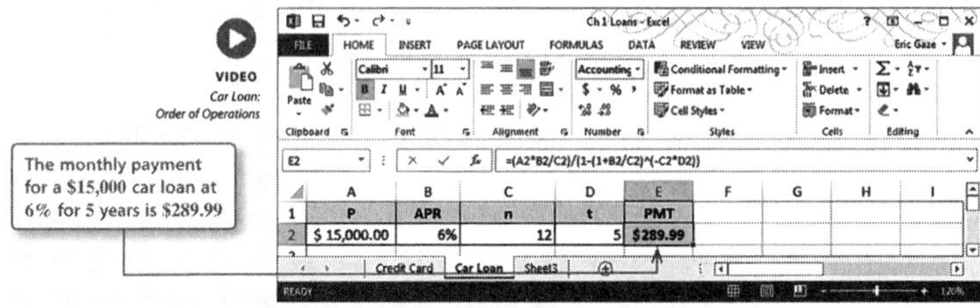

FIGURE 1.8 Computing Monthly Car Loan Payment

SPREADSHEET TUTORIALS Entering Data by Range | Entering Numbers | Formatting Financial Numbers

1.3 Numerical and Graphical Representations: Tables and Charts

OBJECTIVE 1 Use Multiple Inputs to Understand What-If Analysis

OBJECTIVE 2 Convert Tables to Effective Graphs

OBJECTIVE 1 Use Multiple Inputs to Understand What-If Analysis

One powerful use of spreadsheets is to conduct "what-if" analyses. In Example 2, what if we change the APR or the term? How would the monthly payment be affected? We can make a table of values for the car loan from Example 2, showing the monthly payments for different APR values and different terms.

FIGURE 1.9 Table for Monthly Car Payments

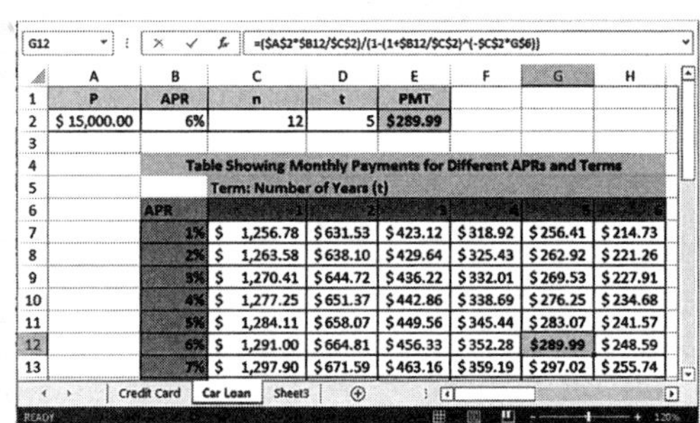

G12: =($A$2*$B12/$C$2)/(1-(1+$B12/$C$2)^(-$C$2*G$6))

P	APR	n	t	PMT
$ 15,000.00	6%	12	5	$289.99

Table Showing Monthly Payments for Different APRs and Terms

	Term: Number of Years (t)					
APR	1	2	3	4	5	6
1%	$ 1,256.78	$631.53	$423.12	$318.92	$256.41	$214.73
2%	$ 1,263.58	$638.10	$429.64	$325.43	$262.92	$221.26
3%	$ 1,270.41	$644.72	$436.22	$332.01	$269.53	$227.91
4%	$ 1,277.25	$651.37	$442.86	$338.69	$276.25	$234.68
5%	$ 1,284.11	$658.07	$449.56	$345.44	$283.07	$241.57
6%	$ 1,291.00	$664.81	$456.33	$352.28	$289.99	$248.59
7%	$ 1,297.90	$671.59	$463.16	$359.19	$297.02	$255.74

The formula for the monthly payment in the table is the same as in Example 2, but now we must be careful with **absolute cell references** versus **relative cell references,** since we are going to fill this formula starting in cell **C7**.

The **APR** should change when we fill down and be fixed when we fill across, **$B7**, while the **term** should be fixed when we fill down but change when we fill across, **C$6**. These are **mixed cell references.**

We will treat the **principal,** *P*, and number of **periods** in a year, *n*, as fixed and so use **absolute cell references, $A$2** and **$C$2**, for them.

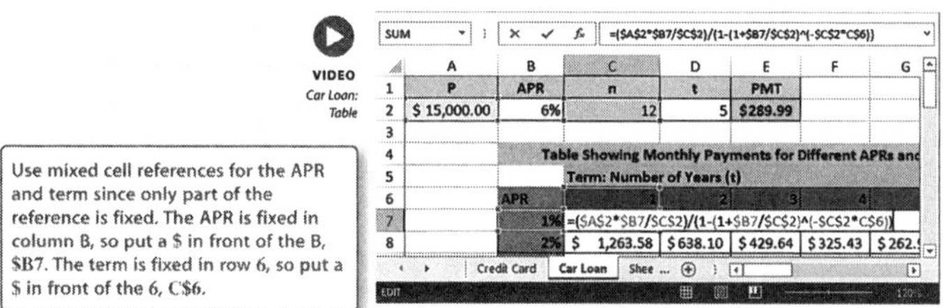
VIDEO
Car Loan: Table
Use mixed cell references for the APR and term since only part of the reference is fixed. The APR is fixed in column B, so put a $ in front of the B, $B7. The term is fixed in row 6, so put a $ in front of the 6, C$6.
SUM
=($A$2*$B7/$C$2)/(1-(1+$B7/$C$2)^(-$C$2*C$6))
A
B
C
D
E
F
G
P
APR
n
t
PMT
$ 15,000.00
6%
12
5
$289.99
Table Showing Monthly Payments for Different APRs and
Term: Number of Years (t)
APR
1%
2%
$ 1,263.58
$638.10
$429.64
$325.43
Credit Card
Car Loan
EDIT

FIGURE 1.10 Formula in Cell **C7** for Monthly Car Payments

SPREADSHEET TUTORIALS Copying Formulas Containing Absolute Cell References Using Merge and Center and Applying Cell Styles

The finished table illustrates the power of using spreadsheets for conducting what-if analyses. Taking a longer term reduces the monthly payment but ends up costing you more over the longer time frame. (Multiply the monthly payment by 12 and then by the number of years for the total payout.)

Having good credit qualifies you for a lower APR and greatly lowers your monthly payment, as shown in the table.

Tables of numbers, however, can be hard to decipher; so next we look at converting tables into effective charts.

Harming your credit by missing payments on credit cards will raise the APR you can receive for a car loan. Look at the difference in monthly payment between a person with good credit (1% APR) versus a person with poor credit (10% APR)!

TABLE 1.2 What-If Analysis for Monthly Car Payments

Table Showing Monthly Payments for Different APR's and Terms						
	Term: Number of Years (t)					
APR	1	2	3	4	5	6
1%	$ 1,256.78	$ 631.53	$ 423.12	$ 318.92	$ 256.41	$ 214.73
2%	$ 1,263.58	$ 638.10	$ 429.64	$ 325.43	$ 262.92	$ 221.26
3%	$ 1,270.41	$ 644.72	$ 436.22	$ 332.01	$ 269.53	$ 227.91
4%	$ 1,277.25	$ 651.37	$ 442.86	$ 338.69	$ 276.25	$ 234.68
5%	$ 1,284.11	$ 658.07	$ 449.56	$ 345.44	$ 283.07	$ 241.57
6%	$ 1,291.00	$ 664.81	$ 456.33	$ 352.28	$ 289.99	$ 248.59
7%	$ 1,297.90	$ 671.59	$ 463.16	$ 359.19	$ 297.02	$ 255.74
8%	$ 1,304.83	$ 678.41	$ 470.05	$ 366.19	$ 304.15	$ 263.00
9%	$ 1,311.77	$ 685.27	$ 477.00	$ 373.28	$ 311.38	$ 270.38
10%	$ 1,318.74	$ 692.17	$ 484.01	$ 380.44	$ 318.71	$ 277.89

OBJECTIVE 2 Convert Tables to Effective Graphs

The table of monthly payments we just created on the previous screen offers an opportunity to practice making effective charts. If we highlight the APR and the 5-year monthly payment columns in the table and make a column chart, we get the following not-so-helpful chart:

FIGURE 1.11
Ineffective Chart of Car Payment Table

VIDEO
Car Loan: Graph

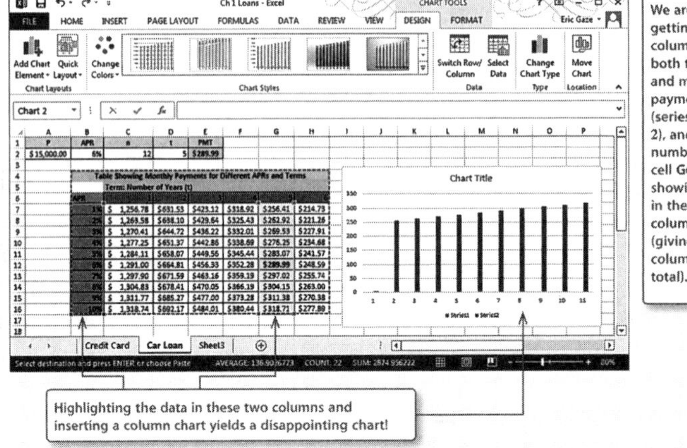

We are getting a column for both the APR and monthly payment (series 1 and 2), and the number 5 in cell **G6** is showing up in the first column (giving us 11 columns total).
Highlighting the data in these two columns and inserting a column chart yields a disappointing chart!

To make effective charts, you must try to understand what Excel is doing with the data that you highlight. Once you understand why your chart came out a certain way, you can fix it. Watch the video for a more in-depth analysis of what went wrong with the chart shown above.

Example 3 Create an Effective Chart

Create an effective chart of the monthly car payments for a 5-year term with varying APR.

SOLUTION Highlighting only the monthly payments in cells **G7:G16** gives us a starting column chart. We can then add the APR values as **Category x-axis Labels** by clicking on the **Select Data** icon.

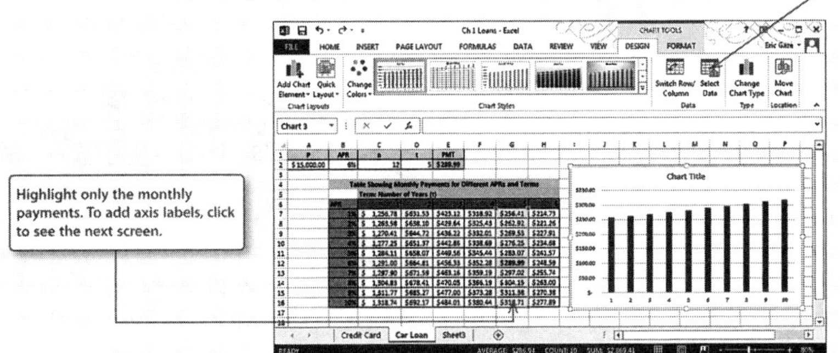

Highlight only the monthly payments. To add axis labels, click to see the next screen.

FIGURE 1.12 Using Select Data to Add Category x-axis Labels to a Chart

Once the Select Data Source dialog box is open, click Edit in the Horizontal (Category) Axis Labels space and then click and drag over the APR values in cells **B7:B16**. Click OK, and the APR values will appear on the x-axis, as shown on next screen.

FIGURE 1.13 Using Select Data Source to Add Horizontal (Category) Axis Labels to a Chart

Highlight only the monthly payments and add in the APR values, using the Select Data icon and inserting them into the Horizontal (Category) Axis Labels box.

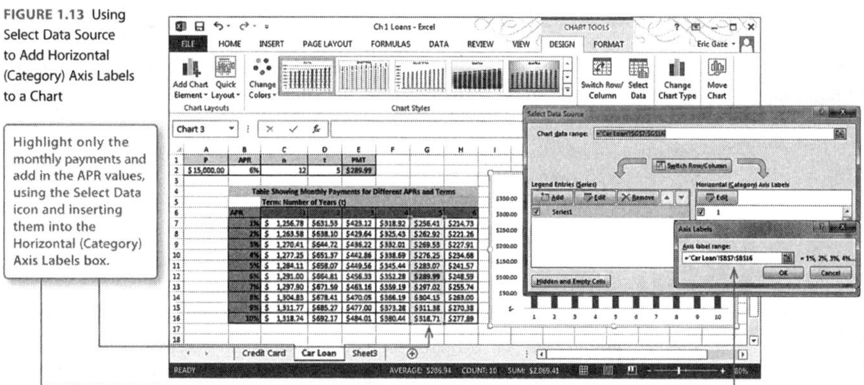

Now that the x-axis labels are in place, you can use the Add Chart Element menu under the Chart Tools Design tab to add titles and format your axes by right clicking on the axis and choosing Format Axis (or choosing Format Selection under the Cart Tools Format tab). The following chart has the vertical axis start at $250 so the differences in monthly payments are more easily seen.

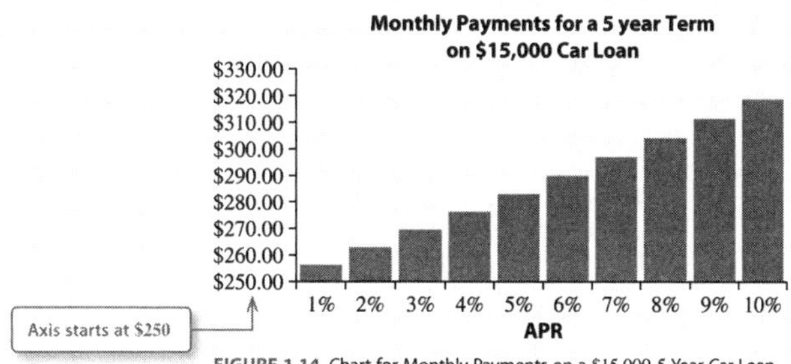

FIGURE 1.14 Chart for Monthly Payments on a $15,000 5-Year Car Loan

1.4 Spotlight on Statistics

OBJECTIVE 1 Learn Descriptive Statistics

OBJECTIVE 2 Create Histograms

OBJECTIVE 1 Learn Descriptive Statistics

The discipline of statistics deals with collecting, organizing, analyzing, and displaying data. A **statistic** is a number you compute related to a data set, which gives you information about that data set. The word comes from "statists," the name given to 18th-century mathematicians who studied demographic data in Europe and analyzed it for the state.

For example, the 2010 U.S. Census estimated the population of the United States to be 308,745,538 people, of which 50.8% were female, and to have a median age of 35.7 years. The overall 2010 population represents a 9.7% increase from the 2000 population, while the 62 and over population grew by 21.1% over this same time period. These facts are all statistics.

Functions play an important role in statistics, with the eight basic descriptive statistics (**mean, median, mode, standard deviation, max, min, range,** and **count**) all being functions of the data values, for whatever data set you may be working with.

Here are eight basic **descriptive statistics** we can calculate for a given quantitative data set:

1. **Mean:** the arithmetic average of the data set.
2. **Median:** the middle of the ordered data set (half above, half below, 50th percentile).
3. **Mode:** the most frequently occurring value in the data set.
4. **Standard deviation:** the "average distance" of the data values from the mean.
5. **Max:** the largest value in the data set.
6. **Min:** the smallest value in the data set.
7. **Range:** the difference between the largest and smallest data values (Max − Min).
8. **Count:** the number of values (usually referred to as N) in the data set.

The eight basic descriptive statistics can each be thought of as a **function** of a given set of data values. The median, mode, max, min, and count don't have equations to represent them but can be computed using Excel's built-in functions of the same names. Even though we do not have equations to represent these functions, there are algorithms, or procedures, to follow.

For example, given a quantitative data set (numbers), order them from smallest to largest. The **median** is the value in the middle if there are an odd number of data values, or the average of the two middle values if there are an even number of data values.

The remaining three descriptive statistics—mean, standard deviation, and range—are all functions that can be represented with equations.

The **range** is simply the **max** minus the **min:** Range = Max − Min

The **mean** is the sum of the data values divided by the count and can be represented by the following equation, with $\overline{X}$, or "*X*-bar," representing the mean, and x_i or "*x*-sub-*i*," representing the ith data value:

$$\overline{X} = \frac{\Sigma x_i}{N}$$

Note: The capital Greek letter sigma, Σ, stands for sum in the formula.

This is technically the arithmetic mean and can be computed using Excel's built-in **AVERAGE** function.

The **standard deviation** is given by the equation: $\text{SD} = \sqrt{\frac{\Sigma (x_i - \overline{X})^2}{N - 1}}$

To compute the standard deviation:

1. Subtract the mean from each data value.
2. Square each of these differences, or "deviations."
3. Sum all the squared deviations.
4. Divide by the count minus 1.
5. Take the square root.

Or just use Excel's **STDEV** function!

Example 4 | **Compute Descriptive Statistics for the CAT Scores Data Set**

Open the Excel workbook *Data Sets* and scroll to the *CAT Scores* worksheet, which contains a data set consisting of 98 student scores on a Critical Thinking Assessment Test (CAT). Compute the eight basic **descriptive statistics** for the data set of scores found in cells **B4:B101**.

SOLUTION Excel has a built-in function with the same name (as shown in the spreadsheet) for each of the eight basic descriptive statistics except for the **mean** (for which you use **AVERAGE**), and the **range** (for which you use **MAX − MIN**). Watch the video for the detailed solution.

FIGURE 1.15 Descriptive Statistics for CAT Scores

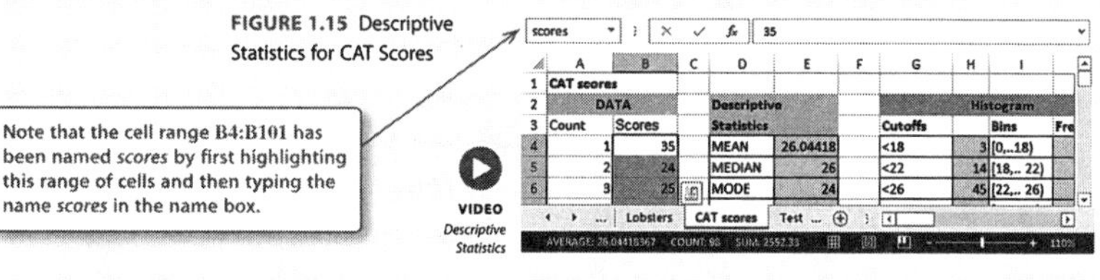

Note that the cell range B4:B101 has been named *scores* by first highlighting this range of cells and then typing the name *scores* in the name box.

VIDEO *Descriptive Statistics*

SPREADSHEET TUTORIALS Defining a Name | Using Define Names in Formula | Using the Median Function | Using the MIN and MAX Functions | Using the Sum and Average Functions

OBJECTIVE 2 Create Histograms

The video for Example 4 showed how to use the **COUNTIF** function to count how many of each score there are and make an associated column chart, shown below. This column chart is called a **histogram**, and the counts are called **frequencies**.

The resulting chart is a picture of the **distribution**, or shape, of your data. In this example, our CAT scores have a bell-shaped distribution.

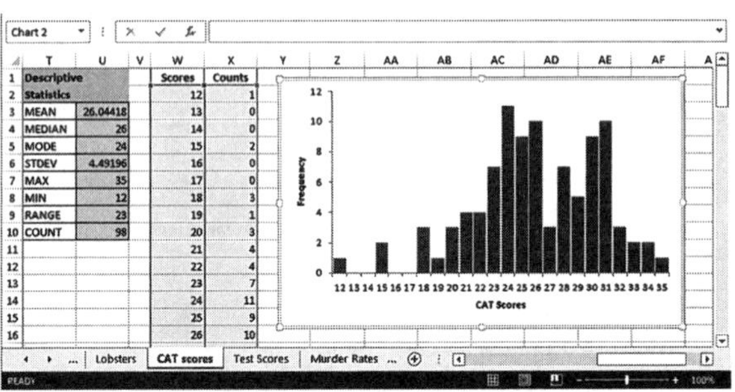

FIGURE 1.16 Basic Histogram for CAT Scores

We have just seen an example of one of the most common visual displays of a data set, called a **histogram**. Often we do not count the number of each data value but put the data values into **bins**, which are essentially intervals determined by cutoff values. You *bin your data* by counting the number of data values that fall into each bin.

Example 5 Create a Histogram with Binned Data

Open the Excel workbook *Data Sets* and scroll to the *CAT Scores* worksheet. Complete the Histogram table by counting how many scores fall below each cutoff and then count how many fall into each bin.

FIGURE 1.17 Creating a Table for a Histogram

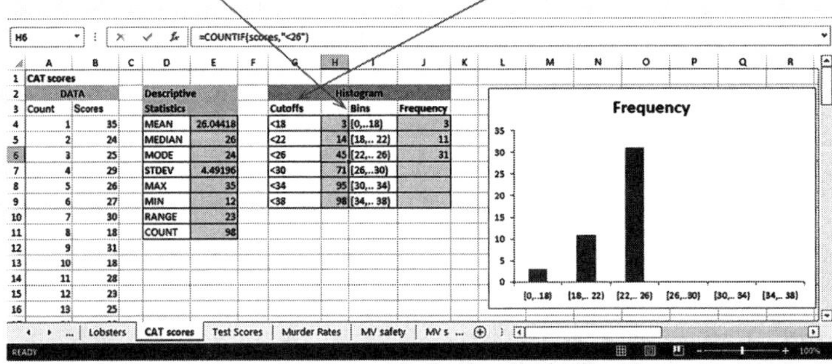

SOLUTION To count the number of values in each **bin**, called a **frequency,** we first count all the data below each cutoff using the **COUNTIF** function.

VIDEO *Histograms*

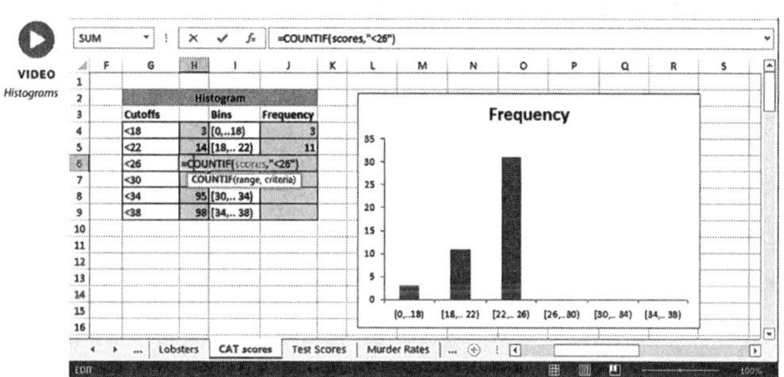

FIGURE 1.18 Counting Values in Bins for a Histogram

Next, we subtract the number of values below the previous cutoff to get the number of values in a bin. For example, to count the number of values between 18 and 22, first count all values below 22 and then subtract the number of values below 18.

SPREADSHEET TUTORIALS Defining a Name Using Define Names in Formula Using COUNTIF

We then create the histogram by making a column chart of the bins and frequency columns and formatting it nicely.

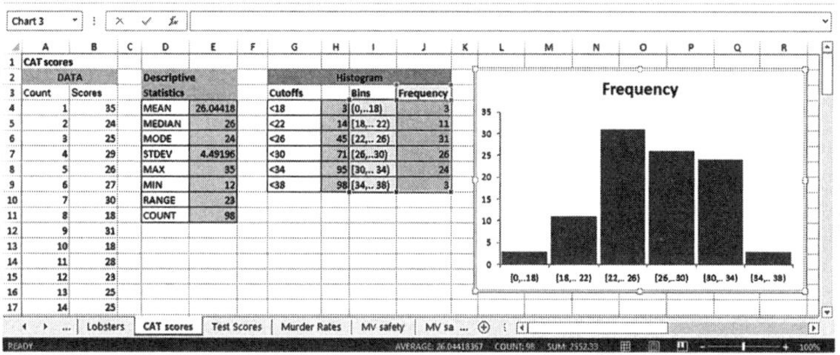

FIGURE 1.19 Histogram for Binned Data

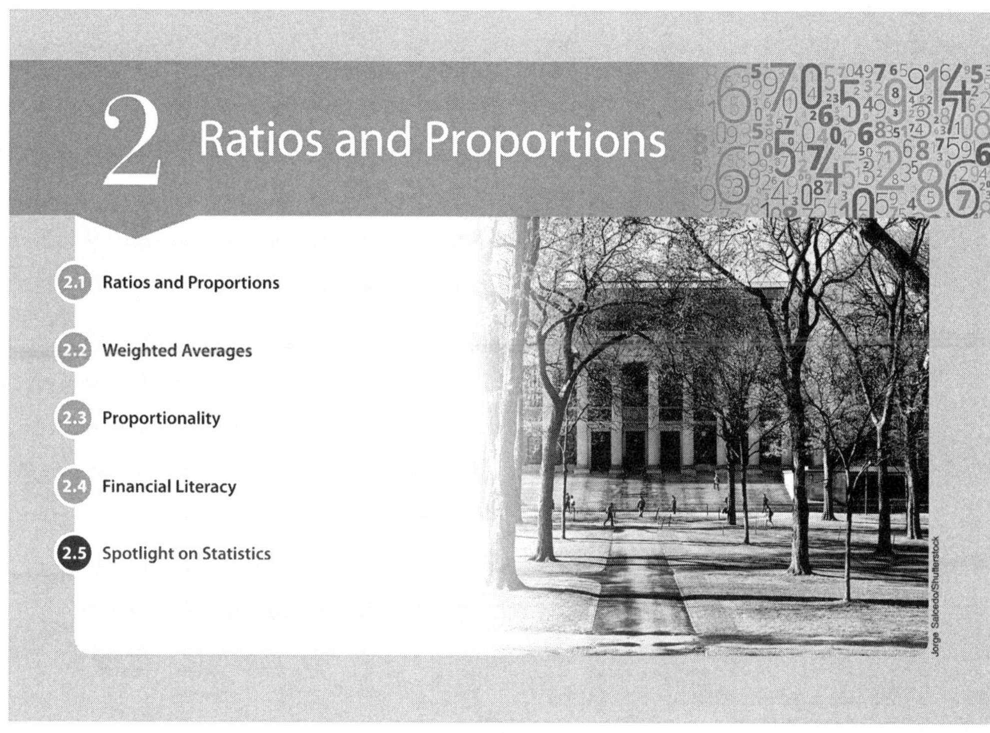

2 Ratios and Proportions
2.1 Ratios and Proportions
2.2 Weighted Averages
2.3 Proportionality
2.4 Financial Literacy
2.5 Spotlight on Statistics
Jorge Salcedo/Shutterstock

2.1 Ratios and Proportions

OBJECTIVE 1 **Understand Ratios**

OBJECTIVE 2 **Use Ratio Tables to Set Up Proportions**

OBJECTIVE 3 **Learn Ratio Vocabulary**

OBJECTIVE 4 **Contrast Part-to-Part and Part-to-Whole Ratios**

OBJECTIVE 1 Understand Ratios

Statistics without comparisons, such as "there were 32,367 motor vehicle deaths (MVD) in 2011 in the U.S." lack meaning. Is this a lot? Often we want to track change over time. There were 43,510 MVD in 2005, and 32,367 MVD in 2011 is 25% less than the 2005 statistic. This seems significant, but maybe there were fewer people in 2011 than in 2005. Or maybe there were fewer vehicles, or people drove fewer miles.

To make meaningful comparisons, we use **ratios**. Ratios are the most basic form of a relationship, simply comparing the relative sizes of two quantities. We can transform the original statistic, 32,367 MVD in 2011, into various **rates** that allow us to make meaningful comparisons between 2005 and 2011.

Comparing 32,367 MVD to the total population:

10.39 motor vehicle deaths per 100,000 people,

or to the number of vehicles:

12.57 MVD per 100,000 motor vehicles,

or to the amount of driving:

1.10 MVD per 100 million miles driven,

makes the statistic come alive and "talk to us." We can now make fair comparisons with the 2005 statistic.

Ratios will unify all numeracy topics in this text, demonstrating that "everything is relative." Rates will be fully explored in Chapter 3.

We can now compare the 32,367 MVD in 2011 with the 43,510 MVD in 2005 using **Table 2.1** from the National Highway Traffic Safety Administration. It is clear that the motor vehicle death rates have decreased from 2005 to 2011, no matter what rate we use. Learning how to compute such statistics and effectively use them to communicate is a major focus of this course.

Rates will be fully explored in Chapter 3. For now just know that a rate is a type of ratio. Ratios are defined on the next screen.

TABLE 2.1 Traffic Safety Data

Year	Killed	Resident Population (Thousands)	Fatality Rate per 100,000 Population	Licensed Drivers (Thousands)	Fatality Rate per 100,000 Licensed Drivers	Registered Motor Vehicles (Thousands)	Fatality Rate per 100,000 Registered Vehicles	Vehicle Miles Traveled (Billions)	Fatality Rate per 100 Million VMT
				Killed					
2002	43,005	287,625	14.95	194,602	22.10	225,685	19.06	2,856	1.51
2003	42,884	290,108	14.78	196,166	21.86	230,633	18.59	2,890	1.48
2004	42,836	292,805	14.63	198,889	21.54	237,949	18.00	2,965	1.44
2005	43,510	295,517	14.72	200,549	21.70	245,628	17.71	2,989	1.46
2006	42,708	298,380	14.31	202,810	21.06	251,415	16.99	3,014	1.42
2007	41,259	301,231	13.70	205,742	20.05	257,472	16.02	3,031	1.36
2008	37,423	304,094	12.31	208,321	17.96	259,360	14.43	2,977	1.26
2009	33,883	306,772	11.05	209,618	16.16	258,958	13.08	2,957	1.15
2010	32,999	309,330	10.67	210,115	15.71	257,312	12.82	2,967	1.11
2011	32,367	311,592	10.39	211,875	15.28	257,512	12.57	2,946	1.10

Data from: U.S. Department of Transportation National Highway Traffic Safety Administration Traffic Safety Facts 2011 Data April 2013, http://www-nrd.nhtsa.dot.gov/Pubs/811753.pdf

In addition to making comparisons over time, we often make group or geographic comparisons. In 2011, Great Britain had 1,901 MVD. Does this mean Brits are safer drivers than Americans? Again, we need to take into account other factors, such as the larger U.S. population. **Table 2.2** illustrates that Brits are indeed safer drivers across all measures.

TABLE 2.2 Traffic Safety Data, Great Britain and the United States

	MVD (2011)	MVD per 100,000 people	MVD per 100,000 MV	MVD per 100 Million Vehicle Miles
Great Britain	1,901	3.09	5.6	0.60
U.S.	32,367	10.39	12.57	1.10

Data from: Reported Road Casualties for Great Britain: 2011 Annual Report, https://www.gov.uk/government/statistical-data-sets/ras40-reported-accidents-vehicles-and casualties

Europeans use the metric system, so the last **rate** in the row for Great Britain was actually given as 3.7 MVD per 1 billion km driven. To make the comparison with the U.S., we had to convert **units**; such conversions will be covered Chapter 3, along with rates. First we need to learn about ratios.

DEFINITION

A **ratio** is a comparison of the *relative* sizes of two or more quantities. If the ratio of quantity A to quantity B is 2 to 5, or 2 : 5, then for every 2 units of quantity A, there are 5 units of quantity B. The comparison is *multiplicative*, meaning the fraction $\frac{a}{b} = \frac{2}{5}$ for a units of quantity A and b units of quantity B.

Note that the ratio 2 : 5 means you also always have 10 units of quantity B for every 4 units of quantity A. So the ratio 2 : 5 is equivalent to 4 : 10 and vice versa.

VIDEO *Ratio Definition*

TABLE 2.3 Ratio Example

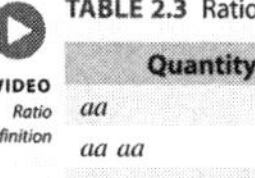

Quantity A	Quantity B	Ratio
aa	*bbbbb*	2 : 5
aa aa	*bbbbb bbbbb*	4 : 10
aa aa aa	*bbbbb bbbbb bbbbb*	6 : 15

OBJECTIVE 2 Use Ratio Tables to Set Up Proportions

Example 1 Compute the Ratio of Private Tuition and Fees to Public Four-Year In-State Tuition and Fees

VIDEO *Ratio Tables*

Table 2.4 shows what full-time undergraduate students paid on average in the United States for the 2013-14 school year. Compute the ratio of Private Tuition and Fees to Public Four-Year In-State Tuition and Fees. Represent this ratio in two different ways:

1. Scale the second quantity to 1.
2. Scale the first quantity to 100.

SOLUTION The **ratio** of Private Four-Year Tuition and Fees to Public Four-Year In-State Tuition and Fees is $30,094 to $8,893, or 30,094 : 8,893. Scaling these quantities to more manageable numbers helps us make sense of this ratio.

TABLE 2.4 Average Published Charges, Full-Time Undergraduate Students

	Tuition and Fees				Room and Board				Total Charges			
Sector	2013-14	2012-13	$ Change	% Change	2013-14	2012-13	$ Change	% Change	2013-14	2012-13	$ Change	% Change
Public Two-Year In-State	$3,264	$3,154	$110	3.5%	$7,466	$7,342	$124	1.7%	$10,730	$10,496	$234	2.2%
Public Four-Year In-State	$8,893	$8,646	$247	2.9%	$9,498	$9,171	$327	3.6%	$18,391	$17,817	$574	3.2%
Public Four-Year Out-of-State	$22,203	$21,533	$670	3.1%	$9,498	$9,171	$327	3.6%	$31,701	$30,704	$997	3.2%
Private Nonprofit Four-Year	$30,094	$28,989	$1,105	3.8%	$10,823	$10,458	$365	3.5%	$40,917	$39,447	$1,470	3.7%
For-Profit	$15,130	$15,060	$70	0.5%	—	—	—	—	—	—	—	—

Source: *Trends in College Pricing 2013*. Data derived from the *Annual Survey of Colleges*. Copyright ©2013. The College Board. www.collegeboard.org. Reproduced with permission.

Recall that the statistic $30,094 for Private Tuition and Fees is meaningless without comparison. We unconsciously make comparisons in our head, given our sense of how much money this is. Using a **ratio table** is a nice way to visualize ratios and keep track of the quantities involved.

A **ratio table** has a column for each quantity; order is important in a ratio, so you must be consistent about which quantity is first and which is second. The first row lists the names of the quantities, the second row gives the known values, the third row scales the second quantity to 1, and the fourth row scales the first quantity to 100.

TABLE 2.5 Ratio Table for Tuition and Fees, 2013-14 Full-Time Undergraduates

Private Tuition and Fees	Public Four-Year In-State Tuition and Fees
\$30,094	\$8,893
x	1
100	x

Scale 1st quantity to 100.

Scale 2nd quantity to 1.

To solve for the first quantity, Private Tuition and Fees, we can set up a **proportion** and cross multiply:

$$\frac{30{,}094}{8{,}893} = \frac{x}{1} \longrightarrow 30{,}094 \cdot 1 = 8{,}893 \cdot x \longrightarrow x = \frac{30{,}094}{8{,}893} \approx 3.4$$

Note that there are no hard-and-fast rules for how many decimal places to use. Use your best judgment for effective communication.

This ratio, 3.4 : 1, tells us that the first quantity, Private Tuition and Fees, is 3.4 times as much as Public Four-Year In-state Tuition and Fees. Thus the 100 in the last row is approximately 3.4 times x, solving gives the second ratio, 100 : 29.4, as shown in the video. This estimate is good enough for a ballpark figure, but using 3.4 has introduced round-off error. If we instead set up the proportion, 30,084 is to 8,893 as 100 is to x, we get the ratio 100 : 29.6.

For every \$3.40 a full-time undergraduate pays for tuition and fees at a private school, a public in-state fulltime student pays \$1; or for every \$100 a full-time undergraduate pays for tuition and fees at a private school, a public in-state full-time student pays \$29.60.

02-6

Example 2 **Compute Ratios for Private Four-Year : Public Four-Year In-State: Public Two-Year**

VIDEO *Proportions*

We can use a ratio table to keep track of more than two quantities. Compare the tuition and fees for Public Two-Year In-State to Private Four-Year and Public Four-Year In-State for full-time undergraduates.

SOLUTION We can add a third column to our ratio table and compute the ratios as before by setting up a proportion and cross multiplying.

TABLE 2.6 Ratio Table for Tuition and Fees, 2013-14 Full-Time Undergraduates for Three Types of Institutions

Private Tuition and Fees	Public Four-Year Tuition and Fees In-State	Public Two-Year Tuition and Fees In-State
\$30,094	\$8,893	\$3,264
3.4	1	x
100	29.6	

Note that to solve for x, we have two choices for setting up a proportion. We can compare x to Private (3.4) or to Public Four-Year (1); making this choice determines the other two numbers in the proportion.

02-7

These four highlighted cells would work to set up a **proportion** and solve for x:

To solve for x, you have two choices for setting up the proportion.

TABLE 2.7 Ratio Table for Tuition and Fees, 2013-14 Full-Time Undergraduates, First Choice for Setting Up a Proportion

Private Tuition and Fees	Public Four-Year Tuition and Fees In-State	Public Two-Year Tuition and Fees In-State
$30,094	$8,893	$3,264
3.4	1	x
100	29.6	

As would these four highlighted cells:

TABLE 2.8 Ratio Table for Tuition and Fees, 2013-14 Full-Time Undergraduates, Second Choice for Setting Up a Proportion

Private Tuition and Fees	Public Four-Year Tuition and Fees In-State	Public Two-Year Tuition and Fees In-State
$30,094	$8,893	$3,264
3.4	1	x
100	29.6	

The first choice is better since a cell has the number 1 in it. This allows us to set up the proportion $\frac{x}{1} = \frac{3,264}{8,893}$, which gives us $x \approx 0.37$.

Note that a **proportion** can be set up horizontally or vertically, so $\frac{8,893}{1} = \frac{3,264}{x}$ would also work, but now we have to cross multiply to get x.

We now have the ratio of Private Four-Year to Public Four-Year to Public Two-Year as 3.4 : 1 : 0.37. To fill in the last missing number in the ratio table, note the relationships between rows and columns. The value 1 in the third row and second column gives us an easy comparison between the third and fourth rows and the second and third columns.

TABLE 2.9 Ratio Table for Tuition and Fees, 2013-14 Full-Time Undergraduates, Relationships Between Rows and Columns

Private Tuition and Fees	Public Four-Year Tuition and Fees In-State	Public Two-Year Tuition and Fees In-State
$30,094	$8,893	$3,264
3.4	1	0.37
100	29.6	x

Multiply by 29.6

Multiply by 0.37

So we can multiply the 0.37 (in row three, column three) by 29.6 to solve for x.

TABLE 2.10 Ratio Table for Tuition and Fees, 2013-14 Full-Time Undergraduates, Filling in Last Value

Private Tuition and Fees	Public Four-Year Tuition and Fees In-State	Public Two-Year Tuition and Fees In-State
$30,094	$8,893	$3,264
3.4	1	0.37
100	29.6	10.95

OBJECTIVE 3 Learn Ratio Vocabulary

Recall that this text is about communicating with numbers and that ratio is the foundational concept that ties together the material from one chapter to the next. Keep in mind that several phrases indicate a ratio:

for every: There are a units of quantity A for every b units of quantity B.

For every \$100 a full-time undergraduate student spent on tuition and fees at a private four-year school in 2013-14, a public four-year in-state student spent \$29.60.

times as much: Quantity A is a times as much as quantity B (assuming a ratio of $a:1$).

Full-time undergraduate students at private four-year schools spent 3.4 *times as much* as students at public four-year in-state schools on tuition and fees in 2013-14.

a fraction of: Quantity A is a/b of quantity B (assuming $a < b$; if $a > b$, typically use *for every*).

Tuition and fees at private two-year schools were $\frac{1}{9}$ *of* the tuition and fees at private four-year schools in 2013-14.

Note that there are not hard-and-fast rules regarding how to round. The one-ninth mentioned in the last sentence is an approximation; being too exact would only cause confusion here.

OBJECTIVE 4 Contrast Part-to-Part and Part-to-Whole Ratios

The ratios we have seen so far have included comparisons across time or between groups; now we consider comparisons within a group.

It is important to remember that a ratio is an ordered pair of numbers; it is "ordered" because it matters which number comes first. The fact that the ratio 4 : 1 is the same as 8 : 2 and 12 : 3 and 100 : 25 should remind you of equivalent fractions. Fractions can also be thought of as ordered pairs, just written vertically instead of horizontally.

The distinction between fractions and ratios can confuse students, especially when dealing with **part-to-part** versus **part-to-whole ratios**. The part-to-whole interpretation of a fraction is so common that students often mistake part-to-part ratios as part-to-whole ratios.

Example 3 | Compare Parts of the Total Cost of Attending College

VIDEO *Part-to-Part Ratios*

Given the breakdown of costs for public two-year students given in **Table 2.11**, compute the part-to-part ratio of Tuition and Fees to Room and Board, with Room and Board scaled to 1. Also compute the part-to-whole ratios for these two parts.

TABLE 2.11 Ratio Table for Expenses, Public Two-Year, 2013-14 Full-Time Undergraduates

Tuition and Fees	Books and Supplies	Room and Board	Transportation	Other Expenses	Total
\$3,264	\$1,270	\$7,466	\$1,708	\$2,225	\$15,933

Room and Board is one part of the total expense.

SOLUTION We first create a **part-to-whole ratio** of Tuition and Fees to Total Expense. We typically scale the second quantity to 100 in a part-to-whole ratio so it can be interpreted as a percentage (covered in Chapter 4). Setting up the proportion $\frac{a}{100} = \frac{3,264}{15,933}$, we can solve for $a \approx 20.5$. Similarly, we can solve for $b \approx 46.9$:

TABLE 2.12 **Part-to-Whole Ratios** for Expenses, Public Two-Year, 2013-14 Full-Time Undergraduates

Tuition and Fees	Books and Supplies	Room and Board	Transportation	Other Expenses	Total
\$3,264	\$1,270	\$7,466	\$1,708	\$2,225	\$15,933
a		b			100

Scale the total or whole to 100.

Next we can solve for the **part-to-part ratio** Tuition and Fees to Room and Board:

TABLE 2.13 **Part-to-Part Ratio** for Expenses, Public Two-Year, 2013-14 Full-Time Undergraduates

Tuition and Fees	Books and Supplies	Room and Board	Transportation	Other Expenses	Total
\$3,264	\$1,270	\$7,466	\$1,708	\$2,225	\$15,933
20.5		46.9			100
x		1			

Tuition and Fees cost \$20.50 for every \$100 spent on total expenses.

Setting up the proportion $\frac{x}{1} = \frac{20.5}{46.9}$, we can solve for $x \approx 0.44$, which tells us that Tuition and Fees cost \$0.44 for every \$1 spent on Room and Board.

2.2 Weighted Averages

OBJECTIVE 1 **Compute Weighted Averages**

OBJECTIVE 1 Compute Weighted Averages

Most students are familiar with the idea of averages, in particular computing **arithmetic averages (mean)** such as average tuition and fees by adding up all possible tuitions and fees at different schools and dividing by the number of schools. Thus an average can be thought of as a ratio. A **weighted average** is an important variation of this concept. We will start with an example to illustrate.

Example 4 **Compute the Weighted Average of Cost per Pound of Fruit**

VIDEO *Weighted Averages*

You purchase 9 pounds of grapes at \$2.00 a pound and 3 pounds of blueberries at \$6.00 a pound. What is the average price you pay per pound of fruit?

SOLUTION The average is given by the total amount you spend divided by the total weight in pounds:

The costs are weighted by the 9 and 3.

$$\frac{9 \cdot \$2.00 + 3 \cdot \$6.00}{9 + 3} = \frac{\$36}{12 \text{ lb}} = \$3.00 \text{ per pound}$$

Instead of just averaging the \$2.00 and \$6.00, you *weight* these prices respectively by the different quantities purchased: 9 lb and 3 lb. The resulting weighted average is thus closer to the \$2.00 you paid per pound for grapes, since you bought more grapes.

Now that we have seen an example of a weighted average, here is a more formal definition:

DEFINITION

Given a sequence of values, x_k, occurring with different weights, weight_k, the **weighted average** is the ratio of the sum of the products, $\text{weight}_k \cdot x_k$, to the sum of the weights:

$$\text{Weighted average} = \frac{\Sigma\,(\text{weight}_k \cdot x_k)}{\Sigma\,\text{weight}_k}$$

Recall that we denote a sum using the Greek letter sigma, Σ

Note that the actual weights are not as important as the ratio of the weights to each other. In the fruit example above, we can use the fact that the ratio of the weight of grapes (9 lb) to the weight of blueberries (3 lb) is 3 : 1, and use these as our weights:

$$\frac{3 \cdot \$2.00 + 1 \cdot \$6.00}{3 + 1} = \frac{\$12}{4\text{ lb}} = \$3.00 \text{ per pound}$$

Using the correct ratio of weights is what really matters. Both 9 : 3 and 3 : 1 give the same weighted average of $3 per pound.

2.3 Proportionality

OBJECTIVE 1 **Understand Proportionality**

OBJECTIVE 2 **Compute the Constant of Proportionality**

OBJECTIVE 3 **Use Equations $y = k \cdot x$**

OBJECTIVE 1 Understand Proportionality

Continuing the fruit example from the last section, saying that the ratio of the weights is 3 : 1 leads to the idea of equivalent fractions. The actual weights of 9 lb : 3 lb can be represented by an infinite number of ratios: 3 : 1, 6 : 2, 9 : 3, etc.

CAUTION Saying the ratio is *equivalent* to 3 : 1 is different from saying that people must *always* buy grapes and blueberries so that the ratio of weights is *constant* at 3 : 1. If you go to the store the next week and decide to buy twice as many blueberries (i.e., 6 lb), there is no reason that you have to also double the amount of grapes (i.e., 18 lb) so that the ratio 18 lb : 6 lb is *constant*, at 3 : 1. ●

DEFINITION

Two quantities are **proportional** or **in proportion** if their ratio is always constant, in a multiplicative sense: doubling one doubles the other, tripling one triples the other, etc.

There is a special relationship between proportional quantities; changing one necessitates a precise quantifiable change in the other:

$$na : nb = \frac{na}{nb} = \frac{a}{b} = a : b$$

If Quantity A is proportional to Quantity B, then increasing the amount of A by a factor, n, implies that B increases by the same factor. Thus the ratio remains constant.

Technically, we have defined *directly proportional*. Quantities are *inversely proportional* if doubling one cuts the other in half, etc.

Example 5 **Fill in a Ratio Table for Proportional Currencies**

The ratio of euros to dollars at the currency exchange booth is 4 : 5, given by the currency rate 0.8 EUR = 1 USD. The amount of euros you will receive is proportional to the amount of dollars you hand in. How many euros do you receive if you hand in \$15? \$30?

SOLUTION We can use ratio tables as before for **proportional** quantities. To solve for the missing values, we exploit the fact that if you multiply your dollars by a factor, the euros also get multiplied by that factor.

TABLE 2.14
Currency Conversion Ratio Table

	Euros (€)	Dollars (\$)	
	0.8	1	
Multiply by 5	4	5	Multiply by 5
Multiply by 3	?	15	Multiply by 3
Multiply by 2	?	30	Multiply by 2

If you hand in twice as many dollars, then you will receive twice as many Euros; there is a definite quantifiable **relationship** between euros and dollars.

So you would receive 12€ in exchange for \$15 and 24€ in exchange for \$30.

CAUTION Determining whether two quantities are proportional can be subtle. It is certainly true that the exchange rate may vary, so tomorrow the ratio of euros to dollars might be 3 : 5. The point is that once fixed, the ratio of euros to dollars will be constant. ●

OBJECTIVE 2 Compute the Constant of Proportionality

DEFINITION

Given two proportional quantities, the decimal equivalent of the constant ratio is referred to as a **constant of proportionality**. It is also referred to as the *scaling factor* or the *conversion factor* and can be computed by scaling one of the quantities to 1. Thus there are two possible constants! The relationship between proportional quantities can be represented by the equation $y = k \cdot x$, where k is either of the constants of proportionality.

Example 6 **Compute a Constant of Proportionality for Currency Conversion**

VIDEO *Proportionality*

The ratio of euros to dollars at the currency exchange booth is €4 : \$5. Determine one of the **constants of proportionality** and represent the relationship between euros and dollars using an equation of the form $y = k \cdot x$.

SOLUTION The given ratio €4 : \$5 is equivalent to €0.8 : \$1; thus 0.8 is a constant of proportionality. The equation is $y = 0.8 \cdot x$. But where did this equation come from, and what do x and y represent?

To answer this, we set up our trusty proportion and cross multiply, but now instead of solving just for x, we use a variable for both euros and dollars:

There is a definite quantifiable relationship between euros and dollars that can be expressed using two different equations. Note that E and D represent the numbers of euros and dollars, respectively.

$$\frac{E}{D} = \frac{4}{5}$$

$$5E = 4D$$

$$E = \frac{4}{5}D \qquad D = \frac{5}{4}E.$$

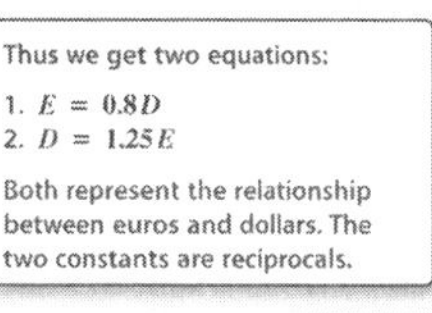
Thus we get two equations:
1. $E = 0.8D$
2. $D = 1.25E$

Both represent the relationship between euros and dollars. The two constants are reciprocals.

OBJECTIVE 3 Use Equations: $y = k \cdot x$

Example 7 Convert Currency Using an Equation

Given \$35, compute the number of euros, assuming an exchange rate of €4 : \$5.

SOLUTION In the last example, we saw that the relationship between euros and dollars can be represented using either of two equations: $E = 0.8D$ or $D = 1.25E$. We can substitute $D = 35$ into either of these, but it makes more sense to use $E = 0.8D$, which has E as the desired output:

We can simply substitute into the equation to solve for one of the variables, we don't have to set up a proportion and cross multiply. E and D represent the number of euros and dollars.

$$E = 0.8 \times 35 = €28$$

CAUTION We have just moved from the familiar solid world of arithmetic, \$1 = €0.8 so \$2 = €1.6, i.e. doubling, to the potentially more powerful world of algebra. Many students misread the equation $E = 0.8D$ as 1 euro equals 0.8 dollars, but that is incorrect. The variable E stands for any amount of euros, not just 1 euro. Compare the following three ways to represent the relationship between euros and dollars:

The 0.8 in the first bullet is in front of the EUR, but it moves in front of the D in the equation. Hmmmmm... tricky!

- 0.8 EUR = 1 USD . . . 0.8 euro equals 1 dollar (no **variables** here, EUR and USD are **units**).
- $E = 0.8D$ . . . The number of euros equals 0.8 times the number of dollars (no **units** here, E and D are **variables**).
- €28 = \$35 ●

Using the equation $E = 0.8D$ is an extremely concise, powerful way to represent the proportional relationship between euros and dollars. It expresses the relationship in compact input/output form; we input dollars into the equation, and the equation will output euros.

Equations are crucial when we use technology to explore these proportional relationships:

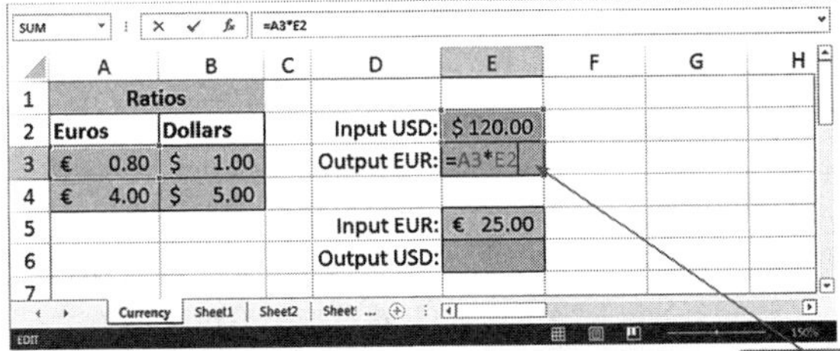

FIGURE 2.1 Entering a Proportionality Equation into a Spreadsheet

The output cell is where you type your formula linking to the input cell.

VIDEO Proportionality as Function

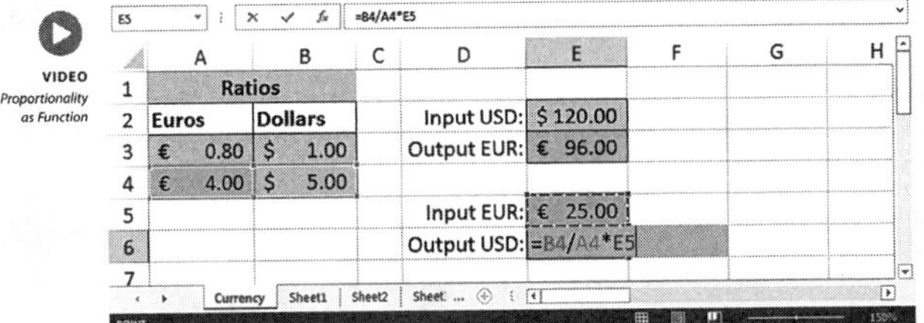

FIGURE 2.2 Entering a Second Proportionality Equation into a Spreadsheet

If we want to solve for D and have dollars as the output, we need to use the other equation:

$$D = \frac{5}{4}E$$

$$D = 1.25E$$

The constant of proportionality is thus 1.25 for this equation.

SPREADSHEET TUTORIALS Fill Formulas | Fill Formulas with Abs. Cell Ref. | Enter Data | Enter Numbers | Format \$ | Do Arithmetic

Given two random quantities, we can always take their ratio; for example, your weight to the price of a gallon of gas might be 160 lb : \$4.00, or 40 lb : \$1.

You may be tempted to model this relationship with the equation $W = 40G$, but this makes no sense. If the cost of gas rises to \$5 a gallon, the equation would predict you would then weigh 200 lb! Since your weight and the cost of gas will not remain in a constant ratio, they are not **proportional** and therefore cannot be modeled with an equation.

Only if two quantities are proportional can we write down an equation for their special relationship. In particular, one quantity is a **function** of the other, as discussed in Chapter 1. We can use the equation to make a table of values for our function and equivalently a graph. Let's look at different ways to represent the proportional relationship between euros and dollars, $E = 0.8D$.

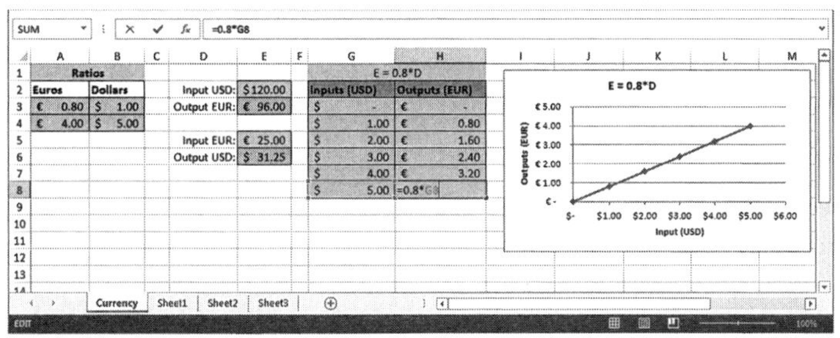

FIGURE 2.3 Representing a Proportional Relationship

Screenshots from Microsoft ® Excel ®. Used by permission of Microsoft Corporation.

We have just seen that the equation $E = 0.8\,D$ is but one way to represent the special relationship between the two quantities, euros and dollars.

TABLE 2.15 Comparison of Direct and Inverse Proportionality

	Directly Proportional	Inversely Proportional
Definition	Quantity A is directly proportional to quantity B if their ratio is constant: $\frac{a}{b} = k$.	Quantity A is inversely proportional to quantity B if their product is constant: $a \cdot b = k$.
Equation	$A = k \cdot B$ or $y = k \cdot x$	$A = \frac{k}{B}$ or $y = \frac{k}{x}$
Table	Doubling one quantity doubles the other.	Doubling one quantity cuts the other in half.
Graph	Straight line through the origin.	Look at graph below.

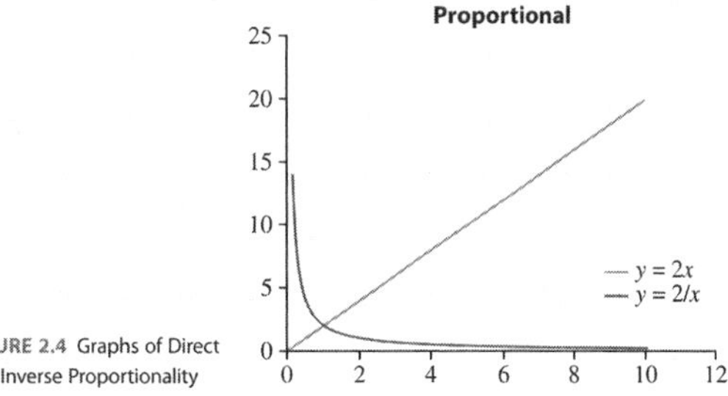

FIGURE 2.4 Graphs of Direct and Inverse Proportionality

2.4 Financial Literacy

OBJECTIVE 1 Understand PE Ratios and Stock Quotes

OBJECTIVE 2 Understand Inflation and the CPI

OBJECTIVE 3 Compute Money Ratios for Retirement

OBJECTIVE 1 Understand PE Ratios and Stock Quotes

We will introduce some basic financial literacy ratios that every numerate person should understand. We start with the **price-to-earnings ratio (PE ratio)** of a **stock**. Say that you start a company that sells pies. If your company gets big enough, you might want to sell shares in it to people to raise money so your company can expand.

Investors buy stock in your company by purchasing **shares**, making them part owners and giving them the opportunity to share in the profits, called **dividends**. Also, if the company does well, investors may at some point sell their shares to someone else for a higher price than they originally paid.

Owning stocks and bonds should be part of everyone's **retirement plan**. These topics will be covered in more detail in Chapter 9. Right now we just want to look at the PE ratio.

Example 8 **Compute the PE Ratio for AT&T on January 21, 2011**

One share of AT&T was selling for $28.40 on January 21, 2011; this is the price of the stock. Every **quarter** (three months), a company must report its **earnings**, or **profit**. Earnings from the most recent four quarters are added together to determine the earnings for the past 12 months. These earnings are divided by the number of shares giving the **earnings per share** for the year. For AT&T, the earnings per share for 2010 was $3.55. Compute the PE ratio for AT&T by comparing the price per share to the earnings per share.

SOLUTION We can create a ratio table to visualize the information:

TABLE 2.16 Ratio Table to Compute the PE Ratio

AT&T on January 21, 2011	
Price per Share	Earnings per Share
$28.40	$3.55
x	1

We scale the earnings per share to 1 and set up the proportion, $\frac{x}{1} = \frac{28.40}{3.55} = 8.0.$

The PE ratio is often referred to as the multiple; in this case, it is written 8.0x. This PE ratio tells us that the share price of AT&T is 8 times the earnings per share. We will analyze this statistic in more depth on the next screen.

In the last example we computed a PE ratio of 8, but we don't have any context for this. Is this good? We will compare two stock quotes for AT&T to generate some insight into this question. A **stock quote** gives basic information about the shares of a company. Below are the stock quotes for AT&T on January 21, 2011, and August 19, 2013. Between these two dates, the PE ratio had jumped from 8 to 25.6.

This stock quote gives basic statistics about AT&T stock, including the number of shares in the company, the PE ratio, and the earnings per share.

Why the big increase? Remember that the PE ratio is computed by dividing **price per share** by **earnings per share**. A fraction increases in value if either the numerator increases or the denominator decreases. In the case of AT&T, both of these happened!

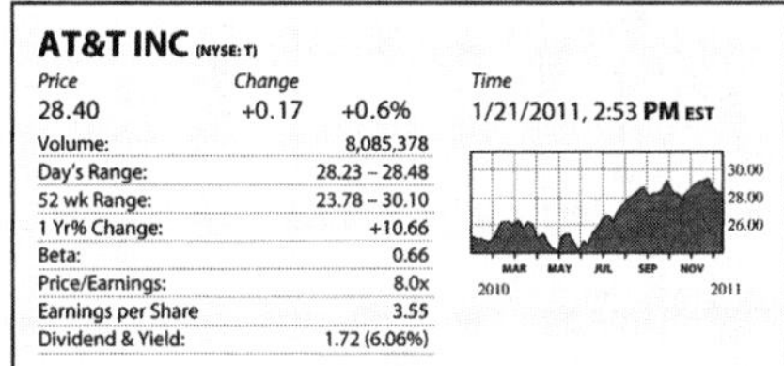

FIGURE 2.5 AT&T 1/21/11
Data from: CNBC.com

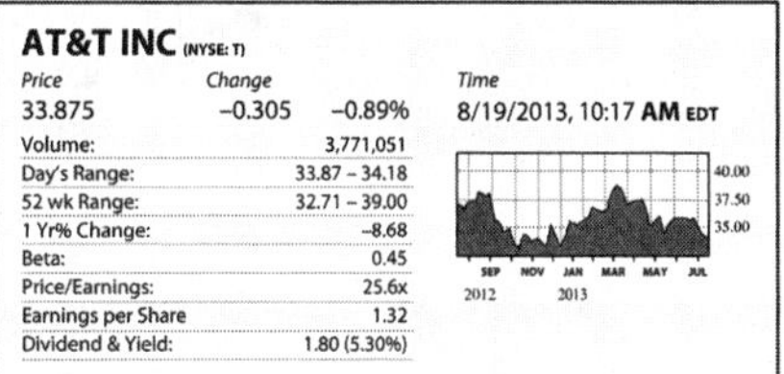

FIGURE 2.6 AT&T 8/19/13
Data from: CNBC.com

Let's continue to put these PE ratios into context. Which is better: a PE ratio of 8.0 or 25.6?

Well, it depends. A higher share price, $33.88, is good if you own the stock, but the big question is whether you believe the share price can go higher. The lower earnings per share, $1.32, is not good, as it means the company is making less money.

Historically, the average PE ratio for the stock market is around 15, meaning people are usually willing to pay 15 times what a company earns to buy a share of the company's stock. The PE ratio of 25.6 is higher than this, so you should be cautious in expecting the share price to go higher. There is always risk in investing in a stock. A low PE ratio may indicate a low price due to a belief that the company will struggle in the future, and a high PE ratio may just be irrational exuberance!

TABLE 2.17 Comparing AT&T Stock over Time

AT&T	1/21/11	8/19/13
Price per Share	$28.40	$33.88
Earnings per Share	$3.55	$1.32

This stock quote from August 19, 2013, shows that the PE ratio has risen to 25.6 due to an increase in the price per share, $33.88, and a decrease in the earnings per share, $1.32.

AT&T INC (NYSE: T)
Price 33.875
Change −0.305 −0.89%
Time 8/19/2013, 10:17 AM EDT
Volume: 3,771,051
Day's Range: 33.87 – 34.18
52 wk Range: 32.71 – 39.00
1 Yr% Change: −8.68
Beta: 0.45
Price/Earnings: 25.6x
Earnings per Share 1.32
Dividend & Yield: 1.80 (5.30%)

FIGURE 2.7 AT&T 8/19/13
Data from: CNBC.com

Speaking of irrational exuberance, recall the average **PE ratio** for the stock market is around 15. The following graphic is based on data from *Irrational Exuberance* by Robert J. Shiller:

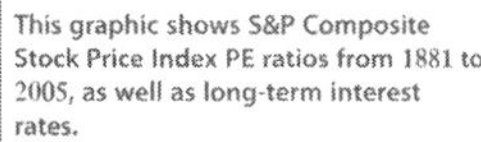

This graphic shows S&P Composite Stock Price Index PE ratios from 1881 to 2005, as well as long-term interest rates.

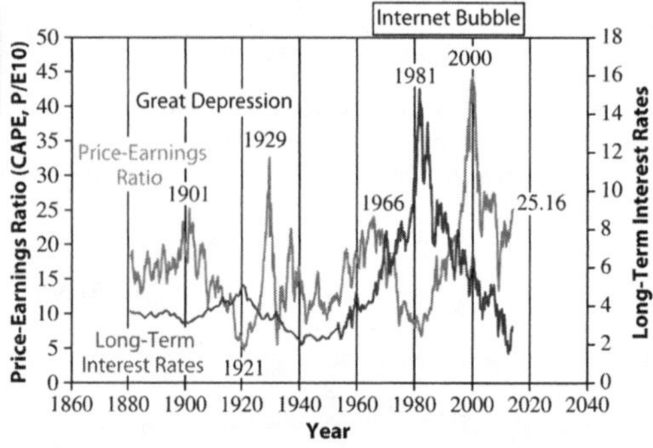

FIGURE 2.8 Schiller's Graphic, Showing Historical PE Ratios Against Interest Rates
Data from: *Irrational Exuberance* by Robert J. Shiller

We can see that it is very uncommon for PE ratios for the market as a whole to stay above 20 for long. The PE ratio is like a rubber band connecting stock prices to earnings; we can certainly stretch the rubber band past 25, but it is going to snap back!

OBJECTIVE 2 Understand Inflation and the CPI

Another financial ratio, called the **Consumer Price Index (CPI)**, has to do with **inflation**. The CPI is related to the cost of goods and services and typically rises each year. For example, a movie ticket in 1990 that cost $6.50 might have cost $10 in 2013. Thus a dollar in 1990 (1990$) was worth more than a dollar in 2013 (2013$).

It is helpful to think of 1990$ and 2013$ as different currencies in much the same way that dollars and euros are different currencies. We need to convert between these currencies, and the CPI allows us to do that.

The CPI is a measure of the cost of a basket of goods and services in a given year. It is called an *index* because it is arbitrarily set to 100 for the cost of this basket in 1983$. These same goods and services would have cost 130.7 in 1990$ and 233 in 2013$.

Example 9 Use CPI to Convert Currency

Convert the cost of a $6.50 movie ticket in 1990 to 2013$.

VIDEO *Financial Literacy*

Open the *CPI* worksheet in *Data Sets* to see historical CPI values, found on the Bureau of Labor Statistics website: http://www.bls.gov/cpi/tables.htm

SOLUTION By setting up a ratio table, we can compute that an item costing $6.50 in 1990 would be $11.59 in 2013, when adjusted for inflation

A movie ticket that costs 6.50 in 1990$ would cost 11.59 in 2013$ due to inflation.

TABLE 2.18 Comparing 1990 and 2013 Costs

	CPI	Cost of an Item
1990$	130.7	6.50
2013$	233.0	x

Data from: Bureau of Labor Statistics, http://www.bls.gov/cpi/tables.htm

Data sets that involve monetary values every year should be converted to a single year's $ so they can be compared. For example, open the *U.S. Receipts 2013* worksheet in *Data Sets*. **Table 2.19** shows the money collected (receipts) by the U.S. government for both the given years' current dollars and as adjusted to other years' $.

The values in bold on the diagonal are the receipts collected for that year in the year's current dollars. These numbers make it appear that the receipts were steadily increasing, but when we convert everything to 2005$, using the CPI values from the *CPI* worksheet in *Data Sets*, we see the government actually collected less in 2005 than in 2000 in real dollars (i.e., dollars adjusted for inflation).

The values in any column represent the receipts for a given year adjusted to other years' $.

In 2005 the U.S. collected less money than in 2000, as evidenced by reading across any of the rows.

TABLE 2.19 U.S.Government Receipts in Both Current and Adjusted Dollars

		1990	2000	2005
	CPI	U.S. Receipts (billions)		
1990$	130.7	1,032	1,537	1,441
2000$	172.2	1,360	2,025	1,899
2005$	195.3	1,542	2,297	2,154

Data from: White House Budget Office Historical Tables, http://www.whitehouse.gov/omb/budget, Table 1.3

The money values in this table are in billions ... add 9 zeros to the end of each number!

The slight discrepancy between these values computed using the CPI and the values in the *U.S. Receipts* worksheet are due to the more sophisticated analysis undertaken by the Bureau of Labor Statistics.

OBJECTIVE 3 Compute Money Ratios for Retirement

Our last collection of financial ratios are related to financial planning and come from the terrific book *Your Money Ratio$* by Charles Farrell. Each of the four middle columns gives a ratio comparing an important monetary amount to your income or earnings.

Capital is the amount you have saved to date.

Savings is the amount you save each year.

TABLE 2.20 *Your Money Ratios:* Ages 25-65

Your age	Capital: Income	Saving: Income	Mortgage: Income	Education: Earnings	Stock: Bonds
25	0.1	12%	2.0	0.75	50 : 50
30	0.6	12%	2.0	0.45	50 : 50
35	1.4	12%	1.9	0.00	50 : 50
40	2.4	12%	1.8	X	50 : 50
45	3.7	15%	1.7	X	50 : 50
50	5.2	15%	1.5	X	50 : 50
55	7.1	15%	1.2	X	50 : 50
60	9.4	15%	0.7	X	40 : 60
65	12.0	15%	0.0	X	40 : 60

Mortgage is the amount you owe on your home loan.

Education is the amount of your student loans.

Data from: *Your Money Ratio$: 8 Simple Tools for Financial Security at Every Stage in Your Life* by Charles Farrell

Notice the three different ways the ratios in the first row are represented in this table:

1. Single numbers
2. Percentages
3. Ratios

Example 10 **Use the Money Ratios**

You are 30 years old and make \$50,000 a year (Income). Use the table to compute your five money ratios:

TABLE 2.21 *Your Money Ratios*: Age 30

Your age	Capital: Income	Saving: Income	Mortgage: Income	Education: Earnings	Stock: Bonds
25	0.1	12%	2.0	0.75	50:50
30	0.6	12%	2.0	0.45	50:50
35	1.4	12%	1.9	0.00	50:50

Data from: *Your Money RatioS : 8 Simple Tools for Financial Security at Every Stage in Your Life* by Charles Farrell

SOLUTION Your *Capital: Income* ratio is 0.6. Capital refers to the total amount of money you should have saved by this age. We get: $\frac{Capital}{50{,}000} = \frac{0.6}{1}$, or $Capital = 0.6 \cdot 50{,}000 = \$30{,}000$.

This \$30,000 should be invested in a retirement portfolio that holds 50% in *Stocks* and 50% in *Bonds*. (See Chapter 9 for descriptions of these terms.)

You should be saving 12% of your *Income* this year ($Savings = 12\% \cdot 50{,}000 = \$6{,}000$) and investing it in your retirement portfolio.

Finally, in terms of debt (what you owe), your *Mortgage* (home loan) should be no more than twice your income: $\frac{Mortgage}{50{,}000} = \frac{2}{1}$, or $Mortgage = \$100{,}000$; and you should owe only 0.45 times your *Earnings*: $\frac{Education}{50{,}000} = \frac{0.45}{1}$, or $Education = \$22{,}500$, in student loans, which should all be paid off by the time you are 35.

2.5 Spotlight on Statistics

OBJECTIVE 1 **Compute *z*-Scores and Standardized Scores**

OBJECTIVE 2 **Explore the Normal Distribution**

OBJECTIVE 1 Compute *z*-Scores and Standardized Scores

VIDEO *z-Score Definition*

In Chapter 1's *Spotlight on Statistics*, we introduced the basic measures of central tendency and spread. The **mean** is the arithmetic average of the data set, and the **standard deviation** is the average distance from the mean. Given these two descriptive statistics, we can put into perspective the location of individual data points within the overall distribution of values. As explained at the beginning of this chapter, statistics are virtually meaningless without comparison.

Example 11 **Use z-Scores for Statistical Comparison**

You get a 63 on a test. Statistically speaking, is this a bad score?

SOLUTION To answer this, we need to know how this score compares to the rest of the class. Assuming that the mean is 51, we now know you scored above average, but how far above average? To answer this, we need to know how spread out the scores are. If all the other scores are between 49 and 53, then you did extremely well (A+), but if a bunch of people got in the 90s and a bunch got in the teens, then you just did average (C). Assuming that the standard deviation (average distance from the mean) is 5 points, your 63 is more than twice that distance above the mean.

In fact, your 63 is 12 points above the mean, and the distance of 12 is 2.4 times the average distance of 5 points. The number +2.4 is your *z*-score, and it indicates that you are 2.4 times the standard deviation above the mean. Someone who got a 39 is 12 points below the mean and would have a *z*-score of −2.4. So a 63 is a good score, maybe a B+/A− on this test.

DEFINITION

The **z-score** of a data value, x, is the ratio of the data value's distance from the mean, $\overline{X}$, to the average distance from the mean (standard deviation, or SD):

$$z = \frac{x - \overline{X}}{\text{SD}} = \text{number of standard deviations from the mean.}$$

A **z-score** is an example of a standardized score. Any data set of raw values can be converted into *z*-scores, which makes for nice comparisons to other data sets.

Hmmm, nice comparisons seem to be a theme of this chapter.

TABLE 2.22 Raw Data and z-Scores

Data						Mean	SD
Raw Scores	69	72	75	78	81	75	4.74
Z-scores	−1.27	−0.63	0.0	0.63	1.27	0	1

Note that the standardized *z*-scores have a mean of 0 and a standard deviation of 1. There are other common standardized scores: The *T*-scores center at 50 and have a standard deviation of 10, while NCE-scores also center at 50 but spread out more, with $SD = 21$.

TABLE 2.23 Standardized Scores

Data						Mean	SD
Raw Scores	69	72	75	78	81	75	4.74
Z-scores	−1.27	−0.63	0.0	0.63	1.27	0	1
T-scores $= 50 + 10 \cdot z$	37.4	43.7	50	56.3	62.6	50	10
NCE $= 50 + 21 \cdot z$	23.54	36.77	50	63.23	76.46	50	21
IQ $= 100 + 15 \cdot z$	81.1	90.6	100	109.5	118.9	100	15
SAT $= 500 + 100 \cdot z$	374	437	500	563	626	500	100

Notice that the actual value of a number in a data set is not important. What matters is the comparison of each number relative to all other values in the data.

A test score of 75 could be reported as a zero (z-score), a 50 (*T*-score), a 100 (IQ-score), or a 500 (SAT score), depending on your choice of scale.

OBJECTIVE 2 Explore the Normal Distribution

Z-scores essentially strip raw scores of unnecessary trappings and present a data set in terms of the most basic center (0) and spread (1). Many data sets have the same general shape (think **histogram** or column chart of binned data), with most values clustered in the middle and the number of values gradually diminishing the farther out from the mean we go. This distribution of data values gives us a **bell-shaped curve:**

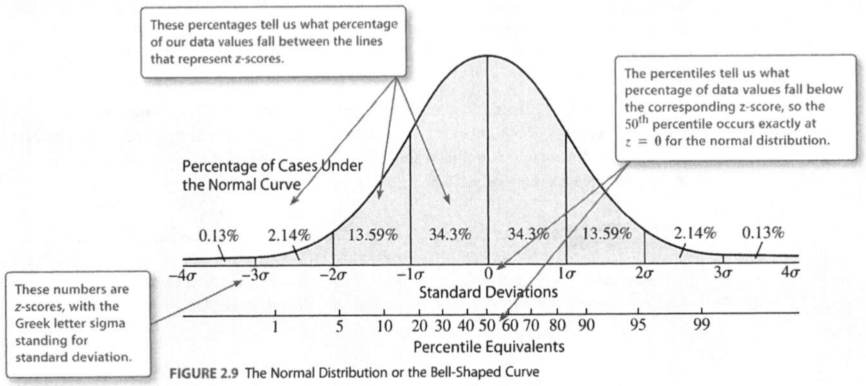
These percentages tell us what percentage of our data values fall between the lines that represent z-scores.
The percentiles tell us what percentage of data values fall below the corresponding z-score, so the 50th percentile occurs exactly at z = 0 for the normal distribution.
These numbers are z-scores, with the Greek letter sigma standing for standard deviation.
Percentage of Cases Under the Normal Curve
0.13% 2.14% 13.59% 34.3% 34.3% 13.59% 2.14% 0.13%
−4σ −3σ −2σ −1σ 0 1σ 2σ 3σ 4σ
Standard Deviations
1 5 10 20 30 40 50 60 70 80 90 95 99
Percentile Equivalents

FIGURE 2.9 The Normal Distribution or the Bell-Shaped Curve

CAUTION As Nassim Taleb points out in his book *The Black Swan*, only certain data sets are normal (e.g., physical characteristics like height and weight), but most socioeconomic data is not normal. ●

Notice that on the **normal curve**, over 99% of the data values are within three standard deviations of the mean:

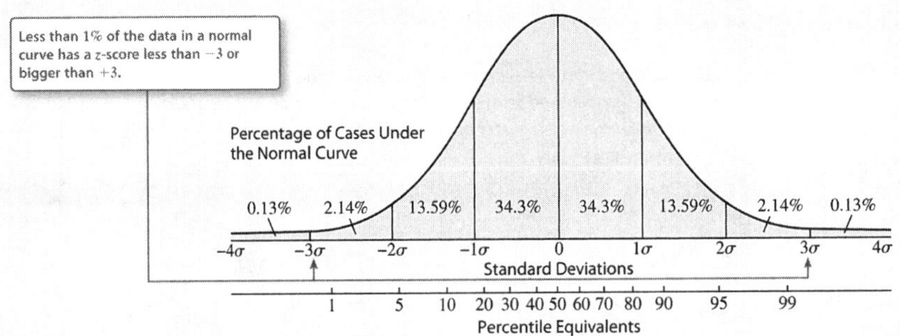
Less than 1% of the data in a normal curve has a z-score less than −3 or bigger than +3.
Percentage of Cases Under the Normal Curve
0.13% 2.14% 13.59% 34.3% 34.3% 13.59% 2.14% 0.13%
−4σ −3σ −2σ −1σ 0 1σ 2σ 3σ 4σ
Standard Deviations
1 5 10 20 30 40 50 60 70 80 90 95 99
Percentile Equivalents

FIGURE 2.10 The Normal Distribution

Socioeconomic data like U.S. household income is *not* normal. In 2005, the top 11,000 U.S. households averaged \$35 million in income compared to the mean U.S. household income of \$84,800, giving these top households a z-score of 92!

Socioeconomic data can have a **fat tail**, meaning a significant number of data values are far away from the mean, as measured by z-scores.

> 11,000 household incomes in the U.S. had a z-score of 92. A woman with a height 92 standard deviations above the mean would be 27 feet tall!
>
> Data from: Congressional Budget Office, http://www.cbo.gov/, *Historical Effective Federal Tax Rates: 1979 to 2005*, **Table 3**

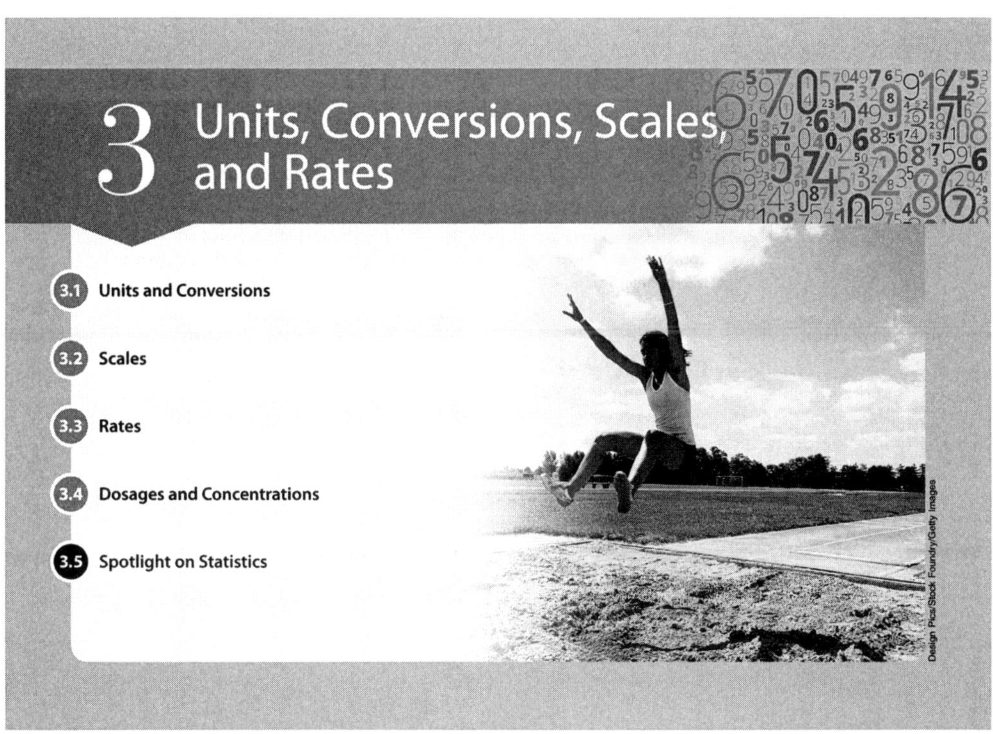

03-1

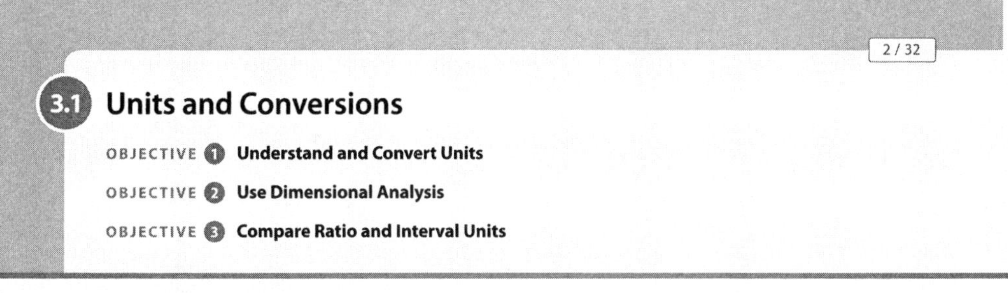

2 / 32
3.1 Units and Conversions
OBJECTIVE 1 Understand and Convert Units
OBJECTIVE 2 Use Dimensional Analysis
OBJECTIVE 3 Compare Ratio and Interval Units

OBJECTIVE 1 Understand and Convert Units

In Chapter 2 we studied **ratio, proportion**, and **proportional** quantities. In this chapter we formalize the concept of units that has already appeared in many of our examples. The act of measuring a quantity requires us to decide what units or system of measurement will be used. When we say a quantity is 4, the units answer the question: "Four what?"

DEFINITION

In measuring a quantity, the **units** refer to the choice of measurement system. There are two distinct types of units:

Units of observation These units pertain to a quality or category such as nationality: American, Indian, Mexican, etc. A data value or observation either belongs to a category or it does not.

Units of measurement These units pertain to a quantity such as length, using an agreed-upon standard: feet, cm, miles, etc. A data value for a given quantity can be measured using any associated unit of measurement, each of which can be converted to the other units of measurement.

03-2

Note that some data have both units of observation and units of measurement.

For example, income can be measured in both units of observation—individuals or households—and in units of measurement—dollars or constant 2005$.

The key distinction between **units of observation** and **units of measurement** is that we can always convert between different choices of units of measurement. Given any **unit of length**, we can convert this to any other unit of length, whereas we cannot convert a category of people into another category.

DEFINITION

A **conversion** is a ratio used to compare two different systems of measurement. A conversion indicates a change in units of measurement, which are typically proportional to one another. The constant of proportionality is called the *conversion factor*.

TABLE 3.1 Length Conversions

Length Conversion Table		
1 centimeter (cm)	=	10 millimeters (mm)
1 inch	=	2.54 centimeters (cm)
1 foot	=	0.3048 meters (m)
1 foot	=	12 inches
1 yard	=	3 feet
1 meter (m)	=	100 centimeters (cm)
1 meter (m)	≈	3.280839895 feet
1 furlong	=	660 feet
1 kilometer (km)	=	1000 meters (m)
1 kilometer (km)	≈	0.62137119 miles
1 mile	=	5280 ft
1 mile	=	1.609344 kilometers (km)
1 nautical mile	=	1.852 kilometers (km)

The second column is giving the **conversion factors**, so to convert miles into kilometers, simply multiply the number of miles by 1.609344.

Example 1 Convert Length Units

VIDEO *Length Conversion*

Convert 5 feet into inches and centimeters by using a **ratio table**.

SOLUTION We will use the ratios 1 ft : 12 in. and 1 in. : 2.54 cm in the ratio table:

TABLE 3.2 Ratio Table for Converting Lengths

Feet (ft)	Inches (in.)	Centimeters (cm)
1	12	
	1	2.54
5	I	C

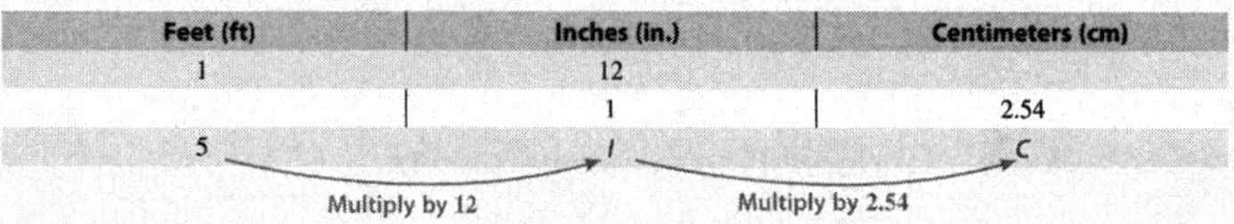

We can use the ratio table to set up **proportions**, cross multiply, and solve:

$$\frac{1}{5} = \frac{12}{I} \rightarrow I = 5 \cdot 12 = 60 \text{ in.}$$

Using this value of 60 in., we can set up the second proportion:

$$\frac{1}{60} = \frac{2.54}{C} \rightarrow C = 60 \cdot 2.54 = 152.4 \text{ cm}$$

Multiplying by the **conversion factors** gives us equations: $I = 12 \cdot F$, $C = 2.54 \cdot I$

Note how the units get added in at the end of the calculation, determined by what column the variable is in.

Alternatively, we can use the **proportional** relationship between columns given by the associated **conversion factors**, 12 and 2.54, and equations $I = 12 \cdot F$ and $C = 2.54 \cdot I$. We substitute $F = 5$ ft into the first equation $I = 12 \cdot 5 = 60$ in., which can then be substituted into the second equation $C = 2.54 \cdot 60 = 152.4$ cm.

CAUTION Remember not to confuse the equations with the ratios:

12 in. : 1 ft
2.54 cm : 1 in. ●

OBJECTIVE 2 Use Dimensional Analysis

A technique called **dimensional analysis** can help us keep track of our **units** and **conversion factors**. Notice that converting 5 feet to centimeters in Example 1 was a two-step process. We can combine these two steps into one computation by canceling units:

Because 12 inches = 1 foot, this fraction is 1. We are simply multiplying by 1, which changes only the units.

$$5\ \cancel{\text{ft}} \cdot \frac{12\ \cancel{\text{in.}}}{1\ \cancel{\text{ft}}} \cdot \frac{2.54\ \text{cm}}{1\ \cancel{\text{in.}}} = 5 \cdot 12 \cdot 2.54\ \text{cm}$$

Example 2 Use Dimensional Analysis

VIDEO *Dimensional Analysis*

Convert 120 euros to dollars, using the ratio 4 EUR : 5 USD.

SOLUTION Students are often confused about whether to multiply by 4/5 or 5/4 in order to solve this problem. The technique of canceling units (dimensional analysis) takes all the confusion out of this process. If we start with 120 EUR and need to cancel EUR to get to USD, we must multiply by the conversion factor with EUR in the denominator:

$$120\ \cancel{\text{EUR}} \cdot \frac{5\ \text{USD}}{4\ \cancel{\text{EUR}}} = \frac{120 \cdot 5}{4}\ \text{USD} = 150\ \text{USD}$$

This also helps us write down an equation for proportional quantities:

$$D = \frac{5\ \text{USD}}{4\ \text{EUR}} \cdot E$$

Assuming that euros will be the input, the 4 EUR goes in the denominator so that euros cancel when we substitute a value for E.

$$D = \frac{5\ \text{USD}}{4\ \cancel{\text{EUR}}} \cdot 120\ \cancel{\text{EUR}} = \frac{5 \cdot 120}{4}\ \text{USD} = 150\ \text{USD}$$

OBJECTIVE 3 Compare Ratio and Interval Units

There do exist **units** for the same quantity which are not **proportional**, which may seem odd. The best example is units for temperature. Doubling the number of degrees Fahrenheit does not correspond to a doubling of degrees Celsius.

Example 3 Convert Degrees Fahrenheit to Degrees Celsius

Convert 27°F and 54°F to degrees Celsius.

SOLUTION To convert temperature from degrees Fahrenheit to degrees Celsius, we use the equation:

$$C = \frac{5}{9} \cdot F - \frac{160}{9}$$

This is a linear equation, which we will study in Chapter 5. Substituting 27 for F, we can solve:

$$C = \frac{5}{9} \cdot 27 - \frac{160}{9} \approx 15 - 17.78 \approx -2.78°\text{C}$$

Similarly, substituting 54 for F, we get 12.22°C. Notice that the doubling from 27°F to 54°F does not transfer to degrees Celsius.

Doubling does not work for these units because they do not have a well-defined zero, which represents the absence of something. Zero degrees Fahrenheit was chosen to represent the freezing point of a brine solution—a totally arbitrary choice of zero—and 0°C corresponds to the freezing point of water. Units like feet and dollars have a well-defined zero that represents the absence of the underlying quantity (no length or money, respectively).

DEFINITION

There are two distinct types of measurement units:

1. **Ratio units** have a well-defined zero that represents the absence of something, such as feet, dollars, etc. It makes sense to talk about doubling these units.
2. **Interval units** do not have a well-defined zero that represents the absence of something, such as degrees Fahrenheit, IQ scores, etc. It does not make sense to double these units; we can only talk about the interval between them; for example, 10°F is 5° warmer than 5°F, not twice as hot.

Note that it is possible for a quantity to have both ratio and interval units. For example, temperature has **interval units**, °F, and **ratio units**, degrees Kelvin, with absolute zero representing the absence of molecular motion.

3.2 Scales

OBJECTIVE 1 **Compare Measurement and Model Scales**

OBJECTIVE 2 **Understand Unit-less Scales**

OBJECTIVE 1 Compare Measurement and Model Scales

Units of measurement involve the notion of scale, which we now define:

DEFINITION

There are two types of **scales** we encounter:

1. A **measurement scale** is a system of ordered marks, such as rulers and thermometers, used as a reference standard. These can be *ratio scales* or *interval scales*, depending on whether the units are **ratio units** or **interval units**.
2. A **model scale** is a ratio used to determine the size relationship between a model and that which it represents. A model scale indicates a change in magnitude. A model scale is typically given with the first quantity scaled to 1 and always between **proportional** quantities, with the **constant of proportionality** called the *scaling factor*.

Example 4 **Use a Model Scale**

On a map, the scale is given as 1 inch : 10 miles, meaning 1 inch on the map corresponds to 10 miles of actual distance. If two towns on the map are 3.6 inches apart, how far apart are they actually?

SOLUTION Set up a proportion and solve:

$$\frac{\text{Model (in.)}}{\text{Actual (mi)}} = \frac{1}{10} = \frac{3.6}{x}$$

$$x = 10 \cdot 3.6 = 36 \text{ mi.}$$

Note the difference between **scales**, which are changes in magnitude, and **conversions**, which are changes in units.

OBJECTIVE 2 Understand Unit-less Scales

A **model scale** indicates a change in magnitude between a model and that which it represents (the actual quantity). It is possible for the **units** of both quantities in a **ratio** to be the same, in which case the units cancel.

Model airplanes are usually on a 1 : 72 scale, meaning 1 inch (or cm, miles, etc.) of model length corresponds to 72 inches (or cm, miles, etc.) of actual length. This 1 : 72 scale is increasingly popular worldwide for die-cast toys and Japanese anime characters. In the United States, the 1 : 48 scale is still more prevalent. Note that this scale works for any units (as did the 1 : 72 scale): 1 cm corresponds with 48 cm and 1 foot corresponds with 48 feet.

Example 5 **Use a Unit-less Scale**

VIDEO *Unit-less Scale*

Given a 1 : 72 model scale, determine how many inches in the model corresponds to 1 foot in the actual.

SOLUTION This **scale** is **unit-less**, so we use any units we want for both quantities in the ratio of model to actual, such as 1 in. : 72 in.

We are asked to convert the units of the actual quantity to feet, which we can do by using the conversion 12 in. : 1 ft:

$$72 \cancel{\text{in.}} \cdot \frac{1 \text{ ft}}{12 \cancel{\text{in.}}} = \frac{72}{12} \text{ ft} = 6 \text{ ft}$$

We can now replace the 72 in. in the given scale with 6 ft and use a ratio table to scale the second quantity to 1:

Photocreo Bednarek/Fotolia

TABLE 3.3 Ratio Table for Model Scale

Model (in.)	Actual (ft)
1	6
x	1

The model scale 1 : 72 is **unit-less**. We can decide on units, such as 1 in. : 72 in., and then convert one of the quantities so that the scale is no longer unit-less, to 1 in. : 6 ft.

Setting up a proportion and solving, it is clear that $x = 1/6$ inch.

In both the map and model plane examples, the model is **in proportion** to the actual quantity. Thus we can use an equation to represent these relationships.

Example 6 **Use an Equation for a Model Scale**

On a map, the scale is given as 1 inch : 10 miles. Represent this proportional relationship with an equation and determine how far apart two towns are on the map if they actually are 64 miles apart.

SOLUTION Using the idea of dimensional analysis, we can write down the equation with actual (mi) as input:

$$\text{Model} = \frac{1 \text{ in.}}{10 \text{ mi}} \cdot \text{Actual}$$

The 10 mi goes in the denominator so that the units will cancel when we input the actual distance of 64 mi:

$$\text{Model} = \frac{1 \text{ in.}}{10 \cancel{\text{mi}}} \cdot 64 \cancel{\text{mi}} = \frac{64}{10} \text{ in.} = 6.4 \text{ in.}$$

Note the different use of units. The map scale 1 in. : 10 mi requires us to use inches and miles. The model scale 1 : 72 is **unit-less.**

Example 7 **Use an Equation for a Unit-less Model Scale**

Model airplanes are usually built on a 1 : 72 scale. Represent this proportional relationship with an equation and determine how long a model plane will be if the actual plane is 64 feet long.

SOLUTION We again can write down the equation with Actual as input, but we now have to set up a proportion and cross multiply to get the equation:

$$\frac{\text{Model}}{\text{Actual}} = \frac{1}{72} \rightarrow \text{Model} = \frac{1}{72} \cdot \text{Actual}$$

Now we substitute 64 feet into the equation. Since there are no units to cancel, the output will also be in feet:

$$\text{Model} = \frac{1}{72} \cdot 64 \text{ ft} = \frac{8}{9} \text{ ft}$$

A plane 64 feet in length will have a model that is 8/9 foot in length. Note also that this means a plane 64 meters in length will have a model that is 8/9 meter in length.

Photocreo Bednarek/Fotolia

The model scale 1 : 72 is **unit-less.** This means that whatever units we use for the input, the output will then have the same units.

3.3 Rates

OBJECTIVE 1 **Understand Compound Units**

OBJECTIVE 1 Understand Compound Units

We have just been looking at **unit-less ratios**, where both quantities involved had identical units that canceled. If the units are different, we often scale the second quantity to a "nice" number (one, one hundred, one thousand, etc.) and create a rate, as shown in **Figure 3.1**.

> **DEFINITION**
>
> A **rate** is a ratio between quantities with different units, with the second quantity scaled to a "meaningful standard" and read using the word "per." Rates have ***compound units*** like meters per second (m/s) or miles per gallon (mi/gal).

This figure gives the **ratio** of students to teachers as a single number, such as 12.29 in 2010–11 for the state of Maine.

How can a ratio be a single number?

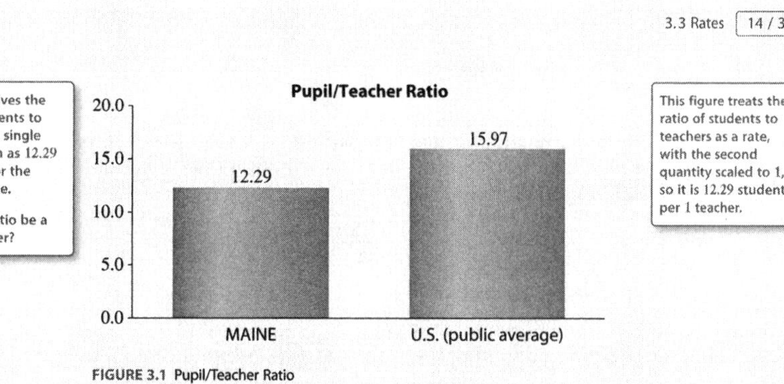

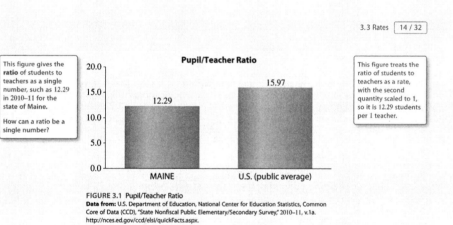

This figure treats the ratio of students to teachers as a rate, with the second quantity scaled to 1, so it is 12.29 students per 1 teacher.

FIGURE 3.1 Pupil/Teacher Ratio
Data from: U.S. Department of Education, National Center for Education Statistics, Common Core of Data (CCD), "State Nonfiscal Public Elementary/Secondary Survey," 2010–11, v.1a. http://nces.ed.gov/ccd/elsi/quickFacts.aspx.

Average rates typically are per 1, such as miles per hour, students per computer, etc. Population statistics tend to give rates per 1,000 people or 100,000 people, such as death rates, poverty rates, etc. Rates of return are percentages, meaning per 100, and are discussed in Chapter 4.

Example 8 **Verify Motor Vehicle Death Rates**

VIDEO *Rates*

At the beginning of Chapter 2, we saw the data shown in **Table 3.4**, giving motor vehicle deaths (MVD) in the U.S. as different rates. Verify the rate per 100,000 population and the rate per 100 million vehicles miles traveled (VMT) for 2011.

SOLUTION The fatality rate per 100,000 population is computed by comparing the MVD to the population. Note that the population is given in *thousands*, meaning each population number should be multiplied by 1,000:

$$\frac{32{,}367 \text{ MVD}}{311{,}592 \text{ thousand people}} = \frac{32{,}367 \text{ MVD}}{311{,}592{,}000 \text{ people}} = 1.039\text{ E} - 4$$

$$= 1.039 \cdot 10^{-4} \text{ MVD per person}$$

TABLE 3.4 Traffic Safety Data

Year	Killed	Resident Population (Thousands)	Fatality Rate per 100,000 Population	Licensed Drivers (Thousands)	Fatality Rate per 100,000 Licensed Drivers	Registered Motor Vehicles (Thousands)	Fatality Rate per 100,000 Registered Vehicles	Vehicle Miles Traveled (Billions)	Fatality Rate per 100 Million VMT
				Killed					
2002	43,005	287,625	14.95	194,602	22.10	225,685	19.06	2,856	1.51
2010	32,999	309,330	10.67	210,115	15.71	257,312	12.82	2,967	1.11
2011	32,367	311,592	10.39	211,875	15.28	257,512	12.57	2,946	1.10

Data from: U.S. Department of Transportation National Highway Traffic Safety Administration Traffic Safety, Facts 2011 Data April 2013, http://www-nrd.nhtsa.dot.gov/Pubs/811753.pdf

Notice that we are using scientific notation; the E−4 means to multiply by 10^{-4}, or move the decimal place four places to the left. This is a very small number and the reason these statistics are listed per 100,000:

$$\frac{1.039 \cdot 10^{-4} \text{ MVD}}{1 \text{ person}} \cdot \frac{100{,}000}{100{,}000} = \frac{10.39 \text{ MVD}}{100{,}000 \text{ people}}$$

Next, we look at the VMT:

$$\frac{32{,}367 \text{ MVD}}{2{,}946 \text{ billion VMT}} = \frac{32{,}367 \text{ MVD}}{2{,}946{,}000{,}000{,}000 \text{ VMT}} = 1.10\text{ E} - 8$$

$$= 1.10 \cdot 10^{-8} \text{ MVD per VMT}$$

As above, we now can convert the denominator to 100 million VMT:

$$\frac{1.10 \cdot 10^{-8} \text{ MVD}}{1 \text{ VMT}} \cdot \frac{100{,}000{,}000}{100{,}000{,}000} = \frac{1.10 \text{ MVD}}{100 \text{ million VMT}}$$

3.4 Dosages and Concentrations

OBJECTIVE 1 **Compare Dosage and Concentration**

OBJECTIVE 2 **Understand Density**

OBJECTIVE 1 Compare Dosage and Concentration

An important application of the concepts in this chapter involves medication dosages. Over-the-counter medications, such as aspirin and cough syrup, come with clearly labeled dosage amounts, such as "2 tablets every 2 hours" or "1 teaspoon every 6 hours for adults and children 12 years and over." Doctors, nurses, and veterinarians, however, are faced with a vast array of medications in varying concentrations (mg/ml, units/cc, %, etc.) and dosage amounts (mg/kg, units/lb, g/lb, etc.).

DEFINITION

The **concentration** of a solution is the ratio of the amount of one substance mixed with the amount of another substance. This is typically a weight-to-volume ratio but can also be a weight-to-weight ratio. The **dosage** of a given medicine is the ratio of the amount of a medicine to the weight of a patient.

Example 9 Use Concentration to Compute Medication

Dilantin at 0.5 g per dose is ordered and is available as 15 mg per 3 ml. Compute how many ml need to be administered.

SOLUTION The medication Dilantin is a powder that has been mixed into a solution with a concentration of 15 mg per 3 ml. We need to determine how much of the solution contains the 0.5 g we need.

First, convert 0.5 g to mg: $0.5\,\cancel{g} \cdot \frac{1{,}000\text{ mg}}{1\,\cancel{g}} = 500\text{ mg}$. Then convert this to ml, using the concentration:

$$500\,\cancel{\text{mg}} \cdot \frac{3\text{ ml}}{15\,\cancel{\text{mg}}} = 100\text{ ml}$$

Note that we inverted the concentration so that the 15 mg is in the denominator. We could have also set up a proportion here to solve for the ml.

It is important to note that in Example 9, we had two solution method options to solve for the 100 ml to administer. It is good to understand both approaches. The two approaches have nearly identical mathematics but subtly different thought processes:

1. **Dimensional analysis:** $500\,\cancel{\text{mg}} \cdot \frac{3\text{ ml}}{15\,\cancel{\text{mg}}} = x\text{ ml}$

2. Set up a **proportion** $\frac{3\text{ ml}}{15\text{ mg}} = \frac{x\text{ ml}}{500\text{ mg}}$

Example 10 | Use a Ratio Table for a Complicated Medication Problem

VIDEO *Dosage*

You have a sick alpaca and need to administer the de-worming paste Safeguard, with active ingredient Fenbendazole. The 25 g tube of Safeguard has a Fenbendazole **concentration** of 100 mg/g (10%), and the vet recommends you give a **dosage** of 20 mg/kg. Your alpaca weighs 122 lb. What do you do?

SOLUTION We can create a **ratio table** to keep track of all the information in this problem:

Using a ratio table is a nice way to organize all this information!

TABLE 3.5 Ratio Table for Medication Problem

	Fenben (mg)	Paste (g)	Alpaca (lb)	Alpaca (kg)
Dosage	20			1
Concentration	100	1		
Weight			122	

We need to determine how much paste to give the alpaca that weighs 122 lb:

We need to use the **conversion** 2.2 lb : 1 kg

TABLE 3.6 Ratio Table for Medication Problem with Variables

	Fenben (mg)	Paste (g)	Alpaca (lb)	Alpaca (kg)
Dosage	20		2.2	1
Concentration	100	1		
Weight	*F*	*P*	122	*A*

The ratio table allows us to break this problem into manageable steps.

First, we convert the alpaca's weight to kg:

$$\frac{A}{1} = \frac{122}{2.2} \rightarrow A \approx 55.5 \text{ kg}$$

Eric Gaze

Next, we determine the correct amount of Fenben needed, using the **dosage**:

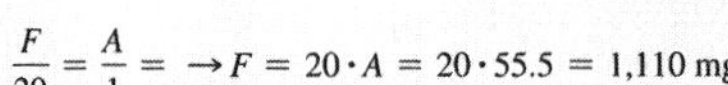

$$\frac{F}{20} = \frac{A}{1} = \rightarrow F = 20 \cdot A = 20 \cdot 55.5 = 1{,}110 \text{ mg}$$

Finally, we use the **concentration** to solve for the right amount of paste:

$$\frac{P}{1} = \frac{F}{100} \rightarrow P = \frac{1{,}110}{100} = 11.1 \text{ g}$$

Now for the hard part: The syringe has a plunger with a measurement scale marking off grams of paste, and you need to set the stopper to 11 *g* and prepare to squirt paste into your alpaca's mouth (and hope she will like it).

OBJECTIVE 2 Understand Density

The following table of weight and volume **conversions** is very helpful when dealing with **dosages** and **concentrations**. It is also useful for computing densities, which we discuss next.

Medicine often comes in solution, which means the concentrations will be: weight of medicine (not weight of liquid) to volume--for example, g/ml.

Note that a cubic centimeter is a cc and is equal to 1 ml.

TABLE 3.7 Conversion Table for Weight and Volume

Weight			Volume		
1 milligram (mg)	=	0.001 gram (g)	**1 U.S. tablespoon**	=	3 U.S. teaspoons
1 gram (g)	=	0.001 kilogram (kg)	**1 U.S. fluid ounce (fl oz)**	≈	29.57353 milliliters (ml)
1 gram (g)	≈	0.035273962 ounce	**1 U.S. cup**	=	16 U.S. tablespoons
1 ounce (oz)	=	28.34952312 grams (g)	**1 U.S. cup**	=	8 U.S. fluid ounces
1 ounce (oz)	=	0.0625 pound	**1 U.S. pint**	=	2 U.S. cups
1 pound (lb)	=	16 ounces	**1 U.S. pint**	=	16 U.S. fluid ounces
1 pound (lb)	=	0.45359237 kilogram (kg)	**1 liter (l)**	≈	33.8140227 U.S. fluid ounces
1 kilogram (kg)	=	1000 grams	**1 liter (l)**	=	1000 milliliters (ml)
1 kilogram (kg)	≈	35.273962 ounces	**1 milliliter (ml)**	=	1 cubic centimeter (cc)
1 kilogram (kg)	≈	2.20462262 pounds (lb)	**1 U.S. quart**	=	2 U.S. pints

DEFINITION

The **density** of an object is the ratio of its weight to the volume it occupies.

The **density** of a material refers to how much mass of the material occupies a fixed space. This explains why certain materials are heavier than others. A block of ice (916.7 kg/m^3) weighs less than a same-size block of lead (11,340 kg/m^3), which in turn weighs less than a same-size block of gold (19,320 kg/m^3). Please refer to the *Densities* sheet in ***Data Sets*** for the actual densities for these and other materials.

Densities often involve volume units like cubic meters (m^3) and cubic inches (in.^{3}). We have seen that 1 inch = 2.54 cm, so a square inch (in.^{2}), which is a square that measures 1 in. on each side, will have 2.54 cm on each side. The area of 1 in.^{2} in cm^2 is thus:

$$1 \text{ in.}^2 = 2.54^2 \text{ cm}^2$$

CAUTION Many students do not square the 2.54 when converting from square inches to square cm. Technically, we square the 1 on the left as well, but $1^2 = 1$. ●

Similarly, we can compare cubic inches and cubic centimeters:

1 cubic inch = the volume of a cube that is 1 inch on each side

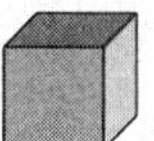

$$1 \text{ in.}^3 = 2.54^3 \text{ cm}^3$$
$$1 \text{ in.}^3 = 16.4 \text{ cm}^3$$

1 cubic cm is much smaller than 1 cubic inch! A cubic inch holds over 16 cubic cm.

Example 11 **Compare Masses Using Density**

VIDEO
Density

Determine the mass of a shoe box full of gold and the same shoe box full of lead. The shoe box has dimensions 12 inches long by 6 inches wide by 5 inches high.

SOLUTION: First, we determine the volume of the shoe box using Volume $= L \cdot W \cdot H = 12 \cdot 6 \cdot 5 = 360$ in.^{3}.

Next, we convert the density of gold and lead to kilograms per cubic inches:

$$\text{Gold: } \frac{19{,}300 \text{ kg}}{1\cancel{m}^3} \cdot \frac{1\cancel{m}^3}{100^3\cancel{cm}^3} \cdot \frac{2.54^3\cancel{cm}}{1 \text{ in.}^3} = 0.316 \text{ kg per in.}^3.$$

Similarly, lead is 0.186 kg per in.^{3}. Multiplying both of these by the volume, 360 in.^{3}, we get the masses:

$$\text{Gold: } \frac{0.316 \text{ kg}}{1\ \cancel{in}^3} \cdot 360\ \cancel{in.}^3 = 113.76 \text{ kg and Lead: : } \frac{0.186 \text{ kg}}{1\ \cancel{in.}^3} \cdot 360\ \cancel{in.}^3 = 66.96 \text{ kg}$$

In Example 11, we converted the **density** of gold in kg per m^3 to kg per in.^{3}. This involved converting just one of the two **units** in the **compound units**. If you are asked to convert both units in a compound units problem, focus on one quantity at a time.

Example 12 **Convert Compound Units**

VIDEO
Compound Units

Convert the density of water, 1,000 kg/m^3, to lb/gal.

SOLUTION We will proceed step by step, first converting the volume: multiplying by **conversion factors** to change cubic meters into cubic centimeters, then into ml and liters and gallons. Finally, we will convert the weight, multiplying by the conversion factor for kilograms to pounds:

When converting compound units focus on one unit at a time, taking intermediate steps using known **conversions**.

$$1{,}000 \text{ kg/m}^3 = \frac{1000 \text{ kg}}{1\ \cancel{m}^3} \cdot \frac{1\cancel{m}^3}{100^3\ \cancel{cm}^3} \cdot \frac{1\ \cancel{cc}}{1\ \cancel{ml}} \cdot \frac{1000\ \cancel{ml}}{1\ \cancel{l}} \cdot \frac{3.785\ \cancel{l}}{1 \text{ gal}} = 3.785\ \frac{\cancel{kg}}{\text{gal}} \cdot \frac{2.2 \text{ lb}}{1\cancel{kg}} = 8.327\ \frac{\text{lb}}{\text{gal}}$$

The term *density* also refers to population densities, meaning people per unit area. In the Chapter 2 homework on **ratios**, you were asked to compute the ratios of population to total area for each region listed in **Table 3.8**. These ratios are actually population densities.

TABLE 3.8 Population Densities United Nations *World Population Prospects 2012*

Region	Total Area (square km)	Total Landmass Percentage	Population (2010)	Total Population Percentage	Population Density per Square km
Asia	31,919,080	21.2%	4,165,440,000	60.2%	130.5
Europe	23,062,555	15.3%	740,308,000	10.7%	32.1
Africa	30,326,000	20.2%	1,031,084,000	14.9%	34.0
North America	21,792,516	14.5%	346,501,000	5.0%	15.9
Latin America and Caribbean	20,558,310	13.7%	596,191,000	8.6%	29.0
Oceania	8,525,349	5.7%	36,659,000	0.5%	4.3
Antarctica	14,285,714	9.5%	1,000	0.0%	0.0

Data from: United Nations, Department of Economic and Social Affairs, *World Population Prospects: 2012*. http://esa.un.org/wpp/

3.5 Spotlight on Statistics

OBJECTIVE 1 **Understand Standard Error of the Mean**

OBJECTIVE 1 Understand Standard Error of the Mean

In the *Spotlight on Statistics* in Chapter 2, we introduced the **z-score** as a way to compare a data value to the **center** and **spread** of the overall **distribution** of data. The *z*-score is actually a **unit-less ratio** because a data value's distance from the mean will have the same units as the **standard deviation**.

Example 13 Compute a *z*-Score as a Unit-less Ratio

VIDEO *z-Scores*

Using the height data in **Table 3.9,** compute the *z*-score of a U.S. woman who is 5 feet, 7 inches tall and interpret this score as a unit-less ratio.

SOLUTION Recall the definition of *z*-score:

$$z = \frac{x - \overline{X}}{\text{SD}} = \text{number of standard deviations from the mean.}$$

TABLE 3.9 Height in Inches for U.S. Females 20 Years of Age and Older By Race and Ethnicity and Age, Mean, Standard Error of the Mean, and Selected Percentiles, 2003–2006

Race and Ethnicity and Age	Number Examined	Mean	Standard Error	Percentile								
				5th	10th	15th	25th	50th	75th	85th	90th	95th
All race and ethnicity groups								Inches				
20 years and over	4,857	63.8	0.06	59.3	60.3	61.0	62.1	63.8	65.6	66.6	67.2	68.2
20–29 years	1,061	64.3	0.12	59.9	60.9	61.6	62.5	64.2	66.1	66.9	67.5	68.0
30–39 years	842	64.3	0.13	60.0	60.8	61.5	62.5	64.2	66.0	67.1	67.7	68.6
40–49 years	784	64.2	0.12	59.9	60.6	61.4	62.4	64.2	66.0	66.9	67.7	68.5
50–59 years	604	63.9	0.13	59.3	60.4	61.2	62.2	63.8	65.7	66.4	67.1	67.9
60–69 years	691	63.7	0.13	59.8	60.5	61.1	62.1	63.7	65.3	66.1	66.9	67.5
70–79 years	463	62.7	0.13	58.6	69.4	60.1	61.0	62.6	64.4	65.2	65.9	66.7
80 years and over	412	61.4	0.15	57.5	58.3	58.8	59.7	61.3	62.9	63.9	64.7	65.4

Data from: National Health Statistics Report No. 10, October 2008, Anthropometric Reference Data, U.S. 2003–06

The average height of the 4,857 women 20 years and older in this sample was 63.8 inches. The height data for men is in the homework.

The **mean** of this sample of 4,857 women is given as $\overline{X} = 63.8$ inches, and the data value in question is 5 feet, 7 inches tall, $x = 67$ inches. To compute the **z-score**, we also need the **standard deviation**, but it is not given in the table, so we will have to estimate the standard deviation, using our knowledge of the **normal distribution** and associated **percentiles**. (We can assume the distribution of heights to be normal.)

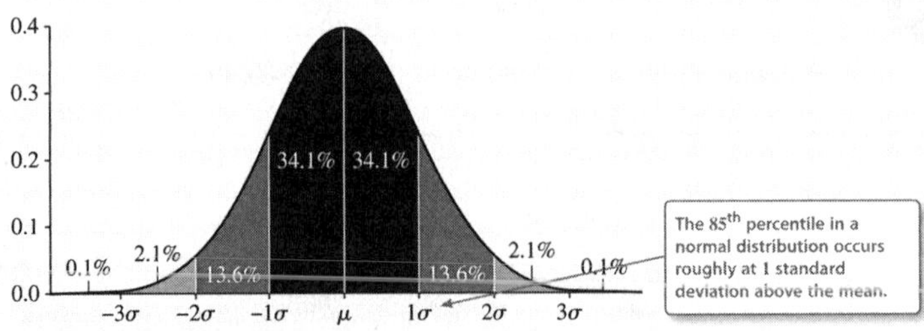

FIGURE 3.2 The Normal Distribution

Notice that in the normal distribution, 34.1% of the data lies between the mean, μ, and 1σ (which represents 1 standard deviation above the mean). Adding the 50% of the data to the left of the mean, we get that 1σ represents the 84.1 percentile (84.1% of the data lie to the left of 1σ). Thus the distance between the 85th percentile, 66.6 inches, and the mean, 63.8 inches is roughly 1 SD, 2.8 inches.

TABLE 3.10 Heights in Inches for U.S. Females 20 Years of Age and Older By Race and Ethnicity and Age, Mean, Standard Error of the Mean, and Selected Percentiles, 2003–2006

Race and Ethnicity and Age	Number Examined	Mean	Standard Error	Percentile								
				5th	10th	15th	25th	50th	75th	85th	90th	95th
All race and ethnicity groups								Inches				
20 years and over	4,857	63.8	0.06	59.3	60.3	61.0	62.1	63.8	65.6	66.6	67.2	68.2
20–29 years	1,061	64.3	0.12	59.9	60.9	61.6	62.5	64.2	66.1	66.9	67.5	68.0
30–39 years	842	64.3	0.13	60.0	60.8	61.5	62.5	64.2	66.0	67.1	67.7	68.6
40–49 years	784	64.2	0.12	59.9	60.6	61.4	62.4	64.2	66.0	66.9	67.7	68.5
50–59 years	604	63.9	0.13	59.3	60.4	61.2	62.2	63.8	65.7	66.4	67.1	67.9
60–69 years	691	63.7	0.13	59.8	60.5	61.1	62.1	63.7	65.3	66.1	66.9	67.5
70–79 years	463	62.7	0.13	58.6	59.4	60.1	61.0	62.6	64.4	65.2	65.9	66.7
80 years and over	412	61.4	0.15	57.5	58.3	58.8	59.7	61.3	62.9	63.9	64.7	65.4

Data from: National Health Statistics Report No. 10, October 2008, Anthropometric Reference Data, U.S. 2003–06

> We can estimate the standard deviation of the sample of 4,857 heights by subtracting the mean, 63.8, from the 85th percentile, 66.6, giving us 2.8 inches.

The *z*-score can now be computed for a woman who is 5 feet, 7 inches tall:

$$z = \frac{x - \overline{X}}{\text{SD}} = \frac{67 \text{ in.} - 63.8 \text{ in.}}{2.8 \text{ in.}} = \frac{3.2 \text{ in.}}{2.8 \text{ in.}} = 1.14$$

Notice that the units cancel, and we get the **unit-less ratio**, 1.14, meaning a height of 5 feet, 7 inches is 1.14 standard deviations above the mean of 63.8 inches.

We were given the sample mean height of 63.8 inches from a sample of 4,857 women, but instead of giving the standard deviation, **Table 3.10** gives a statistic called the standard error, 0.06. If we took another sample of women, we would get a different sample mean. The variability in these sample means is measured by the standard error.

DEFINITION

The **standard error of the mean** is the standard deviation of the distribution of sample means. The standard error can be estimated using a standard deviation from a sample $\mathrm{SE} \approx \frac{\mathrm{SD}}{\sqrt{N}}$, where N is the number of values in the sample.

The **distribution of sample means** refers to the data set we could create by repeatedly sampling 4,857 random representative women and computing their mean height. Every time we did this we would get a different sample mean height. This is an important and subtle point that deserves special care!

Statistics is the study of variability. We characterize variability by describing the shape of the distribution (bell shape, skewed, etc.), the center of the distribution (mean, median, mode), and the spread of the distribution (standard deviation, range, count, max, min). The shape, center, and spread are the **three essences of variability**. We encounter **two types of variability**: natural variability (heights, IQ scores etc.) and sampling variability (e.g., different means from repeated sampling).

The **standard error** (SE) measures sampling variability; it is the **standard deviation** of the **distribution of the sample means**. The central limit theorem tells us that this distribution of sample means will be approximately normal, so we can use our knowledge of the **normal distribution** and **percentiles** to interpret the standard error. First, we will interpret the standard deviation of a normal distribution.

Example 14 Interpret the Standard Deviation of a Normal Distribution

VIDEO *95% rule*

Use the standard deviation, 2.8 inches, for the sample of 4,857 U.S. women's heights from Example 13 to determine the intervals about the sample mean, 63.8 inches, which contain 68% of women's heights, 95% of women's heights, and 99.7% of women's heights.

SOLUTION Using the facts about the normal distribution in **Figure 3.3**, we can say the following:

68% of women's heights are in the interval 63.8 in. $\pm$ 2.8 in., which is 61 in. $\leftrightarrow$ 66.6 in.

95% of women's heights are in the interval 63.8 in. $\pm$ $2 \cdot (2.8 \text{ in.})$, which is 58.2 in. $\leftrightarrow$ 69.4 in.

99.7% of women's heights are in the interval 63.8 in. $\pm$ $3 \cdot (2.8 \text{ in.})$, which is 55.4 in. $\leftrightarrow$ 72.2 in.

Notice that we are simply adding and subtracting multiples of the SD from the mean. The fact that 95% of data in a normal distribution are within 2 SD of the mean is called the **95% Rule**.

In the normal curve, 68% of the data is within 1 SD of the mean, 95% within 2 SD, and 99.7% within 3 SD of the mean.

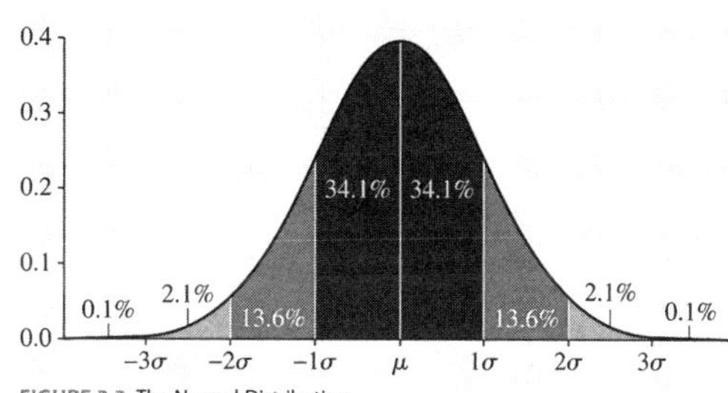

FIGURE 3.3 The Normal Distribution

The natural variability in women's heights is given by the ±1 SD, ±2 SD, ±3 SD in the sentences above.

The **standard error** measures the spread of the **distribution of sample means**, and tells us how accurate our **sample mean** is in terms of estimating the true population mean. The sample mean, 63.8 inches, of 4,857 women estimates the true mean height of all U.S. women. We can interpret the standard error just as we did for the **standard deviation**, but note how much smaller the standard error, 0.06 inches, is than the sample standard deviation, 2.8 inches. There is a good chance a random woman has a height over 5 ft 6 inches (which is less than 1 SD from the mean), but there is basically zero chance a random sample of 4,857 women has a sample mean height over 5 ft 6 inches (which is about 36 SE from the mean).

Example 15 Interpret the Standard Error

VIDEO *Standard Error Rule*

Interpret the meaning of the standard error of the mean, 0.06 inches, for this sample mean of 63.8 inches with respect to the true population mean.

SOLUTION Using the facts about the normal distribution in **Figure 3.4**, we can say the following:

There is a 68% chance that 63.8 in. is within 0.06 in. of the **true population mean.**

There is a 95% chance that 63.8 in. is within 2 • (0.06 in.) of the true population mean.

There is a 99.7% chance that 63.8 in. is within 3 • (0.06 in.) of the true population mean.

Notice that as we increase our certainty of being right, the error is doubled from 0.06 to 0.12 and then tripled to 0.18. The fact that tripling the error gives us almost 100% certainty comes from the normal curve and 3 SD from the mean capturing 99.7% of the data.

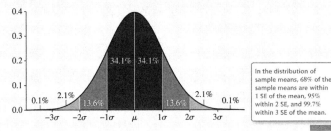

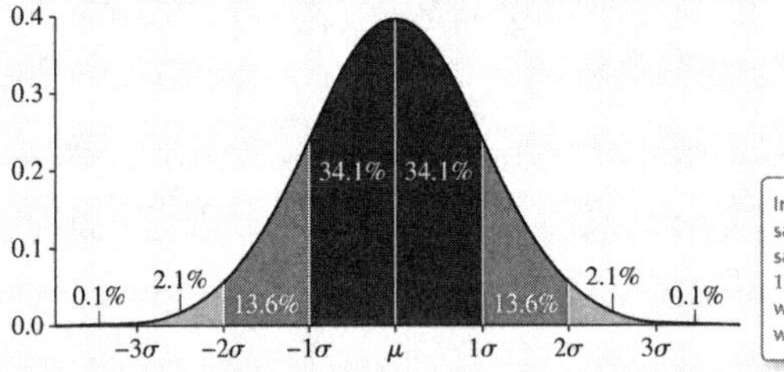

FIGURE 3.4 The Normal Distribution

In the distribution of sample means, 68% of the sample means are within 1 SE of the mean, 95% within 2 SE, and 99.7% within 3 SE of the mean.

Example 15 interpreted the **standard error** slightly differently than we did for the **standard deviation** in Example 14. In Example 14, we knew the mean of the data set and computed intervals about 63.8 inches. In Example 15, we did not know the true population mean so we talked about the probability of being close to this unknown mean. These probabilities can be turned into intervals about the sample mean. Watch the video for an explanation of how the sentences below in Example 16 follow from Example 15.

Example 16 Interpret the Standard Error to Estimate the True Mean

VIDEO *Mu*

Translate the general interpretations from Example 15 of the standard error of the mean, 0.06 inches, into specific intervals about the sample mean.

SOLUTION Using the facts about the normal distribution in **Figure 3.4,** we can say the following:

There is a 68% probability that the average height of women in the U.S. is 63.8 in. ± 0.06 in., which is 63.74 in. ↔ 63.86 in.

There is a 95% probability that the average height of women in the U.S. is 63.8 in. ± 0.12 in., which is 63.68 in. ↔ 63.92 in.

There is a 99.7% probability that the average height of women in the U.S. is 63.8 in. ± 0.18 in., which is 63.62 in. ↔ 63.98 in.

Notice that as we increase our certainty of being right, the error is doubled from 0.06 to 0.12 and then tripled to 0.18. The fact that tripling the error gives us almost 100% certainty comes from the normal curve and 3 SD from the mean capturing 99.7% of the data.

The error is given by the ±1 SE, ±2 SE, ±3 SE in the sentences above.

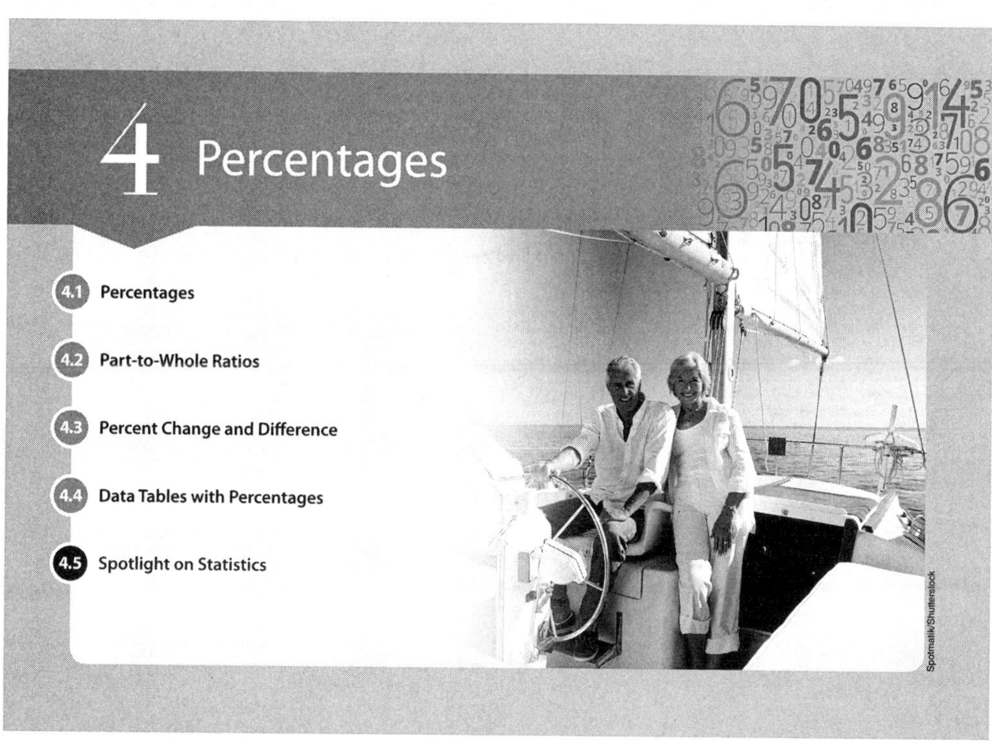

04-1

2 / 28

4.1 Percentages

OBJECTIVE 1 **Understand Rates per 100**

OBJECTIVE 2 **Represent Percentages as Fractions and Decimals**

04-2 (second slide, continued)

OBJECTIVE 1 Understand Rates per 100

Percentages are perhaps the most common type of **ratio**, and we have already seen several examples including the **APR** associated with loans in Chapter 1. In Chapter 3 we studied **rates**, and percentages are a special type of rate with the second quantity scaled to 100.

DEFINITION

A **percentage** is a *ratio* where the second quantity has been scaled to 100 (e.g., $x : 100$). The first quantity is then said to be x percent (x %) of the second. The second quantity is referred to as the *base*. Percentages are sometimes referred to as *rates* because they are *per 100*, with interest rates and rates of return (comparing interest gained to the initial investment) being the two most common examples of this. The word *percent* originally was two words, *per cent*, meaning "per one hundred". The symbol % contains a line and two zeros, like the numeral 100.

04-2

Example 1 Interpret a Rate of Return

VIDEO
Annuity

In **Figure 4.1** use the 1 year **rate of return** to determine the ending balance on 2/28/2014 of an account with a starting balance of $50,000 on 2/28/2013.

An **annuity** is a type of retirement account that allows you to invest money without paying income tax on the deposit. This money can then be withdrawn after retirement. A traditional annuity is a contract guaranteeing a distribution of income over time, based on premiums paid into the annuity.

GUARANTEED
TIAA Traditional Annuity - Group Retirement Annuity
Rates of Return for the Period Ending 02/28/2014

Current Rates	1 Year	3 Year	5 Year
3.75% AS OF CLOSE 02/28/2014	^ 3.00%	^ 3.89%	^ 4.18%

The TIAA Traditional Annuity is a guaranteed annuity account backed by TIAA's claims-paying ability. It guarantees your principal and a contractually specified minimum interest rate, plus it offers the opportunity for additional amounts in excess of this guaranteed rate. These additional amounts are declared on a year-by-year basis by the TIAA Board of Trustees.

FIGURE 4.1 TIAA Traditional Annuity Rates of Return
Data from: Values from TIAA Traditional Annuity. Published by TIAA-CREF, © 2014.

SOLUTION The 1 year **rate of return** is 3%, or 3 : 100, meaning we will get $3 of interest for every $100 invested.

TABLE 4.1 Rate of Return

Interest Earned	Starting Balance
3	100
x	50,000

Setting up a **proportion** and cross multiplying, we can solve for x:

$$\frac{3}{100} = \frac{x}{50{,}000} \rightarrow 3 \cdot 50{,}000 = 100 \cdot x \rightarrow x = \frac{3}{100} \cdot 50{,}000 = \$1{,}500$$

Thus our ending balance is the starting balance plus the interest:

$$\$50{,}000 + \$1{,}500 = \$1{,}500 = \$51{,}500$$

Notice that in our solution, we arrived at the equation:

$$x = \frac{3}{100} \cdot 50{,}000 = 3\% \cdot 50{,}000$$

Note that rates of return (and **interest rates**) are an exception to the rule that **rates** are **ratios** comparing different **units**.

This leads to the sentence *$1,500 is 3% of $50,000* and the equation:

$$\text{Interest} = \text{rate} \cdot \text{Principal}$$
$$I = r \cdot P$$

Taking 3% of a quantity means we multiply the quantity by 3%.

OBJECTIVE 2 Represent Percentages as Fractions and Decimals

The fact that a **percentage** is a **rate** per 100 allows us to write percentages as fractions and hence decimals. This leads to memorizing rules about moving the decimal point two places left or right, which can be easy to apply for percentages such as $75\% = 0.75$ but may cause confusion when working with percentages less than 1% or greater than 100%. We will always focus on the rate per 100 aspect to help avoid this confusion.

Example 2 Represent Percentages as Fractions and Decimals

Fill in the missing values in **Table 4.2**:

SOLUTION

The numerals in the first column are the numerators in the fractions. Dividing by 100 moves the decimal point two places to the left in the third column.

TABLE 4.2 Percentages as Fractions and Decimals

Percentages	Fractions	Decimals
75%	$^{75}/_{100}$	0.75
4.5%		
	$^{275}/_{100}$	
		0.0023
100%		

TABLE 4.3 Percentages as Fractions and Decimals Solved

Percentages	Fractions	Decimals
75%	$^{75}/_{100}$	0.75
4.5%	$^{4.5}/_{100}$	0.045
275%	$^{275}/_{100}$	2.75
0.23%	$^{0.23}/_{100}$	0.0023
100%	$^{100}/_{100}$	1

CAUTION Many people incorrectly state that to write a decimal as a percentage, *multiply by 100*. The correct statement is to *multiply by 100%*, which equals one. This moves the decimal point two places right and inserts the % symbol. ●

Example 3 Use a Percentage Less Than 1%

You take out a 5-year car loan for $18,000, with a 6% **APR**. The fixed monthly payment is $347.99. How much **interest** do you owe after one month? How much interest do you pay over the life of the loan?

SOLUTION Recall from Chapter 1 that the **monthly interest rate (periodic rate)** is $^{6\%}/_{12} = 0.5\%$.

The interest charged each month is thus $0.5 per $100 on the balance that you owe at the start of the month. If you owe $18,000 at the start of the first month, you can compute the interest as follows:

$$\frac{0.5}{100} = \frac{\text{Interest}}{18{,}000} \rightarrow \text{Interest} = \frac{0.5}{100} \cdot 18{,}000 = \$90$$

To compute the total interest charged over the entire term, we could build a spreadsheet as we did in Chapter 1. Note that the new balance is the starting balance minus the payment plus the interest charged.

In Chapter 9 we will explore using built-in financial functions to compute the monthly payment. For now, look back at the payment function in Chapter 1.

TABLE 4.4 Car Loan Payoff Schedule

Month	Balance	Payment	Interest	New Balance
1	$18,000.00	($347.99)	$ 90.00	$17,742.01
2	$17,742.01	($347.99)	$ 88.71	$17,482.73
59	$690.80	($347.99)	$ 3.45	$346.26
60	$346.26	($347.99)	$ 1.73	($0.00)

We could then sum the Interest column, or we could simply multiply our monthly payments by the number of months and subtract the $18,000 borrowed:

$$\$347.99 \cdot 60 - \$18{,}000 = \$2{,}879.40$$

CAUTION When using Excel, the Accounting format presents negative numbers in red with parentheses. Subtracting a negative number results in addition! ●

SPREADSHEET TUTORIALS Entering Data by Range | Entering Numbers | Copying a Formula Using the Fill Handle | Constructing a Formula and Using the SUM Function | Using Arithmetic Operators | Formatting Financial Numbers

4.2 Part-to-Whole Ratios

OBJECTIVE 1 Understand Part-to-Part Ratios

OBJECTIVE 2 Evaluate Concentrations

OBJECTIVE 1 Understand Part-to-Part Ratios

The most common interpretation of a **percentage** is as a **part-to-whole ratio**. Indeed many people define percentages as part-to-whole ratios, which can cause much confusion when dealing with other uses of percentages.

Example 4 Use a Percentage for a Part-to-Part Ratio

The **ratio** of boys to girls in a class is 2 : 3. Interpret this **part-to-part ratio** as a percentage and compute the associated part-to-whole ratios.

SOLUTION Recall from Chapter 2 that when dealing with part-to-part ratios, we use a **ratio table** and include a column for the whole:

TABLE 4.5 Part-to-Part Ratios

Boys (part)	Girls (part)	Students (whole)
2	3	5
x	100	
B	G	**100**

First, we scale the second quantity in the 2 : 3 ratio to 100 and solve for x:

$$\frac{2}{3} = \frac{x}{100} \rightarrow 2 \cdot 100 = 3 \cdot x \rightarrow x \approx 66.7$$

So the boy-to-girl **ratio** of 2 : 3 has been scaled to 66.7 : 100. Interpreting this leads to incorrect statements such as:

1. WRONG: The number of boys is 66.7% of the number of students in class.
2. WRONG: 66.7% of the girls are boys.

The first sentence is mistaking the **part-to-part** ratio as a **part-to-whole ratio**. The second sentence is obviously silly, but it is trickier to determine what is wrong with it. The correct statement is as follows:

3. CORRECT: The number of boys is 66.7% of the number of girls.

TABLE 4.6 Part-to-Part Ratios

Boys (part)	Girls (part)	Students (whole)
2	3	5
66.7	100	
B	G	100

CAUTION It is very easy to misinterpret a part-to-part ratio as part-to-whole. ●

Next, we can compute the respective part-to-whole ratios:

$$\frac{2}{5} = \frac{B}{100} \rightarrow 2 \cdot 100 = 5 \cdot B \rightarrow B = 40$$

$$\frac{3}{5} = \frac{G}{100} \rightarrow 3 \cdot 100 = 5 \cdot G \rightarrow G = 60$$

So the ratio of boys to students is 40 : 100 and girls to students is 60 : 100, meaning that 40% of the class are boys and 60% are girls. And notice that the 40 : 60 ratio of boys to girls is also equivalent to 66.7 : 100.

Another example illustrates the care needed when dealing with **part-to-part ratios**.

Example 5 Compute Merchandise Mark-down

Eddie Bauer is having a storewide clearance sale. Everything is 70% off, and the Weather Edge Rain Parka you have been wanting is now \$45. What was the original price?

SOLUTION In this example, we have to determine the two parts that make up the whole (original price). If we label one part mark-down, meaning the amount the price was reduced, then the second part would be the new price, or what is left after we reduce.

TABLE 4.7 Part-to-Part Mark-down

Mark-down (part)	New Price (part)	Original Price (whole)
x	45	P
70	30	100

This problem is interesting in that information is hidden. Knowing that the mark-down is 70% means we save \$70 for every \$100 of the original price. Knowing this is a **part-to-whole ratio** helps us see that the missing part is \$30.

We can now solve for the original price by using the **ratio table**:

$$\frac{30}{100} = \frac{45}{P} \rightarrow 30 \cdot P = 100 \cdot 45 \rightarrow P = \$150$$

We can subtract the \$45 from the original price of \$150 to get that the mark-down is \$105. Notice that in setting up the **proportion**, we could have written $\frac{30}{100} \cdot P = 45$, or 30% of P is \$45, and then solved for P. This is a great sale, and you hope they don't just have XXL in purple paisley left!

CAUTION Notice how we needed the missing part, 30%, to solve this problem. ●

OBJECTIVE 2 Evaluate Concentrations

In Chapter 3 we studied **concentration** and **dosage**. Sometimes a concentration is given as a **percentage**.

Example 6 Use Concentration as a Percentage

VIDEO Concentration

Your veterinarian is administering a sedative to your 25-pound dog. The sedative is mixed in saline solution. Unfortunately, the solution is premixed at 0.5% for a horse, and it needs to be a 0.05% concentration to be administered at 5 ml per pound for your dog. How much saline solution needs to be added to the current solution to reduce the concentration to 0.05% and make the correct dosage for the dog?

SOLUTION The 0.5% refers to a **part-to-whole ratio** of 0.5 ml of sedative to 100 ml of solution. As always, we put all this information into a **ratio table**:

TABLE 4.8 Part-to-Whole Concentrations as Percentages

Part	Whole #1 (0.5%)	Whole #2 (0.05%)	
Sedative (ml)	Original Solution (ml)	New Solution (ml)	Dog (lb)
0.5	100		
0.05		100	
		5	1
S	O	N	25

Dilution is an important concept for anyone interested in the biological sciences. In general, if we add 100 ml of saline solution to 100 ml of the 0.5% solution, we will have 0.5 ml of sedative to 200 ml of solution, reducing the concentration to 0.25%:

$$\frac{0.5}{200} = \frac{0.25}{100} = 0.25\%$$

CAUTION It is *very* important to remember that the saline solution contains only water and salt. The solution for the horse contains both saline solution and the sedative. We add saline solution to the solution in order to reduce the concentration of the sedative. ●

Once we have our **ratio table** filled in, it is just a matter of setting up **proportions**. Looking back at **Table 4.8**, we will first solve for the amount of the new solution, N, our dog needs. Then we will determine the amount of sedative, S, in this solution; finally, we will determine how much of the old solution, O, has this same amount of sedative:

$$\frac{N}{25} = \frac{5}{1} \rightarrow N = 125 \text{ ml}$$

$$\frac{S}{0.05} = \frac{N}{100} \rightarrow 100 \cdot S = 0.05 \cdot N \rightarrow S = \frac{0.05}{100} \cdot 125 = 0.0625 \text{ ml}$$

$$\frac{S}{0.5} = \frac{O}{100} \rightarrow 100 \cdot S = 0.5 \cdot O \rightarrow O = \frac{100}{0.5} \cdot 0.0625 = 12.5 \text{ ml}$$

TABLE 4.9 Part-to-Whole Concentrations as Percentages

Part	Whole #1 (0.5%)	Whole #2 (0.05%)	
Sedative (ml)	Original Solution (ml)	New Solution (ml)	Dog (lb)
0.5	100		
0.05		100	
		5	1
0.0625	12.5	125	25

CAUTION There are two different wholes in this table. •

Now we use the concept of **dilution**. We know that 12.5 ml of the original 0.5% solution has the correct amount of the sedative, as does 125 ml of the new 0.05% solution. So we take 12.5 ml of the original 0.5% solution and add 112.5 ml of saline water to it to get 125 ml of the new 0.05% solution.

4.3 Percent Change and Difference

OBJECTIVE 1 **Compare Total and Relative Change**

OBJECTIVE 2 **Compare Total and Relative Difference**

OBJECTIVE 3 **Use Growth/Decay Rates/Factors**

OBJECTIVE 1 Compare Total and Relative Change

In Chapter 2 we saw the data in **Table 4.10** on the costs of attending college in 2013–14. Notice that we are given the costs in 2012–13 also for comparison purposes, and it is clear that costs have increased in each sector and category. We can quantify this increase by subtracting the two values and get the **total change**, or **$ change**. In addition, the table lists **percent change, or % change**, and this is our next application of percentages.

TABLE 4.10 Average Published Charges, Full-Time Undergraduate Students.

	Tuition and Fees				Room and Board				Total Charges			
Sector	2013–14	2012–13	$ Change	% Change	2013–14	2012–13	$ Change	% Change	2013–14	2012–13	$ Change	% Change
Public Two-Year In-State	$3,264	$3,154	$110	3.5%	$7,466	$7,342	$124	1.7%	$10,730	$10,496	$234	2.2%
Public Four-Year In-State	$8,893	$8,646	$247	2.9%	$9,498	$9,171	$327	3.6%	$18,391	$17,817	$574	3.2%
Public Four-Year Out-of-State	$22,203	$21,533	$670	3.1%	$9,498	$9,171	$327	3.6%	$31,701	$30,704	$997	3.2%
Private Nonprofit Four-Year	$30,094	$28,989	$1,105	3.8%	$10,823	$10,458	$365	3.5%	$40,917	$39,447	$1,470	3.7%
For-Profit	$15,130	$15,060	$70	0.5%	—	—	—	—	—	—	—	—

Source: *Trends in College Pricing 2013*. Data derived from the *Annual Survey of Colleges*. Copyright ©2013. The College Board. www.collegeboard.org. Reproduced with permission.

Many find percent change confusing and ask why bother with it if we have total change. Look again at **Table 4.10**. Notice that the tuition and fees for *Public Four-Year Out-of-State* undergraduate students increased by $670 compared to only a $110 increase for *Public Two-Year In-State*; but the % change for *Four-Year* is actually less, 3.1% compared to 3.5%, for the *Two-Year*. The percent change puts the total change in perspective by comparing it to the original value, once again demonstrating the power of ratios. An increase of $670 is significant if we start with $1,000, but not so much if we start with $100,000.

DEFINITION

When a quantity changes in value from an original value to a new value, there are two ways to quantify this change:

1. **Total** (Absolute) **change** = New − Original.
2. **Percent** (Relative) **change** = (Total Change)/Original

The percent change is a ratio of total change to the original value and is read as a percentage of the original. We say, "The new value is $x\%$ more (or less) than the original."

Example 7 Compute Total and Percent Change

VIDEO *Change*

Verify both the \$ change and % change for *Public Four-Year Out-of-State* tuition and fees from 2012–13 to 2013–14 given in **Table 4.10**.

SOLUTION The tuition and fees went from \$21,533 to \$22,203:

$$\$ \text{ change} = \$22{,}203 - \$21{,}533 = \$670$$
$$\% \text{ change} = \$670/\ \$21{,}533 \approx 0.031 = 3.1\%$$

Thus tuition and fees increased by 3.1% from 2012–13 to 2013–14 for *Public Four-Year Out-of-State* undergraduate students; or the 2013–14 tuition and fees are 3.1% more than the 2012–13 tuition and fees. Using an arrow diagram is a nice way to keep track of the quantities involved:

$$\underset{\text{2012–13 (original)}}{\$21{,}533} \xrightarrow[\mathbf{+3.1\%}]{\mathbf{+\$670}} \underset{\text{2013–14 (new)}}{\$22{,}203}$$

SPREADSHEET TUTORIALS Calculating a Value after an Increase Calculating the Percentage Rate of Increase

OBJECTIVE 2 Compare Total and Relative Difference

We compute the percent change when we are referring to the same quantity changing over time. If we are comparing the sizes of two different quantities, we compute the total and percent difference.

DEFINITION

The difference in size between two quantities can be measured in two ways:

1. **Total** (Absolute) **difference** = 2nd Quantity − 1st Quantity
2. **Percent** (Relative) **difference** = (Total Difference)/(1st Quantity)

The percent difference is a ratio of total difference from the first quantity and is read as a percentage of the first quantity. We say "The second quantity is $x\%$ more (or less) than the first quantity."

Example 8 Compute Total and Percent Difference

Compute the total and percent difference between the tuition and fees for *Public Four-Year Out-of-State* undergraduate students and *Private Nonprofit Four-Year* in 2013–14 from **Table 4.10**.

SOLUTION The tuition and fees for *Public Four-Year Out-of-State* were \$22,203 versus \$30,094 for *Private Nonprofit Four-Year* in 2013–14. We will set up two arrow diagrams:

$$\underset{\text{Public }(1^{\text{st}})}{\$22{,}203} \xrightarrow[\frac{7{,}891}{22{,}203} = \mathbf{+35.5\%}]{\mathbf{+\$7{,}891}} \underset{\text{Private }(2^{\text{nd}})}{\$30{,}094}$$

$$\underset{\text{Private }(1^{\text{st}})}{\$30{,}094} \xrightarrow[\frac{-7{,}891}{30{,}094} = \mathbf{-26.2\%}]{\mathbf{-\$7{,}891}} \underset{\text{Public }(2^{\text{nd}})}{\$22{,}203}$$

OBJECTIVE 3 Use Growth/Decay Rates/Factors

We now know how to compute change in both number and percent, as given in **Table 4.11**. In this section, we introduce a new way of using the **percent change** to compute the new value from the original. This approach will be crucial for understanding exponential growth in Chapter 6, so this is more than just an academic exercise.

TABLE 4.11 Population Change for the Ten Most Populous and Ten Fastest-Growing Metropolitan Statistical Areas, 2000 to 2010

Metropolitan statistical area	Population		Change	
	2000	2010	Number	Percent
Most Populous				
New York-Northern New Jersey-Long Island, NY-NJ-PA	18,323,002	18,897,109	574,107	3.1
Los Angeles-Long Beach-Santa Ana, CA	12,365,627	12,828,837	463,210	3.7
Chicago-Joliet-Naperville, IL-IN-WI	9,098,316	9,461,105	362,789	4.0
Dallas-Fort Worth-Arlington, TX	5,161,544	6,371,773	1,210,229	23.4
Philadelphia-Camden-Wilmington, PA-NJ-DE-MD	5,687,147	5,965,343	278,196	4.9
Houston-Sugar Land-Baytown, TX	4,715,407	5,946,800	1,231,393	26.1
Washington-Arlington-Alexandria, DC-VA-MD-WV	4,796,183	5,582,170	785,987	16.4
Miami-Fort Lauderdale-Pompano Beach, FL	5,007,564	5,564,635	557,071	11.1
Atlanta-Sandy Springs-Marietta, GA	4,247,981	5,268,860	1,020,879	24.0
Boston-Cambridge-Quincy, MA-NH	4,391,344	4,552,402	161,058	3.7
Fastest-Growing				
Palm Coast, FL	49,832	98,696	48,864	98.1
St. George, UT	90,354	138,115	47,761	52.9
Las Vegas-Paradise, NV	1,375,765	1,951,269	575,504	41.8
Raleigh-Cary, NC	797,071	1,130,490	333,419	41.8
Cape Coral-Fort Myers, FL	440,888	618,754	177,866	40.3
Provo-Orem, UT	376,774	526,810	150,036	39.8
Greeley, CO	180,926	252,825	71,899	39.7
Austin-Round Rock-San Marcos, TX	1,249,763	1,716,289	466,526	37.3
Myrtle Beach-North Myrtle Beach-Conway, SC	196,629	269,291	72,662	37.0
Bend, OR	115,367	157,733	42,366	36.7

For information on confidentiality protection, nonsampling error, and definitions, see www.census.gov/prod/cen2010/doc/pl97-171.pdf
Data from: *Population Distribution and Change: 2000 to 2010, U.S. Census Bureau, 2010 Census,* http://www.census.gov/prod/cen2010/briefs/c2010br-01.pdf

Example 9 Use a Growth Rate

VIDEO *Growth Decay Rates*

In **Table 4.11** the Dallas-Fort Worth Metropolitan area had an estimated population of 5,161,544 people, according to the 2000 census, and it grew by 23.4% over the ensuing decade. What was the estimated population in 2010?

SOLUTION We can draw an arrow diagram, with x representing the unknown new population in 2010:

$$\underset{\substack{2000\text{ (original)}\\100\%}}{5{,}161{,}544} \xrightarrow{\quad +23.4\% \quad} \underset{\substack{2010\text{ (new)}\\123.4\%}}{x}$$

It is helpful to represent the original value with 100%. If this grows by 23.4%, then the new value will be 123.4%. We are now ready to solve for the new value, using two different solution techniques:

Solution #1: The new value is the original value plus 23.4% of the original:

$$x = \mathbf{5{,}161{,}544} + 23.4\% \cdot \mathbf{5{,}161{,}544}$$

Factoring out the 5,161,544, we get a very important simplification:

$$x = \mathbf{5{,}161{,}544} \cdot (1 + 23.4\%)$$
$$x = 5{,}161{,}544 \cdot (\mathbf{1.234})$$
$$= 6{,}369{,}345$$

Note that we do not get exactly the same population estimate as shown in **Table 4.11**, due to round-off error in the 23.4%.

The **growth rate** of 23.4% has a **growth factor** of 1.234. If something grows by 23.4%, we multiply it by 1.234.

Note that we do not need to use 100% and 123.4% in the proportion. The denominators of 100 will cancel out when we solve for x.

Solution #2: The arrow diagram above looks like a ratio table, and we can use the values to set up a proportion:

$$\frac{5{,}161{,}544}{100} = \frac{x}{123.4} \rightarrow x = \frac{123.4}{100} \cdot 5{,}161{,}544 = 6{,}369{,}345$$

Example 9 introduced the notion of growth rates and growth factors.

DEFINITION

Given a percent change of $x\%$, the rate at which a quantity increased (**growth rate**) or decreased (**decay rate**); the number given by $1 \pm x\%$ is called the **growth/decay factor**. The new value may be computed two different ways:

1. **Growth/decay rate:** $\text{New} = \text{Original} \pm x\% \cdot \text{Original}$
2. **Growth/decay factor:** $\text{New} = \text{Original} \cdot (1 \pm x\%)$

CAUTION A decay rate will be negative, but the corresponding decay factor will be positive and less than one. ●

Example 10 Use a Decay Rate

VIDEO *Decay*

The price of 1 ounce of gold closed on March 4, 2014, at $1,338.10. The quote below indicates that the 1 Year % Change in the price of gold was −15.45%. What was the closing price of gold on March 4, 2013?

SOLUTION We can draw an arrow diagram:

x (3/4/13 (original), 100%) —— **−15.45%** ——→ $1,338.10 (3/4/14 (new), **84.55%**)

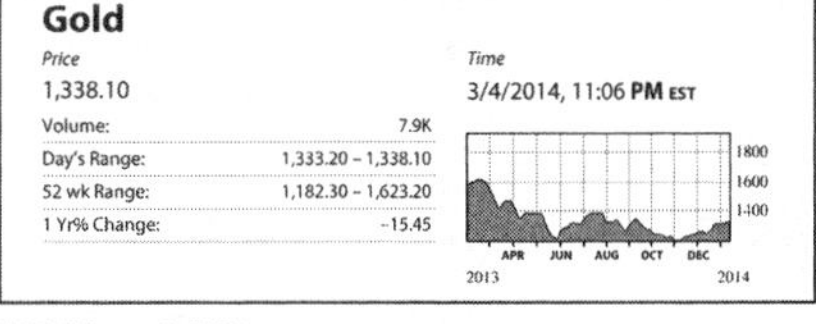

FIGURE 4.2 Gold Price
Data from: CNBC, http://data.cnbc.com/quotes/%40GC.1

Using the decay factor:

$$1{,}338.10 = x \cdot (1 - 15.45\%)$$
$$1{,}338.10 = x \cdot 0.8455$$
$$x = \frac{1{,}338.10}{0.8455} = \mathbf{\$1{,}582.61}$$

Using the proportion:

$$\frac{x}{100} = \frac{1{,}338.10}{84.55} \rightarrow x = \frac{100}{84.55} \cdot 1{,}338.10 = \mathbf{\$1{,}582.61}$$

4.4 Data Tables with Percentages

OBJECTIVE 1 **Interpret Percentage Points**

OBJECTIVE 2 **Use Two-Way Tables**

OBJECTIVE 1 Interpret Percentage Points

Percent change requires extra caution when dealing with a change in **percentages** as opposed to numerical amounts. Consider the following table from *How a Nation Engages with Art*, published by the National Endowment for the Arts. Results are from the *Survey of Public Participation in the Arts*, conducted by the Census Bureau.

TABLE 4.12 Percent of U.S. Adults Who Read at Least One Work of Literature (Novels or Short Stories, Poetry, or Plays), by Type: 2002, 2008, and 2012

				2008–2012	
	2002	**2008**	**2012**	**Change**	**Rate of Change**
Novels or Short Stories	45.1%	47.0%	45.1%	−1.9pp**	−4%**
Poetry	12.1%	8.3%	6.7%	−1.6pp**	−19%**
Plays	3.6%	2.6%	2.9%	0.3pp**	12%**

pp = percentage points
**change is statistically significant at the 95 percent confidence level
Data from: Literary Reading from *How a Nation Engages with Art, September 2013, NEA*, http://arts.gov/sites/default/files/highlights-from-2012-SPPA.pdf

Note that total change is given in units of pp, **percentage points**, and percent change is listed as *Rate of Change*.

DEFINITION

The total change between two percentages is given in units of **percentage points** (pp).

Example 11 Use Percentage Points

Compute the **total change** and **percent change** in the **percentage** of adults reading poetry from 2002 to 2012 given in **Table 4.13**.

SOLUTION We can draw an arrow diagram:

$$\underset{\text{2002 (original)}}{12.1\%} \longrightarrow \underset{\text{2012 (new)}}{6.7\%}$$

The total change is given by $6.7\% - 12.1\% = $ **−5.4 pp.**

CAUTION We can't list the total change as -5.4% because it would then be confused with the true percent change of -44.6%. ●

Percent change is now:

$$\frac{-5.4}{12.1} = -0.446 = -44.6\%$$

TABLE 4.13 Percent of U.S. Adults Who Read at Least One Work of Literature (Novels or Short Stories, Poetry, or Plays), by Type: 2002, 2008, and 2012

				2008–2012	
	2002	**2008**	**2012**	**Change**	**Rate of Change**
Novels or Short Stories	45.1%	47.0%	45.1%	−1.9pp**	−4%**
Poetry	12.1%	8.3%	6.7%	−1.6pp**	−19%**
Plays	3.6%	2.6%	2.9%	0.3pp**	12%**

pp = percentage points
**change is statistically significant at the 95 percent confidence level
Data from: Literary Reading from How a Nation Engages with Art, September 2013, NEA, http://arts.gov/sites/default/files/highlights-from-2012-SPPA.pdf

OBJECTIVE 2 Use Two-Way Tables

When encountering a **percentage**, the first question one should ask is, "Percentage of what?" The "what" is known as the **base** of a percentage. For example, why are the percentages declining, but not the number of literary readers in **Table 4.14**? Are the bases of each percentage the same?

Example 12 Use Percentages to Compute the Base

VIDEO *Base*

Use the percentages in **Table 4.14** to determine the number of U.S. adults for each year in the table.

SOLUTION In 1982, we are given that 56.9% (96 million) of U.S. adults, x, were literary readers:

$$56.9\% \cdot x = 96 \text{ million}$$

$$x = \frac{96}{0.569} = 168.7 \text{ million}$$

The adult population of the U.S. in 1982 was 168.7 million

Similar calculations for 1992, $x = \frac{100}{0.54} = 185.2$ million, and 2002, $x = \frac{96}{0.467} = 205.6$ million, show that we are dealing with different populations and therefore give the different **bases** of the percentages. We are actually taking a smaller percentage of a growing population, resulting in a relatively flat number of literary readers.

CAUTION Always ask "Percentage of what?" before interpreting percentages. •

TABLE 4.14 Decline in Literary Reading

	1982	1992	2002
% of U.S. Adult Population Reading Literature	56.9	54.0	46.7
Number of Literary Readers (in millions)	96	100	96

Data from: Decline in Literary Reading from *Reading at Risk*, June 2004, NEA, http://arts.gov/publications/reading-risk-survey-literary-reading-america-0

Understanding the **base** of a percentage is intimately related to **two-way tables**, which we use when our data involves two **categorical variables**, like gender or political affiliation.

Example 13 Use a Two-Way Table

VIDEO *Two-Way Table*

Table 4.15 shows a two-way table for an experiment involving a skin cream to treat a rash. People with the rash were randomly divided into two groups. One group used the cream for two weeks, and the other group did not. Results for whether the rash got better or worse are tabulated in the two-way table. Does this experiment indicate that the cream makes the rash better?

TABLE 4.15 Skin Cream Experiment Results

	Result	
	Rash Got Better	Rash Got Worse
Patients who did use the new skin cream	223	75
Patients who did not use the new skin cream	107	21

Data from: Table from *Motivated Numeracy and Self-Government*, the Cultural Cognition Project Paper #116. Published by Yale Law School, © 2013.

SOLUTION We have two categorical variables: whether you did or did not use the cream and whether the rash got better or worse. Two-way tables basically organize our results (and are very similar to Venn diagrams). We cannot compare the actual numbers in **Table 4.15** because there are different totals for each column and row. We need to turn these numbers into **percentages (rates)** to make an accurate comparison, and there are two choices:

CAUTION Many people will make the mistake of saying that more people who used the cream got better (223) than any other category, and thus the cream makes the rash better. •

TABLE 4.16 Skin Cream Experiment Percentages #1

	Rash Got Better	Rash Got Worse	Totals
Did use cream	223 (67.6%)	75 (78.1%)	**298**
Did not use cream	107 (32.4%)	21 (21.9%)	**128**
Totals	**330 (100%)**	**96 (100%)**	

TABLE 4.17 Skin Cream Experiment Percentages #2

	Rash Got Better	Rash Got Worse	Totals
Did use cream	223 (74.8%)	75 (25.2%)	**298 (100%)**
Did not use cream	107 (83.6%)	21 (16.4%)	**128 (100%)**
Totals	**330**	**96**	

Notice that the number 223 now has two **percentages** associated to it: 67.6% in **Table 4.16** and 74.8% in **Table 4.17**. To determine what the **base** of the percentage is, we must check in which direction the percentages add to 100%. The 67.6% and the 32.4% add to 100% in the *Rash Got Better* column, indicating that these are percentages of the group of people whose rash got better. Thus we can say that 67.6% of those whose rash got better used the skin cream. Similarly, we can say that 74.8% of those who did use the cream got better. This sounds like the cream works, until you notice that 83.6% of those who did not use the cream also got better! Thus you would have a better chance of getting better by not using the cream.

Example 14 Interpret Percentages

VIDEO *Art Museum*

Now that we understand the care needed in dealing with percentages, take a look at **Table 4.18** and interpret the meaning of the number 11.6.

SOLUTION It is tempting to say that 11.6% of those attending art museums did not read literature, but the percentages for *Read Literature* and *Did Not Read Literature* don't add to 100%. This means the base of the 11.6% is the U.S. adult population who did not read literature; so only 11.6% of the U.S. adult population who did not read literature in 2002 attended an art museum that same year.

It is easy enough to compute percentages of the attendees who read or don't read, given in the last column: $42/55 \approx 76.4\%$ of attendees read literature, while only 23.6% of attendees do not read literature. This seems to be the point the NEA is trying to make: Reading is an important factor in appreciation for the arts and the reason the NEA is publishing a document on the decline of literary reading. The ratio of those who read to those who didn't read is 3 : 1 for attendees of art museums in 2002.

TABLE 4.18 Art Museum Attendance by U.S. Adults, 2002

	% Attending	Number of Attenders (millions)
All adults	26.5%	55
Did not read literature	11.6	13
Read literature	43.5	42
*Light book readers (1–5 books)	34.9	15
*Moderate book readers (6–11 books)	47.2	9
*Frequent book readers (12–49 books)	53.1	13
*Avid book readers (50 books or more)	50.9	5

***Note:** Books can be of any type, literary and non-literary
Data from: Art Museum Attendance from *Reading at Risk*, June 2004, NEA, http://arts.gov/publications/reading-risk-survey-literary-reading-america-0

CAUTION Many people will make the mistake of saying that 11.6% of art museum attendees did not read literature. ●

Let's try one more example before moving on to **percentiles**. The following text is taken verbatim from the National Highway Traffic Administration Safety Report, 2011:

> Drivers are considered to be alcohol-impaired when their blood alcohol **concentration** (BAC) is .08 grams per deciliter (g/dL) or higher. Thus, any fatality occurring in a crash involving a driver with a BAC of .08 or higher is considered to be an alcohol-impaired-driving fatality. The term "driver" refers to the operator of any motor vehicle, including a motorcycle. In 2011, there were 9,878 alcohol-impaired-driving fatalities. This is a decrease of 2.5 percent compared to 2010 (10,136), and it represents an average of one alcohol-impaired-driving fatality every 53 minutes. The 9,878 alcohol-impaired-driving fatalities in 2011 (31% of total traffic fatalities) represent a 27-percent decrease from the 13,472 alcohol-impaired-driving fatalities reported in 2002 (31% of the total).

There's lots of numeracy vocabulary in here, but let's focus on the one-third of traffic fatalities due to drunk drivers in both 2002 and 2011. This means two-thirds of traffic fatalities are due to sober drivers, which seems to imply that sober drivers are twice as dangerous! The solution to this puzzler is that there are, of course, many more sober drivers than drunk drivers, so we would expect sober drivers to have more accidents. We would like to compare the percentage of all drunk drivers who have accidents (the **base** here being the number of drunk drivers as opposed to the number of accidents) to the percentage of sober drivers who have accidents. Unfortunately, we do not know the actual number of drunk drivers on the road, so let's do an example where we do know the numbers in question to illustrate the point.

Example 15 Compute Percentage of What

VIDEO *Drivers*

In 2009, 25- to 34-year-olds got into 10 times as many accidents as 16-year-olds. This seems to imply that 25- to 34-year-olds are 10 times as dangerous on the road as 16-year-olds? Explain why this is not so.

SOLUTION **Table 4.19** shows the data on the number of drivers for both age categories (the numbers we wish we had for drunk and sober drivers). Thus we can take **percentages** not just of accidents but of number of drivers, shown in **Table 4.20**. Thus 22.9% of 16-year-old drivers were involved in accidents in 2009, a much higher rate than the 8.9% for 25- to 34-year-olds.

TABLE 4.19 Accidents by Age Group

	Number of Accidents, 2009	Number of Drivers
16-year-olds	300,000	1,311,000
25- to 34-year-olds	3,270,000	36,694,000

Data from: US Census Statistical Abstract 2012.

TABLE 4.20 Accidents as Percentages of Age Group

	Number of Accidents, 2009	Number of Drivers
16-year-olds	22.9	100
25- to 34-year-olds	8.9	100

Data from: US Census Statistical Abstract 2012.

Spotlight on Statistics

OBJECTIVE 1 **Understand Percentiles**

OBJECTIVE 2 **Use Frequency Polygons**

OBJECTIVE 1 Understand Percentiles

In the Chapter 3 *Spotlight on Statistics*, we looked at **percentages** associated with the **normal distribution** and heights of U.S. women. In **Figure 4.3** we can see two different scales on the x-axis. First, we are given z-scores (or number of **standard deviations** from the **mean**), and second we are given the cumulative percent of data up to each **z-score**.

DEFINITION

A **percentile** is a value below which a certain percentage of ordered data fall:

- *Deciles*: 10th, 20th, . . . , 100th
- *Quintiles*: 20th, 40th, 60th, 80th, 100th
- *Quartiles*: 25th, 50th, 75th, 100th

FIGURE 4.3 Normal Distribution

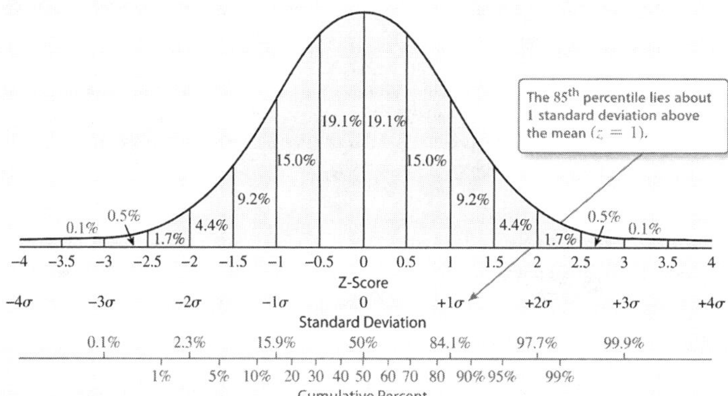

Example 16 Use Percentiles

Answer the following questions about the data for men 20 years and over in **Table 4.21**:

1. What **percentage** of data lies between 66.3″ and 72.6″?
2. What is the 90th **percentile**?
3. What are the middle three **quartiles**?
4. What is the probability of a random male having a height less than 65.6″?

SOLUTION

1. These two heights are at the 15th and 85th percentiles, respectively, so 70% of the data is in between.
2. The 90th percentile occurs at 73.2″.
3. The middle three quartiles are the 25th: 67.4″, 50th: 69.4″, and 75th: 71.5″.
4. 65.6″ lies at the 10th percentile, so there is a 10% chance.

We can interpret the percentiles as probabilities.

TABLE 4.21 Height in Inches for U.S. Males 20 Years of Age and Older By Race and Ethnicity and Age, Mean, Standard Error of the Mean, and Selected Percentiles, 2003–2006

Race and Ethnicity and Age	Number Examined	Mean	Standard Error	Percentile 5th	10th	15th	25th	50th	75th	85th	90th	95th
All race and ethnicity groups								Inches				
20 years and over	4,482	69.4	0.07	64.4	65.6	66.3	67.4	69.4	71.5	72.6	73.2	74.3
20–29 years	808	69.4	0.13	64.7	65.8	66.6	67.8	70.0	72.0	73.0	73.5	74.8
30–39 years	742	69.4	0.13	64.1	65.3	66.1	67.5	69.5	71.5	72.7	73.4	74.7
40–49 years	769	69.7	0.11	65.2	66.2	66.8	67.9	69.7	71.6	72.7	73.3	74.0
50–59 years	591	69.5	0.15	65.0	65.8	66.5	67.5	69.5	71.5	72.7	73.4	74.4
60–69 years	668	69.0	0.11	64.2	65.4	66.1	67.1	69.0	71.1	71.9	72.7	73.7
70–79 years	555	68.4	0.16	63.8	64.6	65.5	66.4	68.5	70.3	71.0	72.0	73.1
80 years and over	349	67.2	0.14	62.7	63.6	64.3	65.5	67.2	68.9	70.0	70.5	71.3

Data from: National Health Statistics Report No. 10, October 2008, Anthropometric Reference Data, U.S. 2003–06

OBJECTIVE 2 Use Frequency Polygons

Recall that the **normal distribution** in **Figure 4.3** is just a **histogram**, with the **percentages** giving the number of data values in **bins**. **Figure 4.4** shows a histogram that gives the **relative frequencies** of words of varying lengths from samples of Mark Twain's writings, with data given in **Table 4.22**.

Due to rounding, the sums for the cumulative frequencies won't all be exact.

Note that the relative frequencies are just percentages of the total number of words, and the **cumulative frequencies** simply sum the relative frequencies up to each word length (i.e., they are **percentiles**).

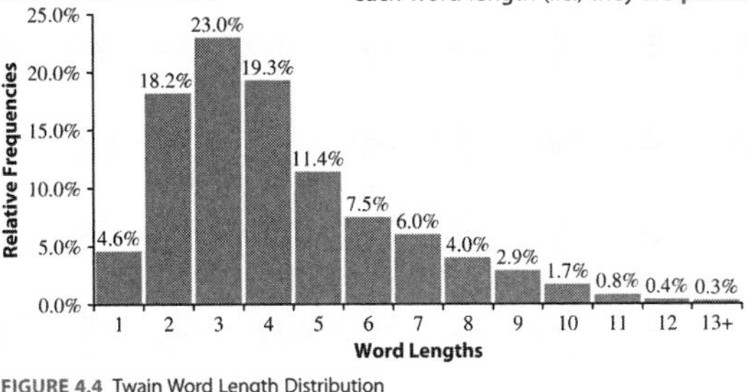

FIGURE 4.4 Twain Word Length Distribution

Data from: Twain data from Brinegar, Claude S., "Mark Twain and the Quintus Curtius Snodgrass Letters: A Statistical Test of Authorship," *Journal of the American Statistical Association*, Vol. 58, No. 301 (March 1963), pp. 85–96

TABLE 4.22 Twain Data

Word Length	Frequency	Relative Frequency	Cumulative Frequency
1	502	4.6%	4.6%
2	1,991	18.2%	22.7%
3	2,523	23.0%	45.7%
4	2,116	19.3%	65.0%
5	1,254	11.4%	76.5%
6	818	7.5%	83.9%
7	659	6.0%	89.9%
8	440	4.0%	94.0%
9	320	2.9%	96.9%
10	187	1.7%	98.6%
11	86	0.8%	99.4%
12	40	0.4%	99.7%
13+	29	0.3%	100.0%

SPREADSHEET TUTORIALS Entering Data by Range | Entering Numbers | Copying a Formula Using the Fill Handle | Constructing a Formula and Using the SUM Function | Using Arithmetic Operators | Formatting Cells with the Percent Style

If instead of making a **histogram** of the **relative frequencies** we make a line graph, we get what is called a **relative frequency polygon**. Graphing the cumulative frequencies yields a **cumulative frequency polygon**. This graph is a "fingerprint" of sorts for an author and can be used to help determine authorship of anonymous works.

During the Civil War, a series of letters were written by someone using the pseudonym Quintus Curtius Snodgrass (QCS). It was thought that the true author was Mark Twain. We can compare the frequency polygons for both authors to see if their "fingerprints" are similar. **Figure 4.5** plots the frequency polygons for samples of both authors' letters. There seems to be a slight discrepancy for words of length 2 and 3. Read the cited article in the source to get a more definitive answer to this question of authorship.

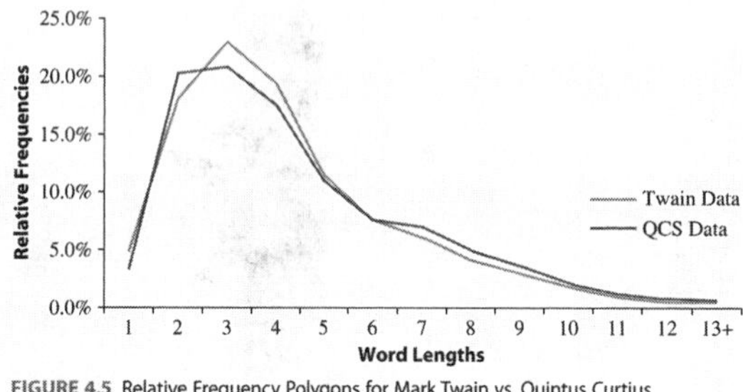

FIGURE 4.5 Relative Frequency Polygons for Mark Twain vs. Quintus Curtius Snodgrass

Data from: Twain vs. QCS from Brinegar, Claude S., "Mark Twain and the Quintus Curtius Snodgrass Letters: A Statistical Test of Authorship," *Journal of the American Statistical Association*, Vol. 58, No. 301 (March 1963), pp. 85–96

TABLE 4.23 QCS Data

Word Length	Frequency	Relative Frequency	Cumulative Frequency
1	424	3.2%	3.2%
2	2,685	20.4%	23.6%
3	2,752	20.9%	44.5%
4	2,302	17.5%	62.0%
5	1,431	10.9%	72.8%
6	992	7.5%	80.3%
7	896	6.8%	87.1%
8	638	4.8%	92.0%
9	465	3.5%	95.5%
10	276	2.1%	97.6%
11	152	1.2%	98.8%
12	101	0.8%	99.5%
13+	61	0.5%	100.0%

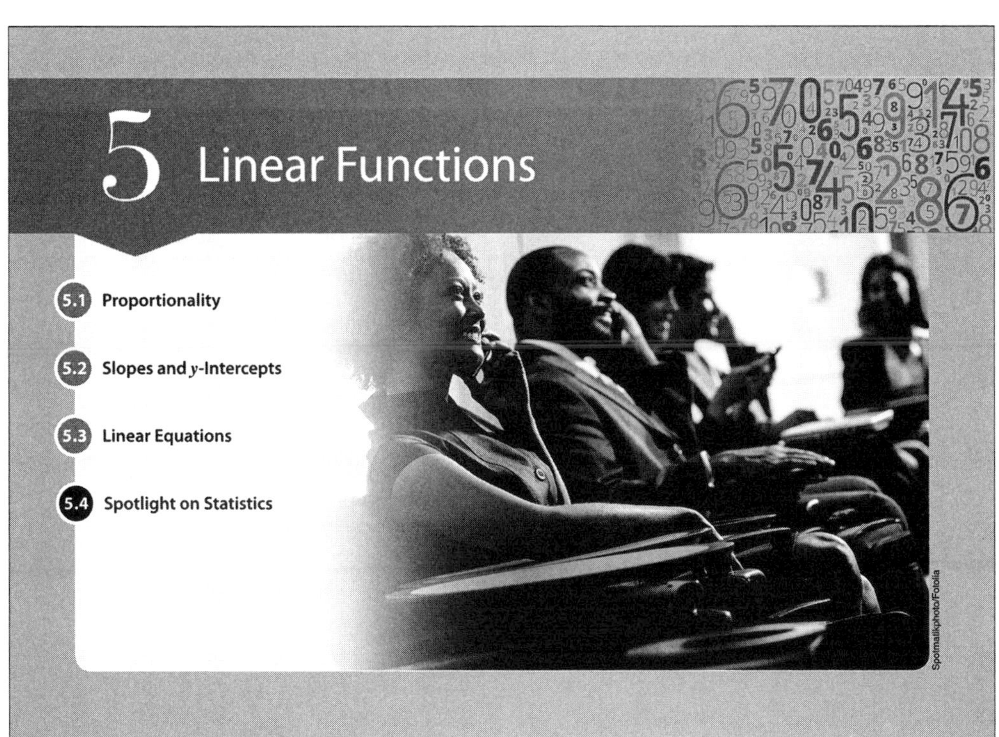
5 Linear Functions
5.1 Proportionality
5.2 Slopes and y-Intercepts
5.3 Linear Equations
5.4 Spotlight on Statistics
Spotmatikphoto/Fotolia

05-1

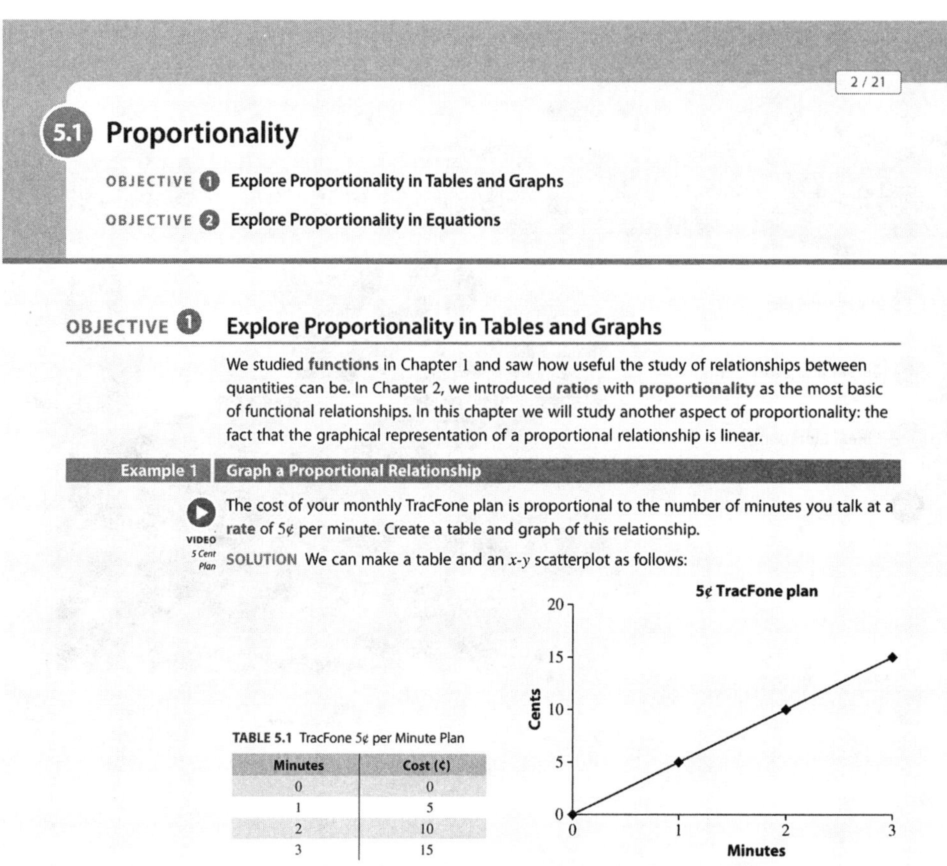

5.1 Proportionality

OBJECTIVE 1 Explore Proportionality in Tables and Graphs

OBJECTIVE 2 Explore Proportionality in Equations

OBJECTIVE 1 Explore Proportionality in Tables and Graphs

We studied **functions** in Chapter 1 and saw how useful the study of relationships between quantities can be. In Chapter 2, we introduced **ratios** with **proportionality** as the most basic of functional relationships. In this chapter we will study another aspect of proportionality: the fact that the graphical representation of a proportional relationship is linear.

Example 1 Graph a Proportional Relationship

VIDEO *5 Cent Plan*

The cost of your monthly TracFone plan is proportional to the number of minutes you talk at a **rate** of 5¢ per minute. Create a table and graph of this relationship.

SOLUTION We can make a table and an x-y scatterplot as follows:

TABLE 5.1 TracFone 5¢ per Minute Plan

Minutes	Cost (¢)
0	0
1	5
2	10
3	15

FIGURE 5.1 TracFone 5¢ per Minute Plan

SPREADSHEET TUTORIALS Entering Data by Range | Entering Numbers | Copying a Formula Using the Fill Handle | Using Arithmetic Operators

From **Table 5.1** we created the graph (x-y scatterplot) in **Figure 5.1**, which gives us a visual display of the relationship between the inputs and outputs of the function. We can see that the points all fall on a line, starting at the origin. Increasing the input by 1 minute necessitates an increase of 5 cents in the output. The **rate**, 5¢ per minute, thus gives a measure of how steep the line is; a plan that charges 7¢ per minute would have a steeper line (i.e., greater rate of incline), as shown in **Figure 5.2**. The rate is therefore called the **slope** of the line and will be formally defined shortly.

Example 2 | **Compare the 5¢ per Minute Plan and the 7¢ per Minute Plan**

VIDEO *5 vs. 7 Cent Plan*

Graph the relationship between cost and minutes for each monthly plan and represent both relationships using an equation.

The **rate** is associated with how steep the line is.

SOLUTION

TABLE 5.2 TracFone 5¢ and 7¢ per Minute Plans

Minutes	Cost (5¢)	Cost (7¢)
0	0	0
1	5	7
2	10	14
3	15	21

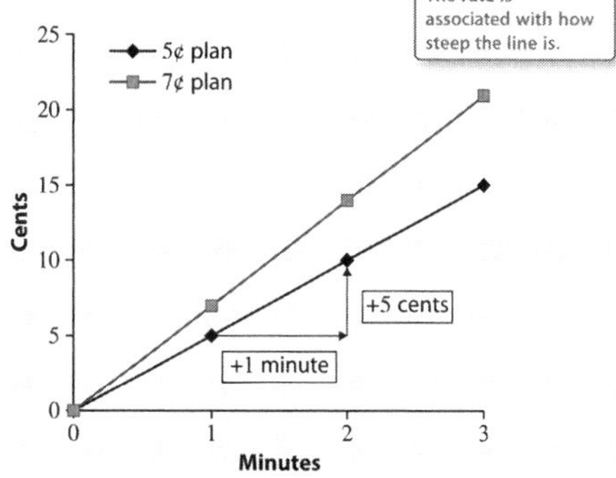

FIGURE 5.2 TracFone 5¢ and 7¢ per Minute Plans

Each rate is the associated **constant of proportionality** in the equation.

Recall from Chapter 3 that all proportional relationships can be represented with an equation of the form $y = k \cdot x$:

$$\text{Cost} = 5 \cdot \text{Minutes} \qquad \text{Cost} = 7 \cdot \text{Minutes}$$
$$C = 5 \cdot M \qquad C = 7 \cdot M$$

OBJECTIVE 2 Explore Proportionality in Equations

We have just seen that the **constant of proportionality** is a **rate** that determines the steepness of the line that graphs the **proportional** relationship. Note that the lines go through the origin for proportional quantities, and you should be able to convince yourself that any line through the origin implies that the input and output are proportional. What about a linear graph that does not go through the origin?

Example 3 | **Determine the Equation of a Line Not Through the Origin**

VIDEO *Monthly Fee*

The cost of your monthly TracFone plan is proportional to the number of minutes you talk at a rate of 5¢ per minute, plus there is a monthly fee of \$20. Create a table and graph of this relationship and determine the equation for this **function**.

SOLUTION

TABLE 5.3 TracFone with Monthly Fee

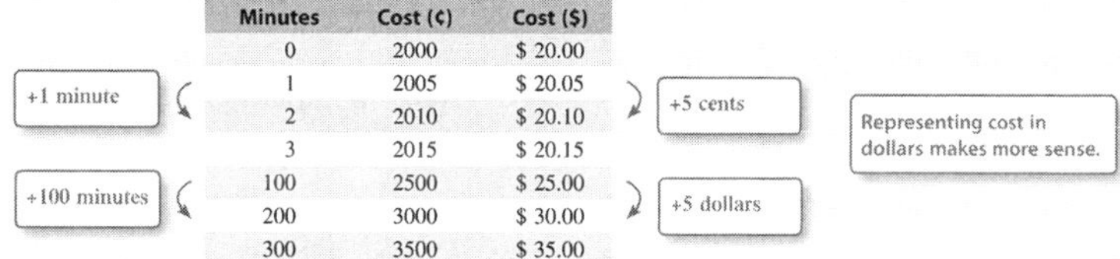

Minutes	Cost (¢)	Cost ($)
0	2000	$ 20.00
1	2005	$ 20.05
2	2010	$ 20.10
3	2015	$ 20.15
100	2500	$ 25.00
200	3000	$ 30.00
300	3500	$ 35.00

Representing cost in dollars makes more sense.

CAUTION Changing units from ¢ to \$ does not change the constant of proportionality. 5¢ per minute is equivalent to \$5 per 100 minutes; the **ratio** is *constant*. ●

If we graph cost ($) as a **function** of minutes using the values from **Table 5.3,** we get the line starting at $20.00 in **Figure 5.3**.

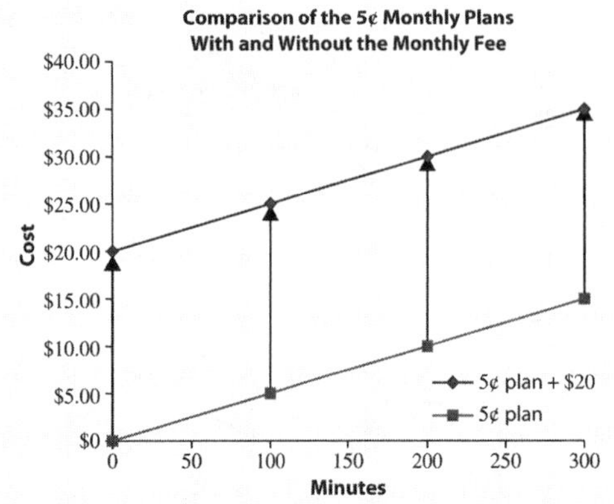

FIGURE 5.3 TracFone Plan Comparison

To find the equation of the monthly plan with a $20 monthly fee, our cost starts at $20, and we add in the 5¢ per minute:

$$\text{Cost} = \$20.00 + \$0.05 \cdot \text{Minutes}$$
$$C = \$0.05 \cdot M + \$20$$

Note that this is not the equation of a proportional relationship, $y = k \cdot x$.

CAUTION Equations are typically written with x and y, such as $y = 0.05x + 20$, but you must use care in determining what each variable represents and what the units are. ●

Adding in a $20 monthly fee raises the graph of the line up 20 units. Note that it does not affect the slope, or steepness, of the line.

5.2 Slopes and y-Intercepts

OBJECTIVE 1 Interpret Slopes as Rates

OBJECTIVE 2 Interpret y-Intercepts as Initial Values

OBJECTIVE 1 Interpret Slopes as Rates

The TracFone examples have shown that the **rate** associated with a **proportional** relationship (i.e., 5¢ per minute) has a geometric interpretation as the steepness or slope of the line we get when we graph the **function**. The linearity of the graph is captured by the **constant of proportionality**. In general, given any two points, we can draw a line connecting them. The steepness of this line is measured by the **ratio** of the total change in y-values to the total change in x-values.

The notation Δx and Δy indicates change in x and change in y respectively. The slope is thus the ratio of change in y to change in x.

DEFINITION

Let (x_1, y_1) and (x_2, y_2) be points in the coordinate plane such that $x_1 \neq x_2$. The **slope** of the straight line that passes through these two points is given by:

$$m = \frac{y_2 - y_1}{x_2 - x_1} = \frac{\Delta y}{\Delta x} = \frac{\text{Rise}}{\text{Run}}$$

The slope is a *ratio* of the total change in the output to the total change in the input, and it has two interpretations:

1. The steepness of the line connecting the two points. A negative slope indicates that the line slants down, moving from left to right.
2. The constant *rate of total change* between the input and output quantities. If the line goes through the origin, this is the constant of proportionality. This rate of total change is also referred to as the *average change, difference quotient,* or *rate of change*.

CAUTION When interpreting the slope as a rate, think: The <output> is changing by <slope> <y-units> per <x-units>. For example, from Example 2: The cost is changing by 5 cents per minute. ●

Example 4 Find the Slope and Interpret in Real-World Terms

VIDEO *Chemical Concentration*

A chemical is spilled into a pond, and the **concentration** at this time (day zero) is 100 ppm (parts per million). After 10 days, the concentration is down to 92 ppm. Assuming that concentration is a function of days, find the **slope** between the two given points and interpret the slope in real-world terms and geometrically.

SOLUTION Recall that y (the output variable) is a **function** of x (the input variable); so the concentration being a function of days from the spill indicates y = concentration and x = days. We can now write down two points, (0 days, 100 ppm) and (10 days, 92 ppm), and compute the slope:

$$\text{Slope} = \frac{92 \text{ ppm} - 100 \text{ ppm}}{10 \text{ days} - 0 \text{ days}} = \frac{-8 \text{ ppm}}{10 \text{ days}}$$

CAUTION Don't say decreasing by -8 ppm every 10 days; this is a double negative. •

We can interpret this ratio as a constant **rate**: The concentration is decreasing by 8 ppm every 10 days, or -0.8 ppm per day. Note that if we say "decreasing," we drop the negative to avoid a double negative. Graphing the line between these two points, we can interpret the slope as the "steepness" of the line:

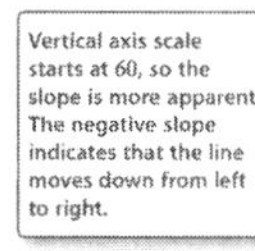

Vertical axis scale starts at 60, so the slope is more apparent. The negative slope indicates that the line moves down from left to right.

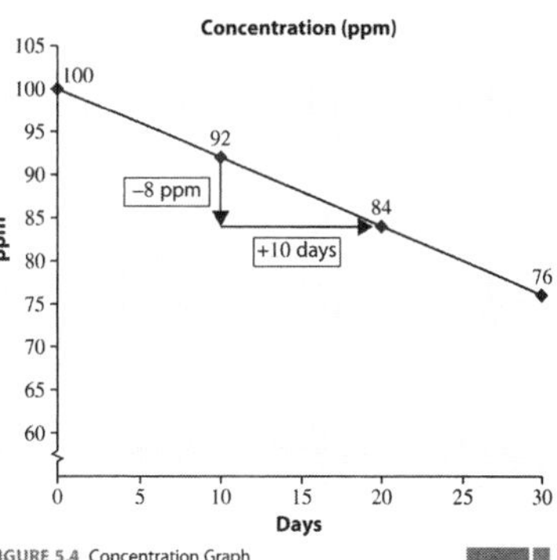

FIGURE 5.4 Concentration Graph

Example 5 Interpret Slope as a Rate

VIDEO *Interest*

In Chapter 4 we saw an example of computing the monthly interest on a car loan. **Table 5.4** shows the **interest** computed as a **function** of the beginning **balance**. Find the **slope** and interpret.

SOLUTION Recall that y (the output variable) is a function of x (the input variable); so the interest being a function of the balance indicates y = interest and x = balance. We can choose any two points and compute the slope. Using the first two months, we have (\$18,000, \$90) and (\$17,742.01, \$88.71):

$$\text{Slope} = \frac{\$88.71 - \$90}{\$17{,}742.01 - \$18{,}000} = \frac{-\$1.29}{-\$257.99} \approx 0.005 = 0.5\%$$

Recall that this is the constant monthly, or **periodic, rate**; we can calculate the **APR** using $\text{APR}/12 = 0.5\%$, which gives APR = 6%. We are being charged \$0.50 in interest for every \$100 we owe each month.

TABLE 5.4 Car Loan Table

Month	Balance	Payment	Interest	New Balance
1	\$18,000.00	\$347.99	\$90.00	\$17,742.01
2	\$17,742.01	\$347.99	\$88.71	\$17,482.73
59	\$690.80	\$347.99	\$3.45	\$346.26
60	\$346.26	\$347.99	\$1.73	\$0.00

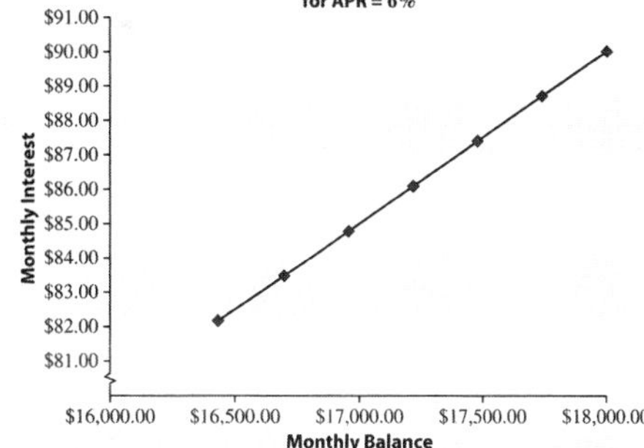

FIGURE 5.5 Car Loan Graph

CAUTION It does not matter what two points you choose to compute the **slope**, but you must be consistent in the order in which you subtract terms in the slope formula. •

SPREADSHEET TUTORIALS Entering Data by Range | Entering Numbers | Copying a Formula Using the Fill Handle | Constructing a Formula and Using the SUM Function | Using Arithmetic Operators

OBJECTIVE 2 Interpret y-Intercepts as Initial Values

Every line has two key characteristics: its steepness, as measured by the **slope**, and its location. Recall the TracFone examples where we added \$20 as a monthly fee, which raised the graph of the line up 20 units in Figure 5.3 but did not change the slope. We characterize the location of the line by specifying where it intercepts the y-axis.

DEFINITION

The **y-intercept** of any straight nonvertical line refers to the y-value of the point where the line crosses the y-axis—that is, where the x-coordinate is zero.

The y-intercept has two interpretations:

1. The location of the line in the x-y coordinate system—that is, where it hits the y-axis.
2. The *initial value* of the output variable when the input variable is time. The y-intercept has an x-coordinate of zero, so if the input variable is time, the y-intercept is referred to as the starting value.

Example 6 Find y-Intercepts

VIDEO *Intercepts*

For the three examples studied so far, TracFone with monthly fee, concentration, and monthly interest, determine the y-intercept and interpret both geometrically and as an initial value.

SOLUTION In Example 3 we derived an equation for the relationship between cost and minutes: $C = \$0.05 \cdot M + \$20.00$. Letting the minutes equal zero, we get $C = \$20.00$, thus the line hits the y-axis at the point (0, 20), and the y-intercept is \$20.00. The y-intercept represents the initial cost of \$20 before we use any minutes. **Figure 5.3** shows the line crossing the y-axis at $y = 20$.

In Example 4 we graphed the **concentration** as a function of days since the spill and can see that the line hits the y-axis at (0 days, 100 ppm). Thus 100 ppm is the **y-intercept** and represents the initial concentration on the day of the spill. We write an equation in which the concentration starts at 100 ppm and decreases by 0.8 ppm per day:

$C = 100 - 0.8 \cdot d$. Letting the input variable equal zero, we get the y-intercept $C = 100$. **Figure 5.4** shows the line crossing the y-axis at $y = 100$.

In Example 5 we considered the **proportional** relationship between monthly **interest** and the **balance** owed at the start of the month. The proportional equation is $I = 0.5\% \cdot B$, with the monthly **periodic rate** as the constant of proportionality. **Figure 5.6** shows the graph, which can be deceiving when trying to identify the y-intercept. It appears that the line will hit just below \$81.00, but this is not the y-axis, it is the line $x = \$16{,}000$. The y-axis occurs where $x = 0$, which is 16,000 units to the left! Substituting $B = 0$ into our equation, we get $I = 0$ (i.e., there is zero interest for a zero balance). The y-intercept is the origin, just as it is for all proportional equations, $y = k \cdot x$.

This is *not* the y-axis! It is $x = \$16{,}000$. We are deliberately keeping the graph as created in Excel and not adding jagged starts to the x-axis to illustrate why caution is needed.

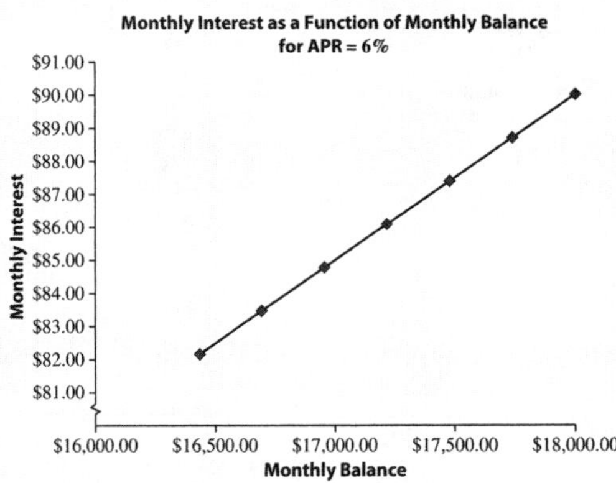

FIGURE 5.6 Car Loan Graph with Confusing Axes

CAUTION When determining the y-intercept from a graph, make sure you are at $x = 0$. Many graphs created with graphing software, such as Excel, will only include the domain of interest, with a vertical axis drawn at the leftmost endpoint. ●

5.3 Linear Equations

OBJECTIVE 1 Evaluate the Slope-Intercept Form

OBJECTIVE 1 Evaluate the Slope-Intercept Form

We have encountered three equations in this chapter representing **functions** with a graph that is a straight line:

1. $C = \$0.05 \cdot M + \$20.00$
2. $C = 100 - 0.8 \cdot d$
3. $I = 0.5\% \cdot B$

All three of these equations can be rewritten in the form $y = m \cdot x + b$:

1. $y = 0.05 \cdot x + 20$
2. $y = -0.8 \cdot x + 100$
3. $y = 0.005 \cdot x + 0$

CAUTION The y-intercept of a proportional relationship will be zero and is usually not written in the equation. •

The coefficient of x is the **slope** of the line, or the constant rate of total change between the input and output variables. The constant at the end of the equation is the **y-intercept**, or y-value that occurs when $x = 0$.

DEFINITION

A function that can be represented with an equation of the form

$$y = m \cdot x + b,$$

where m and b can be any real numbers, is called a **linear function**. The constant m is the *slope* of the linear function; the constant b is the *y-intercept*. This equation is called the *slope-intercept form* of a *linear equation*.

Example 7 Determine the Slope-Intercept Equation for a Linear Function

VIDEO *Houston*

Table 5.5 shows that the Houston Metropolitan area experienced the largest **total change** in metropolitan population from 2000 to 2010. Assuming that population is a **linear function** of time, find the **slope-intercept** equation, interpret the **slope** and **y-intercept**, and graph the function.

SOLUTION Remembering that y is a **function** of x, we have y = population and x = year and the two points (2000, 4,715,407) and (2010, 5,946,800). We can compute the **slope**:

$$m = \frac{5{,}946{,}800 - 4{,}715{,}407}{2010 - 2000} = \frac{1{,}231{,}393 \text{ people}}{10 \text{ years}}$$

So the **average change** in population for the Houston metropolitan area from 2000 to 2010 is 123,139.3 people per year.

CAUTION Even though the data is given every decade, the slope is a **rate** per year. This is because the independent variable (i.e., the input) is given as years (i.e., 2000 and 2010), not decades. •

TABLE 5.5 Population Change for the Ten Most Populous and Ten Fastest-Growing Metropolitan Statistical Areas: 2000 to 2010

Metropolitan statistical area	Population		Change	
	2000	2010	Number	Percent
MOST POPULOUS				
New York-Northern New Jersey-Long Island. NY-NJ-RA	18,323,002	18.897.109	574.107	3.1
Los Angeles-Long Beach-Santa Ana. CA	12.365,627	12.828.837	463.210	3 7
Chicago-Joliet-Naperville. IL-IN-WI	9,098,316	9,461,105	362.789	4.0
Dallas-Fort Worth-Arlington, TX	5,161,544	6,371,773	1,210.229	23.4
Philadelphia-Oamden-Wilmington. PA-NJ-OE-MD	5.687.147	5.965.343	278.196	4.9
Houston-Sugar Land-Baylown. TX	4,715,407	5.946.800	1.231.393	26.1
Washington-Artington-Alexandria. DC-VA-MD-WV	4,796,183	5.582,170	785.987	16.4
Miami-Fort Lauderdale-Pompano Beach, FL	5,007,564	5,564,635	557.071	11.1
Atlanta-Sandy Springs-Marietta, GA	4.247,981	5.268.860	1.020.879	24.0
Boston-Cambridge-Quincy. MA-NH	4,391,344	4,552.402	161.058	3.7
FASTEST-GROWING				
Palm Coast. FL	49,832	95.696	45.864	92.0
SL George. UT	90,354	138,115	47.761	52.9
Las Vegas-Paradise. NV	1,375,765	1.951.269	575.504	41.8
Raleigh-Cary. NC	797,071	1,130.490	333.419	41.8
Cape Coral-Fort Myers. FL	440.888	618.754	177.866	40.3
Provo-Orem. UT	376.774	526.810	150.036	39.8
Greeley, CO	180,926	252,825	71.899	39.7
Austin-Round Rock-San Marcos. TX	1,249,763	1,716.289	466.526	37.3
Myrtle Beach-North Myrtle Beach-Conway. SC	196.629	269.291	72.662	37.0
Bend. OR	115,367	157.733	42.366	36.7

Note: The full names of the metropolitan statistical areas are shown in this table: abbreviated versions of the names are shown in the text.
Data from: Largest and Fastest-Growing Cities, U.S. Census Bureau, 2010 Census, http://www.censhs.gov/prod/cen2010/briefs/c2010br-01.pdf

SPREADSHEET TUTORIALS Entering Data by Range Entering Numbers Editing Values in a Worksheet

To compute the y-intercept we use the fact that the equation will be of the form $y = m \cdot x + b$. We can substitute one of the points (2000, 4,715,407) and the slope 123,139.3 in order to solve for b:

$$4{,}715{,}407 = 123{,}139.3 \cdot 2000 - b$$
$$b = -241{,}563{,}193$$

CAUTION If x = year, then the y-intercept refers to $x = 0$ CE, which usually will have no meaning in the real-world context of the problem. •

Thus our **slope-intercept equation** is:

$$y = 123{,}139.3 \cdot x - 241{,}563{,}193$$

The y-intercept is the initial value, but when years = 0, the population of the Houston metropolitan area is −241,563,193 people! Hopefully you appreciate that this make no sense. **Figure 5.7** shows a graph of the line connecting our two original points, with both axes not starting at zero. To see the y-intercept, we would have to graph everything from 0 CE up to 2010, as in **Figure 5.8,** which again makes no sense.

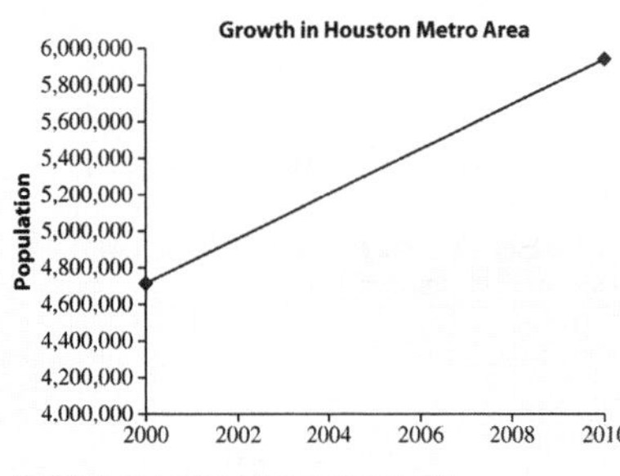

FIGURE 5.7 Houston Population Growth, 2000–2010

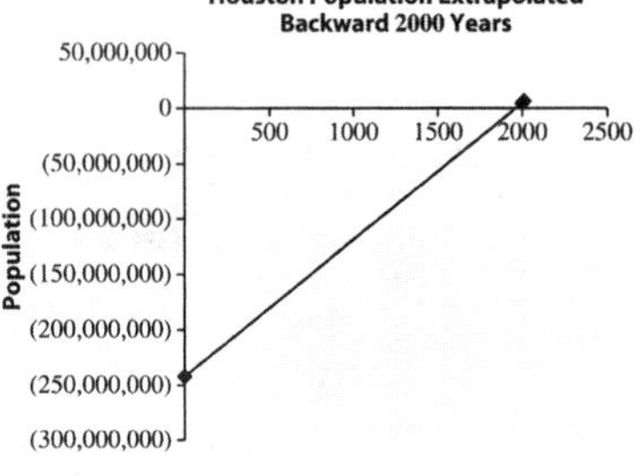

FIGURE 5.8 Houston Population from 0 CE to 2010?

CAUTION Houston did not exist in 0 CE. Seriously. •

Example 7 highlights the problem with using years as the unit on the x-axis when finding a **linear equation**. The y-**intercept** will typically have no meaning in a real-world context and will cause much confusion. To address this problem, we rescale our x-axis by measuring time from a more recent year, such as years since 2000.

Example 8 | Use Years Since 2000 to Find Slope-Intercept Equation

VIDEO *Houston 2000*

Rescale the data for Houston in **Table 5.5** so that years are measured since 2000. Assuming that population is a **linear function** of years since 2000, find the **slope-intercept equation,** interpret the **slope** and y-intercept in real-world terms, and graph the line.

SOLUTION Remembering that y is a **function** of x, we have y = population and x = years since 2000 and the two points (2000, 4,715,407) and (2010, 5,946,800), which become (0, 4,715,407) and (10, 5,946,800). We can compute the slope:

$$m = \frac{5{,}946{,}800 - 4{,}715{,}407}{10 - 0} = \frac{1{,}231{,}393 \text{ people}}{10 \text{ years}}$$

So the **average change** in population for the Houston metropolitan area from 2000 to 2010 is 123,139.3 people per year. Notice that the slope is exactly the same as for Example 7: The change in x is still 10 years.

To compute the y-intercept, we use the fact that the equation will be of the form $y = m \cdot x + b$. We can plug in one of the points (0, 4,715,407) and the slope 123,139.3 in order to solve for b:

$$4{,}715{,}407 = 123{,}139.3 \cdot 0 - b$$
$$b = 4{,}715{,}407$$

Thus our slope-intercept equation is:

$$y = 123{,}139.3 \cdot x + 4{,}715{,}407$$

The y-intercept now represents the population when

$x = 0$ years since 2000 (i.e., in the year 2000).

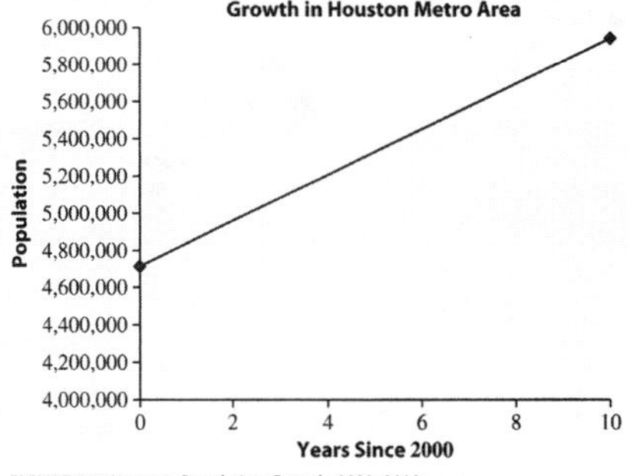

FIGURE 5.9 Houston Population Growth, 2000–2010

The y-intercept is now the population in the year 2000.

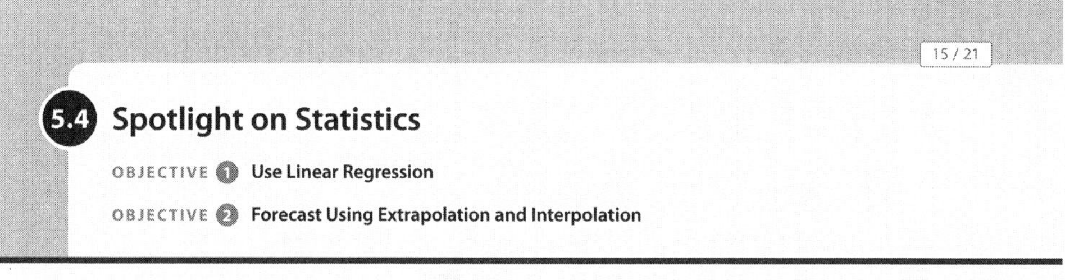

OBJECTIVE 1 Use Linear Regression

In the real world, quantities do not usually vary in a perfectly linear fashion, as in Example 4 on pollutant **concentration** or Example 8 on the population of Houston. The concentration levels or population would be measured regularly, and then a *linear trend* might be observed, in which case a *linear model* would be constructed to help quantify and describe the way in which the concentration levels are dropping or the population is increasing. Consider, for example, the data on Social Security outlays (expenditures or costs) in the U.S. shown in **Table 5.6** and graphed in **Figure 5.10**:

TABLE 5.6 U.S. Budget Social Security Outlays

Year	Social Security Outlays (millions $)
1975	64,658
1980	118,547
1985	188,623
1990	248,623
1995	335,846
2000	409,423
2005	523,305
2010	706,737
2013	813,551

Data from: U.S. Budget Social Security Outlays, http://www.whitehouse.gov/omb/budget/Historicals

We will rescale the axis at the end of Example 9.

Social Security Outlays

Millions $: 0; 100,000; 200,000; 300,000; 400,000; 500,000; 600,000; 700,000; 800,000; 900,000
Years: 1975 1980 1985 1990 1995 2000 2005 2010 2015

FIGURE 5.10 U.S. Budget Social Security Outlays

Example 9 Fit a Trendline to Data and Interpret

VIDEO *Social Security*

Have Excel fit a **linear trendline** to the data given in **Table 5.6** and display the equation. Interpret the **slope** and **y-intercept**.

SOLUTION Entering the data from **Table 5.6** into a spreadsheet, we can create a scatterplot and then add a trendline by using the *Add Chart Element* menu under *Chart Tools: Design,* as shown in **Figure 5.11**. Select *Trendline, More Trendline Options* and then in the *Format Trendline* dialog box, check off *Linear* and *Display Equation on Chart,* as shown in **Figure 5.12**.

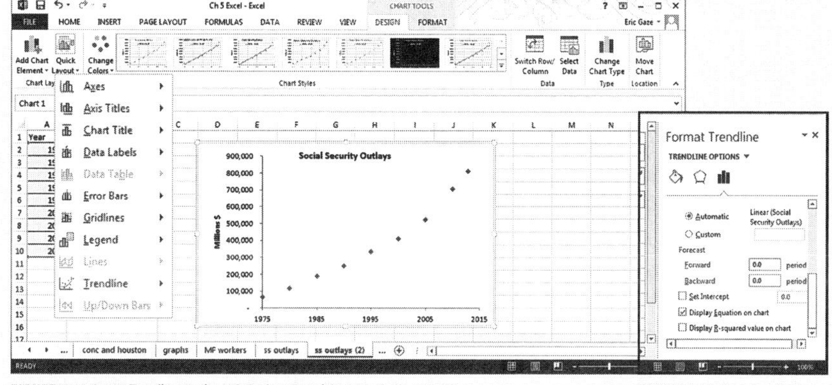

FIGURE 5.11 Insert Trendline in the U.S. Budget Social Security Outlays Graph

FIGURE 5.12 Trendline Options to Display Equation on Graph

SPREADSHEET TUTORIALS Entering Data by Range | Entering Numbers | Formatting Financial Numbers

Adding the **linear trendline** and displaying the equation results in the graph shown in **Figure 5.13**. Note that Excel somehow chooses the "best fitting" line through the scatterplot. (The algorithm behind this procedure will be discussed in Chapter 8.) Excel has also given us the equation of the line $y = 19{,}024 \cdot x - 4 \cdot 10^7$, where we have interpreted the scientific notation, $-4E + 07$, as a power of 10. To interpret the **slope**, we can use the sentence template in the Caution! box:

The *Social Security outlays* are changing by 19,024 *millions $* per *year*.

The **y-intercept**, −40,000,000, makes no sense, as explained in Example 7. We include it here to show how Excel rounds off large numbers when displaying equations and to remind you to rescale your units of years as years since a certain year. In this example, we can rescale to $x =$ years since 1975, and we get the y-intercept of $2,555.5 million, which estimates the Social Security outlays in 1975.

CAUTION When interpreting the slope as a rate, think: The <output> is changing by <slope> <y-units> per <x-units>. ●

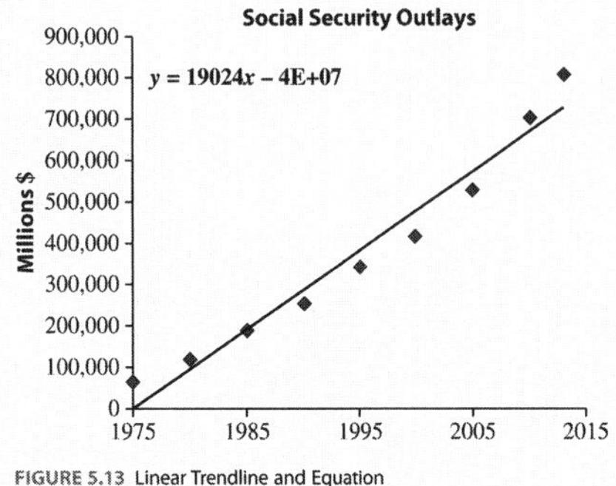

FIGURE 5.13 Linear Trendline and Equation

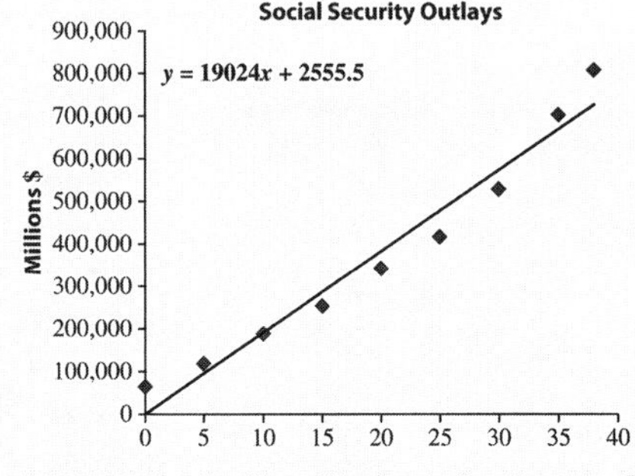

FIGURE 5.14 Linear Trendline and Equation with Years Since 1975

OBJECTIVE 2 Forecast Using Extrapolation and Interpolation

In Example 9, we had Excel fit a **linear trendline** to Social Security data. Notice that the line does not go through all or even most of the points in the scatterplot in **Figure 5.14**. In addition, we said that the **y-intercept** of $2,555.5 million estimates the Social Security outlays in 1975, which we know to be $64,658 million from **Table 5.6**. This may seem strange to you. Why estimate a known value?

The point is that this trendline captures the *trend* of Social Security outlays and can now be used to make predictions in the future.

DEFINITION

Given a scatterplot of data points, we can fit through the data a **linear trendline** that captures the overall trend. This can be accomplished in various ways:

- We can simply draw by hand a line that seems to run through the *middle* of the data points.
- We can select two data points that seem to capture the trend and use the line between them.
- We can use a computer program, like Excel, which will compute the *best-fit* line, also called the *least-squares* line or *regression* line. (Chapter 8 will explain these terms.)

Example 10 Use a Trendline to Make a Prediction

Use the trendline in **Figure 5.14** to predict the Social Security outlays in 2015.

SOLUTION The scatterplot in **Figure 5.14** displays the equation $y = 19{,}024x + 2555.5$, where $y =$ Social Security Outlays in millions $ and $x =$ years since 1975. The year 2015 is 40 years after 1975, so we can substitute $x = 40$ into the equation:

$$y = 19{,}024 \cdot 40 + 2555.5 = 763{,}515.5$$

Thus our trendline predicts the Social Security outlays to be $763,515.5 million in 2015. This is an underestimate, as the actual outlays in 2013 were $813,551 million. We can see the underestimate in **Figure 5.14** as the data points start curving upward above the line.

In Example 10, we used a trendline to make a prediction in the future; this is called extrapolation.

DEFINITION

Given a scatterplot of data points, we can use the trendline to make predictions by substituting x-values.

- If the x-values substituted lie within the domain of inputs for the scatterplot, this is called **interpolation.**
- If the x-values substituted are outside the domain of inputs for the scatterplot, this is called **extrapolation.**

Excel has built-in functions that can perform these calculations for us. The FORECAST function has three arguments (inputs): = **FORECAST** (x, known_y's, known_x's). **Figure 5.15** shows the result of typing this FORECAST function into Excel using the Social Security data and $x = 40$. We get $y = 763{,}524.8$ for the year 2015, which is different from the value 763,515.5 we got by substituting into the equation $y = 19024x + 2555.5$ in Example 10. The discrepancy is due to round-off error in the **slope** and **y-intercept** terms in the equation.

The actual slope is not exactly 19024. Excel rounded off to display the equation. To get the actual slope and y-intercept, we can use the **SLOPE** and **INTERCEPT** functions, both of which have two arguments, (known_y's, known_x's).

Therefore, to make the most accurate predictions using our trendline, we should compute the slope and intercept by using the Excel built-in functions and then use cell references when computing (or just use the **FORECAST** function!).

TABLE 5.7 Slope and Intercept Values from Excel Built-in Functions

Slope	19024.23337
Intercept	2555.495473

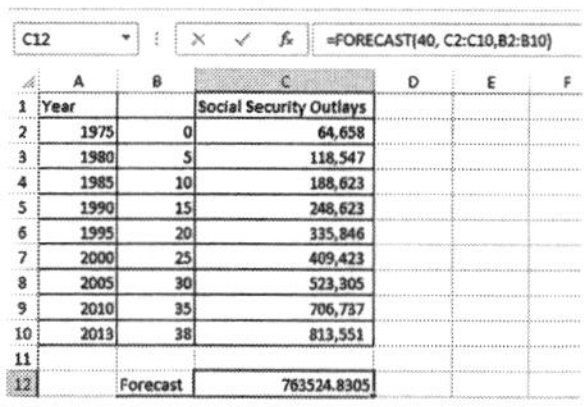

C12 =FORECAST(40, C2:C10,B2:B10)

	A	B	C	D	E	F
1	Year		Social Security Outlays			
2	1975	0	64,658			
3	1980	5	118,547			
4	1985	10	188,623			
5	1990	15	248,623			
6	1995	20	335,846			
7	2000	25	409,423			
8	2005	30	523,305			
9	2010	35	706,737			
10	2013	38	813,551			
11						
12		Forecast	763524.8305			

FIGURE 5.15 Using the FORECAST Function

SPREADSHEET TUTORIALS Inserting and Deleting Rows and Columns | Using Arithmetic Operators | Copying a Formula Using the Fill Handle

Excel also has a **TREND** function that is almost identical to **FORECAST** except that it makes predictions for more than one x-value. Thus the output of this function will be multiple y-values (one for each x-value), and thus it is called an array function. To calculate all the y-values, you must highlight the cell with the **TREND** function and as many other cells as there are y-values. So for three y-values, highlight the cell with the **TREND** function and two other cells next to it, press the **F2** key, and then press **Ctrl+Shift+Enter**. This will be demonstrated in the video for the next example.

Example 11 **Use the Forecast Functions**

VIDEO *Forecast*

Using the data in **Table 5.8,** make a scatterplot of the percentage of U.S. adult population as literary readers in 1982, 1992, and 2002.

- Add a trendline and display the equation.
- Use the **FORECAST** function to predict the value in 2012.
- Use the **SLOPE** and **INTERCEPT** functions to get accurate values of these constants and interpret them.
- Finally, use **TREND** to predict the values in 2012–2014.

TABLE 5.8 Rates of Decline in Literary Reading

	1982	1992	2002
% of U.S. Adult Population	56.9	54.0	46.7
Percentage Point (pp) Decline	—	−2.9 pp	−7.3 pp
Rate of Decline	—	−5%	−14%

Data from: Decline in Literary Reading from *Reading at Risk,* June 2004, NEA, http://arts.gov/publications/reading-risk-survey-literary-reading-america-0

SOLUTION Enter the data from **Table 5.9** into Excel and create the scatterplot shown in **Figure 5.16.**

TABLE 5.9 Decline in Literary Reading from *Reading at Risk*, June 2004, NEA

1	A Years Since 1980	B Percentage of U.S. Adults
2	2	56.9
3	12	54
4	22	46.7
5		
6	32	
7	33	
8	34	

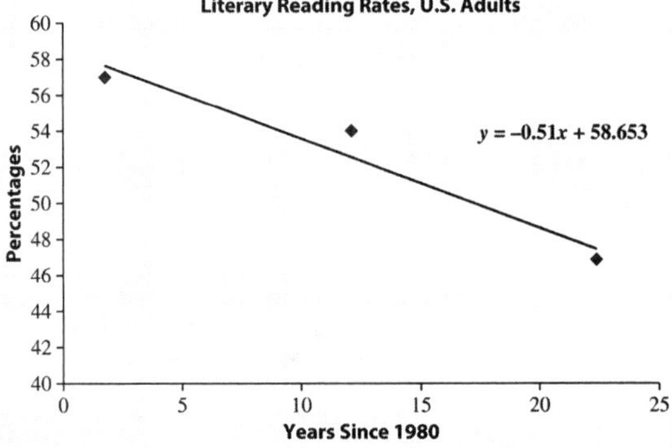

FIGURE 5.16 Literary Reading Scatterplot

Entering the function =**FORECAST**(32, **B2:B4**, **A2:A4**), we get 42.3. In 2012, it's predicted that the literary reading rate will be 42.3%.

Entering the function =**SLOPE**(**B2:B4**, **A2:A4**), we get −0.51. The literary reading rate has been declining by 0.51 percentage points per year since 1982.

Entering the function =**INTERCEPT**(**B2:B4**, **A2:A4**), we get 58.653. The literary reading rate in 1980 was 58.6%.

In cell **B6** enter the function =**TREND**(**B2:B4**, **A2:A4**, **A6:A8**), and we get 42.3. Now highlight **B6:B8**, press **F2**, and then press **Ctrl+Shift+Enter**. Now we get 41.8% and 41.3% for 2013 and 2014, respectively.

Note that the actual literary reading rate was 47.0% in 2012, so past performance is no guarantee of future results!

SPREADSHEET TUTORIALS Entering Data by Range | Entering Numbers | Editing Values in a Worksheet | Formatting Cells with the Percent Style

6 Exponential Functions

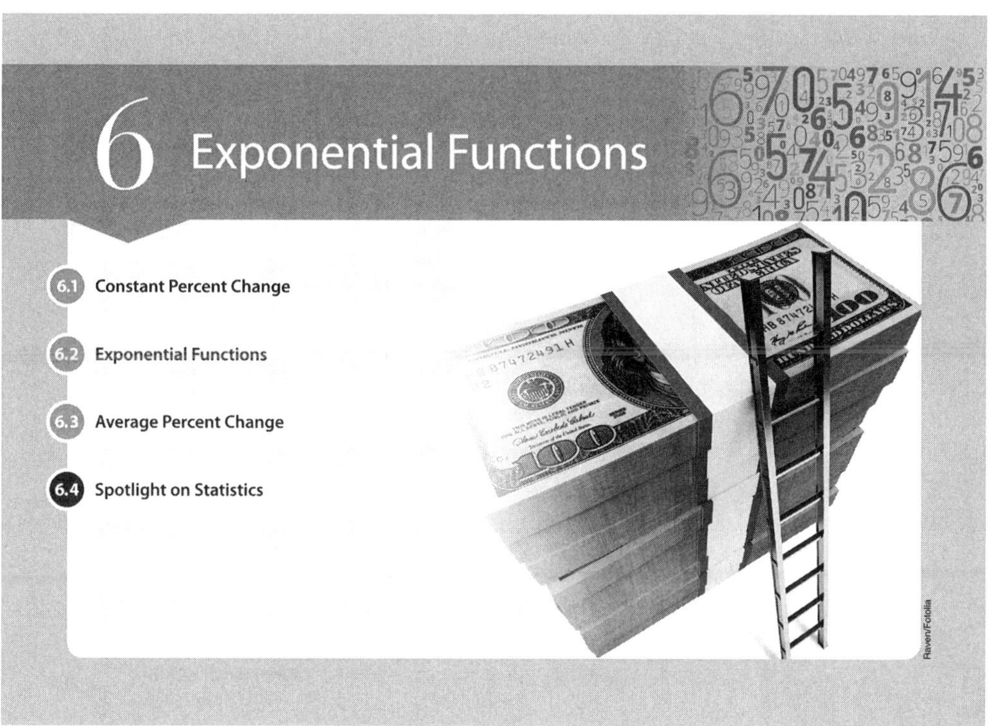

Raven/Fotolia

6.1 Constant Percentage Change

OBJECTIVE 1 Explore Compound Interest

OBJECTIVE 2 Understand Repeated Multiplication as Exponentiation

OBJECTIVE 1 Explore Compound Interest

In Chapter 5 on **linear functions** we saw that the key to linearity is **slope**. We can actually use the idea of slope to define a linear function as one in which the **total change** in output is **proportional** to the total change in input. Mathematicians commonly say linear functions have constant change, referring to the **constant of proportionality**. The phrase "constant change" is misleading, however, because there are two different types of change: total change and **percent change**! Linear functions have constant total change. What type of function would we get if the outputs change by a constant percent change? Let's start with an example of this type of function, dealing with compound interest.

Example 1 **Explore Constant Percent Change**

VIDEO *Compound Interest*

You deposit \$500 into a savings account with an **APR** of 6%. How much money will you have in 10 years?

SOLUTION After 1 year you will have:

Factor out the \$500.

$$\$500 + 6\% \cdot \$500 = \$500 \cdot (1 + 6\%) = \$500 \cdot 1.06 = \$530.$$

We can create **Table 6.1** in Excel in the same fashion as the loan examples in Chapter 1. The major difference is that now we are gaining **interest**, not being charged interest (i.e., our investment is growing over time).

TABLE 6.1 $500 Investment with 6% APR

Year	Beginning	Interest	End
1	**$500.00**	$30.00	$530.00
2	$530.00	$31.80	$561.80
3	$561.80	$33.71	$595.51
4	$595.51	$35.73	$631.24
5	$631.24	$37.87	$669.11
6	$669.11	$40.15	$709.26
7	$709.26	$42.56	$751.82
8	$751.82	$45.11	$796.92
9	$796.92	$47.82	$844.74
10	$844.74	$50.68	**$895.42**

The interest is compounding: We are getting interest on our interest from the constant percent change of 6%.

Notice how the interest is growing every year: 6% of $500 is $30.00, while 6% of $530 is $31.80. The extra $1.80 comes from 6% of the $30 in interest from year 1. At the end of year 10 we have $895.42. Compound interest can be modeled by an exponential function, which will be explained further in the next objective.

SPREADSHEET TUTORIALS Entering Data by Range | Entering Numbers | Copying a Formula Using the Fill Handle | Constructing a Formula and Using the SUM Function | Using Arithmetic Operators | Formatting Financial Numbers

OBJECTIVE 2 Understand Repeated Multiplication as Exponentiation

Taking another look at Example 1, note that all the values in the **End** column in **Table 6.2** can be computed from the previous year's value by multiplying by 1.06:

TABLE 6.2 $500 Investment with 6% APR

Year	End
0	$500.00
1	$530.00
2	$561.80
3	$595.51
4	$631.24
5	$669.11
6	$709.26
7	$751.82
8	$796.92
9	$844.74
10	**$895.42**

$\cdot$ 1.06

$\cdot$ 1.06

$\cdot$ 1.06

Multiply by 1.06 to increase by 6%:

$$\$500 + 6\% \cdot \$500 = \$500 \cdot (1 + 6\%) = \$500 \cdot 1.06$$

Thus the value at the end of the 10th year, $895.42, comes from starting at $500 and multiplying by 1.06 a total of 10 times, i.e., $\$895.42 = \$500 \cdot 1.06^{10}$, or $P = \$500 \cdot 1.06^t$, where P = principle and t = years. We are using the fact that *repeated multiplication is exponentiation*, giving us an **exponential function** (the input variable is an exponent).

Before we more formally define *exponential function*, let's take a closer look at our interest example. There are two ways to think of the value of our investment as a **function**:

1. The value at the end of a year, P_{t+1}, is a function of the previous year's ending value, P_t. This leads to a **recursive formula** for our function: $P_{t+1} = 1.06 \cdot P_t$.
2. The value at the end of the year, P, is a function of the number of years, t, that have passed. This leads to a **closed formula** for our function: $P = 500 \cdot 1.06^t$.

Example 2 Use Both Recursive and Closed Formulas

VIDEO *Recursion*

Create an Excel spreadsheet that calculates the value of our investment for three years using both recursive and closed formulas.

SOLUTION Columns **C** and **D** in **Table 6.3** show the appropriate formulas you would enter and fill down. Both formulas show the amounts in column **B**. The recursive formula always multiplies the previous cell above by 1.06, while the closed formula always starts with the $500 in cell **D2** and multiplies by 1.06 raised to the year in column **A**.

The recursive formula uses a relative cell reference since we are multiplying the previous year's amount by 1.06; the closed formula uses an absolute cell reference since we are always multiplying $500 by a power of 1.06.

TABLE 6.3 Recursive and Closed Formulas

	A	B	C	D
1	Year	Amount	Recursive Formula = Previous*1.06	Closed Formula = $500*1.06^Year
2	0	$500.00	$500.00	$500.00
3	1	$530.00	=C2*1.06	=$D$2*1.06^A3
4	2	$561.80	=C3*1.06	=$D$2*1.06^A4
5	3	$595.51	=C4*1.06	=$D$2*1.06^A5

Recursion, simply multiplying the previous value by 1.06, works great for spreadsheets. In addition, the repeated multiplication of recursion leads us to the exponentiation of the **closed formula**. The closed formula $P = 500 \cdot 1.06^t$, where t = years and P = amount ($) is very powerful. If we want to know how much money our investment will be worth in 35 years, we simply substitute $t = 35$ into the closed formula.

SPREADSHEET TUTORIALS Copying a Formula Using the Fill Handle | Constructing a Formula and Using the SUM Function | Using Arithmetic Operators | Formatting Financial Numbers | Copying Formulas Containing Absolute Cell References

Example 3 Compare Linear and Exponential Growth

VIDEO *Linear vs. Exponential*

Compare the exponential growth equation $P = 500 \cdot 1.06^t$ with linear growth that starts at \$500 and grows by \$30 every year. Find the linear equation and determine the value for both equations at 35 years. Create a scatterplot of both equations out to 35 years and display the equations.

SOLUTION From Chapter 5 we know that the **growth rate** of \$30 per year will be the **slope** of the **linear function**, and \$500 will be the **y-intercept**: $P = 30 \cdot t + 500$. Note that the repeated addition of \$30 every year appears as multiplication, $30 \cdot t$, in the equation. We can now substitute $t = 35$ into both equations:

- $P = 500 \cdot 1.06^t = 500 \cdot 1.06^{35} = \$3{,}843.04$
- $P = 30 \cdot t + 500 = 30 \cdot 35 + 500 = \$1{,}550.00$

Closed formulas are perfect for computing values for a specific year. Exponential growth gives a much larger value than linear growth!

We can build a table of values using recursion for both types of growth. The **linear function** simply adds \$30 to the previous value, while the **exponential function** multiplies the previous value by 1.06.

	A	B	C
1	Years	Linear	Exponential
2	0	\$ 500.00	\$ 500.00
3	1	\$ 530.00	\$ 530.00
4	2	\$ 560.00	\$ 561.80
5	3	=B4+30	\$ 595.51

FIGURE 6.1 Linear Recursion

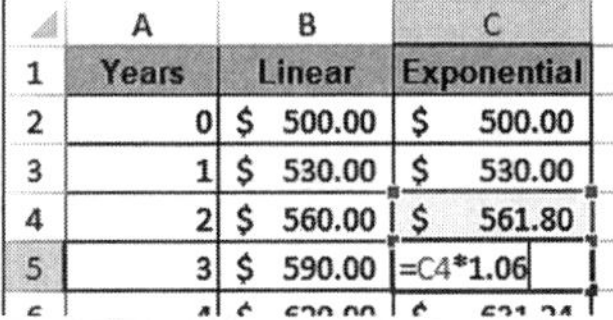

	A	B	C
1	Years	Linear	Exponential
2	0	\$ 500.00	\$ 500.00
3	1	\$ 530.00	\$ 530.00
4	2	\$ 560.00	\$ 561.80
5	3	\$ 590.00	=C4*1.06

FIGURE 6.2 Exponential Recursion

Filling the formulas down to 35 years and inserting a scatterplot, we can insert linear and exponential trendlines and display equations for both:

CAUTION Excel represents exponential equations using $y = a \cdot e^{k \cdot x}$, not $y = a \cdot (1 + r)^x$. They are equivalent, but converting from one form to another requires care. ●

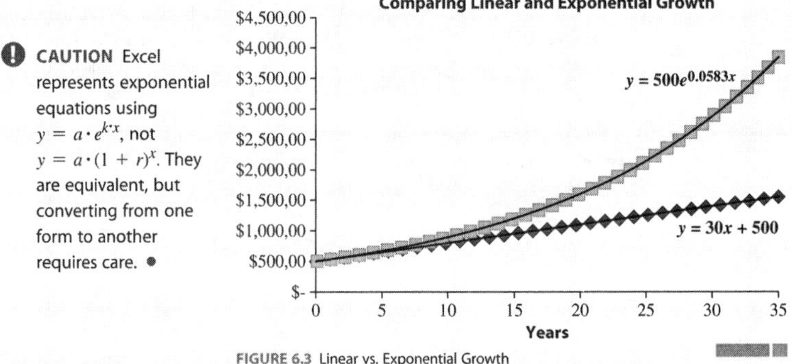

FIGURE 6.3 Linear vs. Exponential Growth

SPREADSHEET TUTORIALS Copying a Formula Using the Fill Handle | Using Arithmetic Operators | Formatting Financial Numbers

Exponential Functions

OBJECTIVE 1 **Use Growth/Decay Rates/Factors**

OBJECTIVE 2 **Understand the Continuous Form**

OBJECTIVE 1 Use Growth/Decay Rates/Factors

We have just seen Excel display the exponential equation, $P = 500 \cdot 1.06^t$, as $y = 500 \cdot e^{0.0583 \cdot x}$. Both of these are of the form $y = a \cdot b^x$, implying that $1.06 \approx e^{0.0583}$. The letter e represents Euler's (pronounced "oiler's") number, which is an irrational number like pi and thus can only be *approximated* by a decimal representation: 2.718282 . . . . In Chapter 7 we will actually derive e and provide the precise mathematical definition. (Recall that pi is the **ratio** of the circumference of any circle to its diameter.) For now we need to know how to calculate with e because Excel is going to give us the equation of our exponential trendlines using Euler's number.

We will use the built-in function =**EXP**(n) to calculate e^n. In particular, if you type in =**EXP**(0.0583), you get 1.06003, confirming the approximation above: $e^{0.0583} \approx 1.06$. Excel is rounding off the decimal, which is why it is not an exact equality. All scientific calculators have an e^n button for this calculation. Note that 0.0583 is very close to 0.06, and both can be interpreted as percentages: 5.83% and 6%. The **APR** is given by 6% and represents the annual **rate**; 5.83% represents the **continuous growth rate** per year and will be explained fully in Chapter 7.

DEFINITION

A function with an equation of the form:

$$y = a \cdot b^x$$

is called an **exponential function**. The constant a is called the *initial value*, and the positive constant b is called the *growth/decay factor*, or the *base*. Compound interest is a standard example of an exponential function, in which the equation is written using P for principle (P_0 is its initial value), r for the *growth/decay rate*, $1 + r$ for the *growth/decay factor*, and t for time:

$$P = P_0 \cdot (1 + r)^t$$

A negative growth rate, r, results in a decay factor.

Quantities in nature change continuously (not just once or 12 times a year), and thus scientists prefer to use the following representation of the equation:

$$y = a \cdot e^{k \cdot x}$$

where e is Euler's number, and k is the *continuous growth rate* ($k > 0$) or *continuous decay rate* ($k < 0$).

There are many examples of exponential growth and decay in the natural world. Populations of many species will grow exponentially for a period of time until they approach the carrying capacity of their environment, which is the maximum population size their ecosystem can support. Human beings in particular are very adept at adapting to their environment, and thus exponential growth models are very accurate for our species. Radioactive decay is an important example of exponential decay.

The fact that every exponential equation can be written in the form $P = P_0 \cdot (1 + r)^t$ illustrates our discussion at the start of the chapter regarding constant percent change. The growth/decay rate, r, is the constant rate of percent change. Let us explore this important concept in a few examples.

Example 4 Find the Growth Rate of the U.S. Population

VIDEO *U.S. Population*

Using the data in the *U.S. Population 1790–2010* spreadsheet in *Data Sets*, create a scatterplot and display the exponential equation. Find both the **continuous growth rate** and the **growth rate.**

SOLUTION The scatterplot is shown below, with the equation and also the *R*-squared value. Let's interpret each number with care:

- **3E-09:** This is the initial value, $3 \cdot 10^{-9} \approx 0$. As discussed in Chapter 5, this refers to 0 CE and makes no sense. We could rescale to years since 1790 to get a more meaningful number.
- **0.0196:** This is the continuous growth rate, 1.96%, implying that the U.S. population has been growing continuously at a rate of 1.96% every year since 1790.
- **0.9625:** This is the *R*-squared value, which will be discussed in detail in Chapter 8. For now just know that it is a measure of how good a fit our trendline is to the data, and it will be between 0 and 1 (perfect fit).

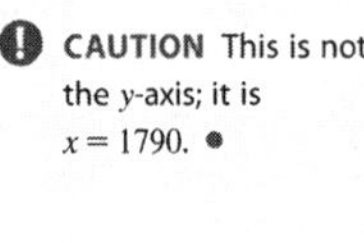

CAUTION This is not the *y*-axis; it is $x = 1790$. ●

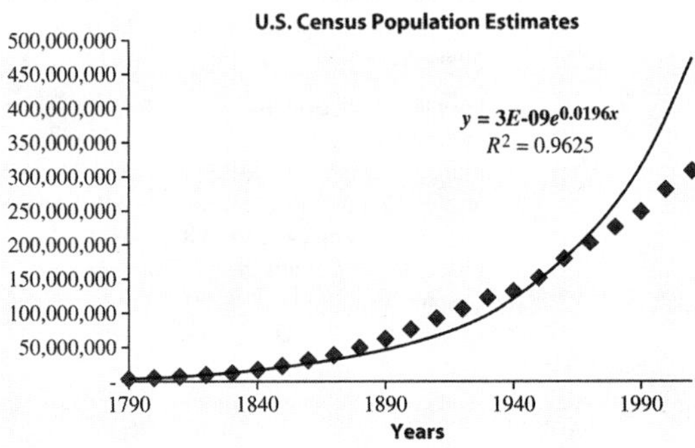

FIGURE 6.4 U.S. Population Graph

Data from: U.S. Census Bureau, http://www.census.gov/population/censusdata/table-4.pdfCT1970p2-13.pdf

Recall from our discussion at the beginning of the objective that we can compute the **growth rate** for the U.S. population by evaluating $e^{0.0196} \approx 1.0198$. Remembering that this is the **growth factor**, $1 + r = 1.0198$, we subtract one and get $r = 0.0198 = 1.98\%$. This implies that the U.S. population has been growing by 1.98% annually (not continuously per year). The distinction between the **continuous rate** and **annual rate** is subtle and will be explored more fully in Chapter 7.

Notice that the data points in the scatterplot begin to fall below the exponential trendline in **Figure 6.4**. As birth rates and immigration rates fell in the 20th century, the U.S. was not able to sustain 1.98% annual growth. We can plot just the data from 1900 to 2010 and get a more accurate growth factor: $e^{0.0126} \approx 1.0127$. Subtracting one from this factor gives us an annual growth rate of 1.27% since 1900.

Also note that the *R*-squared value is 0.9947, which is very close to 1, indicating a better fit to the data for this exponential trendline, or model, than in the previous model (where $R^2 = 0.9625$).

CAUTION It is very easy to mistake the growth factor 1.0127 for the growth rate. ●

The data points in the scatterplot are all very close to the exponential trendline (model).

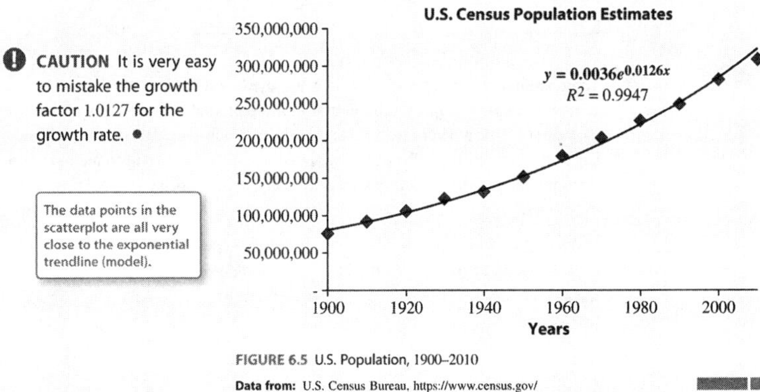

FIGURE 6.5 U.S. Population, 1900–2010

Data from: U.S. Census Bureau, https://www.census.gov/

OBJECTIVE 2 Understand the Continuous Form

Example 4 highlighted the relationship between the **continuous growth rate** and the **growth rate**. In particular, we used two important identities:

- $e^k = 1 + r$
- Factor $= 1 + r$, or $r =$ Factor $- 1$

Let's try an example where we are given the factor and have to work backward to find the rate.

Example 5 Use Decay Factor to Find Rates

VIDEO *Carbon-14*

Carbon-14 decays according to the formula $C = C_0 \cdot 0.88606^m$, where $C =$ grams of carbon-14, $C_0 =$ initial amount, and $m =$ millennia. Determine the **decay rate** per millennium and the **continuous decay rate** per millennium. Given a mass of 100 grams of carbon-14, determine how much will be left in 1,000 years.

SOLUTION We are given the **decay factor**, $1 + r = 0.88606$ and are solving for $r = -0.11394 \approx -11.4\%$. This is the decay rate per millennium. So 100 grams of C-14 right now will lose 11.4% of its mass in 1,000 years, and 88.6 grams will be left. (Notice that this is 88.6% of the original amount.) To find the continuous decay rate per millennium, we need to solve the following for k:

$$e^k = 0.88606$$

To solve the equation for k, we need logarithms, which we will study in Chapter 7. So how can we find k without logarithms? Use Excel! Create an x-y table of values using the given equation $C = C_0 \cdot 0.88606^m$ and then create a scatterplot and insert the equation. Note that we can use any initial value and then a recursive formula,

$$C_{m+1} = C_m \cdot 0.88606:$$

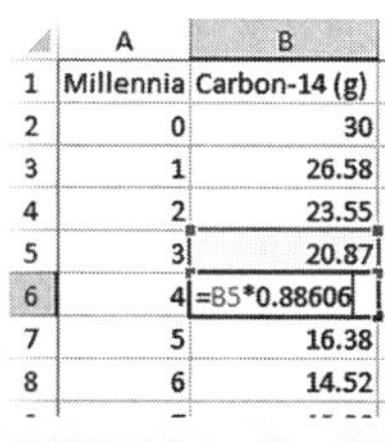

	A	B
1	Millennia	Carbon-14 (g)
2	0	30
3	1	26.58
4	2	23.55
5	3	20.87
6	4	=B5*0.88606
7	5	16.38
8	6	14.52

FIGURE 6.6 Carbon-14 x-y Table

CAUTION The **initial value** does not affect the **decay rate**. You may use any initial value you wish, the rate will be the same. ●

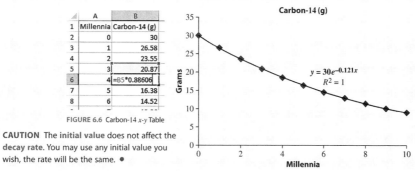

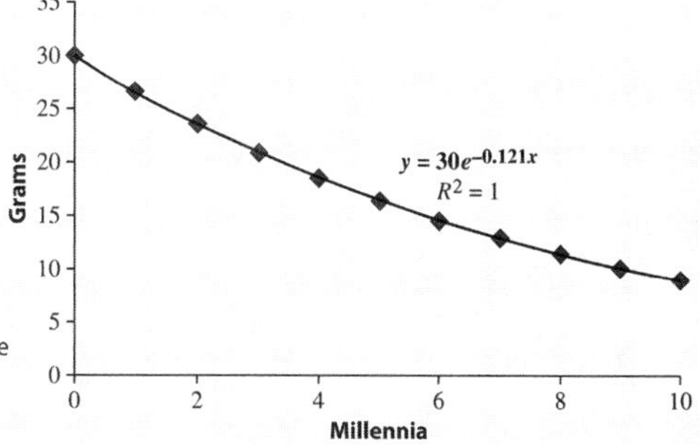

FIGURE 6.7 Carbon-14 Scatterplot

Using the displayed equation $y = 30 \cdot e^{-0.121 \cdot x}$, we get that the continuous decay rate is 12.1% per millennium. This example purposefully illustrates how spreadsheets and recursion can be used to solve problems in lieu of sophisticated algebraic techniques (i.e., logarithms). Hopefully you are somewhat intrigued to see how logarithms can solve this problem in Chapter 7.

SPREADSHEET TUTORIALS Entering Data by Range | Entering Numbers | Copying a Formula Using the Fill Handle | Using Arithmetic Operators

Let us return to the statement characterizing **exponential functions**, that they experience constant **percent change**:

$$r = \frac{P_{t+1} - P_t}{P_t}$$

The fact that this is constant means the **total change** is **proportional** to the amount of the quantity:

$$P_{t+1} - P_t = r \cdot P_t$$

Thus the more people a country has, the more babies will be born in a given year; for example, China will have more newborn babies than Luxemburg in a year. Consider again the investment in **Figure 6.1** with 6% APR. Basically the total change from year to year is the interest, and we have the proportional relationship

$$\text{Interest every year} = 6\% \cdot \text{Principal}$$

The larger the **principal**, the greater the **interest**; they are proportional. Similarly, the carbon-14 example demonstrated that the total change in carbon-14 over one millennium is −11.4% of the original:

$$\text{Total change per millennium} = -11.4\% \cdot \text{Original}$$

In the real world, we usually do not get exactly the same or a constant percent change every time period. For instance, the U.S. population may average 1.27% growth each year, but the actual **growth rate** will vary above and below this value. Next we will look at how to compute an average percent change from a series of regular percent changes.

6.3 Average Percent Change

OBJECTIVE 1 Compare Geometric, Arithmetic, and Harmonic Means

OBJECTIVE 2 Compute Average Percent Change

OBJECTIVE 1 Compare Geometric, Arithmetic, and Harmonic Means

We have characterized exponential growth in terms of constant **percent change** over a fixed time period, such as 6% per year or −11.4% per millennium. This constant percent change is often referred to as the average percent change, in much the same way as the **slope** of a **linear function** is referred to as the average **total change** (or **average change**).

Example 6 Compute Average Rate of Return

VIDEO *Average Rate of Return*

You invest money in a mutual fund that returns 8.5% the first year, −2.3% the second year, and 16.9% the third year. Determine the average rate of return per year.

SOLUTION A very common mistake is to simply sum these percentages and divide by 3—that is, compute the **arithmetic mean**:

$$\frac{8.5\% - 2.3\% + 16.9\%}{3} = 7.7\%$$

CAUTION You *cannot* find average percent change by using the arithmetic mean. This answer is *incorrect*. ●

How do we know this answer, 7.7%, is incorrect? Assume that you originally invest \$1,000, and it goes up 8.5% in year 1, down 2.3% in year 2, and up 16.9% in year 3. We can compute the value of the investment at the end of the three years by using **growth/decay factors**:

$$\$1{,}000 \cdot (1 + 8.5\%) \cdot (1 - 2.3\%) \cdot (1 + 16.9\%)$$
$$= \$1{,}000 \cdot 1.085 \cdot 0.977 \cdot 1.169 = \$1{,}239.19$$

The original amount does not matter, so use a nice number like \$1,000.

Similarly, we can compute the value of a \$1,000 investment that returns 7.7% each year:

$$\$1{,}000 \cdot (1 + 7.7\%) \cdot (1 + 7.7\%) \cdot (1 + 7.7\%)$$
$$= \$1{,}000 \cdot 1.077^3 = \$1{,}249.24$$

Clearly, averaging 7.7% per year does not give the correct value after three years. This does, however, point to the correct solution procedure: We replace 7.7% with the unknown rate, r, and set it equal to the correct amount above:

$$\$1{,}000 \cdot 1.085 \cdot 0.977 \cdot 1.169 = \$1{,}239.19 = \$1{,}000 \cdot (1 + r) \cdot (1 + r) \cdot (1 + r)$$
$$\$1{,}239.19 = \$1{,}000 \cdot (1 + r)^3$$

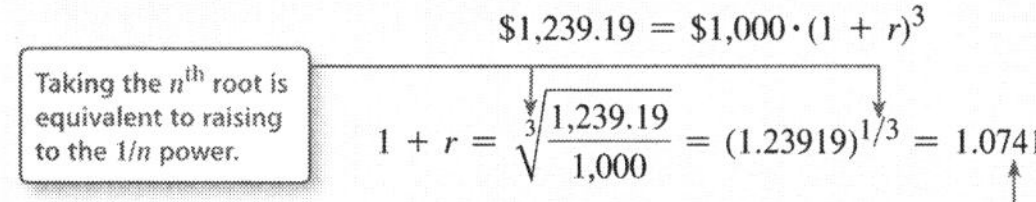
Taking the nth root is equivalent to raising to the $1/n$ power.

$$1 + r = \sqrt[3]{\frac{1{,}239.19}{1{,}000}} = (1.23919)^{1/3} = 1.0741$$

CAUTION This is the **growth factor**; subtract 1 to find the **rate**. ●

Therefore, the correct average rate of return is $r = 7.41\%$.

SPREADSHEET TUTORIALS Calculating a Value after an Increase Calculating the Percentage Rate of Increase

In Example 6 we computed the average rate of return by first calculating the end value, \$1,239.19, from a hypothetical start value of \$1,000 and then using:

$$1 + r = \sqrt[3]{\frac{1{,}239.19}{1{,}000}}$$

This is the **growth/decay factor**; subtract 1 to get the **rate**.

We could have avoided the calculation of the end value and used the growth/decay factors:

$$\$1{,}000 \cdot 1.085 \cdot 0.977 \cdot 1.169 = \$1{,}000 \cdot (1 + r) \cdot (1 + r) \cdot (1 + r)$$
$$1.085 \cdot 0.977 \cdot 1.169 = (1 + r)^3$$
$$1 + r = \sqrt[3]{1.085 \cdot 0.977 \cdot 1.169}$$

This example demonstrates that one way to find average **percent change** involves the nth root of a product of **growth factors**. This type of average is called the geometric mean.

DEFINITION

Given n numbers $a_1, a_2, \cdots, a_n$ we can add them and divide by n to obtain the *arithmetic mean*, or we can multiply them and take the nth root to obtain the *geometric mean*. There is also a third type of average, called the *harmonic mean*.

- The **arithmetic mean** of n numbers (in common usage average value refers to arithmetic mean) is:

$$\frac{a_1 + a_2 + \cdots + a_n}{n}$$

- The **geometric mean** of n numbers (used for growth factors to find average percent change) is:

$$\sqrt[n]{a_1 \cdot a_2 \cdot \cdots \cdot a_n}$$

Taking the nth root is equivalent to raising to the $1/n$ power.

- The **harmonic mean** of n numbers (used for average rates) is:

$$\frac{n}{\frac{1}{a_1} + \frac{1}{a_2} + \cdots + \frac{1}{a_n}}$$

CAUTION There are three different ways to take the mean. ●

Example 7 **Compute the Harmonic Mean**

VIDEO *Harmonic Mean*

You go on a trip and average 20 mph for the first 25 miles and then 80 mph for the next 25 miles. What is your average speed for the entire trip?

SOLUTION Our average speed will be the total distance divided by the total time. The total distance is clearly 50 miles, but the total time requires a calculation using the formula $t = \frac{D}{r}$. The time over each 25-mile segment is:

$$t_1 = \frac{25\text{ miles}}{20\text{ mph}} = 1.25\text{ hours} \qquad t_2 = \frac{25\text{ miles}}{80\text{ mph}} = 0.3125\text{ hours}$$

Thus the average speed is $r = \dfrac{50}{1.25 + 0.3125} = 32$ mph. If we don't solve for the individual times, we can simplify the fraction and arrive at the formula for the harmonic mean:

$$r = \frac{2\cdot(25)}{\frac{25}{20}+\frac{25}{80}} = \frac{2}{\frac{1}{20}+\frac{1}{80}} = 32$$

CAUTION Notice how the 25 miles cancels out, giving us the formula for the **harmonic mean.** •

The average speed for the trip is 32 mph not 50 mph, which is the **arithmetic mean** of 20 and 80. If we had averaged 50 mph for a 50-mile trip, then the total time would have been 1 hour exactly, but our first 25 miles at 20 mph took over 1 hour alone.

06-16

The **harmonic mean** is not familiar to most people and requires care. Basically, if you want to average **rates**, r_i, that are comparing two quantities, a_i: b_i, you may use the harmonic mean formula if the first quantity, a_i, is the same for all the rates. In our average speed example, speed is a rate that compares distance to time, and our first quantity was the same, 25 miles, for both speeds.

Example 8 **Compute the Harmonic Mean**

VIDEO *Alloy*

You mix equal weights of lead at 11,340 kg/m^3, iron at 7,874 kg/m^3, and gold at 19,300 kg/m^3. What is the average **density** of the new alloy?

SOLUTION Density is a rate of weight to volume. We are told the first quantity, weight, is the same for all three densities, so we can use the harmonic mean formula:

$$\frac{3}{\frac{1}{11{,}340}+\frac{1}{7{,}874}+\frac{1}{19{,}300}} \approx 11{,}236.1$$

Thus the average density is 11,236.1 kg/m^3.

There is a famous story of Archimedes, one of the great mathematicians of antiquity, solving a problem involving density while taking a bath. The king was concerned that his jeweler was mixing lead in with gold given to him to make a crown and keeping the extra gold for himself. Archimedes realized the new alloy would be less dense than gold and therefore would take up a larger volume (assuming that the weight was the same). Placing the crown in a tub full of water, one can measure the water displaced and compare that to the water displaced by an equal weight of gold. If the volume of water displaced differs, then the jeweler may lose his head.

06-17

OBJECTIVE 2 Compute Average Percent Change

VIDEO *Average Percent Change*

Recall that the geometric mean provides a method for computing the average percent change. Let's look at a few more examples.

Example 9 Compute Average Percent Change

A town increases in population by 20% in one year and then by 80% the next year. What is the average percent increase per year?

SOLUTION We now know that we cannot simply add these and divide by two to get 50%. We need to take the geometric mean of the growth factors:

$$1 + r = \sqrt[2]{1.20 \cdot 1.80} \approx 1.47$$

Solving for the growth rate gives $r = 47\%$.

Example 10 Compute Average Percent Change

Apple Inc. had a net profit of \$57 million in 2003 and a net profit of \$14,013 million in 2010. What was the average percent change of Apple's net profit over this 7-year period?

SOLUTION We are looking for the unknown **growth factor**, which when the initial value, 57, is multiplied by this growth factor seven times will give 14,013:

$$57 \cdot (1 + r)^7 = 14{,}013$$
$$1 + r = \sqrt[7]{14{,}013/57} \approx 2.195$$
$$r = 1.195 = 119.5\%$$

A growth rate over 100% implies that the quantity is more than doubling each period. Note that the factor is 2.195.

Examples 9 and 10 demonstrate two different ways to compute **average percent change**, depending on the information given in the problem:

- $1 + r = \sqrt[n]{(1 + r_1) \cdot (1 + r_2) \cdots (1 + r_n)}$
- $1 + r = \sqrt[n]{\dfrac{\text{New}}{\text{Original}}} = \left(\dfrac{\text{New}}{\text{Original}}\right)^{1/n}$

Note that both of these formulas are computing the average **growth/decay factor**; you must subtract one to get the **rate**. As we saw in Example 6, we can always use the second of these equations by making up an original value and using the given growth rates to compute a new value. In general, given any two (input, output) data points, we can think of the input and output values as the original and new values. We can compute **average total change** or **average percent change**, per input unit.

DEFINITION

Given any two (input, output) data points (x_1, y_1) and (x_2, y_2), we can compute two types of average change:

The **average total change** is given by the formula

$$r = \frac{y_2 - y_1}{x_2 - x_1}$$

The **average percent change** is given by the formula

$$r = \left(\frac{y_2}{y_1}\right)^{\left(\frac{1}{x_2 - x_1}\right)} - 1$$

6.4 Spotlight on Statistics

OBJECTIVE 1 Forecast with LOGEST and GROWTH

OBJECTIVE 1 Forecast with LOGEST and GROWTH

The following graph gives the personal savings rate as a **percentage** of disposable personal income; the data can be found on the *FRED Graph* sheet in Data Sets. Personal savings is computed from the formulas

Personal Savings = Disposable Income − Expenses and *Disposable Income* = Personal Income − Taxes

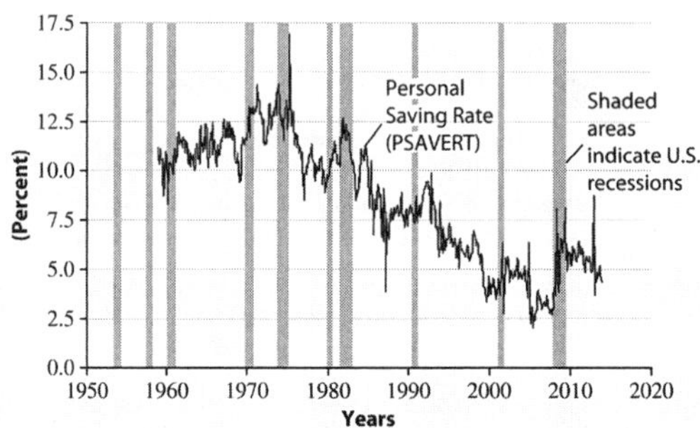

FIGURE 6.8 U.S. Personal Savings Rate:
Data from: Data from U.S. Department of Commerce; Bureau of Economic Analysis; FRED Economic Data, Federal Reserve Bank of of St. Louis, http://research.stlouisfed.org/fred2/series/PSAVERT

Example 11 Fit a Trendline to Data and Interpret

VIDEO *Personal Savings*

Transform the monthly data from the *FRED Graph* sheet in Data Sets to years since 1/1/1959. Create a scatterplot of this data and have Excel fit an exponential trendline and display the equation. Interpret the **continuous growth rate** and **initial value**. Use the equation to predict the personal savings rate on 1/1/2019.

SOLUTION **Figure 6.9** shows how the monthly data is converted to years since 1/1/59. Creating the scatterplot and displaying the equation as explained in the video results in **Figure 6.10**. The initial value represents a personal savings rate of 14.5% on January 1,1959. This rate has been declining continuously by 2.3% each year. On 1/1/19 (60 years after 1/1/59), this exponential model predicts the personal savings rate to be:

$$y = 14.534 \cdot e^{-0.023 \cdot 60} \approx 3.66$$

CAUTION The y-values are meant to be interpreted as **percentages**; you do not move the decimal place. In 2019 the predicted rate is 3.66%. •

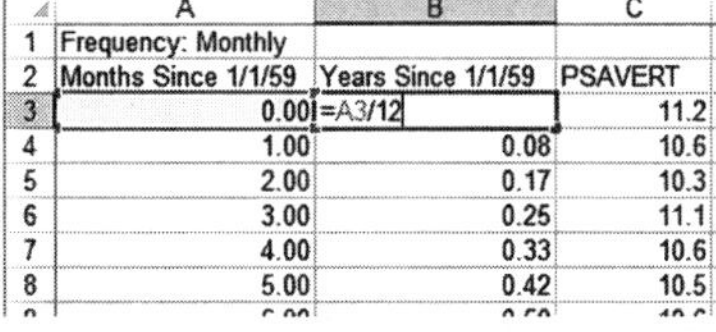

	A	B	C
1	Frequency: Monthly		
2	Months Since 1/1/59	Years Since 1/1/59	PSAVERT
3	0.00	=A3/12	11.2
4	1.00	0.08	10.6
5	2.00	0.17	10.3
6	3.00	0.25	11.1
7	4.00	0.33	10.6
8	5.00	0.42	10.5

FIGURE 6.9 Personal Savings Data, Monthly, and Yearly Since 1/1/59

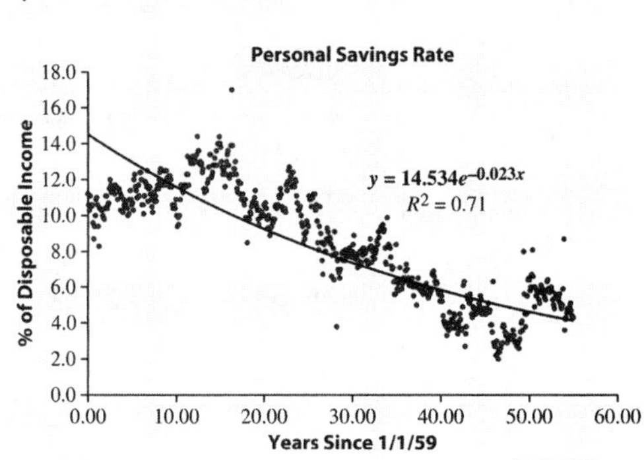

FIGURE 6.10 Exponential Trendline, Personal Savings Rate

SPREADSHEET TUTORIALS Entering Data by Range | Entering Numbers | Inserting and Deleting Rows and Columns | Copying a Formula Using the Fill Handle | Using Arithmetic Operators

Just as it does for **linear functions** (see Chapter 5), Excel has built-in functions that can be used to make predictions for exponential growth. The **LOGEST** function will return the **growth/decay factor** and the **initial value** of the **exponential function** associated with a scatterplot. For linear trendlines, we had two functions, **SLOPE** and **INTERCEPT**, to compute the two constants found in a linear equation.

LOGEST is an *array* function, meaning it has two outputs: The first is the growth/decay factor, and the second is the initial value. There are two options to see both outputs:

1. First enter the **LOGEST** function into a cell: **=LOGEST**(known_*y*'s, known_*x*'s)
    1. Highlight the cell with the **LOGEST** function and the cell right next to it. Press the **F2** key and then press **Ctrl+Shift+Enter**. You should see both outputs next to each other.
2. Alternatively, you can use the **INDEX** function to access the two outputs one at a time: **=INDEX(LOGEST**(known_*y*'s, known_*x*'s), #).
    1. If you enter 1 for the #, then you will get the first output, the growth/decay factor, and if you enter 2 for the #, you will get the second output, the initial value.

CAUTION Note that the **LOGEST** function returns the growth/decay factor associated with the $P = P_0 \cdot (1 + r)^t$ equation. ●

The **GROWTH** function will calculate an output by using the exponential trendline equation. You can forecast a single value or a series of outputs:

1. Enter the **GROWTH** function for a single input: **=GROWTH**(known_*y*'s, known_*x*'s, new_*x*'s).
2. For a series of inputs, enter these *x*-values in a column; then enter the **GROWTH** function next to the first input.
    1. For the new_*x*'s argument, enter the range containing the series of inputs and then press Enter.
    2. Now highlight the cell with the **GROWTH** function and all cells below corresponding to the number of inputs. Press the **F2** key and then press **Ctrl+Shift+Enter**.

Example 12 Use LOGEST and GROWTH

VIDEO *Personal Savings LOGEST and GROWTH*

For the data in Example 11 on personal savings rates, use the **LOGEST** function to find the decay factor and initial value on 1/1/1959 and the **GROWTH** function to predict the personal savings rate on 1/1/2019, 1/1/2020, and 1/1/2021.

SOLUTION In **Figure 6.9** our inputs are in the cells **B3:B663** and outputs are in **C3:C663**.

=LOGEST(C3:C663, B3:B663) returns 0.97744 for the annual decay factor and 14.53393 for the personal savings rate on 1/1/59. Note that 0.97744 − 1 = −2.256% for the annual **decay rate**.

=GROWTH(C3:C663,B3:B663,E9:E11

	B	C	D	E	F	G	H
ly							
'59	Years Since 1/1/59	PSAVERT		LOGEST Function			
0.00	0.00	11.2		Decay Factor	Initial Value		
1.00	0.08	10.6		0.977442145	14.53393461		
2.00	0.17	10.3					
3.00	0.25	11.1		GROWTH Function			
4.00	0.33	10.6		Inputs	Outputs		
5.00	0.42	10.5		Years Since 1/1/59	PSAVERT		
6.00	0.50	10.6		60	=GROWTH(C3:C663,B3:B663,E9:E11		
7.00	0.58	9.6		61	GROWTH(known_y's, [known_x's], [new_x's], [const])		
8.00	0.67	8.7		62			
9.00	0.75	9.4					

FIGURE 6.11 Using **LOGEST** and **GROWTH**

CAUTION After entering the **LOGEST** function in cell **E4**, highlight the range **E4:E5**, press **F2**, and then press **Ctrl+Shift+Enter**. ●

CAUTION After entering this **GROWTH** function in cell **F9**, highlight the range **F9:F11**, press F2, and then press **Ctrl+Shift+Enter.** ●

=GROWTH(C3:C663, B3:B663, 60) returns 3.697 for the personal savings rate in 2019, which is slightly different from the 3.66 we got in Example 11, 3.614 for 2020, and 3.532 for 2021.

Example 13 **Use the GROWTH and LOGEST Functions**

VIDEO
Predicting Bachelors Degrees

Using the data in **Table 6.4**, make a scatterplot of the **percentage** of 25- to 29-year-olds in the U.S. with a bachelor's degree.

- Add an exponential trendline and display the equation.
- Use the **GROWTH** function to predict the value in 2020.
- Use the **LOGEST** function to get more accurate values of the **growth factor** and **initial value**. Interpret these and compare to the ones given in the equation from the scatterplot.

SOLUTION We enter the date from **Table 6.4** into Excel and create the scatterplot shown in **Figure 6.12.** Note that we have not scaled the data to years since 1970, so the **initial value**, 1E-10 ≈ 0, is not going to make sense as discussed in Chapter 5 for linear functions. It refers to 0 CE.

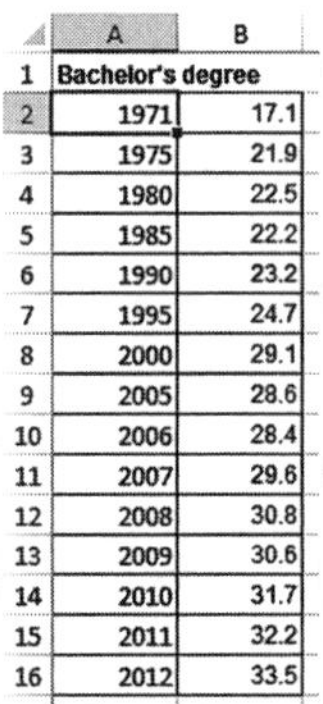

	A	B
1	Bachelor's degree	
2	1971	17.1
3	1975	21.9
4	1980	22.5
5	1985	22.2
6	1990	23.2
7	1995	24.7
8	2000	29.1
9	2005	28.6
10	2006	28.4
11	2007	29.6
12	2008	30.8
13	2009	30.6
14	2010	31.7
15	2011	32.2
16	2012	33.5

TABLE 6.4 Percentage of 25- to 29-Year-Olds with Bachelor's Degree

Data from: National Center for Education Statistics, https://nces.ed.gov/programs/digest/d12/tables/dt12_009.asp

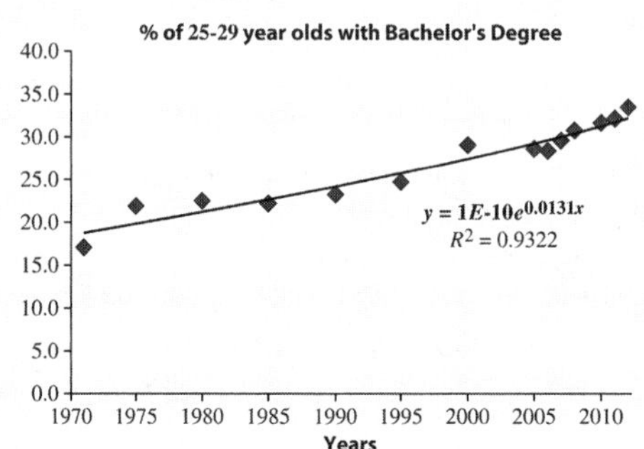

FIGURE 6.12 Exponential Trendline, Educational Attainment

SPREADSHEET TUTORIALS Entering Data by Range Entering Numbers

Entering the **function** =**GROWTH(B2:B16, A2:A16**, 2020), we get 35.75. This is the prediction for 2020, that 35.75% of 25- to 29-year-olds will have a bachelor's degree. Again note that we are using the actual year 2020. We substitute this value into the equation

$$y = 10^{-10} \cdot e^{0.0131 \cdot 2020} = 31.07$$

The round-off in the constants displayed in the equation from the scatterplot introduces error, which is why this value is not close to the actual value of 35.75 from the **GROWTH** function.

The **LOGEST** function will give more precise values for the constants in the exponential equations. Entering the function =**LOGEST(B2:B16, A2:A16**), we get 1.0132. Now highlight the cell with this function and the cell to the right of it, press **F2**, and then press **Ctrl+Shift+Enter**. The initial value, 1.05491E-10, should appear next to the **growth factor**, as shown in **Table 6.5.**

TABLE 6.5 Outputs from the LOGEST Function

Growth Factor	Initial Value
1.013229728	1.05491E-10

The growth factor is giving us the annual **growth rate** (subtract one), $r = 1.323\%$, which is slightly larger than the **continuous growth rate** of 1.31% from the scatterplot. The initial value is showing more decimal places for the 1E-10 from the scatterplot.

In Chapter 7 we will explore the distinction between the annual and continuous rates.

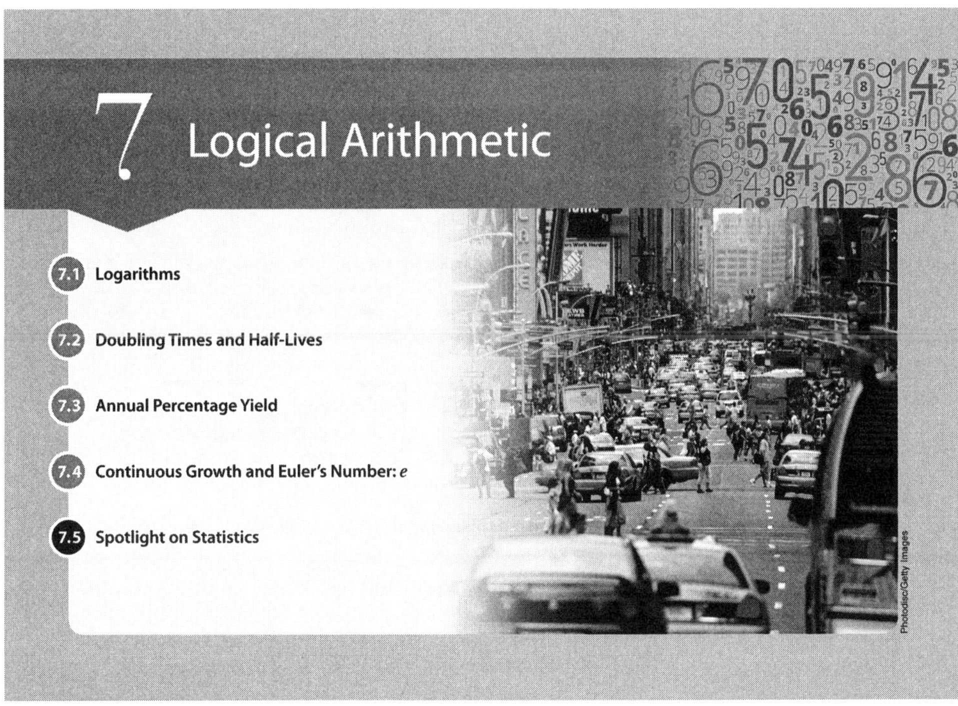

7.1 Logarithms

OBJECTIVE 1 Undo the Exponent

OBJECTIVE 2 Understand Logarithms

OBJECTIVE 1 Undo the Exponent

In Chapter 6 we encountered two different forms of the exponential equation, $y = a \cdot b^x$:

- $P = P_0 \cdot (1 + r)^t$, which uses the **growth/decay rate**, r.
- $y = a \cdot e^{k \cdot x}$, which uses the **continuous growth/decay rate**, k.

Excel will display the second form as shown in **Figure 6.5** for the U.S. population from 1900 to 2010. We interpreted the continuous growth rate per year of the U.S. population to be 1.26%, compared to 1.27% annual growth. In this chapter, we will explore in detail the distinction between these two rates. First, we look at the operation of exponentiation and its associated inverse operation, taking the logarithm.

Example 1 **Undo an Exponent**

VIDEO *Population*

Looking at the U.S. population data in **Table 7.1**, how long will it take for the population to double?

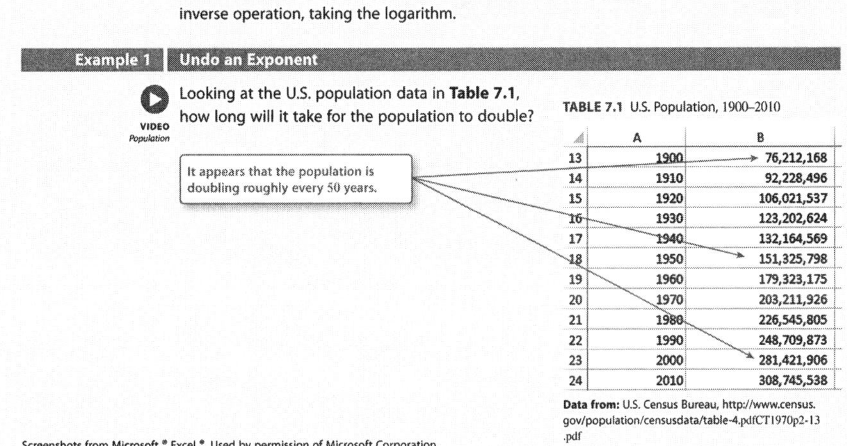

It appears that the population is doubling roughly every 50 years.

TABLE 7.1 U.S. Population, 1900–2010

	A	B
13	1900	76,212,168
14	1910	92,228,496
15	1920	106,021,537
16	1930	123,202,624
17	1940	132,164,569
18	1950	151,325,798
19	1960	179,323,175
20	1970	203,211,926
21	1980	226,545,805
22	1990	248,709,873
23	2000	281,421,906
24	2010	308,745,538

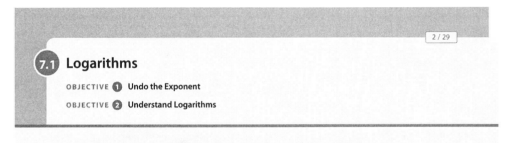

Data from: U.S. Census Bureau, http://www.census.gov/population/censusdata/table-4.pdfCT1970p2-13.pdf

SOLUTION In **Table 7.1**, it appears that the 1900 population doubles around 1950, which then doubles around 2000. We can choose between the two equations:

- $P = P_0 \cdot (1.0127)^t$, which uses the annual **growth/decay rate**, 1.27%.
- $y = a \cdot e^{0.0126 \cdot x}$, which uses the **continuous growth/decay rate**, 1.26%.

Recall that these are just two different representations of the same function, $e^{0.0126} \approx 1.0127$, so we will use the first, which is "simpler." We will perform two separate calculations to find the time required for the population to double—one using the 1900 population as the initial value and one using the 1950 population:

Substitute twice the initial population for P.

Since P is twice the initial population, when we divide both sides by the initial population, we get two.

TABLE 7.2 Finding Doubling Time for U.S. Population, Assuming 1.27% Annual Growth

1900 Initial Population	1950 Initial Population
$P = 76{,}212{,}168 \cdot (1.0127)^t$	$P = 151{,}325{,}798 \cdot (1.0127)^t$
$152{,}424{,}336 = 76{,}212{,}168 \cdot 1.0127^t$	$302{,}651{,}596 = 151{,}325{,}798 \cdot 1.0127^t$
$2 = 1.0127^t$	$2 = 1.0127^t$

Notice that the initial value does not matter when solving for the doubling time. We need to find the time that solves the equation:

$$2 = 1.0127^t$$

It is important to compare the equation we are trying to solve with other common situations:

$$2 = 1.0127^t$$

TABLE 7.3 Comparison of Equation Types and Solution Techniques

Taking the nth root is equivalent to raising to the $1/n$.

Equation Type	Power	Linear	Exponential
Inverse operation	Roots	Reciprocals	Logarithms
Equation	$t^{1.0127} = 2$	$1.0127 \cdot t = 2$	$1.0127^t = 2$
Solution	$t = 2^{1/1.0127}$	$t = 2/1.0127$	?

Before we introduce **logarithms**, let's solve our equation using the most important technique of all, guess and check! Using a spreadsheet, we can easily create tables of values to find the power of 1.0127 that equals two:

TABLE 7.4 Two Is Closer to 1.879 Than 2.132, so t Is Closer to 50 Than 60

t	1.0127^t
30	1.460
40	1.656
50	**1.879**
60	**2.132**

TABLE 7.5 Two Is Closer to 2.002 Than 1.977, so t Is Closer to 55 Than 54

t	1.0127^t
52	1.927
53	1.952
54	**1.977**
55	**2.002**

TABLE 7.6 Two Is Closer to 1.99989 Than 2.00014, so t Is Closer to 54.92 Than 54.93

t	1.0127^t
54.91	1.99964
54.92	**1.99989**
54.93	**2.00014**
54.94	2.00039

Table 7.6 indicates $t \approx 54.92$. Thus the U.S. population doubles every 54.92 years.

SPREADSHEET TUTORIALS Entering Data by Range | Entering Numbers | Copying a Formula Using the Fill Handle | Using Arithmetic Operators

OBJECTIVE 2 Understand Logarithms

Table 7.3 compares three different common types of equations: power, linear, and exponential. To solve these equations, we must use **inverse operations**; to undo a square, we take the square root; to undo a product, we divide; and to undo an exponent, we use logarithms.

DEFINITION

A **logarithm** of x to the base b, $\log_b x$, is the *power* of b equal to x (for x and b both positive). Taking a logarithm to the base b is the inverse operation of raising the base to a power, b^y, just as taking the nth root of a number is the inverse operation of raising that number to the nth power:

$$y = \sqrt[n]{x} \underset{\textit{is equivalent to}}{\Longleftrightarrow} x = y^n$$

$$y = \log_b x \underset{\textit{is equivalent to}}{\Longleftrightarrow} x = b^y$$

The number, b, is called the *base* of the logarithm (also the base of the exponential on the right). If $b = 10$, then this is called the **common logarithm**, and the base is not written:

$$y = \log x \underset{\textit{is equivalent to}}{\Longleftrightarrow} y = \log_{10} x$$

If $b = e$ (Euler's number), then this is called the **natural logarithm** and is written as follows:

$$y = \ln x \underset{\textit{is equivalent to}}{\Longleftrightarrow} y = \log_e x$$

A logarithm is a power or an exponent. Don't miss this important concept in the long definition above.

Example 2 Evaluate Logarithms

VIDEO *Logarithms*

Evaluate the following **logarithms** without using a calculator:

1. $\log_2 8 =$
2. $\log 100 =$
3. $\log 0.1 =$
4. $\log_7 7^{19} =$
5. $\ln e^{23} =$

SOLUTION We can rewrite each of these logarithms as a problem involving exponents:

1. $\log_2 8 = y \underset{\text{is equivalent to}}{\Longleftrightarrow} 2^y = 8 \underset{\text{implies}}{\Longrightarrow} y = 3$
2. $\log 100 = y \Leftrightarrow 10^y = 100 \Rightarrow y = 2$
3. $\log 0.1 = y \Leftrightarrow 10^y = 0.1 \Rightarrow y = -1$
4. $\log_7 7^{19} = y \Leftrightarrow 7^y = 7^{19} \Rightarrow y = 19$
5. $\ln e^{23} = y \Leftrightarrow e^y = e^{23} \Rightarrow y = 23$

Note the general rule that is being used here, based on the definition of a logarithm:

$$\log_b b^k = k$$

Notice that once we have rewritten each of these in exponential form, we can solve it in our head since we are so much more familiar with exponential equations. Watch the video for a nice technique on rewriting a logarithm as an exponent.

Example 2 illustrates the inverse relationship between **logarithms** and exponents. Exponents have many well-known properties; for each of these properties, there is an analogous property of logarithms. We use **common logarithms** in the following table, but the properties are valid for all bases. Watch the video for a detailed derivation of these properties.

VIDEO *Properties*

TABLE 7.7 Properties of Logarithms

Property of Exponents	Property of Logarithms	General Property of Logarithms
$10^3 = 1{,}000$	$\log 1{,}000 = 3$	$\log_b b^k = k$
$10^0 = 1$	$\log 1 = 0$	$\log_b b^0 = 0$
$10^{-5} = 0.00001$	$\log 0.00001 = -5$	$\log_b b^{-k} = -k$
$10^2 \cdot 10^6 = 10^{2+6}$	$\log(10^2 \cdot 10^6) = \log 10^2 + \log 10^6$	$\log_b(a \cdot c) = \log_b a + \log_b c$
$10^2/10^6 = 10^{2-6}$	$\log(10^2/10^6) = \log 10^2 - \log 10^6$	$\log_b(a/c) = \log_b a - \log_b c$
$(10^2)^6 = 10^{2 \cdot 6}$	$\log(10^2)^6 = 6 \cdot \log 10^2$	$\log_b a^k = k \cdot \log_b a$

The fact that the log of a product is the sum of the logs is why "logarithm" stands for "logical arithmetic." In the 1600s, when computation was done by hand, addition was easier than multiplication; you can add a column of numbers all at once, but multiplication requires multiplying numbers two at a time. Thus to multiply a column of numbers, scientists would first look up the log of each factor in a table, sum these to find the log of the unknown product, and then convert back, using the same tables. Life sure was simpler back then.

7.2 Doubling Times and Half-Lives

OBJECTIVE 1 Use Properties of Logarithms

OBJECTIVE 1 Use Properties of Logarithms

We saw in Example 1 that when finding the time it takes for the U.S. population to double using the equation $P = P_0 \cdot (1.0127)^t$, it did not matter what the initial population was. For exponential growth, the doubling time depends only on the growth rate.

DEFINITION

Given a quantity that grows or decays exponentially, $P = P_0 \cdot (1 + r)^t$, the length of time before the quantity doubles or is cut in half is called the **doubling time** ($r > 0$) or **half-life** ($r < 0$), respectively.

- *Doubling time*: $t = \dfrac{\log 2}{\log(1 + r)}$
- *Half life*: $t = \dfrac{\log(1/2)}{\log(1 + r)}$

Note for half-life that the rate cannot be less than -100%. It is impossible to lose more than 100% of what you have.

Example 3 Find the Doubling Time

VIDEO *Doubling Time*

Assuming that the U.S. population grows at 1.27% annually, find the doubling time.

SOLUTION As in Example 1, we know that we can substitute any initial population:

$$P = 76{,}212{,}168 \cdot (1.0127)^t$$

Substituting twice the initial population for P gives us:

$$152{,}424{,}336 = 76{,}212{,}168 \cdot (1.0127)^t$$

Dividing both sides by the initial population yields:

$$2 = 1.0127^t$$

To solve for t, we can take the **logarithm** of both sides of the equation:

$$\log 2 = \log 1.0127^t$$

Now, using the property of logarithms, $\log a^k = k \cdot \log a$:

This is the crucial property of logarithms that "undoes" the exponent. Note how the exponent, t, pops out front so we can solve for it.

$$\log 2 = t \cdot \log 1.0127$$

$$t = \frac{\log 2}{\log 1.0127} \approx 54.924$$

And we arrive at a **doubling time** of 54.924 years, just as in Example 1.

We did not use the formula from the definition for doubling time so we could show its derivation, but we will use the formula in the next example, on half-life.

CAUTION Do not take the logarithm of a negative number; there is no such thing. ●

Example 4 Find a Half-Life

VIDEO *Half Life*

Find the **half-life** of carbon-14, which decays by −11.4% per millennium, and create a graph using the half-life.

SOLUTION The **decay rate** of 11.4% implies a **decay factor** of 0.886, which we can plug into the formula:

$$t = \frac{\log 0.5}{\log 0.886} = 5.727 \text{ millennia}$$

1 + rate = factor
1 − 0.114 = 0.886

We can create a scatterplot using the **half-life** by first generating a table of values assuming an initial value of 100 grams of carbon-14. We know we will lose half of the carbon-14 every 5.727 millennia. Plotting the data in **Table 7.8,** we can then create a scatterplot.

Note the tell-tale shape of exponential decay in the graph. Any quantity that has a fixed half-life will be an **exponential function**. This graph will *never* touch the x-axis. (Google "Zeno's Paradox.")

TABLE 7.8 Carbon-14 Values Using Half-life

Millennia	Carbon-14 (g)
0.000	100.00
5.727	50.00
11.454	25.00
17.181	12.50
22.908	6.25
28.635	3.13
34.362	1.56
40.089	0.78

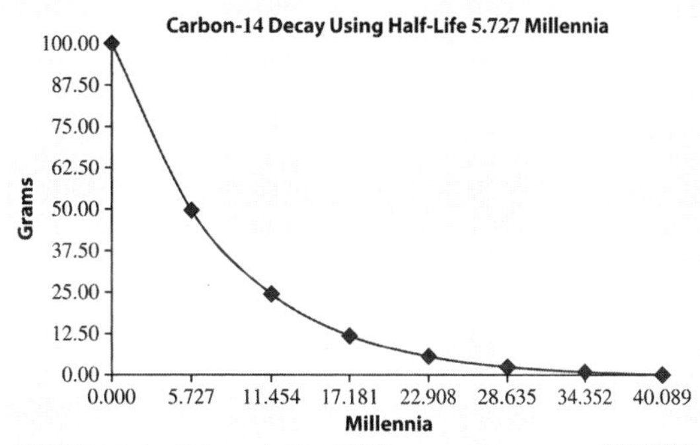

FIGURE 7.1 Carbon-14 Scatterplot Using Half-Life

CAUTION Note the intervals on the x-axis are every 5.727 units, which is exactly how long it takes for the amount of Carbon-14 to be cut in half. ●

SPREADSHEET TUTORIALS Entering Data by Range | Entering Numbers | Copying a Formula Using the Fill Handle | Using Arithmetic Operators

7.3 Annual Percentage Yield

OBJECTIVE 1 Understand Compounding Periodically

OBJECTIVE 2 Compute the Yield (APY)

OBJECTIVE 1 Understand Compounding Periodically

We have defined exponential growth in terms of a constant **percent change**, using the equation $P = P_0 \cdot (1 + r)^t$. This equation works for **periodic rates** as well. Recall that if we have a 6% **APR** compounded monthly, the periodic rate, or monthly rate, is $\frac{6\%}{12} = 0.5\%$.

Example 5 Use Periodic Rate

VIDEO *Periodic Rate*

You invest \$1,000 with a 6% APR, compounded monthly. Write the equation for the value of your investment as a **function** of months and determine the value after three years.

SOLUTION We are given the APR of 6%, which, as mentioned above, implies that the monthly rate is 0.5%. Substituting into our equation for exponential growth:

$$P = 1{,}000 \cdot (1 + 0.5\%)^m$$

where m = months and P = the principal, or value of our investment after m months. In 3 years, or 36 months, we will have:

$$P = 1{,}000(1.005)^{36} = \$1{,}196.68$$

This example of 6% **APR** compounded monthly leads us to a generalization of our exponential equation. First, we write the equation without solving for the **periodic rate**:

$$P = 1{,}000 \cdot \left(1 + \frac{6\%}{12}\right)^m$$

Next, we replace the **variable** for m = months with an expression involving t = years. In our last example, we wanted the value of our investment after three years, and had to convert in our heads to 36 months. In general, the world of finance likes to have years as the standard input variable. Recalling our work in Chapter 3, the **ratio** 1 year : 12 months, yields the equation $m = 12 \cdot t$, which we can substitute into the equation above:

$$P = 1{,}000 \cdot \left(1 + \frac{6\%}{12}\right)^{12 \cdot t}$$

This leads us to the **periodic compounding form** of an exponential equation:

$$P = P_0 \cdot \left(1 + \frac{\text{APR}}{n}\right)^{n \cdot t}$$

> This equation may seem more complicated than the one we used in Example 5. The point is that we want all of our equations to have years as the input variable.

where P_0 = the initial value and n = the number of periods in one year.

OBJECTIVE 2 Compute the Yield (APY)

The **periodic compounding form** of an exponential equation is a bit messy, but it allows us to compare different investments because the input variable will always be years. Also, given an APR and period, we can simply "fill in the blanks" in the general form.

Example 6 Simplify the Periodic Compounding Form of an Exponential Equation

VIDEO *Yield*

Assume that you invest \$1,000 and get an **APR** of 6%, compounded monthly. Represent this relationship with an equation of the form $P = 1{,}000 \cdot (1 + r)^t$ and interpret the **rate**, r.

SOLUTION We have just seen that we can represent this investment using the equation:

$$P = 1{,}000 \cdot \left[\left(1 + \frac{6\%}{12}\right)^{12}\right]^t$$

We are using the property of exponents, which tells us to multiply exponents in this situation.

Notice that everything in the square brackets is a number. Typing this all into a calculator, we can simplify:

$$P = 1{,}000 \cdot (1.061678)^t$$

this looks much more manageable, and notice that it is of the form $P = 1{,}000 \cdot (1 + r)^t$, implying that the **growth rate**, r, is 6.1678%. This represents what an **APR** of 6% compounded monthly will yield at the end of the year. If we substitute $t = 1$, we get \$1,061.68—that is, we get 6.1678% interest. This new rate is called the annual percentage yield, or APY.

DEFINITION

The yield, or **annual percentage yield** (APY), of an investment is the *effective interest rate* required to create the total amount of interest generated over the course of one year. For an investment with no additional deposits or payments and an APR compounded n times per year, we have:

$$APY = \left(1 + \frac{APR}{n}\right)^n - 1$$

The yield for a loan is more complicated since there are almost always monthly payments, which affects the interest charged. Often, this is referred to as the *effective interest rate* for a loan:

$$APY = \frac{\text{Total Interest for 1 Year}}{\text{Initial Balance}}.$$

Example 7 Compute the APY

Determine the APY for an investment with an APR of 8%, compounded daily.

SOLUTION

$$\left(1 + \frac{8\%}{365}\right)^{365} \approx 1.083278$$

Thus the APY = 8.3278%.

CAUTION You must use more than two decimal places to distinguish the APY from the APR. •

SPREADSHEET TUTORIALS Using Arithmetic Operators | Entering Numbers | Formatting Cells with the Percent Style

Continuous Growth and Euler's Number: e

OBJECTIVE 1 Explore Compounding Continuously

OBJECTIVE 1 Explore Compounding Continuously

The **periodic compounding form** of an exponential equation will lead us to e and the concept of the **continuous growth/decay rate**. The idea is simple enough: If we can compound our interest 12 times a year—that is, every month—then we can compound more often: every day, every minute, every second, every nanosecond, etc.

As n, the number of periods in a year, gets larger, the associated period of time gets smaller. Eventually the period of time will be so short that it will be indistinguishable from continuous compounding. It is similar to a movie, which is a collection of pictures flashed before us so quickly that our eyes cannot distinguish the "flip rate," and it appears continuous.

Let's explore what happens to the periodic compounding form of an exponential equation as n (the number of periods in one year) gets larger and larger. We will use 6% for the **APR** and make use of three different forms of the equation: the first with the period as the input variable, the second with years as the input variable, and the third with everything simplified:

$$P = 1{,}000 \cdot \left(1 + \frac{6\%}{12}\right)^{m} \rightarrow P = 1{,}000 \cdot \left(1 + \frac{6\%}{12}\right)^{12 \cdot t} \rightarrow P = 1{,}000 \cdot (1.061678)^{t}$$

This last equation gives the **growth factor** for the **APY**.

Table 7.9 illustrates what happens as the number of periods in one year gets large. Note that the **APY** settles down to 6.1837%, and we do not include the initial value to save space:

VIDEO *APY Table*

TABLE 7.9 Periodic Compounding for 6% **APR**, Going to Infinity

Period	n	Equation	Input	t = years	APY
Annually	1	$(1 + \frac{6\%}{1})^{t}$	t	$(1 + \frac{6\%}{1})^{t}$	$(1.06)^{t}$
Bi-annually	2	$(1 + \frac{6\%}{2})^{b}$	$b = 2 \cdot t$	$(1 + \frac{6\%}{2})^{2 \cdot t}$	$(1.0609)^{t}$
Quarterly	4	$(1 + \frac{6\%}{4})^{q}$	$q = 4 \cdot t$	$(1 + \frac{6\%}{4})^{4 \cdot t}$	$(1.061364)^{t}$
Monthly	12	$(1 + \frac{6\%}{12})^{m}$	$m = 12 \cdot t$	$(1 + \frac{6\%}{12})^{12 \cdot t}$	$(1.061678)^{t}$
Bi-weekly	26	$(1 + \frac{6\%}{26})^{bi}$	$bi = 26 \cdot t$	$(1 + \frac{6\%}{26})^{26 \cdot t}$	$(1.061763)^{t}$
Weekly	52	$(1 + \frac{6\%}{52})^{w}$	$w = 52 \cdot t$	$(1 + \frac{6\%}{52})^{52 \cdot t}$	$(1.061800)^{t}$
Daily	365	$(1 + \frac{6\%}{365})^{d}$	$d = 365 \cdot t$	$(1 + \frac{6\%}{365})^{365 \cdot t}$	$(1.061831)^{t}$
Hourly	8,760	$(1 + \frac{6\%}{8760})^{h}$	$h = 8760 \cdot t$	$(1 + \frac{6\%}{8760})^{8760 \cdot t}$	$(1.061836)^{t}$
Minutely	525,600	$(1 + \frac{6\%}{525600})^{min}$	$min = 525600 \cdot t$	$(1 + \frac{6\%}{525600})^{525600 \cdot t}$	$(1.061837)^{t}$
Secondly	31,536,000	$(1 + \frac{6\%}{31536000})^{s}$	$s = 31536000 \cdot t$	$(1 + \frac{6\%}{31536000})^{31536000 \cdot t}$	$(1.061837)^{t}$

This last equation gives the growth factor for the APY.

SPREADSHEET TUTORIALS Using Arithmetic Operators Entering Numbers

Table 7.9 shows that there is a limit to the **effective rate** of return we can get by increasing the number of compounding periods in a given year. The **APY** approaches 6.1837% for an **APR** of 6%. Let's now formalize this limit, prove that the APY does not get any higher than 6.1837% (to four decimal places of accuracy), and in the process meet an old friend.

VIDEO
e Euler's Constant

We start with the periodic compounding form of the exponential equation with an APR of 6%:

$$P = P_0 \cdot \left(1 + \frac{6\%}{n}\right)^{n \cdot t} = P_0 \cdot \left[\left(1 + \frac{6\%}{n}\right)^{n}\right]^{t}$$

Next, we make a strange substitution to get the 6% out of the parentheses (the video explains in more detail why this is justified):

$$\frac{1}{N} = \frac{6\%}{n} \quad \Rightarrow \quad n = 6\% \cdot N$$

CAUTION These are equivalent expressions: As n goes to infinity, so does N. ●

Giving us:

$$P = P_0 \cdot \left[\left(1 + \frac{1}{N}\right)^{N}\right]^{6\% \cdot t}$$

Now let's see what happens to $\left(1 + \frac{1}{N}\right)^{N}$ as N gets larger and larger and goes to infinity (∞).

Note the battle taking place in this expression. The quantity in the parentheses, the base, wants to go to 1 when N gets large (since $1/N$ gets smaller and smaller); but raising a number bigger than 1 to a larger and larger power wants to make the entire expression huge. So what will happen? Will the entire expression go to 1, or will it go to infinity, or will it go somewhere in between?

Table 7.10 shows that the expression, which starts out at 2, gets to 2.7 pretty quickly. But then the competing tensions of the base going to 1 while the exponent goes to infinity seem to balance out, and the result settles down at 2.71828, with five decimal places of accuracy:

TABLE 7.10 Evaluating Limit as N Goes to Infinity to Five Decimal Places of Accuracy

N	1	100	1,000	100,000	1,000,000	1,000,000,000
$\left(1 + \frac{1}{N}\right)^{N}$	2	2.70481	2.71692	2.71827	2.71828	2.71828

As N continues to get large, the result will continue to grow so that the actual decimal expansion will continue, never ending or repeating, but never getting above 2.71829. We can get as many decimal places of accuracy as we want by substituting large enough numbers. Thus a fixed number begins to appear, one decimal place at a time, 2.718281828459 . . . , and this number has a special name.

DEFINITION

Euler's number, pronounced "oiler's number," is defined as the limit of the process:

$$e = \lim_{N \to \infty} \left(1 + \frac{1}{N}\right)^{N} = 2.718281828459 \cdots$$

SPREADSHEET TUTORIALS Entering Numbers Copying a Formula Using the Fill Handle Using Arithmetic Operators

We can now go back to our equation and finish our analysis of what happens as the number of compounding periods in one year goes to infinity:

$$P = P_0 \cdot \left[\left(1 + \frac{1}{N}\right)^N\right]^{6\% \cdot t}$$

As N goes to infinity, the expression in the square brackets goes to e, giving us the equation:

$$P = P_0 \cdot [e]^{6\% \cdot t}$$

This is exactly the continuous growth form of an exponential equation, $y = a \cdot e^{k \cdot x}$, that we saw in Chapter 6. Now we know that the word *continuous* is referring to getting interest compounded continuously throughout the year.

Example 8 Contrast Periodic Compounding

Write an equation for a \$1,000 investment with an **APR** of 4% for each of the following situations: compounded **a)** annually, **b)** monthly, and **c)** continuously. Determine the value of the investment after one year in each case and compute the **APY**.

SOLUTION

a) The equation is $P = 1{,}000 \cdot (1.04)^t$. In one year, $P(1) = \$1{,}040$; APY = 4%.

b) The equation is $P = 1{,}000 \cdot \left(1 + \frac{0.04}{12}\right)^{12 \cdot t} = 1{,}000 \cdot (1.04074)^t$. In one year, $P(1) = \$1{,}040.74$; APY = 4.074%.

c) The equation is $P = 1{,}000 \cdot (e)^{0.04 \cdot t} = 1{,}000 \cdot (1.04081$. In one year, $P(1) = \$1{,}040.81$ APY = 4.081%

Note that this is the highest possible APY. You cannot do better than compounding continuously.

The continuous form of the exponential equation is not restricted to financial applications.

Example 9 Compute Continuous Decay Rate

VIDEO Air Pressure

Air pressure is an **exponential function** of altitude given by the equation $P = 14.7 \cdot 0.958^h$, where P = air pressure measured in pounds per square inch (psi) and h = altitude measured in thousands of feet ($h = 1$ refers to 1,000 feet above sea level). Determine the **decay rate** of air pressure, the **continuous decay rate**, and the air pressure at 30,000 feet. Interpret the initial value in real-world terms.

SOLUTION We are given the **decay factor**, $0.958 = 1 + r$; therefore, $r = -4.2\%$ and the decay rate is 4.2%. Air pressure drops 4.2% every 1,000 feet in altitude. To determine the continuous decay rate, we need our equation in the continuous form:

$$P = 14.7 \cdot 0.958^h = 14.7 \cdot e^{k \cdot h}$$

In other words, we need to solve the equation:

$$0.958 = e^k$$

Here we are using the property of logarithms, $\log_b b^k = k$. We use the natural logarithm because it is base e.

Taking the **natural logarithm** of both sides of the equation:

$$\ln 0.958 = \ln e^k = k$$

Thus $k = \ln 0.958 \approx -0.0429$. Thus the continuous decay rate is 4.29%.

Substituting $h = 30$ into our first equation (to avoid round-off error in k), we get:

$$P = 14.7 \cdot 0.958^{30} = 4.06 \text{ psi}$$

Finally, the 14.7 represents the air pressure when $h = 0$, so at sea level, the air pressure is 14.7 psi.

One last example puts everything together before we move on to log scales.

Example 10 Connect Everything Together

Fill in the following table:

VIDEO Connections

TABLE 7.11 Growth/Decay Factor Example

Annual Growth/ Decay Rate	Doubling Time/ Half-Life	Growth/Decay Factor per Year	Continuous Rate per Year	Growth/Decay Factor per Decade	Growth/Decay Rate per Decade
30%		1.30		13.79	
	9.0 years	1.08	7.70%		
				0.197	

SOLUTION The key to the table lies in the **growth/decay factor**; once we have this, we can find all the other numbers by using the formulas (see the video for derivations):

TABLE 7.12 Growth/Decay Factor Example Solved

Annual Growth/ Decay Rate	Doubling Time/ Half-Life	Growth/Decay Factor per Year	Continuous Rate per Year	Growth/Decay Factor per Decade	Growth /Decay Rate per Decade
r	$\frac{\log 2}{\log(1+r)}$ $\frac{\log 1/2}{\log(1+r)}$	$1 + r$	$\ln(1 + r)$	$(1 + r)^{10}$	$(1 + r)^{10} - 1$
Annual Growth/ Decay Rate	**Doubling Time/ Half-Life**	**Growth/Decay Factor per Year**	**Continuous Rate per Year**	**Growth/Decay Factor per Decade**	**Growth /Decay Rate per Decade**
30%	2.64 years	1.30	26.2%	13.79	1,279%
8%	9.0 years	1.08	7.70%	2.16	116%
−15%	4.27 years	0.85	−16.3%	0.197	−80.3%

CAUTION To work backward to the decay rate, take the 10th root. ●

SPREADSHEET TUTORIALS Using Arithmetic Operators Entering Numbers Formatting Cells with the Percent Style

7.5 Spotlight on Statistics

OBJECTIVE 1 Understand Log Scales

OBJECTIVE 1 Understand Log Scales

There is one other prevalent use of **logarithms** related to graphing: the **log scale**. This occurs in the Richter scale for measuring earthquake magnitudes and the decibel scale for measuring loudness of sounds. These examples are explored in the homework. A log scale is effective when data varies over a huge range of numbers, like the planetary distances from the sun in our solar system, as shown in **Figure 7.2**.

Note the **linear scale** on the y-axis. It increases in even increments of 1,000.

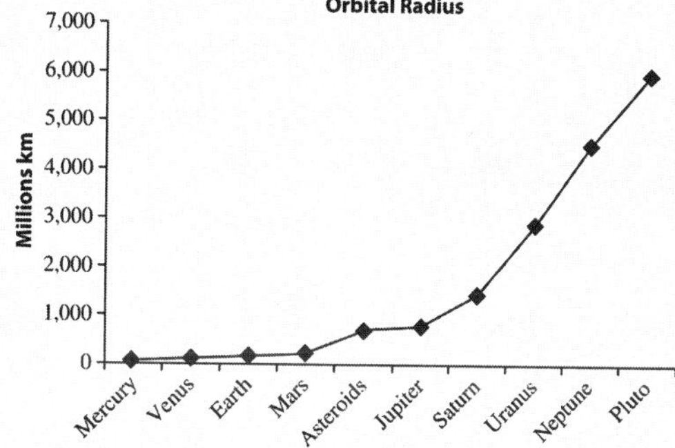

FIGURE 7.2 Orbital Radii

The graph in **Figure 7.2** is difficult to read because the first four radius values are so much smaller than the later radii, so the first four look almost like they are zero, squished down on the x-axis. To deal with this, scientists create what is called a log plot, using a log scale.

DEFINITION

A **logarithmic scale** is a measurement scale that displays intervals measured by order of magnitude (e.g., powers of 10) rather than equally spaced intervals, as in a *linear scale*. A *semi-log plot* is a scatterplot where one axis uses a logarithmic scale and the other a linear scale. A *log-log plot* is a scatterplot where both axes use logarithmic scales.

Example 11 Use a Logarithmic Scale

VIDEO Log Scales

Create a graph of the orbital radius data in **Table 7.13**, using a logarithmic scale.

SOLUTION In Excel it is simple to format an axis using a logarithmic scale. Simply create a line graph (note that this is not a scatterplot since we have only one quantitative variable) and then right-click a value on the y-axis and choose *Format Axis*. Check the box next to *Logarithmic Scale*, and you are done.

TABLE 7.13 Orbital Radii

Planet/ Object	Orbital Radius (Millions km)
Mercury	57.9
Venus	108.2
Earth	149.6
Mars	227.9
Asteroids	686.1
Jupiter	778.3
Saturn	1,429.4
Uranus	2,875.0
Neptune	4,504.5
Pluto	5,915.8

Note the logarithmic scale on the y-axis. It increases by powers of 10.

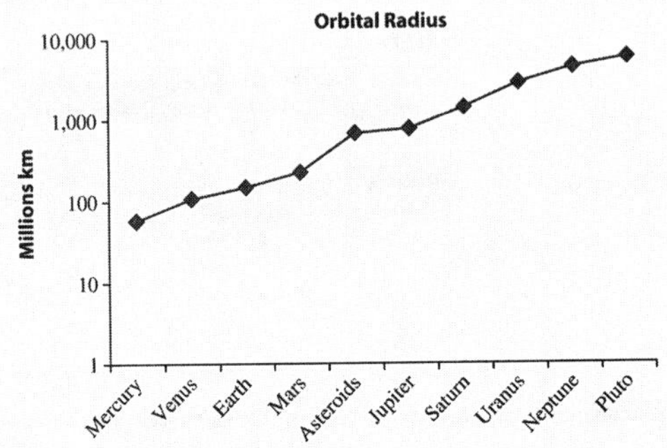

FIGURE 7.3 Orbital Radii, Using Logarithmic Scale

Note that the **logarithmic scale** turned what looked like an exponential curve in **Figure 7.2** into a linear curve in **Figure 7.3**. A logarithmic scale will always turn an exponential graph into a linear graph; we'll see why after the next example, which illustrates this phenomenon.

SPREADSHEET TUTORIAL Entering Data by Range

Example 12 Create a Semi-log Plot

VIDEO Semi Log

The March 2011 tsunami in Japan crippled the reactors at the Fukushima Daiichi Nuclear Power Station, releasing airborne radioactive particles. Of most concern were the particles of cesium-137, which has a half-life of 30 years. Fill in an x-y table for the amount of cesium-137 as a **function** of years. Create a scatterplot of this data and insert an exponential trendline with equation. Create a **semi-log plot** and compare the two graphs side-by-side.

SOLUTION We can fill in the x-y table using the half-life of 30 years and making up a convenient initial value of 80 g. Next, we create a scatterplot and insert an exponential trendline.

TABLE 7.14 Exponential Decay of Cesium-137

Years	Cesium-137 (g)
0	80
30	40
60	20
90	10
120	5

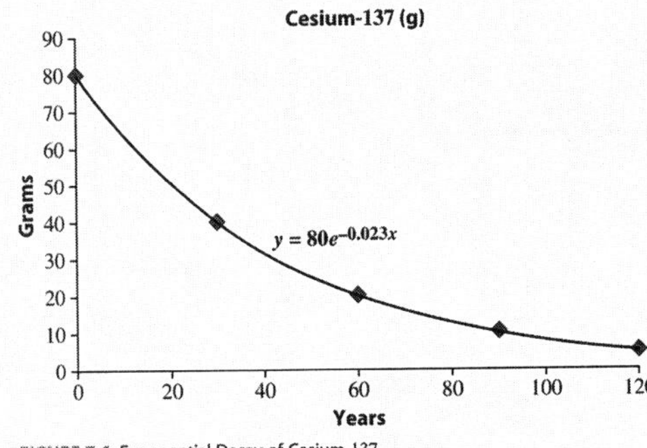

FIGURE 7.4 Exponential Decay of Cesium-137

SPREADSHEET TUTORIALS Entering Data by Range Entering Numbers Copying a Formula Using the Fill Handle Using Arithmetic Operators

Next we create the **semi-log plot** and compare it to our original scatterplot:

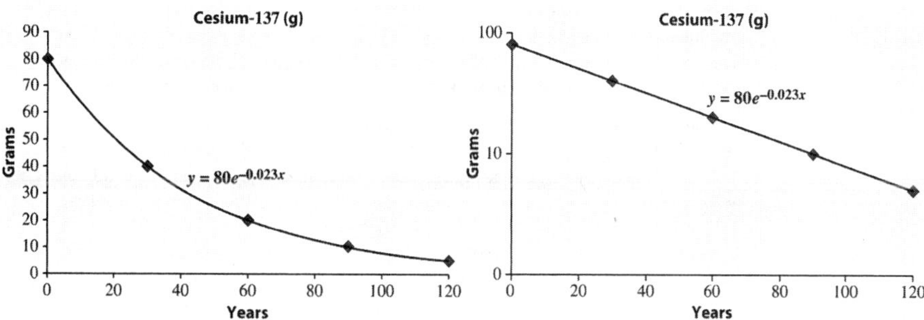

FIGURE 7.5 Exponential Decay of Cesium-137

FIGURE 7.6 Semi-log Plot Exponential Decay of Cesium-137

Note that the semi-log plot turns the exponential curve into a linear curve. We can see why this happens by taking the **logarithm** of the exponential equation.

$$\ln y = \ln\left(80 \cdot e^{-0.023 \cdot x}\right)$$

Using properties of logs, the log of a product is the sum of the logs:

$$\ln y = \ln 80 + \ln\left(e^{-0.023 \cdot x}\right)$$

And $\ln e^k = k$:

$$\ln y = \ln 80 - 0.023 \cdot x$$

We can see that the logarithm of the outputs will be a linear function of the inputs!

Example 13 Take the Log of the Outputs

VIDEO *Exponential to Linear*

Using the data in **Table 7.14**, take the **natural logarithm** of the y-values. Graph these new outputs with the same x-values, add a **linear trendline** to the scatterplot, and display the equation. Compare this equation to the one we just derived: $\ln y = -0.023 \cdot x + \ln 80$.

SOLUTION **Table 7.15** shows the data in Excel with a third column that is simply taking the natural logarithm of the y-values. Graphing the years and $\ln(y)$ data, we get the scatterplot in **Figure 7.7**, with the linear equation:

$$y = -0.0231 \cdot x + 4.382$$

The slope of this equation, −0.0231, is identical to the one derived above. The y-intercept, 4.382, is the same as ln 80 to three decimal places. Therefore, using a **logarithmic scale** on the y-axis has the same effect on the scatterplot as plotting ln (y) against x.

TABLE 7.15 x-y Table Taking the Natural Logarithm of the y-values

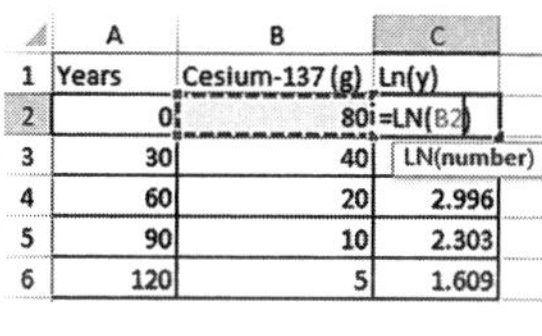

	A	B	C
1	Years	Cesium-137 (g)	Ln(y)
2	0	80	=LN(B2)
3	30	40	LN(number)
4	60	20	2.996
5	90	10	2.303
6	120	5	1.609

Note that we used the natural logarithm for this problem, but any base will work for **semi-log plots**.

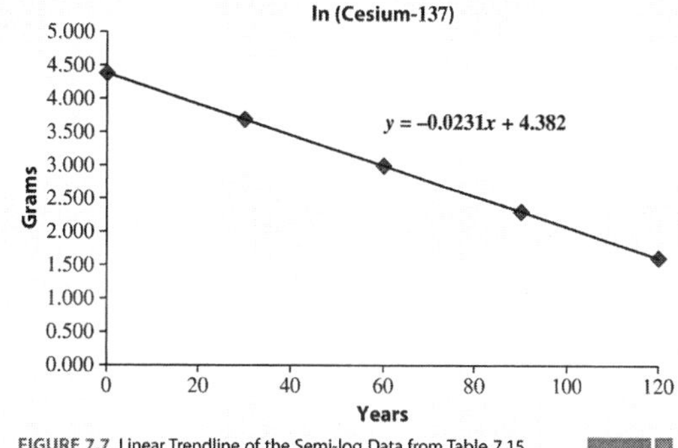

FIGURE 7.7 Linear Trendline of the Semi-log Data from Table 7.15

SPREADSHEET TUTORIALS Entering Data by Range Entering Numbers Copying a Formula Using the Fill Handle Using Arithmetic Operators

Screenshots from Microsoft ® Excel ®. Used by permission of Microsoft Corporation.

Our last example looks at a **log-log plot** and associated **power-law distribution.** Many phenomena have the characteristic of large numbers of small-scale events and fewer large-scale events; for example, there are many small earthquakes and very few devastating earthquakes, and there are many cities with small populations but very few mega-cities. The choice of "small" and "large" is, of course, relative, and these observations are generally based on a ranking of the events. We can use the Richter scale to rank earthquakes and populations to rank cities.

The American linguist George Zipf studied this phenomenon for the frequency of words in a written text and formulated his well-known Zipf's law, which states that the frequency of a word is roughly inversely proportional to its rank (high rank corresponds to low number, as in 1st place, while low rank corresponds to a high number, as in 100th place). The most common word (typically *the*, rank = 1), occurs very often, while very low-ranking words occur infrequently. Recall that *inversely proportional* implies an equation of the form $y = k \cdot x^{-1}$. In general, a power-law distribution refers to the frequency as a function of rank having an equation of the form:

$$y = k \cdot x^{-a}$$

We can rank households by income and create a frequency distribution with a tell-tale power-law shape that we will explore in the next example:

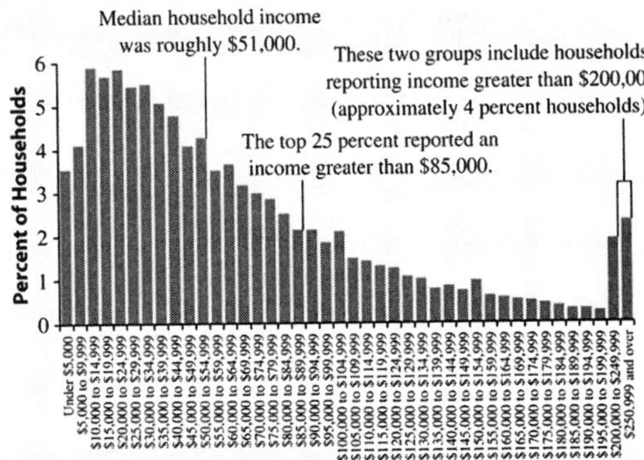

FIGURE 7.8 U.S. Household Income Distribution, 2012

Data from: U.S. Census Bureau, Current Population Survey, 2012 Annual Social and Economic Supplement

Figure 7.8 shows a **power-law distribution** for household income in the United States in 2012. We will use the data from 2005 in **Table 7.16** as it gives more detail at the high end of the spectrum, which the Congressional Budget Office stopped reporting after 2008.

Example 14 **Log-log Plot of Income**

VIDEO *Power Law*

Using the data in **Table 7.16**, create a scatterplot and insert a *Power* trendline. Take the **logarithm** of both the x- and y-values. Graph these new values, add a linear trendline to the scatterplot, and display the equation.

SOLUTION Typing the data into Excel, it is easy enough to get the scatterplot:

TABLE 7.16 Number of Households with Average Income in 2005

	A	B	C
1	Income	Hshlds (1000's)	Percentiles
2	$ 15,900	24,116	0 - 20
3	$ 37,400	21,990	21 - 40
4	$ 58,500	22,153	41 - 60
5	$ 85,200	22,571	61 - 80
6	$ 120,600	11,420	81 - 90
7	$ 161,800	5,924	91 - 95
8	$ 269,800	4,672	96 - 99
9	$ 588,100	564	99 - 99.5
10	$ 1,207,200	451	99.6 - 99.9
11	$ 4,699,500	99	99.9 - 99.99
12	$35,473,200	11	99.99 - 100

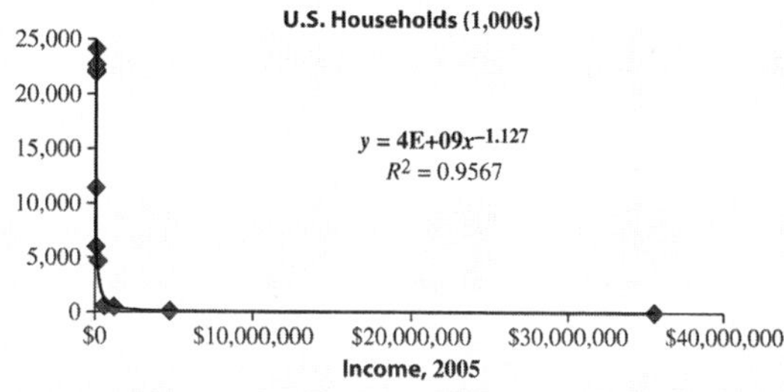

FIGURE 7.9 U.S. Household Income Distribution, 2005

Note the **power-law equation** $y = 4 \cdot 10^9 \cdot x^{-1.127}$. We want to use a **log-log plot** because this scatterplot is so difficult to read.

SPREADSHEET TUTORIAL **Entering Data by Range**

Figure 7.10 shows the **log-log plot** for the data in **Table 7.17**. Notice how the power-law equation, $y = 4 \cdot 10^9 \cdot x^{-1.127}$, gets transformed into a **linear function**. As with the **semi-log plot**, we can see why by taking the log of both sides of this equation:

$$\log y = \log\left(4 \cdot 10^9 \cdot x^{-1.127}\right)$$

Note that the signature of a **power-law distribution** is linearity of the log-log plot. The **slope** is the power of the power-law equation.

Using the log of a product is the sum of the logs:

$$\log y = \log\left(4 \cdot 10^9\right) + \log x^{-1.127}$$

And now, using $\log a^k = k \cdot \log a$:

$$\log y = 9.602 - 1.127 \cdot \log x$$

This is almost identical to the equation in **Figure 7.9**, with $\log y$ as a function of $\log x$. The discrepancy in the y-intercept comes from the rounding off of $4 \cdot 10^9$ in the **power-law equation**.

TABLE 7.17 The Number of Households with Average Income in 2005 with Log-log

	A	B	C	D	E
1	Income	Hshlds (1000's)	Percentiles	Log(Income)	Log(Households)
2	$ 15,900	24,116	0 - 20	=LOG(A2)	4.382
3	$ 37,400	21,990	21 - 40	LOG(number, [base])	4.342
4	$ 58,500	22,153	41 - 60	4.767	4.345
5	$ 85,200	22,571	61 - 80	4.930	4.354
6	$ 120,600	11,420	81 - 90	5.081	4.058
7	$ 161,800	5,924	91 - 95	5.209	3.773
8	$ 269,800	4,672	96 - 99	5.431	3.670
9	$ 588,100	564	99 - 99.5	5.769	2.751
10	$ 1,207,200	451	99.6 - 99.9	6.082	2.654
11	$ 4,699,500	99	99.9 - 99.99	6.672	1.996
12	$35,473,200	11	99.99 - 100	7.550	1.041

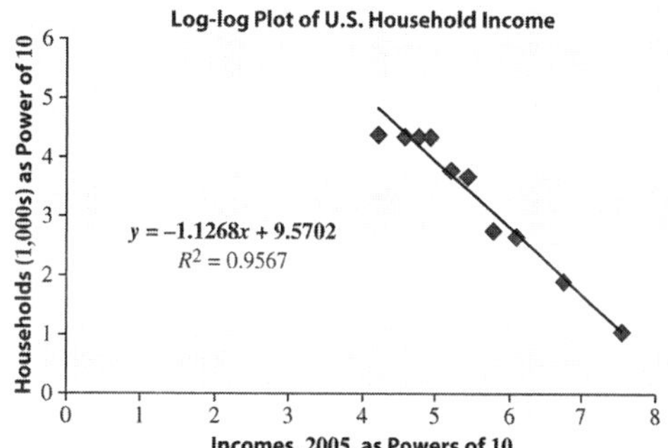

FIGURE 7.10 U.S. Household Income Distribution, 2005, Log-log Plot

SPREADSHEET TUTORIALS **Entering Data by Range** **Entering Numbers** **Copying a Formula Using the Fill Handle** **Using Arithmetic Operators**

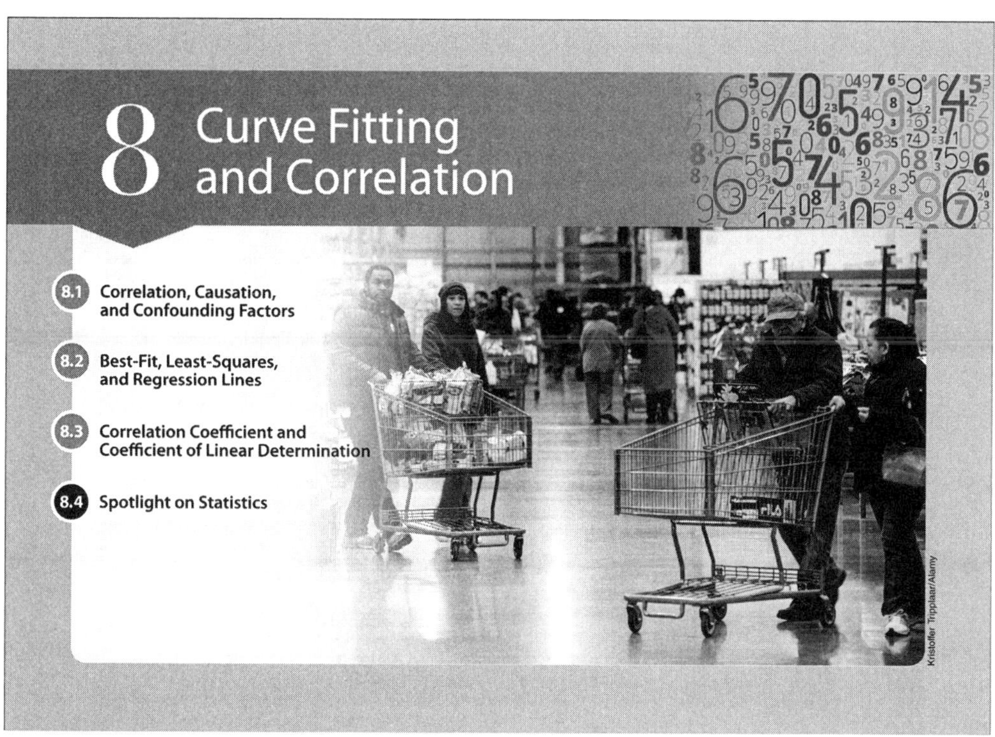

08-1

2 / 31

8.1 Correlation, Causation, and Confounding Factors

OBJECTIVE 1 Understand Correlation

OBJECTIVE 2 Explore Bivariate Data

OBJECTIVE 1 Understand Correlation

Spread of Wal-Mart Supercenters Linked to Obesity, read the March 9, 2011, Harvard Business Review Daily Stat headline. The caption went on to state:

> Research suggests that one additional Wal-Mart Supercenter per 100,000 residents increases individuals' probability of being obese by 2.3 **percentage points**. The researchers, published in the *Journal of Urban Economics*, say their study implies the proliferation of Wal-Mart Supercenters, which offer food at highly discounted prices, explains 10.5% of the U.S. rise in obesity since the late 1980's.

Please read the caption carefully again and try to understand what the researchers are supposedly claiming is the link between supercenters and obesity. Also try to think about how they would possibly measure such statistics. Previous headlines, like *Mobile-Phone Purchases Reduce Tobacco Use in the Philippines* or *Thin Men Get Lower Pay Than Average Weight Men*, offer more titillating relationships. Apparently men who are thin from smoking should buy an iPhone in Manila and move next to a Walmart Supercenter in order to get a raise.

08-2

This chapter goes over the mathematics behind such statements. Before proceeding, a few things need to be pointed out about the caption above.

The caption is implying a **causal** link between supercenters and obesity–namely, that access to mass quantities of inexpensive unhealthy food at supercenters contributes to unhealthy weight gain. The caption claims that supercenters are part of the cause of people becoming obese.

This claim may seem plausible, but having objective data takes us from the realm of speculation to science.

The researchers most definitely can point to a **correlation**; people who live in an area with a higher density of supercenters (relative to the population) are heavier than people who live in a less supercenter-dense area. In fact, the researchers are saying that if a city has two supercenters per 100,000 people and 6% of these people are obese, then another city with three supercenters per 100,000 people would have 8.3% of the population obese. Correlation, however, does not imply **causation**, which does not disprove the researchers' claim of causation; but does mean that one must carefully read the research article which details the study and methods for taking confounding factors into account. **Confounding factors** are other possible factors that could cause the observed behavior. For instance, maybe there are more supercenters built in poorer areas, and obesity is higher in poorer regions in general.

Precise-sounding statistics like "2.3 **percentage points**" and "10.5% of the rise in obesity" lend an air of authority and credibility to the researchers' claims. Certainly they must be right if they were able to compute such precise numerical values. Interpreting such statistics requires care; in this chapter, we will attempt to get a sense of where these numbers come from.

08-3

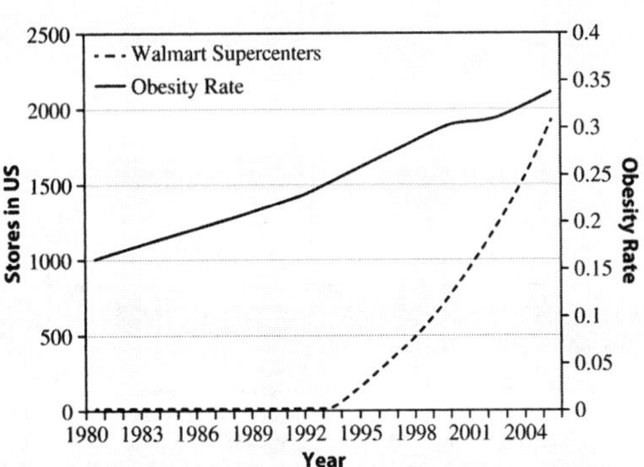

FIGURE 8.1 Rise in Supercenters and Obesity Rate
Data from: *Journal of Urban Economics*, Vol. 69, Issue 2, March 2011, pp. 165–181. http://dx.doi.org/10.1016/j.jue.2010.09.005

CAUTION The fact that obesity rates were already rising before Walmart Supercenters opened indicates that many other factors contribute to obesity. Note the two vertical scales on this graphic. ●

The graphic shows the steady rise of obesity rates in the U.S. and the number of Walmart Supercenters. Note that the first supercenter opened in 1988, and there were 10 in 1993, 239 in 1995, and 1,674 by 2004.

Obesity is defined as having a **body mass index** greater than 30. The Centers for Disease Control and Prevention (CDC) reports that in 2010, 35.7% of U.S. adults were obese.

08-4

The maps in **Figure 8.4** and **Figure 8.5** definitely convey a visual correlation between high obesity rates and locations of Walmart Supercenters. It's not always easy to see the differences between **correlation** and **causation**, and we will spend this chapter going over the basics. Charles Seife's excellent book *Proofiness: The Dark Arts of Mathematical Deception* contains many examples of inaccurate causal claims.

Obesity Trends* Among U.S. Adults

BRFSS, 1990, 2000, 2010

(*BMI ≥30, or about 30 lbs. overweight for 5′4″ person)

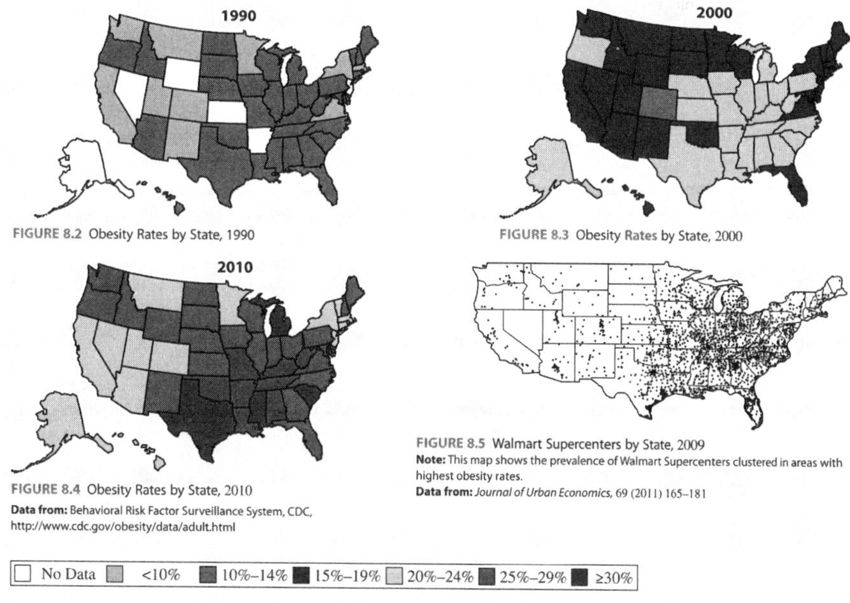

FIGURE 8.2 Obesity Rates by State, 1990

FIGURE 8.3 Obesity Rates by State, 2000

FIGURE 8.4 Obesity Rates by State, 2010
Data from: Behavioral Risk Factor Surveillance System, CDC, http://www.cdc.gov/obesity/data/adult.html

FIGURE 8.5 Walmart Supercenters by State, 2009
Note: This map shows the prevalence of Walmart Supercenters clustered in areas with highest obesity rates.
Data from: *Journal of Urban Economics*, 69 (2011) 165–181

A 2005 article in *Nature* claimed that wearing red (instead of blue) led to more victories in Olympic events. This was based on data from the 2004 Olympics and a scientific study of zebra finches who acted aggressive when wearing red. It took only four years for this notion to be debunked in the following Olympics. This was simply a case of **extrapolating** from *too small a* data set (and concentrating on birds for whom red is the dominant color).

The CDC announced in 2004 that obesity was the cause of 400,000 of the approximately 2.4 million deaths per year. However, the CDC did not control for a very important **confounding factor**: old age. Older people tend to be heavier, and they also tend to die in greater numbers than younger people. The CDC revised its estimate to 24,000 deaths from obesity the following year.

The journal *Social Science and Medicine* published an article claiming that credit card debt made people ill. While the researchers certainly discovered a correlation between debt and bad health, they got the *causation backward*: People who are sick tend to rack up large debt from medical bills.

Many people have heard NutraSweet causes cancer. In the mid-1990s the *Journal of Neuropathology and Experimental Neurology* published a paper showing nothing more than that brain tumor rates started rising about 3 years after NutraSweet came on the market in the 1970s. Now if nothing else in the whole world were also increasing and nothing new were created over this 20-year time period, then we would have found our culprit. However, the population was increasing, as were military spending, and sea levels, and the use of personal computers, and even the use of MRI machines to scan for brain tumors. So the increase in brain tumor diagnoses and NutraSweet usage could just be a case of *randomly rising phenomena*.

OBJECTIVE 2 Explore Bivariate Data

Mathematics classes tend to deal with data pairs (x, y), where y is a **function** of x and the data follow a perfect pattern, such as $y = 3 \cdot x + 7$. In statistics, we have been looking at a single variable, such as X = women's heights, and then describing the variability of this **univariate data** according to the shape of the **distribution** and measures of center and spread. In this chapter we look at **bivariate data**, such as X = Walmart Supercenter density and Y = obesity rates for regions. The intent with bivariate data analysis is to try to explain causal relationships using scatterplots and measures of correlation.

DEFINITION

There are several terms associated with working with bivariate data:

- **Univariate data** refers to a single variable, such as X = women's heights.
- **Bivariate data** refers to two variables, such as X = gas prices and Y = oil prices.
- **Correlation** refers to a relationship between bivariate data in which the two variables are co-related, meaning that they both increase together (*positive correlation*) or one decreases while the other increases (*negative correlation*). There is *perfect correlation* if one variable is a linear function of the other.
- **Causation** refers to a *causal relationship* between bivariate data in which the change in one variable is directly attributed to the change of the other. For example, there is a causal relationship between electricity usage and the temperature: Extremely high and low temperatures cause people to stay indoors and use more electricity to heat or cool their homes. *Reverse causation* refers to mixing up which variable causes the other (high use of electricity does not cause extreme temperature events in the short term!).
- **Confounding factors** are *hidden variables* that are the real *causal agents* behind the correlation of bivariate data, such as the CDC mistakenly attributing 400,000 deaths to obesity, when the true causal agent behind most of these deaths was old age. Mistaken attribution is said to be *spurious*.

Example 1 Compare Oil and Gas Prices

VIDEO *Oil and Gas*

Create time series line graphs of monthly gasoline prices using the *Gasoline-M* worksheet in *Data Sets* for both real and nominal values. Create a scatterplot of gasoline and crude oil real monthly prices, add a **linear trendline** and R^2 value, and identify the highest and lowest real prices of gasoline on the scatterplot.

SOLUTION The time series line graphs for real and nominal monthly gasoline prices is shown in **Figure 8.6**. The real prices (in blue) are above the nominal prices (in green) because we are scaling to March 2014 $.

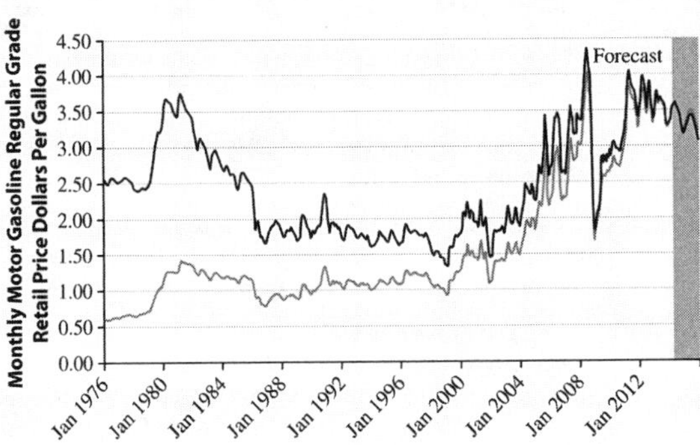

FIGURE 8.6 U.S. Energy Information Administration
Data from: U.S. Energy Information Administration, http://www.eia.gov/forecasts/steo/realprices/

CAUTION Recall that the real prices (in blue) are adjusted for inflation using the CPI. Here they are adjusted using the March 2014 CPI, so these are March 2014 $. The nominal prices (in green) are what people actually paid in a given year, using that year's dollar. ●

SPREADSHEET TUTORIAL Entering Data by Range

Compare the time series line graphs in **Figure 8.6** with the scatterplot of oil and gas prices in **Figure 8.7**. The time series graphs show the change in price of gasoline over time, whereas the scatterplot does not show time. The highest/rightmost data point refers to the highest real price of gasoline/oil from January 1976 to March 2014, which occurred in June 2008, at the start of the financial crisis from which the global economy was still struggling to recover in 2014. The lowest real price of oil and gas occurred in February 1999, at the end of the 1990s economic boom and the height of the dot-com bubble. In general, notice that oil and gas prices are highly **positively correlated**.

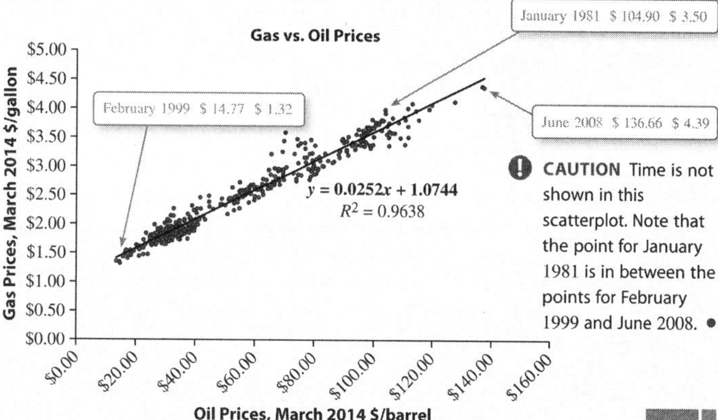

FIGURE 8.7 Oil and Gas Prices, January 1976 to March 2014
Data from: U.S. Energy Information Administration, http://www.eia.gov/forecasts/steo/realprices/

CAUTION Time is not shown in this scatterplot. Note that the point for January 1981 is in between the points for February 1999 and June 2008. ●

8.2 Best-Fit, Least-Squares, and Regression Lines

OBJECTIVE 1 Understand Sum of the Squared Errors

OBJECTIVE 2 Explore Perfect Linear Fit

OBJECTIVE 1 Understand Sum of the Squared Errors

Figure 8.7 shows a **linear trendline** fit to the scatterplot of oil and gas prices. Note how linear this **bivariate data** looks. As oil prices rise, the price of a gallon of gasoline rises in sync and appears to model a true **causal relationship**; rising oil prices cause the price of gas to also rise. We will now explain where the linear trendline comes from and why the R^2 value is a measure of how good a fit this linear model is to the bivariate data.

Example 2 Compare Linear Trendlines

VIDEO *Two Lines*

Using the two points ($14.77, $1.32) in February 1999 and ($104.90, $3.50) in January 1981 in **Figure 8.7**, find the equation of the line between these points and compare it to the linear trendline $y = 0.0252 \cdot x + 1.0744$. In both cases, interpret the **slope** and **y-intercept**.

SOLUTION: First, we find the slope of the line between the two points:

$$m = \frac{3.50 - 1.32}{104.90 - 14.77} = \frac{2.18}{90.13} \approx 0.0242$$

Substituting the first point (14.77, 1.32) into the equation $y = m \cdot x + b$, we get:

$$1.32 = 0.0242 \cdot 14.77 + b$$
$$b \approx 0.9626$$

Giving us the equation:

$$y = 0.0242 \cdot x + 0.9626$$

The **slope** is telling us that the real price of gasoline per gallon in March 2014 \$ is increasing by \$0.0242 per \$1 increase in the real price per barrel of oil. In other words, gas increases by 2.42 cents per gallon for every \$1 per barrel increase in oil (using March 2014 \$). The **linear trendline** in Figure 8.7 instead has an increase of 2.52 cents per gallon. The **y-intercept**, 0.9626, is telling us the price of a gallon of gas, \$0.96, if oil costs nothing (i.e., $x = 0$). This seems silly, assuming that oil would ever be free; but for the sake of comparison, the linear trendline has a y-intercept of \$1.07.

CAUTION The **y-intercept** refers to free oil, which does not seem likely. •

Which of these two lines is a better model for the price of gasoline as a **linear function** of the price of oil? If we wish to make predictions about the future price of gas, assuming that oil prices increase, which model should we use? To answer these questions, we will look at the criteria that statisticians have agreed upon for choosing the best-fit linear model. Using the term *error* or *deviation* for the vertical distance each data point is from the line, we seek a **best-fit line** that minimizes the sum of the squared errors. Thus the best fit line is also called the **least-squares lines**.

CAUTION We minimize the sum of the **squared** errors not the sum of the errors. The errors will be both positive and negative, which will effectively cancel each other when summed. Thus we use the squared errors to make everything non-negative. Squaring rewards small errors and penalizes larger errors. •

Example 3 Compute the Sum of Squared Deviations

VIDEO *Sum of Squares*

For both the **linear trendline** in Figure 8.7, $y = 0.0252 \cdot x + 1.0744$, and the **linear equation** from Example 2, $y = 0.0242 \cdot x + 0.9626$, compute the sum of the squared deviations of each data point to the lines and determine which is a better fit.

SOLUTION Please watch the video for a detailed explanation of the following screenshots. First, we compute the gas prices (y-values) for each line, using the oil prices as the x-values.

	A	B	C	D	E	F	G
1		Bivariate Data		Best fit Line	Example 2 Line	Squared Deviations	
2	Month	Oil (\$/barrel)	Gas (\$/gallon)	y=0.0252x+1.0744	y=0.0242x+0.9626	y=0.0252x+1.0744	y=0.0242x+0.9626
3	January 1976	\$ 55.99	\$ 2.55	=0.0252*B3+1.0744	\$ 2.32	0.004545728	0.055326964
4	February 1976	\$ 55.85	\$ 2.53	\$ 2.48	\$ 2.31	0.002059373	0.045382997
5	March 1976	\$ 56.80	\$ 2.50	\$ 2.51	\$ 2.34	6.94839E-05	0.025685912

FIGURE 8.8 Computing y-Values for Each Linear Model

Then we compute the squared deviations: For each x-value, we subtract the original data's y-value from each line's corresponding y-value and square this difference. (The difference represents how far the original data value is from the line.)

SPREADSHEET TUTORIALS Entering Data by Range | Entering Numbers | Copying a Formula Using the Fill Handle | Constructing a Formula and Using the SUM Function | Using Arithmetic Operators | Formatting Financial Numbers | Using Format Painter | Using Merge and Center and Applying Cell Styles | Aligning Text and Adjusting Size of Columns

	A	B	C	D	E	F	G
1		Bivariate Data		Best fit Line	Example 2 Line	Squared Deviations	
2	Month	Oil ($/barrel)	Gas ($/gallon)	y=0.0252x+1.0744	y=0.0242x+0.9626	y=0.0252x+1.0744	y=0.0242x+0.9626
3	January 1976	$ 55.99	$ 2.55	$ 2.49	$ 2.32	=(D3-C3)^2	0.055326964
4	February 1976	$ 55.85	$ 2.53	$ 2.48	$ 2.31	0.002059373	0.045382997
5	March 1976	$ 56.80	$ 2.50	$ 2.51	$ 2.34	6.94839E-05	0.025685912

FIGURE 8.9 Computing Squared Deviations for Each Linear Model

Now that we have the squared deviation of each data value from each line. We sum these and compare:

458	December 2013	$ 90.90	$ 3.29	$ 3.37	$ 3.16	0.005884131	0.015874743
459	January 2014	$ 98.84	$ 3.32	$ 3.57	$ 3.35	0.060162047	0.001199905
460	February 2014	$ 104.98	$ 3.36	$ 3.72	$ 3.50	0.128531444	0.020088193
461							
462					Sum of Squared Deviations	8.40	21.51

FIGURE 8.10 Computing Sum of Squared Deviations

The sum for the **linear trendline** from Figure 8.7 is 8.40, while the sum of the squared deviations for the linear model we constructed in Example 2 is 21.51. Thus, according to this measure, the linear trendline from **Figure 8.7** is a better fit as it has smaller "error"–that is, the data points are closer to this line. An algorithm can determine the line that has the least such error, and this is what Excel uses to find a linear trendline.

SPREADSHEET TUTORIALS Entering Data by Range | Entering Numbers | Copying a Formula Using the Fill Handle | Constructing a Formula and Using the SUM Function | Using Arithmetic Operators | Formatting Financial Numbers | Using Format Painter | Using Merge and Center and Applying Cell Styles | Aligning Text and Adjusting Size of Columns

DEFINITION

The **least-squares line** is the linear function that *best fits* bivariate data in the sense that it makes the sum of the *squared deviations* from the line as small as possible. This line is also called the *line of best fit,* or the *regression line.*

Example 4 Use the Line of Best Fit to Make a Prediction

Use the line of best fit from Figure 8.7, $y = 0.0252 \cdot x + 1.0744$, to predict the price of gasoline if the cost of oil goes up to $175 a barrel (using March 2014 $).

SOLUTION Recalling that the x-values represent the cost of a barrel of oil in March 2014 $, we can substitute $x = 175$ into the equation:

$$y = 0.0252 \cdot 175 + 1.0744$$
$$y = 5.48$$

Recall that making predictions outside the domain of data is called **extrapolation.** We hope the cost of oil never gets that high, but remember that correlation does not imply causation. The following quote from Mark Twain illustrates the dangers in extrapolation:

> In the space of one hundred and seventy-six years the Lower Mississippi has shortened itself two hundred and forty-two miles. That is an average of a trifle over one mile and a third per year. Therefore, any calm person, who is not blind or idiotic, can see that in the Old Oolitic Silurian Period, just a million years ago last November, the Lower Mississippi River was upward of one million three hundred thousand miles long, and stuck out over the Gulf of Mexico like a fishing-rod. And by the same token any person can see that seven hundred and forty-two years from now the Lower Mississippi will be only a mile and three-quarters long, and Cairo [Illinois] and New Orleans will have joined their streets together, and be plodding comfortably along under a single mayor and a mutual board of aldermen. There is something fascinating about science. One gets such wholesale returns of conjecture out of such a trifling investment in fact.
>
> Mark Twain
> *Life on the Mississippi*

OBJECTIVE 2 Explore Perfect Linear Fit

Bivariate data from the real world is typically not perfectly linear, as are the **functions** studied in many math classes. This is why we say the **best-fit line** *models* the bivariate data; it helps us see any trends, and thus we use the term *trendline*. Occasionally we do encounter perfectly linear bivariate data, and this of course makes us happy.

Example 5 Compute a Perfect Linear Fit

Table 8.1 shows the distances and tolls from Exit 24 (Albany) on the New York State Thruway and other exits, heading west toward Syracuse and Rochester (Exit 46). Create a scatterplot and display the trendline equation and R^2 value. Interpret the **slope** and **y-intercept**.

SOLUTION The slope tells us the tolls increase by $0.0387, or 3.87 cents, per mile; the y-intercept refers to a distance of 0 miles so is not relevant. The fact that $R^2 = 1$ is how we know for sure that the data is perfectly linear; we explore this next.

TABLE 8.1 NY State Thruway Tolls

Exit #	Miles	Toll	Exit #	Miles	Toll
24	0	0	34	114	$4.45
25	6	$0.25	35	131	$5.10
26	14	$0.60	38	138	$5.40
27	26	$1.00	40	157	$6.10
28	34	$1.35	41	173	$6.70
29	46	$1.80	42	180	$7.00
30	72	$2.80	43	193	$7.50
31	85	$3.30	44	200	$7.75
32	96	$3.75	45	204	$7.90
33	105	$4.10	46	215	$8.35

Data from: 2007 Toll Card

FIGURE 8.11 I-90 Tolls, as a Function of Distance from Albany

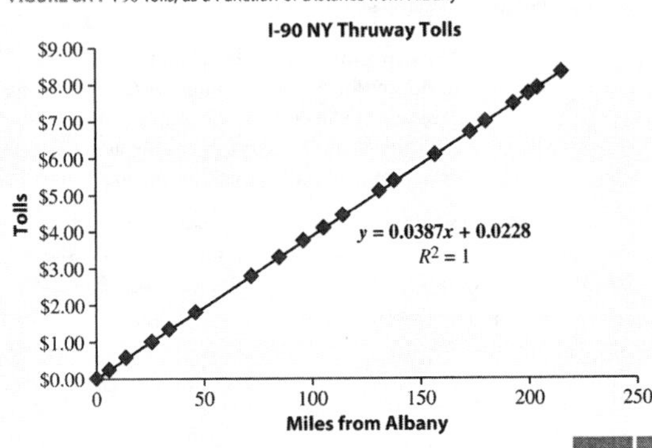

SPREADSHEET TUTORIAL Entering Data by Range

8.3 Correlation Coefficient and Coefficient of Linear Determination

OBJECTIVE 1 **Understand R and R^2**

OBJECTIVE 2 **Understand Best-Fit Exponential Trendlines**

OBJECTIVE 1 Understand R and R^2

Figure 8.11 shows a perfect linear fit. Note that the R^2 value is 1, which tells us that this is a perfect fit, as we now discuss. In general, scatterplots of **bivariate data** will not be perfectly linear, as in **Figure 8.7**. Two persons looking at the same scatterplot can subjectively assess different "degrees of linearity" in the data. It would be helpful if we had a quantitative measure for a model's linearity—some kind of score to attach to a set of data points. There is such a score. We are talking about a famous statistic called the **correlation coefficient**, or its very close cousin, the **coefficient of linear determination**. Since Excel will handle the calculations for us, we will skip directly to interpreting these measures and cover the formulas at the end of the chapter, in the Spotlight on Statistics.

The correlation coefficient, denoted by the letter R, is a single number associated with bivariate data. It always falls between −1 and +1; that is, bivariate data can have an R-value of, say, 0.45 or −0.12, but never 3.14 or −50.

TABLE 8.2 Interpretations of the Correlation Coefficient, R

How R Measures the Strength of the Relationship Between Two Variables				
Very Strong, Negative −1.0	Moderately Strong, Negative −0.5	Absolutely No Relationship 0	Moderately Strong, Positive 0.5	Very Strong, Positive 1.0

DEFINITION

The **correlation coefficient,** R, is a measure of the strength and direction of the linear relationship for bivariate data and will be between −1 and 1, as indicated in **Table 8.2**.

The **coefficient of linear determination,** R^2, is a measure of linearity and will be between 0 and 1, with a value of 1 indicating perfect linearity. Technically, it is the proportion of variability of one variable in bivariate data that can be attributed to variability in the other variable.

R^2 can easily be interpreted as a percentage (which is why Excel reports R^2 and not R in scatterplots), using the following important sentence:

$R^2 \cdot 100\%$ *of the variability in the output can be attributed to variability in the input.*

Thus in **Figure 8.7** we can say that 96.38% of the variability in gas prices is due to variability in oil prices.

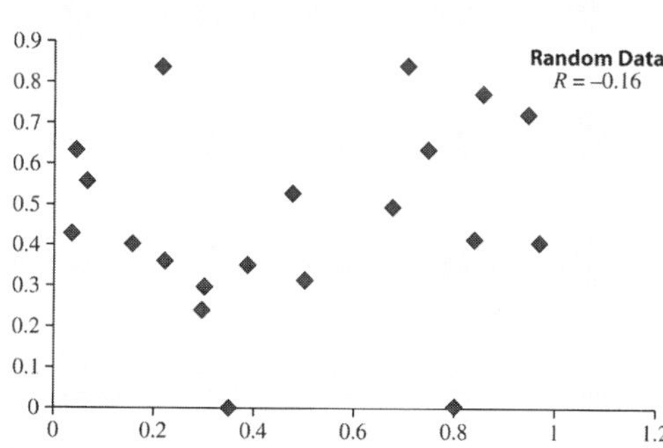

FIGURE 8.12 Random Data; No Correlation

Made-up Data
$R = -0.674$

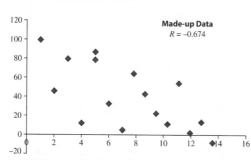

FIGURE 8.13 Made-up Data; Moderate Negative Correlation

The scatterplots on the left show different R-values to give you a sense of how R corresponds visually to **bivariate data**. The data in **Figure 8.12** was generated using Excel's **RAND** function, which generates random numbers between zero and one.

Using data from the *Crime Data* worksheet in *Data Sets*, we can create the time series plot of the violent crime **rate** in the United States from 1960 to 2012, as shown in **Figure 8.14**. Violent crime in the United States had been steadily increasing, from 160.9 violent crimes per 100,000 people in 1960 to an all-time high of 758.2 in 1991. Headlines at that time talked of the rising crime wave and the unavoidable police state we were heading toward, when the rates unexpectedly began to drop. Many explanations have been given, and many have tried to claim credit, but the reasons still remain unclear for the drop in crime. Perhaps law enforcement began arresting criminals at a greater rate during this period.

Note that random data will have a correlation coefficient close to zero. A negative correlation indicates that the points "slope downward."

FIGURE 8.14 Violent Crime Rate Time Series, 1960-2012, FBI Uniform Crime Reports
Data from: Federal Bureau of Investigation, http://www.ucrdatatool.gov/Search/Crime/State/RunCrimeStatebyState.cfm

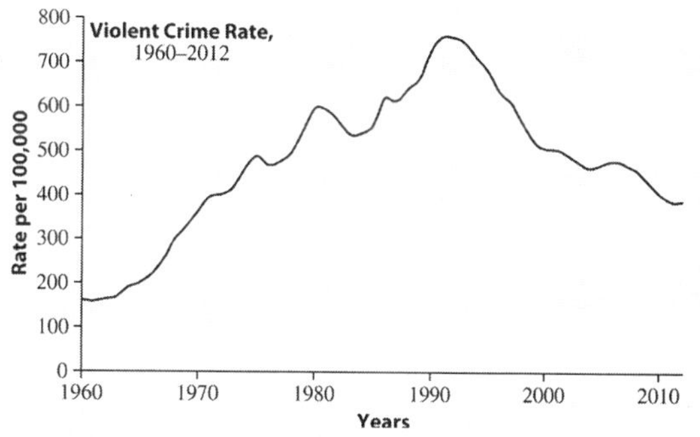

Example 6 **Interpret R^2**

VIDEO *R quared*

Create a scatterplot of the violent crime rate and arrest rate from 1980 to 2011, using the *Arrest* worksheet in Data Sets. Test the hypothesis that increasing arrest rates may correlate with decreasing violent crime rates. Insert a trendline and R^2 value and interpret the **slope** and R^2 values in real-world terms.

SOLUTION To test the hypothesis that the mysterious (and welcome!) drop in the U.S. violent crime rate after 1991 is due to law enforcement making more arrests–that is, police locking up more criminals (for any crime), causing the violent crime rates to decline—we can make a scatterplot of arrest rates and violent crime rates.

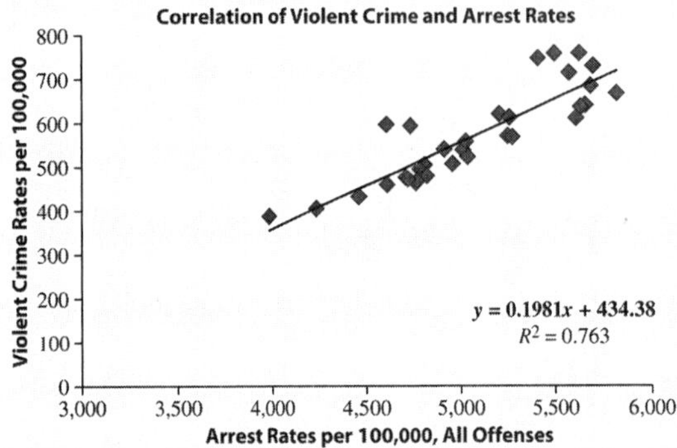

FIGURE 8.15 Violent Crime Rate and Arrest Rates for Any Offense, FBI Uniform Crime Reports and Bureau of Justice Statistics

Data from: Bureau of Justice Statistics, http://www.bjs.gov/index.cfm?ty=datool&surl=/arrests/index.cfm#

If we are correct in our hypothesis, we would expect to see the violent crime rates decline as arrest rates increase–that is, a **negative correlation**. However, **Figure 8.15** shows the opposite: Higher overall arrest rates correspond to years with higher violent crime rates and lower arrest rates for years with lower violent crime rates.

The R^2 value of 0.763 tells us that 76.3% of the variability in violent crime rates can be attributed to variability in arrest rates. The **slope** tells us that the violent crime rate is increasing by 19.81 violent crimes per 100,000 people for every increase of 100 arrests per 100,000 people.

SPREADSHEET TUTORIAL Entering Data by Range

Example 6 concluded that the drop in violent crime rates after 1991 cannot be attributed to higher arrest rates. Perhaps the explanation lies in not just arresting criminals but keeping them behind bars so they cannot commit violent crimes. Our hypothesis now is that violent crime rates should drop as incarceration rates increase.

Example 7 **Test a Hypothesis**

VIDEO *Crime Rates*

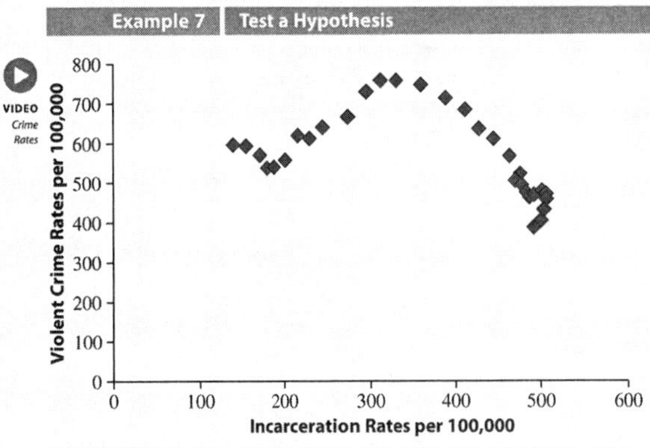

FIGURE 8.16 Violent Crime Rates and Incarceration Rates 1980–2011, Bureau Justice Statistics

Data from: Bureau of Justice Statistics, http://www.bjs.gov/index.cfm?ty=nps

Note that the U.S. had one of the highest incarceration rates in the world in 2011, with about 500 prisoners per 100,000 people

Create a scatterplot of the violent crime rate and incarceration rate from 1980 to 2011, using the *Prisoner* worksheet in Data Sets, and test the hypothesis that violent crime rates will drop as incarceration rates increase.

SOLUTION The scatterplot is inconclusive since it shows that the violent crime rate is low for both very low incarceration rates around 200 and very high incarceration rates around 500. The incarceration rates have been steadily increasing since 1980, so the scatterplot is also a time-series graph showing the peak in 1991 and the decline to the 2011 low. Thus we cannot rule out some other confounding factor that may have occurred in 1991. Further analysis is warranted!

OBJECTIVE 2 Understand Best-Fit Exponential Trendlines

At this point, you might be wondering how Excel can assign an R^2 value to an exponential trendline, as we did in Chapter 6, since R^2 is a measure of linearity. The answer lies in the brief comment in Chapter 7 regarding **log scales**. When a data set is exponential, the **logarithm** of the outputs will be linear with respect to the inputs, and it is this linear fit that is assigned an R^2 value.

Example 8 Interpret R^2 for an Exponential Trendline

VIDEO *Psychology*

A psychology student conducted a memory experiment, using other students as subjects. The objective was to see how well the subject could memorize a random string of letters and how the length of the string affected the outcome. A subject was shown a string such as YGOPFGZ for 5 seconds, then had to wait 10 seconds, and then was asked to repeat the string. The data below summarizes the student's results. Given that the **percentage** of subjects correctly recalling the entire string can never go below zero, the student decided to fit her data with an exponential trendline. Create a scatterplot with an exponential model and interpret both R^2 and the **continuous growth rate**.

TABLE 8.3 Memory Experiment Data

Length of Random String of Letters						
6	7	8	9	10	11	12
Percentage of Subjects Correctly Recalling String						
98	89	76	58	14	4	2

SOLUTION By entering the data from **Table 8.3** into Excel, we can create the scatterplot shown in **Figure 8.17**. The R^2 value 0.8838 says that 88.38% of the variability of the subjects' ability to correctly remember the string of letters can be attributed to variability in the length of the string. This implies that about 12% of the response variable can be attributed to other factors besides how long the string is, such as variation between subjects. The **percentage** answering correctly is declining continuously by 69.9% per additional letter added to the length of the string. The length of the string is discrete: You cannot have 7.2 letters, so it makes more sense to convert the continuous form to the "annual" form:

$$e^{-0.699} \approx 0.497 = 1 + r$$

So $r = -50.3\%$ implies that the percentage answering correctly is declining by 50.3% per additional letter added to the string.

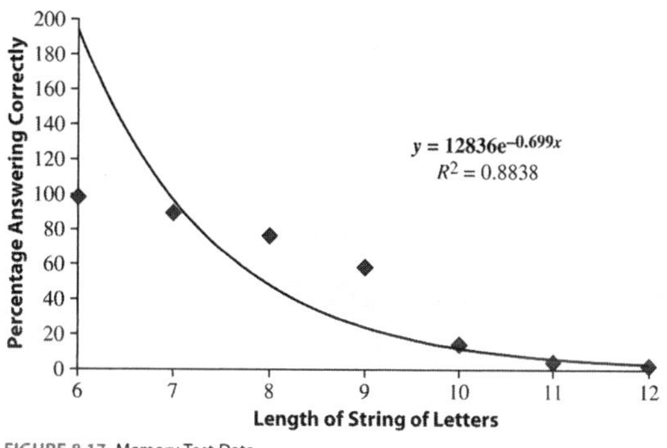

FIGURE 8.17 Memory Test Data

8.4 Spotlight on Statistics

OBJECTIVE 1 Understand Covariance and Correlation

OBJECTIVE 2 Explore $y = \overline{Y} + R \cdot \frac{SD_Y}{SD_X} \cdot (x - \overline{X})$

OBJECTIVE 1 Understand Covariance and Correlation

Figure 8.7 shows a very strong **positive correlation** between gas prices and oil prices. In this section, we will formally define the **correlation coefficient** in terms of a related statistic, the **covariance.** Then we will derive the equation of best fit, using intuitive notions of correlation and **Z-scores.** To start, recall the formula for the **standard deviation:**

$$\mathrm{SD} = \sqrt{\frac{\Sigma(x_i - \overline{X})^2}{N - 1}}$$

Squaring the standard deviation gives the variance of a data sample:

$$\mathrm{Var} = \frac{\Sigma(x_i - \overline{X})^2}{N - 1} = \mathrm{SD}^2$$

Both of these formulas are for **univariate data;** for **bivariate data,** we compute the covariance:

$$\mathrm{Covar} = \frac{\Sigma(x_i - \overline{X}) \cdot (y_i - \overline{Y})}{N - 1}$$

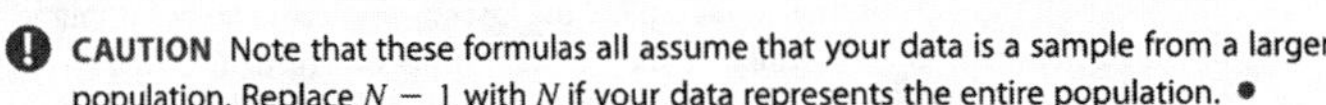

CAUTION Note that these formulas all assume that your data is a sample from a larger population. Replace $N - 1$ with N if your data represents the entire population. ●

Note that the quotient of the **variance** and the **standard deviation** squared for **univariate data** is 1:

$$\frac{\mathrm{Var}}{\mathrm{SD}^2} = 1$$

This motivates (but does not prove!) the following inequality for **bivariate data:**

$$-1 \leq \frac{\mathrm{Covar}}{\mathrm{SD}_x \cdot \mathrm{SD}_Y} \leq 1$$

We have created a new statistic that is trapped between −1 and 1. Any guesses what this is?

DEFINITION

The **variance** for sample univariate data is the standard deviation squared, $\text{Var} = \frac{\Sigma(x_i - \overline{X})^2}{N - 1} = \text{SD}^2$. The **covariance** for sample bivariate data is a measure of how correlated the two variables are and is given by an equation similar to the variance, $\text{Covar} = \frac{\Sigma(x_i - \overline{X}) \cdot (y_i - \overline{Y})}{N - 1}$. The **correlation coefficient** is defined by the formula $R = \frac{\text{Covar}}{\text{SD}_X \cdot \text{SD}_Y}$ and will lie between -1 and 1. Squaring the correlation coefficient gives the **coefficient of linear determination**, R^2.

Excel has built-in functions for these statistics: **CORREL** gives the correlation coefficient, and **COVARIANCE.S** gives the sample covariance defined above.

CAUTION Note that these formulas all assume that your data is a sample from a larger population. Replace $N - 1$ with N if your data represents the entire population. •

Example 9 Use CORREL and COVARIANCE.S

VIDEO CORREL

The scatterplot for oil and gas prices is re-created in **Figure 8.19**. Using the *Oil and Gas* worksheet in *Data Sets*, verify the **coefficient of linear determination** by using the **CORREL** and **COVARIANCE.S** functions.

SOLUTION The coefficient of linear determination from the scatterplot is $R^2 = 0.9638$. To verify this, we can compute R using **CORREL** and then square the result:

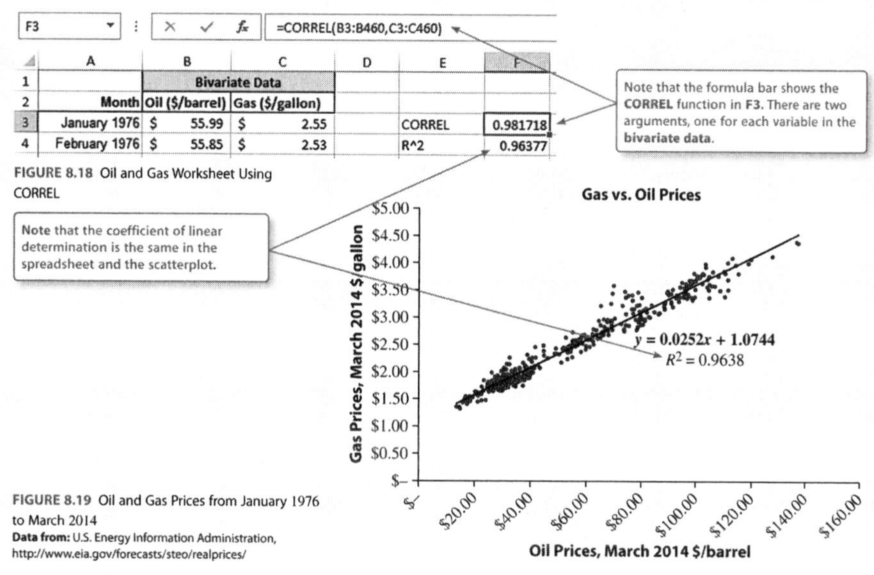
F3
=CORREL(B3:B460,C3:C460)
Note that the formula bar shows the CORREL function in F3. There are two arguments, one for each variable in the bivariate data.
Note that the coefficient of linear determination is the same in the spreadsheet and the scatterplot.
Gas vs. Oil Prices
Gas Prices, March 2014 $/gallon
Oil Prices, March 2014 $/barrel
y = 0.0252x + 1.0744
R² = 0.9638
$5.00
$4.50
$4.00
$3.50
$3.00
$2.50
$2.00
$1.50
$1.00
$0.50
$-
$20.00
$40.00
$60.00
$80.00
$100.00
$120.00
$140.00
$160.00

	A	B	C	D	E	F
1		Bivariate Data				
2	Month	Oil ($/barrel)	Gas ($/gallon)			
3	January 1976	$ 55.99	$ 2.55		CORREL	0.981718
4	February 1976	$ 55.85	$ 2.53		R^2	0.96377

FIGURE 8.18 Oil and Gas Worksheet Using CORREL

FIGURE 8.19 Oil and Gas Prices from January 1976 to March 2014
Data from: U.S. Energy Information Administration, http://www.eia.gov/forecasts/steo/realprices/

SPREADSHEET TUTORIAL **Entering Data by Range**

Next we can compute R, using the following formula involving **COVARIANCE.S**:

$$R = \frac{\text{Covar}}{\text{SD}_X \cdot \text{SD}_Y}$$

To use this formula, we must first compute the **standard deviation** of each variable in the **bivariate data** and then divide the **COVARIANCE.S** by the product of the standard deviations:

Note that the formula bar shows the **function** in **F9**, which computes R using the **COVARIANCE.S** in **F8** and the standard deviations in **F6** and **F7**. We get exactly the same result for R as in cell **F3** using **CORREL**. Squaring will thus give the same coefficient of linear determination.

F9 =F8/(F7*F6)

	A	B	C	D	E	F
1		Bivariate Data				
2	Month	Oil ($/barrel)	Gas ($/gallon)			
3	January 1976	$ 55.99	$ 2.55		CORREL	0.981718
4	February 1976	$ 55.85	$ 2.53		R^2	0.96377
5	March 1976	$ 56.80	$ 2.50			
6	April 1976	$ 56.20	$ 2.48		SD.oil	27.72543
7	May 1976	$ 55.98	$ 2.50		SD.gas	0.71207
8	June 1976	$ 55.98	$ 2.56		COVAR	19.38151
9	July 1976	$ 55.81	$ 2.57		R	0.981718

FIGURE 8.20 Oil and Gas Worksheet Using COVARIANCE.S

SPREADSHEET TUTORIALS Entering Data by Range Using Arithmetic Operators

OBJECTIVE 2 Explore $y = \overline{Y} + R \cdot \frac{SD_Y}{SD_X} \cdot (x - \overline{X})$

The equation in this objective certainly looks daunting, but it will actually tie together many of the statistics we have been learning, going back to Chapters 1 and 2 on **standard deviation** and **Z-scores**, and incorporating these concepts with the line of best fit from Chapter 5. The equation above is a general formula for the line of best fit. The basic idea is simple: We want to use the **line of best fit** from a scatterplot for **bivariate data** to make predictions.

Example 10 Predict Gas Prices

Using the scatterplot for oil and gas prices in **Figure 8.19**, use the **linear equation** of the line of best fit to predict the price of a gallon of gas when the price of a barrel of oil is \$200 in March 2014 \$.

SOLUTION We can substitute $x = \$200$ into the linear equation $y = 0.0252 \cdot x + 1.0744$ and get $y = \$6.11$ in March 2014 \$.

So what does this simple example have to do with z-scores? Let's think about what we are doing. We know from **Figure 8.19** that oil and gas prices are highly **correlated.** In fact, $R^2 = 0.9638$ tells us that 96.38% of the variation in gas prices is due to variation in oil prices. Only 4% of the variability in gas prices can be attributed to such vagaries as the weather and the local gas station manager.

Thus, knowing the oil price tells us a lot about the associated gas price. Consider $x = \$200$ for the oil price. It is clearly well above the average price for a barrel of oil in March 2014 \$, so we would expect the associated gas price to be well above the mean for gas prices. How far above the mean? Recall from Chapter 2 that we put a data value into context by talking about its **Z-score**, or how many **standard deviations** above or below the mean the value is. If the oil price is five standard deviations above the mean, we would expect the gas price to also be five standard deviations above its own mean–or maybe not quite five since oil and gas are not **perfectly correlated**, but maybe $96\% \cdot 5$ standard deviations.

Example 11 **Compute Z-scores**

VIDEO *Best Fit Equation*

Compute the z-scores for the oil price of \$200 and the associated gas price of \$6.11.

SOLUTION First we must compute the mean and standard deviation for both oil and gas prices:

TABLE 8.4 Oil and Gas Statistics

March 2014 \$	Oil Price per Barrel	Gas Price per Gallon
Mean	\$54.28	\$2.44
Standard deviation	27.725	0.712

Now we can compute the z-scores for each:

$$z_{\text{oil}} = \frac{200 - 54.28}{27.725} = 5.256$$

$$z_{\text{gas}} = \frac{6.11 - 2.44}{0.712} = 5.154$$

Note that z_Y / z_X in this example is $5.154/5.256 = 0.98$, which is the **correlation coefficient**!

CAUTION The z-score for the output variable in **bivariate data** will be a fraction of the z-score for the input variable. The more correlated the bivariate data, the closer that fraction will be to 1. That fraction is R. Thus $z_y = R \cdot z_x$, not R^2, as suggested before Example 11. ●

In Example 11 we saw that the z-**score** of the output variable was a fraction of the z-score for the input variable, and that fraction was the **correlation coefficient**, R. This is true in general, and we can use this fact to determine any y-value from a given x-value. We want the y-value to be as many **standard deviations** from the **mean** as its associated x-value is from the mean of it's data set, adjusted by the factor of the correlation coefficient. We use R because it can be both positive or negative and thus will work for **bivariate data** that is **negatively correlated**. Given an x-value, the associated y-value will be:

Note that we replace $z_Y = R \cdot z_X$ in this step. Thus the correlation coefficient can be defined as the ratio of z-scores for bivariate data, $R = \frac{z_Y}{z_X}$.

$$y = \overline{Y} + z_Y \cdot \text{SD}_Y$$

$$\downarrow$$

$$y = \overline{Y} + R \cdot z_X \cdot \text{SD}_Y$$

Now we can use the formula for the z-score:

$$y = \overline{Y} + R \cdot \frac{x - \overline{X}}{\text{SD}_X} \cdot \text{SD}_Y$$

Rearranging gives us a formula for the line of best fit:

$$y = \overline{Y} + R \cdot \frac{\text{SD}_Y}{\text{SD}_X} \cdot (x - \overline{X})$$

CAUTION Note that x and y are the only variables in this equation; everything else is a constant. Substitute for the constants and get a linear equation: $y = m \cdot x + b$. ●

Example 12 **Compute Best-Fit Equation**

Use the values in **Table 8.4** and $R = 0.982$ to verify the linear equation in **Figure 8.19**.

SOLUTION Substituting the values from **Table 8.4** and $R = 0.982$, we get:

$$y = 2.44 + \mathbf{0.982} \cdot \frac{\mathbf{0.712}}{\mathbf{27.725}} \cdot (x - 54.28)$$
$$y = 2.44 + 0.0252 \cdot (x - 54.28)$$
$$y = 0.0252 \cdot x + 1.07$$

CAUTION Using the **order of operations**, compute the product in bold first (which gives the slope), then distribute, then add the constant 2.44 last. ●

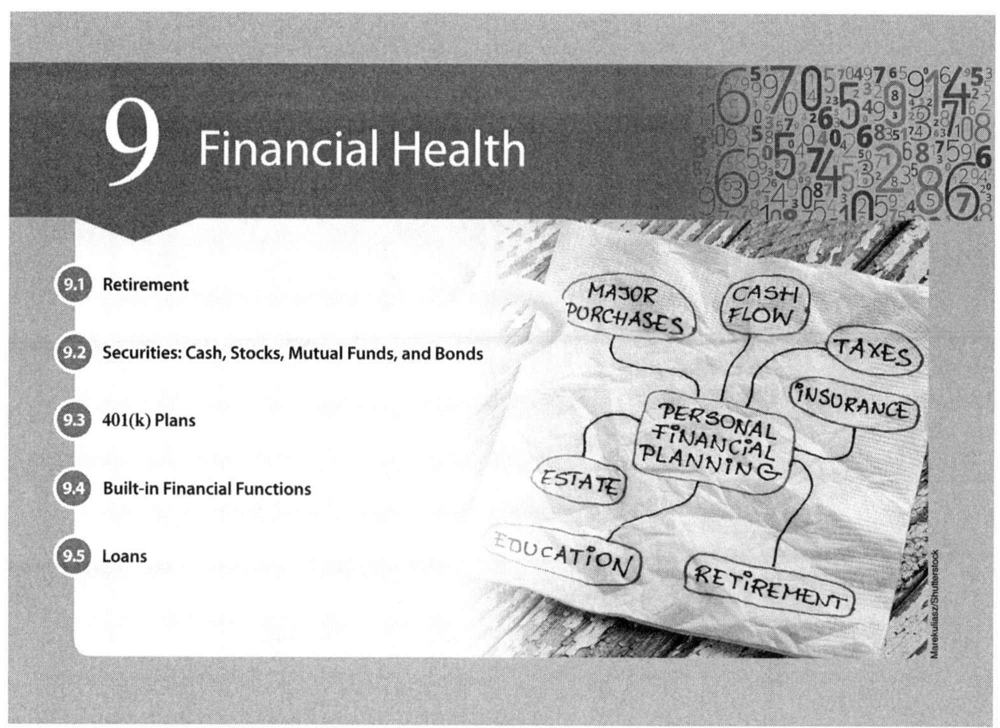

09-1

2 / 33

9.1 Retirement

OBJECTIVE 1 Plan for Retirement

09-2

OBJECTIVE 1 Plan for Retirement

We begin our chapter on financial health by looking at how to save for **retirement**. Investments are called **securities** because they make you feel secure knowing you have money available for retirement or other life choices. Unfortunately, not everyone is saving money, as we saw in **Figure 6.10** on the personal savings rate and as also shown in **Table 9.1**.

TABLE 9.1
Before-Tax Family Income and Percentage of Families That Saved By Age of Head of Household, 2007 & 2010

Family characteristic	2007 Income Median	2007 Income Mean	2007 Percentage of families that saved	2007 Percentage of families	2010 Income Median	2010 Income Mean	2010 Percentage of families that saved	2010 Percentage of families
All families	49.6	88.3	56.4	100.0	45.8	78.5	52.0	100.0
Age of head (years)								
Less than 35	39.2	54.2	58.9	21.6	35.1	47.7	54.6	21.0
35–44	59.3	87.7	56.4	19.6	53.9	81.0	47.6	18.2
45–54	67.2	117.8	55.8	20.8	61.0	102.2	51.8	21.1
55–64	57.2	116.5	58.4	16.8	55.1	105.8	51.4	17.5
65–74	40.8	96.8	56.7	10.5	42.7	75.8	53.6	11.5
75 or more	23.9	47.9	49.4	10.6	29.1	46.1	54.1	10.7

Note that only 52% of families saved in 2010, and the average household income (**median** and **mean**) declined from 2007 to 2010.

Note: In thousands of 2010 dollars except as noted
Data from: "Changes in U.S. Family Finances from 2007 to 2010: Evidence from the Survey of Consumer Finances," Jesse Bricker, Arthur B. Kennickell, Kevin B. Moore, and John Sabelhaus, *Federal Reserve Bulletin*, vol. 98, no. 2, (February 2012), pp. 1–80, http://www.federalreserve.gov/econresdata/scf/scf_2010.htm

Table 9.1 states that average incomes declined from 2007 to 2010, making it even harder for families to save. You may be interested in seeing what people are saving for (see **Table 9.2**) or the different types of financial assets people are investing their savings in (see **Table 9.3**).

TABLE 9.2 Reasons Respondents Gave as Most Important for Their Families' Saving Distributed by Percent, 2001–2010

	Reason Distributed by percent			
Type of reason	2001	2004	2007	2010
Education	10.9	11.6	8.4	8.2
For the family	5.1	4.7	5.5	5.7
Buying own home	4.2	5.0	4.2	3.2
Purchases	9.5	7.7	10.0	11.5
Retirement	32.1	34.7	34.0	30.1
Liquidity	31.2	30.0	32.0	35.2
Investments	1.0	1.5	1.6	1.2
No particular reason	1.1	.7	1.1	1.4
When asked for a reason, reported do not save	4.9	4.0	3.3	3.5
Total	100	100	100	100

Data from: Reasons for Saving, *Federal Reserve Bulletin*, vol. 98, no. 2, (February 2012), pp. 1–80, http://www.federalreserve.gov/econresdata/scf/scf_2010.htm

TABLE 9.3 Value of Financial Assets of all Families Distributed by Percent, 2001–2010

Transaction accounts are checking and savings accounts.

	Value of Financial Assets Distributed by Percent			
Type of financial asset	2001	2004	2007	2010
Transaction accounts	11.4	13.1	10.9	13.3
Certificates of deposit	3.1	3.7	4.0	3.9
Savings bonds	.7	.5	.4	.3
Bonds	4.5	5.3	4.1	4.4
Stocks	21.5	17.5	17.8	14.0
Pooled investment funds (excluding money market funds)	12.1	14.6	15.8	15.0
Retirement accounts	29.0	32.4	35.1	38.1
Cash value life insurance	5.3	2.9	3.2	2.5
Other managed assets	10.5	7.9	6.5	6.2
Other	1.9	2.1	2.1	2.3
Total	**100**	**100**	**100**	**100**
MEMO				
Financial assets as a share of total assets	42.2	35.8	34.0	37.9

Data from: Type of Financial Asset, *Federal Reserve Bulletin*, vol. 98, no. 2, (February 2012), pp. 1–80, http://www.federalreserve.gov/econresdata/scf/scf_2010.htm

We are going to cover most of the different types of financial assets listed in **Table 9.3**. The majority of Americans are woefully unprepared for their **retirement**, but it is important that you be well versed in your financial options. **Figure 9.1** shows that 65% of the retirees in 2007 accounted for only 4.6% of the financial assets for this demographic group. The **median** value of financial assets for these low-net-worth retirees was a meager $10,800 (**mean** was $22,652) in 2007.

Notice the wealth inequality: 5.6% of retirees in 2007 owned 64% of the financial assets. Financial illiteracy is a major cause of this inequity.

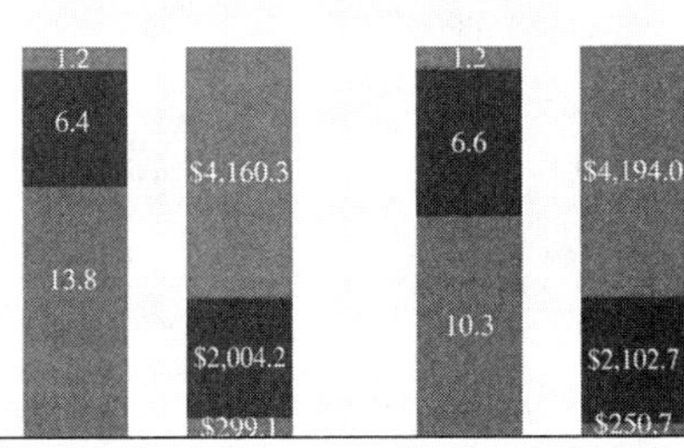

	Number of retirees (in millions)	Retiree assets (in billions)	Number of pre-retirees (in millions)	Pre-retiree assets (in billions)
High-net-worth ($1 million or more)	1.2	$4,160.3	1.2	$4,194.0
Middle Market & Affluents ($100K-$999K)	6.4	$2,004.2	6.6	$2,102.7
Low Net Worth (<$100K)	13.8	$299.1	10.3	$250.7

FIGURE 9.1 2007 Retiree Financial Assets
Data from: Retiree Financial Assets, *LIMRA Factbook on Retirement Income 2010*

The 13.8 million low-net-worth retirees in 2007 discussed in **Figure 9.1** are completely dependent on the government—that is **Social Security** and **Medicare**—and their families to take care of them in their old age. Even retirees with higher net worth are running out of **retirement** savings because of the escalating costs of health care and the longer life spans shown in **Figure 9.2**.
Typically U.S. adults retire at 62 and hope to enjoy 18 years of the good life, but instead many are faced with financial worry and are forced to continue working into their 70s.

Retiring with enough money to live on comfortably is within reach of all Americans. It simply requires a disciplined savings and investing strategy, starting from the day you begin work. Then you just sit back and let the power of compound interest and exponential growth take over!

Let's first look at an example that illustrates how the typical retirement package works.

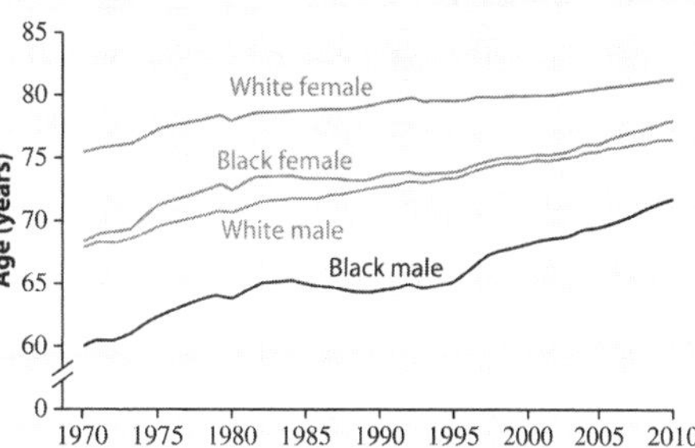

FIGURE 9.2 U.S. Life Expectancy By Race and Sex, 1970–2010
Data from: Life Expectancy, *National Vital Statistics Report*, vol. 61, no. 4, May 8, 2013, http://www.cdc.gov/nchs/data/nvsr/nvsr61/nvsr61_04.pdf

Life expectancy continues to rise. In 2014 the Centers for Disease Control and Prevention (CDC) reported an average life expectancy of 78.7 years in the U.S. (81.0 for women and 76.2 for men), with Hispanics living significantly longer, at 81.2 years (83.8 for women and 78.5 for men).

Example 1 Plan for Retirement

VIDEO *Retirement*

Create an Excel spreadsheet that maps out your annual withdrawals from a **retirement** account, assuming initial savings of $1,000,000 and a 5% starting withdrawal rate that increases with **inflation**. Assuming an inflation rate of 3% and a **rate of return** on your investment of 6%, determine how long your money will last.

Note that in addition to your annual withdrawal, you can also expect to receive **Social Security** and **Medicare**.

SOLUTION The spreadsheet in **Figure 9.3** illustrates how a retirement account works once you are ready to begin withdrawing funds (see video for details). Note that there are three **interest rates** to keep track of, the first is the **percentage** of your savings you will withdraw in the first year, the second is the inflation rate, which increases your annual payout to keep up with inflation, and the third is the rate of return of your investment.

	A	B	C	D	E	F	G	H
1	Initial Savings	$ 1,000,000		Year	Balance	Withdrawal	New Balance	End Balance
2	Withdrawal Rate	5%		1	$1,000,000	$ 50,000	$ 950,000	=G2*(1+$B$4)
3	Inflation Rate	3%		2	$1,007,000	$ 51,500	$ 955,500	$ 1,012,830
4	Rate of Return	6%		3	$1,012,830	$ 53,045	$ 959,785	$ 1,017,372

FIGURE 9.3 Retirement Withdrawal Worksheet

Your retirement account actually grows for the first five years before your rising payout begins to overtake the interest you earn. You will run out of money in 29 years with this scenario. If you can get by with an initial withdrawal rate of only 4%, your money will continue to grow much longer, leaving behind a legacy of $1,091,012 after 29 years.

CAUTION There are assumptions built into this model, most importantly the rate of return of your investment at 6%. ●

SPREADSHEET TUTORIALS Entering Data by Range · Entering Numbers · Copying a Formula Using the Fill Handle · Constructing a Formula and Using the SUM Function · Using Arithmetic Operators · Formatting Financial Numbers · Using Format Painter · Using Merge and Center and Applying Cell Styles · Moving Data and Resolving ####Error · Projecting Income and Expenses by Filling Formulas · Using a Data Table to Calculate Options using What If Analysis

9.2 Securities: Cash, Stocks, Mutual Funds, and Bonds

OBJECTIVE 1 Understand Certificates of Deposit

OBJECTIVE 2 Understand Bonds

OBJECTIVE 3 Understand Stocks

OBJECTIVE 4 Understand Mutual Funds

OBJECTIVE 1 Understand Certificates of Deposit

Now that we have a better sense of why saving for **retirement** is important and how you can use your retirement account to generate income, let's figure out how to get the $1,000,000 we saw in Example 1 into your retirement account. Looking back at **Figure 9.3**, the first two financial assets mentioned are transaction accounts and **certificates of deposits**.

Transaction accounts are checking and savings accounts and are the first step to financial security. Unfortunately, 25% of all U.S. households were either underbanked, or unbanked, according to the 2010 U.S. Census.

Unbanked means the household does not have a checking or savings account. *Underbanked* refers to households that do have such accounts but also rely on money orders, pawn shops, check-cashing services, rent-to-own agreements, or payday loans. All these services should be avoided literally at all costs. They are a financial plague to the poor and financially illiterate.

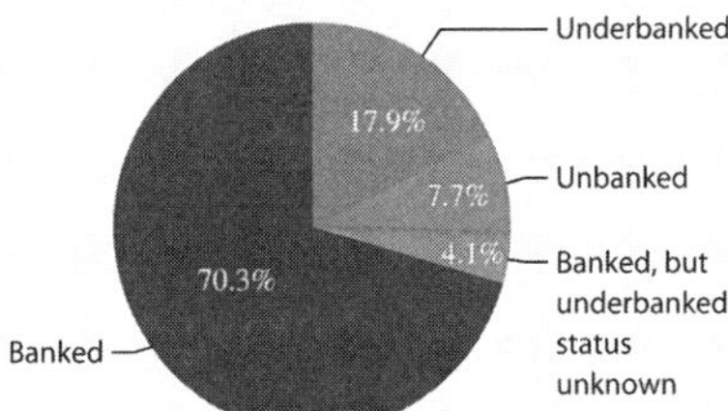

FIGURE 9.4 Banking Status of U.S. Households 2010
Note: Percentages are based on 118.6 million U.S. households; based on data from FDIC.
Data from: The Unbanked and Underbanked, http://www.mybanktracker.com/news/2010/06/02/nearly-8-of-americans-are-unbanked-18-are-underbanked/

Checking and savings accounts are basically a cash investment. It is always nice to keep cash on hand, and there are several ways to keep your money safe and earn a modest return. The Federal Deposit Insurance Corporation (FDIC) guarantees the money that you deposit in a bank account up to a specified amount. FDIC insurance covers all deposit accounts, including checking and savings accounts, money market deposit accounts, and certificates of deposit. The standard insurance amount is $250,000 per depositor, per insured bank, for each account ownership category (as of 2014). If you have more cash than this, you can simply open accounts at different banks.

Checking/savings/money market accounts are ultra-safe investments and correspondingly offer low **rates of return**. There are slight differences between savings and money market accounts, most noticeably that money markets often have checks. In 2014 the average **APY** was typically below 0.5% at most banks with the best offering 0.87% with no minimum deposit. If **inflation** is 3% a year, these accounts have a negative real rate of return. You can withdraw your money at any point with no penalty.

TABLE 9.4 Money Market Accounts (MMA)

Avg Rate April 2014	Latest	Change	Last Week
MMA	0.36%	⬇	0.37%
$10K MMA	0.33%	–	0.33%

Certificates of deposits (CDs) require you to invest your cash for a fixed period of time and give a fixed APY. Withdrawing early will result in penalties. The longer you guarantee the bank your cash, the better the return. Again, CDs are ultra-safe with corresponding negative real rates of return.

TABLE 9.5 Certificates of Deposit

Avg Rate April 2014	Latest	Change	Last Week
6 month CD	0.35%	–	0.35%
1 yr CD	0.64%	⬇	0.66%
5 yr CD	1.35%	⬇	1.38%

Example 2 Compare CDs

VIDEO
Compare CDs

Compute the value of a \$10,000 six-month **CD** at 1% APY after six-months and after one year, assuming that you leave the six-month CD in for one full year at 1% APY. Compute the value of a \$10,000 one-year CD at 1.25% **APY** at the end of one year.

SOLUTION Recall that APY refers to the effective interest rate or yield for an investment over a one-year period. We do not know the **APR** but do know that the six-month CD will be compounded biannually, or twice in one year. Using the formula $APY = \left(1 + \frac{APR}{n}\right)^n - 1$, we can substitute in 1% for the APY and 2 for the number of periods in one year and solve for the APR:

$$1\% = \left(1 + \frac{APR}{2}\right)^2 - 1 \rightarrow 1.01 = \left(1 + \frac{APR}{2}\right)^2 \rightarrow \sqrt{1.01} = 1 + \frac{APR}{2}$$

Solving for the APR gives APR $\approx 0.009975 = 0.9975\%$.

Recall the **periodic compounding form** of an exponential equation:

$P = P_0 \cdot \left(1 + \frac{APR}{n}\right)^{n \cdot t}$

Thus after one biannual period (i.e., six months, or $t = \frac{1}{2}$ year) we will have:

$$10{,}000 \cdot \left(1 + \frac{0.009975}{2}\right)^1 = \$10{,}049.88$$

To find the value of the six-month CD at the end of one year, we will have:

$$10{,}000 \cdot \left(1 + \frac{0.009975}{2}\right)^2 = \$10{,}100.00$$

CAUTION We could also have used the APY = 1% for the six month CD after one year. •

To find the value of the one-year CD at the end of one year, we can simply use the APY of 1.25%:

$$10{,}000 \cdot (1 + \text{APY}) = 10{,}000 \cdot 1.0125 = \$10{,}125.$$

Who is in charge of setting all the **interest rates**? It all starts with the **discount rate**, which the Federal Open Market Committee (the Fed) sets eight times a year. This is the rate banks are charged for borrowing from the Fed. Next, banks set the **federal funds rate**, which is what they charge each other for overnight loans. This then influences the **prime rate** the banks charge their best customers, which then affects credit card rates, typically a fixed value plus the prime rate. The **yields** on **Treasuries** are determined at auction and are affected by the rates above since banks are investing their reserve cash in these bonds.

CAUTION The federal funds rate was basically zero in 2013; there is nowhere for rates to go from there except up. •

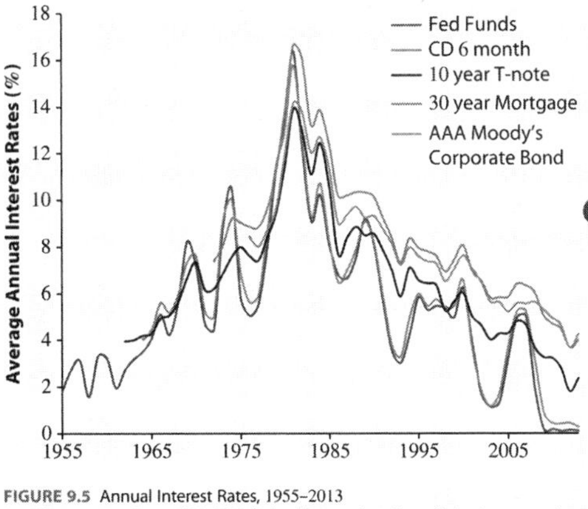

FIGURE 9.5 Annual Interest Rates, 1955–2013
Data from: Interest Rates, 1955–2013, Federal Reserve, http://www.federalreserve.gov/releases/h15/data.htm

T-notes and AAA **Corporate** are **bonds**, which we discuss next. **Mortgages** are loans for home purchases and are discussed at the end of the chapter.

OBJECTIVE 2 Understand Bonds

The **rate of return** for **savings bonds** is similar to that for savings accounts and CDs. The difference is that with a savings bond, you are in effect lending money to the federal government to pay its bills. In return the government will give you interest on the amount you loan (i.e., the value of the bond). There are two types of savings bonds: I bonds, which have an **interest rate** that varies with **inflation** (1.38% composite rate in April 2014), and EE bonds, which have a fixed rate (0.10% in April 2014). You can get more information and purchase government savings bonds online at TreasuryDirect; **Table 9.6** provides details.

TABLE 9.6 Treasury Direct Savings Bonds

	EE Bonds and I Bonds
Purchase price	Electronic: **Face value** (a $50 bond costs $50)
Available electronic bonds	Any amount of $25 or more to the penny For example, electronically, you could buy an EE or an I Bond for $50.23.
Maximum amount you can buy	$10,000 each calendar year for each Social Security number. In any one year for one Social Security Number: You may buy up to $10,000 in electronic EE Bonds. You may also buy up to $10,000 in electronic I Bonds and up to $5,000 in paper I Bonds with your tax refunds.
Redeeming (cashing in the bond)	After 12 months
When interest is earned and compounded	Interest is earned monthly and **compounded semiannually** up to 30 years.
Penalty for cashing in early	Loss of last three months of interest if you redeem the bond during the first five years. For example, if you redeem the bond after 18 months, you get the first 15 months of interest.
Income tax	Federal: Yes State and Local: No Tax benefits may be available when you use the money for higher education.

Data from: Treasury Direct Savings Bonds, U.S. Department of the Treasury, http://www.treasurydirect.gov/

Savings bonds are a nice safe investment but are similar to CDs in terms of the rate of return.

In addition to **savings bonds**, the federal government "sells" **treasuries**, which come in three flavors, depending on the **term**. You can buy them online through Treasury Direct or through a bank or broker. They are sold in denominations of $100.

DEFINITION

Treasuries are bonds issued by the U.S. federal government:

1. **Treasury bills**, or T-bills, are issued in terms of 4 weeks, 13 weeks, 26 weeks, and 52 weeks. They are sold at a discount to their face value and are redeemed for the full face value at the end of the term. For example, if you buy a $1,000 bill at a price per $100 of $99.986111, then you pay $999.86 ($1,000·0.99986111 = $999.86111). When the bill matures, you will be paid its face value, $1,000.
2. **Treasury notes**, or T-notes, are issued in terms of 2, 3, 5, 7, and 10 years, and pay the bearer simple interest every 6 months until maturity. When a Treasury note matures, the bearer is repaid its face value.
3. **Treasury bonds**, or T-bonds, are issued in terms of 30 years and pay the bearer simple interest every 6 months until maturity. When a Treasury bond matures, the bearer is repaid its face value.

TABLE 9.7 Treasury Direct T-note Interest Rates

Security Term	CUSIP	Reopening	Issue Date	Maturity Date	High Yield	Interest Rate
7-Year	912828C57	No	03/31/2014	03/31/2021	2.258%	2.250%
5-Year	912828C65	No	03/31/2014	03/31/2019	1.715%	1.625%
2-Year	912828C40	No	03/31/2014	03/31/2016	0.469%	0.375%
10-Year	912828C66	Yes	03/17/2014	02/15/2024	2.729%	2.750%
3-Year	912828C32	No	03/17/2014	03/15/2017	0.802%	0.750%

Data from: Table from Treasury Direct T-note Interest Rates. Published by US Department of Treasury. http://www.treasurydirect.gov/

The discrepancy between the **High Yield** and **interest Rate** in Table 9.7 is due to the fact that Treasuries are auctioned off. The interest rate is the fixed annual rate (or **coupon rate**) for each bond. The high yield reflects what was bid for these and is not relevant for the average investor!

Example 3 **Evaluate a T-Note Purchase**

VIDEO
T-Note

You purchase a 10-year **T-note** with a face value of $10,000 and a **coupon rate** of 2.75%. Compute the total return of this investment and the average **rate of return**.

SOLUTION **Treasuries** pay simple interest semiannually. In this case, the **APR** of 2.75% implies annual interest of $275 on the $10,000 T-note. This **interest** is paid to you in $137.50 increments every 6 months for 10 years, at which time you are repaid the $10,000. The total return is thus:

$$10{,}000 + 275 \cdot 10 = \$12{,}750$$

The average rate of return is given by:

$$10{,}000 \cdot (1 + r)^{10} = 12{,}750$$

$$r = \sqrt[10]{12{,}750/10{,}000} - 1 \approx 2.46\%$$

CAUTION The coupon rate for a Treasury is an APR, but it generates simple interest. The interest does not compound like the APR for a savings account. •

FIGURE 9.6 Treasury 10-Year Note Rates
Data from: Treasury 10-Year Note Rates, U.S. Department of the Treasury, http://www.treasury.gov/resource-center/data-chart-center/interest-rates/Pages/Historic-LongTerm-Rate-Data-Visualization.aspx

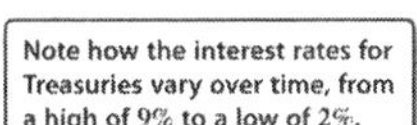

Note how the interest rates for Treasuries vary over time, from a high of 9% to a low of 2%.

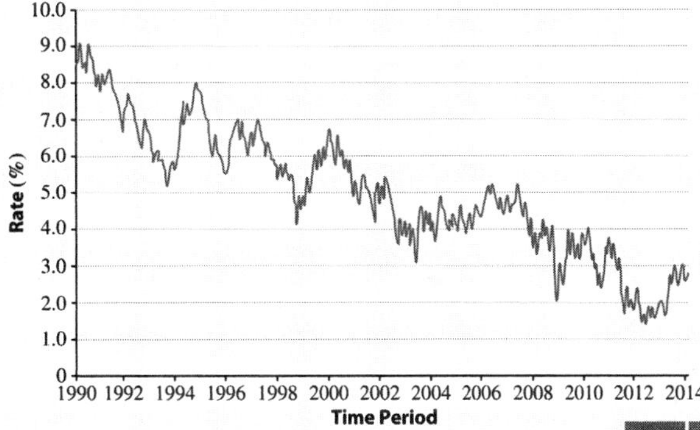

Bonds are essentially loans to either the federal government (**treasuries**), local governments or municipalities (**munis**), or companies (**corporate bonds**). All three of these types of bonds traditionally pay simple interest semiannually. Bonds are rated by independent agencies based on the bond issuer's ability to pay back the loan, in just the same way people are given credit scores. Bonds are rated from best (AAA), to worst (C, or junk bonds). Bondholders thus have a lender/creditor stake.

Example 4 **Evaluate a Municipal Bond Purchase**

VIDEO
Municipal Bonds

Your town wants to build a $20 million athletic complex. To raise the money, the town issues 10,000 bonds for $2,000 each, with a **coupon rate** of 5% interest and a 10-year term. Compute the total return for one $2,000 bond and the average **rate of return**.

SOLUTION The bondholders will get 5% of their $2,000 ($100) paid to them semiannually ($50 every 6 months) for 10 years, at which point the town will pay back the entire $2,000.

The total return is thus:

$$2{,}000 + 100 \cdot 10 = \$3{,}000$$

The average rate of return is given by:

$$2{,}000 \cdot (1 + r)^{10} = 3{,}000$$

$$r = \sqrt[10]{3{,}000/2{,}000} - 1 = 4.14\%$$

Bonds are referred to as *fixed-income assets* because they typically generate a fixed payment every six months for the entire term.

Every investment has risk; the more risk, the higher the rate of return. **Treasuries** are considered the safest investment in the world since they are backed by the U.S. government. **Corporate bonds** carry the risk of default by the company issuing the **bond**. For example, on June 1, 2009, General Motors filed for bankruptcy for a variety of reasons, foremost among them its inability to fund its pension obligations to all its retirees. At the time of bankruptcy, roughly $29 billion worth of GM bonds were being held. The bankruptcy settlement, completed in April 2011, allotted bondholders about 10% of the new GM (worth about $4 billion) by giving them **shares of stock** in the new company. This roughly translated into bondholders receiving only 30 cents for every dollar they loaned GM (i.e., a 70% loss). Bonds can also lose value if **interest rates** rise.

Example 5 | Sell a Bond Early

VIDEO *Sell a Bond*

You own a 30-year $10,000 **T-bond** with a **coupon rate** of 3%. After five years, you unexpectedly need to sell the bond for cash. Unfortunately, interest rates on T-bonds have risen to 6%. Compute how much your bond is worth.

SOLUTION You have been receiving $300 a year for five years, and your T-bond promises to pay the new holder $300 a year for an additional 25 years plus the $10,000 face value, for a total of $17,500:

$$\$10{,}000 + 3\% \cdot \$10{,}000 \cdot 25 = \$17{,}500$$

Instead of buying your bond, however, the investor could purchase a new $10,000 T-bond at 6%, which would return $600 a year for 25 years, equaling $25,000. So there is no way someone will pay you $10,000 for your bond. Instead, we must replace $10,000 with x and 3% with 6% in the equation above:

$$x + 6\% \cdot x \cdot 25 = \$17{,}500 \quad \rightarrow \quad 2.5 \cdot x = 17{,}500 \quad \rightarrow \quad x = \$7{,}000$$

So someone would not pay you more than $7,000 for your bond since they could buy a new T-bond at 6% for $7,000 which would return them $17,500 after 25 years.

To read more about the GM bankruptcy, see http://www.bloomberg.com/news/2011-04-06/old-gm-bondholders-getting-shares-in-new-general-motors-may-depress-price.html.

CAUTION Rising interest rates force the bond prices down for anyone needing to sell a bond before it matures. •

OBJECTIVE 3 Understand Stocks

We have just learned that the safest investments do not have very high **rates of return.**

Stocks are shares of a company that you can buy through an online brokerage firm like E*TRADE and TD Ameritrade. When you buy shares of a company, you have an ownership/equity stake in the company. This means you get to vote at shareholder meetings, with your number of votes equal to your number of shares. If you buy more than half the stock in a company, you have a controlling interest and can control who gets elected to the board of directors and thus who controls the company.

For example, consider the stock quote for GM shown in **Figure 9.7** from Google Finance on March 28, 2014. You could buy one share of GM for $34.71 and own a piece of the company. When GM emerged from bankruptcy on November 26, 2010 until March 28, 2014, the shares had only gone up by 1.69% compared with a 51.39% gain for the entire **S&P 500.**

CAUTION Buying stock in just one company can be very risky. It is much easier to buy a mutual fund for the entire S&P 500, which essentially gives you ownership of 500 companies and diversifies your risk. •

Note that every company with publicly traded stock has a ticker **symbol.** The symbol for General Motors is GM, and for Apple it is AAPL.

FIGURE 9.7 General Motors Stock Quote
Data from: Yahoo Finance, March 28, 2014, https://www.google.com/finance?q=NYSE%3AGM&ei=1bE1U9iYCoq8qAGf7QE

Example 6 Read a Stock Quote

Interpret all the information shown in the stock quote for GM in **Figure 9.8.**

VIDEO *Stock Quote*

SOLUTION The *price* of one **share** of the **stock** was \$34.71 at 3:00 EDT PM 3/28/14, which is up \$0.20 (0.58%) from the closing price the day before. The price so far this day has traded in the range from a low of \$34.59 to a high of \$35.02. Over the past year, GM shares have traded in the *range* from a low of \$27.11 to a high of \$41.85. The share price *opened* the day at \$34.64, and as of 3:00 PM, 10.9 million shares had been traded compared to an *average volume* of 26.11 million shares traded daily. Multiplying the share price by the number of shares that can be traded gives the **market capitalization** of the company, which in this case is \$55.40 billion. The **ratio** of the share price to the **earnings per share** (from the past 12 months or four quarters of earnings) gives the **PE ratio** of 14.65. People are willing to pay 14.65 times what the company earns per share, which is roughly equal to the historical average PE ratio. Each quarter, GM will pay its shareholders a *dividend* of \$0.30 per share (\$1.20 per share for the year, which is 3.44% of the current share price). GM *earned* \$2.38 per share in profit over the past year, and there are 1.59 billion shares on the market. *Beta* measures the volatility of a stock; anything over 1 implies more volatility than in the market at large, so GM shares are 69% more volatile than the market. Finally, 76% of GM shares are owned by large *institutional investors.*

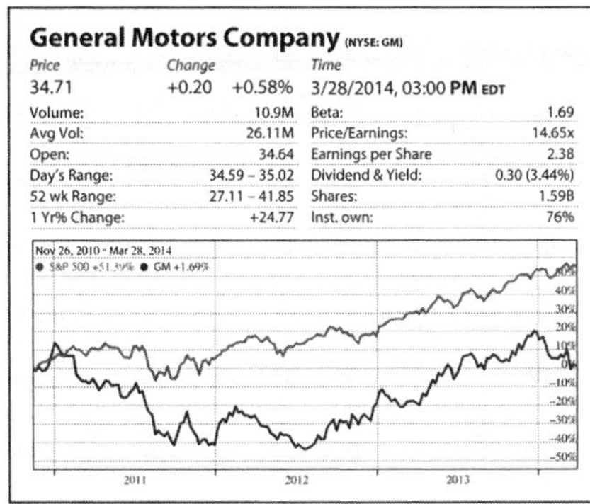

General Motors Company (NYSE: GM)

Price	Change		Time	
34.71	+0.20	+0.58%	3/28/2014, 03:00 **PM** EDT	

Volume:	10.9M	Beta:	1.69
Avg Vol:	26.11M	Price/Earnings:	14.65x
Open:	34.64	Earnings per Share	2.38
Day's Range:	34.59 – 35.02	Dividend & Yield:	0.30 (3.44%)
52 wk Range:	27.11 – 41.85	Shares:	1.59B
1 Yr% Change:	+24.77	Inst. own:	76%

FIGURE 9.8 General Motors Stock Quote
Data from: Yahoo Finance, March 28, 2014, https://www.google.com/finance?q=NYSE%3AGM&ei=1bE1U9iYCoq8qAGf7QE

CAUTION The price of a stock fluctuates because there are people bidding on it. In order to buy a share of stock, someone must sell; thus someone is betting the stock will go up while someone is betting the stock will go down. Trying to guess about such volatility on a daily basis is a fool's errand for most investors. •

Example 7 Test Your Stock Knowledge

VIDEO *Cake Company*

You want to start a small business selling cakes and need to raise \$60,000 to run the business for the first year. You have \$30,000 of your own savings and get two friends to invest \$15,000 each. You decide to give your friends 1,000 **shares** of the company each and keep 2,000 shares for yourself. At the end of the year, you make a **profit** of \$16,000 and decide to reinvest half into the business and pay out the rest as **dividends** to the owners. Determine the number of shares, the price per share, and the **market capitalization** of your company. Next, compute the earnings per share and the **PE ratio**. Finally, compute the dividends as \$ per share and as a **percentage** of the share price.

SOLUTION We will solve this one step at a time:

> Note that each friend made \$2,000 in dividends and still owns 1,000 shares, and each friend could sell shares to someone wanting to buy into this company.

- The number of shares is 4,000.
- Dividing the total invested by the 4,000 shares, we get a price per share of \$15.
- Market capitalization equals the number of shares times share price, which has already been given to us: \$60,000. In other words, the market capitalization is **proportional** to the number of shares and the **constant of proportionality** is the share price.
- The profit of \$16,000 divided by the 4,000 shares gives \$4 **earnings per share** (EPS).
- The PE ratio is the ratio of share price to EPS, so \$15 : \$4, or 3.75.
- The dividends per share is the total amount of dividends paid, \$8,000, divided by the number of shares, 4,000, giving \$2 per share. As a percentage of the share price, 2/15 = 13.3%.

OBJECTIVE  Understand Mutual Funds

Choosing what **stocks** to buy on your own can be intimidating. It can also be difficult to *diversify* your holdings. If you have only $1,000 to invest, you most likely will buy shares of only one or two companies. An online brokerage firm charges you $9.95 per order (approximately), so if you buy 20 shares of one company at $50, you get charged $9.95, but if you buy one share each of 20 companies (20 separate orders), you get charged 20 times $9.95 = $199. A **mutual fund** is a pool of money from many investors that is invested for them by a manager who charges a fee for this service.

One of the greatest investors of our time, Warren Buffett, CEO of Berkshire Hathaway, the "Oracle of Omaha," and second wealthiest individual in the world (2014) with a net worth of $63.4 billion, offers very simple investing advice, telling us we don't need to be experts to achieve satisfactory returns:

"If 'investors' frenetically bought and sold farmland to one another, neither the yields nor the prices of their crops would be increased. So ignore the chatter, keep your costs minimal, and invest in stocks as you would in a farm. Put 10% of cash in short-term government **bonds** and 90% in a very low-cost **S&P 500** index fund."

Then put your faith in the American economy and let your money grow. Constantly digging up your seeds and replanting them is a good way to destroy your crop.

Warren Buffett advises buying a low-cost **index fund**, which is a type of **mutual fund** where the pooled money is invested in an index (like the **S&P 500**) by a computer program. Let's take a look at one of the most popular index funds that tracks the S&P 500 and is offered by the Vanguard Corporation.

Eric Gaze

FIGURE 9.9 Tequila's Iceman Gaze Acres Alpacas

Read Warren Buffet's article "Why I Like to Think of Stocks Like Farms," *Fortune*, March 17, 2014. Then read the rest of the magazine and continue to read it every month. *Money* is another good financial read every month. If you seriously want to grow your money, then you need to get savvy and do something about it.

Example 8 | Read a Mutual Fund Quote

VIDEO *Mutual Funds*

Interpret all the information shown in the quote for the Vanguard 500 Index Fund in **Figure 9.10**.

SOLUTION The **net asset value** (NAV) of 171.27 is a measure of the fund's value, so we can track its performance over time. On March 28, 2014, the NAV increased by 0.80 (0.47%). Funds have ticker symbols like stocks; VFINX is the ticker symbol for this fund. The fund controls or invests assets worth $27.7 billion. Vanguard charges 0.17% of your investment each year as a fee for investing your money for you. Some funds also charge an up-front fee, called a **front end load**, or a deferred fee, called a deferred load. Vanguard does not do this for this fund.

FIGURE 9.10 Vanguard's 500 Index Fund Quote
Data from: www.cnbc.com

Note the expense fee for an **index fund** is typically much lower than the fee for an actively managed mutual fund.

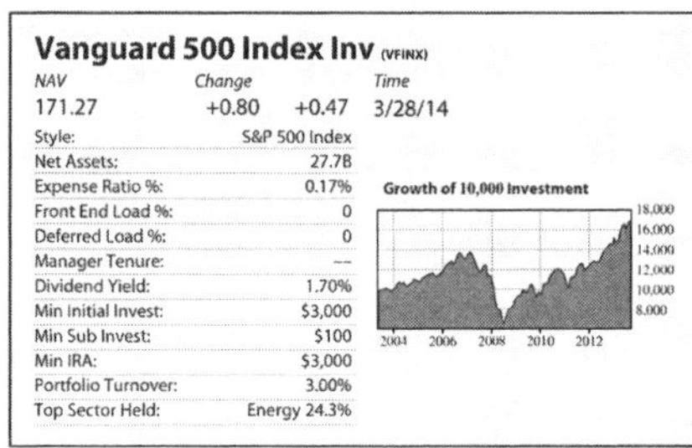

Vanguard 500 Index Inv (VFINX)

NAV	*Change*		*Time*
171.27	+0.80	+0.47	3/28/14

Style:	S&P 500 Index
Net Assets:	27.7B
Expense Ratio %:	0.17%
Front End Load %:	0
Deferred Load %:	0
Manager Tenure:	—
Dividend Yield:	1.70%
Min Initial Invest:	$3,000
Min Sub Invest:	$100
Min IRA:	$3,000
Portfolio Turnover:	3.00%
Top Sector Held:	Energy 24.3%

In **Figure 9.10**, manager tenure refers to how long the current fund manager has been managing this fund. An **index fund** by definition simply tracks an index, using a computer program, so there is no manager. The Vanguard 500 Index fund tracks the **S&P 500** index, which consists of 500 of the largest U.S. companies, spanning many different industries and accounting for about three-fourths of the U.S. stock market's value. **Table 9.8** shows the Vanguard 500 Index fund's top 10 holdings as of March 28, 2014, weighted by the **market capitalization** of the companies (i.e., Apple Inc. had the largest market capitalization of all U.S. companies at this time). This fund pays out a **dividend** because many of the 500 individual companies pay dividends. Currently, the dividend yield is 1.7% of your investment. The minimum initial investment is $3,000, and you can set up a minimum recurring payment of $100 into this fund. The minimum investment for an IRA (individual retirement account) is also $3,000. The portfolio of **stocks** turns over, or sells, 3% of its holdings each year. Finally, 24.3% of the fund assets are invested in energy companies like Exxon, GE, and Chevron. Energy is the largest sector of the fund's holdings. If you had invested $10,000 a decade ago, it would currently be worth $16,520.90.

TABLE 9.8 Vanguard 500 Index Fund Top 10 Holdings

Security	Net Assets
Apple Inc (AAPL)	2.83%
Exxon Mobil Corporation (XOM)	2.52%
Google Inc Class A (GOOG)	2.04%
Microsoft Corporation (MSFT)	1.74%
Johnson & Johnson (JNJ)	1.56%
General Electric (GE)	1.54%
Wells Fargo & Co (WFC)	1.33%
Chevron Corp (CVX)	1.33%
Procter & Gamble Co (PG)	1.28%
JP Morgan Chase & Co (JPM)	1.28%

Data from: Google Finance, https://www.google.com/finance?q=MUTF%3AVFINX&ei=nAU2U-mwHIi7sQeCEw

9.3 401(k) Plans

OBJECTIVE 1 Explore Saving for Retirement

OBJECTIVE 1 Explore Saving for Retirement

To save for **retirement**, you need to open a retirement account, which generally is a 401(k), named after the legislation that created this type of account. *Money's* article "Building the New Retirement" in the March 2014 issue gives us some history of the 401(k).

In 1978 almost half of workers had pensions, a fixed salary to be paid to them during retirement from their company (or government). A new pension law passed in that year, subsection 401(k) of the Internal Revenue Code, made 401(k) plans possible. Basically, employers can offer a retirement plan with a defined annual contribution to your retirement account that is deducted from your paycheck before taxes (up to $17,500 in 2014). Employers can also offer to match a fraction of your contribution. Typically employers offer to match 50 cents for every dollar you contribute, up to 6% of your salary. Unfortunately, many workers do not take advantage of this free money! You should always max out your employer match. If your employer matches up to 6% and you only contribute 4%, you are leaving free money on the table.

By 1990 only 32% of workers were covered by traditional pensions, and about 28% had 401(k) accounts, and by 2014 only 14% of private-sector workers had traditional pensions. The Bureau of Labor Statistics reported that 68% of civilian American workers in 2013 had access to some form of retirement plan, but only 54% were participating (see http://www.bls.gov/news.release/ebs2.t01.htm). These percentages are lower for just private industry: 64% access and 49% participation in 2013. Taking away the 14% of private-sector workers with pensions, this gives us the estimate of 35% of private-sector workers participating in 401(k) plans in 2013.

Example 9 | Compare 401(k) Contributions

VIDEO
401k Plans

Three friends, Sal, Cal, and Val, all work for the same company and all earn the same salary of $40,000. The company will match half of their contributions to the 401(k) plan, up to 6% of their salary. Sal decides to contribute $100 a month to his 401(k), Cal decides not to contribute anything and invest what is left of 6% of his salary after taxes on his own, and Val decides to contribute $400 a month to her 401(k). Determine how much money each will have invested at the end of the year.

SOLUTION 6% of their $40,000 salary is $2,400, or $200 per month. The company will thus match half of their contribution up to a maximum of $100 a month.

Sal contributes $100 a month, the company matches $50 a month, and Sal ends up investing 12 times $150, or $1,800 for the year.

Val contributes $400 a month, the company matches the max of $100 a month since she is contributing 12%, and Val ends up investing 12 times $500, or $6,000 for the year.

Cal does not contribute to his 401(k), so 6% of his salary, or $2,400 gets taxed at a 25% rate, leaving him with $1,800 to invest, the same as Sal. So Sal and Cal have the same amount to invest, but Sal only "spent" $1,200 while Cal "spent" $2,400, twice as much!

CAUTION Not investing in your 401(k) is a double whammy: You miss out on the company match, and you get taxed on your full income. ●

When contributing to a 401(k), you are given options of **mutual funds** to invest in. Mutual funds come in many different varieties. There are **index funds**, **bond** funds, and funds that invest in sectors like energy. If you are looking for good funds to invest in, start with the Money 50, http://money.cnn.com/magazines/moneymag/bestfunds/.

09-23

9.4 Built-in Financial Functions

OBJECTIVE 1 Use RATE, NPER, PMT, PV, and FV (RNPPF)

OBJECTIVE 1 Use RATE, NPER, PMT, PV, and FV (RNPPF)

In Example 1 we explored how to model withdrawing from your **retirement account** by using a spreadsheet. Excel has built-in financial **functions** that can greatly speed up these "what-if" analyses.

DEFINITION

Excel has five built-in financial functions. The arguments for each function are the other four financial functions, in order. Thus the mnemonic device RNPPF is helpful to remember this order:

Rover Needs Poopy Paper Fast.

=**RATE**(nper, pmt, pv, fv)**:** Calculates the *periodic* rate required to achieve some financial goal.
=**NPER**(rate, pmt, pv, fv)**:** Calculates the number of periods required to achieve some financial goal.
=**PMT**(rate, nper, pv, fv)**:** Calculates the payment required to achieve some financial goal.
=**PV**(rate, nper, pmt, fv)**:** Calculates the present value required to achieve some financial goal.
=**FV**(rate, nper, pmt, pv)**:** Calculates the future value required to achieve some financial goal.

09-24

CAUTION You must enter any value that comes out of your pocket (like a payment to the bank or your retirement account) as a negative. Any value like a loan that you borrow from the bank is positive, since this is money going into your pocket. •

CAUTION RATE gives you the periodic rate, not the APR; you must multiply by the number of periods in one year to get the **APR**. NPER gives the number of periods for the entire term of the investment/loan, not the number of **periods** in one year. •

Example 10 Compute a Future Value

Note that as of 2014, the stock market had returned roughly 10% a year since 1927.

VIDEO *Future Value*

You deposit $450 a month into a **mutual fund** in your **401(k)**, which has averaged a 10% annual **rate of return**. What will be the value of this investment after 30 years?

SOLUTION We will use the **FV** function, remembering that **RATE** is the **periodic rate**, **NPER** is the number of months (since we are making monthly payments), the payments must be entered as negatives (since they go out of our pocket into the 401(k)) and the present value is zero:

$$= FV\,(10\%/12, 30 \cdot 12, -450, 0)$$

D5 =FV(D1,D2,D3,D4)

	A	B	C	D
1	APR:	10%	RATE:	0.83%
2	Years:	30	NPER:	360
3			PMT:	($450.00)
4			PV:	$ -
5			FV:	$1,017,219.57

FIGURE 9.11 Future Value Function

Figure 9.11 shows that the result is $1,017,219.57 and answers the question from Example 1 of where the million dollars came from. You could retire a millionaire; it just takes disciplined investing over a long enough time horizon.

We just saw how to accumulate $1,000,000 in your **retirement account**. Now let's use Excel and find out what happens if we get different **rates of return** for different lengths of time.

SPREADSHEET TUTORIALS Entering Numbers | Using Arithmetic Operators | Formatting Financial Numbers | Inserting PMT Financial Function | Moving Data and Resolving ####Error

Example 11 Compare APR and NPER

VIDEO *FV What If Analysis*

Assume that you deposit $450 a month into your **401(k)**. Create a table that computes the future value for 6%, 8%, 10%, and 12% and for 10, 20, 30, and 40 years.

SOLUTION We will again use the **FV** function, remembering that **RATE** is the **periodic rate**, **NPER** is the number of months since we are making monthly payments, the payments must be entered as negatives since they go out of our pocket into the 401(k), and the present value is zero:

$$= \text{FV}\,(\text{APR}/12, \text{Years} \cdot 12, -450, 0)$$

Figure 9.12 shows the results, with the formula in the formula bar displaying the proper **mixed cell references**. Notice how important time is to building your nest egg. If you start investing in your 40s and have only have 20 years of compound growth, you don't even reach $500,000 at 12%.

FIGURE 9.12 What-If Analysis

Note that the growth is not **linear** as a **function** of **APR** or as a function of years.

B4 =FV(B$3/12,$A4*12,$B$1,0)

	A	B	C	D	E
1	PMT:	($450.00)			
2		APR			
3	Years	6%	8%	10%	12%
4	10	$73,745.71	$82,325.72	$92,180.24	$103,517.41
5	20	$207,918.40	$265,059.19	$341,715.98	$445,164.91
6	30	$452,031.77	$670,661.75	$1,017,219.57	$1,572,733.86
7	40	$896,170.83	$1,570,953.52	$2,845,835.81	$5,294,147.63

SPREADSHEET TUTORIALS Entering Data by Range | Entering Numbers | Copying a Formula Using the Fill Handle | Constructing a Formula and Using the SUM Function | Using Arithmetic Operators | Formatting Financial Numbers | Using Format Painter | Using Merge and Center and Applying Cell Styles | Moving Data and Resolving ####Error | Projecting Income and Expenses by Filling Formulas | Using a Data Table to Calculate Options using What If Analysis | Inserting PMT Financial Function

9.5 Loans

OBJECTIVE 1 Explore Credit Cards

OBJECTIVE 2 Understand Amortized Loans

OBJECTIVE 1 Explore Credit Cards

In this section, we will explore the flip side of investing—that is, borrowing money or taking out a loan. Loans in and of themselves are not necessarily bad for you financially. It makes sense to take out a **mortgage** (a loan to buy a house) at 4% if your money is invested at 10%. Credit cards offer convenience, and using them is a good way to build your credit score. The trick is to avoid fees and interest by paying off the credit card in a timely manner. Consider **Table 9.9** which shows an actual credit card offer.

TABLE 9.9 Credit Card Offer

Annual Percentage Rate (APR) for Purchases	0% introductory APR through your 06/2012 billing period. After that, your APR will be 10.9%, 14.9% or 18.9% based on your creditworthiness. This APR will vary with the market based on the Prime Rate
APR for Transfers	0% introductory APR through your 06/2012 billing period. After that, your APR will be 10.9%, 14.9% or 18.9% based on your creditworthiness. This APR will vary with the market based on the Prime Rate
APR for Cash Advances	24.9%. This APR will vary with the market based on the Prime Rate.
Penalty APR and When It Applies	29.4% This APR will vary with the market based on the Prime Rate. This APR may be applied to your account if you make a late payment. How Long will the penalty APR Apply?; If APRs are increased for a payment that is more than 60 days late, the Penalty APR will apply indefinitely unless you make the next six consecutive minimum payments on time following the rate increase.
Paying Interest	Your due date is at least 25 days after the close of each month. We will begin charging interest on cash advances on the transaction date.

CAUTION Note the three possible **interest rates** you can be charged, based on your credit score. It is crucial that you maintain good credit by paying bills on time. •

The credit card offer in **Table 9.9** displays three possible **interest rates**, depending on your credit score: 10.9%, 14.9%, and 18.9%.

Example 12 **Compare Different APRs**

VIDEO
Credit Cards

You charge a spring break trip to Cancun with your friends and come back with a nice tan, many happy memories, and a balance of $1,652 on your credit card. Compute how long it will take to pay off the card, assuming that you can make a $100 payment each month, for each of the three **APRs** 10.9%, 14.9%, and 18.9%. Compute the total **interest** paid in each scenario.

> Note that there is an optional fifth argument, *Type*, which allows you to switch from the default of making the payment at the end of the period to making the payment at the beginning.

SOLUTION We want to find how long it will take to pay off our balance, so we will use the **NPER** function, remembering that **NPER** is the number of months since we are making monthly payments, **RATE** is the **periodic rate**, the payments must be entered as negatives since they go out of our pocket to the credit card company, the present value is $1,652, and the future value of this loan is zero:

$$= \text{NPER}(\text{APR}/12, -100, 1652, 0).$$

The total interest paid will be the number of months times the payment of $100 minus the amount borrowed:

$$\text{Interest} = \text{NPER} \cdot \$100 - \$1{,}652$$

Table 9.10 shows the outcomes for the three different **APRs**. Notice that a person with the worst credit score and highest APR pays out $130.39 more than a person with the best credit score and lowest APR.

TABLE 9.10 Credit Card What-If Analysis

	APR		
	10.9%	14.9%	18.9%
NPER	17.98	18.60	19.28
Interest	$146.05	$208.33	$276.44

SPREADSHEET TUTORIALS Entering Data by Range | Entering Numbers | Copying a Formula Using the Fill Handle | Constructing a Formula and Using the SUM Function | Using Arithmetic Operators | Formatting Financial Numbers | Using Format Painter | Using Merge and Center and Applying Cell Styles | Moving Data and Resolving ####Error | Projecting Income and Expenses by Filling Formulas | Using a Data Table to Calculate Options using What If Analysis | Inserting PMT Financial Function

Credit cards are different from loans for a car, education, or a home because there is not a mandatory fixed payment due each month. Credit cards have a minimum payment due, based on your balance, but you are free to pay whatever you wish above and beyond the minimum. In addition, there is not a fixed term, or length of time, in which to pay back the loan. Car loans, student loans, and home loans have a fixed monthly payment and a fixed term in which to pay off the loan. Loans of this type are called **amortized**.

OBJECTIVE 2 Understand Amortized Loans

An **amortized loan** has a fixed monthly payment and fixed **term**. In Chapter 1 we looked at car loans and used a complicated payment formula. Now let's consider a home loan, called a **mortgage**, and use the **PMT** function to build a payment schedule, called an **amortization schedule**, detailing each month's payment and **interest**.

Example 13 Create an Amortization Schedule

VIDEO *Mortgage*

You take out a 30-year fixed mortgage for $150,000, with an APR of 4.3%. Congratulations! **Figure 9.5** tells us you have received a historically low **APR** for your loan. Create an amortization schedule for your loan.

SOLUTION The amortization schedule is shown in **Figure 9.13**.

FIGURE 9.13 Amortization Schedule

C6 =PMT($B$2/12,$B$3*12,$B$1,0)

	A	B	C	D	E	F
1	Principal:	$ 150,000				
2	APR:	4.30%				
3	Term:	30	years			
4						
5	Month	Beginning Balance	Monthly Payment	Interest Payment	Principal Payment	Ending Balance
6	1	$ 150,000	($742.31)	$ 537.50	($204.81)	$149,795.19
7	2	$149,795.19	($742.31)	$ 536.77	($205.54)	$149,589.65
8	3	$149,589.65	($742.31)	$ 536.03	($206.28)	$149,383.37
363	358	$ 2,211.06	($742.31)	$ 7.92	($734.38)	$ 1,476.67
364	359	$ 1,476.67	($742.31)	$ 5.29	($737.02)	$ 739.66
365	360	$ 739.66	($742.31)	$ 2.65	($739.66)	$ (0.00)

Note the root "mort" in amortize, as in mortality, or death. You are gradually killing off your debt.

SPREADSHEET TUTORIALS Entering Data by Range | Entering Numbers | Copying a Formula Using the Fill Handle | Copying Formulas Containing Absolute Cell References | Constructing a Formula and Using the SUM Function | Using Arithmetic Operators | Formatting Financial Numbers | Using Format Painter | Using Merge and Center and Applying Cell Styles | Moving Data and Resolving ####Error | Projecting Income and Expenses by Filling Formulas | Using a Data Table to Calculate Options using What If Analysis | Inserting PMT Financial Function

Referring to the amortization schedule shown in **Figure 9.13**, let's go over each column for Month 1:

- *Beginning Balance*: In Month 1 this is simply the **principal** in cell B1,
  - =*Principal.*
- *Monthly Payment*: This is the **PMT** function shown in the formula bar, and it is fixed for each month:
  - =**PMT**(APR/12, Term·12, Principal, 0)
- *Interest Payment*: The monthly payment is split into two pieces, the **interest** payment (goes to the bank as a fee) and the principal payment (goes to pay down your loan). The interest payment is the **periodic rate** times the beginning balance for each month,
  - =*Beginning Balance*·APR/12.
- *Principal Payment:* This is what is left over from your monthly payment after the bank takes the interest portion as a fee. Careful here- the monthly payment is negative, but the interest payment is positive so we add, not subtract,
  - =*Monthly PMT* + *Interest PMT.*
- *Ending Balance*: We can finally reduce our balance by the principal payment. Careful here- the principal payment is negative so we add, not subtract,
  - =*Beginning Balance* + *Principal PMT.*
- *Beginning Balance:* In Month 2 we need to link the beginning balance to the ending balance of Month 1, before we can fill down,
  - =*Ending Balance*

Now fill in the rest of the formulas for each column in Month 2 and fill all the way down to 360 months. To compute the total interest paid, we can either **SUM** the *Interest Payment* column or multiply *Monthly Payment* by 360 and subtract the *Principal*, which gives $117,230.58. You paid almost as much in interest as you borrowed!

CAUTION The monthly payment will be negative because we used the PMT function, and anything coming out of your pocket is a negative. We used a simple percentage formula for the interest payment and left it positive to emphasize that it does not get subtracted from your principal. The principal payment is what gets subtracted from your principal, and thus we chose to make it negative. This is tricky: Remember that adding together a positive and a negative is like subtracting. ●

When researching mortgage rates, you see two different **interest rates**, the mortgage rate and the **APR**. The mortgage rate assumes that the costs associated with getting a mortgage are included in the **principal**; the APR does not.

Example 14 Compare Mortgage Rate and APR

VIDEO *Mortgage Rate*

You get a mortgage for $100,000, which includes the **closing costs** of $1,000 for 30 years fixed at 5%. Compute your monthly payment and the APR.

SOLUTION First, we compute the monthly payment using the PMT function, =**PMT**(5%/12, 360, 100000, 0), which gives $536.82. The APR is based on just the amount of the loan which goes toward purchasing the home—that is, $99,000. We use the RATE function to compute the APR and multiply by 12 since this will give the periodic rate, =**RATE**(360, −536.82, 99000, 0)·12, which gives 5.09%.

CAUTION Closing costs are associated with every mortgage and must be taken into account when choosing a mortgage. ●

SPREADSHEET TUTORIALS Entering Numbers | Using Arithmetic Operators | Formatting Financial Numbers | Inserting PMT Financial Function

Example 15 Compare 30-Year Mortgage Offers

Which is better, a mortgage for $100,000 that includes closing costs of $1,000 at 5% or a mortgage for $100,000 that includes closing costs of $4,000 at 4.5%?

SOLUTION The APR allows us to compare these two offers. We know that the first has an APR of 5.09% from above. The second will have a monthly payment of =**PMT**(4.5%/12, 360, 100000, 0), which gives $506.69. The APR is given by =**RATE**(360, −506.69, 96000, 0)·12, which gives 4.85%. Thus the second has a lower APR and is a better deal if you plan on staying in the home for a long period of time. If you move after only a couple of years, you will not make back the higher closing costs with your lower monthly payment.

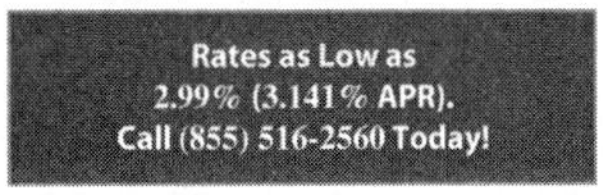

Rates as Low as
2.99% (3.141% APR).
Call (855) 516-2560 Today!

FIGURE 9.14 Mortgage Rate vs. APR

SPREADSHEET TUTORIALS Entering Numbers | Using Arithmetic Operators | Formatting Financial Numbers | Inserting PMT Financial Function

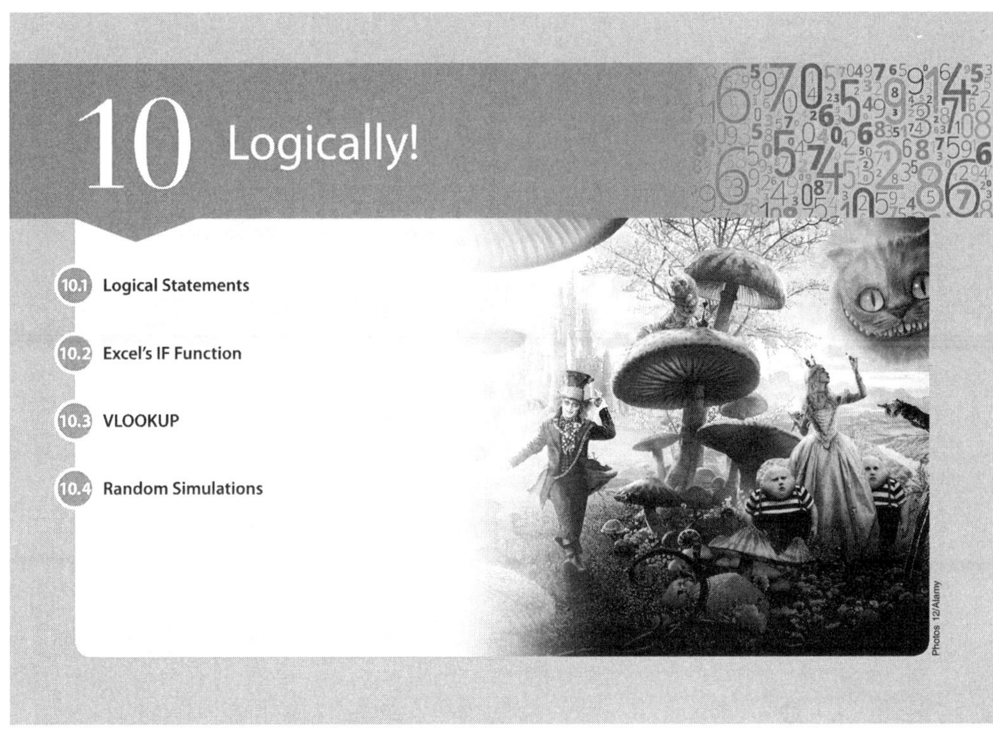

10 Logically!
10.1 Logical Statements
10.2 Excel's IF Function
10.3 VLOOKUP
10.4 Random Simulations
Photos 12/Alamy

10-1

10.1 Logical Statements

OBJECTIVE 1 Understand Logic Vocabulary

OBJECTIVE 1 Understand Logic Vocabulary

It is standard to start a chapter on logic with a quote from *Alice's Adventures in Wonderland* by Lewis Carroll. My favorite quote comes from the mad tea party, right after the Mad Hatter has asked Alice why a raven is like a writing-desk, and is dissatisfied with her response:

> "Then you should say what you mean," the March Hare went on. "I do," Alice hastily replied; "at least—I mean what I say—that's the same thing you know." "Not the same thing a bit!" said the Hatter. "Why, you might just as well say that 'I see what I eat' is the same as 'I eat what I see'!" "You might just as well say," added the March Hare, "that 'I like what I get' is the same thing as 'I get what I like'!" "You might just as well say," added the Dormouse, which seemed to be talking in its sleep, "that 'I breathe when I sleep' is the same thing as 'I sleep when I breathe'!"

FIGURE 10.1 The Mad Hatter's Tea Party

We will use this quotation to explore the basics of logic and associated terminology. Then we will apply this foundation to creating random simulations using Excel's built-in logic functions. This approach will hopefully give you a feel for the utility of these ideas, outside the contrived textbook examples involving people who live on islands and always lie or always tell the truth.

> Lewis Carroll did offer an answer to the riddle regarding the raven and writing desk in the preface to the 1896 edition of the book: "Because it can produce a few notes, tho they are *very* flat; and it is nevar put with the wrong end in front!"
>
> After he died, later editions corrected the intentional misspelling of *never*, making it logically correct but not nearly as clever. Can you see why Carroll misspelled it this way?

10-2

The foundation of logic is the *If-Then* statement, called a **conditional statement**. Such statements in textbooks tend to be straightforward: *If it is sunny then I will go to the beach*. But in the real world, it is not always clear what the conditional statement is. The Lewis Carroll quotation on the previous screen is filled with conditionals; can you find them? Alice's statement *I mean what I say* can be rephrased *"If I say it then I mean it."* The Hatter is trying to make the point that this is different from *"I say what I mean"* or *"If I mean it then I say it."* His example involving eating and seeing is easier to understand, so we will use that to illustrate the various types of statements:

TABLE 10.1
Types of Logic Statements

Type of Statement	If-Then Statement	Translation
Conditional:	*If I eat it then I see it.* (*If P then Q.*)	*I see what I eat.*
Converse:	*If I see it then I eat it.* (*If Q then P.*)	*I eat what I see.*
Contrapositive:	*If I don't see it then I don't eat it.* (*If not Q then not P.*)	*I don't eat what I don't see.*
Inverse:	*If I don't eat it then I don't see it.* (*If not P then not Q.*)	*I don't see what I don't eat.*
Negation:	*I eat it and I don't see it.* (*P and not Q.*)	*I don't always see what I eat.*

We can now see from this table that the confusion on Alice's part has to do with the **converse** of the conditional. Many people mistakenly think these statements are **logically equivalent** when they clearly are not, as the Hatter's example points out. Eating whatever you see is much different than seeing what you eat!

CAUTION The converse is not the same as the conditional; mistaking these two as logically equivalent is called making a **converse error** ●.

10-3

In **Table 10.1** we have introduced the abstract notation *If P then Q* to help remember the different statements. The **contrapositive** and **inverse** both involve the **negation** of the two pieces of the **conditional**. The **converse** and contrapositive both reverse the order of the two pieces and start with *Q* or *not Q*, while the inverse and negation both start with *P* or *not P*. The **negation** is the final statement in **Table 10.1**; notice that it is not an If-Then statement. It is easy to negate the statement *I see it*; you simply say *I don't see it*; negating a conditional is trickier and often causes confusion.

DEFINITION

A **conditional statement** is an *If-Then statement*, which may be true or false, that connects a hypothesis to a conclusion. The hypothesis may also be true or false. If the conditional and hypothesis are both true, then the conclusion must necessarily be true also. Given the conditional statement *If P then Q*, we can form four associated logical statements:

1. **Converse**: *If Q then P.*
2. **Contrapositive**: *If not Q then not P.*
3. **Inverse**: *If not P then not Q.*
4. **Negation**: *P and not Q.*

10-4

Example 1 **Evaluate a Conditional**

Write down the four associated statements for the conditional statement *If it is sunny then we will go to the beach.*

SOLUTION

1. Converse: *If we go to the beach then it is sunny.*
2. Contrapositive: *If we don't go to the beach then it is not sunny.*
3. Inverse: *If it is not sunny then we will not go to the beach.*
4. Negation: *It is sunny and we do not go to the beach.*

CAUTION The negation of a conditional statement is an AND statement, not another conditional. To make the conditional not true, it must be sunny AND we don't go to the beach. ●

CAUTION The negation of a conditional statement is **not** the inverse statement. The word *inverse* in mathematics does imply *undoing*, which causes confusion here. Note that the original conditional does not say anything about what we will do if it is not sunny, which is what the inverse starts with. ●

Two statements are said to be **logically equivalent** if they "mean the same thing." There is a technical definition of this involving truth tables, but we will not go into the details, just report two important facts:

1. The **converse** is *not* logically equivalent to its **conditional**.
2. The **contrapositive** is logically equivalent to its conditional.

Note that this means the **inverse** and converse are logically equivalent.

DEFINITION

A **converse error** refers to mistakenly assuming that the converse is logically equivalent to the original conditional.

Example 2 **Explore the Converse Error**

Explain the converse error for the conditional statement *If it is sunny then we will go to the beach.*

SOLUTION The statement *If it is sunny then we will go to the beach* does not say anything about what will happen if it is not sunny. Many people mistakenly assume that the given conditional implies that the only way we go to the beach is if it is sunny, but this is not true. Assuming that we go to the beach *only if* it is sunny is called making the converse error. The given conditional does guarantee that we go to the beach if it is sunny; thus if we are not at the beach then it cannot be sunny. This explains why the contrapositive is logically equivalent to the original conditional.

The statement *We go to the beach only if it is sunny* is the same as *If we go to the beach then it is sunny.*

The converse error is common because it is so easy to make. The example above is simplistic to illustrate the concept, but in real life, the converse error is dangerous. For example, while it may be true that if men are inherently better at math then they will do better than women on standardized math tests, it certainly is not true that if men do better on standardized math tests then they are inherently better at math than women. Cultural norms that encourage men and discourage women to study math may explain the difference in scores.

CAUTION The converse error is subtle and sometimes hard to spot. ●

There are times when both the conditional and the converse are equivalent, often when giving a definition, such as *A number is even if and only if it is a multiple of 2.* This definition consists of two separate conditionals:

CAUTION A biconditional statement, *P if and only if Q*, is actually two conditional statements: *If P then Q* and *If Q then P* ●.

1. If a number is even, then it is a multiple of 2.
2. If a number is a multiple of 2, then it is even.

DEFINITION

A **biconditional statement** consists of a conditional statement and its converse, which are either both true or both false. The biconditional is read *P if and only if Q*.

Biconditional statements appear in many real-world contexts. A company may wish to give free shipping for orders over $99. Think about this for a second: Is there a biconditional statement lurking in the last sentence?

Example 3 | Explore Biconditional Statements

Explain the biconditional statement implied by the offer of free shipping for orders over $99. Assume that no other promotions are given regarding shipping, which regularly costs $5.99.

SOLUTION Offering free shipping for orders over $99 clearly gives the conditional statement *If the order is over $99 then you get free shipping.*

What is also implied but not stated is that you get free shipping *only if* the order is over $99. Assuming that no other promotions are given regarding shipping, which regularly costs $5.99, when you place an order for less than $99, you would have no reason to expect free shipping. Thus there is another conditional implied: *If there is free shipping then the order was over $99.*

Taken together, we can see that the free shipping promotion amounts to the statement: Free shipping occurs if and only if the order is over $99; otherwise, it will cost $5.99.

10.2 Excel's IF Function

OBJECTIVE 1 Use IF-THEN-ELSE Syntax

OBJECTIVE 2 Explore Nested IF Functions

OBJECTIVE 1 Use IF-THEN-ELSE Syntax

The free shipping example illustrates what is called a **piecewise function**, where the output consists of two possible functions (free or regular shipping) determined by a criterion (order > $99). Excel has a built-in **IF function** that allows for piecewise functions, depending on the truth value of the criterion.

Example 4 | Use the IF Function

VIDEO *IF Shipping*

Retailers often offer free shipping if you order more than a specified amount, such as $99. Create a spreadsheet that outputs the shipping as free if an order is over $99, else it is $5.99.

$$\text{shipping} = \begin{cases} \$0 & \text{order} > \$99 \\ \$5.99 & \text{order} \le \$99 \end{cases}$$

SOLUTION The criterion in this example is whether the order is over $99. We create a spreadsheet that has a cell for the cost of the order and one for shipping. In **Figure 10.2** on the next screen we have the order amount in cell **B1** and the shipping in cell **B2**.

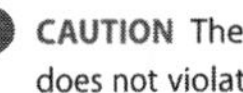

CAUTION The **IF** function is a piecewise function, making it appear to have two outputs. This does not violate the definition of a function because for every order amount there is one and only one shipping cost. ●

The first argument of the **IF** function will be the criterion, called a *logical test*, because it is either true or false (over \$99 or not). In **Figure 10.2** we have entered the logical test in **D2**, **=B1** > 99. Notice that this formula returns the value FALSE because the order is *not* greater than \$99.

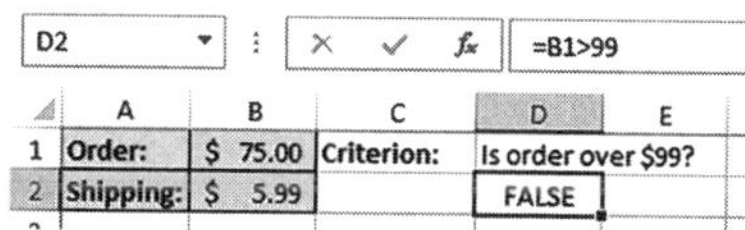

D2 =B1>99

	A	B	C	D	E
1	Order:	\$ 75.00	Criterion:	Is order over \$99?	
2	Shipping:	\$ 5.99		FALSE	

FIGURE 10.2 Free Shipping Logical Test

It is important to understand that the value of a logical test is TRUE or FALSE, as shown in **Figure 10.2**. The **IF function** we enter for the shipping costs begins with evaluating the logical test:

$$= \text{IF}(\text{Order} > \$99, \text{THEN charge } \$0, \text{ELSE charge } \$5.99)$$

Depending on the truth value of the logical test, the function will output 0 or 5.99; the actual syntax is shown in **Figure 10.3**

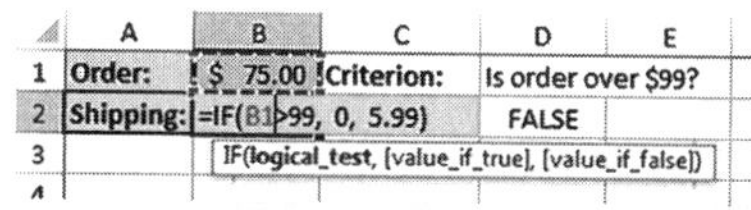

	A	B	C	D	E
1	Order:	\$ 75.00	Criterion:	Is order over \$99?	
2	Shipping:	=IF(B1>99, 0, 5.99)		FALSE	
3		IF(logical_test, [value_if_true], [value_if_false])			

FIGURE 10.3 Free Shipping IF Function

SPREADSHEET TUTORIALS Entering Numbers Using Arithmetic Operators Formatting Financial Numbers Using the IF Function

Let's look at another example that involves running your own business.

Example 5 Use the IF Function

VIDEO *IF Candles*

You run a business making candles and offer customers a 20% discount on their order if they order 20 or more candles. Create a spreadsheet that has a cell for the logical test, Order >= 20, and uses the **IF** function to compute the total cost of the order if a single candle costs \$2.50.

SOLUTION We can create a spreadsheet as in Example 4. Our piecewise function now is based on the criterion of the order being greater than or equal to 20:

$$\text{Price per Candle}\begin{cases} 80\% \cdot \$2.50 & \text{order} \geq 20 \\ \$2.50 & \text{order} < 20 \end{cases}$$

Figure 10.4 shows the formula for the price of a candle as 80% of \$2.50 if the order is 20 or more candles.

Note that a 20% discount means you are charged 80% of the full price.

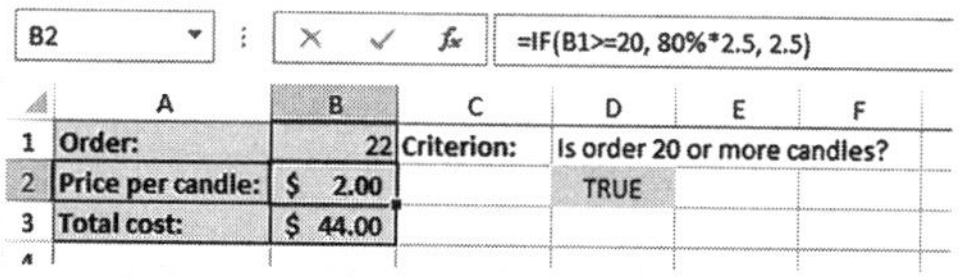

B2 =IF(B1>=20, 80%*2.5, 2.5)

	A	B	C	D	E	F
1	Order:	22	Criterion:	Is order 20 or more candles?		
2	Price per candle:	\$ 2.00		TRUE		
3	Total cost:	\$ 44.00				

FIGURE 10.4 Candle Order

We compute the total cost of the order in cell **B3** using the formula =**B2*B1**. Note that we could have just computed the total cost in the **IF** function, using the formula =**IF(B1** > = 20, 80%* 2.5***B1**, 2.5***B1**), but chose to compute price per candle first to break the problem into simpler steps. **Table 10.2** gives the symbols used by Excel for inequalities in logical tests.

TABLE 10.2 Symbols for Logical Tests

<	less than
>	greater than
<=	less than or equal to
>=	greater than or equal to
<>	does not equal

SPREADSHEET TUTORIALS Entering Numbers Using Arithmetic Operators Formatting Financial Numbers Using the IF Function

OBJECTIVE 2 Explore Nested IF Functions

The previous two examples illustrate using the **IF function** to handle two possible outputs in a piecewise function. Using a tree diagram can help keep track of the outputs.

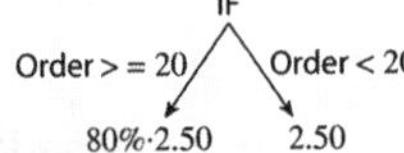

FIGURE 10.5 Candle Order Tree Diagram

We can handle more than two outputs by using nested **IF** functions.

Example 6 | Use Nested IF Functions

VIDEO Nested IF Candles

Your candle company has four possible discounts, based on the number of candles ordered, as shown in **Table 10.3**. Create a spreadsheet using nested **IF** functions to handle the four possible outputs of price per candle.

TABLE 10.3 Candle Order Discounts

No. Candles Ordered	Discount
1–9	0%
10–19	10%
20–49	20%
50 or more	30%

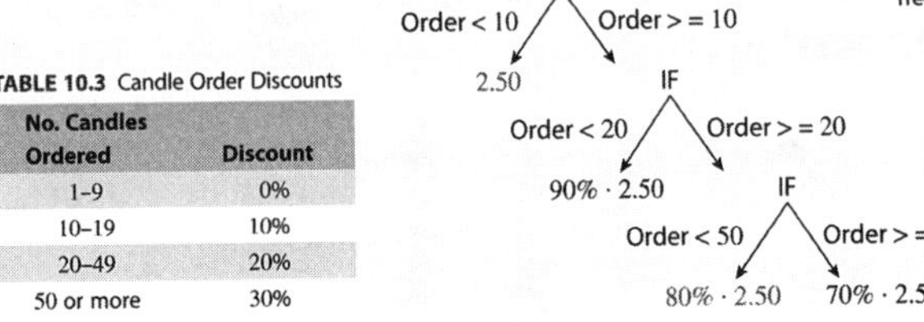

FIGURE 10.6 Nested **IF** Candle Order Tree Diagram

Not that the criterion Order < 20 also implies greater than or equal to 10. The only way to get to this branch on the tree is to first travel down the Order ≥ 10 branch.

SOLUTION The tree diagram in **Figure 10.6** breaks down the possible outputs.

Figure 10.6 illustrates why tree diagrams can assist in tracking all the possible outputs. Note that the right branch represents the ELSE option in the IF-THEN-ELSE format; with more than two possible outputs, this third ELSE option becomes another **IF function**, as shown in **Figure 10.7.**

CAUTION You must apply criteria in order; starting with Order < 50 will not work. •

	A	B	C	D	E	F	G
1	Order:	22					
2	Price per candle:	=IF(B1<10, 2.5, IF(B1<20, 90%*2.5,IF(B1<50, 80%*2.5,70%*2.5)))					
3	Total cost:	$ 44.00					
4			Hypotheses:	Order < 10?	FALSE		
5				Order < 20?	FALSE		
6				Order < 50?	TRUE		
7				Order >= 50?	FALSE		
8							

FIGURE 10.7 Nested IF functions

Note that the fourth criterion, Order > = 50, is unnecessary. It will always have the opposite truth value of the third criterion, Order < 50. Thus we only need three **IF** functions.

CAUTION! There are four possible outputs but only three **IF** functions. The third **IF** function handles the third and fourth outputs, as shown in **Figure 10.7.** •

You may be excited to learn that Excel can handle any number of possible outcomes, but you may also be sobered by the fact that nesting **IF** functions gets very cumbersome. To handle more than two or three outcomes, we will almost always use the **VLOOKUP** function. We will enter a table similar to **Table 10.3** and then instruct Excel to *look up* the order size in the table and take the value from the second column as the output.

SPREADSHEET TUTORIALS Entering Numbers | Using Arithmetic Operators | Formatting Financial Numbers | Using the IF Function

10.3 VLOOKUP

OBJECTIVE 1 Understand VLOOKUP Syntax

OBJECTIVE 2 Use AND, OR, and NOT

OBJECTIVE 1 Understand VLOOKUP Syntax

Instead of using nested **IF** functions to solve Example 6, it is much more efficient to use **Table 10.3** and the **VLOOKUP function.**

Example 7 Use VLOOKUP

VIDEO *VLOOKUP Candles*

Your candle company has four possible discounts, based on the number of candles ordered, as shown in **Table 10.3**. Create a spreadsheet using the **VLOOKUP** function to handle the four possible outputs of price per candle.

SOLUTION In order to use the **VLOOKUP** function, we must first enter the table into Excel. Notice that we have ranges for the size of the order. Excel cannot "read" a range, so we need to enter the left endpoint for each interval, just as we did for the binned data when creating histograms in Chapter 1. **Table 10.4** shows how the table must be formatted for use in Excel.

TABLE 10.4 Candle Order Discounts, Formatted for Excel

No. Candles Ordered	Left Endpoints	Discount
1–9	1	0%
10–19	10	10%
20–49	20	20%
50 or more	50	30%

We can enter this table into Excel and then use **VLOOKUP**, which has three arguments:

= **VLOOKUP** (Lookup this Value, in this Table, get Output from this Column)

The first two arguments, as shown in **Figure 10.8**, are self-explanatory: We want to look up the size of the order in the table in cells **A7:B10**. The order is an input cell, and any value may be input into cell **B1**. The third argument, *col_index_num*, requires care; it is the number of the column that you want for your output from the **VLOOKUP** function. In this case, we want to find the discount factor in *column 2*, so we enter *2* for the third argument.

CAUTION Excel always looks in the first column of the table for the lookup value. Remember that 10 in the first column stands for the range 10–19. ●

FIGURE 10.8 Using **VLOOKUP**

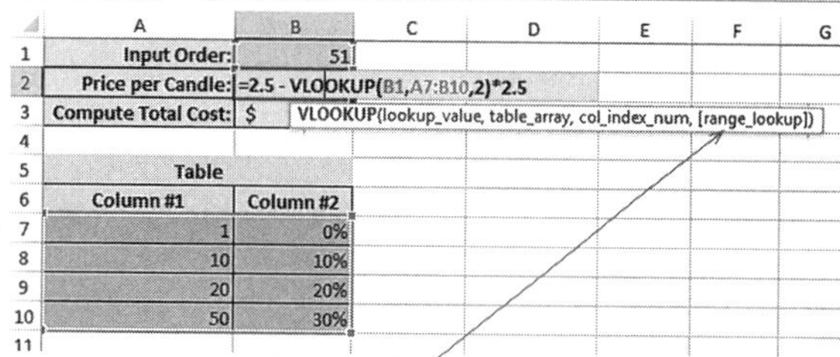

Note that there is a fourth argument, *range_lookup*, which is optional. If it is omitted, Excel will look for the ***value in a range*** given by the left endpoints in *column 1*; if you enter FALSE for this fourth argument, Excel will look for an ***exact match*** in *column 1*.

Note that the **VLOOKUP** function is giving the discount percentage. To compute the price per candle, we multiply this by $2.50 and subtract from $2.50. Watch the video to see how this spreadsheet works: Simply enter any order, and **VLOOKUP** will find the correct discount percentage in the table.

SPREADSHEET TUTORIALS Entering Numbers | Entering Data by Range | Using Arithmetic Operators | Using Merge and Center and Applying Cell Styles | Formatting Financial Numbers | Formatting Cells with Percent Style | Using the IF Function | Inserting VLOOKUP

Besides values, we can also look up words using **VLOOKUP**. Setting the fourth argument to FALSE will cause Excel to look for an exact match (which is useful for phone numbers and addresses), and alphabetical ordering is used if the fourth argument is omitted.

Example 8 | Look Up a Name

VIDEO *VLOOKUP Names*

You are overseeing testing of students who have been assigned room numbers by their last name, according to the chart in **Table 10.5**. Create a spreadsheet that looks up a student's last name and gives his or her room number.

SOLUTION Now the left endpoint will be a letter, and when you omit the fourth argument, Excel will search for a given name alphabetically, as in **Figure 10.9**. This may seem silly to you since we can just look at the table and determine what room someone is in. But imagine that you have to automatically generate room numbers for thousands of students; in such a case having a formula to fill down is a huge time saver (just remember your proper absolute/mixed cell references). Watch the video to see how this works.

TABLE 10.5 Room Assignments

First Letter of Last Name	Room Number
A – D	143
E – H	217
I – N	118
O – S	314
T – Z	223

FIGURE 10.9 Using **VLOOKUP** with Alphabetical Ordering

E2 =VLOOKUP(E1,A3:B7,2)

	A	B	C	D	E	F
1	Table			Name:	Johnson	
2	Column #1	Column #2		Room:	Room 118	
3	A	Room 143				
4	E	Room 217				
5	I	Room 118				
6	O	Room 314				
7	T	Room 223				

CAUTION Excel always looks in the first column in the table for the lookup value. ●

SPREADSHEET TUTORIALS Entering Numbers | Entering Data by Range | Using Merge and Center and Applying Cell Styles | Inserting VLOOKUP

The next example will require an exact match, so the optional fourth argument must be set to FALSE.

Example 9 | Lookup a Grade

Create a spreadsheet that looks up a letter grade and returns the numerical value from the four-point scale.

SOLUTION **Figure 10.10** shows the typical four-point scale. Note that the **VLOOKUP function** entered in cell **E2** has the optional fourth argument set to FALSE, requiring an exact match for looking up the grade value. If you do not set this to FALSE, Excel will return 3.67 for the grade B-. This is because B- comes after A- but before B+, in the symbolic ordering scheme used by Excel.

E2 =VLOOKUP(E1,A1:B11,2,FALSE)

	A	B	C	D	E	F	G
1	A	4		Grade:	B-		
2	A-	3.67		4-pt. scale:	2.67		
3	B+	3.33					
4	B	3					
5	B-	2.67					
6	C+	2.33					
7	C	2					
8	C-	1.67					
9	D+	1.33					
10	D	1					
11	F	0					

FIGURE 10.10 Using **VLOOKUP** with Exact Match Required

CAUTION The fourth argument must be set to FALSE in order to get an exact match. ●

Remember that using **VLOOKUP** applies the logic principles studied at the beginning of the chapter. **VLOOKUP** is used in place of complicated nested **IF** functions.

SPREADSHEET TUTORIALS Entering Numbers | Entering Data by Range | Using Merge and Center and Applying Cell Styles | Inserting VLOOKUP

OBJECTIVE 2 Use AND, OR, and NOT

There may be times when you want to test for multiple criteria at once. To allow you to do this, Excel has additional logic **functions AND**, **OR**, and **NOT**, which can be used to make compound logical tests.

Example 10 **Purchase Hotel and Airfare OR Car and Airfare**

VIDEO *Use AND, OR, NOT*

Expedia is offering a deal: 20% off your purchase if, when you book airfare, you also book either a hotel or a car (or both). Create a spreadsheet that allows you to enter the price of airfare, hotel, and car rental. If airfare and hotel are both purchased, or airfare and car are both purchased, take 20% off of the whole package price.

SOLUTION This is a complicated problem, so we will break it down into manageable pieces. First, we need to introduce the logic functions **AND** and **OR**. In **Figure 10.11** we have named cells **B2**, **B3**, and **B4** *Hotel*, *Air* and *Car*, respectively.

The formula =**AND**(Air $>$ 0, Car $>$ 0) will be true only if both inequalities are true. Similarly, for the formula in cell D2 for hotel and air, =**AND**(Hotel $>$ 0, Air $>$ 0).

CAUTION Note the strange syntax, **AND** is out front, not between the two inequalities. ●

	A	B	C	D	E	F	G
1	Costs		Logical Tests				
2	Hotel:	$ 480.00	Hotel&Air:	TRUE			
3	Airfare:	$ 555.00	Car&Air:	=AND(Air>0,Car>0)			
4	Car:	$ -	D2 OR D3:	AND(logical1, [logical2], [logical3], ...)			
5	Discount %:	20%					
6	SubTotal:	$1,035.00					
7	Discount:	$ 207.00					
8	Total:	$ 828.00					

FIGURE 10.11 Using **AND**

SPREADSHEET TUTORIALS Entering Numbers Entering Data by Range Using Arithmetic Operators Using Merge and Center and Applying Cell Styles Formatting Financial Numbers Formatting Cells with Percent Style Using the IF Function Inserting VLOOKUP Defining a Name Using Define Names in Formula

We will get the 20% discount if either of the two **AND functions** is TRUE. Thus cell **D4** contains the formula =**OR**(**D2**, **D3**), which will be TRUE as long as one or both of **D2** and **D3** are TRUE.

The formula for the discount is now a straightforward **IF** function:

$$= \text{IF}(\mathbf{D4}, 20\%, 0\%)$$

Remember that cell **D4** contains a logical test, which is why we can use it as the first argument in the **IF** function. The subtotal is a sum of all three cells, and the discount and total are straightforward arithmetic.

CAUTION Cell **D4** contains a logical test, so its value is TRUE or FALSE and thus can be used as the first argument for an **IF** function. ●

CAUTION The word "or" is often used as an "exclusive or", as in *I will go jogging or play golf at 4 PM.* The implication here is one or the other, but not both. The **OR** function is not exclusive; it means one or the other or both. ●

> Note that an **AND** function will be TRUE only if all of its arguments (which are logical tests) are TRUE. An **OR** function will be FALSE only if all of its arguments (which are all logical tests) are FALSE. The **NOT** function will simply output the opposite truth value of whatever logical test is its argument; for example, =NOT(D4) will be FALSE.

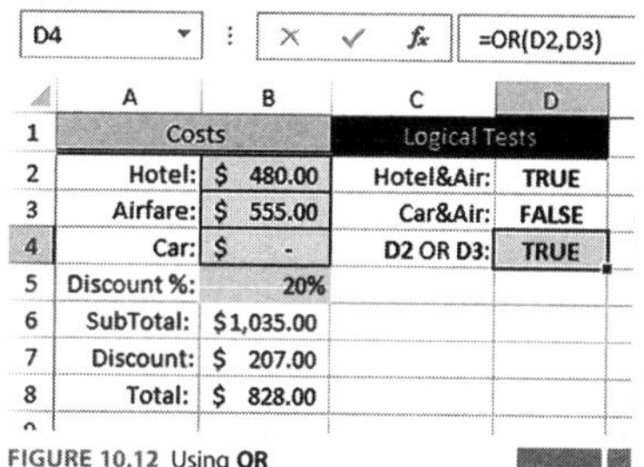

	A	B	C	D
1	Costs		Logical Tests	
2	Hotel:	$ 480.00	Hotel&Air:	TRUE
3	Airfare:	$ 555.00	Car&Air:	FALSE
4	Car:	$ -	D2 OR D3:	TRUE
5	Discount %:	20%		
6	SubTotal:	$1,035.00		
7	Discount:	$ 207.00		
8	Total:	$ 828.00		

FIGURE 10.12 Using **OR**

SPREADSHEET TUTORIALS Entering Numbers Entering Data by Range Using Arithmetic Operators Using Merge and Center and Applying Cell Styles Formatting Financial Numbers Formatting Cells with Percent Style Using the IF Function Inserting VLOOKUP Defining a Name Using Define Names in Formula

Here's a last candle example, utilizing the logic functions just discussed.

Example 11 **Sell Candle Varieties**

VIDEO *Candle Varieties*

Your candle business is booming, so you decide to offer four sizes (Mini, Maxi, Venti, Grande) and three shapes (Cylinder, Cube, Yoda-shaped). The prices are shown in **Table 10.6**. Create a spreadsheet that accepts an input for size and an input for shape and outputs the correct price.

TABLE 10.6 Candle Pricing

	A	B	C	D
1		Shape		
2	Size	Cylinder	Cube	Yoda
3	Mini	$ 2.50	$ 3.25	$ 9.00
4	Maxi	$ 4.50	$ 5.50	$ 12.50
5	Venti	$ 6.00	$ 8.00	$ 20.00
6	Grande	$ 7.50	$ 10.00	$ 32.00

SOLUTION You may be tempted to use 11 nested **IF functions** and logical tests using **AND**, such as Mini AND Cylinder. Hopefully you realize that there is a better way, using **VLOOKUP**. Once again, we will break the problem into manageable steps. We would like to look up a given size in the table and output the price from the correct column. This is problematic because there are three possible price columns. Remember that there are four columns total and that Excel always looks in the first column of the table for the lookup value. **Figure 10.13** shows the spreadsheet. We have named cells **G2** and **G3** *size* and *shape*, respectively, so our formulas will be easier to read.

Name box: size | Formula bar: Venti

	A	B	C	D	E	F	G
1		Shape				Order Form	
2	Size	Cylinder	Cube	Yoda		Size:	Venti
3	Mini	$ 2.50	$ 3.25	$ 9.00		Shape:	Yoda
4	Maxi	$ 4.50	$ 5.50	$ 12.50		Column #:	4
5	Venti	$ 6.00	$ 8.00	$ 20.00		Price:	$ 20.00
6	Grande	$ 7.50	$ 10.00	$ 32.00			

Note that cell **G2** has been named *size*, as displayed in the name box. We can type the word "size" into a formula instead of using the cell reference G2.

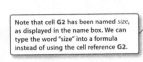

FIGURE 10.13 Candle Pricing Order Form

SPREADSHEET TUTORIALS Entering Numbers | Entering Data by Range | Using Arithmetic Operators | Using Merge and Center and Applying Cell Styles | Formatting Financial Numbers | Formatting Cells with Percent Style | Using the IF Function | Inserting VLOOKUP | Defining a Name | Using Define Names in Formula

We have taken an intermediate step of finding the column number (and naming cell **G4** *col_num*) before trying to type in the **VLOOKUP function.** Note how we can set **shape** equal to cells **B2** and **C2**; we could have used **shape** = "Cylinder," and **shape** = "Cube," but this is unnecessary and could lead to a typo.

	A	B	C	D	E	F	G	H	I	J
1			Shape			Order Form				
2	Size	Cylinder	Cube	Yoda		Size:	Venti			
3	Mini	$ 2.50	$ 3.25	$ 9.00		Shape:	Yoda			
4	Maxi	$ 4.50	$ 5.50	$ 12.50		Column #:	=IF(shape=B2, 2, IF(shape=C2, 3, 4))			
5	Venti	$ 6.00	$ 8.00	$ 20.00		Price:	IF(logical_test, [value_if_true], [value_if_false])			
6	Grande	$ 7.50	$ 10.00	$ 32.00						

FIGURE 10.14 Candle Pricing Order Form Column #

Now that we have the correct column number, the **VLOOKUP** is simple. Remember that cells **G2** and **G3** are input cells—you type in the size and shape—and have been named *size* and *shape*, respectively, so these names rather than the cell references appear in the formula.

	A	B	C	D	E	F	G	H	I	J	K	L
1			Shape			Order Form						
2	Size	Cylinder	Cube	Yoda		Size:	Venti					
3	Mini	$ 2.50	$ 3.25	$ 9.00		Shape:	Yoda					
4	Maxi	$ 4.50	$ 5.50	$ 12.50		Column #:	4					
5	Venti	$ 6.00	$ 8.00	$ 20.00		Price:	=VLOOKUP(size, A3:D6, col_num, FALSE)					
6	Grande	$ 7.50	$ 10.00	$ 32.00			VLOOKUP(lookup_value, table_array, col_index_num, [range_lookup])					

FIGURE 10.15 Candle Pricing Order Form Price

We need the optional fourth argument to make sure a typo in the input does not give an incorrect price. Therefore, anything entered that does not match a size or shape will result in **#N/A**, which tells you the answer is not available.

SPREADSHEET TUTORIALS Entering Numbers | Entering Data by Range | Using Arithmetic Operators | Using Merge and Center and Applying Cell Styles | Formatting Financial Numbers | Formatting Cells with Percent Style | Using the IF Function | Inserting VLOOKUP | Defining a Name | Using Define Names in Formula

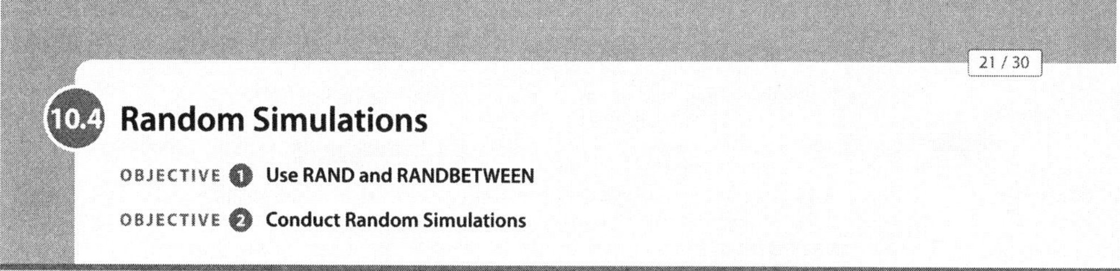

10.4 Random Simulations

OBJECTIVE 1 Use RAND and RANDBETWEEN

OBJECTIVE 2 Conduct Random Simulations

OBJECTIVE 1 Use RAND and RANDBETWEEN

The logic **functions** studied in this chapter open up a new range of problems that have more than one output, based on evaluating criteria. We will finish the chapter with a powerful application of these new tools, modeling real-world phenomena using random simulations. The idea is to use a random number generator, either **RAND** or **RANDBETWEEN**, and **VLOOKUP** to randomly choose possibilities such as possible stock returns or gas prices. First, we must introduce the **RAND** function, which generates a random number between zero and one:

CAUTION The **RAND** function does not have any arguments but requires the open and close parentheses. ●

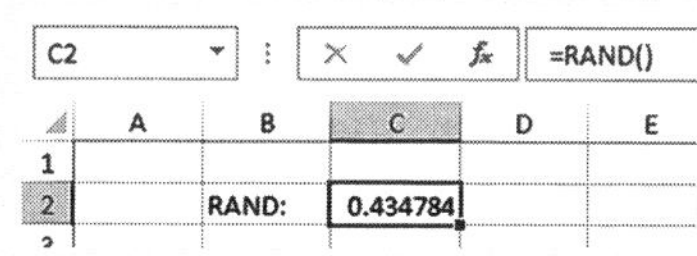

FIGURE 10.16 RAND function

Typing =**RAND**() into Microsoft Word or PowerPoint and pressing Enter gives a random surprise.

Example 12 Simulate Rolling a Die

VIDEO
Rolling Dice

Create a spreadsheet that simulates rolling a single die, using three different approaches: **IF**, **VLOOKUP**, and **RANDBETWEEN**.

SOLUTION There are six possible outcomes, so we need five nested **IF functions**, as in **Figure 10.17**:

	A	B	C	D	E	F	G	H	I
1	RAND:	0.823046							
2	Die #1:	=IF(B1<1/6, 1, IF(B1<2/6, 2, IF(B1<3/6, 3, IF(B1<4/6, 4, IF(B1<5/6, 5, 6)))))							
3		IF(logical_test, [value_if_true], [value_if_false])							
4									

Press F9 (or the **Command** and = keys on Mac) to recalculate all formulas, including **RAND**. Any time you enter anything into the spreadsheet, Excel automatically recalculates all formulas.

FIGURE 10.17 Rolling a Die Using **IF**

CAUTION You must create a separate cell for the random number. If you use **RAND()**<1/6, **RAND()**<2/6, etc., you will get a different random number for each **RAND()**, and your die will not be fair. ●

Instead of using nested **IF** functions, we can use a **VLOOKUP** with a table, as in **Figure 10.18**:

	A	B	C	D	E	F	G	H	I	J	K	L	M
1	RAND:	0.581291		Table			RAND:	0.011815					
2	Die #1:	4		Interval	Left Endpoints	Die	Die #2:	=VLOOKUP(H1,E3:F8,2)					
3				0 .. 1/6	0.000	1		VLOOKUP(lookup_value, table_array, col_index_num, [range_lookup])					
4				1/6 .. 2/6	0.167	2							
5				2/6 .. 3/6	0.333	3							
6				3/6 .. 4/6	0.500	4							
7				4/6 .. 5/6	0.667	5							
8				5/6 .. 1	0.833	6							

FIGURE 10.18 Rolling a Die Using **VLOOKUP**

Finally, we could just type in = **RANDBETWEEN** (1,6), which will generate a random integer between one and six, including the endpoints.

SPREADSHEET TUTORIALS Entering Numbers | Entering Data by Range | Using Arithmetic Operators | Using Merge and Center and Applying Cell Styles | Using the IF Function | Inserting VLOOKUP

OBJECTIVE 2 Conduct Random Simulations

So now that we can roll a die, we can simulate investment returns for retirement.

Example 13 Simulate Retirement Withdrawals

VIDEO
Random Simulation

Recall Example 1 from Chapter 9, which modeled a **retirement account** starting with $1,000,000 and an annual withdrawal rate starting at 4% (i.e., $40,000), with the withdrawal amount growing by the **inflation rate** of 3% each year. We also assumed that the remaining principal would grow by 6% each year. Create a random simulation where the **rate of return** can fluctuate between −9% and 21%.

H3 =G3*(1+$B$4)

	A	B	C	D	E	F	G	H
1	Initial Savings	$ 1,000,000		Year	Balance	Withdrawal	New Balance	End Balance
2	Withdrawal Rate	4%		1	$1,000,000	$ 40,000	$ 960,000	$ 1,017,600
3	Inflation Rate	3%		2	$1,017,600	$ 41,200	$ 976,400	$ 1,034,984
4	Rate of Return	6%		3	$1,034,984	$ 42,436	$ 992,548	$ 1,052,101
5				4	$1,052,101	$ 43,709	$ 1,008,392	$ 1,068,895
6				5	$1,068,895	$ 45,020	$ 1,023,875	$ 1,085,307
38				37	$ 728,703	$ 115,931	$ 612,771	$ 649,538
39				38	$ 649,538	$ 119,409	$ 530,129	$ 561,936
40				39	$ 561,936	$ 122,991	$ 438,945	$ 465,282
41				40	$ 465,282	$ 126,681	$ 338,601	$ 358,917

Note that assuming a constant rate of 6% left us with $358,917 remaining in the account after 40 years.

FIGURE 10.19 Retirement Scenario

SPREADSHEET TUTORIALS Entering Data by Range | Entering Numbers | Copying a Formula Using the Fill Handle | Constructing a Formula and Using the SUM Function | Using Arithmetic Operators | Formatting Financial Numbers | Using Format Painter | Using Merge and Center and Applying Cell Styles | Moving Data and Resolving ####Error | Projecting Income and Expenses by Filling Formulas | Using a Data Table to Calculate Options using What If Analysis

SOLUTION We will add a new column to the spreadsheet in **Figure 10.20**, which generates a random **rate of return** between −9% and 21% inclusive, using =**RANDBETWEEN**(−9, 21)/100. The ending balance then grows or decays, using this rate of return. Recall that #### means the number is too large to be displayed so the column needs to be widened, and that the simulation ends once the End Balance becomes negative.

H2 =RANDBETWEEN(-9,21)/100

	A	B	C	D	E	F	G	H	I
1	Initial Savings	$ 1,000,000		Year	Balance	Withdrawal	New Balance	Rate of return	End Balance
2	Withdrawal Rate	4%		1	$1,000,000	$ 40,000	$ 960,000	-6%	$ 902,400
3	Inflation Rate	3%		2	$ 902,400	$ 41,200	$ 861,200	11%	$ 955,932
4	Rate of Return	6%		3	$ 955,932	$ 42,436	$ 913,496	-3%	$ 886,091
40				39	#########	$ 122,991	$ (1,562,792)	10%	$ (1,719,071)
41				40	#########	$ 126,681	$ (1,845,752)	9%	$ (2,011,870)

FIGURE 10.20 Retirement Scenario with Random Rate of Return

Figure 10.20 shows that you may end up running out of money much sooner than 40 years, while **Figure 10.21** shows you may end up with much more money than you started with. Investing where gains/losses can fluctuate so widely is very risky!

H2 =RANDBETWEEN(-9,21)/100

	A	B	C	D	E	F	G	H	I
1	Initial Savings	$ 1,000,000		Year	Balance	Withdrawal	New Balance	Rate of return	End Balance
2	Withdrawal Rate	4%		1	$1,000,000	$ 40,000	$ 960,000	19%	$ 1,142,400
3	Inflation Rate	3%		2	$1,142,400	$ 41,200	$ 1,101,200	8%	$ 1,189,296
4	Rate of Return	6%		3	$1,189,296	$ 42,436	$ 1,146,860	9%	$ 1,250,077
40				39	$3,730,943	$ 122,991	$ 3,607,952	13%	$ 4,076,986
41				40	$4,076,986	$ 126,681	$ 3,950,304	6%	$ 4,187,323

FIGURE 10.21 Retirement Scenario with Random Rate of Return, Version 2

SPREADSHEET TUTORIALS Entering Data by Range | Entering Numbers | Copying a Formula Using the Fill Handle | Constructing a Formula and Using the SUM Function | Using Arithmetic Operators | Formatting Financial Numbers | Using Format Painter | Using Merge and Center and Applying Cell Styles | Moving Data and Resolving ####Error | Projecting Income and Expenses by Filling Formulas | Using a Data Table to Calculate Options using What If Analysis

Figure 10.22 shows the result of running this simulation many times with 3 representative instances plotted together (chosen to represent high, low, and middle values). You can press the **F9** key to recalculate all the formulas in the spreadsheet (or the **Command** and = keys on a Mac). This has the effect of recalculating all the random numbers and hence running the simulation again. Notice that the amount left in your **retirement account** after 40 years is highly variable; you should utilize your statistical knowledge to analyze this variability and generate insights into this retirement model.

Note that we are assuming −9% and 21% are just as likely to happen as 6%. Do you think this assumption makes sense?

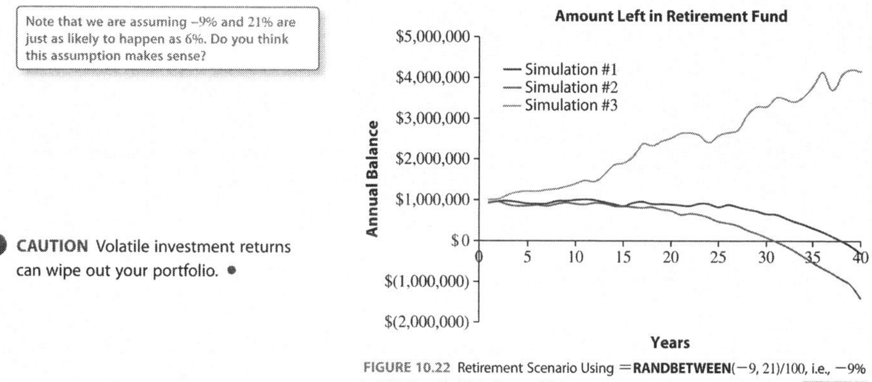

FIGURE 10.22 Retirement Scenario Using =**RANDBETWEEN**(−9, 21)/100, i.e., −9% to 21%, Equally Likely Rates of Return

CAUTION Volatile investment returns can wipe out your portfolio. ●

Example 13 showed extreme possible outcomes because the **rates of return** from –9% to 21% were all equally likely. In practice, the distribution of returns would not be so uniform but more like a **normal distribution**—that is, we would be much more likely to get a value in the middle, around 6%, and much less likely to get a return out near the extreme values of –9% and 21%.

Example 14 Simulate Retirement Withdrawals, Version 2

VIDEO *Random Simulation VLOOKUP*

Re-create a random simulation for the retirement model in Example 13, where the rate of return can fluctuate between −9% and 21%, but this time make getting a rate of return in the middle of the range more likely.

SOLUTION We are given a lot of leeway in creating this model, so we have to make some assumptions about what "getting a rate of return in the middle of the range more likely" actually means in practice. Notice that our range from −9% to 21% can be split up into sixths. Let's assume, as in **Table 10.7**, that there is a 5% chance of getting a rate of return from −9% to −4%, a 10% chance of getting a rate of return from −4% to 1%, a 35% chance from 1% to 6%, a 35% chance from 6% to 11%, a 10% chance from 11% to 16%, and a 5% chance from 16% to 21%.

TABLE 10.7 Random Rates of Returns

5%	–9%...–4%
10%	–4%...1%
35%	1%...6%
35%	6%...11%
10%	11%...16%
5%	16%...21%

Note that these probabilities simulate a normal type of distribution; it's more likely to get a value in the middle and less likely to get a value in the tails. Also note that the probabilities must sum to 100%.

To simulate these possible **rates of return**, we will look up a random number by using **VLOOKUP** and **RAND**. Recall that **RAND** gives a number between 0 and 1—that is, 0% and 100%. We will first turn the probabilities in **Table 10.7** into intervals and endpoints, as shown in **Table 10.8**, where the width of each interval equals the probability.

So now we have the left endpoints necessary for a table involving **VLOOKUP**. We have to generate a random rate of return for each row in the table, which is a perfect job for **RANDBETWEEN**. We will generate a table of rates of return for each of the 40 years in the model. Each year will have a possible rate of return for each interval in **Table 10.8**. Then we will use **VLOOKUP** to look up a random rate of return for each year.

TABLE 10.8 Random Rate of Returns Table for **VLOOKUP**

Probability	Interval	Left Endpoint	Rate of Return
5%	0%...5%	0	–9%...–4%
10%	5%...15%	0.05	–4%...1%
35%	15%...50%	0.15	1%...6%
35%	50%...85%	0.50	6%...11%
10%	85%...95%	0.85	11%...16%
5%	95%...100%	0.95	16%...21%

CAUTION We need to transform **Table 10.7** into a table that can be used with **VLOOKUP**. •

We are ready to enter **Table 10.8** into our spreadsheet, as shown in **Table 10.9**. The left endpoints are identical and will form *Column 1* in the table. *Columns 2* through *41* correspond to *Year 1* through *Year 40*. The rate of return for each row is given by the appropriate **RANDBETWEEN** function. The interval starting at 0.00 has a rate between −9% and −4%, so the function is =**RANDBETWEEN**(−9, −4)/100. The next row will have =**RANDBETWEEN** (−4, 1)/100, etc. We can fill across these formulas for each of the 40 years and then format the results as percentages.

CAUTION Notice that the column number is one more than the year number. ●

TABLE 10.9 Rates of Return Using **RANDBETWEEN**

K	L	M	N	O	P	Q
Table	Rates of Return					
Column #1	Col. #2	Col. #3	Col. #4	Col. #5	Col. #6	Col. #7
Left Endpoints	Year 1	Year 2	Year 3	Year 4	Year 5	Year 6
0.00	=RANDBETWEEN(-9,-4)/100			-7%	-5%	-7%
0.05	RANDBETWEEN(bottom, top)		%	-2%	-1%	-1%
0.15	1%	3%	5%	5%	4%	3%
0.50	7%	10%	11%	6%	8%	10%
0.85	15%	14%	14%	13%	15%	14%
0.95	21%	21%	21%	18%	18%	16%

Now that our table is ready, we can enter the appropriate **VLOOKUP** function in the *Rate of Return* column, as shown in **Figure 10.23**. Remember that the third argument will be the column number, which is one more than the year number.

Figure 10.23 displays the **VLOOKUP** function in cell **H2** that can be filled down. Notice that we are looking up a random number in *column 1* of the table in cells **K4:AY9** and returning a value from the column number that is one more than the year number (as we saw in **Table 10.9**).

D	E	F	G	H	I	J	K	L	M
Year	Balance	Withdrawal	New Balance	Rate of return	End Balance		Table	Rates of Return	
1	$1,000,000	$ 40,000	$ 960,000	=VLOOKUP(RAND(),$K$4:$AY$9,D2+1)				Col. #2	Col. #3
2	$ 988,800	$ 41,200	$ 947,600	VLOOKUP(lookup_value, table_array, col_index_num, [range_lookup])				Year 2	
3	$ 966,552	$ 42,436	$ 924,116	14%	$ 1,053,492		0.00	-8%	-4%
4	$1,053,492	$ 43,709	$ 1,009,783	12%	$ 1,130,957		0.05	0%	0%
5	$1,130,957	$ 45,020	$ 1,085,937	6%	$ 1,151,093		0.15	3%	2%
6	$1,151,093	$ 46,371	$ 1,104,722	14%	$ 1,259,383		0.50	9%	8%
7	$1,259,383	$ 47,762	$ 1,211,621	-6%	$ 1,138,924		0.85	12%	16%
8	$1,138,924	$ 49,195	$ 1,089,729	14%	$ 1,242,291		0.95	21%	20%

FIGURE 10.23 Retirement Scenario with Random Rate of Return, Version 3

You are now ready to run your simulation and see what happens to your million dollars. Pressing the **F9** key on a PC or **Command** and = on a Mac will regenerate all the random numbers in the model. Keep track of the amount of money after 40 years and see if you don't run out or maybe even gain.

The point of creating a model like this is to generate insights, not provide a "correct" answer. After seeing how the model responds to repeated simulations, you may wish to go back and change some assumptions.

Using a spreadsheet to provide such insights to what-if questions is powerful. Enjoy.

SPREADSHEET TUTORIALS Entering Data by Range | Entering Numbers | Copying a Formula Using the Fill Handle | Constructing a Formula and Using the SUM Function | Using Arithmetic Operators | Formatting Financial Numbers | Using Format Painter | Using Merge and Center and Applying Cell Styles | Moving Data and Resolving ####Error | Projecting Income and Expenses by Filling Formulas | Using a Data Table to Calculate Options using What If Analysis | Using the IF Function | Inserting VLOOKUP

Figure 10.24 shows the result of running this simulation many times with 3 representative instances plotted together (chosen to represent high, low, and middle values). Compare results to those in **Figure 10.22**. Notice that this model is less variable: It is still possible to get extreme ending balances, but they happen less frequently.

FIGURE 10.24 Retirement Scenario Using **VLOOKUP** with More Normal Distribution of Rates of Return, i.e., from −9% to 21% but More Likely in the Middle

Note that we are assuming that -9% and 21% are much less likely to occur than values in the middle, from 1% to 11%. Do you think this assumption is more realistic than the uniform distribution of probabilities in Example 13?

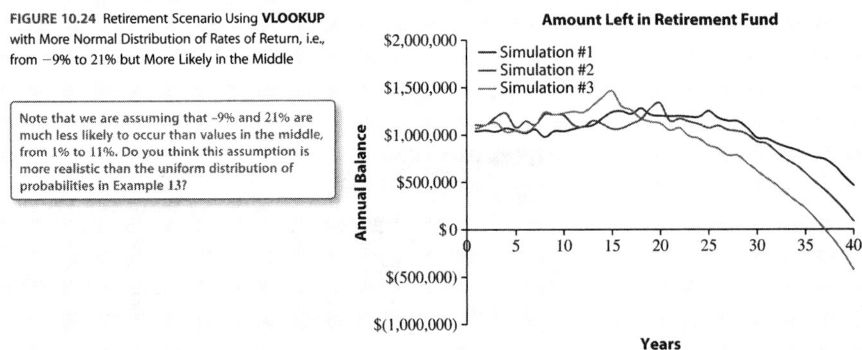

Creating models like this requires you to use all your quantitative reasoning capabilities, from percent change and statistical analysis to reasoning about assumptions made for the model. We hope this course has empowered you to embrace such quantitative analyses in your own life confidently. Best of luck.

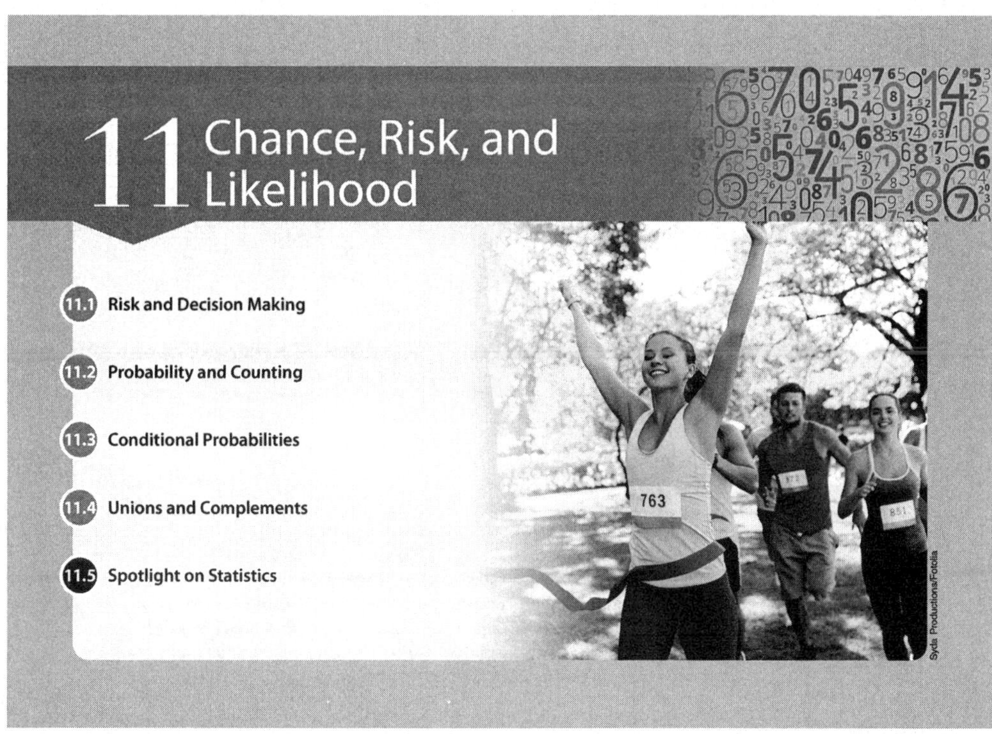

11-1

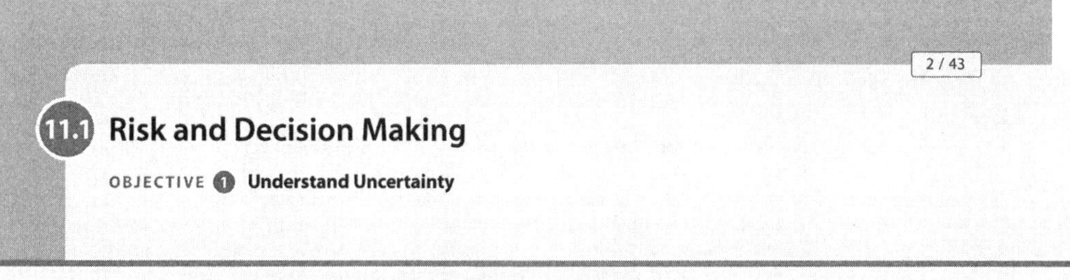

2 / 43
11.1 Risk and Decision Making
OBJECTIVE 1 Understand Uncertainty

OBJECTIVE 1 Understand Uncertainty

This text, *Thinking Quantitatively*, is dedicated to providing you with the quantitative skills needed for informed decision making in your personal, professional, and public life. Often we are faced with situations that involve **chance**, or have incomplete information resulting in **likelihoods** and **risk** assessment. To deal with uncertainty we need a firm grasp of **probability**, which is the focus of this chapter.

Example 1 | **Compare Risks from Smoking**

VIDEO *Smoking*

Use the risk chart given in **Table 11.1** from the excellent book *Know Your Chances* to compare the risk of dying from common diseases due to smoking and answer the following questions:

1. Who is more likely to die in the next 10 years from a heart attack: a 55-year-old man or woman?
2. By what factor does smoking increase the chance of a 55-year-old man or 55-year-old woman dying from lung cancer?

11-2

TABLE 11.1
Death Rates

			Vascular Disease		Cancer					Lung Disease		
Age	Sex	Smoking Status	Heart Attack	Stroke	Lung	Breast	Colon	Prostate	Ovarian	COPD	Accidents	All Causes
55	M	Never Smoked	19	3	1		3	2		1	5	74
55	**M**	**Smoker**	**41**	**7**	**34**		**3**	**1**		**7**	**4**	**178**
55	F	Never Smoked	8	2	2	6	2		2	1	2	55
55	**F**	**Smoker**	**20**	**6**	**26**	**5**	**2**		**2**	**9**	**2**	**110**

Note: Numbers given are deaths per 1,000 of each cohort over the next 10 years
Data from: Steve Woloshin Lisa Schwartz, and H. Gilbert Welch, "The Risk of Death by Age, Sex, and Smoking Status in the U.S.: Putting Health Risks in Context," *Journal of the National Cancer Institute* 100 (2008): 845–853

3. Does smoking cause heart attacks or minimize the **chance** of getting breast cancer?

4. Should you smoke?

Never smoked is defined as having smoked less than 100 cigarettes in lifetime, and *smoker* is defined as having smoked more than 100 cigarettes in lifetime and currently smoking.

SOLUTION

1. **Table 11.1** tells us that for 55-year-old men who have never smoked, 19 in 1,000 will die from a heart attack in the next 10 years while 41 in 1,000 55-year-old male smokers will die from a heart attack in the next 10 years. The rates for 55-year-old women are, respectively, 8 in 1,000 and 20 in 1,000. Therefore 55-year-old men are more likely to die from a heart attack than women whether they smoke or not.

2. For men the risk of dying increases from 1 in 1,000 to 34 in 1,000, or by a factor of 34; for women the rate increases from 2 to 26, or by a factor of 13.

3. This table is observational and does not indicate **causation**, just association (see Chapter 8 for more on **correlation** and causation). It may be that smokers have very poor diets with more meat and dairy, and don't exercise as much as non-smokers. Both diet and exercise could be true **confounding factors** with regard to heart disease. The fact that breast cancer death **rates** are lower for smokers than non-smokers, 5 in 1,000 versus 6 in 1,000, is due to the fact that female smokers have much higher deaths from all causes: 110 in 1,000 versus 55 in 1,000. Thus fewer smokers die from breast cancer; something else kills them first.

4. This is a personal question that only you can answer. To make an informed decision you must find and analyze the relevant data!

CAUTION The fact that some death rates decline for smokers does not indicate a benefit of smoking. It simply means many more smokers are dying from other causes. ●

The data in Example 1 clearly show negative effects from smoking, but it is important to remember that cigarette companies vehemently denied any connection between smoking and lung cancer for decades. Tobacco corporations waged a public relations war, casting doubt on scientific studies and even claiming cigarettes were good for you! This may seem ridiculous now, given the overall acceptance of the dangers of smoking, including bans on smoking in public spaces. Oddly enough, many Americans accept that smoking is bad for us, but believe that filling the air with smoke and greenhouse gases is somehow not bad for the environment and deny that our changing climate has anything to do with human (anthropogenic) behavior.

The Intergovernmental Panel on Climate Change (IPCC) issued its fifth assessment report (AR5) in 2014 and concluded that human greenhouse gas emissions "have been detected throughout the climate system and are *extremely likely* (95–100% certain) to have been the dominant cause of the observed warming since the midtwentieth century."

Note that the **cumulative CO_2 emissions graphic** on the right has error bars indicating *uncertainties* in these measurements, meaning the actual value could be anywhere from the bottom to the top of each bar. The IPCC scientists are careful to indicate the limits of their understanding and use the language of uncertainty and **likelihood** throughout.

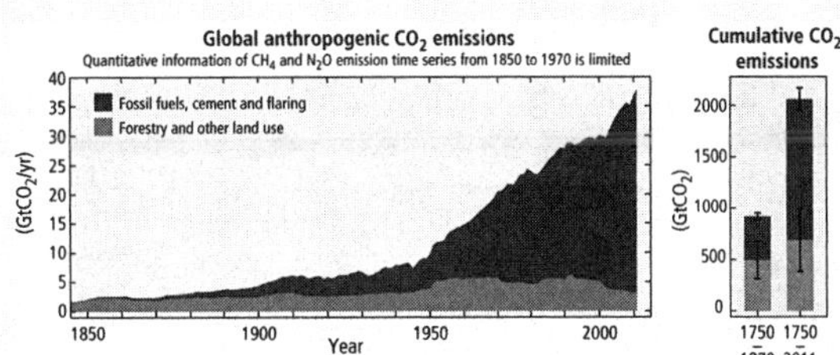

FIGURE 11.1 CO_2 Emissions from Human Sources 1850–2011

Source: Text from Climate Change 2014: Synthesis Report. Contribution of Working Groups I, II and III to the Fifth Assessment Report of the Intergovernmental Panel on Climate Change. [Core Writing Team, Pachauri, R.K. and Meyer, L. (eds.)], pp 45 IPCC, Geneva, Switzerland.

Figure 11.1 shows the massive increase in carbon dioxide pollution from human sources starting in 1950. To deny that such pollution will have any impact on the environment seems as naïve as believing that cigarette smoke will not harm your lungs.

It is important to understand that science does not provide definitive proof, just increased certainty based on available evidence and experimental verification. Greenhouse gases like carbon dioxide will become trapped in the atmosphere and prevent reflected solar heat from escaping into outer space. This should lead to increasing temperatures, less sea ice, higher sea levels, and more extreme weather events.

Note that **Figure 11.2** shows observed data in line with scientists' predictions. Surface temperature is projected to rise over the 21st century under all assessed emission scenarios. It is *very likely* (90–100% certain) that heat waves will occur more often and last longer, and that extreme precipitation events will become more intense and frequent in many regions. The ocean will continue to warm and acidify, and global mean sea level will continue to rise.

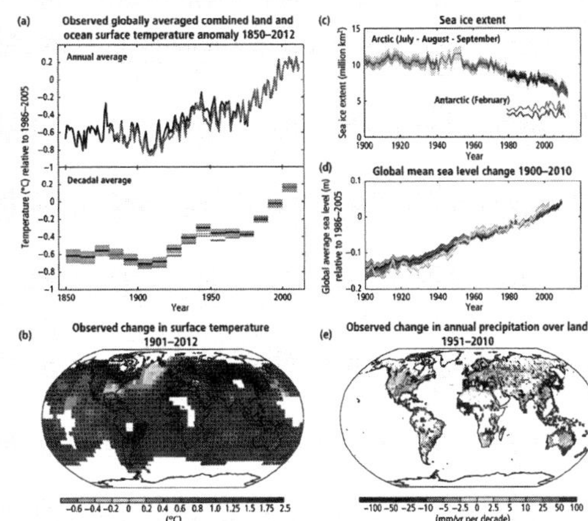

FIGURE 11.2 Observed Changes in Temperature, Sea Ice, Sea Levels, and Precipitation

Source: Text from Climate Change 2014: Synthesis Report. Contribution of Working Groups I, II and III to the Fifth Assessment Report of the Intergovernmental Panel on Climate Change. [Core Writing Team, Pachauri, R.K. and Meyer, L. (eds.)], pp 14 IPCC, Geneva, Switzerland.

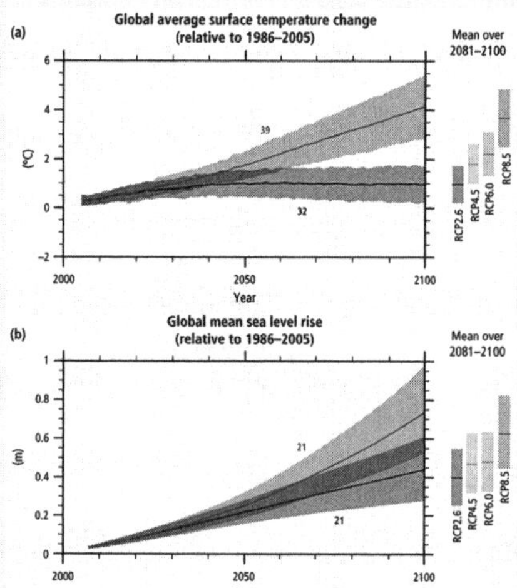

FIGURE 11.3 Projected Simulations for Four Emission Scenarios

Source: Text from Climate Change 2014: Synthesis Report. Contribution of Working Groups I, II and III to the Fifth Assessment Report of the Intergovernmental Panel on Climate Change. [Core Writing Team, Pachauri, R.K. and Meyer, L. (eds.)], pp 11 IPCC, Geneva, Switzerland

Figure 11.3 shows projections for temperature change and sea level rise (both relative to 1986–2005) using two emission scenarios. The blue and red uncertainty shadings indicate possible ranges for each scenario. The mean and associated uncertainties over 2081–2100 are given for all four scenarios as colored vertical bars on the right-hand side of each graphic.

To make an informed decision as a citizen regarding public policy issues one must understand that life is filled with uncertainty. Smoking does not always lead to lung cancer and scientists cannot predict exactly how much temperatures will rise given the best available data on greenhouse gas emissions. We also need to appreciate that **chance** is not absolute but relative to other factors. The chance of a 55-year-old person dying from a heart attack is highly dependent on whether the individual smokes. The chance of dying from a gunshot is 30 times higher in the U.S. than in England. **Table 11.2** compares the risks of dying from a gunshot in other countries with the U.S. and shows living in the United States makes you much more likely to be a gun homicide victim. Living in Chicago in 2015 raises the rate of gun deaths to 178 per million, while being poor, black, male, and living in Chicago raises the rate even more.

In 2015 gun control and race relations were topics that dominated the headlines and polarized the debates of our Presidential hopefuls. Should we vote for stricter gun control measures? Just how dangerous is our society? Does racial profiling impact police tactics such as stop and frisk?

Answering such questions requires understanding risk and assessing various interventions. We can reduce our risk of dying from a car crash to zero by walking everywhere and similarly reduce our risk of a heart attack, stroke, or diabetes by adopting a whole-food, plant-based diet. This chapter will provide you with the quantitative skills to help make such decisions.

TABLE 11.2 Comparison of Death Rates (2007–2012 Averages)

Being killed with a gun in:	Is as likely as dying from ___ in the U.S.	Deaths per million
El Salvador	Heart attack	446.3
United States	Car accident	31.2
China	Plane crash	1.6
Japan	Lightning strike	0.1

Data from: http://www.nytimes.com/2015/12/05/upshot/in-other-countries-youre-as-likely-to-be-killed-by-a-falling-object-as-a-gun.html?_r=0

CAUTION The chance of dying from the causes in **Table 11.2** is highly dependent on other factors. In 2010 blacks accounted for 55% of gun homicide victims, but made up only 13% of the population, giving a gun homicide rate for blacks of 132 per million. •

11.2 Probability and Counting

OBJECTIVE 1 **Explore Events, Outcomes, and Sample Spaces**

OBJECTIVE 2 **Understand Permutations and Combinations**

OBJECTIVE 1 Explore Events, Outcomes, and Sample Spaces

The **probability** of an **event** occurring is a measure of the **likelihood** or **chance** of it happening. This idea of quantifying the uncertain is inherently unintuitive. Indeed human beings have been gambling and playing games of chance since before recorded history, yet mathematicians did not formally "discover" the laws of probability until the 17th century. This is probably because they viewed "chance" or "fate" as coming from divine intervention: the Romans worshipped the goddess Fortuna of luck and chance, and ancient oracles used dice and bones to divine fates predetermined by the gods (the I-Ching is still very popular today). If chance is due to the caprice of the gods why bother trying to quantify it? The mathematics of probability is not terribly sophisticated, just counting and **ratios**. We will start with a simple example to illustrate the concepts and vocabulary before giving the formal definition.

Example 2 Compute the Probability of a Daughter

VIDEO *Daughter*

You meet with a friend who has two children. What is the probability her second child is a girl? She mentions one of her children is a boy. Given this new information, what is the probability that her second child is a girl? Lastly she tells you the previously mentioned boy was born on a Tuesday. Given this new information, what is the probability that her second child is a girl? Assume the probability of having a boy or girl is equally likely (50%).

SOLUTION The **probability** of the **event**, *2nd child girl*, is the **ratio** of the number of ways this event can occur to all possible **outcomes** of having two children. We can create a table showing the collection of all possible outcomes (called the **sample space**):

TABLE 11.3 Sample Space for Two Children

	Second Child	
First Child	Boy	Girl
Boy	**BB**	**BG**
Girl	**GB**	**GG**

CAUTION Knowing one child is a boy changes the sample space by eliminating the GG possibility. •

So the sample space consists of four possible outcomes: {BB, GB, BG, GG}. The event, *2nd child girl*, consists of two possible outcomes: {BG, GG}. Thus the probability of the second child being a girl is 2 : 4 or 50%.

If we know that one of the children is a boy, our sample space changes: {BB, GB, BG}, so that the event now consists of a single element: {BG}, and the probability is 1 : 3 or 33.3%. As we saw in the previous section, additional information can radically change the **likelihood** of an event!

Finally we are told the aforementioned boy was born on a Tuesday. This seems completely extraneous, yet once again the new information alters the probability of the second child being a girl. Our table now must include days of the week indicating when each child was born.

TABLE 11.4 Sample Space for Two Children with Day Born

	2nd Child									
1st Child	**B_Mon**	**B_Tue**	**B_Wed**	**...**	**B_Sun**	**G_Mon**	**G_Tue**	**...**	**G_Sun**
B_Mon	BB	**BB**	BB	...	BB	BG	BG	...	BG
B_Tue	**BB**	**BB**	**BB**	**...**	**BB**	**BG**	**BG**	**...**	**BG**
B_Wed	BB	**BB**	BB	...	BB	BG	BG	...	BG
B_Thu	BB	**BB**	BB	...	BB	BG	BG	...	BG
B_Fri	BB	**BB**	BB	...	BB	BG	BG	...	BG
B_Sat	BB	**BB**	BB	...	BB	BG	BG	...	BG
B_Sun	BB	**BB**	BB	...	BB	BG	BG	...	BG
G_Mon	GB	**GB**	GB	...	GB	GG	GG	...	GG
G_Tue	GB	**GB**	GB	...	GB	GG	GG	...	GG
G_Wed	GB	**GB**	GB	...	GB	GG	GG	...	GG
G_Thu	GB	**GB**	GB	...	GB	GG	GG	...	GG
G_Fri	GB	**GB**	GB	...	GB	GG	GG	...	GG
G_Sat	GB	**GB**	GB	...	GB	GG	GG	...	GG
G_Sun	GB	**GB**	GB	...	GB	GG	GG	...	GG

CAUTION The event, 2nd child girl, now consists of the last seven elements in this highlighted row. The last BG in this row indicates the 1st child is a boy born on Tuesday and the 2nd child is a girl born on Sunday. •

Our **sample space** now consists of the highlighted row and column for a boy born on Tuesday, with **intersection** at the outcome of two boys both born on a Tuesday. Each row and column consists of 14 possible **outcomes**, but we only count the intersection once, giving 27 possible outcomes in the sample space. The **event**, *2nd child girl*, consists of the 7 outcomes **BG** in the **B_Tue** row, so the new **probability** is 7 : 27 or 25.9%.

This seems bizarre that knowing the day the boy was born would change the probability of the second child being a girl. Probability is notoriously counter-intuitive so it is critical you always determine your sample space with care!

Example 2 illustrated the fundamental importance of determining your **sample space** and counting carefully when computing **probabilities**. We encountered this in Section 11.1 when looking at the **risk** of dying from a heart attack (smoking greatly increases the risk) or a gunshot (living in the U.S. greatly increases the risk). Many probabilities are reported as **percentages** so knowing your sample space is basically answering the question: Percentage of what? We are now ready to define the relevant terms that have been introduced.

DEFINITION

The **probability** of an *event* occurring, **P**(*Event*), is the ratio of the number of ways this event can occur to the total number of *outcomes* possible. The collection of all possible outcomes is called the *sample space*, and the event is considered to be a subset of the sample space. Thus the probability ratio can always be represented as a fraction/decimal between zero and one.

- $0 \le P\ (Event) \le 1$.
- **P** (*Event*) = 0 implies it will not occur, zero chance.
- **P** (*Event*) = 1 implies it will occur, guaranteed 100% certain.

The **odds in favor** of an event occurring are the ratio of the probability of the event occurring to the probability it does not occur (in gambling situations the odds are typically given as the ratio of amount won to the amount bet).

Odds of 2 : 1 imply 2/3 chance of the event occurring and 1/3 chance of it not occurring. The ***certainty***, ***chance***, ***risk***, or ***likelihood*** of an event occurring is the probability of the event occurring using either past data or data from simulations.

It will rain tomorrow with 20% certainty implies that past data with similar conditions resulted in rain on the next day 20% of the time, or that 20% of the simulations modeling these conditions resulted in rain 20% of the time.

A more precise definition of the probability of precipitation is found in the exercises.

Example 3 **Determine Events and Sample Spaces**

VIDEO *Events*

Determine what the **event** and the **sample space** are for the following **probabilities**:

1. In **Table 11.1** the 6 per 1,000 in the *Stroke* column.
2. In **Table 11.2** the 31.2 per million.
3. On screen 8 in the **Caution** Box, the probability given is 132 per million.

SOLUTION

1. The 6 per 1,000 represents the probability of a 55-year-old female smoker dying of a stroke over the next 10 years (starting in 2008). So the sample space consists of all 55-year-old female smokers and the event is the **subset** of those women who die from a stroke over the next 10 years.
2. The 31.2 per million can be interpreted two ways. The first column tells us this is the probability of dying from a gunshot in the U.S. (using 2007–2012 average), while the second column tells us it is also the probability of dying in a car accident in the U.S. The sample space in both cases is the entire population of the U.S. and the first/second event consists of the subset of those who died from a gunshot/car accident.
3. The probability of a black person being killed by a gunshot in the U.S. was 132 per million in 2010. The sample space was all black people and the event was the subset of those who died from a gunshot.

OBJECTIVE 2 Understand Permutations and Combinations

In Example 2 we counted the number of ways you can have two children, with **Table 11.3** showing the four possible outcomes.

Example 4 **Ways to Have Three Children**

VIDEO *Three Children*

Count the number of ways to have three children.

SOLUTION Each child can be a boy or a girl so the eight possibilities are: {BBB, BBG, BGB, BGG, GBB, GBG, GGB, GGG}.

Counting is critical to computing **probabilities**, and Example 4 illustrates what is called the **Fundamental Principle of Counting**. We have three children, or three choices to be made, and two options for each child/choice so we multiply the number of options for each choice: $2 \times 2 \times 2 = 8$.

We can illustrate this with a tree diagram:

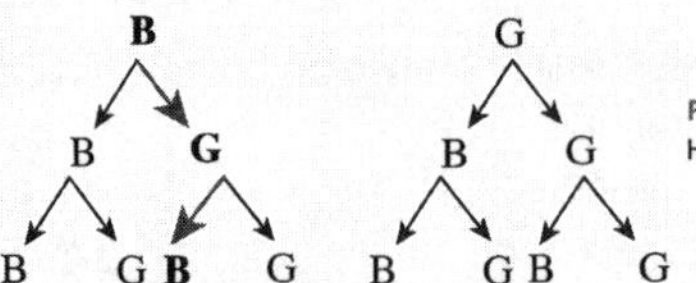

FIGURE 11.4 Tree Diagram Listing Number of Ways to Have Three Children

Each branch of the tree represents a possible way to have three children; the highlighted branch gives BGB. There are eight such branches: we have two options for the first child and for each of these there are two options for the second child, giving four ways to have two children. For each of these four possibilities there are two options for the third child, giving eight total possibilities for three children.

DEFINITION

Given a series of k choices to be made, each with a different number of options: $n_1, n_2, \ldots, n_k$, then the total number of possible ways to choose one option from each of the k choices is the product: $n_1 \times n_2 \times \ldots \times n_k$. This is called the **Fundamental Principle of Counting.**

Example 5 Choose Outfits

Assume you have five shirts to choose from, two pairs of pants and six pair of shoes. How many different outfits can you make?

SOLUTION There are three choices with the respective numbers of options being: five, two, and six. So there are $5 \times 2 \times 6 = 60$ outfits.

We can use spreadsheets to help us estimate probabilities. Consider a simple problem that is often solved incorrectly. If you flip two coins what is the **probability** of getting exactly one head? Many people think the answer is one-third reasoning that the **sample space** consists of three possibilities {0H, 1H, 2H} and our **event** is one out of these three possibilities. The mistake being made here is that the sample space actually consists of all possible **outcomes** {HH, HT, TH, TT}, not all possible events: {0H, 1H, and 2H}. So the correct probability is one-half.

Example 6 Use a Spreadsheet to Flip Coins

VIDEO
Coin Flips

If you flip two coins and count the number of heads you get, what is the probability of getting one head? Use a spreadsheet to estimate this probability.

SOLUTION We will have Excel flip two coins 1,000 times using the approach from Chapter 10 involving **IF** and **RAND**. This in effect will be a **sample space** for our experiment, and by counting the number of heads with the **COUNTIF** function we can approximate the **probability**.

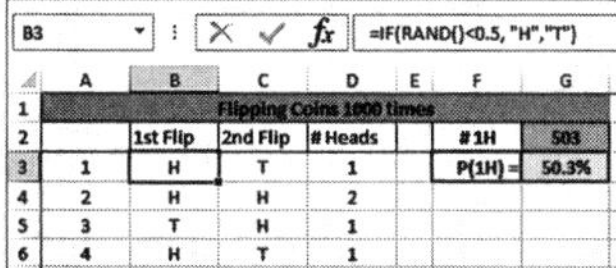

B3 =IF(RAND()<0.5, "H","T")

	A	B	C	D	E	F	G
1	Flipping Coins 1000 times						
2		1st Flip	2nd Flip	# Heads		# 1H	503
3	1	H	T	1		P(1H) =	50.3%
4	2	H	H	2			
5	3	T	H	1			
6	4	H	T	1			

FIGURE 11.5 Spreadsheet Using **RAND** to Flip Two Coins

G2 =COUNTIF(D3:D1002,1)

	A	B	C	D	E	F	G
1	Flipping Coins 1000 times						
2		1st Flip	2nd Flip	# Heads		# 1H	503
3	1	H	T	1		P(1H) =	50.3%
4	2	H	H	2			
5	3	T	H	1			
6	4	H	T	1			

FIGURE 11.6 Spreadsheet Using **COUNTIF** to Flip Two Coins and Count Number of Heads

Press **F9** (**Command** and = keys on a Mac) and try to get the number of times you get one head below 400. You probably won't be able to and you most certainly will never come close to 333, which is what someone with a probability of one-third would have predicted. **P(*1H*)** oscillates between 480 and 520, hovering above and below 500, so the probability of getting one head must be 50%. This empirical approach, running an experiment and simply counting the **outcomes**, is incredibly powerful and fun! It is like being in a science lab (ask your professor for goggles). Remember probability is nothing more than counting.

CAUTION Empirically determining probabilities by running an experiment and counting the number of times an **event** occurs, does not give you the exact result (in this case 50%). Instead there will be variability in each result (the experiment above gives 50.3%). By increasing the number of trials in each experiment (from 1,000 to 10,000 flips) we can reduce the variability. The discipline of statistics quantifies this variability and will be explored in more detail in a forthcoming chapter. •

Associated with the **Fundamental Principle of Counting** are permutations and combinations.

SPREADSHEET TUTORIALS Using Arithmetic Operations | Using COUNTIF | Formatting Cells with Percent Style | Fill Formula | Using the IF Function

DEFINITION

A **permutation** is a selection of r items from a group of n, with no item being selected twice and the order items are selected is counted differently (*abc* is a different permutation than *bca*). The total number of permutations is given by:

$$_nP_r = n \times (n-1) \times (n-2) \times \cdots \times (n-r+1) = \frac{n!}{(n-r)!}$$

A **combination** is a selection of r items from a group of n, with no item being selected twice and the order items are selected is NOT counted differently (*abc* is the same combination as *bca*). The total number of combinations is given by:

$$_nC_r = \binom{n}{r} = \frac{_nP_r}{r!} = \frac{n!}{(n-r)! \cdot r!}$$

Note that $n!$ is read "n factorial" and represents the product $n \times (n-1) \times (n-2) \times \cdots \times 2 \times 1$.

Example 7 Compute Permutations and Combinations

VIDEO *Permutations and Combinations*

Given a group of six people: {Ann, Mei, Suk, Bob, Jim, Rav}, how many ways can these six people finish a race first, second, and third. How many ways can we choose a committee of three?

SOLUTION To finish a race, order does matter. We have six choices for first, then only five choices for second and four choices for third, giving us $6 \times 5 \times 4 = 120$ ways to finish the race or 120 permutations, $_6P_3$. To choose committees, order does NOT matter so we arrange our 120 permutations into groups of six: {abc, acb, bac, bca, cab, cba}, each of which represents a single committee. Thus the number of committees is the number of combinations, $_6C_3 = \frac{_6P_3}{3!} = \frac{120}{6} = 20$ committees.

CAUTION Each combination of three people gives six different permutations. We divide the total number of permutations by the six ways to permute three items. •

11.3 Conditional Probabilities

OBJECTIVE 1 **Understand Conditional Probabilities**

OBJECTIVE 2 **Explore the First Law of Probability**

OBJECTIVE 1 Understand Conditional Probabilities

At the end of Section 11.1 we discussed how chance was highly dependent on other factors or conditions such as where you live and lifestyle choices such as smoking. **Probabilities** that are based on a given condition are called conditional probabilities.

DEFINITION

The **conditional probability** of *A given B* is written **P**(*A* | *B*) and is the ratio of the number of outcomes occurring in both events *A* and *B* to the number of total outcomes in *B*.

Example 8 | Use Conditional Probabilities

Let's use the conditional probabilities **P**(*55-year old male dies from lung cancer in the next 10 years|Smoker*) = 34 per thousand and **P**(*55-year old male dies from lung cancer in the next 10 years|Non-smoker*) = 1 per thousand to compute the probability **P**(*55-year old male dies from*

lung cancer in the next 10 years). Assume the population consists of 10,000 55-year-old male non-smokers and 1,000 55-year-old male smokers.

SOLUTION First note that you cannot simply add the two probabilities 34 + 1 to get 35 per thousand, because the denominators of the two fractions are different (55-year-old non-smokers and smokers). That would be like adding 34 miles per hour and 1 mile per second!

It helps to draw a **Venn diagram** to get a picture of the sets involved:

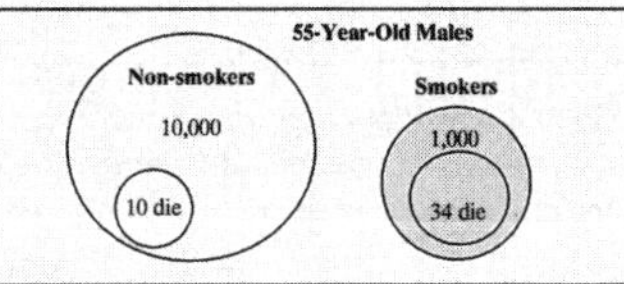

FIGURE 11.7 Venn Diagram Showing Population of 55-Year-Old Males

Note that the non-smokers and smokers are **disjoint**, these **subsets** do not overlap (**intersect**). There would exist some men outside the two circles who were smokers and stopped; these are not included in the statistics.

We can see that there are a total of 44 deaths and 11,000 total men in the two groups. Thus the overall **probability**, **P**(*55-year-old male dies from lung cancer in the next 10 years*) = 4 deaths per thousand. It is weighted toward the **risk** for non-smokers since there are more of these men.

Example 9 **Compute Conditional Probabilities**

VIDEO *Skin Cream*

Recall the two-way table from Section 4.4 involving the use of a skin cream given in **Table 11.5**. Compute the **conditional probabilities**: **P**(*Got Better*|*Used Cream*) and **P**(*Used Cream*|*Got Better*).

SOLUTION We can see from the table that 223 people satisfy both criteria (*Got Better and Used Cream*), and 298 people total used the cream, so the probability that you got better given you used the cream: **P**(*Got Better*|*Used Cream*) = 223/298 = 74.8%.

CAUTION The conditional probabilities have a **sample space** (denominator) restricted by the given condition. ●

TABLE 11.5 Two-Way Table for Skin Cream Experiment

	Rash Got Better	Rash Got Worse	Totals
Did use cream	223	75	**298**
Did not use cream	107	21	**128**
Totals	**330**	**96**	

We can turn **Table 11.5** into a **Venn diagram** as shown in **Figure 11.8** and see that out of the 330 people who got better, 223 used the cream, so the **probability** that you used the cream given you got better: **P**(*Used Cream*|*Got Better*) $= 223/330 = 67.6\%$.

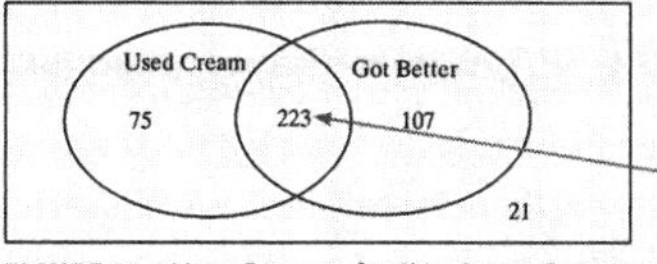

Note that there are 223 people in the **intersection** of the two **subsets**. These are people who used the cream AND got better.

FIGURE 11.8 Venn Diagram for Skin Cream Experiment

Example 9 illustrates a procedure for computing **conditional probabilities**. If we denote the number of elements in a **set** with #(*Set*):

$$\mathbf{P}(\textit{Used Cream} \mid \textit{Got Better}) = \frac{\#(\textit{Used Cream } \textbf{AND} \textit{ Got Better})}{\#(\textit{Got Better})}$$

we can turn the number of elements in a set into a probability by dividing by the total number in the sample space:

$$\mathbf{P}(\textit{Used Cream} \mid \textit{Got Better}) = \frac{\#(\textit{Used Cream } \textbf{AND} \textit{ Got Better}) / 426}{\#(\textit{Got Better}) / 426} = \frac{\mathbf{P}(\textit{Used Cream } \textbf{AND} \textit{ Got Better})}{\mathbf{P}(\textit{Got Better})}$$

which gives us the general rule for computing conditional probabilities (note that we are replacing the word AND with the symbol for the intersection of two sets):

DEFINITION

The **conditional probability** of *A given B* can be computed as follows:

$$\mathbf{P}(A \mid B) = \frac{\mathbf{P}(A \textbf{ AND } B)}{\mathbf{P}(B)} = \frac{\mathbf{P}(A \cap B)}{\mathbf{P}(B)}$$

OBJECTIVE 2 Explore the First Law of Probability

We are now ready to explore the First Law of Probability which is nothing more than a rearrangement of the formula for computing **conditional probabilities.**

DEFINITION

The First Law of Probability says that the probability of event A and event B both occurring is:

$$\mathbf{P}(A \textbf{ AND } B) = \mathbf{P}(A) \cdot \mathbf{P}(B \mid A)$$

If A and B are *independent* events then $\mathbf{P}(B \mid A) = \mathbf{P}(B)$ and the formula is:

$$\mathbf{P}(A \textbf{ AND } B) = \mathbf{P}(A) \cdot \mathbf{P}(B).$$

Flipping two coins are *independent events*; the probability of the second flip does not depend on the first. Choosing two committee members are *dependent* events; the probability of choosing the second member depends on the first choice.

Example 10 Apply the First Law of Probability

VIDEO *First Law*

A subcommittee of two people will be chosen from a group of six: {Sue, Ann, Jill, Bob, Jim, Joe}. The first three listed are women and the last three listed are men. What is the **probability** the subcommittee contains two women?

SOLUTION First, let's draw the **sample space** and compute the probability by counting. Notice how the **permutations** below the diagonal are the same committees as those above. So the total number of committees is given by computing the number of ways to choose two from six: ${}_6C_2 = \frac{{}_6P_2}{2!} = \frac{6 \times 5}{2} = 15$ committees, and three of these have two women.

TABLE 11.6 Subcommittees of Two People

1st slot/2nd slot	Sue	Ann	Jill	Bob	Jim	Joe
Sue		Sue/Ann	Sue/Jill	Sue/Bob	Sue/Jim	Sue/Joe
Ann	Ann/Sue		Ann/Jill	Ann/Bob	Ann/Jim	Ann/Joe
Jill	Jill/Sue	Jill/Ann		Jill/Bob	Jill/Jim	Jill/Joe
Bob	Bob/Sue	Bob/Ann	Bob/Jill		Bob/Jim	Bob/Joe
Jim	Jim/Sue	Jim/Ann	Jim/Jill	Jim/Bob		Jim/Joe
Joe	Joe/Sue	Joe/Ann	Joe/Jill	Joe/Bob	Joe/Jim	

Thus the **probability** of the **event** of choosing two women is: $\mathbf{P}(2W) = 3 : 15 = 20\%$. Now let's apply the **First Law of Probability.** We are asking for the probability that the first choice is a woman ($1stW$) AND that the second choice is a woman ($2ndW$):

$$\mathbf{P}(1stW \textbf{ AND } 2ndW) = \mathbf{P}(1st\ W) \cdot \mathbf{P}(2nd\ W \mid 1st\ W)$$

The first choice is easy enough: $\mathbf{P}(1stW) = 3 : 6 = 50\%$, but the second choice is a **conditional probability** and requires us to think about what happens if the first choice is a women. This would mean there are only two women out of five people left for the second choice: $\mathbf{P}(2ndW \mid 1stW) = 2 : 5 = 40\%$. Thus:

$$\mathbf{P}(1stW \textbf{ AND } 2ndW) = 50\% \cdot 40\% = 20\%$$

CAUTION We can compute the conditional probability, $\mathbf{P}(2ndW \mid 1stW)$, by simply reasoning that if a woman has been chosen, there are only two women left out of five people. We do not need to use the complicated formula. •

Note that in Example 10 the two events *1stW* and *2ndW* are **dependent.** Let's give a brief example involving **independent** events.

Example 11 | Apply the First Law of Probability with Independence

You are having a party and believe the probability of your friend Rav attending, **P**(*Rav*) = 1/5, and the probability of your friend Suk attending, **P**(*Suk*) = 2/3. Rav and Suk do not know each other. What is the probability they both attend?

SOLUTION Given they do not know each other these are independent events and we can use the First Law of Probability for independent events: **P**(*Rav* **AND** *Suk*) = **P**(*Rav*) · **P**(*Suk*) = (1/5) · (2/3) = 2/15.

Note that the joint probability of both attending is smaller than each individual probability!

11.4 Unions and Complements

OBJECTIVE 1 **Explore the Second Law of Probability**

OBJECTIVE 2 **Explore the Third Law of Probability**

OBJECTIVE 1 Explore the Second Law of Probability

In Chapter 10 we saw that Excel has built-in logic functions: **AND, OR,** and **NOT.** The **First Law of Probability** deals with the **AND** situation, the **probability** of this **event** *and* that event occurring (multiply!). Next we will explore the probability of this event *or* that event occurring.

Example 12 | Compute the Probability of a Union

VIDEO
Second Law

Given the **Venn diagram** for the skin cream experiment in **Figure 11.8**, compute the probability of a participant having used the cream **OR** gotten better.

SOLUTION This event consists of the **union** of the two **subsets**, *Used Cream* ∪ *Got Better*. There is a total of 75 + 223 + 107 = 405 people in the union, out of 426 total participants. Thus P(*Used Cream* ∪ *Got Better*) = 405/426 = 95.1%.

CAUTION If we add the elements of both subsets together we double count the **intersection.** There are 298 people who used the cream and 330 who got better, adding these would give 628 people. We need to subtract the intersection to get the correct number in the union: 298 + 330 − 223 = 405. •

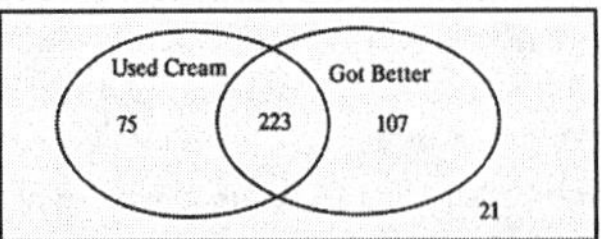

FIGURE 11.9 Venn Diagram for Skin Cream Experiment

Example 12 illustrates the need to subtract the **intersection** when counting elements in a **union** of two **sets** and leads to the Second Law of Probability.

DEFINITION

The **Second Law of Probability** says that the probability of event A or event B occurring is:

$$\mathbf{P}(A \textbf{ OR } B) = \mathbf{P}(A) + \mathbf{P}(B) - \mathbf{P}(A \textbf{ AND } B)$$

$$\mathbf{P}(A \cup B) = \mathbf{P}(A) + \mathbf{P}(B) - \mathbf{P}(A \cap B)$$

If A and B are *disjoint* events then $\mathbf{P}(A \textbf{ AND } B) = 0$ and the formula is: $\mathbf{P}(A \textbf{ OR } B) = \mathbf{P}(A) + \mathbf{P}(B)$. The probability of event A or event B occurring means A or B or both, and is the same as the probability of *at least one* of event A or event B occurring.

CAUTION We often say things like, "I will go for a run or play golf," implying one or the other but not both. In mathematics *or* always means "this or that or both." •

Example 13 Apply the Second Law of Probability

A subcommittee of two people will be chosen from a group of six: {Sue, Ann, Jill, Bob, Jim, Joe}. The first three listed are women and the last three listed are men. What is the **probability** that at least one man is chosen?

SOLUTION The **sample space** is given in **Table 11.7** and we can see there are 12 possible committees with at least one man, so $\mathbf{P}(\textit{at least 1M}) = 12/15 = 80\%$.

TABLE 11.7 Subcommittees of Two People

1st slot/2nd slot	Sue	Ann	Jill	Bob	Jim	Joe
Sue		Sue/Ann	Sue/Jill	Sue/Bob	Sue/Jim	Sue/Joe
Ann	Ann/Sue		Ann/Jill	Ann/Bob	Ann/Jim	Ann/Joe
Jill	Jill/Sue	Jill/Ann		Jill/Bob	Jill/Jim	Jill/Joe
Bob	Bob/Sue	Bob/Ann	Bob/Jill		Bob/Jim	Bob/Joe
Jim	Jim/Sue	Jim/Ann	Jim/Jill	Jim/Bob		Jim/Joe
Joe	Joe/Sue	Joe/Ann	Joe/Jill	Joe/Bob	Joe/Jim	

This **probability** is the same as the probability that the first choice is a man (1st M) or the second choice is a man (2nd M) and the **Second Law of Probability** tells us:

$$\mathbf{P}(\text{1st M } \textbf{OR} \text{ 2nd M}) = \mathbf{P}(\text{1st M}) + \mathbf{P}(\text{2nd M}) - \mathbf{P}(\text{1st M } \textbf{AND} \text{ 2nd M})$$

Now the probabilities of choosing a man first is **P**(1st M) = 3/6 and so is **P**(2nd M) (note these are not **conditional probabilities**). The probability of choosing two men, **P**(1st M **AND** 2nd M) = 3/15, giving us:

$$\mathbf{P}(\text{1st M } \mathbf{OR} \text{ 2nd M}) = \frac{3}{6} + \frac{3}{6} - \frac{3}{15} = \frac{4}{5} = 80\%$$

CAUTION We have computed this probability two different ways. It is always easiest to simply list all possible **outcomes** (15) and count the outcomes for the event in question (12). The second method involves computing **P**(2nd M) = 3/6 which is different from **P**(2nd M | 1st M) = 2/5. •

Sometimes the probability of A and B is zero, for example rolling two dice and getting a 7 and an 11, or being a smoker and a non-smoker. In these situations we can just add the probabilities in the Second Law (this will work for more than two events). For more than two events with non-empty **intersections**, the intersections that you have to subtract from the sum of individual probabilities gets complicated, and we will instead always use the following law.

OBJECTIVE 2 Explore the Third Law of Probability

There is a third way to compute the **probability** of choosing at least one man from Example 13 using the fact that either an **event** occurs or it does not occur but not both: **P**(A) + **P**(**NOT** A) = 1. Thus we can instead compute the probability of NOT getting at least one man which is the same as the probability of getting two women: **P**(*At Least 1M*) + **P**(*2W*) = 1. Looking at **Table 11.7** we have **P**(*2W*) = 3 : 15 = 20%, so **P**(*At Least 1M*) = 80%.

The **complement** of an event A is the event that A does not occur, Not A. An event and its complement make up the entire **sample space** so the sum of their probabilities must be 1.

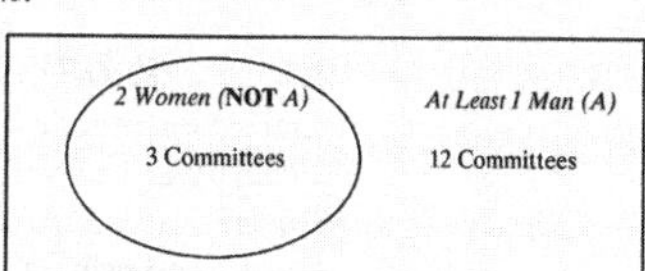

FIGURE 11.10 Venn Diagram for Committees of Two People

Example 14 Find the Complement of a Union

VIDEO *Third Law*

Given the **Venn diagram** for the skin cream experiment in **Figure 11.11**, compute the probability of the complement of the event a participant used the cream **OR** got better.

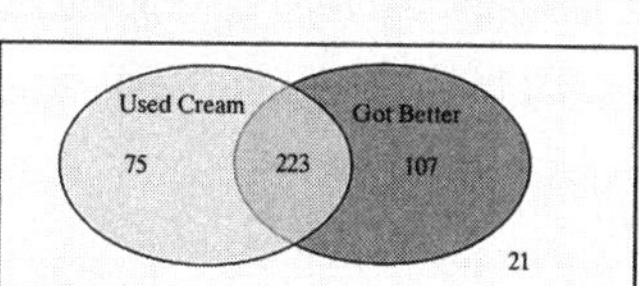

FIGURE 11.11 Venn Diagram for Skin Cream Experiment

SOLUTION This event consists of 405 participants in the shaded regions:

The **complement** of the **event**, *Used Cream* **OR** *Got Better*, consists of participants who did not use the cream **AND** did not get better.

P(NOT(*Used Cream* **OR** *Got Better*)) = **P**(NOT(*Used Cream*) **AND** NOT(*Got Better*))

There are 21 such people so the **probability** is: 21/426 = 4.9%.

We will now combine what we know about complements into the Third Law of Probability:

DEFINITION

The **Third Law of Probability** says that the probability of event *A* is 1 minus the probability of its complement, **NOT** *A*:

P(*A*) = 1 – **P**(NOT *A*)

P(*A* **OR** *B*) = 1 – **P**(NOT *A* **AND** NOT *B*)

For *independent* events we can apply the **First Law** to the last formula and get the **Golden Rule of Probability:**

P(*At Least One Independent Event (A, B, C, …) Occuring*) = 1 – **P**(NOT *A*) × **P**(NOT *B*) × **P**(NOT *C*) × …

Example 15 Apply the Third Law

VIDEO *Aces*

In the excellent book, *Chance*, by Amir Aczel, the gambling paradox of Chevalier de Mere is recounted. The Chevalier enjoyed playing two different dice games in the casinos of 17th century Europe. The first game consisted of rolling four dice and winning if at least one "ace"

(the number one) showed up. The second game consisted of getting 24 rolls of a pair of dice and winning if at least one double ace showed up. The Chevalier incorrectly reasoned that in the first game **P**(*1st Ace* or *2nd Ace* or *3rd Ace* or *4th Ace*) = **P**(*1st Ace*) + **P**(*2nd Ace*) + **P**(*3rd Ace*) + **P**(*4th Ace*) = 4 : 6 or 67%. In the second game the Chevalier made the same type of mistake, reasoning that a single double ace had a probability of 1/36 and he had 24 chances of a double ace giving him a probability of $24 \times \frac{1}{36} = \frac{24}{36} = \frac{2}{3}$. Find the correct probabilities.

SOLUTION In the first game the Chevalier was making the common mistake of forgetting to subtract the **probability** of the **intersections** when using the **Second Law**. His flawed logic would have us believe that if you rolled six dice you were guaranteed to get an ace since 6 times one-sixth = 100%. The second law is difficult to apply here since the sample space has 6^4 = 1,296 possible outcomes and the intersections are too complicated to easily determine. Instead the **Third Law**, and in particular the **Golden Rule** (each die is independent of the others), readily provides the solution:

P(*At least one ace*) = 1 – **P**(*No aces*)

P(*At least 1 ace*) = 1 – **P**(*No ace* **AND** *No ace* **AND** *No ace* **AND** *No ace*)

$$= 1 - \frac{5}{6} \times \frac{5}{6} \times \frac{5}{6} \times \frac{5}{6} = 1 - \left(\frac{5}{6}\right)^4 = 51.8\%$$

In the second game the **sample space** is even larger, consisting of 36^{24} possible outcomes for 24 rolls of a pair of dice! We again invoke the Golden Rule:

$$\mathbf{P}(\textit{at least one double ace}) = 1 - \mathbf{P}(\textit{no double aces})$$

$$\mathbf{P}(\textit{at least 1 double ace}) = 1 - \left(\frac{35}{36}\right)^{24} = 49.1\%$$

In the interest of science the Chevalier spent countless hours and a small fortune doing empirical research in the casinos only to convince himself his probabilities (67%) were way off and close to 50%, with the first game winning slightly more often than the second. He contacted the famous mathematician Blaise Pascal, who in turn corresponded with Pierre Fermat, and modern probability theory was born! It is interesting that the Chevalier's empirical intuition correctly determined the first game was slightly better. Also that even without mathematically determining the probabilities the casinos had created games of chance with very close to even **odds**.

Let's recap our Three Laws of **Probability** with a simple example.

Example 16 **Apply All Three Laws**

VIDEO
All Laws

Flip two coins and determine the probability of getting two heads (*2H*) and the probability of getting at least one head (*At least 1H*).

SOLUTION The probability of getting two heads uses the **First Law** (of **independent** events):

$$\mathbf{P}(2H) = \mathbf{P}(\textit{1st H} \text{ and } \textit{2nd H}) = \mathbf{P}(\textit{1st H}) \times \mathbf{P}(\textit{2nd H})$$

$$\mathbf{P}(2H) = \frac{1}{2} \times \frac{1}{2} = \frac{1}{4}$$

The probability of getting at least one head uses the **Second Law**:

$$\mathbf{P}(\textit{At least 1H}) = \mathbf{P}(\textit{1st H} \text{ or } \textit{2nd H}) = \mathbf{P}(\textit{1st H}) + \mathbf{P}(\textit{2nd H}) - \mathbf{P}(\textit{1st H} \text{ and } \textit{2nd H})$$

$$\mathbf{P}(\textit{At least 1H}) = \frac{1}{2} + \frac{1}{2} - \frac{1}{4} = \frac{3}{4}$$

Or we can use the **Third Law**:

$$\mathbf{P}(\textit{At least 1H}) = 1 - \mathbf{P}(0H)$$

$$= 1 - \frac{1}{4} = \frac{3}{4}.$$

We will finish this section with a nice application of the **Golden Rule of Probability**, and explain why it has such a provocative title.

Example 17 **Apply the Golden Rule**

You are applying to five colleges and believe you have a small 10% **chance** of getting into any one of them. What is the **probability** of getting into at least one of the schools?

SOLUTION Clearly the decisions of the schools are **independent** so we invoke the **Golden Rule** and compute the probability using the fact that there is a 90% chance of NOT getting into each of the five schools:

$$\mathbf{P}(\textit{At least 1 acceptance}) = 1 - \mathbf{P}(\textit{0 acceptances})$$

$$= 1 - 0.9^5 = 41.0\%.$$

And by increasing the number of applications you can raise your probability of at least one acceptance to almost certainty:

TABLE 11.8 Golden Rule Probabilities

No. of Applications with 10% Chance	Probability of at Least One Acceptance
5	41.0%
10	65.1%
20	87.8%
25	92.8%
50	99.5%

Which leads to a nice moral:

> **Moral of the Golden Rule of Probability** Even against long odds, keep trying and you will succeed. Persistence and determination trump luck every time. It's the law!

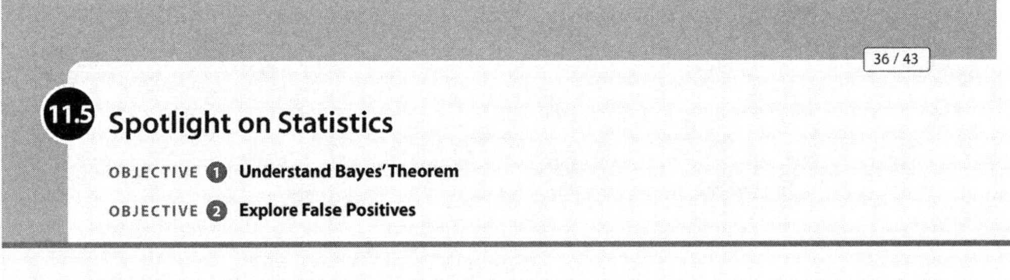

36 / 43
11.5 Spotlight on Statistics
OBJECTIVE 1 Understand Bayes' Theorem
OBJECTIVE 2 Explore False Positives

OBJECTIVE 1 Understand Bayes' Theorem

In the late 1740s the Reverend Thomas Bayes discovered the formula involving **conditional probabilities** that would subsequently be named after him. At the time he was interested in cause and effect, and wished to determine a way to quantify the **probability** of a cause given an observed effect. For example, we know that smoking is a possible cause of heart attacks, and in **Table 11.1** we looked at some probabilities of a heart attack death given smoking, $\mathbf{P}(HA|Smoker)$. Bayes was interested in the inverse probability, given a heart attack death, what is the probability of that person being a smoker, $\mathbf{P}(Smoker|HA)$? Clearly heart attacks don't cause smoking, so this is like working backwards from known data (heart attack) to likely causes (smoking). Bayes in particular wished to work backwards from observing the effect of creation to the probability of its likely cause being a creator. His simple theorem would come to divide generations of statisticians, with Bayesian adherents becoming bitter rivals of the frequentist camp. An excellent historical overview of this and the rise to ascendency of Bayes' Theorem in the modern era (due to increased computational power) is given in Sharon McGrayne's fabulous book, *The Theory That Would Not Die.*

We will start with a familiar example to derive the formula and then move on to more sophisticated applications. Recall from Example 9 that we computed the two **probabilities** $P(\textit{Got Better} \mid \textit{Used Cream}) = 74.8\%$ and $P(\textit{Used Cream} \mid \textit{Got Better}) = 67.6\%$ by looking at the information given in **Table 11.9** and **Figure 11.12**. Clearly using the cream would be the "cause" of the effect, getting better. We are interested in working backwards from effect to cause and we will derive a new formula for computing $P(\textit{Used Cream} \mid \textit{Got Better}) = P(UC \mid GB)$, starting with the formula for **conditional probability**:

$$P(UC \mid GB) = \frac{P(UC \text{ AND } GB)}{P(GB)} = \frac{P(UC) \cdot P(GB \mid UC)}{P(GB)}$$

Now the people who got better (GB) either used cream (UC) or did not (NoC) so:

$$P(GB) = P(GB \cap UC) + P(GB \cap NoC)$$

$$P(GB) = P(GB \mid UC) \cdot P(UC) + P(GB \mid NoC) \cdot P(NoC)$$

Note that we are using the First Law here.

Substituting in for the denominator above gives us:

$$P(UC \mid GB) = \frac{P(UC) \cdot P(GB \mid UC)}{P(GB \mid UC) \cdot P(UC) + P(GB \mid NoC) \cdot P(NoC)}$$

TABLE 11.9 Skin Cream Two-Way Table

	Rash Got Better	Rash Got Worse	Totals
Did use cream	223	75	**298**
Did not use cream	107	21	**128**
Totals	**330**	**96**	**426**

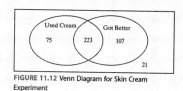

FIGURE 11.12 Venn Diagram for Skin Cream Experiment

VIDEO
Bayes

We are now ready to plug into the formula:

$$P(UC \mid GB) = \frac{P(UC) \cdot P(GB \mid UC)}{P(GB \mid UC) \cdot P(UC) + P(GB \mid NoC) \cdot P(NoC)}$$

$$P(UC \mid GB) = \frac{298/426 \cdot 223/298}{223/298 \cdot 298/426 + 107/128 \cdot 128/426} = \frac{52.3\%}{52.3\% + 25.1\%} = 67.6\%$$

This is obviously WAY more complicated than Example 9 so we will introduce a record keeping table and then look at applications to illustrate the power of this approach. In general the effect will be referred to as the data (D) and the cause will be referred to as the hypothesis (H). We wish to compute $P(H \mid D)$. **Table 11.10** lists the two competing hypotheses given the data that someone got better: either they used the cream or did not. The **priors** are the probabilities that someone did (70%) or did not (30%) use cream, and we update these probabilities to the **posteriors** given the data that someone got better. The **likelihoods** are the **conditional probabilities** $P(D \mid H)$ which are multiplied by the priors in the numerator and denominator of the formula. The denominator in the formula is the sum of the products:

$$\mathbf{P}(H_i \mid D) = \frac{\mathbf{P}(H_i) \cdot \mathbf{P}(D \mid H_i)}{\Sigma_i \mathbf{P}(D \mid H_i) \cdot \mathbf{P}(H_i)}$$

CAUTION This is **Bayes' Formula** and it is messy. We will use tables to keep track of everything. •

We know 70% of the participants used the cream. Given the data that someone got better reduces this prior probability to 67.6%.

TABLE 11.10 Skin Cream Bayes' Table Given the Data That Someone Got Better

Hypotheses (H_i)	Priors $P(H_i)$	Likelihoods $P(D \mid H_i)$	Products $P(H_i) \cdot P(D \mid H_i)$	Posteriors $P(H_i \mid D)$
Did use cream	298/426 = 70.0%	223/298	223/426	223/330 = 67.6%
Did not use cream	128/426 = 30.0%	107/128	107/426	107/330 = 32.4%
Totals	100%		330/426	100%

Example 18 **Apply Bayes' Formula**

VIDEO *Heart Attack*

A 55-year-old male has just had a heart attack. He says he is not smoking but you think there is a 20% **chance** he has been smoking. Given that he has had a heart attack what is the new **probability** that he is smoking? Use the information from **Table 11.1** as approximations for the probability of having a heart attack.

SOLUTION Our two hypotheses are that he is smoking (S) or not smoking (NS), and **Table 11.1** gives us the **likelihood** of a heart attack (A) in both cases: $\mathbf{P}(A \mid S) = 4.1\%$ and $\mathbf{P}(A \mid NS) = 1.9\%$. We can now fill in a Bayes' Table:

TABLE 11.11 Smoking Bayes' Table Given the Data That Someone Had a Heart Attack

Hypotheses (H_i)	Priors $P(H_i)$	Likelihoods $P(D \mid H_i)$	Products $P(H_i) \cdot P(D \mid H_i)$	Posteriors $P(H_i \mid D)$
Smoking	20.0%	4.1%	82	82/234 = 35.0%
Not Smoking	80.0%	1.9%	152	152/234 = 65.0%
Totals	100%		234	100%

CAUTION Note that we can ignore the percentages when computing the products, since the posteriors will be each product divided by the sum of products. •

Thus knowing he had a heart attack increases the probability of being a smoker from 20% to 35%!

This example illustrates the power of Bayes' Theorem. We can update our prior subjective beliefs with new information. If we receive more data we can update these new posteriors, treating them like priors and proceeding as above.

Example 19 **Apply Bayes' Formula with Three Hypotheses**

VIDEO *Galen*

Three siblings (Galen, Mei, and Beau) are equally likely to eat an apple, but the **probability** they leave the core on the counter differs: $\mathbf{P}(Core \mid Galen) = 1/5$, $\mathbf{P}(Core \mid Mei) = 3/5$, and $\mathbf{P}(Core \mid Beau) = 4/5$. If we find a core on the counter, what is the new probability that each sibling was the culprit?

SOLUTION Our three hypotheses are that each sibling ate the apple and left the core on the counter. We can now fill in a Bayes' Table:

TABLE 11.12 Apple Bayes' Table Given the Data That Someone Left a Core on the Counter

Hypotheses (H_i)	Priors $P(H_i)$	Likelihoods $P(D \mid H_i)$	Products $P(H_i) \cdot P(D \mid H_i)$	Posteriors $P(H_i \mid D)$
Galen	1/3	1/5	1/15	1/8 = 12.5%
Mei	1/3	3/5	3/15	3/8 = 37.5%
Beau	1/3	4/5	4/15	4/8 = 50.0%
Totals	100%		8/15	100%

As expected, Beau is the leading culprit with a 50% **posterior** probability.

Note that since the **priors** are equally likely, the **ratio** of the **likelihoods** and the **posteriors** are the same 1 : 3 : 4.

Example 20 Solve the Monty Hall Problem

VIDEO *Monty*

The Monty Hall Problem is a classic **probability** conundrum. It has fooled experts with advanced degrees in statistics and led to public embarrassment as these experts attacked one another in print. The problem states that you are on a game show and must choose one out of three doors. There is a car behind one of the doors. After you have selected your door, the host, Monty Hall, opens another door that does not have the car (he knows where the car is) and asks if you want to change your door. Should you switch?

SOLUTION Our three hypotheses are that the car is equally likely to be behind one of the three doors. Let's assume you pick door A and Monty opens door B, should you switch to door C? The **likelihoods** are the key to this puzzle. The likelihood that Monty opens door B given the car is behind door A is ½ since he could open door B or C, but the likelihood he opens door B given the car is behind door B is zero, since he cannot show you the car! Finally the likelihood he opens door B given the car is behind door C is 100%, since he cannot open door C and show you the car and he cannot open your door A.

Table 11.13 clearly shows you now have a 2/3 chance of getting the car behind door C so YES you should switch! This is so counter-intuitive because people think switching is just 50–50. Think of it this way: if Monty did not open door B but instead you could have both doors B and C would you take those two over door A? Of course you would: two doors gives you twice the probability!

TABLE 11.13 Monty Hall Bayes' Table Given the Data That You Pick Door A and Monty Opens Door B

Hypotheses (H_i)	Priors $P(H_i)$	Likelihoods $P(D \mid H_i)$	Products $P(H_i) \cdot P(D \mid H_i)$	Posteriors $P(H_i \mid D)$
Door A	1/3	1/2	1/6	1/3
Door B	1/3	0	0	0
Door C	1/3	1	1/3	2/3
Totals	100%		1/2	100%

Note that since the priors are equally likely, the likelihoods and posteriors have the same ratio of 1 : 0 : 2.

OBJECTIVE 2 Explore False Positives

One last application of Bayes' Formula for making informed health decisions. There are many tests for diseases. A **false positive** indicates you test positive for the disease (indicating sick) but don't actually have it, while a **false negative** indicates you test negative for the disease (indicating healthy) but actually have it.

Example 21 Predict Illness

VIDEO *False Positives*

A certain disease occurs in 5 out of 1,000 people. A test has a false positive rate of 3% and a false negative rate of 1%. What is the **probability** that a person who tests positive actually has the disease, P(*Sick* | +)?

Note that another way to solve this problem is to make a **two-way table** by assuming there are 100,000 people in the population, and then computing how many are sick and well, and how many test positive and negative. The video shows how to do this.

SOLUTION We are given P(+ | *Well*) = 3% which means P(– | *Well*) = 97%, and we are given P(– | *Sick*) = 1% which means P(+ | *Sick*) = 99%. We can now fill in a Bayes' Table, and get P(*Sick* | +) = 14.2%. This is very surprising given how accurate the test sounds!

TABLE 11.14 False Positive Bayes' Table Given the Data That You Test Positive

Hypotheses (H_i)	Priors $P(H_i)$	Likelihoods $P(D \mid H_i)$	Products $P(H_i) \cdot P(D \mid H_i)$	Posteriors $P(H_i \mid D)$
Sick	5/1,000 = 0.5%	99%	49.5	49.5/348 = 14.2%
Well	995/1,000 = 99.5%	3%	298.5	298.5/348 = 85.8%
Totals	100%		348	100%

CHAPTER 1
An Excel-lent Approach to Relationships
MyMathLab Homework Problems*

* Problems with an asterisk are included in the pre-assigned homework assignment.
! Problems with an exclamation point are new to the Update edition.
To find the problems in MyMathLab online, please refer to the ID code listed below each problem.

!* 1. Which of the following relationships are functions? For each one answer "Yes" if it is a function and "No" if not a function. If it is a function then answer Yes/No to the additional questions below. Answer parts a through e.

Is it a constant function?
Is it a 1-1 function?

a. Inputs: States Outputs: Governors

Is this relation a function? (1) __________

Is it a constant function? (2) __________

Is it a 1-1 function? (3) __________

b. Inputs: Governors Outputs: States

Is this relation a function? (4) __________

Is it a constant function? (5) __________

Is it a 1-1 function? (6) __________

c. Inputs: People at concession stand Outputs: Cost of their order

Is this relation a function? (7) __________

Is it a constant function? (8) __________

Is it a 1-1 function? (9) __________

d. Inputs: Cost of their order Outputs: People at concession stand

Is this relation a function? (10) __________

Is it a constant function? (11) __________

Is it a 1-1 function? (12) __________

e. Inputs: Students at a college Outputs: Mascot of college they are attending

Is this relation a function? (13) __________

Is it a constant function? (14) __________

Is it a 1-1 function? (15) __________

(1) ○ Yes ○ No (2) ○ No ○ Yes (3) ○ Yes ○ No (4) ○ No ○ Yes (5) ○ No ○ Yes (6) ○ No ○ Yes (7) ○ Yes ○ No

(8) ○ No ○ Yes (9) ○ No ○ Yes (10) ○ No ○ Yes (11) ○ No ○ Yes (12) ○ Yes ○ No (13) ○ No ○ Yes

(14) ○ No ○ Yes (15) ○ Yes ○ No

ID: 1.1.1

!* 2. Choose the correct response in each blank for the definition of a function.

A function is a ________ between _____ and ______, in which every ______ is paired with ______ and only one ________.

A function is a (1) ____________ between (2) ____________ and (3) ____________ in which every (4) ____________ is paired with (5) ____________ and only one (6) ____________

(1) ○ ratio ○ difference ○ relationship

(2) ○ inputs ○ numbers ○ variables

(3) ○ variables, ○ outputs, ○ numbers,

(4) ○ range ○ input ○ domain

(5) ○ one ○ infinity ○ two

(6) ○ relationship. ○ output. ○ variable.

ID: 1.1.2

* 3. Graph the points on the same axes.

A(4,3), B(− 8,2),
C(0,0), D(− 2,1)

Choose the correct answer on the right.

○ A.

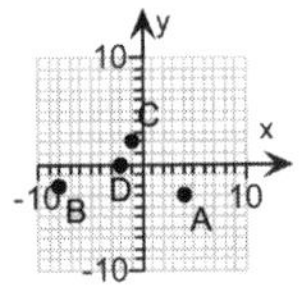

○ B.

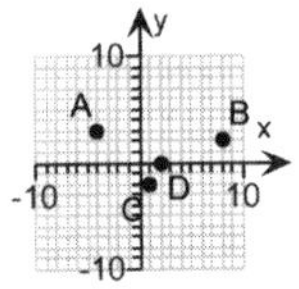

○ C.

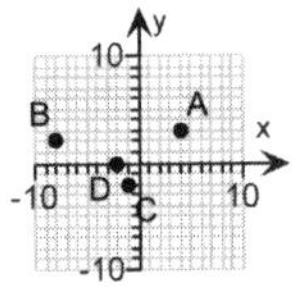

○ D.

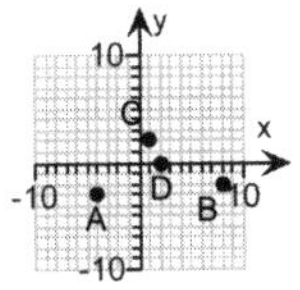

ID: 1.1.3

* 4. In the following situation, state whether two variables are related in a way that might be described by a function. If so, identify the independent and dependent variables.

You jump from an airplane (with a parachute) and
want to know how far you have traveled at various times during your descent.

Determine whether the two variables are related in a way that might be described by a function. If the situation could be described as a function, then identify the independent and dependent variables. Choose the correct answer below.

○ **A.** The situation cannot be described by a function.

○ **B.** The situation can be described by a function. The dependent variable is the time and the independent variable is the distance fallen.

○ **C.** The situation can be described by a function. The dependent variable is the distance fallen and the independent variable is the time.

○ **D.** The situation can be described by a function. There is a dependent variable, but no independent variable. The dependent variable is the distance fallen.

ID: 1.1.4

* 5. In the following situation, state whether two variables are related in a way that might be described by a function. If so, identify the independent and dependent variables.

You have an expensive phone bill and
want to know how the cost of the bill depends on the amount of time you spent on the phone.

Determine whether the two variables are related in a way that might be described by a function. If the situation could be described as a function, then identify the independent and dependent variables. Choose the correct answer below.

○ **A.** The situation can be described by a function. There is a dependent variable, but no independent variable. The dependent variable is cost.

○ **B.** The situation can be described by a function. The dependent variable is the time and the independent variable is the cost.

○ **C.** The situation can be described by a function. The dependent variable is the cost and the independent variable is the time.

○ **D.** The situation cannot be described by a function.

ID: 1.1.5

!* 6. Compute the periodic rate and interest in the first period for a $2,600 loan with 6.5% APR for the following periods.

a. Monthly
b. Daily (use a non-leap year)
c. Quarterly (4 times a year)
d. Biweekly (every 2 weeks)

a. The periodic rate is ___________ %.
(Type an integer or decimal rounded to three decimal places as needed.)

The interest in the first period is $___________.
(Round to the nearest cent as needed.)

b. The periodic rate is ___________ %.
(Type an integer or decimal rounded to three decimal places as needed.)

The interest in the first period is $___________.
(Round to the nearest cent as needed.)

c. The periodic rate is ___________ %.
(Type an integer or decimal rounded to three decimal places as needed.)

The interest in the first period is $___________.
(Round to the nearest cent as needed.)

d. The periodic rate is ___________ %.
(Type an integer or decimal rounded to three decimal places as needed.)

The interest in the first period is $___________.
(Round to the nearest cent as needed.)

ID: 1.1.6

---

* 7. Find the monthly interest payment in the situation described below. Assume that the monthly interest rate is 1 / 12 of the annual interest rate.

You maintain an average balance of $1050 on your credit card, which carries a 12% annual interest rate.

The monthly interest payment is $___________.
(Type an integer or a decimal.)

ID: 1.1.7

---

* 8. Find the monthly interest payment in the situation below. Assume that monthly interest rates are $\frac{1}{12}$ of annual interest rates.

Vic bought a new plasma TV for $2400. He made a down payment of $500 and then financed the balance through the store. Unfortunately, he was unable to make the first monthly payment and now pays 4% interest per month on the balance (while he watches his TV).

What is Vic's monthly interest payment?

$___________ (Round to the nearest dollar as needed.)

ID: 1.1.8

---

* 9. For the example below, prorate the given expenses to find the *monthly* cost.

Sara pays $3700 for tuition and fees for each of the two semesters, plus an additional $230 for textbooks each semester.

The prorated monthly cost for tuition and fees and textbooks is $___________.
(Round to the nearest dollar as needed.)

ID: 1.1.9

---

* 10. Prorate the following expenses and find the corresponding monthly expense.

Lan pays a semiannual premium of $550 for automobile insurance, a monthly premium of $160 for health insurance, and an annual premium of $400 for life insurance.

The monthly expense is $___________.
(Round to the nearest cent as needed.)

ID: 1.1.10

∗ 11. Prorate the following expenses and find the corresponding monthly expense.
In filing his income tax, Raul reported annual contributions of $250 to a public radio station, $220 to a public radio station, $300 to a local food bank, and $281 to other charitable organizations.

The monthly expense is $ ________.
(Round to the nearest cent as needed.)

ID: 1.1.11

∗ 12. Consider the following loan. Complete parts (a)-(c) below.
An individual borrowed $64,000 at an APR of 7%, which will be paid off with monthly payments of $467 for 23 years.

a. Identify the amount borrowed, the annual interest rate, the number of payments per year, the loan term, and the payment amount.
The amount borrowed is $ ________, the annual interest rate is ________%, the number of payments per year is ________, the loan term is ________ years, and the payment amount is $ ________.

b. How many total payments does the loan require? What is the total amount paid over the full term of the loan?
There are ________ payments toward the loan and the total amount paid is $ ________.

c. Of the total amount paid, what percentage is paid toward the principal and what percentage is paid for interest?
The percentage paid toward the principal is ________% and the percentage paid for interest is ________%.
(Round to the nearest tenth as needed.)

ID: 1.1.12

!∗ 13. Rewrite the following Excel formulas as expressions that would appear in a text.
a. = 3 + (4 − 6)/7*3 + 2
b. = 3 + (4 − 6)/(7*3) + 2
c. = 3 + (4 − 6)/7*(3 + 2)
d. = 3 + 4 − 6/7*3 + 2

a. Choose the correct answer below.

- A. $3+4-\frac{6}{7}\times 3+2$
- B. $3+\frac{4-6}{7}\times 3+2$
- C. $3+\frac{4-6}{7}\times(3+2)$
- D. $3+\frac{4-6}{7\times 3}+2$

b. Choose the correct answer below.

- A. $3+4-\frac{6}{7}\times 3+2$
- B. $3+\frac{4-6}{7\times 3}+2$
- C. $3+\frac{4-6}{7}\times 3+2$
- D. $3+\frac{4-6}{7}\times(3+2)$

c. Choose the correct answer below.

- A. $3+4-\frac{6}{7}\times 3+2$
- B. $3+\frac{4-6}{7\times 3}+2$
- C. $3+\frac{4-6}{7}\times 3+2$
- D. $3+\frac{4-6}{7}\times(3+2)$

d. Choose the correct answer below.

- A. $3+\frac{4-6}{7\times 3}+2$
- B. $3+4-\frac{6}{7}\times 3+2$
- C. $3+\frac{4-6}{7}\times 3+2$
- D. $3+\frac{4-6}{7}\times(3+2)$

ID: 1.2.1

!∗ 14. Compute the following in your head.
a. = 2/3*4
b. = 2 + 6/3 + 4
c. = 2 − 14/7
d. = 36^1/2
e. = 36^(1/2)

a. 2/3*4 = ________
(Type an integer or decimal rounded to two decimal places as needed.)

b. 2 + 6/3 + 4 = ________
(Type an integer or decimal rounded to two decimal places as needed.)

c. 2 − 14/7 = ________
(Type an integer or decimal rounded to two decimal places as needed.)

d. 36^1/2 = ________
(Type an integer or decimal rounded to two decimal places as needed.)

e. 36^(1/2) = ________
(Type an integer or decimal rounded to two decimal places as needed.)

ID: 1.2.2

!* 15. Rewrite the following expressions as a formula that can be typed into Excel.

a. $= \frac{2-3}{4} + 6$

b. $= 3 \cdot 4^{5-2}$

c. $= 4 + \frac{5-6}{9 \times 2} + 5$

d. $= \left(\frac{8}{3 \cdot 4^2}\right)^2$

a. Choose the correct answer below.

- ○ **A.** = 2 − 3/4 + 6
- ○ **B.** = (2 − 3)/4 + 6
- ○ **C.** = (2 − 3/4) + 6
- ○ **D.** = ((2 − 3)/(4 + 6))

b. Choose the correct answer below.

- ○ **A.** = 3*4^(5 − 2)
- ○ **B.** = 3*(4)^5 − 2
- ○ **C.** = 3*(4^5 − 2)
- ○ **D.** = 3*4^5 − 2

c. Choose the correct answer below.

- ○ **A.** = 4 + (5 − 6)/9*2 + 5
- ○ **B.** = 4 + (5 − 6/9*2) + 5
- ○ **C.** = 4 + (5 − 6)/(9*2) + 5
- ○ **D.** = 4 + 5 − 6/(9*2) + 5

d. Choose the correct answer below.

- ○ **A.** = (8/(3*4^2))^2
- ○ **B.** = (8/3*4^2)^2
- ○ **C.** = (8/(3*4)^2)^2
- ○ **D.** = (8/3*4)^2^2

ID: 1.2.3

16. Perform the exponentiation by hand. Then use a calculator to check your work.

2^7

$2^7 =$ __________

ID: 1.2.4

17. Perform the exponentiation by hand. Then use a calculator to check your work.

4^4

$4^4 =$ __________

ID: 1.2.5

18. Perform the exponentiation by hand. Then use a calculator to check your work.

-2^2

$-2^2 =$ __________ (Type an integer or a simplified fraction.)

ID: 1.2.6

19. Perform the exponentiation by hand. Then use a calculator to check your work.

$(-8)^2$

$(-8)^2 =$ __________

ID: 1.2.7

20. Perform the exponentiation by hand. Then use a calculator to check your work.

$\left(\frac{3}{8}\right)^3$

$\left(\frac{3}{8}\right)^3 =$ ________
(Simplify your answer.)

ID: 1.2.8

---

21. Perform the indicated operations by hand. Then use a calculator to check your work.

$(2-4)(11-7)$

$(2-4)(11-7) =$ ________ (Type an integer or a simplified fraction.)

ID: 1.2.9

---

22. Perform the indicated operations by hand. Then use a calculator to check your work.

$-6-8\cdot 5$

$-6-8\cdot 5 =$ ________ (Type an integer or a simplified fraction.)

ID: 1.2.10

---

23. Perform the indicated operations by hand. Then use a calculator to check your work.

$\frac{7}{8}-\frac{3}{4}\cdot\frac{1}{2}$

$\frac{7}{8}-\frac{3}{4}\cdot\frac{1}{2} =$ ________ (Simplify your answer.)

ID: 1.2.11

---

* 24. Perform the indicated operations by hand. Then use a calculator to check your work.

$-7(2)^2+3$

$-7(2)^2+3 =$ ________

ID: 1.2.12

---

25. Perform the indicated operations by hand. Then use a calculator to check your work.

$\frac{22-5^2}{11+2^2}$

$\frac{22-5^2}{11+2^2} =$ ________ (Type an integer or a simplified fraction.)

ID: 1.2.13

---

* 26. Use a calculator to perform the indicated operations. Round the result to two decimal places.

$18.85-32.7(19.7)+11.95\div 3.22$

$18.85-32.7(19.7)+11.95\div 3.22 =$ ________
(Round to two decimal places as needed.)

ID: 1.2.14

---

27. Evaluate the following expression for $a = -3$, $b = -6$, and $c = 2$.

$ac-b\div a$

$ac-b\div a =$ ________ (Type an integer or a simplified fraction.)

ID: 1.2.15

---

28. Evaluate the expression for $a = -4$ and $c = 6$.

a^2-c^2

$a^2-c^2 =$ ________

ID: 1.2.16

---

29. Evaluate the following expression for a = − 3, b = − 4, and c = 3.

$$\frac{-b-c^2}{4a}$$

$\frac{-b-c^2}{4a}$ = ________ (Type an integer or a simplified fraction.)

ID: 1.2.17

30. Evaluate $\frac{a-b}{c-d}$ for the given values of a, b, c, and d.

a = − 8, b = 4, c = 9, d = − 1

$\frac{a-b}{c-d}$ = ________ (Type an integer or a simplified fraction.)

ID: 1.2.18

* 31. Evaluate the expression for x = − 4.

$$-9x^2$$

$-9x^2$ = ________

ID: 1.2.19

32. Evaluate the expression for x = − 2.

$$4x^2 - 2x + 5$$

When x = − 2, $4x^2 - 2x + 5$ = ________ (Type an integer.)

ID: 1.2.20

* 33. The salary of members of two governing bodies in 2008 was $166.2 thousand, and has increased by approximately $3 thousand per year since then.
Complete parts **a.** and **b.**

(a) Complete the following table to help find an expression that stands for the salary (in thousands of dollars) of members of the two governing bodies t years since 2008.

Number of years and salaries of members of the two governing bodies.

Years since 2008	Salary (thousands of dollars)
0	(3 • ________) + ________
1	(3 • ________) + ________
2	(3 • ________) + ________
3	(3 • ________) + ________
4	(3 • ________) + ________
t	________

(Do not simplify.)

(b) Evaluate the expression that is found in part **(a)** for t =7. What does your result mean in this situation?

The value of the expression for t = 7 is ________.

This means that the salary will be about $________ thousand in year ________.

ID: 1.2.21

34. The number of pieces of equipment stolen from a country's construction sites was 1384 in 2005, and has increased by approximately 123 pieces per year since then.
Complete parts **a.** and **b.**

(a) Complete the following table to help find an expression that stands for the number of pieces of equipment stolen at t years since 2005.

Number of years and pieces of stolen equipment

Years since 2005	Number of pieces of stolen equipment
0	(123 • ________) + ________
1	(123 • ________) + ________
2	(123 • ________) + ________
3	(123 • ________) + ________
4	(123 • ________) + ________
t	________

(Do not simplify.)

(b). Evaluate the expression that you found in part **(a)** for t = 6. What does your result mean in this situation?

The value of the expression for t = 6 is ________.

This means that the number of pieces of equipment stolen will be about ________ in ________.

ID: 1.2.22

35. The population of a city was about 177 thousand in 1980 and has decreased by about 5 thousand per year since then.
a. Complete the table to help find an expression that stands for the population of this city (in thousands) at t years since 1980. Show the arithmetic to help you see a pattern.
b. Evaluate the expression that you found in part (a) for t = 27.

a.

Years Since 1980	Population (thousands)
0	______
1	______
2	______
3	______
4	______
t	______

b. When t = 27 the population is ______ thousand.

ID: 1.2.23

36. Let x be a number. Translate the following English phrase into a mathematical expression. Then evaluate the expression for $x = -6$.

4 more than the product of -6 and the number

Translate the given English phrase into the mathematical expression.

______ (Do not simplify.)

Evaluate the previous expression for $x = -6$.

______ (Type an integer or a simplified fraction.)

ID: 1.2.24

37. Let x be a number. Translate the following English phrase into a mathematical expression. Then evaluate the expression for $x = -5$.

-4 minus the quotient of 30 and the number

Translate the given English phrase into the mathematical expression.

______

Evaluate the previous expression for $x = -5$.

______ (Type an integer or a simplified fraction.)

ID: 1.2.25

38. Let x be a number. Translate the English phrase or sentence into a mathematical expression. Then evaluate the expression for x = 16.

Subtract 13 from the quotient of the number and 4.

Select the expression that correctly translates the statement.

○ **A.** $\frac{x}{4} - 13$

○ **B.** $13 - \frac{x}{4}$

○ **C.** $\frac{4}{x} - 13$

○ **D.** $(x)(4) - 13$

Evaluate the expression for x = 16.

______

ID: 1.2.26

39. If a cube has sides of length s feet, then the volume of the cube is s^3 cubic feet. Find the volume of a cubic box with sides of length 2 feet.

The volume is ______ cubic feet.

ID: 1.2.27

!* 40. What is the formula you would type into cell E2 (using all cell references) to compute the monthly payment of a car loan for $17,000 at 6% for 5 years?

	A	B	C	D	E
1	P	APR	n	t	PMT
2	$17,000	6%	12	5	$328.66

$$PMT = \frac{P \times \frac{APR}{12}}{\left(1 - \left(1 + \frac{APR}{12}\right)^{-nt}\right)}$$

Choose the correct answer below.

- ○ **A.** = (A2*B2/C2)/1 − (1 + B2/C2)^(− C2*D2)
- ○ **B.** = (A2*B2/C2)/(1 − (1 + B2/C2)^ − C2*D2)
- ○ **C.** = A2*B2/C2/(1 − (1 + B2/C2)^(− C2*D2))
- ○ **D.** = (A2*B2/C2)/(1 − (1 + B2/C2)^(− C2*D2))

ID: 1.2.28

41. Solve.

$5 + n = 8$

The solution is n = ________.
(Simplify your answer.)

ID: 1.2.29

42. Solve.

$n - 14 = 17$

The solution is n = ________.
(Simplify your answer.)

ID: 1.2.30

43. Solve and check.

$7x = 42$

The solution is x = ________.

ID: 1.2.31

* 44. Solve and check.

$9x - 3 = 60$

The solution is x = ________.

ID: 1.2.32

45. Solve the equation for the unknown quantity.

$7y + 6 = 6y - 1$

y = ________ (Simplify your answer.)

ID: 1.2.33

46. Solve the equation.

$5x + 8 = 2x + 44$

x = ________

ID: 1.2.34

47. Use the four basic rules of algebra to solve the following equation.

$6x - 32 = 60 + 4x$

x = ________ (Simplify your answer.)

ID: 1.2.35

48. Solve and check your solution.

$$\frac{x}{5} + 3 = 10$$

x = ____________ (Type an integer or a simplified fraction.)

ID: 1.2.36

---

49. Solve for x.

$$x^2 = 36$$

Select the correct choice below and, if necessary, fill in the answer box to complete your choice.

○ **A.** x = ____________
(Simplify your answer. Type an exact answer, using radicals as needed. Use a comma to separate answers as needed.)

○ **B.** The equation has no real solutions.

ID: 1.2.37

---

50. Solve for x.

$$(x - 5)^2 = 1$$

Select the correct choice below and, if necessary, fill in the answer box to complete your choice.

○ **A.** x = ____________
(Simplify your answer. Type an exact answer, using radicals as needed. Use a comma to separate answers as needed.)

○ **B.** The equation has no real solutions.

ID: 1.2.38

---

51. Use the four basic rules of algebra to solve the following equation.

$$\left(\frac{y}{5}\right)^2 = 81$$

y = ____________
(Simplify your answer. Use a comma to separate answers as needed.)

ID: 1.2.39

---

52. Solve the following equation.

$$u^5 = 243$$

u = ____________
(Type a whole number.)

ID: 1.2.40

---

* 53. Consider a student loan of $25,000 at a fixed APR of 6% for 25 years.

a. Calculate the monthly payment.
b. Determine the total amount paid over the term of the loan.
c. Of the total amount paid, what percentage is paid toward the principal and what percentage is paid for interest.

a. The monthly payment is $ ____________.
(Do not round until the final answer. Then round to the nearest cent as needed.)

b. The total payment over the term of the loan is $ ____________.
(Round to the nearest cent as needed.)

c. Of the total payment over the term of the loan, ____________ % is paid toward the principal and ____________ % is paid toward interest.
(Round to the nearest tenth as needed.)

ID: 1.2.41

---

54. Consider a home mortgage of $175,000 at a fixed APR of 4.5% for 20 years.

a. Calculate the monthly payment.
b. Determine the total amount paid over the term of the loan.
c. Of the total amount paid, what percentage is paid toward the principal and what percentage is paid for interest.

a. The monthly payment is $__________.
(Do not round until the final answer. Then round to the nearest cent as needed.)

b. The total amount paid over the term of the loan is $__________.
(Round to the nearest cent as needed.)

c. Of the total amount paid, __________% is paid toward the principal, and __________% is paid for interest.
(Round to one decimal place as needed.)

ID: 1.2.42

---

55. Consider a home mortgage of $150,000 at a fixed APR of 3% for 25 years.

a. Calculate the monthly payment.
b. Determine the total amount paid over the term of the loan.
c. Of the total amount paid, what percentage is paid toward the principal and what percentage is paid for interest.

a. The monthly payment is $__________.
(Do not round until the final answer. Then round to the nearest cent as needed.)

b. The total amount paid over the term of the loan is $__________.
(Round to the nearest cent as needed.)

c. Of the total amount paid, __________% is paid toward the principal, and __________% is paid for interest.
(Round to one decimal place as needed.)

ID: 1.2.43

---

56. Consider a student loan of $17,500 at a fixed APR of 9% for 4 years.

a. Calculate the monthly payment.
b. Determine the total amount paid over the term of the loan.
c. Of the total amount paid, what percentage is paid toward the principal and what percentage is paid for interest.

a. The monthly payment is $__________.
(Do not round until the final answer. Then round to the nearest cent as needed.)

b. The total amount paid over the course of the loan is $__________.
(Round to the nearest cent as needed.)

c. Of the total amount paid, __________% is paid toward the principal and __________% is paid for interest.
(Round to once decimal place as needed.)

ID: 1.2.44

---

57. Consider a home mortgage of $125,000 at a fixed APR of 12% for 15 years.

a. Calculate the monthly payment.
b. Determine the total amount paid over the term of the loan.
c. Of the total amount paid, what percentage is paid toward the principal and what percentage is paid for interest.

a. The monthly payment is $__________.
(Do not round until the final answer. Then round to the nearest cent as needed.)

b. The total payment over the term of the loan is $__________.
(Round to the nearest cent as needed.)

c. Of the total payment over the term of the loan, __________% is paid toward the principal and __________% is paid toward interest.
(Round to the nearest tenth as needed.)

ID: 1.2.45

---

58. For the following loan, make a table showing the amount of each monthly payment that goes toward principal and interest for the first three months of the loan.

A home mortgage of $142,000 with a fixed APR of 6% for 30 years.

Fill out the table.

End of...	Interest	Payment Toward Principal	New Principal
Month 1	$ ______	$ ______	$ ______

(Round the final answers to the nearest cent as needed. Round all intermediate values to six decimal places as needed.)

Fill out the table.

End of...	Interest	Payment Toward Principal	New Principal
Month 2	$ ______	$ ______	$ ______

(Round the final answers to the nearest cent as needed. Round all intermediate values to six decimal places as needed.)

Fill out the table.

End of...	Interest	Payment Toward Principal	New Principal
Month 3	$ ______	$ ______	$ ______

(Round the final answers to the nearest cent as needed. Round all intermediate values to six decimal places as needed.)

ID: 1.2.46

---

59. Someone needs to borrow $11,000 to buy a car and the person has determined that monthly payments of $250 are affordable. The bank offers a 3-year loan at 7% APR, a 4-year loan at 7.5%, or a 5-year loan at 8% APR. Which loan best meets the person's needs? Explain.

Which loan best meets the person's needs?
(Round the final answer to the nearest cent as needed. Round all intermediate values to six decimal places as needed.)

- ○ **A.** The third loan best meets the person's needs because the monthly payment of $ ______ is less than the maximum budgeted amount of $250 per month.
- ○ **B.** The first loan best meets the person's needs because the monthly payment of $ ______ is less than the maximum budgeted amount of $250 per month.
- ○ **C.** The second loan best meets the person's needs because the monthly payment of $ ______ is less than the maximum budgeted amount of $250 per month.
- ○ **D.** None of the loans meet the person's needs.

ID: 1.2.47

!* 60. Rewrite the Excel formula, = F4 * E7 − H6, after it has been moved as specified below.
a. down 2 cells
b. right 4 cells (starting with formula = F4 * E7 − H6)
c. up 3 cells (starting with formula = F4 * E7 − H6)
d. left 1 cell (starting with formula = F4 * E7 − H6)

a. Choose the correct answer below.

- ○ **A.** = D4 * C7 − F6
- ○ **B.** = F1 * E4 − H3
- ○ **C.** = H4 * G7 − J6
- ○ **D.** = F6 * E9 − H8

b. Choose the correct answer below.

- ○ **A.** = F8 * E11 − H10
- ○ **B.** = J4 * I7 − L6
- ○ **C.** = F1 * E3 − H2
- ○ **D.** = E4 * D7 − G6

c. Choose the correct answer below.

- ○ **A.** = I4 * H7 − K6
- ○ **B.** = F6 * E9 − H8
- ○ **C.** = C4 * B7 − E6
- ○ **D.** = F1 * E4 − H3

d. Choose the correct answer below.

- ○ **A.** = F5 * E8 − H7
- ○ **B.** = E4 * D7 − G6
- ○ **C.** = F3 * E6 − H5
- ○ **D.** = J4 * I7 − L6

ID: 1.3.1

!* 61. Rewrite the Excel formula = E$4*$D$3 − $B2 after it has been moved as specified below.
(a) down 2 cells
(b) right 3 cells (starting with formula = E$4*$D$3 − $B2)
(c) up 1 cell (starting with formula = E$4*$D$3 − $B2)
(d) left 1 cell (starting with formula = E$4*$D$3 − $B2)

(a) Choose the correct answer below.

- **A.** = H$4*$G$3 − $E2
- **B.** = E$4*$D$3 − $B2
- **C.** = E$4*$D$3 − $B4
- **D.** = E$6*$D$5 − $B4

(b) Choose the correct answer below.

- **A.** = H$4*$G$3 − $E2
- **B.** = E$7*$D$6 − $B5
- **C.** = H$4*$D$3 − $B2
- **D.** = E$4*$D$3 − $B5

(c) Choose the correct answer below.

- **A.** = F$4*$E$3 − $C2
- **B.** = E$3*$D$2 − $B1
- **C.** = F$4*$D$3 − $B2
- **D.** = E$4*$D$3 − $B1

(d) Choose the correct answer below.

- **A.** = D$5*$D$4 − $B3
- **B.** = F$4*$E$3 − $C2
- **C.** = E$4*$D$3 − $B3
- **D.** = D$4*$D$3 − $B2

ID: 1.3.2

---

62. Write a short statement that expresses a possible relationship between the variables.
(size of file, time to download the file)

Choose the correct answer below.

- **A.** As the size of a file increases, the time to download the file increases.
- **B.** As the time to download a file increases, the size of the file decreases.
- **C.** As the size of a file increases, the time to download the file decreases.
- **D.** As the time to download a file increases, the size of the file increases.

ID: 1.3.3

---

63. Write a short statement that expresses a possible relationship between the variables.
(volume of gas tank, cost to fill the tank)

Choose the correct answer below.

- **A.** As the volume of a gas tank decreases, the cost to fill the tank increases.
- **B.** As the volume of a gas tank decreases, the cost to fill the tank decreases.
- **C.** As the cost to fill a gas tank decreases, the volume of the tank increases.
- **D.** As the cost to fill a gas tank decreases, the volume of the tank decreases.

ID: 1.3.4

---

64. Write a short statement that expresses a possible relationship between the variables.
(latitude, ocean temperature on a given day)

Choose the correct answer below.

- **A.** As the ocean temperature on a given day increases, the latitude decreases.
- **B.** As the latitude increases, the ocean temperature on a given day decreases.
- **C.** As the latitude increases, the ocean temperature on a given day increases.
- **D.** As the ocean temperature on a given day increases, the latitude increases.

ID: 1.3.5

---

65. Use the graph on the right to answer the following questions.

a. Estimate the pressure at altitudes of 9,000 feet, 18,000 feet, and 21,000 feet.
b. Estimate the altitudes at which the pressure is 23, 19, and 11 inches of mercury.
c. Estimating beyond the boundaries of the graph, at what altitude do you think the atmospheric pressure reaches 5 inches of mercury? Is there an altitude at which the pressure is exactly zero? Explain your reasoning.

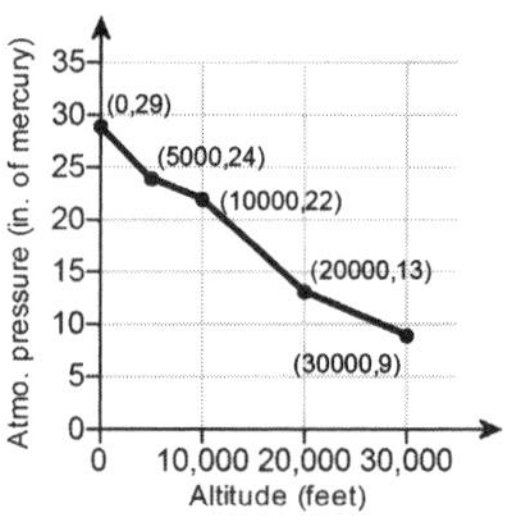

a. The pressure at 9,000 feet is ________ inches of mercury, the pressure at 18,000 feet is ________ inches of mercury, and the pressure at 21,000 feet is ________ inches of mercury.
(Round to the nearest integer as needed.)

b. The altitude for which the pressure is 23 inches of mercury is ________ feet, the altitude for which the pressure is 19 inches of mercury is ________ feet, and the altitude for which the pressure is 11 inches of mercury is ________ feet.
(Round to the nearest thousand as needed.)

c. The altitude at which the atmospheric pressure reaches 5 is approximately ________.
(Round to the nearest thousand as needed.)

Explain whether there is an altitude at which the pressure is exactly zero. Choose the correct answer below.

○ **A.** The pressure reaches zero at an altitude of ________ feet.
○ **B.** The pressure approaches zero, but theoretically never reaches zero.

ID: 1.3.6

---

*66. Consider the graph of the function below.

a. Identify the independent and dependent variables, and describe the domain and range.

b. Describe the function in words.

a. The independent variable is the (1) ________ and the dependent variable is the (2) ________

The domain of the function is the (3) ________ from the minimum value of ________ to the maximum value of ________.

The range of the function is the (4) ________ from the minimum value of ________ billion to the maximum value of ________ billion.
(Round to the nearest integer as needed.)

b. Choose the correct description below.

○ **A.** The function shows a steady increase in population from 1950 to 2000.
○ **B.** The function shows that the rate of increase in population has been increasing since 1950.
○ **C.** The function shows that there has been a relatively constant world population since 1950.
○ **D.** The function shows an initial increase in population, but then a decrease in population closer to 2000.

(1) ○ year ○ population (2) ○ population. ○ year. (3) ○ years ○ populations (4) ○ populations ○ years

ID: 1.3.7

---

*67. The data table below represents a function and shows the average high temperature on certain days of the year.
a. Identify the independent and dependent variables, and describe the domain and the range.
b. Make a clear graph of the function.
c. Describe the function in words.

Jan. 1	Feb. 1	Mar.1	Apr. 1	May 1	June 1	July 1	Aug. 1	Sep. 1	Oct. 1	Nov. 1	Dec. 1	Dec. 31
43°F	39°F	46°F	59°F	68°F	77°F	85°F	81°F	81°F	65°F	54°F	49°F	44°F

a. The independent variable is (1) ________ and the dependent variable is (2) ________ The domain of the function is (3) ________ over the course of a year and the range of the function is temperatures between (4) ________ °F.

***67. (cont.)** b. Choose the correct graph below.

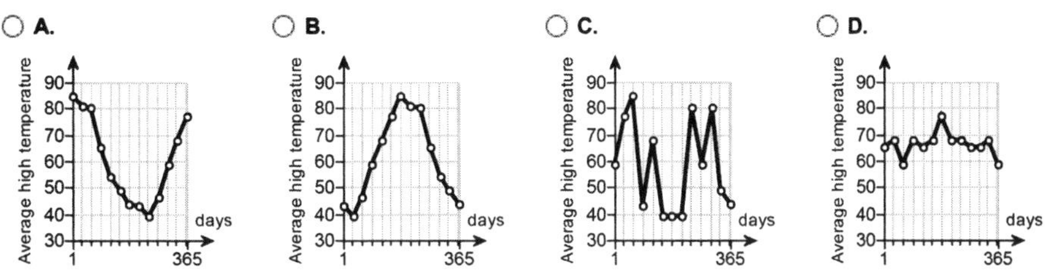

c. Choose the correct description below.

○ **A.** The temperature decreases during the first half of the year and then increases during the second half of the year.

○ **B.** The temperature increases during the first half of the year and then decreases during the second half of the year.

○ **C.** There is no discernible pattern in the temperature throughout the year.

○ **D.** The temperature stays relatively constant throughout the year.

(1) ○ time ○ temperature (2) ○ time. ○ temperature. (3) ○ all days ○ certain days (4) ○ 39 and 85 ○ 43 and 44

ID: 1.3.8

---

68. 10, The following data table represents a function.

a. Identify the independent and dependent variables, and describe the domain and range.

b. Make a clear graph of the function.

c. Describe the function in words.

Speed (mi / hr)	Stopping Distance (reaction plus braking in ft)
10	14
20	38
30	76
40	110
50	166
60	222
70	329

a. The independent variable is (1) ____________ and the dependent variable is (2) ____________

The domain of the function consists of all the (3) ____________ from the minimum value of ____________ to the maximum value of ____________.

The range of the function consists of all the (4) ____________ from the minimum value of ____________ to the maximum value of ____________.

b. Make a clear graph of the function. Choose the correct graph below.

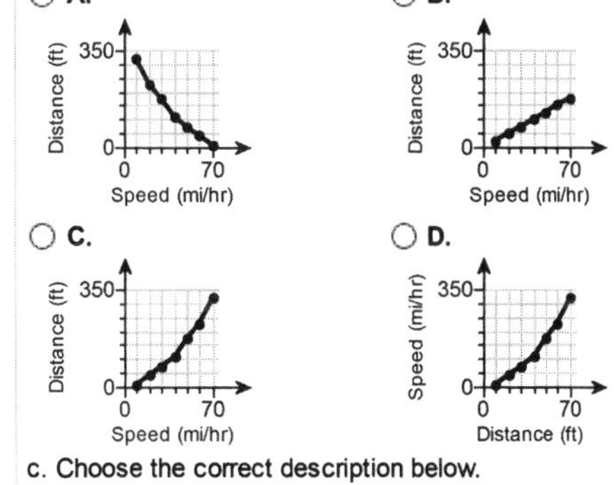

c. Choose the correct description below.

○ **A.** The rate at which the stopping distance decreases grows faster as speed increases.

○ **B.** The function shows a constant rate of increase in stopping distance relative to speed.

○ **C.** The rate at which the stopping distance increases grows faster as speed increases.

○ **D.** The rate at which the speed increases grows faster as stopping distance.

(1) ○ speed ○ stopping distance (2) ○ speed. ○ stopping distance. (3) ○ speeds ○ distances (4) ○ distances

ID: 1.3.9

* 69. Do the following for the function given below.

(altitude, temperature) when climbing a mountain

a. Describe an appropriate domain and range for the function.
b. Make a rough sketch of a graph of the function.
c. Briefly discuss the validity of the graph as a model of the true function.

a. Choose the appropriate domain for the function below.

- **A.** The domain is all altitudes of interest or 0 ft to 15,000 ft.
- **B.** The domain is all temperatures corresponding to altitudes of interest or 0°F to 90°F.
- **C.** The domain is all temperatures corresponding to altitudes of interest or 70°F to 90°F.
- **D.** The domain is all altitudes of interest or 0 ft to 50,000 ft.

Choose the appropriate range for the function below.

- **A.** The range is all altitudes of interest or 0 ft to 50,000 ft.
- **B.** The range is all temperatures corresponding to altitudes of interest or 70°F to 90°F.
- **C.** The range is all temperatures corresponding to altitudes of interest or 0°F to 90°F.
- **D.** The range is all altitudes of interest or 0 ft to 15,000 ft.

b. Make a rough sketch of a graph of the function. Choose the correct graph below. Let a represent altitude of a mountain and F represent temperature in degrees Fahrenheit.

A.

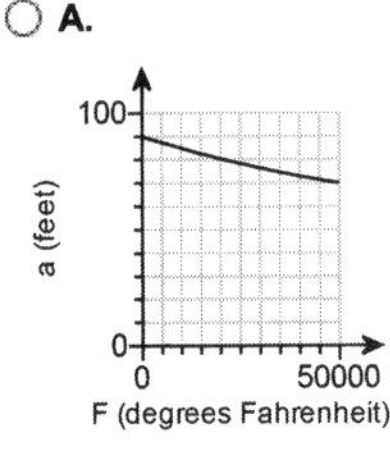

B.

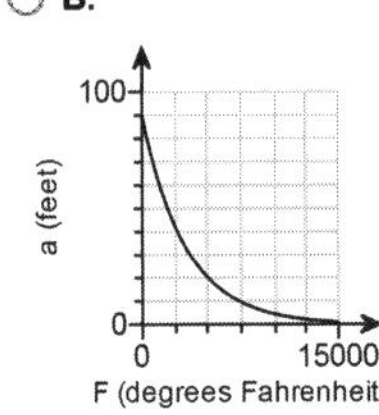

C.

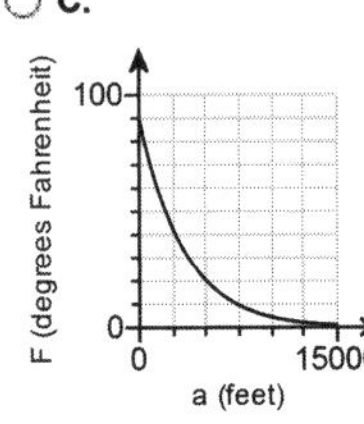

D.

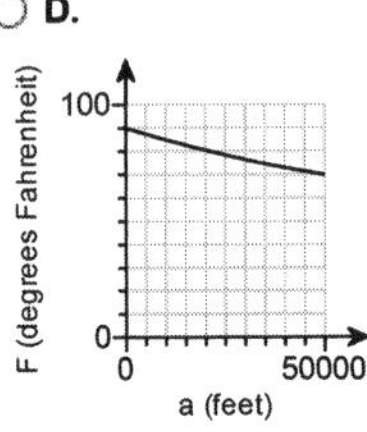

c. Briefly discuss the validity of the graph as a model of the true function. Choose the correct answer below.

- **A.** The graph is not a valid model of the true function.
- **B.** The graph is a valid model of the function because altitude of a mountain decreases as temperature in degrees Fahrenheit increases.
- **C.** The validity of the graph as a model of the true function can never be known.
- **D.** The graph is a valid model of the function because temperature in degrees Fahrenheit decreases as altitude of a mountain increases.

ID: 1.3.10

---

70. For the given function, use your intuition or additional research, if necessary, to complete parts (a) through (c) below.

(weight of car, average gas mileage)

a. Describe an appropriate domain and range for the function.
b. Make a rough sketch of a graph of the function.
c. Briefly discuss the validity of the graph as a model of the true function.

a. Choose the appropriate domain for the function below.

- **A.** The domain is all average gas mileages of cars of various weights or 5 mi / gal to 300 mi / gal.
- **B.** The domain is the typical weights of all cars or 1000 pounds to 8000 pounds.
- **C.** The domain is the typical weights of all cars or 100 pounds to 800 pounds.
- **D.** The domain is all average gas mileages of cars of various weights or 15 mi / gal to 35 mi / gal.

Choose the appropriate range for the function below.

- **A.** The range is all average gas mileages of cars of various weights or 5 mi / gal to 300 mi / gal.
- **B.** The range is the typical weights of all cars or 100 pounds to 800 pounds.
- **C.** The range is the typical weights of all cars or 1000 pounds to 8000 pounds.
- **D.** The range is all average gas mileages of cars of various weights or 15 mi / gal to 35 mi / gal.

b. Make a rough sketch of a graph of the function. Choose the correct graph below. Let w represent weight of a car and m represent gas mileage of a car.

A.

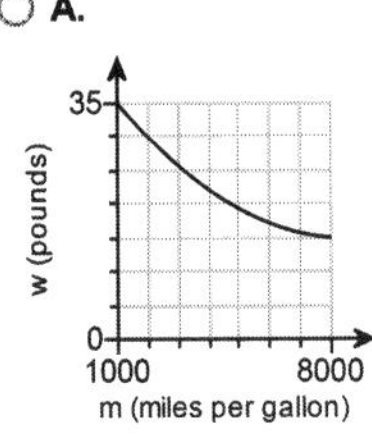

B.

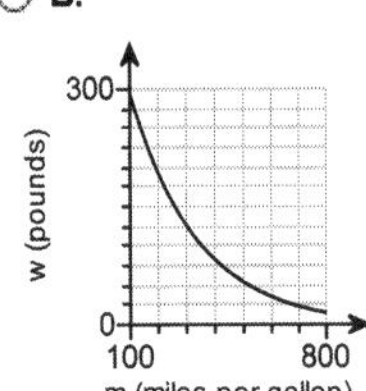

C.

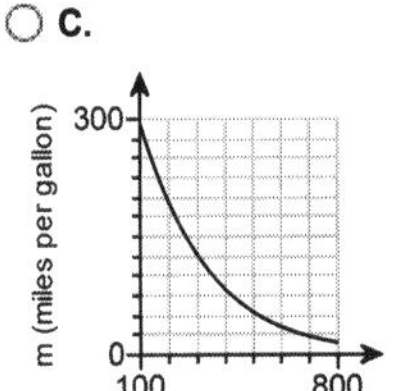

D.

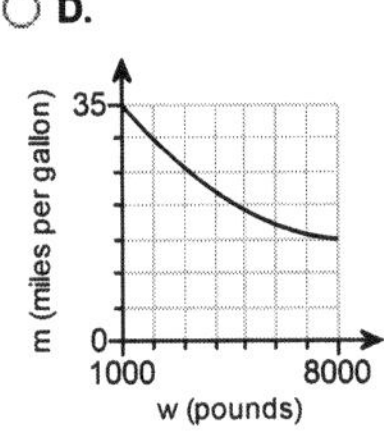

70. (cont.) c. Briefly discuss the validity of the graph as a model of the true function. Choose the correct answer below.

- ○ **A.** The graph is a valid model of the function because gas mileage of a car decreases as weight of a car increases.
- ○ **B.** The validity of the graph as a model of the true function can never be known.
- ○ **C.** The graph is not a valid model of the true function.
- ○ **D.** The graph is a valid model of the function because weight of a car decreases as gas mileage of a car increases.

ID: 1.3.11

---

71. Do the following for the function (time of day, temperature) over the course of one full day in the desert, where t is the number of hours after 7 A.M. Saturday and F is the temperature in degrees Fahrenheit.

a. Describe an appropriate domain and range for the function.
b. Make a rough sketch of a graph for the function.
c. Briefly discuss the validity of your graph as a model of the true function.

a. Choose the appropriate domain for the function below.

- ○ **A.** The domain of the function consists of all temperatures between 85°F and 90°F.
- ○ **B.** The domain of the function consists of all times between 0 and 24.
- ○ **C.** The domain of the function consists of all times between 7 A.M. Saturday and 7 P.M. Sunday.
- ○ **D.** The domain of the function consists of all temperatures between 40°F and 90°F.

Choose the appropriate range for the function below.

- ○ **A.** The range of the function consists of all times between 0 and 24.
- ○ **B.** The range of the function consists of all times between 7 A.M. Saturday and 7 P.M. Sunday.
- ○ **C.** The range of the function consists of all temperatures between 85°F and 90°F.
- ○ **D.** The range of the function consists of all temperatures between 40°F and 90°F.

b. Make a rough sketch of a graph for the function. Choose the correct graph below. Recall that t is the number of hours after 7 A.M. Saturday and F is the temperature in degrees Fahrenheit.

○ **A.**

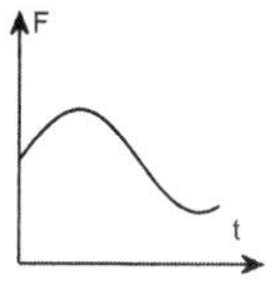

○ **B.**

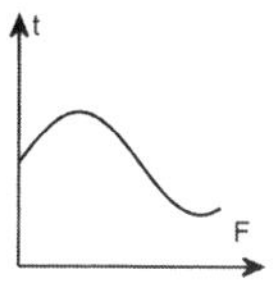

○ **C.**

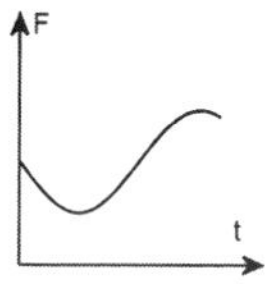

○ **D.**

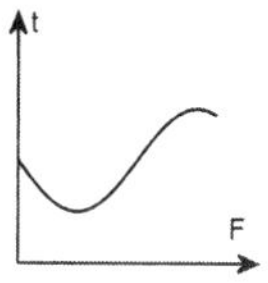

c. Briefly discuss the validity of your graph as a model of the true function. Choose the correct answer below.

- ○ **A.** The graph is a valid model because the temperature in the desert is hot at night and cool during the day.
- ○ **B.** The graph is a valid model because the temperature in the desert is consistently hot throughout the day.
- ○ **C.** The graph is a valid model because the temperature in the desert is consistently cool throughout the day.
- ○ **D.** The graph is a valid model because the temperature in the desert is cool at night and hot during the day.

ID: 1.3.12

---

72. Do the following for the function given below.

(number of inputs to a password, total number of different possible combinations)

a. Describe an appropriate domain and range for the function.
b. Make a rough sketch of a graph of the function.
c. Briefly discuss the validity of the graph as a model of the true function.

a. Describe an appropriate domain and range for the function.

- ○ **A.** The domain and range are interchangeable.
- ○ **B.** There is not enough information given in the problem statement to determine the domain and range.
- ○ **C.** The domain is the total number of different password combinations corresponding to the number of inputs and the range is the number of inputs to a password, say $n = 2$ through $n = 8$.
- ○ **D.** The domain is the number of inputs to a password, say $n = 2$ through $n = 8$ and the range is the total number of different password combinations corresponding to the number of inputs.

72. (cont.) b. Make a rough sketch of a graph of the function. Choose the correct graph below. Let n represent number of inputs to a password and f(n) represent the total number of different password combinations corresponding to the number of inputs.

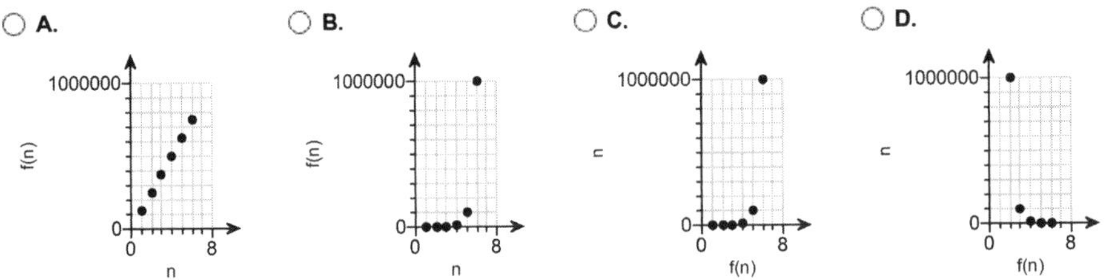

c. Briefly discuss the validity of the graph as a model of the true function. Choose the correct answer below.

- A. The graph is not a valid model of the true function.
- B. The graph is a valid model of the function because number of inputs to a password decreases as the total number of different password combinations corresponding to the number of inputs increases.
- C. The graph is a valid model of the function because total number of different password combinations increases as the number of inputs to the password increases.
- D. The validity of the graph as a model of the true function can never be known.

ID: 1.3.13

---

73. Do the following for the function given below.

(speed, stopping distance of a car)

a. Describe an appropriate domain and range for the function.
b. Make a rough sketch of a graph of the function.
c. Briefly discuss the validity of the graph as a model of the true function.

a. Choose the appropriate domain for the function below.

- A. The domain is stopping distances for each of the given speeds; 10 feet to 350 feet.
- B. The domain is realistic car speeds; 10 feet per second to 70 feet per hour.
- C. The domain is realistic car speeds; 10 miles per hour to 70 miles per hour.
- D. The domain is stopping distances for each of the given speeds; 10 miles to 350 miles.

Choose the appropriate range for the function below.

- A. The range is stopping distances for each of the given speeds; 10 feet to 350 feet.
- B. The range is realistic car speeds; 10 feet per second to 70 feet per hour.
- C. The range is realistic car speeds; 10 miles per hour to 70 miles per hour.
- D. The range is stopping distances for each of the given speeds; 10 miles to 350 miles.

b. Make a rough sketch of a graph of the function. Choose the correct graph below. Let v represent speed in miles per hour and d represent stopping distance in feet.

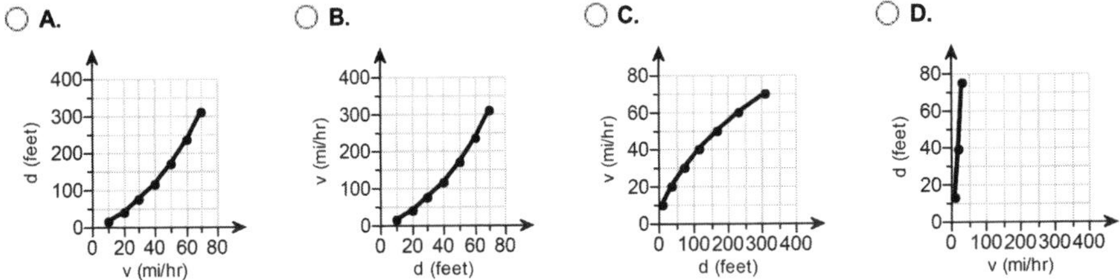

c. Briefly discuss the validity of the graph as a model of the true function. Choose the correct answer below.

- A. The validity of the graph as a model of the true function can never be known.
- B. The graph is not a valid model of the true function.
- C. The graph is a valid model of the function because it is reasonable to assume that stopping distance in feet increases as speed in miles per hour increases.
- D. The graph is a valid model of the function because it is reasonable to assume that speed in miles per hour increases as stopping distance in feet increases.

ID: 1.3.14

74. For the given function, use your intuition or additional research, if necessary, to complete parts (a) through (c) below.

(angle of cannon, horizontal distance traveled by cannonball)

a. Describe an appropriate domain and range for the function.
b. Make a rough sketch of a graph of the function.
c. Briefly discuss the validity of the graph as a model of the true function.

a. Choose the appropriate domain for the function below.

- ○ **A.** The domain is the horizontal distances traveled by the cannon shot at certain angles or 0 ft to 3500 mi.
- ○ **B.** The domain is all angles a cannon could be shot at or 0° to 360°.
- ○ **C.** The domain is all angles a cannon could be shot at or 0° to 90°.
- ○ **D.** The domain is the horizontal distances traveled by the cannon shot at certain angles or 0 ft to 3500 ft.

Choose the appropriate range for the function below.

- ○ **A.** The range is all angles a cannon could be shot at or 0° to 360°.
- ○ **B.** The range is the horizontal distances traveled by the cannon shot at certain angles or 0 ft to 3500 mi.
- ○ **C.** The range is the horizontal distances traveled by the cannon shot at certain angles or 0 ft to 3500 ft.
- ○ **D.** The range is all angles a cannon could be shot at or 0° to 90°.

b. Make a rough sketch of a graph of the function. Choose the correct graph below. Let a represent angle of a cannon and d represent horizontal distance a cannonball travels.

○ **A.** ○ **B.** ○ **C.** ○ **D.**

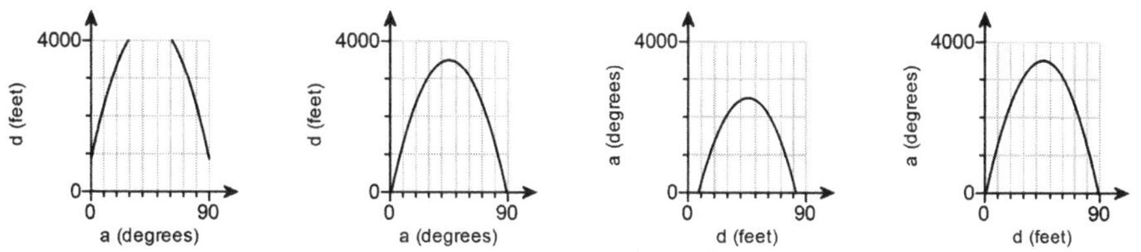

c. Briefly discuss the validity of the graph as a model of the true function. Choose the correct answer below.

- ○ **A.** The validity of the graph as a model of the true function can never be known.
- ○ **B.** The graph is a valid model of the function because angle of a cannon increases then decreases as horizontal distance a cannonball travels increases.
- ○ **C.** The graph is a valid model of the function because horizontal distance a cannonball travels increases then decreases as angle of a cannon increases.
- ○ **D.** The graph is not a valid model of the true function.

ID: 1.3.15

!* 75. Use the Excel screenshot available below to answer parts (a) through (c).
[1] Click the icon to view the screenshot.

a. What type of chart is shown?

- ○ Clustered bar
- ○ Clustered column
- ○ Pie chart
- ○ Stacked 100% bar

b. What do the columns represent?

- ○ **A.** Monthly car payments for a 5 year loan from 1 to 10 months
- ○ **B.** Monthly car payments for 5 months and APR's ranging from 1% to 10%
- ○ **C.** Monthly car payments for a loan with a 5% APR and terms ranging from 1 to 6 years
- ○ **D.** Monthly car payments for a 5 year loan and APR's ranging from 1% to 10%

c. To add the APR values as Category x-axis labels we must click on what icon?

- ○ Select Data
- ○ Switch Row/Column
- ○ Quick Layout
- ○ Add Chart Element

!* 75. (cont.) 1: Excel Screenshot.

	A	B	C	D	E	F	G	H
1	**P**	**APR**	**n**	**t**	**PMT**			
2	$15,000.00	6%	12	5	$289.99			
3								
4		**Table Showing Monthly Payments for Different APRs and Terms**						
5			**Term: Number of years (t)**					
6		**APR**	1	2	3	4	5	6
7		**1%**	$1,256.78	$631.53	$423.12	$318.92	$256.41	$214.73
8		**2%**	$1,263.58	$638.10	$429.64	$325.43	$262.92	$221.26
9		**3%**	$1,270.41	$644.72	$436.22	$332.01	$269.53	$227.91
10		**4%**	$1,277.25	$651.37	$442.86	$338.69	$276.25	$234.68
11		**5%**	$1,284.11	$658.07	$449.56	$345.44	$283.07	$241.57
12		**6%**	$1,291.00	$664.81	$456.33	$352.28	$289.99	$248.59
13		**7%**	$1,297.90	$671.59	$463.16	$359.19	$297.02	$255.74
14		**8%**	$1,304.83	$678.41	$470.05	$366.19	$304.15	$263.00
15		**9%**	$1,311.77	$685.27	$477.00	$373.28	$311.38	$270.38
16		**10%**	$1,318.74	$692.17	484.01$	$380.44	$318.71	$277.89
17								
18								

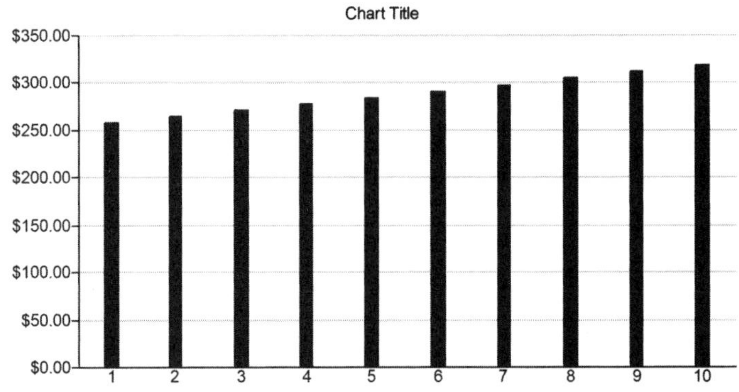

ID: 1.3.16

---

76. Net grain production is the difference between the amount of grain a country produces and the amount of grain its citizens consume. It is positive if the country produces more than it consumes, and negative if the country consumes more than it produces. The figure shows the net grain production of four countries in 1990 and projected for 2030. Complete parts **a** through **c**.

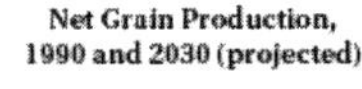

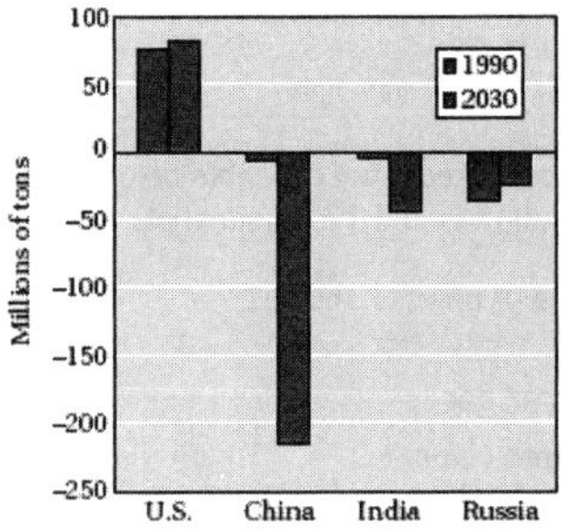

a. Which of the four countries had to import grain to meet its needs in 1990?

☐ **A.** Russia
☐ **B.** China
☐ **C.** U.S.
☐ **D.** India

b. Which of the four countries are expected to need to import grain to meet needs in 2030?

☐ **A.** Russia
☐ **B.** India
☐ **C.** U.S.
☐ **D.** China

c. Given that India and China are the world's two most populous countries, what does this graph tell you about how world agriculture will have to change between now and 2030?

○ **A.** It will need to increase.
○ **B.** It will need to decrease.
○ **C.** It can stay about the same.

ID: 1.3.17

* 77. In this figure, the graphs from top to bottom represent individuals who are not high school graduates, who have some college experience or an associate's degree, and who have a bachelor's degree or higher, in that order. Complete parts (a) and (b) below.

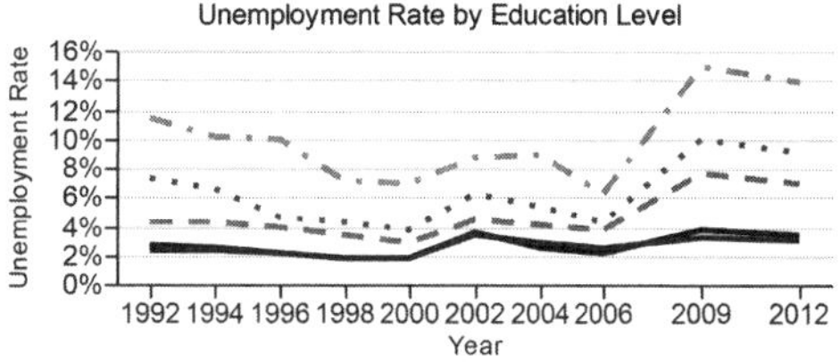

a. Briefly describe how unemployment varies with educational attainment. Choose the correct answer below.

- ○ **A.** As the level of education increases, pay rate decreases.
- ○ **B.** As the level of education increases, pay rate increases.
- ○ **C.** As the level of education increases, unemployment rates tend to increase.
- ○ **D.** Unemployment stays approximately constant regardless of level of education.
- ○ **E.** As the level of education increases, unemployment rates tend to decrease.

b. How much more likely is a high school dropout to be unemployed than a worker with a bachelor's degree?

- ○ **A.** Just as likely
- ○ **B.** About 2 to 3 times as likely
- ○ **C.** About 10 times as likely
- ○ **D.** About 5 times as likely

ID: 1.3.18

78. Consider the data displayed in the figure below. Complete parts (a) and (b).

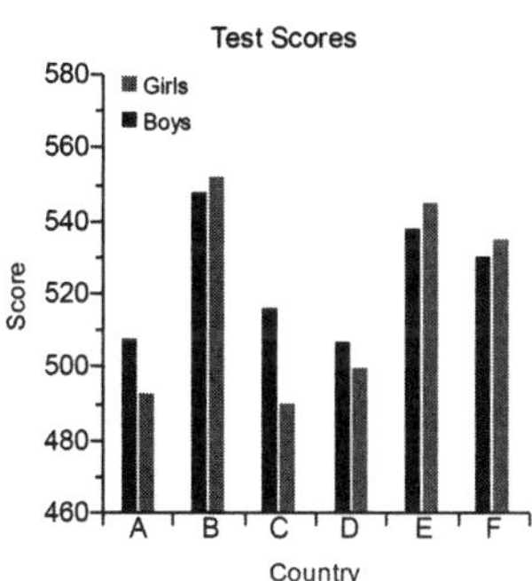

a. The bar for girls from country B is more than twice as long as the bar for girls from country C. Can it be concluded that test scores for girls from country B were more than twice as high as test scores for girls from country C? Explain.

- ○ **A.** No, because the data is only a sample of the entire population.
- ○ **B.** Yes, because the bar is more than twice as long.
- ○ **C.** Yes, because country B does far better than country C.
- ○ **D.** No, because the scale on the vertical axis does not start at 0.

b. Assume that the data in the figure represent overall regional differences in performances. Suppose that country G is in the same region as countries E and F. How can the test scores for boys and girls in country G compare?

- ○ **A.** Boys will probably score higher than girls.
- ○ **B.** Boys and girls will probably score the same.
- ○ **C.** Girls will probably score higher than boys.
- ○ **D.** Nothing can be predicted from the data.

ID: 1.3.19

* 79. Use the data in the graph to answer parts (a) through (c). [2] Click the icon to view the graph.

a. Which category varies the most among the different types of institutions? By how much?

(1) ____________ varies the most. It has a variation of $ ____________.
(Type an integer or a decimal.)

b. Excluding "other expenses" which cost category varies the least among the different types of institutions? Can you explain why this category varies so little?

- ○ **A.** Tuition and fees varies the least because the operational costs for all types of colleges are the same.
- ○ **B.** Books and supplies varies the least because students at all types of colleges need approximately the same number of books and supplies and these don't vary much in cost.
- ○ **C.** Room and board varies the least because it costs all types of colleges the same amount of money to have a student live on campus.
- ○ **D.** Transportation varies the least because students at all types of colleges have the same mode of transportation.

c. Ignoring the "other expenses" category, the general trend is for all categories to cost more as you look down the chart from two-year public colleges to four-year private colleges. However, one category is an exception to this trend. Which category? Can you explain why? (Hint: If more than one category appears to have a downward trend, focus on the category with the largest downward trend.)

- ○ **A.** Transportation because commuters must spend more money to get to school than students living on-campus
- ○ **B.** Room and board because it costs less to live on-campus than to live-off campus
- ○ **C.** Tuition and fees because two-year public colleges need to charge more to attend due to smaller enrollment numbers
- ○ **D.** Books and supplies because two-year public colleges require more books and supplies than four-year private colleges

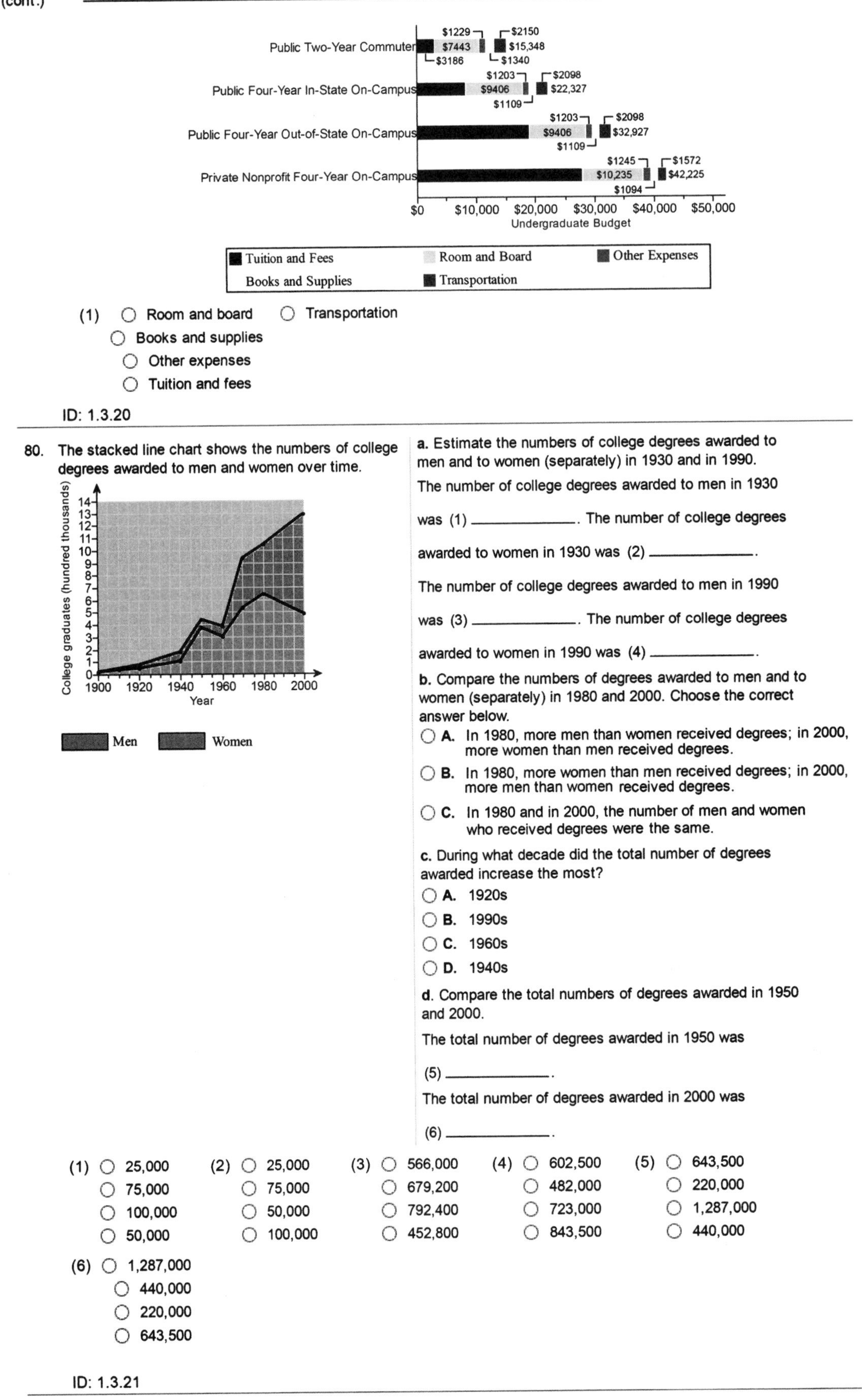

*79. (cont.) 2: Graph

(1) ○ Room and board ○ Transportation
○ Books and supplies
○ Other expenses
○ Tuition and fees

ID: 1.3.20

80. The stacked line chart shows the numbers of college degrees awarded to men and women over time.

a. Estimate the numbers of college degrees awarded to men and to women (separately) in 1930 and in 1990.

The number of college degrees awarded to men in 1930 was (1) ________. The number of college degrees awarded to women in 1930 was (2) ________.

The number of college degrees awarded to men in 1990 was (3) ________. The number of college degrees awarded to women in 1990 was (4) ________.

b. Compare the numbers of degrees awarded to men and to women (separately) in 1980 and 2000. Choose the correct answer below.

○ A. In 1980, more men than women received degrees; in 2000, more women than men received degrees.

○ B. In 1980, more women than men received degrees; in 2000, more men than women received degrees.

○ C. In 1980 and in 2000, the number of men and women who received degrees were the same.

c. During what decade did the total number of degrees awarded increase the most?

○ A. 1920s

○ B. 1990s

○ C. 1960s

○ D. 1940s

d. Compare the total numbers of degrees awarded in 1950 and 2000.

The total number of degrees awarded in 1950 was

(5) ________.

The total number of degrees awarded in 2000 was

(6) ________.

(1) ○ 25,000 ○ 75,000 ○ 100,000 ○ 50,000

(2) ○ 25,000 ○ 75,000 ○ 50,000 ○ 100,000

(3) ○ 566,000 ○ 679,200 ○ 792,400 ○ 452,800

(4) ○ 602,500 ○ 482,000 ○ 723,000 ○ 843,500

(5) ○ 643,500 ○ 220,000 ○ 1,287,000 ○ 440,000

(6) ○ 1,287,000 ○ 440,000 ○ 220,000 ○ 643,500

ID: 1.3.21

81. The accompanying line chart shows the major spending categories of the federal budget over the last 50 years. (Payments to individuals includes Social Security and Medicare; net interest represents interest payments on the national debt; all other represents non-defense discretionary spending.) Complete parts (a) through (c) below.

[3] Click the icon to view the line chart.

a. Find the percentage of the budget that went to net interest in 1980 and 2012.

The percentage of the budget that went to net interest in 1980 is approximately ________ %.
(Round to the nearest integer as needed.)

The percentage of the budget that went to net interest 2012 is approximately ________ %.
(Round to the nearest integer as needed.)

b. Find the percentage of the budget that went to defense in 1990 and 2012.

The percentage of the budget that went to national defense in 1990 is approximately ________ %.
(Round to the nearest integer as needed.)

The percentage of the budget that went to national defense in 2012 is approximately ________ %.
(Round to the nearest integer as needed.)

c. Find the percentage of the budget that went to payments to individuals in 1970 and 2012.

The percentage of the budget that went to payments to individuals in 1970 is approximately ________ %.
(Round to the nearest integer as needed.)

The percentage of the budget that went to payments to individuals in 2012 is approximately ________ %.
(Round to the nearest integer as needed.)

3: Figure

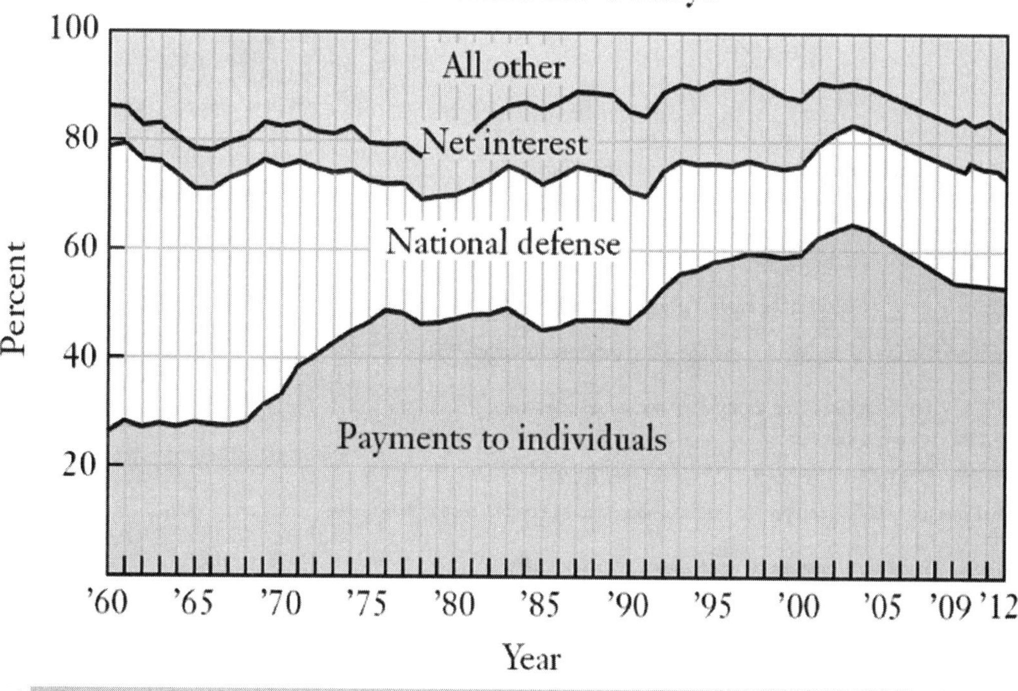

ID: 1.3.22

82. Consider the contour map in the figure, which has six points marked on it. Assume that points A and B correspond to summits, and that the contour lines have 40-foot intervals. Complete parts **a** through **d**.

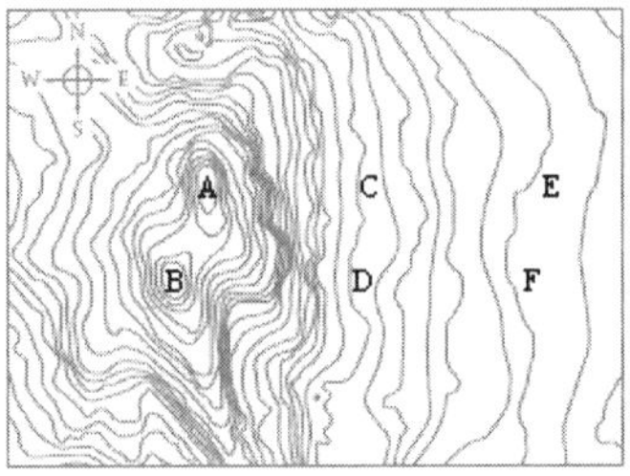

a. If you walk from A to C, do you walk uphill or downhill?

○ downhill
○ uphill

b. Does your elevation change more in walking from B to D or from D to F?

○ D to F
○ B to D

c. If you walk directly from E to F does your elevation increase, decrease, or remain the same?

○ **A.** Your elevation decreases.
○ **B.** Your elevation increases.
○ **C.** Your elevation remains the same.

d. What is your net elevation change if you walk from A to C to D to A?

__________ feet

ID: 1.3.23

*83. The figure shows projections of the age distribution of the U.S. population from 2010 through 2050. Use this graph to answer the following questions. Complete parts **a** through **d**.

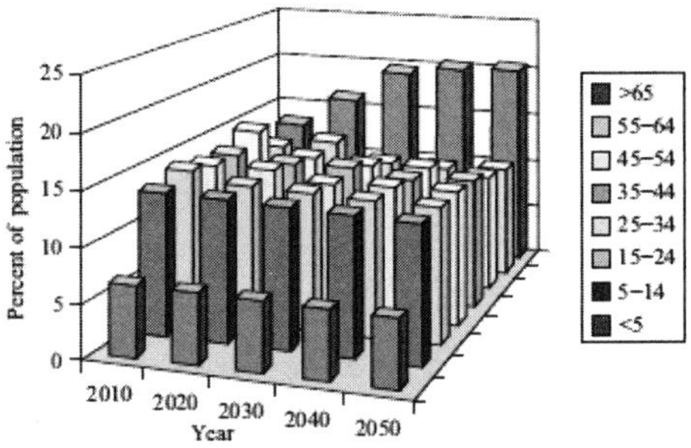

a. What percentage of the population was over age 65 in 2010?

__________ (Round to the nearest integer as needed.)

What percentage of the population is projected to be over age 65 in 2050?

__________ (Round to the nearest integer as needed.)

b. Describe the change in the 45-54 age group between 2010 and 2050.

○ **A.** The group decreases as a percentage of the population.
○ **B.** The group stays about the same as a percentage of the population.
○ **C.** The group increases as a percentage of the population.

c. Does the under-25 segment of the population increase or decrease in size between 2010 and 2050?

○ **A.** The group decreases as a percentage of the population.
○ **B.** The group stays about the same as a percentage of the population.
○ **C.** The group increases as a percentage of the population.

d. In what year did (will) 45- to 54-year-olds comprise the largest percentage of the population?

45- to 54-year-olds comprise the largest percentage in (1) __________

(1) ○ 2020. ○ 2030.
○ 2010.
○ 2050.
○ 2040.

ID: 1.3.24

84. Figure 5.31 uses television sets to represent the number of homes with cable in 1960 and 2008. Note that the heights of the TVs represent the number of homes. Briefly explain how the graph creates a perceptual distortion that exaggerates the true change in the number of homes with cable.

[4] Click the icon to view Figure 5.31.

Choose the correct answer below.

○ **A.** A perceptual distortion is created because the heights of the TVs represent the number of homes, but the human eye tends to focus on the volumes of the TVs, exaggerating the true change to appear too large.

○ **B.** A perceptual distortion is created because the areas of the TV screens represent the number of homes, but the human eye tends to focus on the volumes of the TVs, exaggerating the true change to appear too small.

○ **C.** A perceptual distortion is created by the scale of the graphs. Since the scales vary between the two images, it exaggerates the true change in the number of homes.

○ **D.** A perceptual distortion is created because the volumes of the TVs represent the number of homes, but the human eye tends to focus on the areas of the TV screens, exaggerating the true change to appear too large.

4: Figure

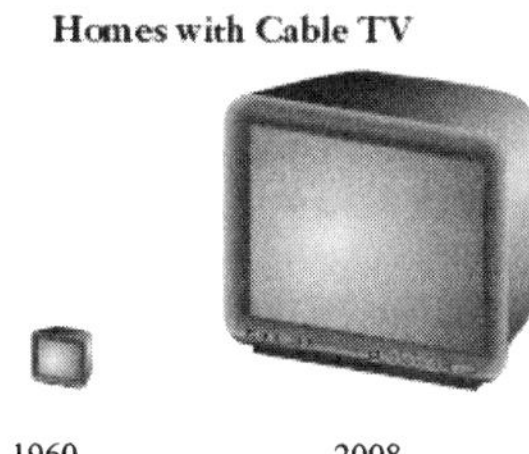

FIGURE 5.31 Homes with Cable TV

ID: 1.3.25

85. The graph to the right compares teaching salaries of women and men at private colleges and universities. What impression does the graph create? Does the graph depict the data fairly? If not, construct a graph that depicts the data fairly.

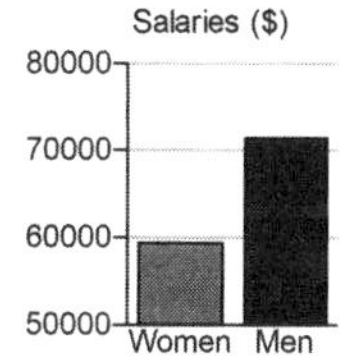

What impression does the graph create?

○ **A.** The graph creates the impression that women have salaries that are slightly higher than that of men.

○ **B.** The graph creates the impression that men have salaries that are more than twice the salaries of women.

○ **C.** The graph creates the impression that men and women have approximately the same salaries.

○ **D.** The graph creates the impression that men have salaries that are slightly higher than that of women.

Does the graph depict the data fairly?

○ **A.** No, because the vertical scale does not start at zero.

○ **B.** Yes, because the vertical scale is appropriate for the data.

○ **C.** No, because the data are two-dimensional measurements.

○ **D.** Yes, because the bars accurately represent each average.

If the graph does not depict the data fairly, which graph below does?

○ **A.**

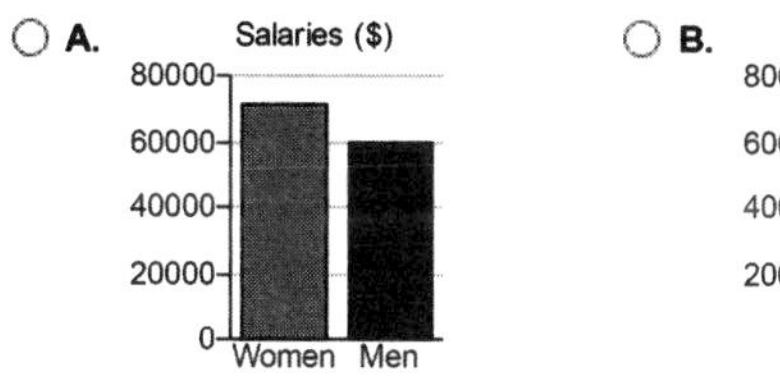

○ **B.**

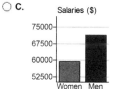

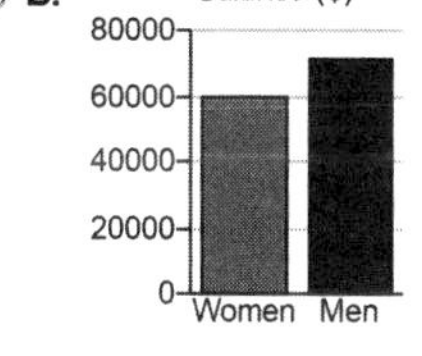

○ **C.**

Salaries ($)
75000
67500
60000
52500
Women Men

○ **D.** The graph depicts the data fairly

ID: 1.3.26

86. The table shows the numbers of cell phone subscriptions. Display the data using an ordinary vertical scale and an exponential vertical scale. Which graph is more useful? Why?
[5] Click the icon to view the table.

Choose the correct graph of the data with an ordinary vertical scale below.

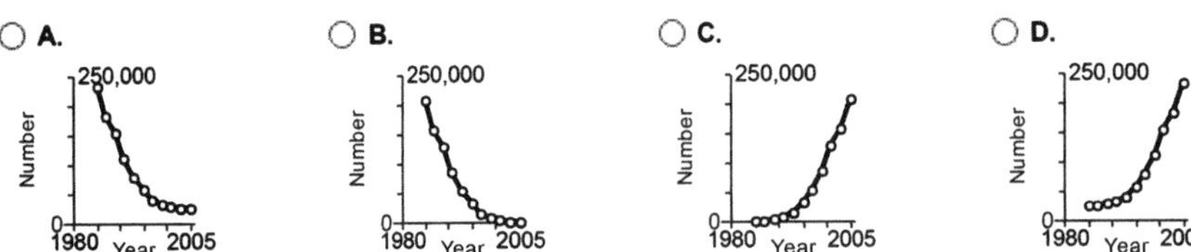

Choose the correct graph of the data with an exponential vertical scale below.

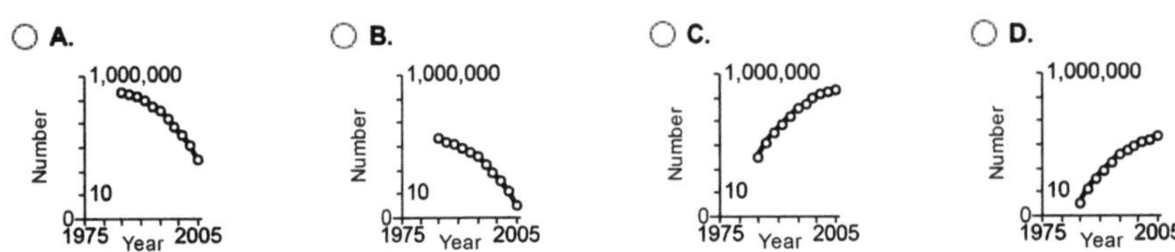

Which graph is more useful? Why?

- **A.** The graph in part a gives a better picture of the true nature of the rate of change. The graph in part b makes it easier to see the changes in the late years.
- **B.** The graph in part a gives a worse picture of the true nature of the rate of change. The graph in part b makes it easier to see the changes in the early years.
- **C.** The graph in part a gives a better picture of the true nature of the rate of change. The graph in part b makes it easier to see the changes in the early years.
- **D.** The graph in part a gives a worse picture of the true nature of the rate of change. The graph in part b makes it easier to see the changes in the late years.

5: Data Table

Year	Number
1985	300
1987	1,240
1989	3,507
1991	7,557
1993	16,009
1995	33,786
1997	55,312
1999	86,046
2001	128,375
2003	158,722
2005	207,800

ID: 1.3.27

87. Recast the population data in the figure with a proper horizontal axis. What trends are clear in your new graph that are not clear in the original? Explain.

[6] Click the icon to view the figure of world population data.

Choose the correct graph below.

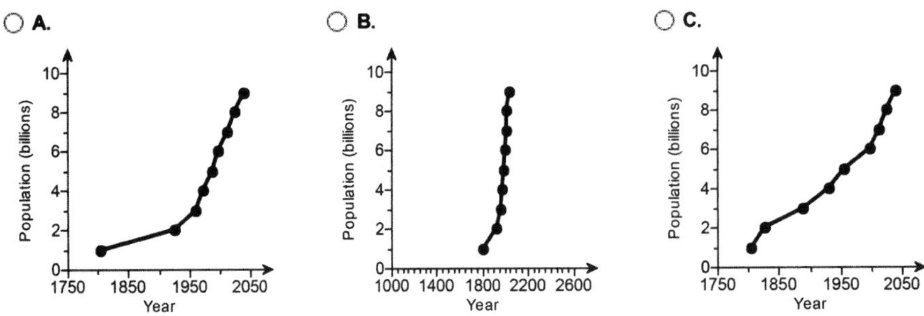

87. (cont.) Observe the graph with a proper horizontal axis found in the previous step. What trends are clear in the new graph that are not clear in the original figure? Explain. Choose the correct answer below.

- ◯ **A.** Most of the growth occurred after 1950. It is not clear in the original figure because the horizontal axis is not linear.
- ◯ **B.** The population grows linearly. It is not clear in the original figure because it has lots of visual impacts.
- ◯ **C.** Most of the growth occurred after 1850. It is not clear in the original figure because the horizontal axis is not linear.
- ◯ **D.** Most of the growth occurred after 1950. It is not clear in the original figure because it has lots of visual impacts.

6: Pictograph of world population

World Population (in billions of people)

1 2 3 4 5 6 7 8 9

1804 1927 1960 1974 1987 1999 2012 2024 2040

Source: United Nations Population Division, future projections based on intermediate-case assumptions.

ID: 1.3.28

88. The graph in the figure show data on the relative risk of schizophrenia among people born in different months. Complete parts **a** and **b**.

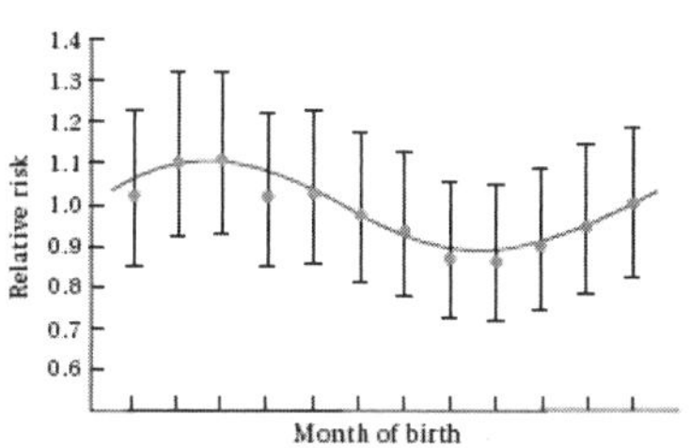

a. Note that the scale of the vertical axis does not include zero. Sketch the same risk curve using an axis that includes zero.

◯ **A.**

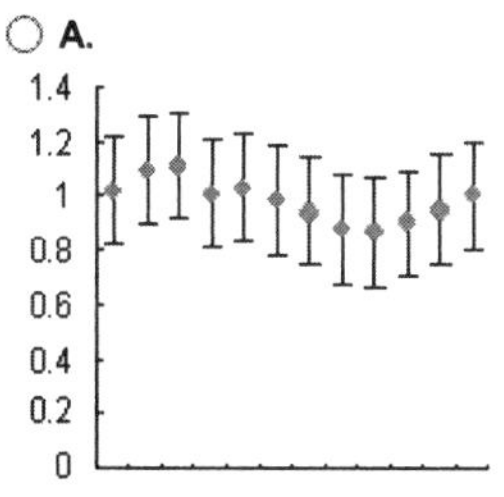

◯ **B.**

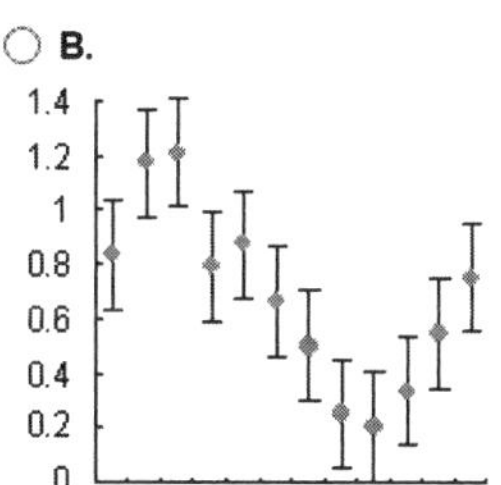

◯ **C.**

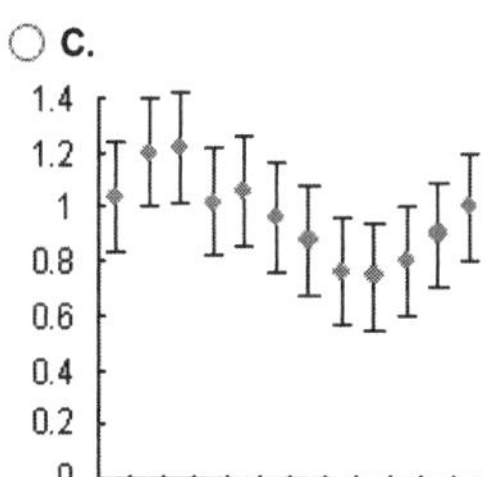

Comment on the effect of this change.

- ◯ **A.** The changes look bigger on the new graph.
- ◯ **B.** The changes look about the same on the new graph.
- ◯ **C.** The changes look smaller on the new graph.

b. Each value of the relative risk is shown with a dot at its most likely value and with an "error bar" indicating the range in which the data value probably lies. The study concludes that "the risk was also significantly associated with the month of birth." Given the size of the error bars, does this claim appear justified? (Is it possible to draw a flat line that passes through all of the error bars?)

- ◯ The claim appears justified.
- ◯ The claim does not appear justified.

ID: 1.3.29

89. The Gapminder HIV Chart 2009 displays the wealth of various countries (per capita income) and the percentage of adults infected with HIV in the same countries. The size of the bubble is proportional to the actual number of HIV-infected adults. Complete parts (a) through (e) below.

[7] Click the icon to view the Gapminder HIV Chart 2009.

a. How is the location of countries indicated on the display? Choose the correct answer below.

- A. The sizes of the bubbles indicate the locations.
- B. The vertical axis indicates the locations.
- C. Names indicate the countries.
- D. Colors indicate the continents.

On what continent is Tanzania located? Choose the correct answer below.

- A. Asia
- B. Europe
- C. Africa
- D. The Americas

b. Approximately how many people in India live with HIV? What is the per capita income in that country? Choose the correct answers below.

- A. Approximately 5 million people; $20,000
- B. Approximately 10 thousand people; $10,000
- C. Approximately 0.1 million people; $12,000
- D. Approximately 1 million people; $3000

c. Approximately how many people in Mexico live with HIV? What is the per capita income in that country? Choose the correct answers below.

- A. Approximately 0.1 million people; $12,000
- B. Approximately 5 million people; $20,000
- C. Approximately 10 thousand people; $10,000
- D. Approximately 1 million people; $3000

d. Discuss how incidence of HIV appears to be related to the wealth of a country.

With some exceptions, HIV incidence (1) ____________ with the wealth of the country.

e. What country is the most notable exception to the conclusion in part (d)? Choose the correct answer below.

- A. Thailand
- B. Russia
- C. Brazil
- D. South Africa

7: Gapminder HIV Chart 2009 (Data from 2007)

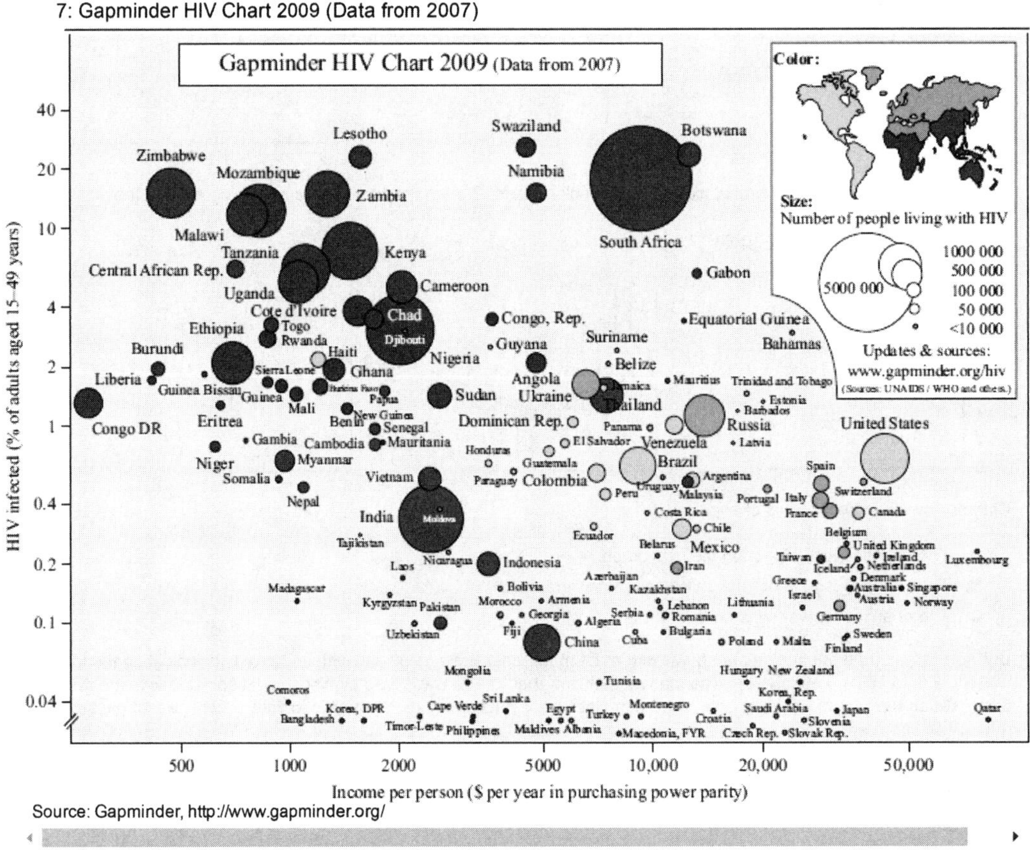

Source: Gapminder, http://www.gapminder.org/

(1) ○ increases ○ decreases

ID: 1.3.30

90. The accompanying table gives the median age of a population between 1920 and 2010. (Half the population is below the median age and half is above the median age.) Choose the type of graphical display that is most appropriate and explain your reasoning. Discuss any interesting features in the data.

[8] Click the icon to view the data set.

Choose the correct answer below.

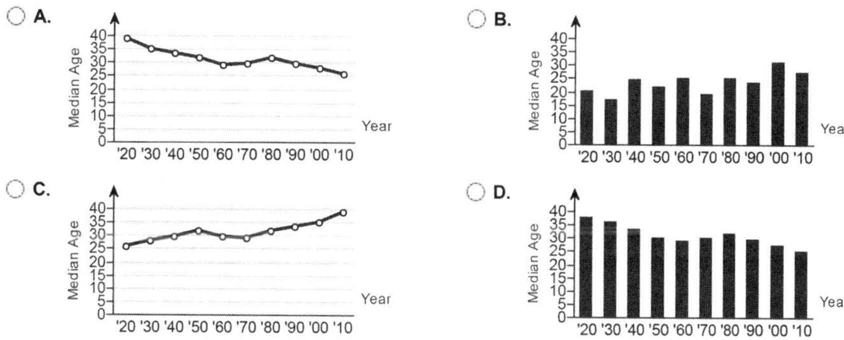

Why was this particular display chosen?

- A. The data set is quantitative and the categories are quantitative, so the bar graph that appropriately matches the data set was chosen.
- B. The data set is qualitative and the categories are quantitative, so the line chart that appropriately matches the data set was chosen.
- C. The data set is quantitative and the categories are quantitative, so the line chart that appropriately matches the data set was chosen.
- D. The data set is qualitative and the categories are qualitative, so the bar graph that appropriately matches the data set was chosen.

Discuss any interesting features of the data. Choose the correct answer below.

- A. The graph increases steadily from 1970 to 1990, with a largest median age occurring in 1990 and the smallest median age occurring in 1970.
- B. The graph increases steadily from 1980 to 2010, with a largest median age occurring in 2010 and the smallest median age occurring in 1920.
- C. The graph has identical median ages occurring in 1990 and 2000, with a largest median age occurring in 1960 and the smallest median age occurring in 1930.
- D. The graph decreases steadily from 1920 to 1960, with a largest median age occurring in 1920 and the smallest median age occurring in 2010.

8: Data Table

Year	Median Age
1920	25.6
1930	27.7
1940	29.8
1950	31.9
1960	29.5
1970	28.9
1980	31.9
1990	33.3
2000	35.3
2010	38.7

ID: 1.3.31

* 91. The accompanying table gives the number of daily newspapers for a particular region and their total circulation (in millions) for selected years since 1920. Make a graphical display of the data. Choose any graphic type that is appropriate to the data set. In addition to making the display, explain why this type of display was chosen and describe interesting patterns in the data.
[9] Click on the icon to view the data table.

Choose the correct graph(s) below.

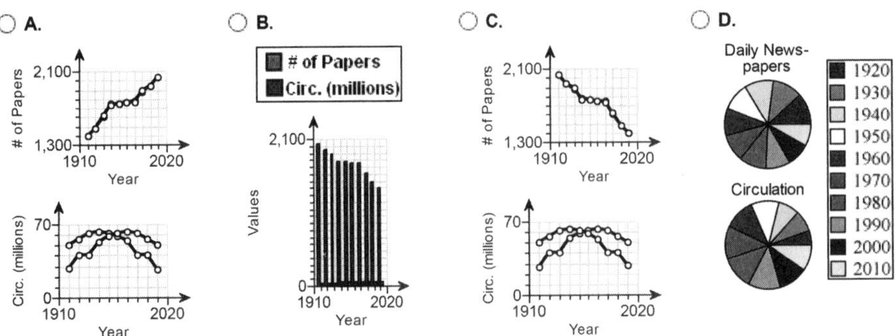

Explain why this type of display was chosen.

Number of daily newspapers and circulation (1) ________ comparable values so it (2) ________ sense to put them together in a single chart. The data are categorized by (3) ________ categories. The sum of data across categories (4) ________ a value of interest. Thus, (5) ________ a good choice.

Describe interesting patterns in the data.

- A. There is a consistent upward trend in the number of newspapers. Newspaper circulation increased steadily until 1940, then it was relatively stable for about 20 years, and it has been decreasing since 1960.
- B. There is a consistent downward trend in the number of newspapers. Newspaper circulation increased steadily until 1970, then it was relatively stable for about 20 years, and it has been decreasing since 1990.
- C. There is a consistent upward trend in the number of newspapers. Newspaper circulation increased steadily until 1970, then it was relatively stable for about 20 years, and it has been decreasing since 1990.
- D. There is a consistent downward trend in the number of newspapers. Newspaper circulation increased steadily until 1940, then it was relatively stable for about 20 years, and it has been decreasing since 1960.

9: Number of daily newspapers and their total circulation since 1920

Year	Number of Daily Newspapers	Circulation (millions)
1920	2,033	27
1930	1,938	40
1940	1,878	41
1950	1,781	54
1960	1,767	59
1970	1,744	62
1980	1,748	63
1990	1,604	62
2000	1,482	56
2010	1,400	50

(1) are not / are
(2) makes / does not make
(3) quantitative / qualitative
(4) is not / is

(5) line charts are / a multiple bar chart is / pie charts are

ID: 1.3.32

!* 92. Use the Excel screenshot to answer parts (a) through (h).

[10] Click the icon to view the Excel screenshot.

(a) The type of chart shown is (1) ___________

(b) The columns in the chart represent (2) ___________ at 3 concerts.

(c) What would be the value of typing in the following function in Excel?

= SUM(C6,E6)

The value of the function would be ___________.

(Type an integer or a decimal rounded to two decimal places as needed. Do not include the $ symbol in your answer.)

(d) What would be the value of typing in the following function in Excel?

= SUM(C6:E6)

The value of the function would be ___________.

(Type an integer or a decimal rounded to two decimal places as needed. Do not include the $ symbol in your answer.)

(e) What would be the value of typing in the following function in Excel?

= AVERAGE(C4:E4)

The value of the function would be ___________.

(Type an integer or a decimal rounded to two decimal places as needed. Do not include the $ symbol in your answer.)

(f) What would be the value of typing in the following function in Excel?

= COUNT(B3:F8)

The value of the function would be ___________.

(Type an integer or a decimal rounded to two decimal places as needed. Do not include the $ symbol in your answer.)

(g) What would be the value of typing in the following function in Excel?

= MAX(D6:E8,F8)

The value of the function would be ___________.

(Type an integer or a decimal rounded to two decimal places as needed. Do not include the $ symbol in your answer.)

(h) What would be the value of typing in the following function in Excel?

= COUNTIF(C4:F10,">75")

The value of the function would be ___________.

(Type an integer or a decimal rounded to two decimal places as needed. Do not include the $ symbol in your answer.)

10: Excel screenshot

	A	B	C	D	E	F	G
1							
2			**Revenue per Item per Concert**				
3			Concert 1	Concert 2	Concert 3	**Totals**	
4		Soda	$58.00	$63.00	$54.00	$175.00	
5		Water	$31.75	$45.00	$48.25	$125.00	
6		Popcorn	$25.50	$27.00	$17.00	$69.50	
7		Cookie	$38.00	$46.00	$47.50	$131.50	
8		Hot Dog	$67.00	$77.00	$56.00	$200.00	
9							
10		**Totals**	$220.25	$258.00	$222.75	$701.00	
11							

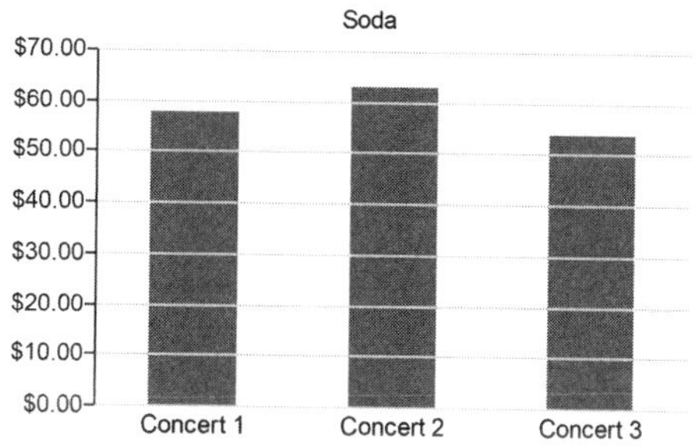

(1) ○ clustered bar.
○ pie chart.
○ clustered column.
○ stacked 100% bar.

(2) ○ number of sodas sold
○ attendance
○ revenues for soda sales
○ total sales

ID: 1.4.1

93. Define and distinguish among mean, median, and mode.

Choose the correct description of the mean below.

- A. The mean is the most common value in a data set. It is not affected by outliers.
- B. The mean is the middle value in a data set. It is not affected by outliers.
- C. The mean is the most common value in a data set. It can be strongly affected by outliers.
- D. The mean is the sum of all the values divided by the number of values. It can be strongly affected by outliers.
- E. The mean is the sum of all the values divided by the number of values. It is not affected by outliers.
- F. The mean is the middle value in a data set. It can be strongly affected by outliers.

Choose the correct description of the median below.

- A. The median is the middle value in a data set. It can be strongly affected by outliers.
- B. The median is the sum of all the values divided by the number of values. It can be strongly affected by outliers.
- C. The median is the middle value in a data set. It is not affected by outliers.
- D. The median is the most common value in a data set. It can be strongly affected by outliers.
- E. The median is the most common value in a data set. It is not affected by outliers.
- F. The median is the sum of all the values divided by the number of values. It is not affected by outliers.

Choose the correct description of the mode below.

- A. The mode is the most common value in a data set. It is not affected by outliers.
- B. The mode is the middle value in a data set. It can be strongly affected by outliers.
- C. The mode is the sum of all the values divided by the number of values. It can be strongly affected by outliers.
- D. The mode is the sum of all the values divided by the number of values. It is not affected by outliers.
- E. The mode is the most common value in a data set. It can be strongly affected by outliers.
- F. The mode is the middle value in a data set. It is not affected by outliers.

ID: 1.4.2

94. What are outliers? Describe the effects of outliers on the mean, median, and mode.

Choose the correct answer below.

- A. An outlier in a data set is a value that is much higher than almost all other values. An outlier can change the median of a data set, but does not affect the mean or mode.
- B. An outlier in a data set is a value that is much higher than almost all other values. An outlier can change the mode of a data set, but does not affect the mean or median.
- C. An outlier in a data set is a value that is much higher or much lower than almost all other values. An outlier can change the mean of a data set, but does not affect the median or mode.
- D. An outlier in a data set is a value that is much higher or much lower than almost all other values. An outlier does not change the mean, median, or mode of a data set.

ID: 1.4.3

95. Briefly describe two possible sources of confusion about the "average."

Choose the correct answer below.

- A. Two possible sources of confusion are not knowing whether the reported average is the mode or the median, and having too many outliers.
- B. Two possible sources of confusion are not knowing whether the reported average is the mean or the median, and not having enough collected data to compute the average.
- C. Two possible sources of confusion are not knowing whether the reported average is the mode or the median, and not having enough information about how the average was computed.
- D. Two possible sources of confusion are not knowing whether the reported average is the mean or the median, and not having enough information about how the average was computed.

ID: 1.4.4

96. What do we mean when we say that a distribution is symmetric? Give simple examples of a symmetric distribution, a left-skewed distribution, and a right-skewed distribution.

What do we mean when we say that a distribution is symmetric?

- ○ **A.** A single-peaked distribution is symmetric if its values are more spread out on the left side of the mode.
- ○ **B.** A single-peaked distribution is symmetric if its left half is a mirror image of its right half.
- ○ **C.** A single-peaked distribution is symmetric if its left half has as many data values as the right half.
- ○ **D.** A single-peaked distribution is symmetric if its values are more spread out on the right side of the mode.

Give a simple example of a symmetric distribution. Choose the correct answer below.

- ○ **A.** The heights of a sample of 100 women is a symmetric distribution.
- ○ **B.** The number of books read during the school year by fifth graders is a symmetric distribution.
- ○ **C.** The speed of cars on a road where a visible patrol car is using radar to detect speeders is a symmetric distribution.
- ○ **D.** The weights of a sample of 500 dogs of varying breed is a symmetric distribution.

Give a simple example of a left-skewed distribution. Choose the correct answer below.

- ○ **A.** The speed of cars on a road where a visible patrol car is using radar to detect speeders is a left-skewed distribution.
- ○ **B.** The weights of a sample of 500 dogs of varying breed is a left-skewed distribution.
- ○ **C.** The heights of a sample of 55 men is a left-skewed distribution.
- ○ **D.** The number of books read during the school year by fifth graders is a left-skewed distribution.

Give a simple example of a right-skewed distribution. Choose the correct answer below.

- ○ **A.** The heights of a sample of 55 men is a right-skewed distribution.
- ○ **B.** The weights of a sample of 500 dogs of varying breed is a right-skewed distribution.
- ○ **C.** The number of books read during the school year by fifth graders is a right-skewed distribution.
- ○ **D.** The number of legs a sample of 40 spiders has is a right-skewed distribution.

ID: 1.4.5

---

97. Decide whether each of the following statements makes sense (or is clearly true) or does not make sense (or is clearly false). Explain your reasoning.

In my data set of 10 exam scores, the mean turned out to be the score of the person with the third highest grade. No two people got the same score.

Choose the correct answer below.

- ○ **A.** The statement makes sense because the mean of a data set can be pulled far to the left or right of the middle of the range of values by outliers.
- ○ **B.** The statement does not make sense because there were no repeated scores, so the distribution does not have a mean.
- ○ **C.** The statement does not make sense because the mean of a data set is always in the middle of the range of values.
- ○ **D.** The statement does not make sense because the mean of a data set is either near the middle of the range of values, or it is decreased by outliers in the data. The mean cannot be increased by outliers.

ID: 1.4.6

---

* 98. Decide whether the following statement makes sense (or is clearly true) or does not make sense (or is clearly false). Explain your reasoning.

In my data set of 10 exam scores, the median turned out to be the score of the person with the third highest grade. No two people got the same score.

Choose the correct answer below.

- ○ **A.** This does not make sense because the median value should be between the fifth and sixth highest scores.
- ○ **B.** This makes sense because outliers do not affect the median, so the people who got a perfect score wouldn't change the median value.
- ○ **C.** This makes sense because the third highest score must be the most common value.
- ○ **D.** This does not make sense because the median value should be the sum of all values divided by the total number of values.

ID: 1.4.7

---

* 99. Decide whether each of the following statements makes sense (or is clearly true) or does not make sense (or is clearly false). Explain your reasoning.

I made a distribution of 15 apartment rents in my neighborhood. One apartment had a much higher rent than all of the others, and this outlier caused the mean rent to be higher than the median rent.

Choose the correct answer below.

- **A.** The statement does not make sense because an outlier with a large value increases the mean and the median by the same amount.
- **B.** The statement does not make sense because an outlier with a large value increases the median, but does not affect the mean.
- **C.** The statement makes sense because an outlier with a large value increases the mean, but does not affect the median.
- **D.** The statement does not make sense because an outlier with a large value decreases the mean, but does not affect the median.

ID: 1.4.8

100. Decide whether the following statement makes sense (or is clearly true) or does not make sense (or is clearly false). Explain your reasoning.

The distribution of grades was left-skewed, but the mean, median, and mode were all the same.

Choose the correct answer below.

- **A.** This makes sense because when outliers have high values, the mean, median, and mode are the same.
- **B.** This makes sense because when outliers have low values, the mean, median, and mode are the same.
- **C.** This does not make sense because the mean and median should lie somewhere to the left of the mode if the distribution is left-skewed.
- **D.** This does not make sense because the mean and median should lie somewhere to the right of the mode if the distribution is left-skewed.

ID: 1.4.9

*101. The numbers of words defined on randomly selected pages from a dictionary are shown below. Find the mean, median, and mode of the listed numbers.

33 55 52 54 78 59 49 77 44 71

What is the mean? Select the correct choice below and, if necessary, fill in the answer box within your choice.

- **A.** The mean is ________. (Round to one decimal place as needed.)
- **B.** There is no mean.

What is the median? Select the correct choice below and, if necessary, fill in the answer box within your choice.

- **A.** The median is ________. (Round to one decimal place as needed.)
- **B.** There is no median.

What is(are) the mode(s)? Select the correct choice below and, if necessary, fill in the answer box within your choice.

- **A.** The mode(s) is(are) ________. (Round to one decimal place as needed. Use a comma to separate answers as needed.)
- **B.** There is no mode.

ID: 1.4.10

102. Blood alcohol concentrations of drivers involved in fatal crashes and then given jail sentences are shown below. Find the mean, median, and mode of the listed numbers.

0.27 0.17 0.17 0.16 0.13 0.24
0.29 0.24 0.14 0.16 0.11 0.16

The mean is ________. (Round to the nearest thousandth as needed.)

The median is ________. (Round to the nearest thousandth as needed.)

What is(are) the mode(s)? Select the correct choice below and, if necessary, fill in the answer box within your choice.

- **A.** The mode(s) is(are) ________ sec. (Use a comma to separate answers as needed.)
- **B.** There is no mode.

ID: 1.4.11

103. Actual times (in seconds) recorded when statistics students participated in an experiment to test their ability to determine when one minute (60 seconds) had passed are shown below. Find the mean, median, and mode of the listed numbers.

55 50 75 62 67 60 47 47

The mean is ________ sec. (Round to the nearest tenth as needed.)

The median is ________ sec. (Round to the nearest tenth as needed.)

What is(are) the mode(s)? Select the correct choice below and, if necessary, fill in the answer box within your choice.

○ **A.** The mode(s) is(are) ________ sec. (Use a comma to separate answers as needed.)

○ **B.** There is no mode.

ID: 1.4.12

---

104. Weights (in grams) of randomly selected chocolate candies are shown below. Find the mean, median, and mode of the listed numbers.

0.957 0.911 0.841 0.927 0.933 0.882
0.914 0.913 0.958 0.945 0.921

The mean is ________ g. (Round to four decimal places as needed.)

The median is ________ g. (Round to four decimal places as needed.)

What is the mode? Select the correct choice below and, if necessary, fill in the answer box within your choice.

○ **A.** The mode(s) is(are) ________ g.
(Use a comma to separate answers as needed.)

○ **B.** There is no mode.

ID: 1.4.13

---

105. Cans of soda vary slightly in weight. Given below are the measured weights of seven cans, in pounds. Find the mean and median of these weights. Which, if any, of these weights would be considered an outlier? What are the mean and median weights if the outlier is excluded?

0.8158 0.8194 0.8163 0.8177 0.7906 0.8145 0.8119

Find the mean and median of the weights.

The mean is ________.
(Round to five decimal places as needed.)

The median is ________.
(Type an integer or a decimal.)

Which, if any, of these weights would be considered an outlier? Select the correct choice below and, if necessary, fill in the answer box to complete your choice.

○ **A.** The outlier is ________.
(Type an integer or a decimal.)

○ **B.** None of the weights would be considered an outlier.

Find the mean with the outlier excluded. Select the correct choice below and, if necessary, fill in the answer box to complete your choice.

○ **A.** The mean without the outlier is ________.
(Round to five decimal places as needed.)

○ **B.** None of the weights would be considered an outlier.

Find the median with the outlier excluded. Select the correct choice below and, if necessary, fill in the answer box to complete your choice.

○ **A.** The median without the outlier is ________.
(Type an integer or a decimal.)

○ **B.** None of the weights would be considered an outlier.

ID: 1.4.14

---

106. State, with an explanation, whether the mean, median, or mode gives the best description of the following average.

The average number of children in a family

Which measurement gives the best description of the given average?

The (1) __________ is the best because the distribution (2) __________

(1) ○ mode
○ mean
○ median

(2) ○ is probably right-skewed with a single peak.
○ probably has several peaks.
○ is probably left-skewed with a single peak.
○ is probably symmetric with a single peak.

ID: 1.4.15

---

107. State, with an explanation, whether the mean, median, or mode gives the best description of the following average.

The average height of women in this country

Which measurement gives the best description of the given average?

The (1) __________ is the best because the distribution (2) __________

(1) ○ mean
○ median
○ mode

(2) ○ is probably left-skewed with a single peak.
○ is probably symmetric with a single peak.
○ probably has several peaks.
○ is probably right-skewed with a single peak.

ID: 1.4.16

---

108. Consider two grocery stores at which the mean time in line is the same but the variation is different. At which store would you expect the customers to have more complaints about the waiting time? Explain.

Choose the correct answer below.

○ **A.** The customers would have more complaints about the waiting time at the store that has more variation because some customers are easily annoyed.

○ **B.** The customers would have more complaints about the waiting time at the store that has less variation because some customers are easily annoyed.

○ **C.** The customers would have more complaints about the waiting time at the store that has more variation because some customers would have longer waits and might think they are being treated unequally.

○ **D.** The customers would have more complaints about the waiting time at the store that has less variation because some customers would have longer waits and might think they are being treated unequally.

ID: 1.4.17

---

109. What are the quartiles of a distribution? How do we find them?

What are the quartiles of a distribution?

○ **A.** The quartiles are values that divide the data distribution into quarters.

○ **B.** When the data distribution is divided equally into four sets, each set of values is called a quartile.

○ **C.** The quartiles consist of the lowest value, the median, and the highest value of the data distribution.

○ **D.** The quartiles consist of the mean, the median, and the standard deviation of the data distribution.

How do we find them?

○ **A.** The lower quartile is the mean of the data values in the first quarter of a data set. The middle quartile is the overall mean. The upper quartile is the mean of the data values in the fourth quarter of data set.

○ **B.** The lower quartile is the mean of the data values in the lower half of a data set. The middle quartile is the overall mean. The upper quartile is the mean of the data values in the upper half of data set.

○ **C.** The lower quartile is the median of the data values in the first quarter of a data set. The middle quartile is the overall median. The upper quartile is the median of the data values in the fourth quarter of data set.

○ **D.** The lower quartile is the median of the data values in the lower half of a data set. The middle quartile is the overall median. The upper quartile is the median of the data values in the upper half of data set.

ID: 1.4.18

---

110. Define the five-number summary, and explain how to depict it visually with a boxplot.

Which five numbers are included in the five-number summary for a data set?

- A. low value, lower quartile, median, upper quartile, and high value
- B. low value, lower quartile, mean, upper quartile, and high value
- C. low value, variance, mean, standard deviation, and high value
- D. low value, variance, median, standard deviation, and high value

Explain how to depict the five numbers visually with a boxplot. Choose the correct answer below. Select all that apply.

- A. Draw a number line that spans all the values in the data set. Enclose the values from the lower to upper quartile in a box. Draw a vertical line through the box at the mean. Add "whiskers" extending to the low and high values.
- B. Draw a number line that spans all the values in the data set. Enclose the values from the lower to upper quartile in a box. Draw a vertical line through the box at the median. Add "whiskers" extending to the low and high values.
- C. Draw a number line that spans all the values in the data set. Enclose the values from the lower to upper quartile in a box.
- D. Draw a number line that spans all the values in the data set. Enclose the values from the lower to upper quartile in a box. Draw a vertical line through the box at the mean.

ID: 1.4.19

---

111. Describe the process of calculating a standard deviation. Give a simple example of its calculation (such as calculating the standard deviation of the numbers 2, 3, 4, 4, and 6). What is the standard deviation if all of the sample values are the same?

Fill in the blanks to complete the process of calculating a standard deviation.

Compute the mean of the data set. Then find the deviation from the mean for every data value by

(1) __________ the data value.

Find the (2) __________ of all the deviations from the mean, and then (3) __________ them together.

Divide this sum by the (4) __________

The standard deviation is the (5) __________ of this quotient.

The standard deviation of the numbers 2, 3, 4, 4, and 6 is approximately __________.
(Round to three decimal places as needed.)

If all of the sample values are the same, then the standard deviation is __________.

(1)
- adding the mean to
- subtracting the mean from
- multiplying the mean by
- dividing the mean by

(2)
- squares
- cubes
- cube roots
- square roots

(3)
- multiply
- add

(4)
- total number of data values minus 1.
- total number of data values.
- total number of data values minus 2.

(5)
- fourth root
- cube
- square root
- square
- cube root

ID: 1.4.20

---

112. Decide whether the following statement makes sense (or is clearly true) or does not make sense (or is clearly false). Explain your reasoning.

Both exams had the same range, so they must have had the same median.

Choose the correct answer below.

- A. This does not make sense because the range is the most common value or group of values in a distribution. It has nothing to do with the median.
- B. This makes sense because the median is equal to half of the range.
- C. This does not make sense because the range is the difference between the highest and lowest data values. It has nothing to do with the median.
- D. This makes sense because the median is equal to the range.

ID: 1.4.21

113. Decide whether the following statement makes sense (or is clearly true) or does not make sense (or is clearly false). Explain your reasoning.

For the 30 students who took the test, the high score was 80, the median was 75, and the low score was 40.

Choose the correct answer below.

- A. The statement does not make sense because the median should divide the lowest fourth of a data set from the upper three-fourths.
- B. The statement makes sense because it is possible that when sorting the 30 scores from low to high, the first value was 40, the highest value was 80, and 75 was halfway between the 14th and the 15th score.
- C. The statement does not make sense because the median should lie halfway between the lowest value and the highest value.
- D. The statement makes sense because it is possible that when sorting the 30 scores from low to high, the first value was 40, the highest value was 80, and 75 was halfway between the 15th and the 16th score.

ID: 1.4.22

---

114. Decide whether the following statement makes sense (or is clearly true) or does not make sense (or is clearly false). Explain your reasoning.

The standard deviation for the heights of a group of 5-year-old children is smaller than the standard deviation for the heights of a group of children who range in age from 3 to 15.

Choose the correct answer below.

- A. The statement makes sense because the range of data for the heights of a group of 5-year-old children is larger than the range of data for the heights of a group of children who range in age from 3 to 15.
- B. The statement does not make sense because the range of data for the heights of a group of 5-year-old children is smaller than the range of data for the heights of a group of children who range in age from 3 to 15.
- C. The statement makes sense because the range of data for the heights of a group of 5-year-old children is smaller than the range of data for the heights of a group of children who range in age from 3 to 15.
- D. The statement does not make sense because the range of data for the heights of a group of 5-year-old children is larger than the range of data for the heights of a group of children who range in age from 3 to 15.

ID: 1.4.23

---

115. Find the mean and median for the waiting times at Big Bank given below. Show your work clearly, and verify that they are the same. The following values are measured in minutes.

Big Bank (three lines): 4.1 5.2 5.6 6.2 6.7 7.2 7.7 7.7 8.5 9.3 11.0

Which of the following shows how to compute the mean?

- A. mean = (sum of all values) × (total number of values)
- B. $\text{mean} = \dfrac{\text{sum of all values}}{\text{total number of values}}$
- C. mean = sum of all values + total number of values
- D. $\text{mean} = \dfrac{\text{total number of values}}{\text{sum of all values}}$

The sum of all values is ________.
(Type an integer or a decimal.)

The total number of values is ________.
(Type a whole number.)

Thus, the mean is ________.
(Round to one decimal place as needed.)

Notice that the data are given in ascending order. How should the median be found in this case? Select the correct choice below and fill in the answer box(es) to complete your choice.

- A. The median is the ________ th value in the sorted data set.
(Type a whole number.)
- B. The median is halfway between the ________ th and ________ th values in the sorted data set.
(Type whole numbers. Use ascending order.)

Thus, the median is ________.
(Type an integer or a decimal.)

ID: 1.4.24

---

116. The table to the right gives the cost of living index (COLI) for six East Coast counties and six Midwest counties (using an index where 100 represents the average cost of living for all participating cities with a population of more than 1.5 million). Answer parts (a) through (e) below.

	East Coast Counties		Midwest Counties
A	104.8	U	96.2
B	128.7	V	92.6
C	314.4	W	94.4
D	134.4	X	87.5
E	123.2	Y	95.9
F	141.9	Z	228.9

a. Find the mean, median, and range for each of the two data sets.

The mean for the East Coast Counties is ___________.
(Type an integer or decimal rounded to two decimal places as needed.)

The median for the East Coast Counties is ___________.
(Type an integer or decimal rounded to two decimal places as needed.)

The range for the East Coast Counties is ___________.
(Type an integer or decimal rounded to two decimal places as needed.)

The mean for the Midwest Counties is ___________.
(Type an integer or decimal rounded to two decimal places as needed.)

The median for the Midwest Counties is ___________.
(Type an integer or decimal rounded to two decimal places as needed.)

The range for the Midwest Counties is ___________.
(Type an integer or decimal rounded to two decimal places as needed.)

b. Give the five-number summary and draw a boxplot for each of the two data sets.

Give the five number summary for the East Coast Counties.

Low Value = ___________ Lower Quartile = ___________

Median = ___________ Upper Quartile = ___________

High Value = ___________

(Type integers or decimals rounded to two decimal places as needed.)

Choose the correct boxplot for the East Coast Counties below.

○ A. ○ B. ○ C.

x
90 130 170 210 250 290 330

Give the five-number summary for the Midwest Counties.

Low Value = ___________ Lower Quartile = ___________

Median = ___________ Upper Quartile = ___________

High Value = ___________

(Type integers or decimals rounded to two decimal places as needed.)
Choose the correct boxplot for the Midwest Counties below.

○ A. ○ B. ○ C.

x
80 120 160 200 240

c. Find the standard deviation for each of the two data sets.

The standard deviation for the East Coast Counties is ___________.
(Type an integer or decimal rounded to two decimal places as needed.)

The standard deviation for the Midwest Counties is ___________.
(Type an integer or decimal rounded to two decimal places as needed.)

116. (cont.) d. Apply the range rule of thumb to estimate the standard deviation of each of the two data sets. How well does the rule work in each case? Briefly discuss why it does or does not work well.

The standard deviation for the East Coast Counties is approximately ___________, using the range rule of thumb.
(Type an integer or decimal rounded to two decimal places as needed.)

The standard deviation for the Midwest Counties is approximately ___________, using the range rule of thumb.
(Type an integer or decimal rounded to two decimal places as needed.)

How well does the rule work in each case? Briefly discuss why it does or does not work well. Choose the correct answer below.

- ○ **A.** They work well in both of the two data sets because there are no outliers in anyone of the two data sets.
- ○ **B.** It works well in the Midwest data set, but it does not work well in the East Coast data set, because there is a outlier in the East Coast data set.
- ○ **C.** They do not work well in both of the two data sets because there are outliers in both of the two data sets.
- ○ **D.** It works well in the East Coast data set, but it does not work well in the Midwest data set, because there is a outlier in the Midwest data set.

e. Based on all the results, compare and discuss the two data sets in terms of their center and variation. Choose the correct answer below. Select all that apply.

- ☐ **A.** The mean of COLI for the six East Coast counties is higher than that for the six Midwest Counties, which means the average level of COLI for the East Coast counties is higher.
- ☐ **B.** The mean of COLI for the six East Coast counties is higher than that for the six Midwest Counties, which means the average level of COLI for the East Coast counties is lower.
- ☐ **C.** The variation of COLI for the six East Coast counties is higher than that for the six Midwest Counties, which means the level of COLI in most Midwest Counties varies in a larger range.
- ☐ **D.** The variation of COLI for the six East Coast counties is higher than that for the six Midwest Counties, which means the level of COLI in most Midwest Counties varies in a smaller range.

ID: 1.4.25

---

117. Researchers at the Pennsylvania State University conducted experiments with poplar trees in which one group of trees was given fertilizer and irrigation while the other group was given no treatment. The weights in kilograms of trees in the two groups are shown in the following table. Complete parts (a) through (e) below.
[11] Click the icon to view the table.

a. Find the mean, median, and range for each of the two data sets.
Find the mean, median, and range for the no treatment group.

Mean = ___________
Median = ___________
Range = ___________
(Type integers or decimals rounded to three decimal places as needed.)

Find the mean, median, and range for the treatment group.

Mean = ___________
Median = ___________
Range = ___________
(Type integers or decimals rounded to three decimal places as needed.)

b. Give the five-number summary and draw a boxplot for each of the two data sets.
Give the five-number summary for the no treatment group.

Low = ___________ Lower quartile = ___________
Median = ___________ Upper quartile = ___________
High = ___________
(Type integers or decimals rounded to two decimal places as needed.)

Give the five-number summary for the treatment group.

Low = ___________ Lower quartile = ___________
Median = ___________ Upper quartile = ___________
High = ___________
(Type integers or decimals rounded to two decimal places as needed.)

117. (cont.) Draw a boxplot for the no treatment group. Choose the correct answer below.

○ A. ○ B. 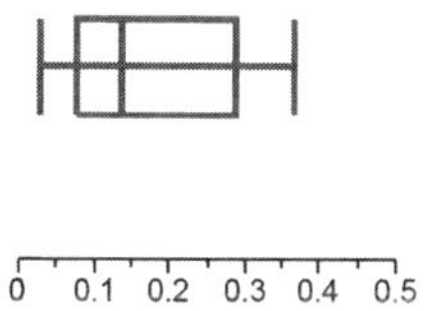 ○ C.

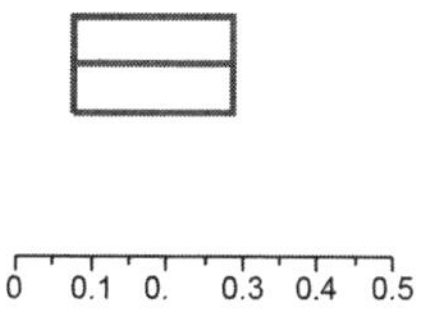

0 0.1 0. 0.3 0.4 0.5 | 0 0.1 0.2 0.3 0.4 0.5 | 0 0.1 0.2 0.3 0.4 0.5

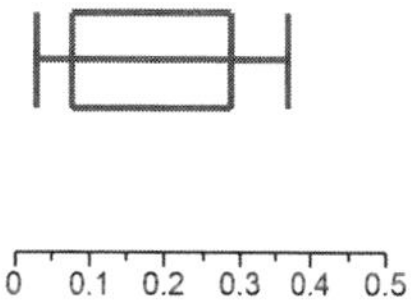

Draw a boxplot for the treatment group. Choose the correct answer below.

○ A. ○ B. 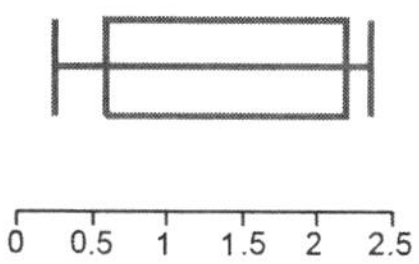 ○ C.

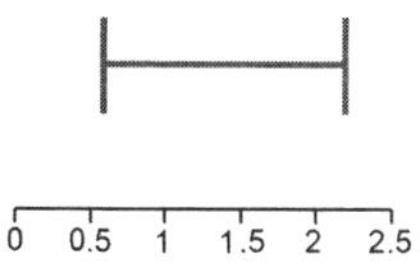

0 0.5 1 1.5 2 2.5 | 0 0.5 1 1.5 2 2.5 | 0 0.5 1 1.5 2 2.5

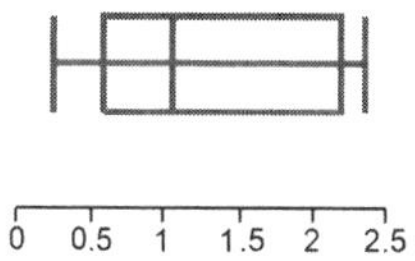

c. Find the standard deviation for each of the two data sets.

The standard deviation for the no treatment group is ____________.
(Round to three decimal places as needed.)

The standard deviation for the treatment group is ____________.
(Round to three decimal places as needed.)

d. Apply the range rule of thumb to estimate the standard deviation of each of the two data sets. How well does the rule work in each case? Briefly discuss why it does or does not work well.

The standard deviation for the no treatment group is approximately ____________, using the range rule of thumb.
(Round to four decimal places as needed.)

The standard deviation for the treatment group is approximately ____________, using the range rule of thumb. (Round to four decimal places as needed.)

How well does the rule work in each case? Briefly discuss why it does or does not work well. Choose the correct answer below.

○ **A.** It works well in the treatment group, but it does not work well in the no treatment group, because the values in the no treatment group aren't distributed evenly.

○ **B.** It works well in both of the two data sets because the values in both groups are distributed evenly.

○ **C.** It does not work well in both of the two data sets because the values in both groups aren't distributed evenly.

○ **D.** It works well in the no treatment group, but it does not work well in the treatment group, because the values in the treatment group aren't distributed evenly.

e. Based on all the results, compare and discuss the two data sets in terms of their center and variation. Choose the correct answer below.

○ **A.** The average weight of trees in the no treatment group is higher than that in the treatment group, but variations in weights of trees in the no treatment group are lower.

○ **B.** The average weight of trees in the no treatment group is higher than that in the treatment group, and variations in weights of trees in the no treatment group are higher.

○ **C.** The average weight of trees in the no treatment group is lower than that in the treatment group, but variations in weights of trees in the no treatment group are higher.

○ **D.** The average weight of trees in the no treatment group is lower than that in the treatment group, and variations in weights of trees in the no treatment group are lower.

11: Data Table

No treatment:	0.14	0.03	0.13	0.37	0.21
Treatment:	2.02	0.27	0.92	1.07	2.36

ID: 1.4.26

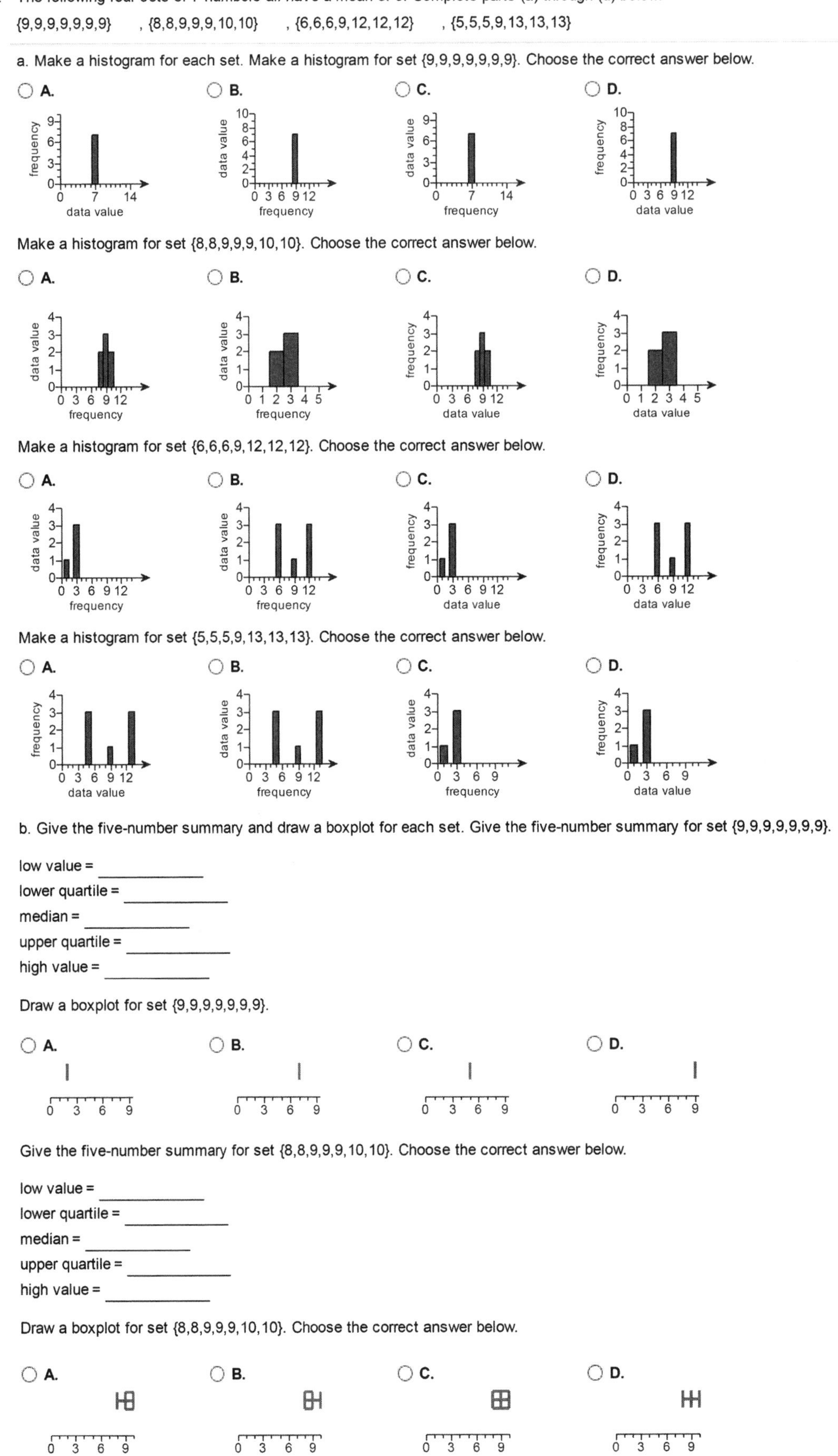

118. The following four sets of 7 numbers all have a mean of 9. Complete parts (a) through (d) below.

{9,9,9,9,9,9,9} , {8,8,9,9,9,10,10} , {6,6,6,9,12,12,12} , {5,5,5,9,13,13,13}

a. Make a histogram for each set. Make a histogram for set {9,9,9,9,9,9,9}. Choose the correct answer below.

○ A. ○ B. ○ C. ○ D.

Make a histogram for set {8,8,9,9,9,10,10}. Choose the correct answer below.

○ A. ○ B. ○ C. ○ D.

Make a histogram for set {6,6,6,9,12,12,12}. Choose the correct answer below.

○ A. ○ B. ○ C. ○ D.

Make a histogram for set {5,5,5,9,13,13,13}. Choose the correct answer below.

○ A. ○ B. ○ C. ○ D.

b. Give the five-number summary and draw a boxplot for each set. Give the five-number summary for set {9,9,9,9,9,9,9}.

low value = ____________

lower quartile = ____________

median = ____________

upper quartile = ____________

high value = ____________

Draw a boxplot for set {9,9,9,9,9,9,9}.

○ A. ○ B. ○ C. ○ D.

Give the five-number summary for set {8,8,9,9,9,10,10}. Choose the correct answer below.

low value = ____________

lower quartile = ____________

median = ____________

upper quartile = ____________

high value = ____________

Draw a boxplot for set {8,8,9,9,9,10,10}. Choose the correct answer below.

○ A. ○ B. ○ C. ○ D.

118. (cont.) Give the five-number summary for set {6,6,6,9,12,12,12}.

low value = ____________

lower quartile = ____________

median = ____________

upper quartile = ____________

high value = ____________

Draw a boxplot for set {6,6,6,9,12,12,12}. Choose the correct answer below.

○ A.

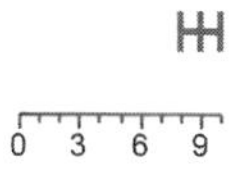

○ B.

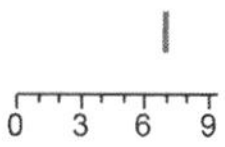

○ C.

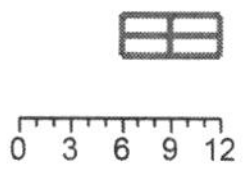

○ D.

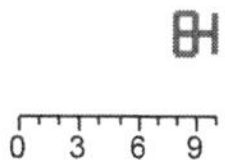

Give the five-number summary for set {5,5,5,9,13,13,13}.

low value = ____________

lower quartile = ____________

median = ____________

upper quartile = ____________

high value = ____________

Draw a boxplot for set {5,5,5,9,13,13,13}. Choose the correct answer below.

○ A.

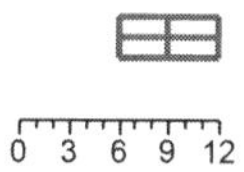

○ B.

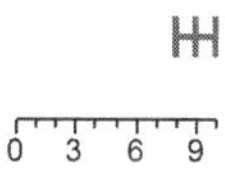

○ C.

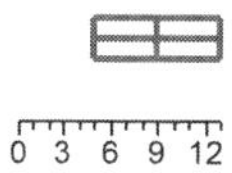

○ D.

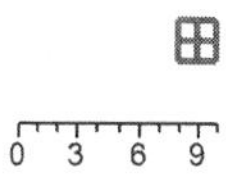

c. Compute the standard deviation for each set. Compute the standard deviation for set {9,9,9,9,9,9,9}.

s = ____________ (Round to the nearest tenth as needed.)

Compute the standard deviation for set {8,8,9,9,9,10,10}.

s = ____________ (Round to the nearest tenth as needed.)

Compute the standard deviation for set {6,6,6,9,12,12,12}.

s = ____________ (Round to the nearest tenth as needed.)

Compute the standard deviation for set {5,5,5,9,13,13,13}.

s = ____________ (Round to the nearest tenth as needed.)

d. Based on your results, briefly explain how the standard deviation provides a useful single-number summary of the variation in these data sets.

The standard deviation is a measure of how widely data values are spread around the (1) ____________ of a data set.

Note that in the first data set the difference between highest and lowest value is (2) ____________ and the standard deviation is 0 and in the last data set the difference between highest and lowest value is (3) ____________ than in other data sets and the standard deviation is the (4) ____________

(1) ○ mean ○ median

(2) ○ not zero ○ zero

(3) ○ lower ○ higher

(4) ○ highest. ○ lowest.

ID: 1.4.27

---

* 119. After recording the pizza delivery times for two different pizza shops, you conclude that one pizza shop has a mean delivery time of 46 minutes with a standard deviation of 4 minutes. The other shop has a mean delivery time of 45 minutes with a standard deviation of 19 minutes. Interpret these figures. If you liked the pizzas from both shops equally well, which one would you order from? Why?

Interpret these figures. Choose the correct answer below.

○ **A.** The variations are nearly equal, but the mean is greater for the first shop than for the second.

○ **B.** Both the means and the variations are nearly equal.

○ **C.** The means are nearly equal, but the variation is significantly greater for the second shop than for the first.

○ **D.** The means are nearly equal, but the variation is significantly lower for the second shop than for the first.

* 119. (cont.) If you liked the pizzas from both shops equally well, which one would you order from? Why? Choose the correct answer below.

- A. Choose the second shop. The delivery time is more reliable because it has a larger mean.
- B. Choose the first shop. The delivery time is more reliable because it has a lower mean.
- C. Choose the second shop. The delivery time is more reliable because it has a larger standard deviation.
- D. Choose the first shop. The delivery time is more reliable because it has a lower standard deviation.

ID: 1.4.28

---

120. A report claims that the returns for the investment portfolios with a single stock have a standard deviation of 0.53, while the returns for portfolios with 31 stocks have a standard deviation of 0.319. Explain how the standard deviation measures the risk in these two types of portfolios.

Choose the correct answer below.

- A. A lower standard deviation means more certainty in the return and less risk. Hence, the returns for portfolios with 31 stocks have less risk than the ones with a single stock.
- B. Compare the ratio of the standard deviation to the number of stocks for each type of portfolio. If the ratio is smaller, than the risk is higher. Hence, the returns for portfolios with 31 stocks have more risk than the ones with a single stock.
- C. A lower standard deviation means less certainty in the return and more risk. Hence, the returns for portfolios with 31 stocks have more risk than the ones with a single stock.
- D. They both have the same risk because the difference in the standard deviation is too small.
- E. Compare the ratio of the standard deviation to the number of stocks for each type of portfolio. If the ratio is smaller, than the risk is higher. Hence, the returns for portfolios with 31 stocks have less risk than the ones with a single stock.

ID: 1.4.29

---

121. For the past 100 years, the mean batting average in the major leagues has remained fairly constant at about 0.253. However, the standard deviation of batting averages has decreased from about 0.042 in the 1910s to 0.028 at present. What does this tell us about the batting averages of players? Based on these facts, would you expect batting averages above .350 to be more or less common today than in the past? Explain.

What do these values say about the batting averages of batters?

- A. This says the batting averages are more varied today because the standard deviation decreased.
- B. This says the batting averages are more varied today because the standard deviation increased.
- C. This says the batting averages are less varied today because the standard deviation increased.
- D. This says the batting averages are less varied today because the standard deviation decreased.

Based on these facts, would you expect batting averages above .350 to be more or less common today than in the past?

- A. Because the mean is unchanged, batting averages above .350 are less common today because the standard deviation is lower, thus it is less probable to have such a high batting average.
- B. Because the mean is unchanged, batting averages above .350 are more common today because the standard deviation is lower, thus it is less probable to have such a high batting average.
- C. Because the mean is unchanged, batting averages above .350 are less common today because the standard deviation is higher, thus it is more probable to have such a high batting average.
- D. Because the mean is unchanged, batting averages above .350 are more common today because the standard deviation is higher, thus it is less probable to have such a high batting average.

ID: 1.4.30

---

122. A nurse rotates between maternity wards in two different hospitals. During one shift at Healing Hospital and one shift at Healthy Hospital, she records the following weights (in pounds) of newborn babies. Complete parts (a) through (c).

Healing:	6.6	7.1	7.6	7.8	8.2	8.4	8.9
Healthy:	5.8	6.3	6.6	6.8	7.4	7.7	8.1

a. Find the mean and median of each data set.

Find the mean and median for the newborn babies at the Healing Hospital.

mean = ____________

median = ____________

(Round to the nearest hundredth as needed.)

Find the mean and median for the newborn babies at the Healthy Hospital.

mean = ____________

median = ____________

(Round to the nearest hundredth as needed.)

122. (cont.) b. Find the standard deviation of each data set.
Find the standard deviation for the newborn babies at the Healing Hospital.

s = ___________ (Round to the nearest hundredth as needed.)

Find the standard deviation for the newborn babies at the Healthy Hospital.

s = ___________ (Round to the nearest hundredth as needed.)

c. Draw a box plot for the newborn babies at the Healing Hospital. Choose the correct answer below.

○ A. ○ B. 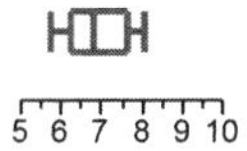 ○ C. 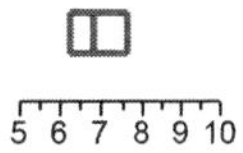 ○ D.

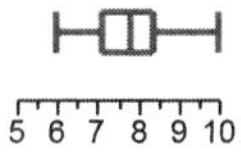

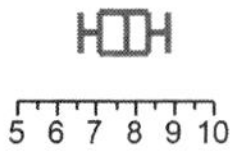

5 6 7 8 9 10 | 5 6 7 8 9 10 | 5 6 7 8 9 10 | 5 6 7 8 9 10

Draw a boxplot for the newborn babies at the Healthy Hospital. Choose the correct answer below.

○ A. ○ B. 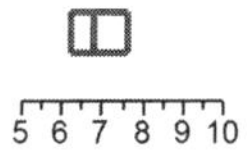 ○ C. 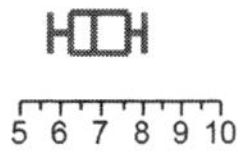 ○ D.

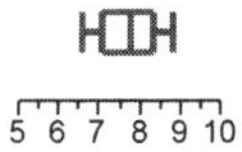

5 6 7 8 9 10 | 5 6 7 8 9 10 | 5 6 7 8 9 10 | 5 6 7 8 9 10

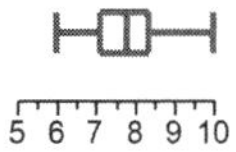

Give a possible explanation for the differences you observe. Choose the correct answer below.

○ **A.** The average weight of newborn babies from the Healing Hospital is lower than the average weight of newborn babies from the Healthy Hospital. This could be because the parents who are patients at the Healing hospital are healthier, and therefore keep control of their weight better, which causes lower weights of newborns.

○ **B.** The average weight of newborn babies from the Healthy Hospital is lower than the average weight of newborn babies from the Healing Hospital. This could be because the parents who are patients at the Healthy hospital are healthier, and therefore keep control of their weight better, which causes lower weights of newborns.

ID: 1.4.31

---

123. An auto transmission manufacturer receives ball bearings from two different suppliers. The ball bearings must have a specified diameter of 16.30 mm with a tolerance of ±0.1 mm. Recent shipments from the two suppliers had ball bearings with the following diameters. Complete parts (a) through (c).

Supplier A:	16.22	16.27	16.31	16.35	16.37	16.42	16.45
Supplier B:	16.18	16.22	16.25	16.35	16.37	16.42	16.45

a. Find the mean and standard deviation for each of the two data sets.

Find the mean and standard deviation for the diameters of the ball bearings from Supplier A.

mean = ___________

s = ___________

(Round to the nearest hundredth as needed.)

Find the mean and standard deviation for the diameters of the ball bearings from Supplier B.

mean = ___________

s = ___________

(Round to the nearest hundredth as needed.)

b. Draw a boxplot for each data set, and mark the tolerance on each boxplot.

Draw a boxplot for the diameters of the ball bearings from Supplier A. Choose the correct answer below.

○ A. ○ B. 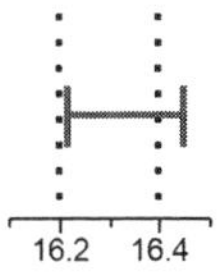 ○ C. 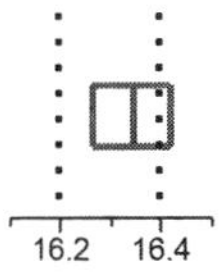 ○ D.

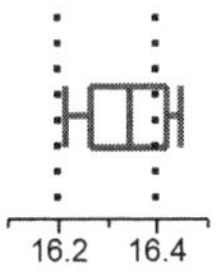

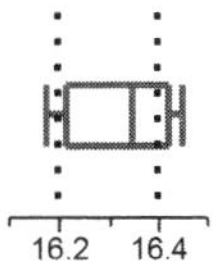

16.2 16.4 | 16.2 16.4 | 16.2 16.4 | 16.2 16.4

Draw a boxplot for the diameters of the ball bearings from Supplier B. Choose the correct answer below.

○ A. ○ B. 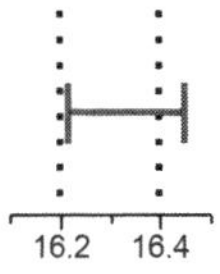 ○ C. 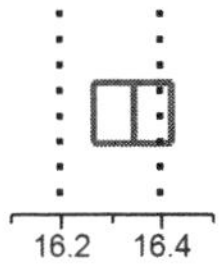 ○ D.

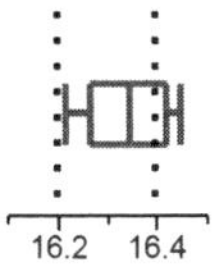

16.2 16.4 | 16.2 16.4 | 16.2 16.4 | 16.2 16.4

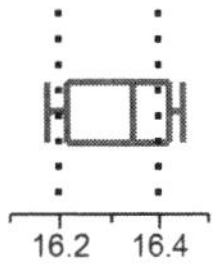

c. What percentage of ball bearings from each supplier meet specifications?

Find the percentage of ball bearings from Supplier A that meet specifications.

___________ % (Round to the nearest integer as needed.)

Find the percentage of ball bearings from Supplier B that meet specifications.

___________ % (Round to the nearest integer as needed.)

ID: 1.4.32

!* 124. For the following data set {3, 7, 2, 3, 5}, compute the mean, median, mode, range, and the distance (deviation) each value is from the mean.

The mean is ________.
(Type an integer or a decimal.)

The median is ________.
(Type an integer or a decimal.)

Determine the mode(s). Select the correct choice below and, if necessary, fill in the answer box to complete your choice.

- A. The mode is ________.
  (Use a comma to separate answers as needed. Type an integer or a decimal.)
- B. There is no mode.

The range is ________.
(Type an integer or a decimal.)

Subtract the mean from each value to find that value's deviation from the mean.

The value 3 has a deviation from the mean of ________.
The value 7 has a deviation from the mean of ________.
The value 2 has a deviation from the mean of ________.
The value 3 has a deviation from the mean of ________.
The value 5 has a deviation from the mean of ________.
(Type integers or decimals.)

ID: 1.4.33

!* 125. Use the Excel screenshot to answer parts (a) through (h).

[12] Click the icon to view the Excel screenshot.

(a) The type of chart shown is referred to in statistics as a (1) ________

(b) What do the columns represent?

- A. The counts of the number of questions on the CAT exam.
- B. The frequency at which the CAT exam was administered.
- C. The number of students who got a given score on the CAT exam.
- D. The scores of students on the CAT exam.

(c) How many students took the exam?

There were ________ students who took the exam.

(d) What was the mean score on the exam?

The mean score was ________ points.
(Type an integer or decimal rounded to two decimal places as needed.)

(e) What was the "average distance" of students' scores from the mean?

The "average distance" was ________ points.
(Type an integer or decimal rounded to two decimal places as needed.)

(f) What was the lowest score?

The lowest score was ________.

(g) What was the most frequently occurring score?

The most frequently occurring score was ________.

(h) What score splits the dataset in half, meaning half the scores above this value and half below this value?

The score that splits the dataset in half is ________.

125. (cont.) 12: Reference

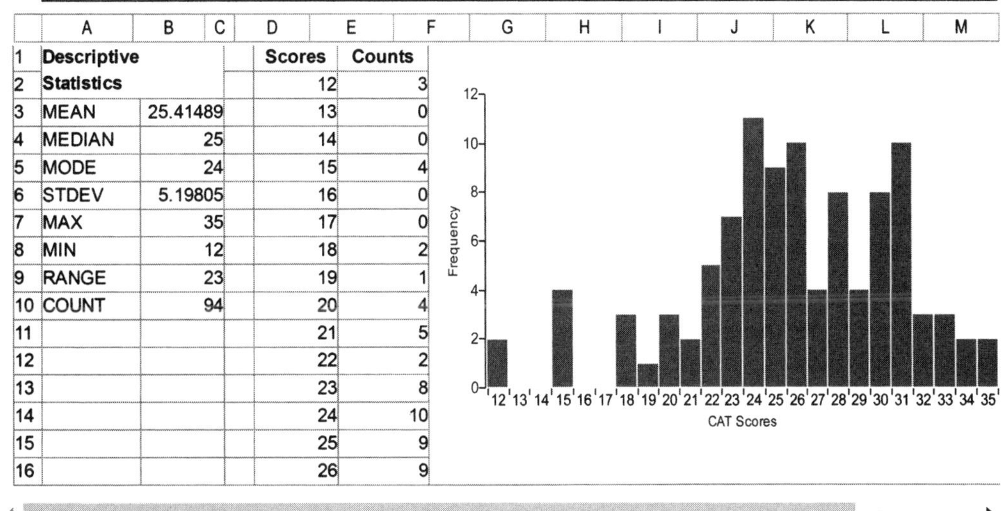

	A	B	C	D	E
1	**Descriptive**			**Scores**	**Counts**
2	**Statistics**			12	3
3	MEAN	25.41489		13	0
4	MEDIAN	25		14	0
5	MODE	24		15	4
6	STDEV	5.19805		16	0
7	MAX	35		17	0
8	MIN	12		18	2
9	RANGE	23		19	1
10	COUNT	94		20	4
11				21	5
12				22	2
13				23	8
14				24	10
15				25	9
16				26	9

(1) ○ normal distribution. ○ histogram.
○ box and whisker plot. ○ scatterplot.

ID: 1.4.34

!* 126. Use the Excel screenshot to answer the following.
(a) The formula in cell H6 is " = COUNTIF(scores," < 26"). What is it computing?
(b) How many students got between a 26 and 30, [26, 30)?
(c) What formula is entered into cell J7?
[13] Click the icon to view the Excel screenshot.

(a) What is the formula computing?

○ **A.** The number of scores below 45.
○ **B.** The number of scores below 26.
○ **C.** The number of scores around 26.
○ **D.** The number of scores below 26 and above 22.

(b) How many students got between a 26 and 30?

○ 26
○ 23
○ 3
○ 45

(c) The formula that should be entered into cell J7 is (1) ____________

13: Reference

	A	B	C	D	E	F	G	H	I	J
1	**CAT Scores**									
2	**DATA**			**Descriptive**			**Histogram**			
3	**Count**	**Scores**		**Statistics**			**Cutoffs**		**Bins**	**Frequency**
4	1	35		MEAN	25.79167		< 18	3	[0,...18)	3
5	2	24		MEDIAN	26		< 22	19	[18,...22)	16
6	3	25		MODE	24		< 26	46	[22,...26)	27
7	4	29		STDEV	4.70813		< 30	72	[26,...30)	
8	5	26		MAX	35		< 34	92	[30,...34)	
9	6	27		MIN	12		< 38	96	[34,...38)	
10	7	30		RANGE	23					
11	8	18		COUNT	96					
12	9	31								
13	10	18								
14	11	28								
15	12	23								
16	13	25								

!* 126.
(cont.)

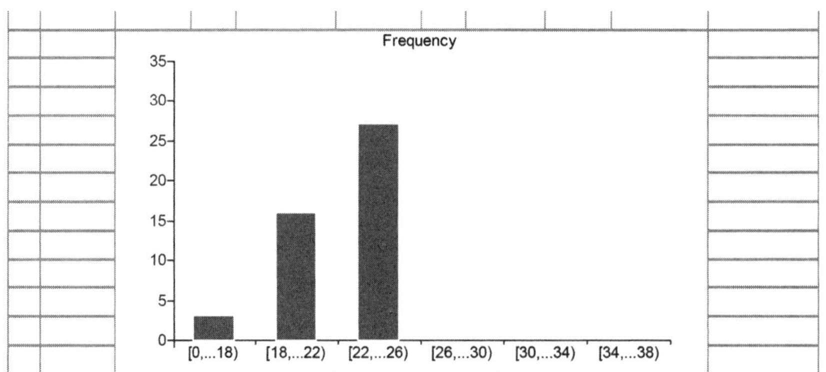

(1) ○ H7 − H6.
○ J7 − J6.
○ = SUM(J4:J6).
○ = SUM(H4:H6).

ID: 1.4.35

---

127. Make a bar graph of the populations of the five most populous states (from census data) in a certain country, with the bars in descending order.

State	Population
A	35.2 million
B	23.3 million
C	20.1 million
D	19.8 million
E	12.6 million

Choose the correct bar graph below.

○ **A.** Populations in Millions (Census Data)

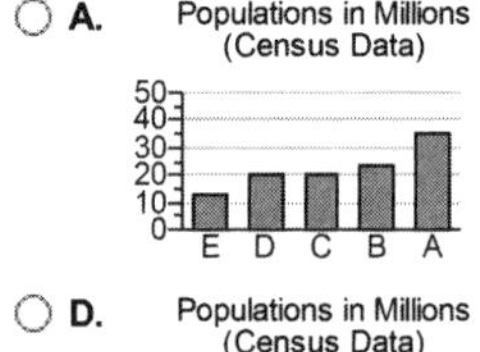

○ **B.** Populations in Millions (Census Data)

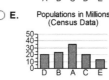

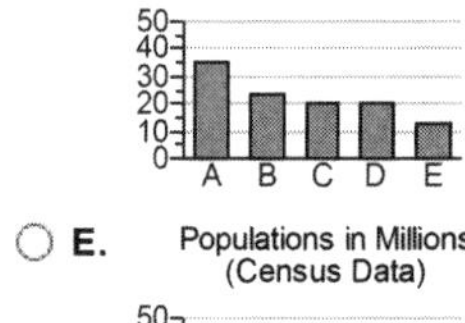

○ **C.** Populations in Millions (Census Data)

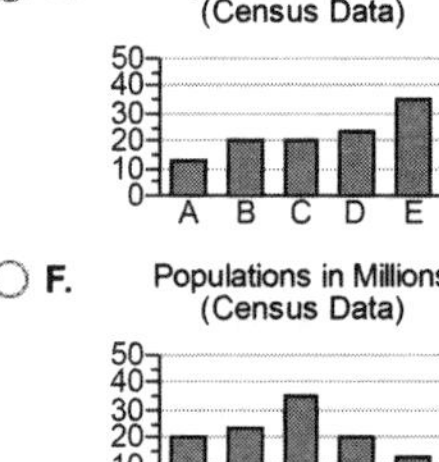

○ **D.** Populations in Millions (Census Data)

50 40 30 20 10 0
E D C B A

○ **E.** Populations in Millions (Census Data)

50 40 30 20 10 0
D B A C E

○ **F.** Populations in Millions (Census Data)

50 40 30 20 10 0
B D E C A

ID: 1.4.36

---

128. Construct a pie chart for the data set in the table to the right. The first step is to compute a percentage for each category in the data set. The annual revenue (in millions of dollars) of the leading food product businesses are shown in the table.

Company	Sales ($ millions)
A	57.3
B	49.2
C	22.2
D	20.5
E	20.1

Choose the correct pie chart below.

○ **A.** Company Revenues

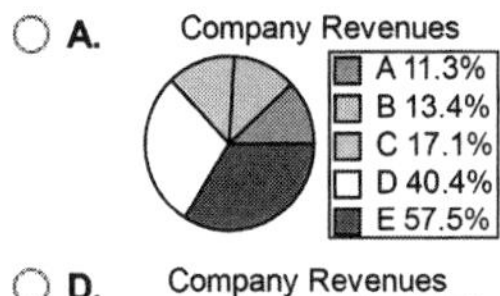

○ **B.** Company Revenues

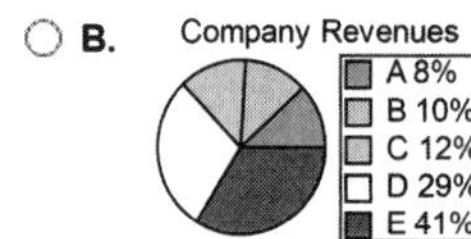

○ **C.** Company Revenues

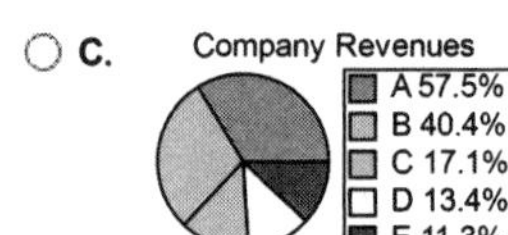

○ **D.** Company Revenues

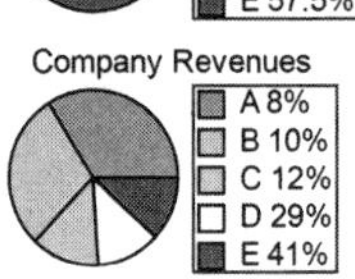

○ **E.** Company Revenues

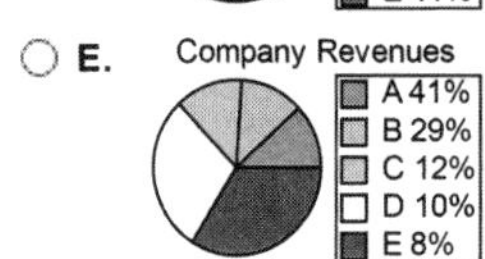

○ **F.** Company Revenues

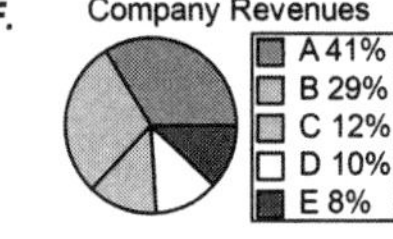

ID: 1.4.37

129. Use the frequency table for the ages of recent award-winning male actors at the time when they won their award to construct the corresponding histogram.
[14] Click the icon to view the frequency table.

Choose the correct graph below.

A.

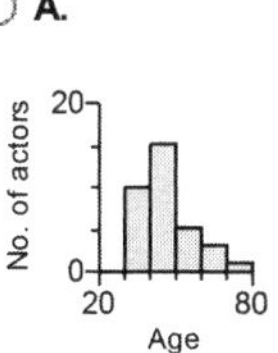

B.

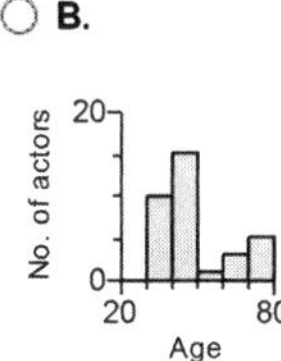

C.

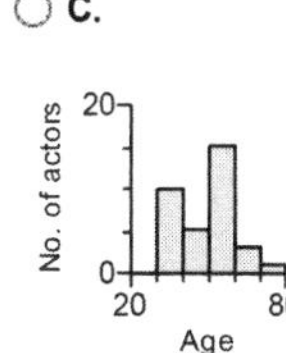

D.

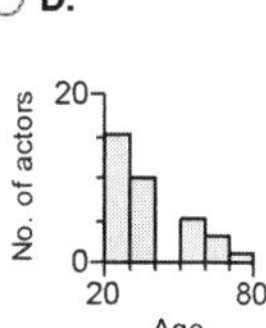

14: Data Table

Age	No. of actors
20 - 29	0
30 - 39	10
40 - 49	15
50 - 59	5
60 - 69	3
70 - 79	1

ID: 1.4.38

130. The accompanying table shows the numbers of cell phone subscriptions (in millions) in a certain country for various years. Construct a time-series graph for the data. Does the graph show straight-line growth (linear growth)? Or is the growth faster than linear?
[15] Click the icon to view the cell phone subscription data.

Construct a time-series graph for the data. Choose the correct graph below.

A.

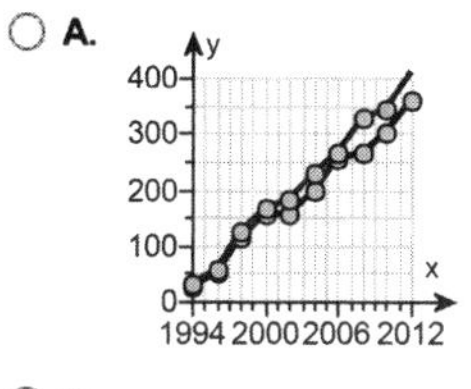

B.

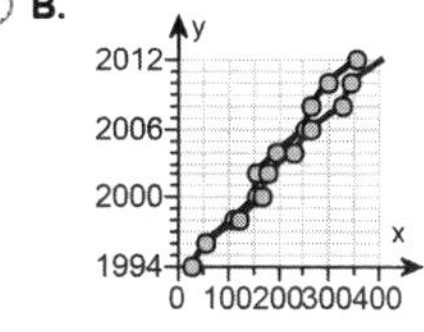

C.

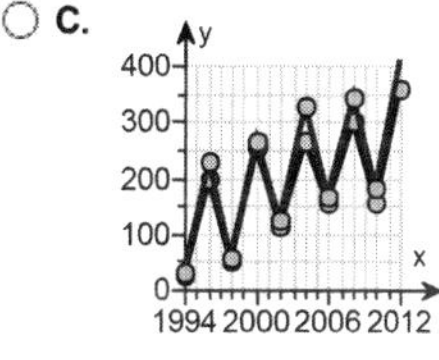

D.

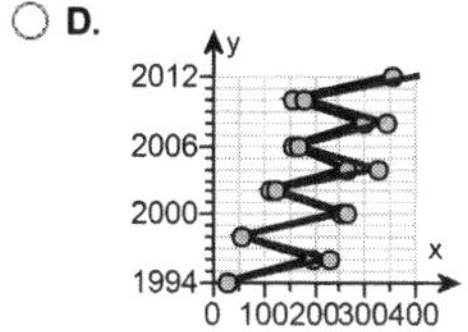

E.

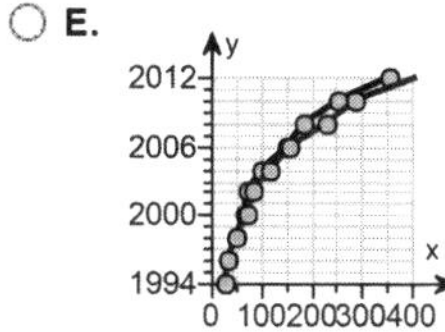

F.

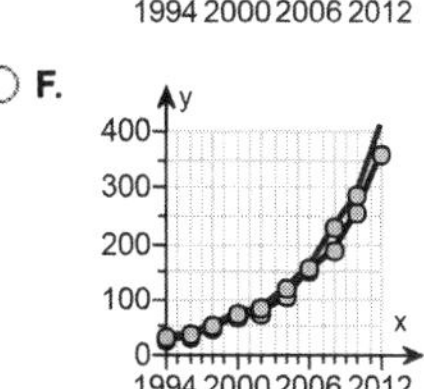

Does the graph show straight-line growth (linear growth)? Or is the growth faster than linear?

- **A.** While the graph varies greatly, it appears to show straight-line growth over the entire time series.
- **B.** The graph shows straight-line growth over the entire time-series.
- **C.** The graphs appears to have faster than linear growth over the entire time-series.
- **D.** While the graph shows straight-line growth at the beginning of the time-series, the growth appears to be faster than linear toward to end.

15: Cell Phone Subscription Data

Year	Number (millions)	Year	Number (millions)
1994	27	2004	196
1996	54	2006	253
1998	115	2008	264
2000	155	2010	301
2002	157	2012	356

ID: 1.4.39

* 131. The frequency table categorizes winners of a prestigious award from 1990 through 2012 by their age at the time they received the award. Complete parts (a) through (c) below.

[16] Click the icon to view the frequency table.

a. State whether the data are qualitative or quantitative.

The data are (1) ____________

b. Draw a pie chart if the data are qualitative. Draw a histogram if the data are quantitative.. Choose the correct graph below.

○ A. ○ B. ○ C. ○ D.

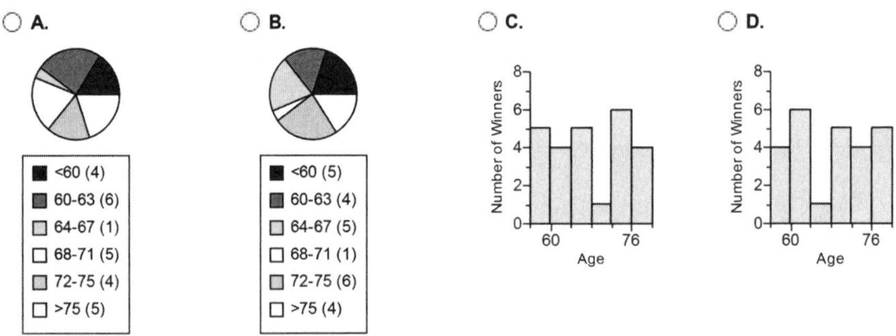

c. Discuss interesting features of the data revealed by the display. Choose the correct answer below.

○ **A.** The frequencies of the categories are approximately equal. Age does not seem to be a factor in determining who receives the award.

○ **B.** Lower ages tend to have greater frequencies. Age seems to be a factor in determining who receives the award, with younger people being more likely to receive it.

○ **C.** Higher ages tend to have greater frequencies. Age seems to be a factor in determining who receives the award, with older people being more likely to receive it.

○ **D.** The frequencies of the categories are approximately equal, though the frequency for one category is markedly less than the frequencies of the other categories. Age does not seem to be a factor in determining who receives the award.

16: Frequency Table

Age	Number of Winners
< 60	4
60-63	6
64-67	1
68-71	5
72-75	4
> 75	5

(1) ○ quantitative.
○ qualitative.

ID: 1.4.40

132. The frequency table shows the number of bachelor's degrees (in thousands) conferred on men and women in selected years (and projected for 2020). Complete parts (a) through (c) below.

[17] Click the icon to view the frequency table.

a. State whether the data are qualitative or quantitative.

The data are (1) ____________

b. Draw a bar graph if the data are qualitative. Draw a line chart if the data are quantitative. Choose the correct graph below.

○ **A.**

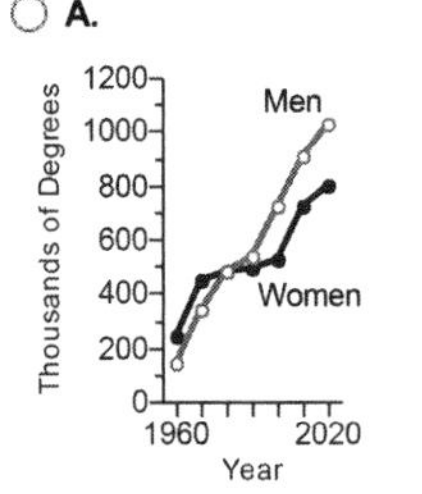

○ **B.**

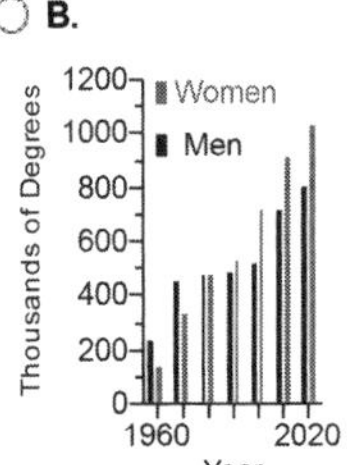

○ **C.**

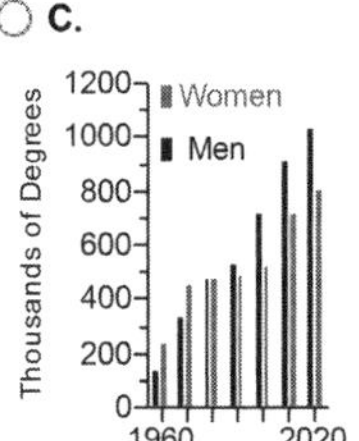

○ **D.**

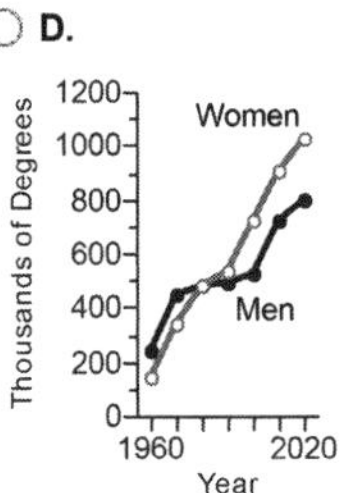

132. (cont.) c. Discuss interesting features of the data revealed by the display. Choose the correct answer below.

- ○ **A.** Over time, more bachelor's degrees were conferred on both men and women each year. The ratio of degrees conferred on men to degrees conferred on women remained fairly constant.
- ○ **B.** Over time, more bachelor's degrees were conferred on both men and women each year. In 1960, more were being conferred on men. By the 1980s, more were being conferred on women.
- ○ **C.** The total number of conferred bachelor's degrees remained fairly constant. In 1960, more were being conferred on men. By the 1980s, more were being conferred on women.
- ○ **D.** Over time, more bachelor's degrees were conferred on both men and women each year. In 1960, more were being conferred on women. By the 1980s, more were being conferred on men.

17: Frequency Table

Year	Men	Women
1960	240	140
1970	450	335
1980	480	475
1990	490	530
2000	520	720
2010	720	910
2020	800	1030

(1) ○ qualitative. ○ quantitative.

ID: 1.4.41

133. The frequency table shows the number of daily newspapers (morning and evening) in a country between 1950 and 2010. Complete parts (a) through (c) below.

[18] Click the icon to view the frequency table.

a. State whether the data are qualitative or quantitative.

The data are (1) ___________

b. Draw a bar graph if the data are qualitative. Draw a line chart if the data are quantitative. Choose the correct graph below.

○ **A.**

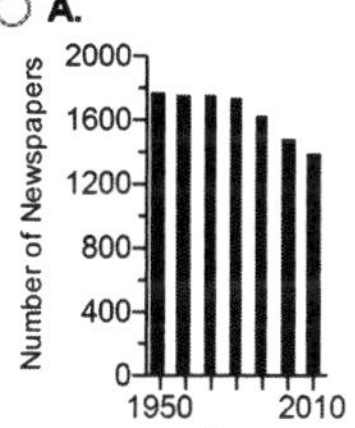

○ **B.**

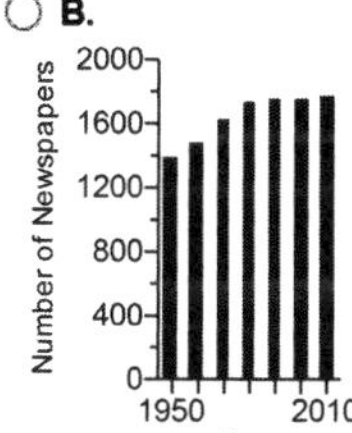

○ **C.**

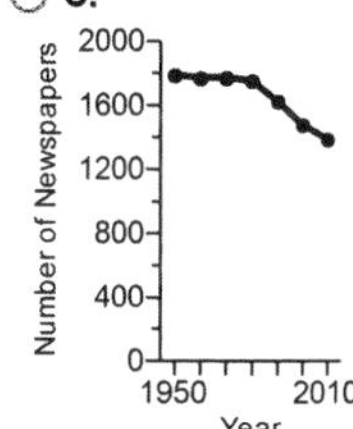

○ **D.**

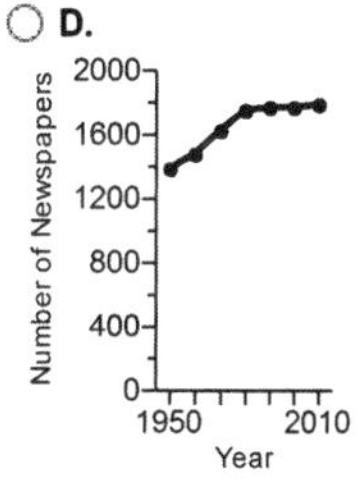

c. Discuss interesting features of the data revealed by the display. Choose the correct answer below.

- ○ **A.** From 1950 to 1980, the number of daily newspapers increased fairly steadily. From 1990 to 2010, the number remained fairly constant.
- ○ **B.** From 1950 to 1980, the number of daily newspapers remained fairly constant. During the 1980s, the number increased. From 1990 to 2010, the number was again fairly constant.
- ○ **C.** From 1950 to 1980, the number of daily newspapers remained fairly constant. During the 1980s, the number decreased. From 1990 to 2010, the number was again fairly constant.
- ○ **D.** From 1950 to 1980, the number of daily newspapers remained fairly constant. Starting in the 1980s, the number decreased fairly steadily, a trend that continued through 2010.

18: Frequency Table

Year	Number of Newspapers
1950	1776
1960	1762
1970	1756
1980	1745
1990	1619
2000	1473
2010	1387

(1) ○ qualitative. ○ quantitative.

ID: 1.4.42

134. The frequency table shows the stated religions of first-year college students in a particular year. Complete parts (a) through (c) below.

[19] Click the icon to view the frequency table.

a. State whether the data are qualitative or quantitative.

The data are (1) ____________ because religions are (2) ____________

b. Draw a bar graph if the data are qualitative. Draw a line chart if the data are quantitative. Choose the correct graph below.

○ A.

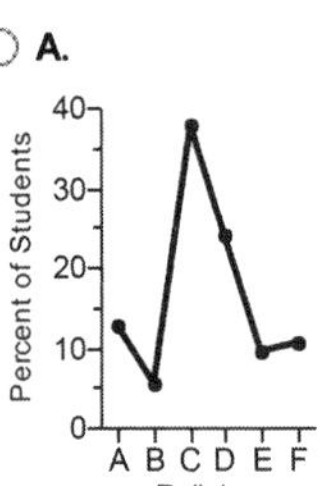

○ B.

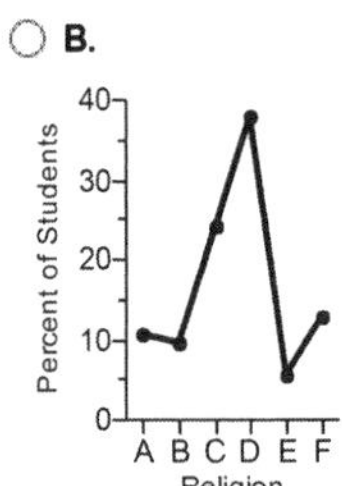

○ C.

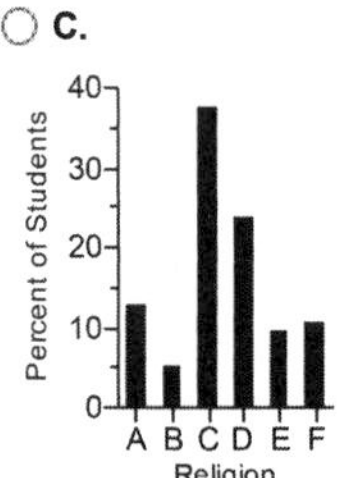

○ D.

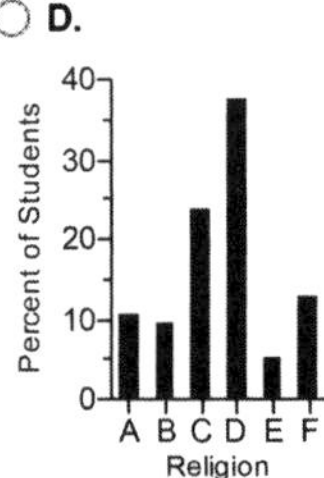

c. Discuss interesting features of the data revealed by the display. Choose the correct answer below.

○ A. There appears to be no percentage that is significantly larger or smaller than the rest of the percentage values. All the data values are roughly the same size.

○ B. Religion C has by far the largest percentage value and religion D has the second largest percentage value. The percentage values for the other religions are relatively similar in magnitude.

○ C. Religion D has by far the largest percentage value and religion C has the second largest percentage value. The percentage values for the other religions are relatively similar in magnitude.

○ D. The percentage increases steadily from religion B to religion E and remains constant from E to F. Religion E has the largest percentage value in the sample.

19: Frequency Table

Religion	Percent of Students
A	12.8
B	5.4
C	37.8
D	23.9
E	9.5
F	10.6

(1) ○ quantitative
○ qualitative

(2) ○ counts or measurements.
○ categories.

ID: 1.4.43

*135. The frequency table shows the percentage of foreign-born citizens in a country between 1940 and 2010. Complete parts (a) through (c) below.

[20] Click the icon to view the frequency table.

a. State whether the data are qualitative or quantitative.

The data are (1) ____________ because years are (2) ____________

b. Draw a bar graph if the data are qualitative. Draw a line chart if the data are quantitative. Choose the correct graph below.

○ A.

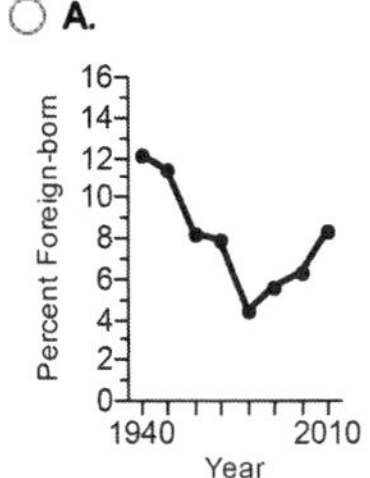

○ B.

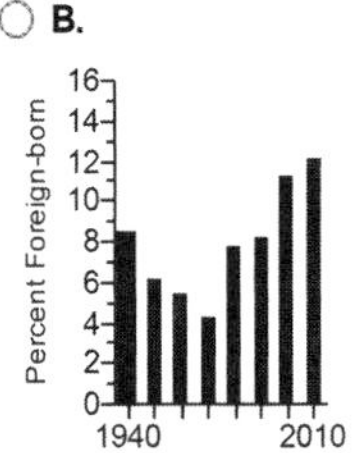

○ C.

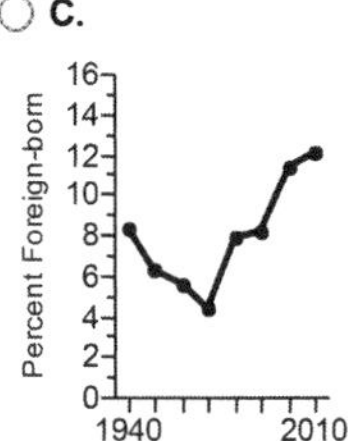

○ D.

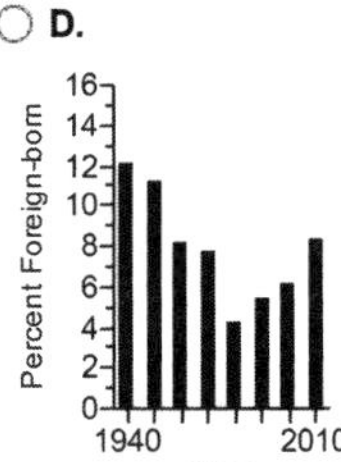

*135. (cont.) c. Discuss interesting features of the data revealed by the display. Choose the correct answer below.

- A. From 1950 to 1990, the percentage of foreign-born citizens remained fairly constant. During the 1990s, the percentage decreased. From 2000 to 2010, the percentage was again fairly constant.
- B. From 1950 to 1990, the percentage of foreign-born citizens remained fairly constant. Starting in the 1990s, the percetnage increased fairly steadily, a trend that continued through 2010.
- C. From 1950 to 1990, the percentage of foreign-born citizens increased fairly steadily. From 1990 to 2010, the percentage remained fairly constant.
- D. From 1950 to 1980, the percentage of foreign-born citizens remained fairly constant. During the 1980s, the percentage increased. From 1990 to 2010, the percentage was again fairly constant.

20: Frequency Table

Year	Percent Foreign-born
1940	8.3
1950	6.2
1960	5.5
1970	4.3
1980	7.8
1990	8.2
2000	11.3
2010	12.1

(1) ○ quantitative ○ qualitative   (2) ○ counts or measurements. ○ categories.

ID: 1.4.44

136. The table gives the order of the presidents of a country and the ages at their inauguration. Complete parts (a) through (d) below.

[21] Click the icon to view the table.

a. Find a creative way to display these data. Choose the correct answer below.

○ A.

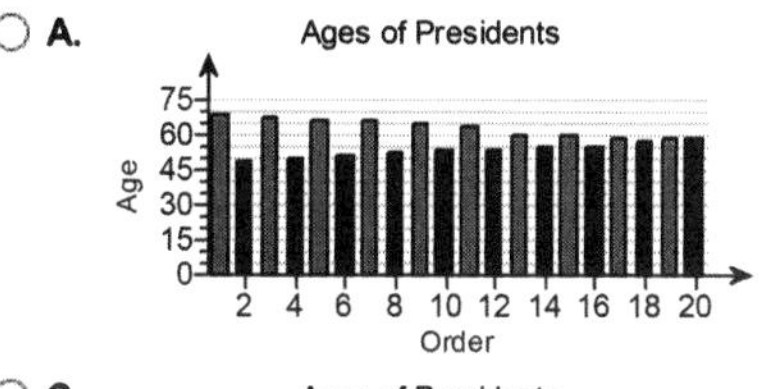

○ B.

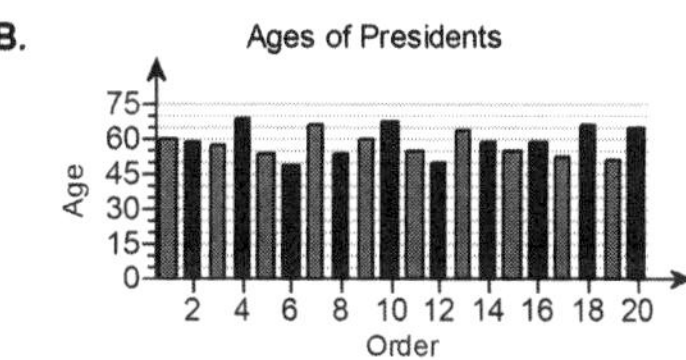

○ C.

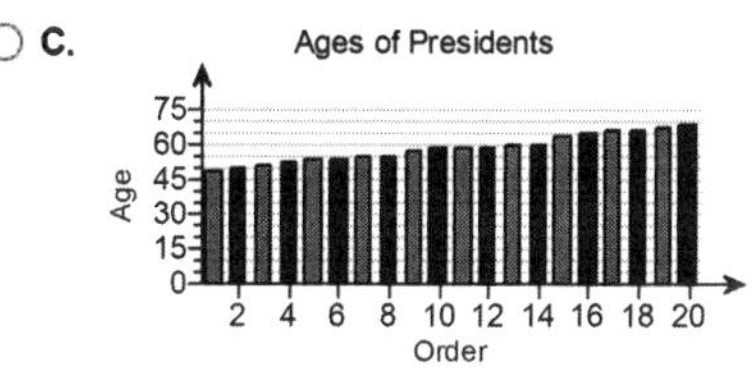

○ D.

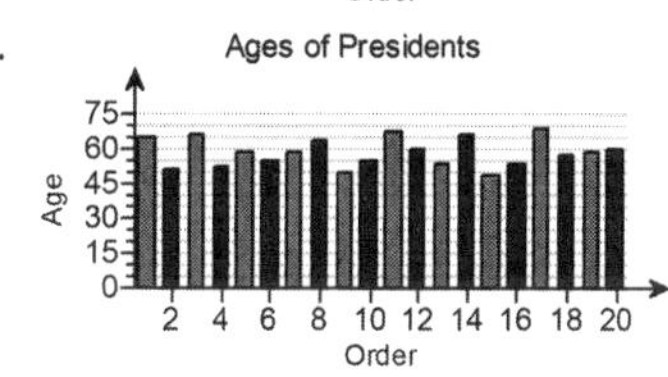

b. Which presidents could have said that they were the *youngest* president (or the same age in years as the youngest) at the time they took office?

The presidents that could have said that they were the youngest president, by the order they took office, are ______.

(Type a whole number. Use a comma to separate answers as needed.)

c. Which presidents could have said that they were the *oldest* president (or the same age in years as the oldest) at the time they took office?

The presidents that could have said that they were the oldest president, by the order they took office, are ______.

(Type a whole number. Use a comma to separate answers as needed.)

d. Describe significant features of the data. Choose the correct answer below.

- A. Each president was between 50 and 60 years old at the time of his or her inauguration. Older presidents tend to be followed by younger presidents and vice versa.
- B. Each president was between 40 and 70 years old at the time of his or her inauguration. There is no particular pattern in those ages.
- C. Each president was between 40 and 70 years old at the time of his or her inauguration. Those ages tend to increase over time.
- D. Each president was between 50 and 60 years old at the time of his or her inauguration. Those ages tend to decrease over time.

21: Table of Presidents' Ages at Inauguration

Order	1	2	3	4	5	6	7	8	9	10
Age	64	51	66	52	58	54	58	63	50	55
Order	11	12	13	14	15	16	17	18	19	20
Age	67	59	53	66	48	53	68	57	58	59

ID: 1.4.45

CHAPTER 2
Ratios and Proportions
MyMathLab Homework Problems*

* Problems with an asterisk are included in the pre-assigned homework assignment.
! Problems with an exclamation point are new to the Update edition.
To find the problems in MyMathLab online, please refer to the ID code listed below each problem.

1. Compare the following pair of numbers A and B in three ways.
   a. Find the ratio of A to B.
   b. Find the ratio of B to A.
   c. Complete the sentence: A is ____ percent of B.

   A = 6 and B = 3

a. The ratio of A to B is ___________. (Type an integer or a simplified fraction.)

b. The ratio of B to A is ___________. (Type an integer or a simplified fraction.)

c. A is ___________ percent of B. (Type an integer or a decimal.)

ID: 2.1.1

---

2. Compare the following pair of numbers A and B in three ways.
   a. Find the ratio of A to B.
   b. Find the ratio of B to A.
   c. Complete the sentence: A is ____ percent of B.

   A = 180 and B = 460

a. The ratio of A to B is ___________. (Type an integer or a simplified fraction.)

b. The ratio of B to A is ___________. (Type an integer or a simplified fraction.)

c. A is ___________ percent of B.
(Type an integer or decimal rounded to one decimal place as needed.)

ID: 2.1.2

---

*3. Compare A and B in three ways, where A = 51,546 is the number of deaths due to a deadly disease in the United States in 2005 and B = 18,717 is the number of deaths due to the same disease in the United States in 2009.
   a. Find the ratio of A to B.
   b. Find the ratio of B to A.
   c. Complete the sentence: A is ____ percent of B.

a. The ratio of A to B is ___________.
(Type an integer or decimal rounded to two decimal places as needed.)

b. The ratio of B to A is ___________.
(Type an integer or decimal rounded to two decimal places as needed.)

c. A is ___________ percent of B.
(Round to the nearest integer as needed.)

ID: 2.1.3

---

4. Compare A and B in three ways, where A = 1.1 million is the 2012 population of city X and B = 2.5 million is the 2012 population of city Y.
   a. Find the ratio of A to B.
   b. Find the ratio of B to A.
   c. Complete the sentence: A is ____ percent of B.

a. The ratio of A to B is ___________.
(Type an integer or decimal rounded to two decimal places as needed.)

b. The ratio of B to A is ___________.
(Type an integer or decimal rounded to two decimal places as needed.)

c. A is ___________ percent of B.
(Round to the nearest integer as needed.)

ID: 2.1.4

---

* 5. Compare A and B in three ways, where A = 1.87 million is the 2012 daily circulation of newspaper X and B = 2.29 million is the 2012 daily circulation of newspaper Y.

a. Find the ratio of A to B.
b. Find the ratio of B to A.
c. Complete the sentence: A is ____ percent of B.

a. The ratio of A to B is ___________.
(Type an integer or decimal rounded to two decimal places as needed.)

b. The ratio of B to A is ___________.
(Type an integer or decimal rounded to two decimal places as needed.)

c. A is ___________ percent of B.
(Round to the nearest integer as needed.)

ID: 2.1.5

---

6. Write this ratio as a fraction in lowest terms.

The ratio of 2 to 5.

The fractional notation for the ratio of 2 to 5 is ___________.

ID: 2.1.6

---

7. Write this ratio as a fraction in lowest terms.

\$100 to \$20

\$100 to \$20 is ___________.
(Simplify your answer. Type a fraction.)

ID: 2.1.7

---

8. Write this ratio as a fraction in lowest terms.

70 minutes to 40 minutes

70 minutes to 40 minutes is ___________.
(Simplify your answer. Type a fraction.)

ID: 2.1.8

---

9. Find the ratio of the following. Simplify, if possible.

86 days to 16 days

The ratio is ___________.
(Type an integer or a fraction.)

ID: 2.1.9

---

10. Write this ratio as fraction in lowest terms.

\$2.36 to \$10.84

\$2.36 to \$10.84 is ___________.
(Simplify your answer. Type a fraction.)

ID: 2.1.10

---

11. Write the ratio as a fraction in lowest terms.

7 to $7\frac{1}{3}$

The ratio is ___________.
(Simplify your answer. Type a fraction.)

ID: 2.1.11

---

12. Write the ratio as a fraction in lowest terms.

$1\frac{1}{4}$ to $1\frac{1}{14}$

The ratio is ___________.
(Simplify your answer. Type a fraction.)

ID: 2.1.12

---

13. Write the ratio as a fraction in lowest terms.

Compare in inches.

2 feet to 21 inches

The ratio is ________.

ID: 2.1.13

---

14. Write the ratio as a fraction in lowest terms.

33 minutes to 2 hours

For help, use the table of measurement relationships.

The ratio is ________.

ID: 2.1.14

---

15. Write the ratio as a fraction in lowest terms. Compare in hours.

48 hours to 3 days

The ratio is ________.

ID: 2.1.15

---

16. A town has six flower shops. Their one-year sales figures are compared in the chart. Find the ratio of sales at Corolla and Sons to those at Radio Flowers.

The ratio is ________.
(Simplify your answer. Type a fraction.)

Store	One-Year Sales ($)
Corolla and Sons	135 thousand
Winnie-the-Florist	310 thousand
Radio Flowers	405 thousand
Flowers of Distinction	540 thousand
Sifter's	640 thousand
Gorilla Flowers	810 thousand

ID: 2.1.16

---

17. Use the circle graph of one family's monthly budget to find the ratio of miscellaneous to total budget, $2000.

The ratio is ________.
(Type a simplified fraction.)

Utilities
Miscellaneous
Transportation
Food
Rent
Taxes

Item	Cost
Utilities	$100
Miscellaneous	$180
Transportation	$200
Food	$320
Rent	$820
Taxes	$380

ID: 2.1.17

---

18. Find the ratio and simplify. In this triangle, find the ratio of the shortest side to the longest.

14.8
4.4
14.1

The simplified ratio is ________.
(Type the ratio as a simplified fraction.)

ID: 2.1.18

---

19. Compare the ratio of the longest side to the shortest side.

The ratio is ________.
(Type the ratio as a simplified fraction.)

$6\frac{1}{4}$
5
$3\frac{1}{4}$
5
$14\frac{1}{2}$

ID: 2.1.19

20. The price of oil recently went from $14.00 to $19.60 per case of 12 quarts. Find the ratio of the increase in price to the original price.

The ratio is ________.
(Type a simplified fraction.)

ID: 2.1.20

21. A production company spent $52\frac{1}{2}$ days filming its first movie. The company's second movie was filmed in $8\frac{3}{4}$ weeks. Find the ratio of the first movie's filming time to the second movie's filming time. Compare in weeks.

The ratio is ________.
(Type a simplified fraction.)

ID: 2.1.21

!* 22. Use the following table comparing motor vehicle deaths (MVD) to answer parts (a) through (d) below.

	MVD (2011)	MVD per 100,000 people	MVD per 100,000 MV	MVD per 100 million vehicle miles
Country A	1,625	3.79	5.7	0.70
Country B	2,125	9.06	13.67	1.50

(a) The 1,625 is giving the number of MVD in Country A for their entire population, while the 3.79 is a ratio giving 3.79 MVD : 100,000 people. Put this information into a ratio table to find the total population of Country A in 2011. Solve for the total population.

MVD (2011)	People
1,625	x
3.79	100,000

x = ________ (Round to the nearest integer as needed.)

(b) Use the same technique to find the population of Country B in 2011, by first filling in the bottom row of the table and then solving for x.

MVD (2011)	People
2,125	x
________	________

(Type integers or decimals.)

Solve for x.

x = ________ (Round to the nearest integer as needed.)

(c) How many motor vehicles (MV) were there in Country B in 2011?

________ (Round to the nearest integer as needed.)

(d) Compute the ratio of the number of motor vehicles in Country A in 2011 to the number of motor vehicles in the Country B in 2011 and scale the second quantity to 1.

The ratio is ________ to 1.
(Type an integer or decimal rounded to one decimal place as needed.)

ID: 2.1.22

!* 23. Use the tables to answer parts (a) and (b).

(a) Compute the ratio of Total Charges for Public Four-Year In-State from 2013-14 to 2012-13 and scale the second quantity to 1.

[1] Click on the icon to view the table for part (a).

(b) Fill in the ratio table for 2013-14, using the values given in the second row of the table to avoid round-off error whenever possible.

[2] Click on the icon to view the table for part (b).

(a) Compute the ratio of Total Changes for Public Four-Year In-State from 2013-14 to 2012-13 and scale the second quantity to 1.

The scaled ratio is ________ : ________.
(Type integers or decimals rounded to three decimal places as needed.)

!* 23. (cont.) **(b)** Fill in the following ratio table for 2013-14, using the values given in the second row of the table to avoid round-off error whenever possible.

Private Room and Board	Public Four-Year Room and Board In-State	Public Two-Year Room and Board In-State
$13,391	**$10,979**	**$7,932**
______	**1**	______
100	______	______

(Type integers or decimals rounded to two decimal places as needed. Do not include the $ symbol in your answer.)

1: Table for part (a)

	Tuition and Fees				Room and Board				Total Charges			
Sector	2013-14	2012-13	$ Change	% Change	2013-14	2012-13	$ Change	% Change	2013-14	2012-13	$ Change	% Change
Public 2-Year In-State	$3,200	$3,116	$84	2.7	$7,485	$7,337	$148	2.0	$10,685	$10,453	$232	2.2
Public 4-Year In-State	$8,841	$8,695	$146	1.7	$10,374	$9,142	$1232	13.5	$19,215	$17,837	$1,378	7.7
Public 4-Year Out-of-State	$22,655	$20,113	$2542	12.6	$9,460	$9,181	$279	3.0	$32,115	$29,294	$2,821	9.6
Private Nonprofit 4-year	$31,636	$27,786	$3850	13.9	$11,272	$10,373	$899	8.7	$42,908	$38,159	$4,749	12.4
For-Profit	$15,214	$15,004	$210	1.4								

2: Table for part (b)

Private Room and Board	Public Four-Year Room and Board In-State	Public Two-Year Room and Board In-State
$13,391	**$10,979**	**$7,932**
	1	
100		

ID: 2.1.23

* 24. Which equality represents the proportion $6 is to 8 cans as $18 is to 24 cans?

Which equation represents the proportion?

○ **A.** $\frac{\$6}{8 \text{ cans}} = \frac{\$18}{24 \text{ cans}}$

○ **B.** $\frac{\$6}{24 \text{ cans}} = \frac{8 \text{ cans}}{\$18}$

○ **C.** $\frac{\$6}{24 \text{ cans}} = \frac{\$18}{8 \text{ cans}}$

○ **D.** $\frac{\$6}{8 \text{ cans}} = \frac{24 \text{ cans}}{\$18}$

ID: 2.1.24

25. Write the proportion.

3.4 hours is to 6.8 hours as

2.4 hours is to 4.8 hours

______ = ______

(Type fractions. Do not simplify.)

ID: 2.1.25

26. Find the missing number in the proportion.

$\frac{5}{2} = \frac{x}{10}$

x = ______

ID: 2.1.26

27. Find the missing number in the proportion.

$\frac{24}{28} = \frac{6}{x}$

x = ______

ID: 2.1.27

28. Solve for m.

$$\frac{m}{6} = \frac{6}{18}$$

m = ____________ (Type an integer or a simplified fraction.)

ID: 2.1.28

---

29. Find the missing number in the proportion.

$$\frac{1}{x} = \frac{2}{16}$$

x =

ID: 2.1.29

---

30. Solve for x.

$$\frac{8}{22} = \frac{x}{99}$$

x = ____________ (Type an integer or a simplified fraction.)

ID: 2.1.30

---

31. Solve for x.

$$\frac{x}{0.22} = \frac{0.6}{0.33}$$

x = ____________ (Type an integer or a decimal.)

ID: 2.1.31

---

32. Solve for m.

$$\frac{10.7}{1.23} = \frac{8.8}{m}$$

m = ____________

(Round to 4 decimal places.)

ID: 2.1.32

---

33. Find the unknown number in the proportion.

$$\frac{3}{1\frac{1}{2}} = \frac{14}{x}$$

x = ____________

ID: 2.1.33

---

34. Solve for t.

$$\frac{3\frac{1}{3}}{4\frac{1}{4}} = \frac{t}{5\frac{1}{5}}$$

The solution is t = ____________. (Type an integer or a simplified fraction.)

ID: 2.1.34

---

35. Solve the proportion in two different ways. First change all the numbers to decimal form and solve. Then change all the numbers to fraction form and solve.

$$\frac{\frac{2}{5}}{x} = \frac{2}{0.8}$$

x = ____________

(Type a decimal.)

x = ____________

(Simplify your answer. Type a fraction.)

ID: 2.1.35

---

*36. Caroline can sketch 8 cartoon strips in ten hours. How long will it take her to sketch 12 strips?

It will take her ___________ hours.

ID: 2.1.36

37. If 4 sweaters cost $39.12, how much would 8 sweaters cost?

The cost for 8 sweaters is $___________.

ID: 2.1.37

38. Set up and solve a proportion for the following application problem. If 2 pounds of grass seed cover 404 square feet, how many pounds are needed for 6868 square feet?

___________ pounds.

ID: 2.1.38

39. Tom makes $145.65 in 3 days. How much does he make in 2 days?

Tom makes $___________ in 2 days.

ID: 2.1.39

40. An 11-ounce bag of rice noodles makes 12 servings. At that rate, find how many ounces of noodles are needed for 19 servings, to the nearest ounce.

How many ounces of noodles are needed for 19 servings?
___________ ounces
(Round to the nearest whole number.)

ID: 2.1.40

41. A contractor finds that 7 gallons of paint will cover 1050 sq ft of wall area. How much wall area could be covered with 21 gallons of paint?

The contractor could cover ___________ sq ft.
(Simplify your answer. Type an integer or a decimal.)

ID: 2.1.41

42. One inch on the plan represents 2 feet. Find the actual dimensions of the study.

From north to south, the actual study measures ___________ feet.

From east to west, the actual study measures ___________ feet.

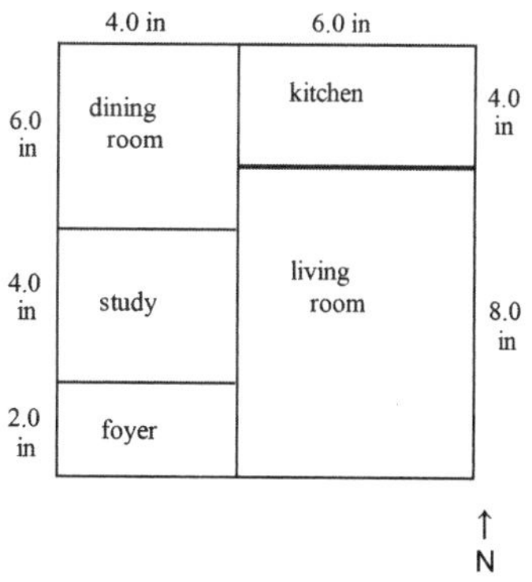

ID: 2.1.42

*43. A particular hybrid car travels approximately 294 mi on 6 gal of gas. Find the amount of gas required for a 931-mi trip.

The car needs ___________ gallons of gas for a 931-mi trip.
(Type an integer or a decimal.)

ID: 2.1.43

44. About 6 out of 10 people entering a community college need to take a refresher mathematics course. If there are 940 entering students, how many will probably need a refresher mathematics course?

About ___________ students will need a refresher mathematics course.

ID: 2.1.44

45. Nearly 4 out of 7 people choose vanilla as their favorite ice cream flavor. If 154 people attend an ice cream social, how many would you expect to choose vanilla?

_________ people will choose vanilla ice cream.

ID: 2.1.45

46. About 9 of 10 U.S. households have TV remote controls. There were 135,400,000 U.S. households in 1998. How many households have TV remote controls? Set up a proportion to solve.

_________ households have remote controls.

ID: 2.1.46

47. The stock market report says that 6 stocks went up for every 7 stocks that went down. If 924 stocks went down yesterday, how many went up? Set up and solve a proportion for the problem.

_________ stocks went up yesterday.

ID: 2.1.47

48. The ratio of the length of an airplane wing to its width is 8 to 1. If the length of a wing is 39.1 meters, how wide must it be?

The airplane wing must be _________ meters wide.
(Round to the nearest hundredth.)

ID: 2.1.48

49. The number of calories you burn depends on your weight. A 150-pound person burns 205 calories during 30 minutes of hiking. Find the number of calories that a 200-pound person would burn during the same activity, assuming they burn calories at the same rate.

How many calories would a 200-pound person burn?
_________ calories
(Round to the nearest whole number.)

ID: 2.1.49

50. At 3 p.m., Coretta's shadow is 1.45 meters long. Her height is 1.75 meters. At the same time, a tree's shadow is 6.8 meters long. How tall is the tree?

The tree is _________ meters tall.
(Round to the nearest hundredth.)

ID: 2.1.50

51. A survey of students at a university shows that 3 out of 4 drink coffee. Of the students who drink coffee, 1 out of 8 adds cream to it. If the university has 22,400 students, find the number of students who drink coffee with cream.

How many students drink coffee with cream?
_________ students

ID: 2.1.51

* 52. The nutrition information on the cereal box says that a 1/2-cup serving provides 150 calories and 6 grams of dietary fiber. At that rate, find how many calories and grams of fiber are in a 2/3-cup serving.

A 2/3-cup serving contains _________ calories.

A 2/3-cup serving contains _________ grams of fiber.

ID: 2.1.52

!* 53. Use the table to answer parts (a) and (b) below.

Private Four-Year Room and Board	**Public Four-Year Room and Board In-State**	**Public Two-Year Room and Board In-State**
$10,918	**$9,210**	**$7,263**
1.19	**1**	0.79
100	84.36	66.52

(a) (1) _________ $100 a student spends on room and board at a private four-year school, a student at a public four-year school spends (2) _________

(b) A student spends (3) _________ times as much on room and board at a private four-year school as a student does at a (4) _________ school.

(1) ○ For every fraction of
○ For every

(2) ○ $84.36.
○ $66.52.

(3) ○ 0.79
○ 1.19

(4) ○ public four-year
○ public two-year

ID: 2.1.53

!* 54. In a particular country, for men born in 1940 the predicted years of receiving retirement benefits is 16.4 for the bottom decile of income earners versus 23.1 years for the top decile.

Answer parts (a) through (d) below.

(a) Compute the ratio of predicted years of receiving retirement benefits for the top decile to the bottom decile and scale the second quantity to 1.

The scaled ratio is ________ : ________.
(Type integers or decimals rounded to two decimal places as needed.)

(b) Fill in the blanks.

A man born in 1940 from the top decile will receive retirement benefits for (1) ________ times as many (2) ________ as a man from the bottom decile.

(c) Compute the ratio of predicted years of receiving retirement benefits for the bottom decile to the top decile and scale the second quantity to 100.

________ : ________
(Type integers or decimals rounded to one decimal place as needed.)

(d) Fill in the blanks.

For every (3) ________ (4) ________ that a man born in 1940 from the bottom decile receives from retirement benefits, a man from the top decile will receive retirement benefits for (5) ________ (6) ________

(1) ○ 1 ○ 0.71 ○ 0.41 ○ 1.41

(2) ○ dollars ○ years

(3) ○ 100 ○ 0.71 ○ 140.9 ○ 71.0

(4) ○ dollars ○ years

(5) ○ 100 ○ 71.0

(6) ○ years. ○ dollars.

ID: 2.1.54

!* 55. Use the following table to answer parts (a) through (c) below.

Tuition and Fees	Books and Supplies	Room and Board	Transportation	Other Expenses	Total
$3,447	$1,478	$6,191	$1,684	$2,490	$15,290
	1				
					100

(a) Compute the part-to-part ratio of room and board to books and supplies and scale the second quantity to 1.

The scaled ratio is ________ : ________.
(Type integers or decimals rounded to two decimal places as needed.)

(b) A student spends (1) ________ times as much on (2) ________ as on (3) ________

(c) Compute the part-to-whole ratio of each part (room and board, and books and supplies) and scale the second quantity to 100.

The scaled part-to-whole ratio for room and board is ________ : ________.
(Type integers or decimals rounded to two decimal places as needed.)

The scaled part-to-whole ratio for books and supplies is ________ : ________.
(Type integers or decimals rounded to two decimal places as needed.)

(1) ○ 3.19 ○ 4.19 ○ 1 ○ 0.24

(2) ○ books and supplies ○ room and board

(3) ○ books and supplies. ○ room and board.

ID: 2.1.55

!* 56. Your GPA is a weighted average; your grades are weighted by the credits for each course. Quality points are the product of the credits for a course and the 4.0 scale of your grades. Complete parts **a.** and **b.** below.

Credits	Grade	4.0 Scale	Quality Points
4	B	3.0	
4	C+	2.33	
3	A	4.0	
		GPA:	

a. Compute the quality points for the three courses listed.

Credits	Grade	4.0 Scale	Quality Points
4	B	3.0	
4	C+	2.33	
3	A	4.0	
		GPA:	

(Type integers or decimals rounded to the nearest hundredth as needed.)

b. Your GPA is then the ratio of your total quality points to total credits. Compute the GPA for the courses listed.

The GPA for the courses listed is ________.
(Type an integer or a decimal rounded to the nearest hundredth as needed.)

ID: 2.2.1

!* 57. In one class, homework is worth 10% of the final grade, each of 3 projects is worth 15%, and a final exam is worth 45%.

(a) If a student has an 83 homework average and a 94 on the first project, what is the student's grade at this point?

(b) If a student gets a 76 on the second project and a 74 on the third project, what is the lowest grade the student can get on the final exam to get an 80 overall in the course?

(a) The grade at this point is ________.
(Simplify your answer. Round to the nearest tenth as needed.)

(b) The lowest possible grade is ________.
(Simplify your answer. Round to the nearest integer as needed.)

ID: 2.2.2

!* 58. For each of the pairs of quantities, identify if they are directly, inversely, or not proportional. Complete parts (a) through (j).

(a) tax ($) charged for buying an item : cost ($) of an item

Choose the correct answer below.

- ○ inversely proportional
- ○ directly proportional
- ○ not proportional

(b) population of a region : area of a region

- ○ not proportional
- ○ directly proportional
- ○ inversely proportional

(c) average speed to work : time it takes

- ○ directly proportional
- ○ not proportional
- ○ inversely proportional

(d) population of New York City : population of New York State

- ○ directly proportional
- ○ not proportional
- ○ inversely proportional

(e) volume of water : weight of water

- ○ not proportional
- ○ directly proportional
- ○ inversely proportional

!* 58. (cont.) **(f)** air pressure : altitude

- ○ inversely proportional
- ○ not proportional
- ○ directly proportional

(g) parent's age : child's age

- ○ not proportional
- ○ inversely proportional
- ○ directly proportional

(h) force of gravity between 2 objects : distance between 2 objects

- ○ not proportional
- ○ directly proportional
- ○ inversely proportional

(i) population of a state : number of representatives in Congress

- ○ not proportional
- ○ directly proportional
- ○ inversely proportional

(j) a person's height : a person's weight

- ○ directly proportional
- ○ not proportional
- ○ inversely proportional

ID: 2.3.1

!* 59. The number of miles driven is proportional to the gas the car uses. Note that driving is assumed to be consistent over time. Complete parts (a) and (b) below.

(a) Fill in the blank.

For two proportional quantities, the decimal equivalent of the fractional representation of their ratio is called a

(1) ____________

(b) Assuming that a person drives 115 miles on 5 gallons of gas, find both constants of proportionality. Express the first as whole number and the second as a fraction in lowest terms.

The constant of proportionality expressed as a whole number is ____________.
(Type an integer or a simplified fraction.)

The constant of proportionality expressed as a fraction is ____________.
(Type an integer or a simplified fraction.)

(1) ○ proportional number.
○ proportional fraction.
○ constant of proportionality.

ID: 2.3.2

---

60. A recipe for 12 bran muffins calls for 1 cup of flour. The number of muffins that can be made varies directly with the amount of flour used. There are $3\frac{1}{2}$ cups of flour available. How many muffins can be made?

____________ muffins

ID: 2.3.3

---

61. Determine whether the equation represents a direct variation. If it does, find the constant of variation.
$3y = 4x + 1$

Choose the correct answer below.

○ **A.** Yes, the equation represents a direct variation. The constant of variation is ____________.
(Type an integer or a simplified fraction.)

○ **B.** No, the equation does not represent a direct variation.

ID: 2.3.4

---

62. Suppose y varies directly with x. Write a direct variation equation that relates x and y. Then find the value of y when $x = 12$.

$y = 9$ when $x = 4$

Write a direct variation equation that relates x and y.

y = ____________ (Simplify your answer.)

What is the value of y when $x = 12$?

y = ____________ (Simplify your answer.)

ID: 2.3.5

*63. Graph the direct variation equation.

$y = 2x$

Use the graphing tool to graph the equation.

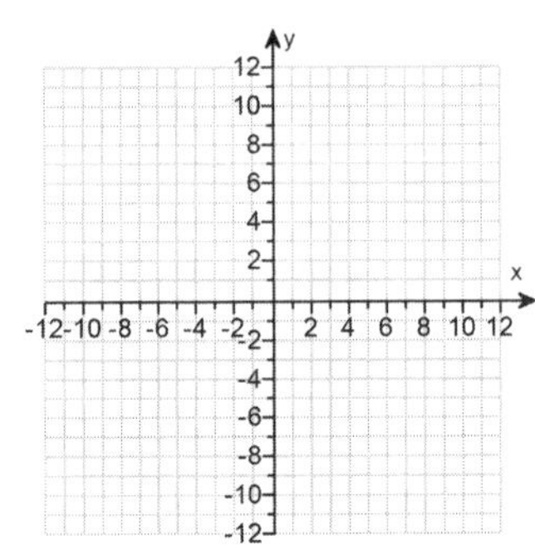

ID: 2.3.6

*64. The distance d you bike varies directly with the amount of time t you bike. Suppose you bike 9.2 mi in 1.25 h. What is an equation that relates d and t? What is the graph of the equation?

Write an equation that relates d and t. Choose the correct answer below.

- A. $d = 7.36t$
- B. $d = 11.50t$
- C. $d = 9.2t$
- D. $d = 1.25t$

Graph the equation. Choose the correct graph below.

A. 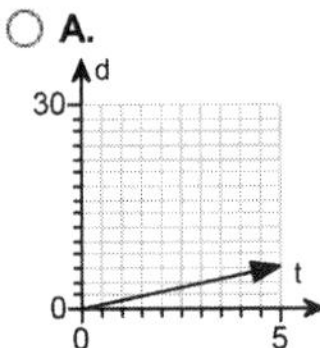

B. 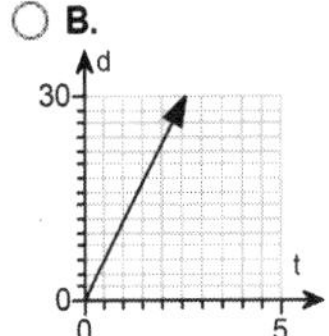

C. 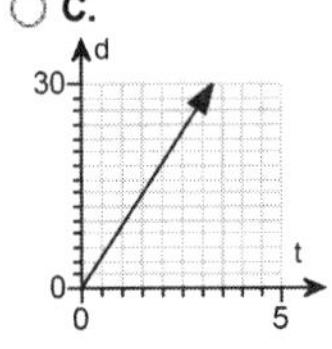

D. 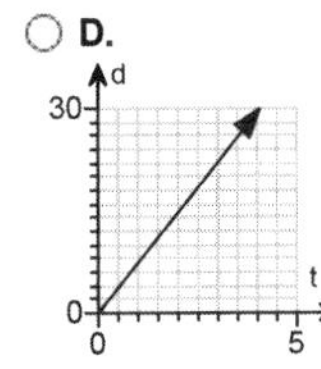

ID: 2.3.7

65. For the data in the table, tell whether y varies directly with x. If it does, write an equation for the direct variation.

x	y
− 10	18
1	− 1.8
20	− 36

Write an equation for the direct variation. Select the correct choice and fill in any answer boxes in your choice below.

- A. y = ____________ (Use integers or decimals for any numbers in the expression.)
- B. There is no direct variation.

ID: 2.3.8

*66. For the data in the table below, does y vary directly with x? If it does, write an equation for the direct variation.

x	2	3	7
y	6	8	16

Choose the correct answer below.

- A. Yes, y varies directly with x. The equation for the direct variation is $y = \frac{8}{3}x$.
- B. Yes, y varies directly with x. The equation for the direct variation is $y = \frac{16}{7}x$.
- C. Yes, y varies directly with x. The equation for the direct variation is $y = 3x$.
- D. No, y does not vary directly with x.

ID: 2.3.9

67. Suppose y varies directly with x. Write a direct variation equation that relates x and y. Then graph the equation.

$y = 6.3$ when $x = 0.9$

The equation of variation is y = ____________.
(Simplify your answer.)

Use the graphing tool to graph the equation.

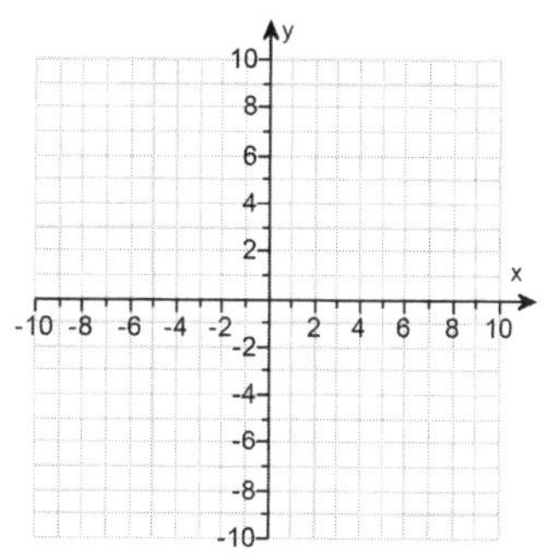

ID: 2.3.10

68. Tell whether the two quantities vary directly. Explain your reasoning.

the score on a test and the number of incorrect answers on the test

Choose the correct answer below.

- ○ **A.** Yes, they vary directly. When one quantity increases, the other quantity also increases.
- ○ **B.** No, they do not vary directly. When one quantity increases, the other quantity does not increase.
- ○ **C.** Yes, they vary directly. When one quantity increases, the other quantity does not increase.
- ○ **D.** No, they do not vary directly. When one quantity increases, the other quantity also increases.

ID: 2.3.11

!* 69. If two quantities are proportional, then their relationship can be represented by an equation of the form $y = k \cdot x$.

(a) Assume that the number of miles driven is proportional to the gas used by the car. If a car can drive 217 miles on 7 gallons of gas, find an equation that represents this relationship.

(b) Assume that the water used in a pancake recipe is proportional to the flour used at a ratio of 3 cups of water to 5 cups of flour. Find an equation that represents this relationship.

(c) Assume that the ratio of currency A to currency B to currency C is 7 : 3 : 840 and that these currencies are proportional to each other. Find equations that represent relationships between pairs of these quantities.

(a) Choose the correct answer below.

- ○ **A.** $G = 31 \cdot M$
- ○ **B.** $G = 217 \cdot M$
- ○ **C.** $M = \frac{1}{31} \cdot G$
- ○ **D.** $M = 31 \cdot G$

(b) Choose the correct answer below.

- ○ **A.** $W = \frac{3}{5} \cdot F$
- ○ **B.** $W = 3 \cdot F$
- ○ **C.** $W = \frac{5}{3} \cdot F$
- ○ **D.** $W = 5 \cdot F$

(c) Select all that apply.

- ☐ **A.** $C = 280 \cdot A$
- ☐ **B.** $B = \frac{3}{7}A$
- ☐ **C.** $B = 280 \cdot C$
- ☐ **D.** $B = \frac{1}{280} \cdot C$
- ☐ **E.** $A = 3 \cdot B$
- ☐ **F.** $C = 280 \cdot B$
- ☐ **G.** $A = 120 \cdot C$

ID: 2.3.12

70. Translate the sentence into an equation.

W varies directly as h.

Choose the correct answer below.

○ **A.** $W = kh^2$
○ **B.** $W = kh$
○ **C.** $W = \frac{k}{h}$
○ **D.** $W = k\sqrt{h}$

ID: 2.3.13

---

71. Write an equation to describe the variation. Use k for the constant of proportionality.

b varies inversely as f

The equation is __________.

ID: 2.3.14

---

72. Translate the equation into a sentence by using the phrase "varies directly" or "varies inversely."

$$W = \frac{k}{h}$$

Choose the correct answer below.

○ **A.** W varies inversely as h.
○ **B.** W varies directly as h.
○ **C.** W varies inversely as the square root of h.
○ **D.** W varies directly as h cubed.

ID: 2.3.15

---

73. Find an equation that meets the given conditions.

c varies directly as u, and $c = 20$ when $u = 4$.

c = __________

ID: 2.3.16

---

*74. Find an equation that meets the conditions p varies inversely as d, and $p = 8$ when $d = 10$.

p = __________ (Simplify your answer.)

ID: 2.3.17

---

*75. If y varies directly as x, and $y = 12$ when $x = 4$, find y when $x = 8$.

y = __________ when $x = 8$.

ID: 2.3.18

---

76. If G varies inversely as r, and $G = 15$ when $r = 4$, find G when $r = 5$.

G = __________ (Simplify your answer.)

ID: 2.3.19

---

77. If I varies inversely as $r + 2$, and $I = 8$ when $r = 4$, find r when $I = 5$.

r = __________ when $I = 5$

ID: 2.3.20

---

78. The distance traveled varies directly as the speed of a car. If the speed decreases, what happens to the distance traveled?

Choose the correct answer below.

- ○ It increases.
- ○ It decreases.

ID: 2.3.21

---

*79. The cost of tuition at a certain college varies directly as the number of credit hours taken. For the academic year 2005 – 2006, the cost of 14 credit hours was $1274. What did 10 credit hours cost?

The cost of 10 credit hours was $__________.

ID: 2.3.22

---

*80. The distance that an object falls varies directly as the square of the time the object is in motion. If an object falls for 3 seconds, it will fall 144.9 feet. To estimate the height of a cliff, a person drops a stone at the edge of the cliff and measures how long it takes for the stone to reach the base. If it takes 3.8 seconds, what is the height of the cliff?

The cliff is about __________ feet high.
(Round to one decimal place as needed.)

ID: 2.3.23

---

81. Assume that the stopping distance of a van varies directly with the square of the speed. A van traveling 40 miles per hour can stop in 60 feet. If the van is traveling 64 miles per hour, what is its stopping distance?

If the van is traveling 64 miles per hour, the stopping distance is __________ feet.
(Type an integer or a decimal.)

ID: 2.3.24

---

82. The force F (in pounds) required to push a sofa across a floor varies directly as the weight w (in pounds) of the sofa. Complete parts (a) through (c) below.

a. A person can push a 100-pound sofa across a carpeted floor by pushing with a force of 60 pounds. Find an equation that describes the relationship between w and F.

F = __________

(Type an equation using w as the variable. Simplify your answer. Use integers or fractions for any numbers in the equation.)

b. How much force is required to push a 75-pound sofa across a carpeted floor?

A force of __________ pounds is required to push a 75-pound sofa across a carpeted floor.
(Type an integer or decimal.)

c. How would an equation of a model for a wood floor compare with the model you found in part (a)? In particular, how would the variation constants compare?

- ○ **A.** The variation constant should increase when changing to a wood floor.
- ○ **B.** The variation constant should stay the same when changing to a wood floor.
- ○ **C.** The variation constant should decrease when changing to a wood floor.

ID: 2.3.25

---

*83. The time T (in seconds) it takes to hear thunder after you see lightning varies directly as the distance d (in feet) from the lightning if the temperature does not vary much during the storm. In a certain storm, it takes 5 seconds to hear thunder when lightning is seen 5525 feet away.

a. Find an equation that describes the relationship between d and T for the storm.

T = __________
(Round to six decimal places as needed.)

b. If it takes 6 seconds for you to hear thunder after you see lightning, how far away was the lightning?

__________ feet
(Round to the nearest foot as needed.)

c. What does the constant k represent in this situation? [Hint: Recall that slope is the rate of change of the dependent variable with respect to the independent variable.]

- ○ **A.** The distance from the lightning increases by k feet for each 1 second it takes to hear thunder.
- ○ **B.** The time it takes to hear thunder increases by k seconds for each 1 foot from the lightning strike.
- ○ **C.** The speed of sound in this storm is k feet per second.
- ○ **D.** The minimum time it takes to hear thunder after you see lightning is k seconds.

*83. (cont.) **d.** There is a rule of thumb that the number of seconds it takes you to hear thunder after you see lightning is equal to the number of miles that you are from the lightning. Is this rule of thumb a good approximation? If yes, explain. If no, find a better rule of thumb. [Hint: There are 5280 feet in 1 mile.]

Is this rule of thumb a good approximation?

- ○ No
- ○ Yes

Find a better rule of thumb if the rule of thumb given above is not a good approximation.

- ○ **A.** The number of seconds divided by 5 is approximately the number of miles to the strike.
- ○ **B.** The rule of thumb given above is a good approximation, it is in accordance with the equation found in part (a).
- ○ **C.** The number of seconds is approximately the number of feet to the strike.
- ○ **D.** The number of seconds multiplied by 5 is approximately the number of miles to the strike.

ID: 2.3.26

---

*84. The weight (in pounds) $w = f(d)$ of an object varies inversely as the square of its distance (in thousands of miles) d from the center of Earth.

a. An astronaut weighs 240 pounds at sea level (about 4 thousand miles from Earth's center). Find an equation of f.

f(d) = ____________

b. How much would the astronaut weigh at 4 thousand miles above Earth's surface?

____________ pounds

c. At what distance from the center of Earth would the astronaut weigh 1 pound?

____________ miles
(Round to the nearest mile as needed.)

d. Estimate how much the astronaut would weigh on the surface of the Moon. The Moon is a mean distance of about 239 thousand miles from Earth.

____________ pounds
(Round to three decimal places as needed.)

Has model breakdown occurred?

- ○ Yes
- ○ No

e. Without finding an equation, discuss how an equation of a model for a 230-pound astronaut would compare with the equation you found in part (a). Discuss how the variation constants would compare.

- ○ **A.** The equations would be the same.
- ○ **B.** The variation constant in the equation would be less than the variation constant of the equation found in part (a).
- ○ **C.** The variation constant in the equation would be greater than the variation constant of the equation found in part (a).

ID: 2.3.27

---

85. The intensity (in watts per square meter, W/m^2) $I = f(d)$ of a television signal varies inversely as the square of the distance d (in kilometers) from the transmitter. The intensity of a television signal is 20 W/m^2 at a distance of 3.3 km. Complete parts (a) through (d) below.

a. Find an equation of f.

f(d) = ____________ (Simplify your answer.)

b. Find f(1), f(2), f(3), and f(4). What do they mean in this situation?

f(1) = ____________ W/m^2
(Round to one decimal place as needed.)

f(2) = ____________ W/m^2
(Round to one decimal place as needed.)

f(3) = ____________ W/m^2
(Round to one decimal place as needed.)

f(4) = ____________ W/m^2
(Round to one decimal place as needed.)

85. (cont.) What do these values mean in this situation?

- ◯ **A.** The intensity of the signal for 1, 2, 3, and 4 television channels.
- ◯ **B.** The distance between transmitters for 1, 2, 3, and 4 television channels.
- ◯ **C.** The intensity of the signal at 1, 2, 3, and 4 kilometers from the transmitter
- ◯ **D.** The distances from the transmitter at which the intensity is 1, 2, 3, and 4 W/m^2

c. Use a graphing calculator to draw a graph of f. What happens to the value of I as the value of d increases, for $d > 0$? What does that mean in this situation?

Choose the correct graph below.

◯ **A.** ◯ **B.** ◯ **C.** ◯ **D.**

As the value of d increases, the value of I (1) ____________. This means that the signal (2) ____________ as the distance from the transmitter increases.

d. What happens to the value of f(d) for an extremely large value of d? What does that mean in this situation?

For an extremely large value of d, the value of I is (3) ____________. This means that the signal is (4) ____________ to be received far from the transmitter.

(1) ◯ decreases ◯ stays the same ◯ increases
(2) ◯ gets stronger ◯ gets weaker ◯ stays the same
(3) ◯ the constant k ◯ extremely large ◯ nearly zero
(4) ◯ strong enough ◯ too weak

ID: 2.3.28

86. As you move away from an object, it appears to decrease in height. To describe this relationship, an algebra professor stood 10 feet from his garage, held a yardstick 1 foot away, and measured the image of his garage. The image of the garage had an apparent height of 14.7 inches. He collected apparent heights of the garage at various distances from it, as shown in the table to the right. Let $a = f(d)$ be the apparent height (in inches) of the garage when the professor was d feet from the garage. Complete parts (a) through (f) below.

Distance from Garage (feet)	Apparent Height of Garage (inches)
10	14.7
20	7.1
30	4.9
40	3.6
50	2.9
60	2.4
70	2.2

a. Use a graphing calculator to draw a scattergram of the data. Choose the correct graph below.

◯ **A.** ◯ **B.** ◯ **C.** ◯ **D.**

b. Find an equation of f. Which equation below best models the data?

- ◯ **A.** $f(d) = 180.45d$
- ◯ **B.** $f(d) = \frac{180.45}{d}$
- ◯ **C.** $f(d) = \frac{146.14}{d}$
- ◯ **D.** $f(d) = 146.14d$

c. In a sentence using the phrase "varies directly" or "varies inversely," describe how the distance from the garage and the apparent height of the garage are related. Complete the following sentence.

The apparent height of the garage varies (1) ____________ as the distance from the garage.

d. Your model f is a decreasing function for $d > 0$. Eplain why that makes sense in this situation. Complete the following explanation.

Since the apparent height of the garage (2) ____________ as the distance from the garage increases, a decreasing function makes sense.

e. Find the apparent height from a distance of 100 feet.

From 100 feet, the apparent height is about ____________ inches.
(Use the answer from part (b) to find this answer. Round to one decimal place as needed.)

f. Esimate the actual height of the garage. [Hint: Think about how the apparent heights were recorded.]

The garage is about ____________ inches tall.
(Use the answer from part (b) to find this answer. Round to two decimal places as needed.)

(1) ◯ directly ◯ inversely (2) ◯ increases ◯ decreases

ID: 2.3.29

87. Let f(L) be the area (in square inches) of a rectangle with width 8 inches and length L (in inches). Write a variation equation in the given variables. State the value of the variation constant k.

f(L) = ____________

The variation constant is k = ____________.

ID: 2.3.30

88. A group of n people win a total of $9 million from a state lottery drawing. Let f(n) be each person's share (in millions of dollars). Write a variation equation in the given variables. State the value of the variation constant k.

Write a variation equation in the given variables.

f(n) = ____________

State the value of the variation constant k.

k = ____________

ID: 2.3.31

89. Suppose that a CD is about to be released. Let n = f (a) be the number of CDs (in millions) to be sold, where a is the advertising budget (in thousands dollars). A graph of f is sketched in the figure.

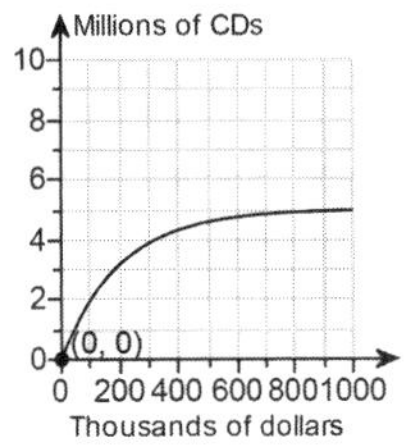

a. Is f an increasing function? Explain.

- ○ Yes, because the graph of the function is increasing.
- ○ No, because the graph of the function is decreasing

b. Does the number of CDs sold vary directly as the amount of money spent on advertising? Explain.

- ○ Yes, as the amount of money spent on advertising increases, the number of CDs sold increases.
- ○ No, for the money spent on advertising to vary directly as the number of CDs sold, the function must be linear.

c. Compare the meanings of these two statements: "One quantity varies directly as another quantity." "One quantity will increase if the other quantity increases." Choose the correct answer.

- ○ **A.** For $k > 0$, the first statement implies that the second statement is true. The second statement never implies that the first statement is true.
- ○ **B.** For $k > 0$, the second statement implies that the first statement is true. The first statement never implies that the second statement is true.
- ○ **C.** For $k > 0$, the first statement implies that the second statement is true and the second statement implies that the first statement is true.

ID: 2.3.32

90. If x varies directly as y, and $x = 25$ when $y = 5$, find x when $y = 7$.

x = ____________

ID: 2.3.33

91. y varies directly as the square of R. If y is 7 when R is 2, find y when R is 6.
a) Write the variation.
b) Find y when R is 6.

a) How are these two variables related?

- ○ **A.** $y = kR$
- ○ **B.** $y = kR^2$
- ○ **C.** $y = \frac{k}{R}$
- ○ **D.** $y = \frac{k}{R^2}$

b) The quantity indicated is ____________.

ID: 2.3.34

92. x varies inversely as the square of P. If x is 9 when P is 8, find x when P is 2.
a) Write the variation.
b) Find x when P is 2.

a) How are these two variables related?

○ **A.** $x = kP$
○ **B.** $x = kP^2$
○ **C.** $x = \frac{k}{P^2}$
○ **D.** $x = \frac{k}{P}$

b) The quantity indicated is ________ (Type an integer or a decimal.)

ID: 2.3.35

---

93. The interest on an investment varies directly as the rate of interest. If the interest is $54 when the interest rate is 10%, find the interest when the rate is 6.1%.

The interest when the rate of interest is 6.1% is $ ________ .
(Simplify your answer. Type an integer or a decimal.)

ID: 2.3.36

---

*94. The time t it takes to set up a circus tent varies inversely with the number E of elephants used. If 3 elephants can set up a tent in 40 hours, how long will it take 4 elephants?

t = ________ hours

ID: 2.3.37

---

95. The weight M of an object on the moon varies directly as its weight E on earth. A person who weighs 168.35 lb on earth weighs 28.62 lb on the moon. How much would a 221.76-lb person weigh on the moon?

A 221.76-lb person would weigh ________ lb on the moon. (Round to the nearest tenth.)

ID: 2.3.38

---

96. The pressure exerted by a certain liquid at a given point varies directly as the depth of the point beneath the surface of the liquid. The pressure at 90 feet is 630 pounds per square inch. What is the pressure at 20 feet?

The pressure at 20 feet is ________ pounds per square inch.

ID: 2.3.39

---

97. If the temperature is constant, the pressure of a gas in a container varies inversely as the volume of the container. If the pressure is 50 pounds per square foot in a container with 8 cubic feet, what is the pressure in a container with 4.5 cubic feet?

The pressure is ________ pounds per square foot.
(Round to the nearest hundredth.)

ID: 2.3.40

---

98. The distance that a spring will stretch varies directly as the force applied to the spring. A force of 90 pounds is needed to stretch a spring 9 inches. What force is required to stretch the spring 21 inches?

A ________-pound force is required to stretch the spring 21 inches.
(Type an integer or a fraction.)

ID: 2.3.41

---

99. The stopping distance d of a car after the brakes are applied varies directly as the square of the speed r. If a car travelling 50 mph can stop in 100 ft, how many feet will it take the same car to stop when it is travelling 75 mph?

It will take the same car to stop in ________ ft.

ID: 2.3.42

!*100. Recall that the PE ratio is the ratio of the price per share to the earnings per share, including earnings from the past 4 quarters. Compute the PE ratios of the following companies.

(a) The share price is $13.73 and the earnings per share is $0.57.

(b) The share price is $36.11, there are 1.4 billion shares, and the company made $2.1 billion in profit over the past 12 months.

(c) The share price is $452.44, and over each of the past 4 quarters, the company made $2.41, $1.53, $1.78, and $2.14 in earnings per share.

(a) The PE ratio is approximately ________.
(Simplify your answer. Round to one decimal place as needed.)

(b) The PE ratio is approximately ________.
(Simplify your answer. Round to one decimal place as needed.)

(c) The PE ratio is approximately ________.
(Simplify your answer. Round to one decimal place as needed.)

ID: 2.4.1

101. Use the stock table below to answer parts **a** through **g**. Assume that the data for Company XYZ stock came from an online quote you looked at during lunch.

Company XYZ (XYZ)			
Last 15.25	Change +0.25	%Change 1.67	Volume 69,000,000
Open 14.39	High 16.13	Low 14.03	
52-Week High 21.85		52-Week Low 11.18	

Market Cap ($ millions)	87,550
P/E ratio	19.14
Dividend (latest quarter)	0.28
Dividend Yield	7.34%
Shares Outstanding (millions)	5741

a. What is the symbol for Company XYZ stock?

The symbol is (1) ________

b. What was the price per share at the end of the day yesterday?

$ ________ (Round to the nearest cent as needed.)

c. Based on the current price, what is the total value of the shares that have been traded so far today?

$ ________ million (Round to the nearest whole number as needed.)

d. What percentage of all Company XYZ shares have been traded so far today?

________ % (Round to the nearest hundredth as needed.)

e. Suppose you own 150 shares of Company XYZ. Based on the current price and dividend yield, what total dividend should you expect to receive this year?

$ ________ (Round to the nearest cent as needed.)

f. What were the earnings per share for Company XYZ?

$ ________ (Round to the nearest cent as needed.)

g. How much total profit did Company XYZ earn in the past year?

$ ________ million (Round to the nearest tenth as needed.)

(1) ○ Company XYZ.
○ XYZ.

ID: 2.4.2

*102. Company XYZ closed at $44.83 per share with a P/E ratio of 14.93. Answer the following questions.

a. How much were earnings per share?
b. Does the stock seem overpriced, underpriced, or about right given that the historical P/E ratio is 12-14?

a. How much were earnings per share?

$__________ (Round to the nearest cent as needed.)

b. Based on the fact that Company XYZ stock historically trades at an average P/E ratio of 12-14, does the stock price seem overpriced, underpriced, or about right?

○ Underpriced
○ Overpriced
○ About right

ID: 2.4.3

---

103. Company XYZ closed at $102.25 per share with a P/E ratio of 10.34. Answer the following questions.

a. How much were earnings per share?
b. Does the stock seem overpriced, underpriced, or about right given that the historical P/E ratio is 12-14?

a. How much were earnings per share?

$__________ (Round to the nearest cent as needed.)

b. Based on the fact that Company XYZ stock historically trades at an average P/E ratio of 12-14, does the stock price seem overpriced, underpriced, or about right?

○ About right
○ Underpriced
○ Overpriced

ID: 2.4.4

---

104. Answer the following questions, assuming that the mutual fund quote below is one that you found online today. Complete parts (a) through (c) below.

A certain Limited-Term Tax-Exempt Fund (CMLTX)

	1-Day Net Change	1-Day Return
NAV. $9.41	$0.00	0.0%

Total Returns (%) 3, 5 and 10 year returns are annualized.

	YTD	1-Yr	5-Yr	10-Yr
Fund	2.82%	3.88%	3.41%	3.16%

a. Suppose you invest $4000 in this fund today. How many shares will you buy?

__________ shares
(Round to two decimal places as needed.)

b. Suppose you had invested $4000 in this fund 5 years ago. How much would your investment be worth now?

$__________
(Round to two decimal places as needed.)

c. Suppose you had invested $4000 in this fund 10 years ago. How much would your investment be worth now?

$__________
(Round to two decimal places as needed.)

ID: 2.4.5

---

105. Decide whether the following statement makes sense (or is clearly true) or does not make sense (or is clearly false). Explain your reasoning.

The price per gallon of gasoline has risen from only a quarter in 1918 to nearly $3 in 2009, thereby making it much more difficult for the poor to afford fuel for their cars.

Choose the correct answer below.

○ **A.** The statement does not make sense because "poor" is too vague a description to be meaningful in this context.

○ **B.** The statement does not make sense because when inflation is taken into account, the two prices are quite comparable.

○ **C.** The statement makes sense because even with inflation taken into account, the price per gallon of gasoline in 1918 was much less than the price in 2009.

○ **D.** The statement makes sense. Gasoline is twelve times as expensive today compared to 1918, so it makes sense that it is more difficult for the poor to afford fuel for their cars.

ID: 2.4.6

106. Decide whether the following statement makes sense or does not make sense. Explain your reasoning.

An 18th-century philosopher once said, "A penny saved is a penny earned," but if he were alive today, he would be talking about a dollar rather than a penny.

Choose the correct answer below.

- ○ **A.** The statement makes sense. Due to inflation, a penny in the 18th century has less purchasing power than a penny today.
- ○ **B.** The statement does not make sense. Due to inflation, a penny in the 18th century has less purchasing power than a penny today.
- ○ **C.** The statement does not make sense. The value of a penny is always 1 cent.
- ○ **D.** The statement makes sense. Due to inflation, a penny in the 18th century has about the same purchasing power as a dollar today.

ID: 2.4.7

* 107. Decide whether the following statement makes sense (or is clearly true) or does not make sense (or is clearly false). Explain your reasoning.

When we chart the price of milk in 1995 dollars we find that it has become slightly more expensive, but when we chart it in 1975 dollars we find that it has become cheaper.

Choose the correct answer below.

- ○ **A.** The statement does not make sense because prices always rise with time.
- ○ **B.** The statement does not make sense because the same trend would be seen regardless of what kind of dollars are used.
- ○ **C.** The statement makes sense because 1995 dollars are worth more than 1975 dollars.
- ○ **D.** The statement makes sense because 1975 dollars are worth more than 1995 dollars.

ID: 2.4.8

108. Suppose the current cost of gasoline is $2.90 per gallon. Find the current price index number, using the 1975 price of 56.7 cents as the reference value.

The current price index number is __________.
(Round to one decimal place as needed.)

ID: 2.4.9

* 109. If it cost $13 to fill a gas tank in 2000, how much would it have cost to fill the same tank in 1990?

Average Gasoline Prices (per gallon)

Year	Price	Price as a Percentage of 2000 Price	Price Index (2000 = 100)
1960	$0.31	19.9%	19.9
1970	$0.36	23.1%	23.1
1980	$1.22	78.2%	78.2
1990	$1.23	78.8%	78.8
2000	$1.56	100.0%	100.0
2010	$2.84	182.1%	182.1

It would have cost $ __________ in 1990.
(Round to the nearest cent as needed.)

ID: 2.4.10

110. If it cost $11 to fill a gas tank in 1990, how much of the same tank could be filled with $11 in 2000?

Average Gasoline Prices (per gallon)

Year	Price	Price as a Percentage of 1970 Price	Price Index (1970 = 100)
1960	$0.31	86.1%	86.1
1970	$0.36	100.0%	100.0
1980	$1.22	338.9%	338.9
1990	$1.23	341.7%	341.7
2000	$1.56	433.3%	433.3
2010	$2.84	788.9%	788.9

About __________ of the same tank could be filled.
(Type an integer or decimal rounded to two decimal places as needed.)

ID: 2.4.11

*111. Suppose you needed $23,000 to maintain a particular standard of living in 1974. How much would you have needed in 1999 to maintain the same standard of living? Assume that all prices have risen at the same rate as the CPI.

How much would you have needed?

$ ___________
(Round to the nearest dollar.)

Average Annual
Consumer Price Index (CPI)
(1982 – 1984 = 100)

Year	CPI	Year	CPI	Year	CPI
1973	44.4	1984	103.9	1995	152.4
1974	49.3	1985	107.6	1996	156.9
1975	53.8	1986	109.6	1997	160.5
1976	56.9	1987	113.6	1998	163.0
1977	60.6	1988	118.3	1999	166.6
1978	65.2	1989	124.0	2000	172.2
1979	72.6	1990	130.7	2001	177.1
1980	82.4	1991	136.2	2002	179.9
1981	90.9	1992	140.3	2003	184.0
1982	96.5	1993	144.5	2004	188.9
1983	99.6	1994	148.2	2005	195.3

ID: 2.4.12

112. Suppose you needed $35,000 to maintain a particular standard of living in 1977. How much would you have needed in 2011 to maintain the same standard of living? Assume that all prices have risen at the same rate as the CPI.

How much would you have needed?

$ ___________
(Round to the nearest dollar.)

Average Annual
Consumer Price Index (CPI)
(1982 – 1984 = 100)

Year	CPI	Year	CPI	Year	CPI
1976	56.9	1989	124.0	2001	177.1
1977	60.6	1990	130.7	2002	179.9
1978	65.2	1991	136.2	2003	184.0
1979	72.6	1992	140.3	2004	188.9
1980	82.4	1993	144.5	2005	195.3
1981	90.9	1994	148.2	2006	201.6
1982	96.5	1995	152.4	2007	207.3
1983	99.6	1996	156.9	2008	215.3
1984	103.9	1997	160.5	2009	214.5
1985	107.6	1998	163.0	2010	218.1
1986	109.6	1999	166.6	2011	224.9
1987	113.6	2000	172.2	2012	229.6
1988	118.3				

ID: 2.4.13

113. Find the inflation rate from 1987 to 1988. Assume that all prices have risen at the same rate as the CPI.

The inflation rate was about ___________%.
(Round to one decimal place as needed.)

Average Annual
Consumer Price Index (CPI)
(1982 – 1984 = 100)

Year	CPI	Year	CPI	Year	CPI
1976	56.9	1989	124.0	2001	177.1
1977	60.6	1990	130.7	2002	179.9
1978	65.2	1991	136.2	2003	184.0
1979	72.6	1992	140.3	2004	188.9
1980	82.4	1993	144.5	2005	195.3
1981	90.9	1994	148.2	2006	201.6
1982	96.5	1995	152.4	2007	207.3
1983	99.6	1996	156.9	2008	215.3
1984	103.9	1997	160.5	2009	214.5
1985	107.6	1998	163.0	2010	218.1
1986	109.6	1999	166.6	2011	224.9
1987	113.6	2000	172.2	2012	229.6
1988	118.3				

ID: 2.4.14

114. Suppose you needed $0.25 to buy a particular box of macaroni and cheese in 1979. How much would it cost to buy the same box of macaroni and cheese in 2005? Assume that all prices have risen at the same rate as the CPI.

How much would it cost?

$ ___________
(Round to the nearest cent.)

Average Annual
Consumer Price Index (CPI)
(1982 – 1984 = 100)

Year	CPI	Year	CPI	Year	CPI
1976	56.9	1989	124.0	2001	177.1
1977	60.6	1990	130.7	2002	179.9
1978	65.2	1991	136.2	2003	184.0
1979	72.6	1992	140.3	2004	188.9
1980	82.4	1993	144.5	2005	195.3
1981	90.9	1994	148.2	2006	201.6
1982	96.5	1995	152.4	2007	207.3
1983	99.6	1996	156.9	2008	215.3
1984	103.9	1997	160.5	2009	214.5
1985	107.6	1998	163.0	2010	218.1
1986	109.6	1999	166.6	2011	224.9
1987	113.6	2000	172.2	2012	229.6
1988	118.3				

ID: 2.4.15

115. Suppose you needed $1,600 to buy a particular car in 1983. How much money would you have needed in 2004 to buy the same car? Assume that all prices have risen at the same rate as the CPI.

How much money would you have needed?

$ ___________
(Round to the nearest dollar.)

Average Annual Consumer Price Index (CPI) (1982 – 1984 = 100)

Year	CPI	Year	CPI	Year	CPI
1976	56.9	1989	124.0	2001	177.1
1977	60.6	1990	130.7	2002	179.9
1978	65.2	1991	136.2	2003	184.0
1979	72.6	1992	140.3	2004	188.9
1980	82.4	1993	144.5	2005	195.3
1981	90.9	1994	148.2	2006	201.6
1982	96.5	1995	152.4	2007	207.3
1983	99.6	1996	156.9	2008	215.3
1984	103.9	1997	160.5	2009	214.5
1985	107.6	1998	163.0	2010	218.1
1986	109.6	1999	166.6	2011	224.9
1987	113.6	2000	172.2	2012	229.6
1988	118.3				

ID: 2.4.16

*116. Suppose admission to a movie cost $8.00 in 2006. What was its price in 1983 dollars? Assume that all prices have risen at the same rate as the CPI.

The price was about $ ___________ in 1983.
(Round to the nearest cent.)

Average Annual Consumer Price Index (CPI) (1982 – 1984 = 100)

Year	CPI	Year	CPI	Year	CPI
1976	56.9	1989	124.0	2001	177.1
1977	60.6	1990	130.7	2002	179.9
1978	65.2	1991	136.2	2003	184.0
1979	72.6	1992	140.3	2004	188.9
1980	82.4	1993	144.5	2005	195.3
1981	90.9	1994	148.2	2006	201.6
1982	96.5	1995	152.4	2007	207.3
1983	99.6	1996	156.9	2008	215.3
1984	103.9	1997	160.5	2009	214.5
1985	107.6	1998	163.0	2010	218.1
1986	109.6	1999	166.6	2011	224.9
1987	113.6	2000	172.2	2012	229.6
1988	118.3				

ID: 2.4.17

117. What is the purchasing power of $1 in 1980 in terms of 1990 dollars?

The purchasing power of $1 in 1980 in terms of 1990 dollars is $ ___________.
(Round to the nearest cent.)

Average Annual Consumer Price Index (CPI) (1982 – 1984 = 100)

Year	CPI	Year	CPI	Year	CPI
1976	56.9	1989	124.0	2001	177.1
1977	60.6	1990	130.7	2002	179.9
1978	65.2	1991	136.2	2003	184.0
1979	72.6	1992	140.3	2004	188.9
1980	82.4	1993	144.5	2005	195.3
1981	90.9	1994	148.2	2006	201.6
1982	96.5	1995	152.4	2007	207.3
1983	99.6	1996	156.9	2008	215.3
1984	103.9	1997	160.5	2009	214.5
1985	107.6	1998	163.0	2010	218.1
1986	109.6	1999	166.6	2011	224.9
1987	113.6	2000	172.2	2012	229.6
1988	118.3				

ID: 2.4.18

118. The following table shows a housing index that can be used to compare housing prices in different cities. Suppose you see a house valued at $180,000 in City G. Find the price of a comparable house in City K, City F, and City D.

City	Index	City	Index
City A	91	City F	100
City B	406	City G	358
City C	141	City H	55
City D	64	City J	95
City E	134	City K	51

If you know the price of a particular home in your town, you can use the index to find the price of a comparable house in another town with the formula below.

$$\underset{\text{(other town)}}{\text{price}} = \underset{\text{(your town)}}{\text{price}} \times \frac{\text{index (other town)}}{\text{index (your town)}}$$

A comparable house in City K would cost about $ ___________.
(Round to the nearest dollar.)

A comparable house in City F would cost about $ ___________.
(Round to the nearest dollar.)

A comparable house in City D would cost about $ ___________.
(Round to the nearest dollar.)

ID: 2.4.19

119. Total spending on health care in a certain region rose from $11 billion in 1976 to $2.7 trillion in 2005. Compare this rise in health care spending to the overall rate of inflation as measured by the Consumer Price Index.

[3] Click the icon to view the Average Annual Consumer Price Index.

Health care spending increased by ____________ %.
(Round to the nearest percent as needed.)

The overall rate of inflation was ____________ %.
(Round to the nearest percent as needed.)

3: Average Annual Consumer Price Index (1982-1984=100)

Year	CPI	Year	CPI	Year	CPI
1976	56.9	1987	113.6	1998	163.0
1977	60.6	1988	118.3	1999	166.6
1978	65.2	1989	124.0	2000	172.2
1979	72.6	1990	130.7	2001	177.1
1980	82.4	1991	136.2	2002	179.9
1981	90.9	1992	140.3	2003	184.0
1982	96.5	1993	144.5	2004	188.9
1983	99.6	1994	148.2	2005	195.3
1984	103.9	1995	152.4	2006	201.6
1985	107.6	1996	156.9	2007	207.3
1986	109.6	1997	160.5	2008	215.3

ID: 2.4.20

120. The average price of a low-fare airline ticket rose from $260 in 1988 to $410 in 2009. Calculate the relative change in price from 1988 to 2009, and compare it to the overall rate of inflation as measured by the Consumer Price Index.

Low-fare airline ticket prices increased by ____________ %.
(Round to the nearest integer as needed.)

The overall rate of inflation was ____________ %.
(Round to the nearest integer as needed.)

The change in low-fare airline ticket prices was

(1) ____________ the overall rate of inflation.

(1) ○ less than
○ equal to
○ greater than

Average Annual Consumer Price Index (CPI) (1982 – 1984 = 100)

Year	CPI	Year	CPI	Year	CPI
1976	56.9	1989	124.0	2001	177.1
1977	60.6	1990	130.7	2002	179.9
1978	65.2	1991	136.2	2003	184.0
1979	72.6	1992	140.3	2004	188.9
1980	82.4	1993	144.5	2005	195.3
1981	90.9	1994	148.2	2006	201.6
1982	96.5	1995	152.4	2007	207.3
1983	99.6	1996	156.9	2008	215.3
1984	103.9	1997	160.5	2009	214.5
1985	107.6	1998	163.0	2010	218.1
1986	109.6	1999	166.6	2011	224.9
1987	113.6	2000	172.2	2012	229.6
1988	118.3				

ID: 2.4.21

121. The average price of tuition and fees at private 4-year colleges and universities increased from $8,400 in 1988 to $24,000 in 2010. Calculate the relative change in price from 1988 to 2010 and compare it to the overall rate of inflation as measured by the Consumer Price Index.

Average tuition and fees in private 4-year colleges and universities increased by ____________ %.
(Round to the nearest integer as needed.)

The overall rate of inflation was ____________ %.
(Round to the nearest integer as needed.)

The increase in tuition and fees in private 4-year colleges was (1) ____________ the overall rate of inflation.

(1) ○ less than
○ equal to
○ greater than

Average Annual Consumer Price Index (CPI) (1982 – 1984 = 100)

Year	CPI	Year	CPI	Year	CPI
1976	56.9	1989	124.0	2001	177.1
1977	60.6	1990	130.7	2002	179.9
1978	65.2	1991	136.2	2003	184.0
1979	72.6	1992	140.3	2004	188.9
1980	82.4	1993	144.5	2005	195.3
1981	90.9	1994	148.2	2006	201.6
1982	96.5	1995	152.4	2007	207.3
1983	99.6	1996	156.9	2008	215.3
1984	103.9	1997	160.5	2009	214.5
1985	107.6	1998	163.0	2010	218.1
1986	109.6	1999	166.6	2011	224.9
1987	113.6	2000	172.2	2012	229.6
1988	118.3				

ID: 2.4.22

122. The average price of tuition and fees at public 4-year colleges and universities increased from $1,800 in 1988 to $6,600 in 2006. Calculate the relative change in price from 1988 to 2006 and compare it to the overall rate of inflation as measured by the Consumer Price Index.

Average Annual Consumer Price Index (CPI) (1982 – 1984 = 100)

Year	CPI	Year	CPI	Year	CPI
1976	56.9	1989	124.0	2001	177.1
1977	60.6	1990	130.7	2002	179.9
1978	65.2	1991	136.2	2003	184.0
1979	72.6	1992	140.3	2004	188.9
1980	82.4	1993	144.5	2005	195.3
1981	90.9	1994	148.2	2006	201.6
1982	96.5	1995	152.4	2007	207.3
1983	99.6	1996	156.9	2008	215.3
1984	103.9	1997	160.5	2009	214.5
1985	107.6	1998	163.0	2010	218.1
1986	109.6	1999	166.6	2011	224.9
1987	113.6	2000	172.2	2012	229.6
1988	118.3				

Average tuition and fees in public 4-year colleges and universities increased by ___________%.
(Round to the nearest integer as needed.)

The overall rate of inflation was ___________%.
(Round to the nearest integer as needed.)

The increase in tuition and fees in public 4-year colleges

was (1) ___________ the overall rate of inflation.

(1) ○ equal to
○ greater than
○ less than

ID: 2.4.23

123. The accompanying table shows federal minimum wages over the past 70 years. According to the table, how much is $2.00 in 1974 dollars worth in 1996 dollars?

[4] Click the icon to view the table of federal minimum wages.

$2.00 in 1974 dollars is worth $___________ in 1996 dollars.

4: Federal Minimum Wage

Year	Actual Dollars	1996 Dollars
1938	$0.25	$2.78
1939	$0.30	$3.39
1945	$0.40	$3.49
1950	$0.75	$4.88
1956	$1.00	$5.77
1961	$1.25	$6.41
1967	$1.40	$6.58
1968	$1.60	$7.21
1974	$2.00	$6.37
1976	$2.30	$6.34
1978	$2.65	$6.38
1979	$2.90	$6.27
1981	$3.35	$5.78
1990	$3.50	$4.56
1991	$4.25	$4.90
1996	$4.75	$4.75
1997	$5.15	$5.03
2007	$5.85	$4.42
2008	$6.55	$4.77
2009	$7.25	$5.12

ID: 2.4.24

124. The accompanying table shows federal minimum wages over the past 70 years. Explain why the minimum wage for 1996 is the same as 1996 dollars.

Choose the correct answer below.

○ **A.** The government passed a decree setting the federa

○ **B.** The value of 1996 dollars is increasing as the years to match its growth.

○ **C.** Since the federal minimum wage in 1996 is in 1996

○ **D.** The federal minimum wage in actual dollars and 199 they happen to be equal in 1996.

Year	Actual Dollars	1996 Dollars
1938	$0.25	$2.78
1939	$0.30	$3.39
1945	$0.40	$3.49
1950	$0.75	$4.88
1956	$1.00	$5.77
1961	$1.25	$6.41
1967	$1.40	$6.58
1968	$1.60	$7.21
1974	$2.00	$6.37
1976	$2.30	$6.34
1978	$2.65	$6.38
1979	$2.90	$6.27
1981	$3.35	$5.78
1990	$3.50	$4.56
1991	$4.25	$4.90
1996	$4.75	$4.75
1997	$5.15	$5.03
2007	$5.85	$4.42
2008	$6.55	$4.77
2009	$7.25	$5.12

ID: 2.4.25

* 125. Use the average annual consumer price index table to convert the 1990 minimum wage from actual dollars to 1996 dollars. Is the result consistent with the entry in the accompanying minimum wage table?
[5] Click the icon to view the table of federal minimum wages.

Average Annual Consumer Price Index (CPI) (1982 – 1984 = 100)

Year	CPI	Year	CPI	Year	CPI
1976	56.9	1989	124.0	2001	177.1
1977	60.6	1990	130.7	2002	179.9
1978	65.2	1991	136.2	2003	184.0
1979	72.6	1992	140.3	2004	188.9
1980	82.4	1993	144.5	2005	195.3
1981	90.9	1994	148.2	2006	201.6
1982	96.5	1995	152.4	2007	207.3
1983	99.6	1996	156.9	2008	215.3
1984	103.9	1997	160.5	2009	214.5
1985	107.6	1998	163.0	2010	218.1
1986	109.6	1999	166.6	2011	224.9
1987	113.6	2000	172.2	2012	229.6
1988	118.3				

The 1990 minimum wage in 1996 dollars is
$__________.
(Round to the nearest cent as needed.)

This result (1) __________ consistent with the entry in the accompanying minimum wage table because the result value is (2) __________ close to the minimum wage table value of $__________.
(Round to the nearest cent as needed.)

5: Federal Minimum Wages

Year	Actual Dollars	1996 Dollars
1938	$0.25	$2.78
1939	$0.30	$3.39
1945	$0.40	$3.49
1950	$0.75	$4.88
1956	$1.00	$5.77
1961	$1.25	$6.41
1967	$1.40	$6.58
1968	$1.60	$7.21
1974	$2.00	$6.37
1976	$2.30	$6.34
1978	$2.65	$6.38
1979	$2.90	$6.27
1981	$3.35	$5.78
1990	$3.50	$4.56
1991	$4.25	$4.90
1996	$4.75	$4.75
1997	$5.15	$5.03
2007	$5.85	$4.42
2008	$6.55	$4.77
2009	$7.25	$5.12

(1) ○ is not ○ is (2) ○ equal or ○ not

ID: 2.4.26

126. The table below shows the federal minimum wages during several years. In what year was the purchasing power of the minimum wage the highest? Explain.

Year	Actual Dollars	1996 Dollars
1938	$0.25	$2.78
1956	$1.00	$5.77
1961	$1.25	$6.41
1974	$2.00	$6.37
1981	$3.35	$5.78
1990	$3.50	$4.56
1997	$5.15	$5.03
2007	$5.85	$4.42

The purchasing power of the minimum wage was the highest in __________ because it was worth
$__________ in 1996, which is greater than the 1996 value of the federal minimum wage in all of the other years.
(Type integers or decimals.)

ID: 2.4.27

!* 127. Use the accompanying table to answer the questions regarding money ratios.
(a) What is the capital a 35-year-old should have with an income of $35,000?
(b) How much should a 45-year-old be saving for retirement with an income of $86,000?
(c) How much in education debt should a 30-year-old have with an income of $59,000?
[6] Click the icon to view the money ratio table.

(a) The 35-year-old should have $__________ in capital.
(Simplify your answer. Do not include the $ symbol in your answer.)

(b) The 45-year-old should be saving $__________ for retirement.
(Simplify your answer. Do not include the $ symbol in your answer.)

(c) The 30-year-old should have $__________ in education debt.
(Simplify your answer. Do not include the $ symbol in your answer.)

!* 127. (cont.) 6: Money Ratio Table

Age	Capital: Income	Savings: Income	Mortgage: Income	Education: Earnings	Stocks: Bonds
25	0.1	12%	2.0	0.75	50:50
30	0.6	12%	2.0	0.45	50:50
35	1.4	12%	1.9	0.00	50:50
40	2.4	12%	1.8	X	50:50
45	3.7	15%	1.7	X	50:50
50	5.2	15%	1.5	X	50:50
55	7.1	15%	1.2	X	50:50
60	9.4	15%	0.7	X	40:60
65	12.0	15%	0.0	X	40:60

ID: 2.4.28

128. The accompanying figure summarizes the average spending patterns for people of different ages in a certain nation. Determine whether the spending pattern given below is equal to, above, or below the national average. Assume that salaries and wages are after taxes.

A single 30-year-old woman with a monthly salary of $4500 spends $1530 per month on rent.

[7] Click the icon to view the figure.

Is the woman's spending pattern equal to, above, or below the national average?

- ○ **A.** The spending pattern is below the national average.
- ○ **B.** The spending pattern is above the national average.
- ○ **C.** The spending pattern is equal to the national average.

7: Figure

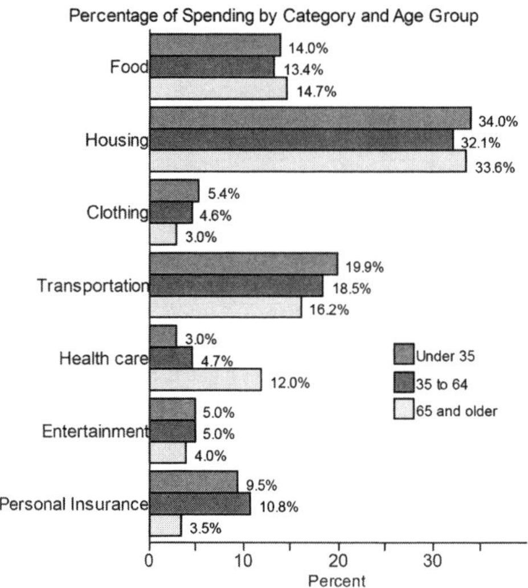

ID: 2.4.29

129. The accompanying figure summarizes the average spending patterns for people of different ages in a certain nation. Determine whether the spending pattern given below is equal to, above, or below the national average. Assume that salaries and wages are after taxes.

A single 56-year-old man with a monthly salary of $3500 spends $380 per month on health care.

[8] Click the icon to view the figure.

Is the man's spending pattern equal to, above, or below the national average?

- ○ **A.** The spending pattern is below the national average.
- ○ **B.** The spending pattern is equal to the national average.
- ○ **C.** The spending pattern is above the national average.

129. (cont.) 8: Figure

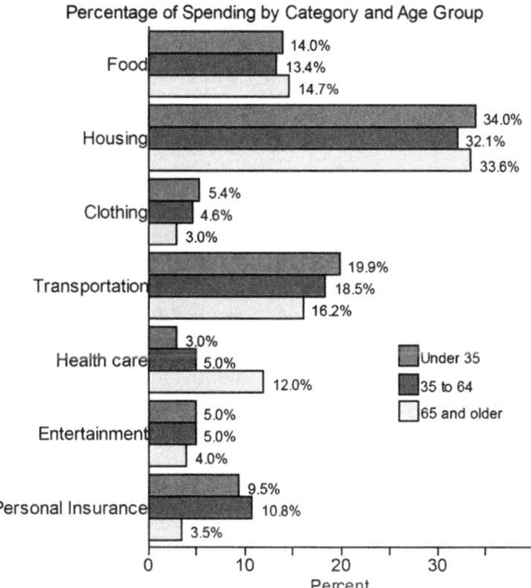

ID: 2.4.30

---

*130. The accompanying figure summarizes the average spending patterns for people of different ages in a certain nation. Determine whether the spending pattern given below is equal to, above, or below the national average. Assume that salaries and wages are after taxes.

A retired couple (over 65 years old) with a fixed monthly income of $3400 spends $730 per month on health care.

[9] Click the icon to view the figure.

Is the couple's spending pattern equal to, above, or below the national average? Select the correct choice below and fill in the answer box within your choice.
(Round to the nearest tenth as needed.)

○ **A.** The couple spends ________ % of the salary on health care per month, which is above the national average.

○ **B.** The couple spends ________ % of the salary on health care per month, which is below the national average.

○ **C.** The couple spends ________ % of the salary on health care per month, which is equal to the national average.

9: Percentage of Spending by Category and Age Group

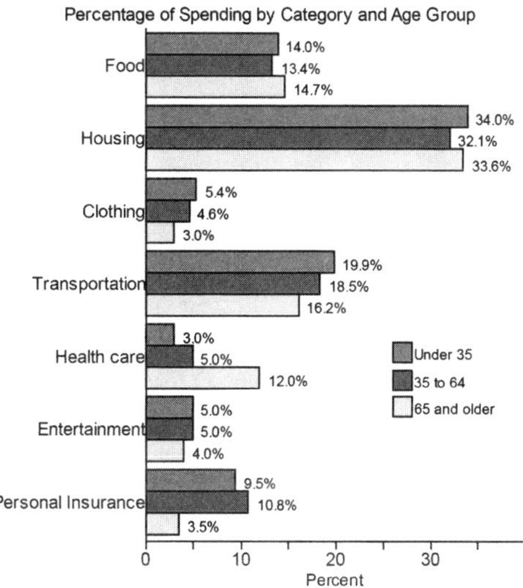

The data show spending per "consumer unit," which is defined to be either a single person or a family sharing a household.

ID: 2.4.31

131. Consider the following situation, which involves two options. Determine which option is less expensive. Are there unstated factors that might affect your decision?

You currently drive 400 miles per week in a car that gets 23 miles per gallon of gas. You are considering buying a new fuel-efficient car for $19,000 (after trade-in on your current car) that gets 41 miles per gallon. Insurance premiums for the new and old car are $800 and $600 per year, respectively. You anticipate spending $2000 per year on repairs for the old car and having no repairs on the new car. Assume gas costs $3.00 per gallon. Over a five-year period, is it less expensive to keep your old car or buy the new car?

Over a five-year period, the cost of the old car is $__________ and the cost of the new car is

$__________. Thus, over a five-year period, it is less expensive to (1) __________
(Round to the nearest dollar as needed.)

Are there unstated factors that might affect your decision? Select all that apply.

- ☐ **A.** Inflation
- ☐ **B.** Time value of money
- ☐ **C.** Government incentives to purchase a new fuel efficient car
- ☐ **D.** Any payments for purchasing the old car and number of payments remaining
- ☐ **E.** No, there are no unstated factors that might affect the decision
- ☐ **F.** Depreciation or future resale value for each car
- ☐ **G.** Interest and number of years on any loans taken out to buy the new car

(1) ○ keep your old car.
○ buy the new car.

ID: 2.4.32

---

132. You must decide whether to buy a new car for $19,000 or lease the same car over a three-year period. Under the terms of the lease, you can make a down payment of $3000 and have monthly payments of $150. At the end of the three years, the leased car has a residual value (the amount you pay if you choose to buy the car at the end of the lease period) of $10,000. Assume you can sell the new car at the end of the three years at the same residual value. Is it less expensive to buy or to lease?

The cost for buying the car and selling it after three years would be $__________.

The cost for leasing the car is $__________.

Is it less expensive to buy or to lease?

○ Buy
○ Lease

ID: 2.4.33

---

133. You have a choice between going to an in-state college where you would pay $6000 per year for tuition and an out-of-state college where the tuition is $10,000 per year. The cost of living is much higher at the in-state college, where you can expect to pay $900 per month in rent, compared to $450 per month at the other college. Assuming all other factors are equal, which is the less expensive choice on an annual (12-month) basis?

The yearly expense of the in-state college is $__________ and the yearly expense of the out-of-state college is

$__________. Thus, on an annual basis, the less expensive choice is the (1) __________ college.
(Simplify your answers.)

(1) ○ in-state
○ out-of-state

ID: 2.4.34

---

134. The table shows median annual earnings for women and men with various levels of education. Assuming the difference in the table remains constant over a 40-year career, approximately how much more does a man with a bachelor's degree earn than a man with a high school education?

	High School Only	Associate's degree Only	Bachelor's degree Only	Professional Degree
Women	$21,138	$39,214	$49,242	$80,677
Men	$40,700	$50,316	$66,475	$119,250

A man with a bachelor's degree earns $__________ more than a man with a high school education over a 40-year career.

ID: 2.4.35

---

*135. The table shows median annual earnings for women and men with various levels of education. As a percentage, how much more does a man with a bachelor's degree earn than a woman with a bachelor's degree? Assuming the difference remains constant over a 40-year career, how much more does the man earn than the woman?

	High School Only	Associate's degree Only	Bachelor's degree Only	Professional Degree
Women	$21,349	$39,437	$49,570	$80,202
Men	$40,482	$50,781	$66,736	$119,198

A man with a bachelor's degree earns ____________ % more annually than a woman with a bachelor's degree.
(Round to the nearest whole number as needed.)

Over a 40-year career, a man with a bachelor's degree earns $ ____________ more than a woman with a bachelor's degree.
(Round to the nearest whole number as needed.)

ID: 2.4.36

---

136. You could take a 15-week, three-credit college course, which requires 10 hours per week of your time for $550 per credit hour in tuition. Or during those hours you could have a job paying $10 per hour. What is the net cost of the class compared to working? Based on your answer and the fact that the average college graduate earns nearly $28,000 per year more than a high school graduate, write a few sentences giving your opinion as to whether the college course is a worthwhile experience.

What is the net cost of the class compare to working?

The net cost of the class compared to working is $ ____________ .

Choose the correct answer below.

○ **A.** A college course is a worthwhile expense because it will be a lot easier to find a job that pays more than $10 per hour than it will be for a high school graduate.

○ **B.** Working is a better idea because it is better to spend time earning money than spending money. College graduates may make $28,000 more per year, but all of the extra time spent working compensates for that difference.

○ **C.** A college course is a worthwhile expense because earning $28,000 per year more than a high school graduate is close to $1 million dollars more over a lifetime.

○ **D.** Working is a better idea because the $10 per hour will increase as the worker gains experience. Although a high school graduate makes $28,000 less per year, this figure doesn't take into account possible promotions and pay wage raises that could be earned.

ID: 2.4.37

!*1. The average life expectancy for one region is 71.74 years with a standard deviation of 8.66 years.
(a) What is the z-score for one city with a life expectancy of 83.57?
(b) What is the T-score for one city with a life expectancy of 83.57?
(c) Assume that the mean life expectancy is rescaled to 500 and that all life expectancies are scaled proportionally so that the new standard deviation is 150. What would the new standardized score for this city be?

(a) The z-score is ____________ .
(Simplify your answer. Round to three decimal places as needed.)

(b) The T-score is ____________ .
(Simplify your answer. Round to two decimal places as needed.)

(c) The new standardized score is ____________ .
(Simplify your answer. Round to one decimal place as needed.)

ID: 2.5.1

---

2. Use the normal distribution of IQ scores, which has a mean of 90 and a standard deviation of 17, and the following table with the standard scores and percentiles for a normal distribution to find the indicated quantity.
[1] Click the icon to view the table.

Percentage of scores greater than 47.5 is ____________ %.
(Round to two decimal places as needed.)

2. (cont.) 1: Data Table

Full data set

Standard Scores and Percentiles for a Normal Distribution
(cumulative values from the left)

Standard score	%	Standard score	%
− 3.0	0.13	0.1	53.98
− 2.5	0.62	0.5	69.15
− 2	2.28	0.9	81.59
− 1.5	6.68	1	84.13
− 1	15.87	1.5	93.32
− 0.9	18.41	2	97.72
− 0.5	30.85	2.5	99.38
− 0.1	46.02	3	99.87
0	50.00	3.5	99.98

ID: 2.5.2

*3. The scores on a psychology exam were normally distributed with a mean of 65 and a standard deviation of 4. A failing grade on the exam was anything 2 or more standard deviations below the mean. What was the cutoff for a failing score? Approximately what percentage of the students failed?

The cutoff for a failing score was ___________.
(Simplify your answer.)

Approximately ___________ percent of the students failed.
(Round to one decimal place as needed.)

ID: 2.5.3

*4. A set of data items is normally distributed with a mean of 90 and a standard deviation of 12. Convert 78 to a z-score.

z_{78} = ___________
(Type an integer or a decimal. Do not round until the final answer. Then round to the nearest hundredth as needed.)

ID: 2.5.4

5. A set of data items is normally distributed with a mean of 20 and a standard deviation of 9. Convert 11 to a z-score.

z_{11} = ___________
(Do not round until the final answer. Then round to the nearest hundredth as needed.)

ID: 2.5.5

6. Find the standard score and use the table below to find the percentile for a data value 2.4 standard deviations above the mean.

z-score	-3.0	-2.8	-2.6	-2.4	-2.2	-2.0	-1.8	-1.6	-1.4	-1.2
Percentile	0.13	0.26	0.47	0.82	1.39	2.28	3.59	5.48	8.08	11.51
z-score	-1.0	-0.8	-0.6	-0.4	-0.2	0.2	0.4	0.6	0.8	1.0
Percentile	15.87	21.19	27.43	34.46	42.07	57.93	65.54	72.57	78.81	84.13
z-score	1.2	1.4	1.6	1.8	2.0	2.2	2.4	2.6	2.8	3.0
Percentile	88.49	91.92	94.52	96.41	97.72	98.61	99.18	99.53	99.74	99.87

The standard score is ___________.

The standard score corresponds to a percentile of ___________.

ID: 2.5.6

*7. Use the accompanying table of standard scores and their percentiles under the normal distribution to find the approximate standard score of the following data values. Then state the approximate number of standard deviations that the value lies above or below the mean.

a. A data value in the 80th percentile
b. A data value in the 60th percentile
c. A data value in the 17th percentile

[2] Click the icon to view the table.

a. The standard score for the 80th percentile is approximately ___________.
(Round to two decimal places as needed.)

The 80th percentile lies approximately ___________ standard deviations (1) ___________ the mean.
(Round to two decimal places as needed.)

*7. (cont.) b. The standard score for the 60th percentile is approximately __________.
(Round to two decimal places as needed.)

The 60th percentile lies approximately __________ standard deviations (2) __________ the mean.
(Round to two decimal places as needed.)

c. The standard score for the 17th percentile is approximately __________.
(Round to two decimal places as needed.)

The 17th percentile lies approximately __________ standard deviations (3) __________ the mean.
(Round to two decimal places as needed.)

2: More Info

Standard Scores and Percentiles for a Normal Distribution

z-score	Percentile	z-score	Percentile	z-score	Percentile	z-score	Percentile
−3.5	0.02	−1.0	15.87	0.0	50.00	1.1	86.43
−3.0	0.13	−0.95	17.11	0.05	51.99	1.2	88.49
−2.9	0.19	−0.90	18.41	0.10	53.98	1.3	90.32
−2.8	0.26	−0.85	19.77	0.15	55.96	1.4	91.92
−2.7	0.35	−0.80	21.19	0.20	57.93	1.5	93.32
−2.6	0.47	−0.75	22.66	0.25	59.87	1.6	94.52
−2.5	0.62	−0.70	24.20	0.30	61.79	1.7	95.54
−2.4	0.82	−0.65	25.78	0.35	63.68	1.8	96.41
−2.3	1.07	−0.60	27.43	0.40	65.54	1.9	97.13
−2.2	1.39	−0.55	29.12	0.45	67.36	2.0	97.72
−2.1	1.79	−0.50	30.85	0.50	69.15	2.1	98.21
−2.0	2.28	−0.45	32.64	0.55	70.88	2.2	98.61
−1.9	2.87	−0.40	34.46	0.60	72.57	2.3	98.93
−1.8	3.59	−0.35	36.32	0.65	74.22	2.4	99.18
−1.7	4.46	−0.30	38.21	0.70	75.80	2.5	99.38
−1.6	5.48	−0.25	40.13	0.75	77.34	2.6	99.53
−1.5	6.68	−0.20	42.07	0.80	78.81	2.7	99.65
−1.4	8.08	−0.15	44.04	0.85	80.23	2.8	99.74
−1.3	9.68	−0.10	46.02	0.90	81.59	2.9	99.81
−1.2	11.51	−0.05	48.01	0.95	82.89	3.0	99.87
−1.1	13.57	0.0	50.00	1.0	84.13	3.5	99.98

(1) ○ above ○ below (2) ○ above ○ below (3) ○ below ○ above

ID: 2.5.7

!*8. Assume that the life expectancy for one region is normally distributed with a mean of 70.14 years and a standard deviation of 7.89 years. Use the accompanying graphic to answer the questions.

(a) What is the approximate percentile for one city with a life expectancy of 74.39?

(b) What percentage of cities in the region have a life expectancy greater than 78.03 (1 standard deviation above the mean)?

(c) Approximately 99% of cities in the region have a life expectancy between what two values?

3 Click the icon to view the normal distribution.

(a) Choose the correct answer below.

○ **A.** 80th percentile
○ **B.** 90th percentile
○ **C.** 10th percentile
○ **D.** 70th percentile

(b) __________ %
(Simplify your answer. Round to two decimal places as needed.)

(c) Choose the correct answer below.

○ **A.** 70.14 and 93.81
○ **B.** 46.47 and 93.81
○ **C.** 46.47 and 70.14
○ **D.** 62.25 and 85.92

!*8. (cont.) 3: Normal Distribution

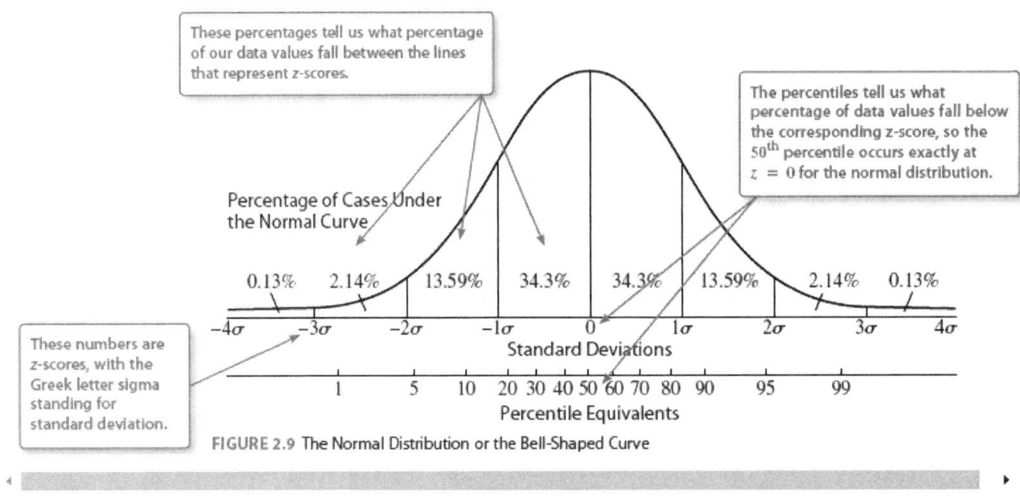
These percentages tell us what percentage of our data values fall between the lines that represent z-scores.
The percentiles tell us what percentage of data values fall below the corresponding z-score, so the 50th percentile occurs exactly at z = 0 for the normal distribution.
Percentage of Cases Under the Normal Curve
0.13% 2.14% 13.59% 34.3% 34.3% 13.59% 2.14% 0.13%
−4σ −3σ −2σ −1σ 0 1σ 2σ 3σ 4σ
Standard Deviations
These numbers are z-scores, with the Greek letter sigma standing for standard deviation.
1 5 10 20 30 40 50 60 70 80 90 95 99
Percentile Equivalents
FIGURE 2.9 The Normal Distribution or the Bell-Shaped Curve

ID: 2.5.8

9. Consider the distribution of exam scores (graded from 0 to 100) for 77 students when 37 students got an A, 24 students got a B, and 16 students got a C. Complete parts (a) through (d) below.

a. How many peaks would you expect for the distribution?

- A. There would probably be many peaks corresponding to the different exam scores that each student had.
- B. There would probably be no peaks. The distribution of grades always tends to be uniform.
- C. There would probably be three peaks, because even though each exam score could be anywhere between 0 and 100, the only grades received were A, B, and C.
- D. There would probably be one peak because there are no obvious reasons why the exam scores would form different groups.

b. Make a sketch of the distribution. Choose the correct answer below.

A.

B.

C.

D.

c. What shape would you expect for the distribution?

- A. The distribution would probably be left-skewed because many of the students got an A, and very few got a C.
- B. The distribution would probably be right-skewed because a lot of students got either a B or a C.
- C. The distribution would probably be symmetric because the only grades received were A, B, and C.
- D. The distribution would probably be symmetric because there are no obvious factors to indicate that there would be a higher or lower exam score for any student.

d. What variation would you expect in the distribution?

- A. The variation would probably be large because many students got an A, some got a B, and a small number got a C.
- B. The variation would probably be moderate because the only grades received were A, B, and C.
- C. The variation would probably be moderate because there are no obvious reasons to expect an especially large or small amount of variation.
- D. The variation would probably be small because all the students would tend to have nearly the same exam score.

ID: 2.5.9

10. Consider the distribution of the annual rainfall in 105 cities selected randomly throughout the United States. Complete parts (a) through (d) below.

a. How many peaks would you expect for the distribution?

- **A.** There would probably be many peaks corresponding to the different amounts of rainfall in each city.
- **B.** There would probably be three peaks, one for the cities with little rainfall, one for the cities with average rainfall, and one for the cities with a lot of rainfall.
- **C.** There would probably be one peak because there are no obvious reasons why the values of the annual rainfall would form different groups.
- **D.** There would probably be no peaks. The annual rainfall tends to form a uniform distribution.

b. Make a sketch of the distribution. Choose the correct answer below.

A. **B.**  **C.**  **D.**

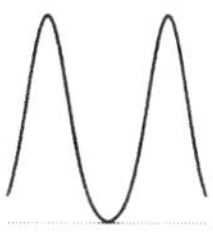

c. What shape would you expect for the distribution?

- **A.** The distribution would probably be symmetric because there are no obvious factors to indicate that there would be more or less rainfall in any city.
- **B.** The distribution would probably be left-skewed because there is a clear minimum amount of rainfall but no obvious maximum amount.
- **C.** The distribution would probably be symmetric because all the cities would tend to have nearly the same amount of rainfall.
- **D.** The distribution would probably be right-skewed because there is a clear minimum amount of rainfall but no obvious maximum amount.

d. What variation would you expect in the distribution?

- **A.** The variation would probably be moderate because there are no obvious reasons to expect an especially large or small amount of variation.
- **B.** The variation would probably be moderate because all the cities would tend to have nearly the same amount of rainfall.
- **C.** The variation would probably be small because all the cities would tend to have nearly the same amount of rainfall.
- **D.** The variation would probably be large because there would likely be several cities with very different amounts of rainfall.

ID: 2.5.10

---

11. Consider the distribution of the monthly sales of snow shovels over a one-year period at a store in Buffalo, NY (the distribution will look best if you start from July rather than January). Complete parts (a) through (d) below.

a. How many peaks would you expect for the distribution?

- **A.** There would probably be three peaks, one for the months with low sales, one for the months with average sales, and one for the months with high sales.
- **B.** There would probably be many peaks corresponding to the different sales each month.
- **C.** There would probably be no peaks. The monthly sales of products tend to form a uniform distribution.
- **D.** There would probably be one peak corresponding to the winter months.

b. Make a sketch of the distribution. Choose the correct answer below.

A. **B.**  **C.**  **D.**

c. What shape would you expect for the distribution?

11. (cont.)

- ○ **A.** The distribution would probably be right-skewed because it is likely that there would be a lot of snow shovels sold during July and August.
- ○ **B.** The distribution would probably be left-skewed because it is likely that there would be a lot of snow shovels sales toward the tail end of the year.
- ○ **C.** The distribution would probably be symmetric because all the months will tend to have the same volume of sales.
- ○ **D.** The distribution would probably be symmetric because the distribution of monthly sales of snow shovels has its peak in the winter months because of the need for snow shovels then.

d. What variation would you expect in the distribution?

- ○ **A.** The variation would probably be moderate because all the months will tend to have the same volume of sales.
- ○ **B.** The variation would probably be small because all the snow shovels would tend to have nearly the same price.
- ○ **C.** The variation would probably be moderate because there are no obvious reasons to expect an especially large or small amount of variation.
- ○ **D.** The variation would probably be large because there would likely be several months with very different numbers of snow shovels sold.

ID: 2.5.11

---

12. Consider the distribution of the prices of 15-pound bags of 16 different brands of dog food. Complete parts (a) through (d) below.

a. How many peaks would you expect for the distribution?

- ○ **A.** There would probably be three peaks, one for the low priced items, one for the average priced items, and one for the high priced items.
- ○ **B.** There would probably be many peaks corresponding to the different brands.
- ○ **C.** There would probably be no peaks. The prices of competing products tend to form a uniform distribution.
- ○ **D.** There would probably be one peak because there are no obvious reasons why the prices of dog food would form different groups.

b. Make a sketch of the distribution. Choose the correct answer below.

○ **A.** ○ **B.** ○ **C.** ○ **D.**

c. What shape would you expect for the distribution?

- ○ **A.** The distribution would probably be symmetric because there are no obvious factors to indicate that there would be more high or low priced items.
- ○ **B.** The distribution would probably be left-skewed because it is likely that there would be a few very high priced brands, but no very low priced brands.
- ○ **C.** The distribution would probably be symmetric because all the brands would tend to have nearly the same price.
- ○ **D.** The distribution would probably be right-skewed because it is likely that there would be a few very low priced brands, but no very high priced brands.

d. What variation would you expect in the distribution?

- ○ **A.** The variation would probably be moderate because all the brands would tend to have nearly the same price.
- ○ **B.** The variation would probably be small because all the brands would tend to have nearly the same price.
- ○ **C.** The variation would probably be large because there would likely be several groups with very different prices.
- ○ **D.** The variation would probably be moderate because there are no obvious reasons to expect an especially large or small amount of variation.

ID: 2.5.12

---

13. Exam results for 100 students are given below. For the given exam grades, briefly describe the shape and variation of the distribution.

median = 21, mean = 77, low score = 16, high score = 95

The distribution is (1) __________ and has (2) __________ variation.

(1) ○ right-skewed ○ left-skewed

(2) ○ high ○ moderate ○ low

ID: 2.5.13

---

14. The histogram to the right shows the times between eruptions of a geyser for a sample of 300 eruptions (which means 299 times between eruptions). Over the histogram, draw a smooth curve that captures its general features. Then classify the distribution according to its number of peaks and its symmetry or skewness.

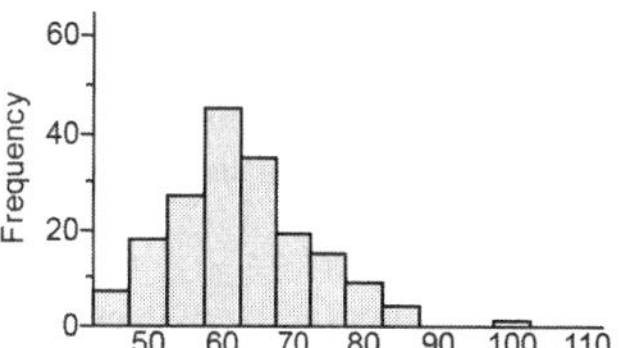

Chose the correct answer below.

- A. one peak, right-skewed, moderate variation
- B. two peaks, left-skewed, wide variation
- C. one peak, symmetric, low variation
- D. three peaks, symmetric, wide variation

ID: 2.5.14

15. The histogram of a sample of the weights of 208 rugby players is shown to right. Draw a smooth curve that captures its important features. Then classify the distribution according to its number of peaks, symmetry or skewness, and variation.

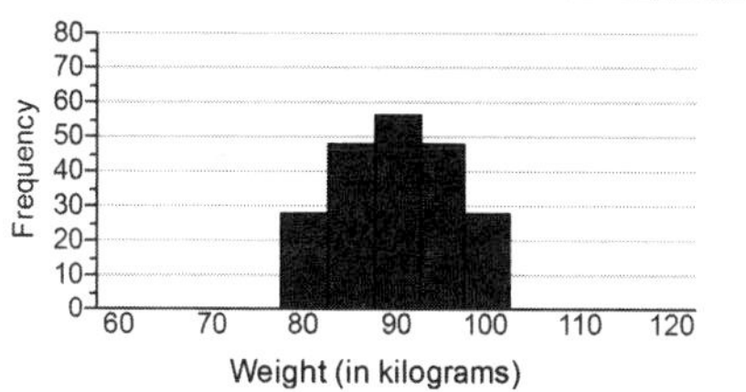

Draw a smooth curve that captures the important features. Choose the correct answer below.

A.

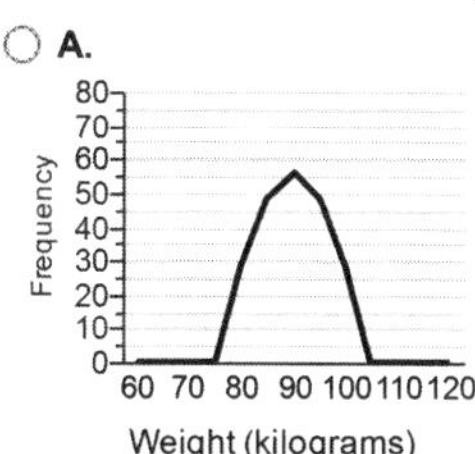

B.

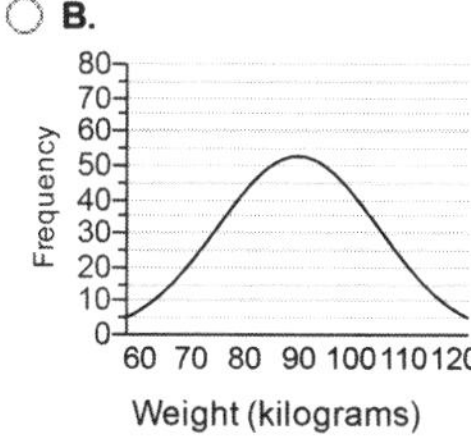

C.

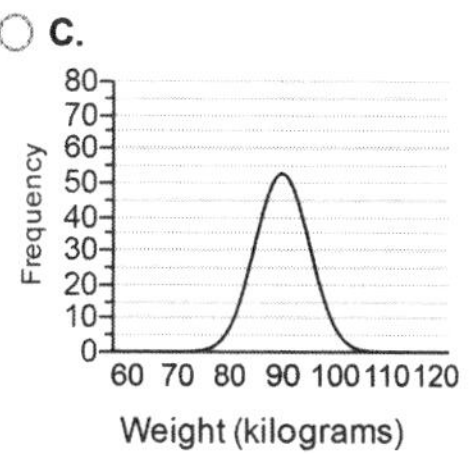

The distribution has ________ peak(s), is (1) ________ and has (2) ________ variation.

(1) symmetric, left-skewed, right-skewed,

(2) fairly low, fairly high, moderate

ID: 2.5.15

*16. Suppose you study family income in a random sample of 300 families. Your results can be summarized as the mean family income was $49,000, the median family income was $35,000, the highest and lowest incomes were $253,000 and $2,500, respectively.

a. Draw a rough sketch of the income distribution, with clearly labeled axes. Choose the correct answer below.

A.

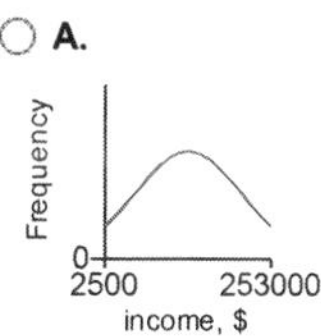

B.

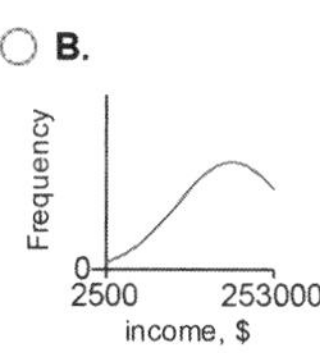

C.

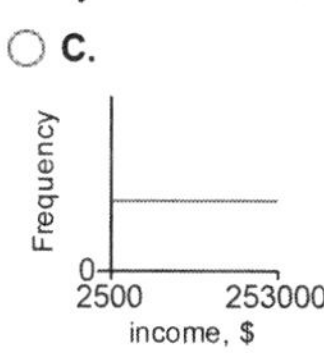

D.

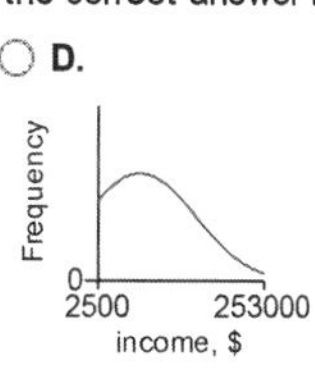

Describe the distribution as symmetric, left-skewed, or right-skewed. Choose the correct answer below.

- symmetric
- right-skewed
- left-skewed

b. How many families in the sample earned less than $35,000? Explain how you know. Choose the correct answer below.

- A. 150 families, because the median is the middle value in the sorted data set.
- B. 75 families, because the mean is the average value of income.
- C. 225 families, because the mode is the most common value in a data set.

c. Based on the given data, can you determine how many families earned more than $49,000? Why or why not? Choose the correct answer below.

- A. No, because the number of families that earned more than $49,000 depends on the distribution.
- B. Yes, because the mean is the middle value in the sorted data set.

ID: 2.5.16

17. A student has completed 14 credits in the table to the right during one semester. Grades are weighted so that A = 4.0; A − = 3.7; B + = 3.4; B = 3.0; and B − = 2.7. Find the student's GPA for the semester.

Course	Credits	Grade
Math 108	3	B
Comparitive Religion 121	3	B +
Spanish 321	4	B −
Astronomy 111	3	B −
Astronomy Lab 112	1	B

The student's GPA is ________.
(Type an integer or decimal rounded to the nearest hundredth as needed.)

ID: 2.5.17

18. What is a normal distribution? Briefly describe the conditions that make a normal distribution.

What is a normal distribution and what conditions make a distribution normal? Choose the correct answer below.

○ **A.** A normal distribution is an asymmetric distribution with a single peak. Its peak corresponds to the mode of the distribution. Its variation is characterized by the standard deviation of the distribution.

○ **B.** A normal distribution is a symmetric, bell-shaped distribution with a single peak. Its peak corresponds to the mean, median, and mode of the distribution. Its variation is characterized by the standard deviation of the distribution.

○ **C.** A normal distribution is a symmetric distribution with two peaks. Its peaks correspond to the maximum and the minimum of the distribution. Its variation is characterized by the standard deviation of the distribution.

○ **D.** A normal distribution is a symmetric, bell-shaped distribution with a single peak. Its peak corresponds to the mean, median, and mode of the distribution. Its variation is characterized by the range of the distribution.

ID: 2.5.18

*19. What is a standard score? How do you find the standard score for a particular data value?

Choose the correct definition of a standard score below.

○ **A.** A standard score is the number of standard deviations a data value lies above or below the mean.

○ **B.** A standard score is a data value that lies within one standard deviation of the mean.

○ **C.** A standard score is the distance between a data value and the nearest outlier.

○ **D.** A standard score is a data value equal to the mean.

Choose the correct formula for computing a standard score below.

○ **A.** The standard score for a particular data value is given by $z = \frac{\text{data value} - \text{mean}}{\text{standard deviation}}$.

○ **B.** The standard score for a particular data value is given by $z = \frac{\text{standard deviation}}{\text{mean} - \text{data value}}$.

○ **C.** The standard score for a particular data value is given by $z = \frac{\text{data value}}{\text{standard deviation}}$.

○ **D.** The standard score for a particular data value is given by $z = \frac{\text{standard deviation}}{\text{data value}}$.

ID: 2.5.19

*20. Decide whether the following statement makes sense or does not make sense.

The heights of male basketball players at a local college are normally distributed with a mean of 6 feet 3 inches and a standard deviation of 3 inches.

Choose the correct answer below.

○ Does not make sense

○ Makes sense

ID: 2.5.20

*21. Decide whether the following statement makes sense or does not make sense.

The weights of babies born at Belmont Hospital are normally distributed with a mean of 6.8 pounds and a standard deviation of 7 pounds.

Choose the correct answer below.

○ Does not make sense

○ Makes sense

ID: 2.5.21

22. Decide whether the following statement makes sense (or is clearly true) or does not make sense (or is clearly false). Explain your reasoning.

My professor graded the final score on a curve, and she gave a grade of A to anyone who had a standard score of 2 or more.

Choose the correct answer below.

- A. This does not make sense because a standard score of 2 or more corresponds to roughly the 97th percentile. This means the lowest test scores are getting curved up to be the highest test scores.
- B. This makes sense because a standard score of 2 or more corresponds to roughly the 97th percentile. Though this curve is stingy on giving out A's to students, it is still giving the top students the highest grade.
- C. This makes sense because now the majority of the class is receiving an A on the test, which is very fair.
- D. This does not make sense because it is rare for test scores to follow the normal distribution.

ID: 2.5.22

---

23. Decide whether the following statement makes sense (or is clearly true) or does not make sense (or is clearly false.) Explain your reasoning.

Jack is in the 50th percentile for height, so he is of median height.

Choose the correct answer below.

- A. This makes sense. The 50th percentile is by definition the mean height.
- B. This does not make sense. The percentile only applies to the standard scores and has no relation to the median of the distribution.
- C. This makes sense. The 50th percentile height means that 50% of all the heights in the data set are less than or equal to Jack's height. The median is the middle value, which means it splits the distribution in half. These two statements are the same.
- D. This does not make sense. Percentile only refers to the mean of a distribution, so the 50th percentile is the average height. This does not necessarily mean that this percentile is the median or middle value.

ID: 2.5.23

---

* 24. Consider the following set of three distributions, all of which are drawn to the same scale. Identify the two distributions that are normal. Of the two normal distributions, which one has the larger variation?

y x (a) y x (b) y x (c)

The two normal distributions are (1) ________, where (2) ________ has the larger standard deviation.

(1)
- (b) and (c)
- (a) and (c)
- (a) and (b)

(2)
- (a)
- (b)
- (c)

ID: 2.5.24

---

25. State, with an explanation, whether you would expect the following data set to be normally distributed.
The delay in departure of trains from a station (note that trains, buses, and airplanes cannot leave early)

Choose the correct answer below.

- A. The data set is not normally distributed. The data set is qualitative and thus is inappropriate for normal appoximation.
- B. This data set is not normally distributed. There is no reason to assume that the mean, median, and mode of this distribution are centered at a central peak in a symmetric, bell-shaped distribution. It is possible that trains never experience delay or frequently encounter very above average delays at this particular station.
- C. This data set is normally distributed. We should expect delay times to cluster toward the mean and become less common farther from the mean.
- D. The data set is not normally distributed. All trains must be delayed by the same amount of time and thus all values cluster toward the mean. This indicates that there is no bell-shape distribution for this data set.

ID: 2.5.25

---

26. State, with an explanation, whether you would expect the following data set to be normally distributed.

The distances between the bull's-eye of a target and 100 darts thrown by an expert

Choose the correct answer below.

○ **A.** This data set is not normally distributed. Dart distance from the bull's-eye will likely have multiple peaks since there will be several clusters of darts in the same vicinity from the bull's-eye.

○ **B.** This data set is not normally distributed. In this case, dart distance from the bull's-eye is completely random, so there is no symmetric bell-curve distribution.

○ **C.** This data set is not normally distributed. There are no genetic, environmental, or other factors that contribute to how the data values are spread.

○ **D.** This data set is approximately normally distributed. On average, an expert will come very close to the bull's-eye, which means that the distances will cluster around some small value. Bad shots and shots that are better than average will correspond to distances greater and smaller than the mean, respectively.

ID: 2.5.26

---

27. State whether you would expect the following data set to be normally distributed or not.

Scores on an easy statistics exam

Choose the correct answer below.

○ Normally distributed
○ Not normally distributed

ID: 2.5.27

---

* 28. Assume that a set of test scores is normally distributed with a mean of 110 and a standard deviation of 5. Use the 68-95-99.7 rule to find the following quantities.

a. The percentage of scores less than 110 is ____________%.
(Round to one decimal place as needed.)

b. The percentage of scores greater than 115 is ____________%.
(Round to one decimal place as needed.)

c. The percentage of scores between 100 and 115 is ____________%.
(Round to one decimal place as needed.)

ID: 2.5.28

---

29. The lengths of pregnancy terms for a particular species of mammal are nearly normally distributed about a mean pregnancy length with a standard deviation of 15 days. About what percentage of births would be expected to occur within 30 days of the mean pregnancy length?

About ____________% of births would be expected to occur within 30 days of the mean pregnancy length.
(Type an integer or a decimal.)

ID: 2.5.29

---

30. The lengths of pregnancy terms for a particular species of mammal are nearly normally distributed about a mean pregnancy length with a standard deviation of 19 days. About what percentage of births would be expected to occur within 57 days of the mean pregnancy length?

About ____________% of births would be expected to occur within 57 days of the mean pregnancy length.
(Type an integer or a decimal.)

ID: 2.5.30

---

* 31. A set of data values is normally distributed with a mean of 80 and a standard deviation of 7. Give the standard score and approximate percentile for a data value of 78.25.
[4] Click the icon to view the table of standard scores and percentiles.

The standard score for 78.25 is $z =$ ____________.
(Do not round until the final answer. Then round to the nearest hundredth as needed.)

The data value 78.25 occurs at about the ____________th percentile.
(Round to the nearest whole number as needed.)

*** 31. (cont.)** 4: More Info

Standard Scores and Percentiles

z-score	Percentile	z-score	Percentile	z-score	Percentile	z-score	Percentile
− 3.5	00.02	− 1.00	15.87	0.00	50.00	1.1	86.43
− 3.0	00.13	− 0.95	17.11	0.05	51.99	1.2	88.49
− 2.9	00.19	− 0.90	18.41	0.10	53.98	1.3	90.32
− 2.8	00.26	− 0.85	19.77	0.15	55.96	1.4	91.92
− 2.7	00.35	− 0.80	21.19	0.20	57.93	1.5	93.32
− 2.6	00.47	− 0.75	22.66	0.25	59.87	1.6	94.52
− 2.5	00.62	− 0.70	24.20	0.30	61.79	1.7	95.54
− 2.4	00.82	− 0.65	25.78	0.35	63.68	1.8	96.41
− 2.3	01.07	− 0.60	27.43	0.40	65.54	1.9	97.13
− 2.2	01.39	− 0.55	29.12	0.45	67.36	2.0	97.72
− 2.1	01.79	− 0.50	30.85	0.50	69.15	2.1	98.21
− 2.0	02.28	− 0.45	32.64	0.55	70.88	2.2	98.61
− 1.9	02.87	− 0.40	34.46	0.60	72.57	2.3	98.93
− 1.8	03.59	− 0.35	36.32	0.65	74.22	2.4	99.18
− 1.7	04.46	− 0.30	38.21	0.70	75.80	2.5	99.38
− 1.6	05.48	− 0.25	40.13	0.75	77.34	2.6	99.53
− 1.5	06.68	− 0.20	42.07	0.80	78.81	2.7	99.65
− 1.4	08.08	− 0.15	44.04	0.85	80.23	2.8	99.74
− 1.3	09.68	− 0.10	46.02	0.90	81.59	2.9	99.81
− 1.2	11.51	− 0.05	48.01	0.95	82.89	3.0	99.87
− 1.1	13.57	− 0.00	50.00	1.00	84.13	3.5	99.98

ID: 2.5.31

32. Suppose you read that the average height of a class of 46 eighth-graders is 51 inches with a standard deviation of 50 inches. Is this likely? Explain.

Choose the correct answer below.

- ○ **A.** This is not likely because heights are usually not approximated by the normal distribution.
- ○ **B.** This is likely because a mean height of 51 inches is a very plausible height for an eighth-grader.
- ○ **C.** This is not likely because a mean of 51 and a standard deviation of 50 would imply that about 5% of the heights differ from the mean by more than 100, which is impossible.
- ○ **D.** This is likely because the heights are often accurately approximated by the normal distribution.

ID: 2.5.32

33. The scores for a certain test of intelligence are normally distributed with mean 75 and standard deviation 12. Find the 90th percentile of these scores.
[5] Click the icon to view the table of standard scores and percentiles.

The 90th percentile is __________. (Round to the nearest whole number as needed.)

5: More Info

Standard Scores and Percentiles

z-score	Percentile	z-score	Percentile	z-score	Percentile	z-score	Percentile
− 3.5	00.02	− 1.00	15.87	0.00	50.00	1.1	86.43
− 3.0	00.13	− 0.95	17.11	0.05	51.99	1.2	88.49
− 2.9	00.19	− 0.90	18.41	0.10	53.98	1.3	90.32
− 2.8	00.26	− 0.85	19.77	0.15	55.96	1.4	91.92
− 2.7	00.35	− 0.80	21.19	0.20	57.93	1.5	93.32
− 2.6	00.47	− 0.75	22.66	0.25	59.87	1.6	94.52
− 2.5	00.62	− 0.70	24.20	0.30	61.79	1.7	95.54
− 2.4	00.82	− 0.65	25.78	0.35	63.68	1.8	96.41
− 2.3	01.07	− 0.60	27.43	0.40	65.54	1.9	97.13
− 2.2	01.39	− 0.55	29.12	0.45	67.36	2.0	97.72
− 2.1	01.79	− 0.50	30.85	0.50	69.15	2.1	98.21
− 2.0	02.28	− 0.45	32.64	0.55	70.88	2.2	98.61
− 1.9	02.87	− 0.40	34.46	0.60	72.57	2.3	98.93
− 1.8	03.59	− 0.35	36.32	0.65	74.22	2.4	99.18
− 1.7	04.46	− 0.30	38.21	0.70	75.80	2.5	99.38
− 1.6	05.48	− 0.25	40.13	0.75	77.34	2.6	99.53
− 1.5	06.68	− 0.20	42.07	0.80	78.81	2.7	99.65
− 1.4	08.08	− 0.15	44.04	0.85	80.23	2.8	99.74
− 1.3	09.68	− 0.10	46.02	0.90	81.59	2.9	99.81
− 1.2	11.51	− 0.05	48.01	0.95	82.89	3.0	99.87
− 1.1	13.57	− 0.00	50.00	1.00	84.13	3.5	99.98

ID: 2.5.33

34. Scores on the quantitative portion of an exam have a mean of 571 and a standard deviation of 154. Assume the scores are normally distributed. What percentage of students taking the quantitative exam score above 586?
[6] Click the icon to view the table of standard scores and percentiles.

What percentage of students taking the quantitative exam score above 586?

__________ % (Round to the nearest whole number as needed.)

6: More Info

Standard Scores and Percentiles

z-score	Percentile	z-score	Percentile	z-score	Percentile	z-score	Percentile
− 3.5	00.02	− 1.00	15.87	0.00	50.00	1.1	86.43
− 3.0	00.13	− 0.95	17.11	0.05	51.99	1.2	88.49
− 2.9	00.19	− 0.90	18.41	0.10	53.98	1.3	90.32
− 2.8	00.26	− 0.85	19.77	0.15	55.96	1.4	91.92
− 2.7	00.35	− 0.80	21.19	0.20	57.93	1.5	93.32
− 2.6	00.47	− 0.75	22.66	0.25	59.87	1.6	94.52
− 2.5	00.62	− 0.70	24.20	0.30	61.79	1.7	95.54
− 2.4	00.82	− 0.65	25.78	0.35	63.68	1.8	96.41
− 2.3	01.07	− 0.60	27.43	0.40	65.54	1.9	97.13
− 2.2	01.39	− 0.55	29.12	0.45	67.36	2.0	97.72
− 2.1	01.79	− 0.50	30.85	0.50	69.15	2.1	98.21
− 2.0	02.28	− 0.45	32.64	0.55	70.88	2.2	98.61
− 1.9	02.87	− 0.40	34.46	0.60	72.57	2.3	98.93
− 1.8	03.59	− 0.35	36.32	0.65	74.22	2.4	99.18
− 1.7	04.46	− 0.30	38.21	0.70	75.80	2.5	99.38
− 1.6	05.48	− 0.25	40.13	0.75	77.34	2.6	99.53
− 1.5	06.68	− 0.20	42.07	0.80	78.81	2.7	99.65
− 1.4	08.08	− 0.15	44.04	0.85	80.23	2.8	99.74
− 1.3	09.68	− 0.10	46.02	0.90	81.59	2.9	99.81
− 1.2	11.51	− 0.05	48.01	0.95	82.89	3.0	99.87
− 1.1	13.57	− 0.00	50.00	1.00	84.13	3.5	99.98

ID: 2.5.34

35. Scores on the verbal Graduate Record Exam (GRE) have a mean of 448 and a standard deviation of 110. Scores on the quantitative GRE have a mean of 655 and a standard deviation of 153. A perfect score on either exam is 800. Assuming the scores are normally distributed, what percentage of students score 800 on the quantitative exam?
[7] Click the icon to view the table of standard scores and percentiles.

The percentage of students that score 800 on the quantitative exam is approximately __________ %.
(Round to the nearest percent as needed.)

7: More Info

Standard Scores and Percentiles for a Normal Distribution

z-score	Percentile	z-score	Percentile	z-score	Percentile	z-score	Percentile
−3.5	0.02	−1.0	15.87	0.0	50.00	1.1	86.43
−3.0	0.13	−0.95	17.11	0.05	51.99	1.2	88.49
−2.9	0.19	−0.90	18.41	0.10	53.98	1.3	90.32
−2.8	0.26	−0.85	19.77	0.15	55.96	1.4	91.92
−2.7	0.35	−0.80	21.19	0.20	57.93	1.5	93.32
−2.6	0.47	−0.75	22.66	0.25	59.87	1.6	94.52
−2.5	0.62	−0.70	24.20	0.30	61.79	1.7	95.54
−2.4	0.82	−0.65	25.78	0.35	63.68	1.8	96.41
−2.3	1.07	−0.60	27.43	0.40	65.54	1.9	97.13
−2.2	1.39	−0.55	29.12	0.45	67.36	2.0	97.72
−2.1	1.79	−0.50	30.85	0.50	69.15	2.1	98.21
−2.0	2.28	−0.45	32.64	0.55	70.88	2.2	98.61
−1.9	2.87	−0.40	34.46	0.60	72.57	2.3	98.93
−1.8	3.59	−0.35	36.32	0.65	74.22	2.4	99.18
−1.7	4.46	−0.30	38.21	0.70	75.80	2.5	99.38
−1.6	5.48	−0.25	40.13	0.75	77.34	2.6	99.53
−1.5	6.68	−0.20	42.07	0.80	78.81	2.7	99.65
−1.4	8.08	−0.15	44.04	0.85	80.23	2.8	99.74
−1.3	9.68	−0.10	46.02	0.90	81.59	2.9	99.81
−1.2	11.51	−0.05	48.01	0.95	82.89	3.0	99.87
−1.1	13.57	0.0	50.00	1.0	84.13	3.5	99.98

ID: 2.5.35

36. Scores on the quantitative portion of an exam have a mean of 563 and a standard deviation of 160. Assume the scores are normally distributed. What percentage of students taking the quantitative exam score below 579?
[8] Click the icon to view the table of standard scores and percentiles.

What percentage of students taking the quantitative exam score below 579?

___________% (Round to the nearest whole number as needed.)

8: More Info

Standard Scores and Percentiles

z-score	Percentile	z-score	Percentile	z-score	Percentile	z-score	Percentile
− 3.5	00.02	− 1.00	15.87	0.00	50.00	1.1	86.43
− 3.0	00.13	− 0.95	17.11	0.05	51.99	1.2	88.49
− 2.9	00.19	− 0.90	18.41	0.10	53.98	1.3	90.32
− 2.8	00.26	− 0.85	19.77	0.15	55.96	1.4	91.92
− 2.7	00.35	− 0.80	21.19	0.20	57.93	1.5	93.32
− 2.6	00.47	− 0.75	22.66	0.25	59.87	1.6	94.52
− 2.5	00.62	− 0.70	24.20	0.30	61.79	1.7	95.54
− 2.4	00.82	− 0.65	25.78	0.35	63.68	1.8	96.41
− 2.3	01.07	− 0.60	27.43	0.40	65.54	1.9	97.13
− 2.2	01.39	− 0.55	29.12	0.45	67.36	2.0	97.72
− 2.1	01.79	− 0.50	30.85	0.50	69.15	2.1	98.21
− 2.0	02.28	− 0.45	32.64	0.55	70.88	2.2	98.61
− 1.9	02.87	− 0.40	34.46	0.60	72.57	2.3	98.93
− 1.8	03.59	− 0.35	36.32	0.65	74.22	2.4	99.18
− 1.7	04.46	− 0.30	38.21	0.70	75.80	2.5	99.38
− 1.6	05.48	− 0.25	40.13	0.75	77.34	2.6	99.53
− 1.5	06.68	− 0.20	42.07	0.80	78.81	2.7	99.65
− 1.4	08.08	− 0.15	44.04	0.85	80.23	2.8	99.74
− 1.3	09.68	− 0.10	46.02	0.90	81.59	2.9	99.81
− 1.2	11.51	− 0.05	48.01	0.95	82.89	3.0	99.87
− 1.1	13.57	− 0.00	50.00	1.00	84.13	3.5	99.98

ID: 2.5.36

CHAPTER 3
Units, Conversions, Scales, and Rates
MyMathLab Homework Problems*

* Problems with an asterisk are included in the pre-assigned homework assignment.
! Problems with an exclamation point are new to the Update edition.
To find the problems in MyMathLab online, please refer to the ID code listed below each problem.

!* 1. Three different countries have currencies A, B, and C. The ratio of currency A to currency B to currency C is 4 : 468 : 9. Use the given information to answer parts **(a)** through **(c)** below.

Currency A	Currency B	Currency C
4	468	9
1		
	1	
		1

(a) Fill in the given table. Be sure to use the values in the 2nd row of the table whenever possible to avoid round-off error.

Currency A	Currency B	Currency C
4	468	9
1	______	______
______	1	______
______	______	1

(Type integers or simplified fractions.)

(b) Each currency is proportional to the other two. Which pair of currencies has a constant of proportionality equal to 52?

Currencies (1) __________ have a constant of proportionality equal to 52.

(c) Write an equation y = k • x expressing the relationship between these two currencies, using 52 as the constant of proportionality.

Select the correct choice below and fill in the answer box to complete your choice.

○ B= __________ A

○ C= __________ A

○ B= __________ C

(1) ○ B and C
○ A and C
○ A and B

ID: 3.1.1

!* 2. Use the given ratios to find the conversion factors in parts **(a)** through **(f)**.

(a) To convert from gallons to quarts, multiply by what? 2 gallons: 8 quarts

Multiply by __________. (Type an integer or a simplified fraction.)

(b) Write down an equation y = k • x expressing the relationship between gallons (G) and quarts (Q).

The equation is Q= __________ G.

(c) To convert from pounds to kilograms, multiply by what? 6.6 pounds: 3 kilograms

Multiply by __________. (Round to two decimal places as needed.)

(d) Write down an equation y = k • x expressing the relationship between pounds (P) and kilograms (K).

The equation is K= __________ P. (Round to two decimal places as needed.)

(e) To convert from furlongs to miles, multiply by what? 40 furlongs: 5 miles

Multiply by __________. (Round to three decimal places as needed.)

(f) Write down an equation y = k • x expressing the relationship between furlongs (F) and miles (M).

The equation is F = __________ M.

ID: 3.1.2

3. Decide whether the following statement makes sense or does not make sense. Explain your reasoning.

   I drove at a speed of 35 miles for the entire trip.

   Choose the correct answer below.

   ○ **A.** The statement makes sense because it is reasonable for a person to go on a 35 mile trip.
   ○ **B.** The statement does not make sense because the indicated speed is much higher than the speed a person can travel.
   ○ **C.** The statement does not make sense because it is not reasonable for a person to go on a 35 mile trip.
   ○ **D.** The statement does not make sense because miles is not a unit of speed.

   ID: 3.1.3

---

4. Decide whether the following statement makes sense or does not make sense. Explain your reasoning.

   I have a box with a volume of 2 square feet.

   Choose the correct answer below.

   ○ **A.** The statement makes sense because it is reasonable to have a box with the stated volume.
   ○ **B.** The statement does not make sense because a box cannot have a volume.
   ○ **C.** The statement does not make sense because square feet is not a unit of volume.
   ○ **D.** The statement does not make sense because the stated volume is too large.

   ID: 3.1.4

---

5. Decide whether the following sentence makes sense or does not make sense. Explain your reasoning.

   I know a professional bicyclist who weighs 300 kilograms.

   Choose the correct answer below.

   ○ **A.** The statement does not make sense because a professional bicyclist cannot be overweight.
   ○ **B.** The statement makes sense because it is reasonable for a professional bicyclist to be 300 kilograms.
   ○ **C.** The statement does not make sense because it is not physically possible for any person to be 300 kilograms.
   ○ **D.** The statement does not make sense because kilogram is not a unit of weight.

   ID: 3.1.5

---

6. Decide whether the following sentence makes sense or does not make sense. Explain your reasoning.

   My car's gas tank holds 12 meters of gasoline.

   Choose the correct answer below.

   ○ **A.** The statement does not make sense because meters is not a unit of volume.
   ○ **B.** The statement does not make sense because the size of the gas tank is too large.
   ○ **C.** The statement makes sense because it is possible for a car's gas tank to hold upwards of 20 meters of gasoline.
   ○ **D.** The statement makes sense because it is reasonable to have a car with the indicated tank volume.

   ID: 3.1.6

---

7. Identify the units of the following quantities. State the units mathematically and in words.

   Your average speed on a long walk, found by dividing distance traveled in feet by time elapsed in seconds.

   What are the units mathematically?

   ○ **A.** $\frac{s}{ft}$
   ○ **B.** s
   ○ **C.** $\frac{ft}{s}$
   ○ **D.** ft

   What are the units in words?

   ○ **A.** seconds
   ○ **B.** feet per second
   ○ **C.** miles
   ○ **D.** miles per seconds

   ID: 3.1.7

---

8. Identify the units you would expect for the quantity described below. State the units in words and mathematically.

The price of apple juice, found by dividing its cost in dollars by its volume in pints.

What are the units in words?

- ○ **A.** pints
- ○ **B.** dollars
- ○ **C.** pints per dollar
- ○ **D.** dollars per pint

What are the units mathematically?

- ○ **A.** pt/$
- ○ **B.** $/pt
- ○ **C.** pt
- ○ **D.** $

ID: 3.1.8

---

*9. Identify the units of the following quantity. State the units mathematically and in words.

The per capita yearly oil consumption by the residents of a town, found by dividing the amount of oil used per year in gallons by the population of the town in people.

What are the units mathematically?

- ○ **A.** $\frac{\text{gal}}{\text{person}}$
- ○ **B.** $\frac{\text{Gal}}{\text{person}}$
- ○ **C.** $\frac{\text{Gal}^3}{\text{person}}$
- ○ **D.** $\frac{\text{L}^3}{\text{person}}$

What are the units in words?

- ○ **A.** gallons per person
- ○ **B.** Gal^3 per town
- ○ **C.** Gal^3 per person
- ○ **D.** gallons per town

ID: 3.1.9

---

10. Convert 27 feet to inches.

27 feet = ____________ inches
(Round to the nearest hundredth as needed.)

ID: 3.1.10

---

11. Convert 42 minutes to seconds.

There are ____________ seconds in 42 minutes.
(Simplify your answer.)

ID: 3.1.11

---

12. Use two or three unit fractions to convert.

9 days = ______ seconds

9 days = ____________ seconds

ID: 3.1.12

---

13. Convert 10 years to hours (neglecting leap years).

10 years = ____________ hours
(Simplify your answer.)

ID: 3.1.13

---

* 14. Find a conversion factor between cubic inches and cubic feet. Write it in three forms.

Complete the conversion factor below.

__________ cubic inches = 1 cubic foot

Write the conversion factor in the form for converting cubic feet to cubic inches. Choose the correct answer below.

- A. $1 = \frac{\text{1 cubic foot}}{\text{1728 cubic inches}}$
- B. $1 = \frac{\text{1728 cubic inches}}{\text{1 cubic foot}}$
- C. $1 = \frac{\text{1728 cubic feet}}{\text{1 cubic inch}}$
- D. $1 = \frac{\text{1 cubic inch}}{\text{1728 cubic feet}}$

Write the conversion factor in the form for converting cubic inches to cubic feet. Choose the correct answer below.

- A. $1 = \frac{\text{1728 cubic inches}}{\text{1 cubic foot}}$
- B. $1 = \frac{\text{1 cubic inch}}{\text{1728 cubic feet}}$
- C. $1 = \frac{\text{1 cubic foot}}{\text{1728 cubic inches}}$
- D. $1 = \frac{\text{1728 cubic feet}}{\text{1 cubic inch}}$

ID: 3.1.14

15. A new sidewalk will be 4 feet wide, 120 feet long, and filled to a depth of 6 inches (0.5 foot) with concrete. How many cubic yards of concrete are needed?

The new sidewalk needs __________ cubic yards of concrete.
(Round to one decimal place as needed.)

ID: 3.1.15

* 16. An air conditioning system can circulate 430 cubic feet of air per minute. How many cubic yards of air can it circulate per minute?

The air conditioning system can circulate about __________ cubic yards of air per minute.
(Type an integer or a decimal rounded to one decimal place as needed.)

ID: 3.1.16

17. Complete the following sentence with a number. The answer should be greater than 1.

A kilometer is ______ times as large as a meter.

A kilometer is __________ times as large as a meter.
(Type an integer or a decimal.)

ID: 3.1.17

18. Complete the following sentence with a number. The answer should be greater than 1.

A decameter is ______ times as large as a meter.

A decameter is __________ times as large as a meter.
(Type an integer or a decimal.)

ID: 3.1.18

19. Complete the following sentence with a number. The answer should be greater than 1.

A cubic decameter is ______ times as large as a cubic meter.

A cubic decameter is __________ times as large as a cubic meter.
(Type an integer or a decimal.)

ID: 3.1.19

*20. Convert the measurement to the units specified.

34 pounds to kilograms

1 in. = 2.540 cm	1 cm = 0.3937 in
1 ft = 0.3048 m	1 m = 3.28 ft
1 yd = 0.9144 m	1 m = 1.094 yd
1 mi = 1.6093 km	1 km = 0.6214 mi
1 lb = 0.4536 kg	1 kg = 2.205 lb

34 pounds = ___________ kg
(Round to two decimal places as needed.)

ID: 3.1.20

21. Convert the following quantities to the indicated units.

17 quarts to liters

17 quarts = ___________ liters
(Round to two decimal places as needed.)

ID: 3.1.21

*22. Express 70 miles per hour in kilometers per hour.

70 mi/hr = ___________ km/hr
(Round to the nearest whole number as needed.)

ID: 3.1.22

23. Convert the following quantities to the indicated units.

13 meters per second to miles per hour

13 meters per second = ___________ miles per hour
(Do not round until the final answer. Then round to two decimal places as needed.)

ID: 3.1.23

24. Convert 370 cubic inches to cubic centimeters.

370 cubic inches is approximately equal to ___________ cubic centimeters.
(Round to the nearest hundredth as needed.)

ID: 3.1.24

*25. Convert the following temperatures from Fahrenheit to Celsius or vice versa.

a. 70°F b. 55°C c. −30°C

a. 70°F = ___________ °C
(Type an integer or decimal rounded to one decimal place as needed.)

b. 55°C = ___________ °F
(Type an integer or decimal rounded to one decimal place as needed.)

c. −30°C = ___________ °F
(Type an integer or decimal rounded to one decimal place as needed.)

ID: 3.1.25

26. Convert the following temperatures from Kelvin to Celsius or vice versa.

a. 80 K b. 190 K c. 35°C

a. 80 K = ___________ °C
(Type an integer or a decimal.)

b. 190 K = ___________ °C
(Type an integer or a decimal.)

c. 35°C = ___________ K
(Type an integer or a decimal.)

ID: 3.1.26

* 27. Use the currency exchange rates in the table for the following question.

You arrive in Mexico City with $380. How many pesos can you buy?

Currency	Dollars per Foreign	Foreign per Dollar
British pound	1.414	0.7072
Canadian dollar	0.7834	1.277
European euro	1.256	0.7965
Japanese yen	0.01007	99.34
Mexican peso	0.06584	15.19

You can buy ________ pesos with $380.
(Simplify your answer. Round to two decimal places as needed.)

ID: 3.1.27

28. You return from a trip with 3700 Mexican pesos. How much are your pesos worth in U.S. dollars? Use the exchange rate shown below.

Currency	U.S. dollars per Mexican peso	Mexican pesos per U.S. dollar
Mexican peso	0.05988	16.70

The 3700 Mexican pesos are equivalent to about $ ________ .
(Round to the nearest cent as needed.)

ID: 3.1.28

!* 29. Use dimensional analysis to find the units in the conversion factors in parts **(a)** through **(c)**.

(a) To convert from 5 gallons to quarts, multiply by a conversion factor. What are the correct units in the numerator and denominator of the factor shown below?

5 gal × (1) ________

(b) To convert 5 pounds to kilograms, multiply by a conversion factor. What are the correct units in the numerator and denominator of the factor shown below?

5 lbs × (2) ________

(c) To convert 5 furlongs to miles, multiply by a conversion factor. What are the correct units in the numerator and denominator of the factor shown below?

5 fur × (3) ________

(1) ○ $\frac{\text{gallons}}{\text{quarts}}$ ○ $\frac{\text{quarts}}{\text{gallons}}$

(2) ○ $\frac{\text{kilograms}}{\text{pounds}}$ ○ $\frac{\text{pounds}}{\text{kilograms}}$

(3) ○ $\frac{\text{miles}}{\text{furlongs}}$ ○ $\frac{\text{furlongs}}{\text{miles}}$

ID: 3.1.29

* 30. How much will a person pay for 10.1 pounds of bananas at a price of $1.16 per pound?

The price the person will pay is ________ (1) ________ (Round to the nearest cent.)

(1) ○ pounds.
○ dollars.

ID: 3.1.30

31. How much will a person earn working for 8 months at a salary of $2,900 per month?

The amount the person will earn is ________ (1) ________ (Type an integer or a decimal.)

(1) ○ months.
○ dollars.

ID: 3.1.31

32. The Kentucky Derby distance is 27 furlongs. How far is the Kentucky Derby in (a) rods? (b) fathoms?

a. The Kentucky Derby is ________ rods.

b. The Kentucky Derby is ________ fathoms.

ID: 3.1.32

33. One cubic foot holds 7.48 gallons of water, and one gallon of water weighs 8.33 pounds. How much does 3.3 cubic feet of water weigh in pounds? in ounces (avoirdupois)?

The weight in pounds is ________ lb.
(Type an integer or decimal rounded to the nearest tenth as needed.)

The weight in ounces (avoirdupois) is ________ oz av. (Round to the nearest integer as needed.)

ID: 3.1.33

---

34. A boat has a top speed of 49 knots (nautical miles per hour). What is this speed in miles per hour?

The boat has a top speed of ________ miles per hour.
(Round to two decimal places as needed.)

ID: 3.1.34

---

35. How many cords of wood could you fit in a room that is 3 yards long, 3 yards wide, and 2 yards high? Use the fact that 1 cord = 128 ft^3 and 1 yd^3 = 27 ft^3.

You could fit ________ cords of wood in a room that is 3 yards long, 3 yards wide, and 2 yards high.
(Round to two decimal places as needed.)

ID: 3.1.35

---

36. Suppose that a certain basketball athlete earned $23,500,000 to play 80 games, each lasting 48 minutes. (Assume no overtime games.)
a. How much did the athlete earn per game?
b. Assuming that the athlete played every minute of every game, how much did he earn per minute?
c. Assuming that the athlete played 2/3 of every game, how much did he earn per minute?
d. Suppose that, averaged over a year, the athlete practiced or trained 30 hours for every game and then played every minute. Including this training time, what was his hourly salary?

a. The athlete earned $________ per game.

b. The athlete earned $________ per minute played if he played the entire game for every game.
(Round to the nearest dollar per minute as needed.)

c. The athlete earned $________ per minute played if he played 2/3 of every game.
(Round to the nearest dollar per minute as needed.)

d. The athlete earned $________ per hour if he trained 30 hours for every game and then played every minute.
(Round to the nearest dollar per hour as needed.)

ID: 3.1.36

---

37. Suppose you have a tablet with a capacity of 16 gigabytes. For a plain text book, one byte typically corresponds to one character and an average page consists of 2000 characters. Assume all 16 gigabytes are used for plain text books.
a. How many pages of text can the tablet hold?
b. How many 500-page books can the tablet hold?

a. The tablet can hold ________ pages of text.
(Type a whole number.)

b. The tablet can hold ________ 500-page books.
(Type a whole number.)

ID: 3.1.37

---

*38. Use the sample currency exchange rates given in the table to answer the following question. State all of the conversion factors that you use.

Suppose that a new fuel-efficient European car travels an average of 27 kilometers on 1 liter of gasoline. If gasoline costs 2.75 euros per liter, how much will it cost to drive 350 kilometers in dollars?

Currency	Dollars per Foreign	Foreign per Dollar
British pound	1.414	0.7072
Canadian dollar	0.7834	1.277
European euro	1.256	0.7965
Japanese yen	0.01007	99.34
Mexican peso	0.06584	15.19

State all of the conversion factors that you use.

☐ **A.** $1 = \frac{350 \text{ km}}{1 \text{ L}}$

☐ **B.** $1 = \frac{2.75 \text{ euros}}{1 \text{ L}}$

☐ **C.** $1 = \frac{1.256 \text{ dollars}}{1 \text{ euro}}$

☐ **D.** $1 = \frac{1 \text{ L}}{1000 \text{ mL}}$

☐ **E.** $1 = \frac{1 \text{ euro}}{1.256 \text{ dollars}}$

☐ **F.** $1 = \frac{1 \text{ L}}{27 \text{ km}}$

If gasoline costs 2.75 euros per liter, it will cost $________ to drive 350 kilometers.
(Do not round until the final answer. Then round to the nearest cent as needed.)

ID: 3.1.38

---

39. Use the sample currency exchange rates given in the table to answer the following question. State all of the conversion factors that you use.

An 0.8-liter bottle of Mexican wine costs 260 pesos. What is the price in dollars per ounce?

Currency	Dollars per Foreign	Foreign per Dollar
British pound	1.414	0.7072
Canadian dollar	0.7834	1.277
European euro	1.256	0.7965
Japanese yen	0.01007	99.34
Mexican peso	0.06584	15.19

State all of the conversion factors that you use.

☐ **A.** $1 = \frac{0.06584 \text{ dollars}}{1 \text{ peso}}$

☐ **B.** $1 = \frac{1000 \text{ mL}}{1 \text{ L}}$

☐ **C.** $1 = \frac{1 \text{ mL}}{0.03381 \text{ oz}}$

☐ **D.** $1 = \frac{1 \text{ peso}}{0.06584 \text{ dollars}}$

☐ **E.** $1 = \frac{1 \text{ L}}{1000 \text{ mL}}$

☐ **F.** $1 = \frac{0.03381 \text{ oz}}{1 \text{ mL}}$

An 0.8-liter bottle of Mexican wine that costs 260 pesos has the price of ________ dollars per ounce.
(Do not round until the final answer. Then round to the nearest cent as needed.)

ID: 3.1.39

40. Use the sample currency exchange rates given in the table to answer the following question. State all of the conversion factors that you use.

Carpet at a British home supply store sells for 22 pounds (currency) per square meter. What is the price in dollars per square yard?

Currency	Dollars per Foreign	Foreign per Dollar
British pound	1.624	0.6158
Canadian dollar	1.005	0.9950
European euro	1.320	0.7576
Japanese yen	0.0120	83.33
Mexican peso	0.07855	12.73

State all of the conversion factors that you use.

☐ **A.** $\frac{1.624 \text{ dollars}}{1 \text{ British pound}}$

☐ **B.** $\frac{0.7665 \text{ dollars}}{1 \text{ euro}}$

☐ **C.** $\frac{0.6158 \text{ British pound}}{1 \text{ dollar}}$

☐ **D.** $\frac{0.5436 \text{ kg}}{1 \text{ lb}}$

☐ **E.** $\frac{0.9144 \text{ m}}{1 \text{ yd}}$

☐ **F.** $\frac{1.094 \text{ yd}}{1 \text{ m}}$

The price is ________ dollar(s) per square yard.
(Round to the nearest cent as needed.)

ID: 3.1.40

41. What is the weight of a 36.35-carat diamond in grams and ounces?

The weight of a 36.35-carat diamond is ________ g.
(Round to two decimal places as needed.)

The weight of a 36.35-carat diamond is ________ oz.
(Round to two decimal places as needed.)

ID: 3.1.41

42. How many ounces of gold are in a 16-karat gold chain that weighs 2.1 ounces?

There are ________ ounces of pure gold in a 16-karat gold chain that weighs 2.1 ounces.
(Round to two decimal places as needed.)

ID: 3.1.42

43. The standard guidelines for fluid intake recommend that a 10–20-kg child should have 1000 mL of fluid plus 50 mL for each full kilogram of body weight over 10 kg per day. How many 8-ounce glasses of fluid should a 43-pound child have each day?

The 43-pound child should drink about ________ 8-ounce glasses of fluid each day.
(Simplify your answer. Round to the nearest glass as needed.)

ID: 3.1.43

!* 44. Complete the sentences in parts **(a)** and **(b)**.

(a) Degrees Celsius are (1) ____________ units because they do not have a well-defined (2) ____________ that represents the absence of something. It does not make sense to (3) ____________ these units.

(b) Dollars are (4) ____________ units because they do have a well-defined (5) ____________ that represents the absence of money. It does make sense to (6) ____________ these units.

(1) ○ ratio ○ interval

(2) ○ mean value ○ zero

(3) ○ convert ○ double ○ subtract

(4) ○ interval ○ ratio

(5) ○ zero ○ mean value

(6) ○ double ○ convert

ID: 3.1.44

45. Convert to Fahrenheit.
45°C

45°C = ____________ °F

ID: 3.1.45

46. Convert to Fahrenheit.
- 5° C

- 5° C = ____________ ° F
(Simplify your answer. Type an integer or a decimal. Round to the nearest tenth as needed.)

ID: 3.1.46

* 47. Convert to Celsius.
26° F

26° F = ____________ ° C
(Simplify your answer. Type an integer or a decimal. Round to the nearest tenth as needed.)

ID: 3.1.47

48. Convert to Celsius.
123° F

123° F = ____________ ° C
(Simplify your answer. Type an integer or a decimal. Round to the nearest tenth as needed.)

ID: 3.1.48

49. Convert 44°C to Fahrenheit.

44°C = ____________ °F
(Simplify your answer. Type an integer or a decimal.)

ID: 3.1.49

50. Convert to Fahrenheit.
- 9° C

- 9° C = ____________ ° F
(Simplify your answer. Type an integer or a decimal. Round to the nearest tenth as needed.)

ID: 3.1.50

51. Convert to Celsius.
45° F

45° F = ____________ ° C
(Simplify your answer. Type an integer or a decimal. Round to the nearest tenth as needed.)

ID: 3.1.51

52. Convert to Celsius.

$-26°F$

$-26° F =$ ____________ $° C$
(Simplify your answer. Type an integer or a decimal. Round to the nearest tenth as needed.)

ID: 3.1.52

53. Convert to Celsius.

390°F

Use the formula $C = \frac{5}{9} \cdot (F - 32)$

The answer is ____________ °C.
(Round to the nearest tenth.)

ID: 3.1.53

* 54. Find the scale ratio for the map described below.

1 centimeter on the map represents 100 meters on the ground.

The scale ratio is 1 to ____________.

ID: 3.2.1

* 55. Find the scale ratio for the map described below.

1 mm (map) = 5 km (actual)

The scale ratio is 1 to ____________.

ID: 3.2.2

* 56. The table to the right gives size and distance data for the planets at a certain point in time. Calculate the scaled size and distance for each planet using a 1 to 10 billion scale model solar system.

Planet	Diameter	Distance from Sun
Mercury	4880 km	60.9 million km
Venus	12,100 km	108.1 million km
Earth	12,760 km	147.2 million km
Mars	6790 km	220.8 million km
Jupiter	143,000 km	750.4 million km
Saturn	120,000 km	1486 million km
Uranus	52,000 km	2891 million km
Neptune	48,400 km	4462 million km

Complete the following table.

(Type integers or decimals rounded to the nearest tenth as needed.)

Planet	Diameter	Distance from Sun
Mercury	________ mm	________ m
Venus	________ mm	________ m
Earth	________ mm	________ m
Mars	________ mm	________ m
Jupiter	________ mm	________ m
Saturn	________ mm	________ m
Uranus	________ mm	________ m
Neptune	________ mm	________ m

ID: 3.2.3

* 57. According to modern science, Earth is about 4.5 billion years old and written human history extends back about 10,000 years. Suppose the entire history of Earth is represented with a 10-meter-long timeline, with the birth of Earth on one end and today at the other end.

a. What distance represents 2 billion years?
b. How far from the end of the timeline does written human history begin?

a. 2 billion years is represented by __________ meters of the timeline.
(Type an integer or decimal rounded to the nearest tenth as needed.)

b. Written human history begins about __________ millimeters from the end of the timeline.
(Type an integer or decimal rounded to the nearest hundredth as needed.)

ID: 3.2.4

!* 58. Complete the sentences in parts **(a)** and **(b)**.

(a) A unit-less scale of 1 : 108 indicates that __________ of an inch in the model corresponds to 1 foot in what the model represents.
(Type an integer or a simplified fraction.)

(b) If a model (M) car is related to the actual (A) car it represents with a scale of 1 : 108, find the equation that represents this relationship.

Choose the correct equation below.

○ $A = 108 \cdot M$

○ $A = \frac{1}{108} \cdot M$

○ $M = 108 \cdot A$

ID: 3.2.5

!* 59. An ant that weighs $\frac{1}{100}$ ounces can lift $\frac{1}{5}$ ounces. Use this information to answer parts **(a)** through **(c)**.

(a) The unit-less scale of what the ant weighs to what it can lift is 1 : __________.

(b) Find the equation that represents this relationship between an ant's weight (W) and the weight of what it can lift (L).

The equation is L = __________ W.

(c) Assume Susan is as strong as an ant and she weighs 180 pounds. How many pounds can she lift? (The correct answer does not have to be realistic.)

Susan can lift __________ pounds.

ID: 3.2.6

!* 60. The 2010 census in a certain country counted 343,764,366 people and there were 32,829,497 births that year.

a) Compute the ratio of births to population and scale the second quantity to 1,000. This is known as the birth rate.
b) The birth rate in part **a)** is 3% **lower** than the 2009 birth rate. Why is the birth rate lower in 2010 even though the population increased between 2009 and 2010?
c) Why are the fertility rates in the given graphic so much higher than the birth rate?

[1] Click the icon to view a graph of the trends in the fertility rate between 1950 and 2013.

a) What is the birth rate, or ratio of births to population? (Compute the ratio of births to population and scale the second quantity to 1000.)

__________ :1000
(Round to two decimal places as needed.)

b) Which of the following are plausible explanations for why the birth rate is lower in 2010 than in 2009 given that the population grew? Select all that apply.

☐ **A.** People are living longer, so there are fewer young people having babies.
☐ **B.** Families are having fewer children due to the increasing costs of raising a child.
☐ **C.** People have fewer babies when the economy is bad.
☐ **D.** More women are working and delaying having children until after age 35.
☐ **E.** There was an increase in immigration into the country.

!* 60. (cont.) **c)** Why are the fertility rates in the given graphic so much higher than the birth rate?

○ **A.** The graph does not single out teen pregnancies.
○ **B.** The fertility rates are per 1000 women of child bearing age, not per 1000 people.
○ **C.** Some women who are fertile and of child bearing age choose not to have babies.

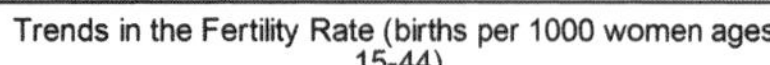

ID: 3.3.1

!* 61. The data in the given table shows the number of motor vehicle deaths (MVD) in a certain country as different rates. Use this information to complete parts **a** and **b**.

[2] Click the icon to view the table of motor vehicle deaths.

a) Compute the fatality rate per 100,000 population in 2005.

__________ (Type an integer or a decimal rounded to two decimal places.)

b) Compute the fatality rate per 100 million vehicle miles traveled in 2014.

__________ (Type an integer or a decimal rounded to two decimal places.)

2: Table of motor vehicle deaths

Year	Killed	Resident Population (Thousands)	Licensed Drivers (Thousands)	Registered Motor Vehicles (Thousands)	Vehicle Miles Traveled (Billions)
2005	43,613	293,191	194,602	255,685	2905
2010	32,130	303,827	210,115	254,312	2925
2014	31,882	309,662	211,875	257,512	2984

ID: 3.3.2

!* 62. Food labels in the U.S. give the number of calories which are units of energy and can be converted to joules (J). Technically these calories are "food calories" and the conversion is 1 food calorie = 4184 joules. A food calorie is also called a kilocalorie (kcal) and equals 1000 thermal calories. So a calorie of heat in a science lab equals 4.184 joules. Many people mistakenly think watts (W) are a unit of energy, when in fact they are units of power. Power is a rate of energy use per unit time, and a watt equals 1 joule per second (J/s). A 100 watt bulb uses 100 joules of energy every second. Electric bills measure energy usage in units of kilowatt-hours (kwh), which is 1000 watts of energy use for 1 hour, or 1000 J/s for 3600 seconds, which is 3,600,000 joules. Use this information to complete parts **a** through **d**.

a) Convert 7 kwh into food calories.

7 kwh = __________ food calories
(Type an integer or a decimal rounded to one decimal place.)

b) You leave a 100 watt bulb on for 8 hours. How many food calories of energy are used?

__________ food calories
(Type an integer or a decimal rounded to one decimal place.)

!* 62. (cont.) **c)** A 220 calorie protein bar costs $3.49. How many food calories per dollar is this?

__________ food calories per dollar
(Type an integer or a decimal rounded to one decimal place.)

d) A 220 calorie protein bar costs $3.49 and a kwh of energy from the local electric company costs 13 cents. How many food calories per dollar is the energy?

__________ food calories per dollar
(Type an integer or a decimal rounded to one decimal place.)

Which is cheaper in terms of food calories per dollar? Choose the correct answer below.

○ protein bar
○ kwh

ID: 3.3.3

---

63. An airliner travels 90 miles in 10 minutes. What is its speed in miles per hour?

The speed is __________ miles per hour.

ID: 3.3.4

---

64. A hose fills a hot tub at a rate of 3.32 gallons per minute. How many hours will it take to fill a 302-gallon hot tub?

It will take __________ hours to fill the hot tub.
(Simplify your answer. Round to two decimal places as needed.)

ID: 3.3.5

---

65. Sid needs 0.9 meters of canvas material to make a carry-all bag for his wheelchair. If canvas is $6.23 per meter, how much will Sid spend? (Note that $6.23 per meter is the same as $6.23 for one meter.)

Sid must spend $__________.
(Round to the nearest cent as needed.)

ID: 3.3.6

---

* 66. Suppose that in 2008, 822,900 citizens died of a certain disease. Assuming the population of the country is 217 million, what was the mortality rate in units of deaths per 100,000 people?

The mortality rate is __________ deaths per 100,000 people.
(Simplify your answer. Round to the nearest integer as needed.)

ID: 3.3.7

---

67. There are approximately 3.7 million births in a country each year. Find the birth rate in units of births per minute.

In this country, there are approximately __________ births per minute.
(Simplify your answer. Round to one decimal place as needed.)

ID: 3.3.8

---

* 68. If your car gets 25 miles per gallon, how much does it cost to drive 300 miles when gasoline costs $2.60 per gallon?

The cost is $__________.
(Simplify your answer. Round to the nearest cent as needed.)

ID: 3.3.9

---

69. A dog kennel uses 85 lb of dog food per day. How many pounds are used in a year?

The kennel uses __________ lb of dog food in a year.

ID: 3.3.10

---

70. Consider the following exam question and student solution. Determine whether the solution is correct. If it is not correct, write a note to the student explaining why it is wrong and give a correct solution.

Exam Question: A candy store sells chocolate for $6.35 per pound. The piece you want to buy weighs 0.35 pound. How much will it cost, to the nearest cent? (Neglect sales tax.)

Student Solution: $0.35 \div 6.35 = 0.055$. It will cost 5.5¢.

Select the correct answer below and, if necessary, fill in the answer box to complete your choice.

- ○ **A.** The student's solution is correct.
- ○ **B.** The student's solution is incorrect. The student's division gives an answer whose units are square pounds per dollar. The desired units are dollars. The correct answer in dollars is $__________.
(Simplify your answer. Round to the nearest cent as needed.)
- ○ **C.** The student's solution is incorrect. The student's division gives an answer that includes part of a cent. Fractional cents cannot be used. The correct answer in cents is __________¢.
(Simplify your answer. Round to the nearest cent as needed.)

ID: 3.3.11

---

71. Consider the following exam question and student solution. Determine whether the solution is correct. If it is not correct, write a note to the student explaining why it is wrong and give a correct solution.

Exam question: You can buy a 32-pound bag of flour for $9 or you can buy a 1-pound bag for $0.44. Compare the per pound cost for the large and small bags.

Student solution: The large bag price is $32 \div \$9 = \$3.56$ per pound, which is much more than the 44¢ per pound price of the small bag.

Select the correct choice below and, if necessary, fill in the answer box to complete your choice.

- ○ **A.** The student's solution is correct.
- ○ **B.** The student's solution is incorrect. The student's division gives an answer with units of pounds per dollar, but he should seek an answer in dollars per pound. The answer in dollars per pound is $__________ per pound, which is less than the $0.44 per pound for the smaller bag. (Round to the nearest cent as needed.)
- ○ **C.** The student's solution is incorrect. The student should have converted 44¢ per pound to dollars per pound before writing the exam solution. He should have converted 44¢ cents per pound to $__________ per pound. (Round to the nearest cent as needed.)

ID: 3.3.12

---

* 72. Decide which of the two given prices is the better deal and explain why.

You can buy shampoo in a 6-ounce bottle for $3.89 or in a 15-ounce bottle for $9.49.

Select the correct choice below and, if necessary, fill in the answer box to complete your choice.

- ○ **A.** The 15-ounce bottle is the better deal because the cost per ounce is $__________ per ounce while the 6-ounce bottle is $__________ per ounce.
- ○ **B.** The 6-ounce bottle is the better deal because the cost per ounce is $__________ per ounce while the 15-ounce bottle is $__________ per ounce.

(Round to the nearest cent as needed.)

ID: 3.3.13

---

73. Decide which of the two given prices is the better deal and explain why.

You can fill a 15-gallon tank of gas for $50.85 or buy gas for $3.50/gallon.

Select the correct choice below and, if necessary, fill in the answer box to complete your choice.

- ○ **A.** The better deal is to fill a 15-gallon tank for $50.85 because the price to fill a 15-gallon tank of gas for $50.85 is $__________ per gallon.
- ○ **B.** The better deal is to buy gas for $3.50 / gallon because the price to fill a 15-gallon tank of gas for $50.85 is $__________ per gallon.

(Round to the nearest cent as needed.)

ID: 3.3.14

---

74. You plan to take a 1428-mile trip in your car, which averages 24 miles per gallon. How many gallons of gasoline should you expect to use? Would a car that has only half the gas mileage require twice as much gasoline for the same trip? Explain.

You should expect to use about ____________ gallons of gasoline.
(Type an integer or a decimal.)

Would a car that has only half the gas mileage (12 miles per gallon) require twice as much gasoline for the same trip? Select the correct choice below and fill in the answer box to complete your choice.
(Type an integer or a decimal.)

○ **A.** Yes; the car would use ____________ gallons, which is twice as many gallons.

○ **B.** No; the car would use ____________ gallons, which is not twice as many gallons.

ID: 3.3.15

---

75. Gas mileage actually varies slightly with the driving speed of a car (as well as with highway vs. city driving). Suppose your car averages 33 miles per gallon on the highway if your average speed is 54 miles per hour, and it averages 26 miles per gallon on the highway if your average speed is 69 miles per hour. Answer parts (a) and (b) below.

a. What is the driving time for a 2900-mile trip if you drive at an average speed of 54 miles per hour? What is the driving time at 69 miles per hour?

The driving time at 54 miles per hour is ____________ hours.
(Type an integer or decimal rounded to two decimal places as needed.)

The driving time is at 69 miles per hour is ____________ hours.
(Round to two decimal places as needed.)

b. Assume a gasoline price of $4.67 per gallon. What is the gasoline cost for a 2900-mile trip if you drive at an average speed of 54 miles per hour? What is the gasoline cost at 69 miles per hour?

The gasoline cost at 54 miles per hour is $____________.
(Round to two decimal places as needed.)

The gasoline cost at 69 miles per hour is $____________.
(Round to two decimal places as needed.)

ID: 3.3.16

---

* 76. The Greenland ice sheet contains about 3 million cubic kilometers of ice. If completely melted, this ice would release about 2.6 million cubic kilometers of water, which would spread out over Earth's approximate 336 million square kilometers of ocean surface. How much would the sea level rise?

The sea level would rise ____________ km. (Round to three decimal places as needed.)

ID: 3.3.17

---

77. Assume running consumes 105 Calories per mile. If you run 11-minute miles, what is your average power output, in watts, during a 2-hour run?

Your average power output is ____________ watts. (Round to the nearest whole number as needed.)

ID: 3.3.18

---

78. Your utility company charges 11 cents per kilowatt-hour of electricity. Complete parts (a) and (b) below.

a. What is the daily cost of keeping lit a 100-watt light bulb for 11 hours each day?
b. How much will you save in a year if you replace the bulb with an LED bulb that provides the same amount of light using only 20 watts of power?

a. The daily cost of keeping lit a 100-watt light bulb for 11 hours each day is $____________.
(Round to three decimal places as needed.)

b. The yearly savings of replacing the 100-watt light bulb with a 20-watt light bulb is $____________.
(Round to two decimal places as needed.)

ID: 3.3.19

---

* 79. A cube of wood measures 8 centimeters on a side and weighs 20 grams. Complete parts (a) and (b) below.

a. What is the density of the cube of wood?
b. Will it float in water?

a. The density of the cube of wood is __________ g/cm^3.
(Round to two decimal places as needed.)

b. Will the cube of wood float in water?

- A. The cube will sink since its density is greater than 1 g/cm^3.
- B. The cube will float since its density is greater than 1 g/cm^3.
- C. The cube will float since its density is less than 1 g/cm^3.
- D. The cube will sink since its density is less than 1 g/cm^3.

ID: 3.3.20

---

* 80. Give the density in appropriate units.

The land area of a country is about 2.0 million square miles, and the population is about 700 million people. What is the average population density?

The average population density is __________ people/mi^2.
(Simplify your answer. Round to one decimal place as needed.)

ID: 3.3.21

---

81. In 1900, a certain country's population was 73,131,292 and its area was 2,833,648 square miles. In 2000, the country's population was 288,109,996 and its area was 3,697,297 square miles. Compute the population densities of both years.

The population density in 1900 was __________ people per square mile.
(Round to the nearest whole number as needed.)

The population density in 2000 was __________ people per square mile.
(Round to the nearest whole number as needed.)

ID: 3.3.22

---

* 82. A certain antihistamine is often prescribed for allergies. A typical dose for a 100-pound person is 24 mg every six hours. Complete parts (a) and (b) below.

a. Following this dosage, how many 12.9 mg chewable tablets would be taken in a week?
b. This antihistamine also comes in a liquid form with a concentration of 12.9 mg/10 mL. Following the prescribed dosage, how much liquid antihistamine should a 100-pound person take in a week?

a. A 100-pound person could take __________ tablets in a week.
(Round to the nearest whole number as needed.)

b. A 100-pound person could take __________ mL in a week.
(Round to the nearest whole number as needed.)

ID: 3.3.23

---

83. A typical glass of wine contains about 20 grams of alcohol. Consider a 99-pound woman, with approximately 6 liters (6000 milliliters) of blood, who drinks two glasses of wine. Complete parts (a) and (b) below.

a. If all the alcohol were immediately absorbed into her bloodstream, what would her blood alcohol content be?

__________ $\frac{g}{100\ mL}$ (Round to two decimal places as needed.)

Note that a blood alcohol content (BAC) of 0.08g/100mL is the legal driving limit in the U.S.A. BAC at or above 0.4g/100mL usually leads to coma or death. Explain why it is fortunate that, in reality, the alcohol is not absorbed immediately. Choose the correct answer below.

- A. It is fortunate because any amount of alcohol consumption can impair brain function.
- B. It is fortunate that alcohol is not absorbed immediately because although this blood alcohol content is below the legal limit, it will impair brain function.
- C. It is fortunate that alcohol is not absorbed immediately because this is a lethal concentration of alcohol and is far beyond the legal limit.
- D. It is fortunate that alcohol is not absorbed immediately because this blood alcohol content is above the legal limit for driving and is a dangerous level of intoxication.

83. (cont.) b. Again assume all the alcohol is absorbed immediately, but now assume her body eliminates the alcohol (through metabolism) at a rate of 10 grams per hour. What is her blood alcohol content 3 hours after drinking the wine?

__________ $\frac{\text{g}}{100 \text{ mL}}$ (Round to two decimal places as needed.)

Is it safe for her to drive at this time? Explain.

- ○ **A.** It is safe to drive. Her blood alcohol content is lower than it was three hours ago.
- ○ **B.** It is not safe to drive. This blood alcohol content means she would either be in a coma or possibly dead.
- ○ **C.** It is safe to drive. Although is it above the legal limit, it is still pretty close.
- ○ **D.** It is not safe to drive. This is over the legal limit.

ID: 3.3.24

---

84. Two races that a student runs every year are the 1 mile race in his hometown and the 1490 meter race in his college town. Complete parts (a) through (d) below.

	Student	Other Students
Hometown	7:31:48	8:47:27
College town	6:37:00	7:19:46

a. Complete the sentence.

The college town race is __________ % of the hometown race in length.

b. Consider the student's personal records shown in the table for the two races. What is the student's average speed in each race in miles per hour?

The student's average speed in the hometown race is __________ mi/hr, and the student's average speed in the college town race is __________ mi/hr.
(Round to two decimal places as needed.)

c. What is the average speed in each race in miles per hour for the other students?

The average speed of the other students in the hometown race is __________ mi/hr and the other students' average speed in the college town race is __________ mi/hr.
(Round to two decimal places as needed.)

d. If the average speed for the college town race were run for the entire length of the hometown race, would the student beat his personal record? Would the other students?

- ○ **A.** If the student runs the hometown race at a different average speed from the college town race, he will beat his personal record. If other students run the hometown race at a different average speed from the college town race, they will beat their record time.
- ○ **B.** If the student runs the hometown race at the same average speed as in the college town race, he will not beat his personal record. If other students run the hometown race at the same average speed as in the college town race, they will not beat their record time.
- ○ **C.** If the student runs the hometown race at the same average speed as in the college town race, he will beat his personal record. If other students run the hometown race at the same average speed as in the college town race, they will beat their record time.
- ○ **D.** If the student runs the hometown race at a different average speed from the college town race, he will not beat his personal record. If other students run the hometown race at a different average speed from the college town race, they will not beat their record time.

ID: 3.3.25

---

85. Assume that when you take a bath, you fill a tub to the halfway point. The tub measures 6 feet by 2 feet by 2.2 feet. When you take a shower, you use a shower head with a flow rate of 2.23 gallons per minute, and you typically spend 8 minutes in the shower. There are 7.5 gallons in one cubic foot. Complete parts (a) through (c) below.

a. Do you use more water taking a shower or taking a bath? Choose the correct answer below.

- ○ **A.** Shower; you use __________ more cubic feet of water than taking a bath.
- ○ **B.** Bath; you use __________ more cubic feet of water than you do taking a shower.

(Round to one decimal place as needed.)

b. How long would you need to shower in order to use as much water as you use taking a bath?

You would need to shower for __________ minutes to use as much water as you use taking a bath.
(Round to the nearest whole number.)

85. (cont.) c. Assuming your shower is in a bath tub, propose a non-mathematical way to compare, in one experiment, the amounts of water you use taking a shower and a bath. Choose the correct answer below.

- ○ **A.** Don't drain the water after taking a bath, and then turn on the shower head to see how much of a change there is.
- ○ **B.** Use a stopwatch to time how long it takes to fill a five-gallon bucket with the shower head.
- ○ **C.** Put the plug in the drain when taking a shower.
- ○ **D.** Only take showers for one month, and then check the water bill at the end of the month.

ID: 3.3.26

---

86. A lake in a certain country has a volume of approximately 2819 cubic kilometers, and its surface area is 67,859 square kilometers. Complete parts (a) through (c) below.

a. What is the average depth of the lake (the depth of a box with the volume and surface area of the lake)?

__________ km
(Round to three decimal places as needed.)

b. In the past six years, the water level of the lake has dropped 13 feet from the depth computed in part (a). Approximately how much water has the lake lost?

Therefore, the lake lost __________ km^3 of water.
(Round to the nearest whole number as needed.)

c. What percentage of the volume has been lost?

The percentage of volume that has been lost is __________ %.
(Round to the nearest whole number as needed.)

ID: 3.3.27

---

87. A particular dam contains approximately 1,500,000,000,000 cubic feet of water. For a week-long spike flood, water was released at a rate of 26,000 cubic feet per second.

a. How much water was released during the flood?
b. What percentage of the dam was released during the flood?

a. The amount of water released during the week-long flood was __________ (1) __________
(Simplify your answer.)

b. __________ % of the dam was released during the flood.
(Type an integer or decimal rounded to the nearest hundredth as needed.)

(1)
- ○ feet per second.
- ○ cubic feet per second.
- ○ feet.
- ○ square feet per second.
- ○ square feet.
- ○ cubic feet.

ID: 3.3.28

---

*88. A 13% dextrous solution (13 mg per 100 mL of solution) is given intravenously. Suppose a total of 3.474 L of the solution is given over a 18-hour period. Complete parts (a) through (c) below.

a. What is the flow rate in units of mL/hr?

__________ mL/hr (Type an integer or decimal rounded to the nearest thousandth as needed.)

What is the flow rate in dextrous per hour?

__________ mg/hr (Type an integer or decimal rounded to the nearest thousandth as needed.)

b. If each mL contains 13 drops (the drop factor is expressed as 13 ggt/mL), what is the flow rate in units of ggt/hr?

__________ ggt/hr (Type an integer or decimal rounded to the nearest thousandth as needed.)

c. During the 18-hour period, how much dextrous is delivered?

__________ mg (Type an integer or decimal rounded to the nearest thousandth as needed.)

ID: 3.3.29

---

89. A solution consisting of 255 mg of dopamine in 15 mL of solution is administered at a rate of 4 ml/hr. Complete parts (a) and (b) below.

a. What is the flow rate in mg of dopamine per hour?

__________ mg/hr (Type an integer or decimal rounded to the nearest thousandth as needed.)

b. If a patient is prescribed to receive 272 mg of dopamine, how long should the infusion last?

__________ hour(s) (Type an integer or decimal rounded to the nearest thousandth as needed.)

ID: 3.3.30

---

90. A doctor administers a drug to a 36-kg patient, using a dosage formula of 45 mg/kg/day. Assume that the drug is available in a 100 mg per 5 mL suspension or in 500 mg tablets.

a. How many tablets should a 36-kg patient take every four hours?
b. The suspension with a drop factor of 10 ggt/mL delivers the drug intravenously to the patient over a twelve-hour period. What flow rate should be used in units of ggt/hr?

a. The patient should take __________ pills every four hours.
(Type an integer or decimal rounded to the nearest hundredth as needed.)

b. The intravenous suspension flow should be set to __________ ggt/hour.
(Type an integer or decimal rounded to the nearest hundredth as needed.)

ID: 3.3.31

---

91. In May you used 1100 kilowatt-hours of energy for electricity.
a. Calculate the total electrical energy use in joules.
b. Calculate your average power use in watts.
c. Assume that your power supplier generates electricity by burning oil. Note that 1 liter of oil releases 12 million joules of energy. How much oil is needed to generate the electricity you use? Give your answer in both liters and gallons.

a. The total electrical energy use was __________ joules.
(Type an integer or a decimal.)

b. The average power use is __________ watts.
(Round to the nearest whole number as needed.)

c. To generate the electricity you used, __________ L is needed.
(Round to the nearest whole number as needed.)

To generate the electricity you used, __________ gal is needed.
(Round to two decimal places as needed.)

ID: 3.3.32

---

92. An outdoor spa (hot tub) draws 1486 watts to keep the water warm. If the utility company charges $0.11 per kilowatt-hour, how much does it cost to operate the spa for four months during the winter (24 hours per day)? Assume each month has 30 days.

It costs $__________ to operate the spa for four months during the winter.
(Round to the nearest whole number as needed.)

ID: 3.3.33

---

93. A new coal-burning power plant can generate 2.3 gigawatts (billion watts) of power. Burning 1 kilogram of coal yields about 450 kilowatt-hours of energy. Complete parts (a), (b), and (c) below.

a. How much energy, in kilowatt-hours, can the plant generate each month?

The plant can generate __________ million kilowatt-hours of energy each month.
(Type an integer.)

b. How much coal, in kilograms, is needed by this power plant each month?

The plant needs __________ million kilograms of coal each month.
(Round to one decimal place as needed.)

c. If a typical home uses 1002 kilowatts-hours per month, how many homes can this power plant supply with energy?

This power plant can supply __________ homes with energy.
(Round to the nearest whole number.)

ID: 3.3.34

---

94. Solar (photovoltaic) cells convert sunlight directly into electricity. If solar cells were 100% efficient, they would generate about 1000 watts of power per square meter of surface area when exposed to direct sunlight. With lower efficiency, they generate proportionally less power. For example, 10% efficient cells generate 100 watts of power in direct sunlight.

Suppose a 1-square-meter panel of solar cells has an efficiency of 30% and receives the equivalent of 6 hours of direct sunlight per day. How much energy, in joules, can it produce each day? What average power, in watts, does the panel produce?

How much energy, in joules, can the solar panel produce each day? Give the value in millions of joules per day.

__________ million joules per day
(Type an integer or decimal rounded to two decimal places as needed.)

What average power, in watts, does the panel produce in a day?

__________ watts
(Type an integer or decimal rounded to one decimal place as needed.)

ID: 3.3.35

---

95. Solar (photovoltaic) cells convert sunlight directly into electricity. If solar cells were 100% efficient, they would generate about 1000 watts of power per square meter of surface area when exposed to direct sunlight. With lower efficiency, they generate proportionally less power. For example, 10% efficient cells generate 100 watts of power in direct sunlight. Suppose you want to supply 1 kilowatt of power to a house by putting solar panels on its roof. For solar cells with the average power of 20 watts per square meter of solar panels, how many square meters of solar panels would you need? Assume you can make use of the average power from the solar cells (by, for example, storing energy in batteries until it is needed).

You would need __________ square meters of solar panels.
(Round to the nearest integer as needed.)

ID: 3.3.36

---

96. A certain region currently has wind farms capable of generating a total of 2700 megawatts (2.7 gigawatts) of power. Complete parts (a) and (b) below.

a. Assuming wind farms typically generate 25% of their capacity, how much energy, in kilowatt-hours, can the region's wind farms generate in one year? Given that the average household in the region uses about 10,000 kilowatt-hours of energy each year, how many households can be powered by these wind farms?

The wind farms can generate __________ kilowatt-hours in one year.
(Simplify your answer.)

The wind farms can power __________ households.
(Simplify your answer.)

b. One of the great advantages of wind power is that it does not produce the carbon dioxide emissions that contribute to global warming. On average, energy produced from fossil fuels generates about 1.5 pounds of carbon dioxide for every kilowatt-hour of energy. Suppose the region did not have its wind farms and the energy were instead produced from fossil fuels. How much more carbon dioxide would be entering the atmosphere each year?

__________ lbs
(Simplify your answer.)

ID: 3.3.37

---

97. A large stand of fir trees occupies 29 hectares. The trees have an average density of 1 tree per 25 m^2. A forester estimates that each tree will yield 300 board-feet. Estimate the yield of the stand if one-tenth of the trees are cut.

The stand will yield __________ (1) __________
(Simplify your answer.)

(1) ○ board-feet. ○ m^2.
○ trees.
○ hectares.
○ m.

ID: 3.3.38

---

98. Choose the best answer to the following question. Explain your reasoning with one or more complete sentences.
To end up with units of speed, what do you need to do?

Choose the correct answer below.

- A. Divide a distance by a time because the units of speed are set up as the units of distance over the units of time.
- B. Multiply a distance by a time because the units of speed are set up as the units of distance times the units of time.
- C. Divide a time by a distance because the units of speed are set up as the units of time over the units of distance.
- D. Divide a time by a distance because one of the variations of the speed formula is d/t.
- E. Divide a distance by a time and then multiply by 100 because it is a ratio of distance to time.
- F. Multiply a distance by a time because one of the variations of the speed formula is $d \cdot t$.

ID: 3.3.39

---

99. Choose the best answer to the following question. Explain your reasoning with one or more complete sentences.
You are given two pieces of information, (1) the price of gasoline in dollars per gallon and (2) the gas mileage of a car in miles per gallon. You are asked to find the cost of driving this car in dollars per mile. What should you do?

Choose the correct answer below.

- A. Divide the car's gas mileage by the price of gas because gallons must not appear in either the numerator or denominator of the resulting units.
- B. Divide the car's gas mileage by the price of gas because dividing by the price of gas will leave dollars in the numerator and miles in the denominator.
- C. Multiply the price of gas by the car's gas mileage because unit conversions should be completed using multiplication, not division.
- D. Multiply the price of gas by the car's gas mileage because dividing by a fraction is the same as multiplying by its reciprocal.
- E. Divide the price of gas by the car's gas mileage because dividing by gas mileage will leave miles in the numerator and dollars in the denominator.
- F. Divide the price of gas by the car's gas mileage because division will remove the units of gallons, leaving only units of dollars and miles in the answer.

ID: 3.3.40

---

100. Choose the best answer to the following question. Explain your reasoning with one or more complete sentences.
You want to know how much total energy is required to operate a 100-watt light bulb. Do you need any more information?

Choose the correct answer below.

- A. Yes; you need to know the temperature of the light bulb when it is on because energy is what makes matter heat up.
- B. Yes; you need to know how long the light bulb is on because time is needed to find power when given an amount of energy.
- C. No; the energy can be determined because watts are related to kilowatt-hours, and kilowatt-hours are a unit of energy.
- D. Yes; you need to know how long the light bulb is on because power is the rate at which energy is used, and watts are units of power.
- E. Yes; you need to know the temperature of the light bulb when it is on because the light bulb does not require energy if it is cold.
- F. No; watts are a unit of energy, so the energy required is given.

ID: 3.3.41

---

101. Choose the best answer to the following question. Explain your reasoning with one or more complete sentences.
The concentration of carbon dioxide in Earth's atmosphere might be stated in which units?

Choose the correct answer below.

- A. Grams per meter may be used because grams can describe the amount of carbon dioxide and meters can describe a height into the atmosphere.
- B. Parts per million may be used because there are millions of carbon dioxide molecules in the atmosphere.
- C. Joules per watt may be used because a unit divided by its corresponding rate gives concentration.
- D. Grams per meter may be used because when looking at a region of air with dimensions of 1 meter, grams describes the mass of material in that region.
- E. Joules per watt may be used because carbon dioxide is used in lightbulbs.
- F. Parts per million may be used because it gives the number of molecules of carbon dioxide in a million molecules of air.

ID: 3.3.42

---

102. Choose the best answer to the following question. Explain your reasoning with one or more complete sentences.

What does a blood alcohol content (BAC) of 0.08 gm/100 mL mean?

Choose the correct answer below.

- A. A person with 4 liters of blood has $0.08 \times 40 = 3.2$ grams of alcohol in his blood because $\frac{0.08\text{ g} \times 40}{100\text{ mL} \times 40} = \frac{3.2\text{ g}}{4\text{ L}}$.
- B. A person with 4 liters of blood has $0.08 \times 40 = 3.2$ grams of alcohol in his blood because 0.08 represents the number of grams of alcohol in a liter of blood, and that needs to be increased by a factor of 40.
- C. A person with 4 liters of blood has $\frac{0.08}{40} = 0.002$ grams of alcohol in his blood because 4 L is 40 times as much as 100 mL.
- D. A person with 4 liters of blood has $\frac{0.08}{4} = 0.02$ grams of alcohol in his blood because dividing the grams of alcohol by the number of liters yields grams per liter.

ID: 3.3.43

---

103. Use the table to express the 1994 fatality rate in deaths per 100 million vehicle-miles traveled.

Year	Population (millions)	Traffic fatalities	Licensed drivers (millions)	Vehicle miles (trillions)
1989	242	40,563	160	1.8
1994	289	40,103	187	2.6
2003	295	40,159	196	3.1

The 1994 fatality rate is ________ deaths per 100 million vehicle-miles.
(Round to the nearest tenth as needed.)

ID: 3.3.44

---

104. Use the table to express the 1994 fatality rate in deaths per 100,000 licensed drivers.

Year	Population (millions)	Traffic fatalities	Licensed drivers (millions)	Vehicle miles (trillions)
1983	245	42,331	164	1.5
1994	283	42,022	180	2.3
2000	307	31,078	203	3.2

The 1994 fatality rate is ________ deaths per 100,000 licensed drivers.
(Round to the nearest tenth as needed.)

ID: 3.3.45

---

105. The table below shows the number of accidents, fatalities, and hours flown for a country's general aviation (non-commercial, personal, corporate, and instructional flights). Compute the accident rate per 100,000 flight hours in 2006 and 2012. By this measure, has general aviation become safer?

Year	Accidents	Fatalities	Hours Flown (millions)
2006	1525	708	24.1
2008	1573	481	22.1
2012	1372	452	20.1

Select the correct choice below and fill in any answer boxes within your choice.
(Round to the nearest tenth as needed.)

- A. General aviation has not become safer because the accident rate in 2006, ________ accidents per 100,000 flight hours, is lower than the accident rate in 2012, ________ accidents per 100,000 flight hours.
- B. General aviation has become safer because the accident rate in 2006, ________ accidents per 100,000 flight hours, is higher than the accident rate in 2012, ________ accidents per 100,000 flight hours.

ID: 3.3.46

---

106. The table shows the leading causes of death in a certain country in a recent year. The population of the country was 319 million. What is the empirical probability of death by chronic respiratory diseases during a single year? How much greater is the risk of death by chronic respiratory diseases than death by kidney disease?

Cause	Deaths
Heart disease	596,300
Cancer	575,600
Chronic respiratory diseases	143,800
Stroke	128,200
Accidents	122,500

Cause	Deaths
Alzheimer's disease	84,500
Diabetes	73,700
Pneumonia/Influenza	53,700
Kidney disease	45,500
Suicide	38,800

The empirical probability of death by chronic respiratory diseases during a single year is __________.
(Round to five decimal places as needed.)

The risk of death by chronic respiratory diseases is about __________ times greater than risk by death of kidney disease.
(Round to one decimal place as needed.)

ID: 3.3.47

107. The table shows the leading causes of death in a certain country in a recent year. The population of the country was 319 million. What was the death rate due to cancer in deaths per 10,000 of the population of the country?

Cause	Deaths
Heart disease	596,600
Cancer	575,500
Chronic respiratory diseases	143,600
Stroke	128,300
Accidents	122,300

Cause	Deaths
Alzheimer's disease	84,500
Diabetes	73,800
Pneumonia/Influenza	53,900
Kidney disease	45,200
Suicide	38,800

There were about __________ deaths from cancer per 10,000 people.
(Round to the nearest tenth as needed.)

ID: 3.3.48

108. The table shows the leading causes of death in a certain country in a recent year. The population of the country was 311 million. If you lived in a typical city of 500,000, how many people would you expect to die of kidney disease each year?

Cause	Deaths
Heart disease	596,500
Cancer	575,400
Chronic respiratory diseases	143,200
Stroke	128,100
Accidents	122,500

Cause	Deaths
Alzheimer's disease	84,100
Diabetes	73,300
Pneumonia/Influenza	53,700
Kidney disease	45,400
Suicide	38,900

About __________ people would be expected to die of kidney disease each year.
(Type a whole number. Round to the nearest person as needed.)

ID: 3.3.49

* 109. Use the graph to estimate the death rate for 55-year-olds. Assuming that there were about 11.6 million 55-year-olds, how many people of this age could be expected to die in a year?

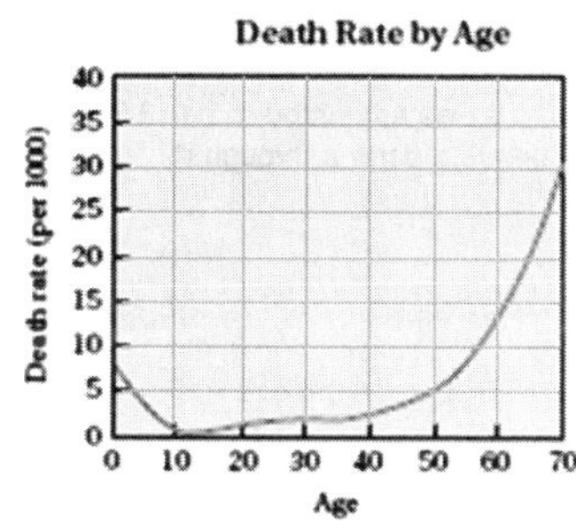

The estimated death rate for 55-year-olds is __________ deaths per 1000 people.
(Round to the nearest whole number as needed.)

Assuming that there were about 11.6 million 55-year-olds, __________ people of this age could be expected to die in a year.
(Simplify your answer.)

ID: 3.3.50

110. Use the graph to determine to what age the average 80-year-old could expect to live.

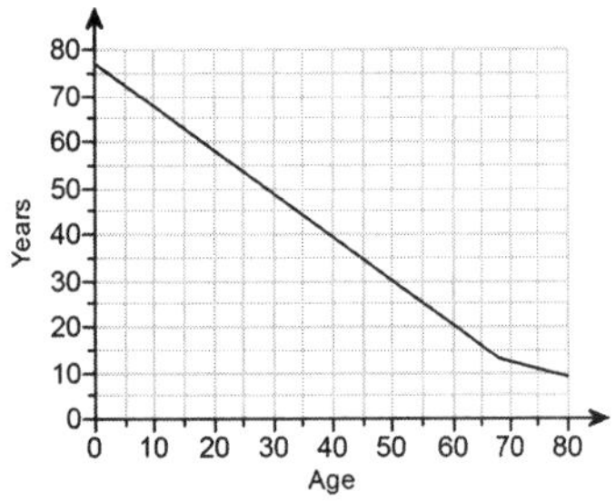

The average 80-year-old could expect to live to ________ years of age.

ID: 3.3.51

---

111. Suppose that a life insurance company insures 1,300,000 fifty-year-old people in a given year. (Assume a death rate of 4 per 1000 people.) The cost of the premium is $500 per year, and the death benefit is $60,000. What is the expected profit or loss for the insurance company?

The insurance company can expect a(n) $ ________ million (1) ________

(Type an integer or decimal rounded to one decimal place as needed.)

(1) ○ loss.
○ profit.

ID: 3.3.52

---

112. In a certain country, the life expectancy for women in 1900 was 45 years and in 2000 it was 82 years. Assuming that life expectancy between 2000 and 2100 increases by the same percentage as it did between 1900 and 2000, what will the life expectancy be for women in 2100?

Assuming the life expectancy between 2000 and 2100 will increase by the same percentage as it did between 1900 and 2000, the life expectancy for women in 2100 will be ________ years.

(Round to the nearest integer as needed.)

ID: 3.3.53

---

113. Country A reported 46,485 births for a year (assume 365 days) with a population of about 2.9 million people. Country B reported 11,959 births with a population of about 1.5 million people.

a. How many people were born each day of the year in Country A?
b. How many people were born each day of the year in Country B?
c. What was the birth rate in Country A in births per 1000 people?
d. What was the birth rate in Country B in births per 1000 people?

a. There were ________ people born each day of the year in Country A.
(Round to the nearest whole number as needed.)

b. There were ________ people born each day of the year in Country B.
(Round to the nearest whole number as needed.)

c. The birth rate in Country A was ________ births per 1000 people.
(Round to the nearest tenth as needed.)

d. The birth rate in Country B was ________ births per 1000 people.
(Round to the nearest tenth as needed.)

ID: 3.3.54

---

114. In a certain year the population of a country reached 300 million. The overall birth rate was estimated to be 13.8 births per 1,000, and the overall death rate was estimated to be 8.5 deaths per 1,000. Complete parts **a** through **d**.

a. Approximately how many births were there in the country?

________ (Simplify your answer. Type an integer or a decimal.)

b. About how many deaths were there in the country?

________ (Simplify your answer. Type an integer or a decimal.)

c. Based on births and deaths alone (that is, not counting immigration and emigration), about how much did the population rise during that year?

________ (Simplify your answer. Type an integer or a decimal.)

114. (cont.) **d.** Ignoring immigration and emigration, what is the rate (in decimal form) of population growth of the country in that year?

___________ (Simplify your answer. Type an integer or a decimal.)

What is the population growth rate expressed as a percentage?

___________ % (Simplify your answer. Type an integer or a decimal.)

ID: 3.3.55

---

115. Each year there are approximately 3 million births in a country, of which 114,000 are twin births (that is, $2 \times 114{,}000$ babies), 3800 are triplet births, and 300 are quadruplet births. Assume that births of five or more babies in one delivery are negligible in number. Complete parts (a)–(c) below.

a. What is the approximate probability that an expectant mother will give birth to more than one baby? Assume that multiple births are randomly distributed in the population.

The probability is approximately ___________.
(Do not round until the final answer. Then round to three decimal places as needed.)

b. What is the approximate probability that a randomly selected newborn is a twin? (Remember that there are two babies for each twin birth.)

The probability is approximately ___________.
(Do not round until the final answer. Then round to three decimal places as needed.)

c. What is the approximate probability that a randomly selected newborn is a twin, a triplet, or a quadruplet?

The probability is approximately ___________.
(Do not round until the final answer. Then round to three decimal places as needed.)

ID: 3.3.56

---

116. There are approximately 3.8 million deaths per year in country A. Express this quantity as deaths per minute.

In country A, there are ___________ deaths/min.
(Type an integer or decimal rounded to one decimal place as needed.)

ID: 3.3.57

---

117. Restate the following fact as indicated.

Approximately 31,700 citizens of a country died in automobile accidents in 2012. Express this toll in deaths per day.

There were approximately ___________ deaths per day due to automobile accidents.
(Round to the nearest whole number as needed.)

ID: 3.3.58

---

118. Restate the following fact as indicated.

In 2012, there were approximately 32,300 firearm fatalities (homicides and suicides). Express this quantity in deaths per hour.

There were approximately ___________ deaths/hour due to firearm fatalities in 2012.
(Round to one decimal place as needed.)

ID: 3.3.59

---

119. A country's people consume 6.3 billion pounds of candy (excluding chewing gum) per year. Express this quantity in terms of pounds per person per month. Note that the population of the country is 308 million.

The amount of candy consumed is approximately ___________ pounds per person per month.
(Type an integer or decimal rounded to the nearest tenth as needed.)

ID: 3.3.60

---

120. Estimates of the number of cells in the human body vary over an order of magnitude. Indeed, the precise number varies from one individual to another and depends on whether you count bacterial cells. Complete parts (a) through (c) below.

a. Assume that an average cell has a diameter of 7 micrometers (7×10^{-6} meter), which means it has a volume of 200 cubic micrometers. How many cells are there in a cubic centimeter?

___________ cells per cm^3

(Use scientific notation. Use the multiplication symbol in the math palette as needed. Round to two decimal places as needed.)

b. Estimate the number of cells in a liter, using the fact that a cubic centimeter equals a milliliter.

___________ cells per liter

(Use scientific notation. Use the multiplication symbol in the math palette as needed. Round to two decimal places as needed.)

c. Estimate the number of cells in a(n) 77-kilogram (170-pound) person, assuming the human body is 100% water (actually it is 60–70% water) and that 1 liter of water weighs 1 kilogram.

___________ cells per person

(Use scientific notation. Use the multiplication symbol in the math palette as needed. Round to two decimal places as needed.)

ID: 3.3.61

---

* 121. An issue of a magazine contained the following statement.

> Dropping less than two inches per mile after emerging from the mountains, a river drains into the ocean. One day's discharge at its mouth, 3.6 trillion gallons, could supply all of country A's households for three months.

Based on this statement, determine how much water an average household uses each month. Assume that there are 300 million households in country A.

Country A uses approximately ___________ gallons per household per month.

(Type a whole number.)

ID: 3.3.62

---

122. A white dwarf is a type of remnant star that will have about the same mass as the star did, but its radius will be much smaller. A certain white dwarf has a mass of 4×10^{30} kg and a radius of about 6200 km.
a. Calculate the average density of the white dwarf in units of kilograms per cubic centimeter.
b.What is the mass of a teaspoon of a material from a white dwarf? (A teaspoon is about 4 cubic centimeters.) Compare this to the mass of something familiar.
c. A neutron star is a type of stellar remnant compressed to even greater densities than a white dwarf. Suppose that a neutron star has a mass 1.6 times greater than the mass of the white dwarf, but has a radius of only 15 kilometers. What is its density? Compare the mass of 1 cubic centimeter of a neutron star to the total mass of Mount Everest (about 5×10^{10} kg).

a. Calculate the density of the white dwarf using the formulas shown below.

$D = \frac{m}{v}$, where D is density, m is mass, and v is volume

$v = \frac{4}{3}\pi r^3$, where v is the volume of a sphere and r is the radius of the white dwarf

The average density of the white dwarf is about ___________ kilograms per cubic centimeter.

(Round to the nearest whole number as needed.)

b. The mass of a teaspoon of white dwarf material is about ___________ kilograms.

(Round to the nearest whole number as needed.)

The mass of a teaspoon of white dwarf material is most comparable to the mass of (1) ___________

c. Calculate the density of the neutron star using the formulas shown below.

$D = \frac{m}{v}$, where D is density, m is mass, and v is volume

$v = \frac{4}{3}\pi r^3$, where v is the volume of a sphere and r is the radius of the neutron star

The density of the neutron star is about ___________ kilograms per cubic centimeter.

(Use scientific notation. Use the multiplication symbol in the math palette as needed. Round to the nearest whole number as needed.)

122. (cont.) Is the mass of one cubic centimeter of neutron star material more or less than the total mass of Mount Everest?

○ More (1) ○ a person.
○ Less ○ a car.
○ a tank.
○ a cat.

ID: 3.3.63

---

123. An organization estimated that in a particular year the population of a country spent \$11.4 trillion in personal consumption. The major categories of these expenditures are durable goods (\$1.7 trillion; for example, cars, furniture, recreational equipment), nondurable goods (\$2.8 trillion; for example, food, clothing, fuel), and services (\$6.6 trillion; for example, health care, education, transportation). Complete parts (a) through (e) below.

a. What is the approximate annual per capita spending for personal consumption? Assume a population of 330 million.

\$ ________ /person/yr
(Round to the nearest dollar as needed.)

b. What is the approximate daily per capita spending for personal consumption?

\$ ________ /person/day
(Round to the nearest dollar as needed.)

c. On average about what percentage of personal spending is devoted to services?

________ %
(Round to the nearest percent as needed.)

d. Spending on health care was estimated to be \$1.3 trillion in that year. About what percentage of all personal spending is devoted to health care?

________ %
(Round to the nearest percent as needed.)

e. Ten years earlier, the total spending on personal consumption was \$7.3 trillion, while health care spending was \$731 billion. Compare the percentage increase in total spending and health care spending over the decade.

The percentage increase in total spending was ________ %, while the percentage increase in health care spending was ________ %. The percentage increase for (1) ________ was greater.
(Round to the nearest percent as needed.)

(1) ○ health care spending
○ total spending

ID: 3.3.64

!* 1. A dosage of 0.2 g of an epilepsy treatment medication is ordered to be given through a nasogastric tube. The medication is available as 42 mg per 6 mL. Complete parts **a** through **c**.

Recall that 1000 mg = 1 g.

a) What is the dosage in mg?

________ mg (Type an integer or a decimal.)

b) What is the concentration in mg per mL?

________ mg/mL (Type an integer or a decimal.)

c) How many mL should be administered?

________ mL (Type an integer or a decimal rounded to two decimal places as needed.)

ID: 3.4.1

!* 2. An anti-inflammatory drug at a dosage of 1.7 mg/kg is ordered for a child weighing 79.2 lbs. The drug is available at a concentration of 120 mg/3 mL. Complete parts **a** through **c**.

Recall that 2.2 lbs = 1 kg.

a) What is the child's weight in kg?

________ kg (Type an integer or a decimal.)

b) What is the dosage in milligrams for this child?

________ mg (Type an integer or a decimal.)

c) How many mL should be administered to the child?

________ mL (Round to three decimal places as needed.)

ID: 3.4.2

!* 3. A nurse is given instructions to give a nitroglycerin drip at 10 mcg/minute. The nitroglycerin is mixed at 60 mg per 600 mL. The flow rate needs to be in mL/hr. Complete parts **a** through **c**.

Recall that 1000 mcg = 1 mg.

a) What is the dosage in milligrams per minute (mg/min)?

___________ mg/min (Type an integer or a decimal.)

b) What is the dosage in milligrams per hour, mg/hr?

___________ mg/hr (Type an integer or a decimal.)

c) How many milliliters per hour, ml/hr, should be administered?

___________ mL/hr (Type an integer or a decimal.)

ID: 3.4.3

---

4. For a water rate of $1.55 per 1000 gallons of water used, what is the water bill if a resident uses 38,100 gallons?

The water bill is $___________.
(Round to the nearest cent.)

ID: 3.4.4

---

5. A nurse must administer 240 micrograms of atropine sulfate. The drug is available in solution form. The concentration of the atropine sulfate solution is 200 micrograms per milliliter. How many milliliters should be given?

___________ milliliters of the atropine sulfate solution should be given.
(Simplify your answer.)

ID: 3.4.5

---

6. Insulin comes in 10 cubic centimeter (cc) vials labeled in the number of units of insulin per cubic centimeter of fluid. A vial marked U40 has 40 units of insulin per cubic centimeter of fluid. If a patient needs 29 units of insulin, how much fluid should be drawn into the syringe from the U40 vial?

The amount of fluid containing 29 units of insulin is ___________ cc.
(Type an integer or a decimal.)

ID: 3.4.6

---

7. Fill in the blank with an appropriate word, phrase, or symbol.

Cubic meters, m^3, are a measure of ______.

Cubic meters, m^3, are a measure of (1) ___________

(1) ○ volume.
○ area.
○ length.

ID: 3.4.7

---

8. Fill in the blank with an appropriate word, phrase, or symbol.

Hectares, ha, are a measure of ______.

Hectares, ha, are a measure of (1) ___________

(1) ○ volume.
○ area.
○ length.

ID: 3.4.8

---

9. Fill in the blank with an appropriate word, phrase, or symbol.

Meters, m, are a measure of _______.

Meters, m, are a measure of (1) _____________

(1) ○ volume.
○ length.
○ area.

ID: 3.4.9

---

10. Fill in the blank with an appropriate word, phrase, or symbol.

Kiloliters, kL, are a measure of _______.

Kiloliters, kL, are a measure of (1) _____________

(1) ○ length.
○ area.
○ volume.

ID: 3.4.10

---

11. Fill in the blank with an appropriate word, phrase, or symbol.

Cubic centimeters, cm^3, are a measure of _______.

Cubic centimeters, cm^3, are a measure of (1) _____________

(1) ○ area.
○ volume.
○ length.

ID: 3.4.11

---

12. Fill in the blank with an appropriate word, phrase, or symbol.

Centiliters, cL, are a measure of _______.

Centiliters, cL, are a measure of (1) _____________

(1) ○ length.
○ volume.
○ area.

ID: 3.4.12

---

13. Indicate the metric unit of measurement that you would use to express the following.
the diameter of a pizza

Choose the correct answer below.

○ km
○ cm
○ mm
○ m

ID: 3.4.13

---

* 14. Indicate the metric unit of measurement that you would use to express the following.
The thickness of a cat's tooth

Choose the correct answer below.

○ km
○ cm
○ mm
○ m

ID: 3.4.14

---

15. Indicate the metric unit of measurement that you would use to express the following.

    The distance between two lakes

    Choose the correct answer below.

    ○ **A.** km
    ○ **B.** mm
    ○ **C.** m
    ○ **D.** cm

    ID: 3.4.15

---

16. A building is about how tall?

    Choose the correct answer below.

    ○ 350 km
    ○ 350 m
    ○ 350 cm

    ID: 3.4.16

---

17. Ted is driving near Tokyo and sees a road sign which gives the distance to the city. Choose the most reasonable measurement.

    Choose the correct answer below.

    ○ 19 cm
    ○ 19 mm
    ○ 19 km

    ID: 3.4.17

---

*18. The diameter of a coffee cup is about how long?

    Choose the correct answer below.

    ○ 8 mm
    ○ 8 m
    ○ 8 cm

    ID: 3.4.18

---

19. An auditorium is about how tall?

    Choose the correct answer below.

    ○ 25 km
    ○ 25 cm
    ○ 25 m

    ID: 3.4.19

---

20. Estimate the length of a car in metric units.

    Choose the correct answer below.

    ○ **A.** 0.5 m
    ○ **B.** 5 km
    ○ **C.** 0.5 cm
    ○ **D.** 50 km
    ○ **E.** 50 m
    ○ **F.** 5 m

    ID: 3.4.20

---

21. Indicate the metric unit of measurement you would use to express the area of a kitchen table.

    Choose the correct answer below.

    ○ Cubic kilometers
    ○ Square kilometers
    ○ Cubic meters
    ○ Square meters

    ID: 3.4.21

---

22. Indicate the metric unit of measurement you would use to express the area of a sheet of paper.

Choose the correct answer below.

- ◯ Square kilometers
- ◯ Cubic kilometers
- ◯ Cubic centimeters
- ◯ Square centimeters

ID: 3.4.22

---

* 23. Indicate the metric unit of measurement you would use to express the area of a pen cap.

Choose the correct answer below.

- ◯ Square centimeters or square millimeters
- ◯ Cubic centimeters
- ◯ Square kilometers
- ◯ Square centimeters or square meters

ID: 3.4.23

---

24. Indicate the metric unit of measurement you would use to express the area of the Yukon Territory.

Choose the correct answer below.

- ◯ Square millimeters
- ◯ Square kilometers
- ◯ Cubic millimeters
- ◯ Cubic kilometers

ID: 3.4.24

---

25. What is the approximate area of a business envelope?

Choose the correct answer below.

- ◯ $240\ km^2$
- ◯ $240\ cm^2$
- ◯ $240\ mm^2$

ID: 3.4.25

---

26. What is the approximate area of a bed sheet?

Choose the correct answer below.

- ◯ $7\ mm^2$
- ◯ $7\ km^2$
- ◯ $7\ m^2$

ID: 3.4.26

---

* 27. What is the approximate area of a playground?

Choose the correct answer below.

- ◯ **A.** $\frac{4}{5}$ ha
- ◯ **B.** $\frac{4}{5}\ m^2$
- ◯ **C.** $\frac{4}{5}\ km^2$

ID: 3.4.27

---

28. What is the approximate area of one side of a postage stamp?

Choose the correct answer below.

- ○ **A.** 5 cm^2
- ○ **B.** 5 mm^2
- ○ **C.** 5 km^2

ID: 3.4.28

---

29. The area of a county fairgrounds is about how big?

Choose the correct answer below..

- ○ **A.** 2 m^2
- ○ **B.** 2 cm^2
- ○ **C.** 2 km^2

ID: 3.4.29

---

30. Estimate the area of a $20 bill in metric units.

Choose the correct answer below.

- ○ **A.** 105 cm^2
- ○ **B.** 1050 cm^2
- ○ **C.** 10.5 cm^2
- ○ **D.** 1050 m^2
- ○ **E.** 105 mm^2
- ○ **F.** 105 m^2

ID: 3.4.30

---

31. Determine the metric unit that would best be used to measure the volume of liquid in a small cylinder.

Choose the correct answer below.

- ○ Milliliters
- ○ Kiloliters
- ○ Millimeters
- ○ Kilometers

ID: 3.4.31

---

*32. Determine the metric unit that would best be used to measure the volume of a large trash can.

Choose the correct answer below.

- ○ Milliliters
- ○ Kilometers
- ○ Millimeters
- ○ Liters

ID: 3.4.32

---

33. Determine the metric unit that would best be used to measure the volume of a barrel.

Choose the correct answer below.

- ○ Kilometers
- ○ Cubic millimeters
- ○ Cubic meters
- ○ Meters

ID: 3.4.33

---

34. Choose the best answer to indicate the volume of a tube of super glue.

The volume of a tube of super glue is about how much?

- ○ 30 mm^3
- ○ 30 cm^3
- ○ 30 dm^3

ID: 3.4.34

---

*35. You bought a bottle of juice at the store. Choose the most reasonable measurement for its contents.

Choose the correct answer below.

- ○ 0.28 kL
- ○ 0.28 L
- ○ 0.28 mL

ID: 3.4.35

---

36. Choose the best answer to indicate the volume of a carry-on suitcase.

The volume of a carry-on suitcase is about how much?

- ○ 0.04 cm^3
- ○ 0.04 m^3
- ○ 0.04 mm^3

ID: 3.4.36

---

37. Estimate the volume in metric units and compute the actual volume of air in the cardboard box that is 51 cm long, 60 cm wide, and 57 cm tall. (Use V = LWH.)

The exact volume of air in the cardboard box is ___________ cm^3.

ID: 3.4.37

---

38. Compute the volume of oil in a barrel that has a height of 10 m and a diameter of 0.5 m.

The volume of oil in the barrel is about ___________ m^3.
(Type an integer or a decimal rounded to two decimal places as needed.)

ID: 3.4.38

---

39. One liter of liquid has the equivalent volume of which of the following: a cubic centimeter, a cubic decimeter, or a cubic meter?

One liter of liquid has the equivalent volume of (1) ___________

(1) ○ a cubic decimeter.
○ a cubic centimeter.
○ a cubic meter.

ID: 3.4.39

---

40. One milliliter of liquid has the equivalent volume of which of the following: a cubic centimeter, a cubic decimeter, or a cubic meter?

One milliliter of liquid has the equivalent volume of (1) ___________

(1) ○ a cubic centimeter.
○ a cubic meter.
○ a cubic decimeter.

ID: 3.4.40

---

41. A house 31 m by 9 m is surrounded by a walkway 1.7 m wide.

a) Find the area of the region covered by the house and the walkway.
b) Find the area of the walkway.

a) The area of the region covered by the building and the walkway is ___________ m^2.
(Round to the nearest whole number as needed.)

b) The area of the walkway is ___________ m^2.
(Round to the nearest whole number as needed.)

ID: 3.4.41

---

*42. Mr. Hershman has purchased a farm that is in the shape of a rectangle. The dimensions of the piece of land are 2.7 km by 3.06 km. How many square kilometers did he buy, and how many hectares did he purchase?

How many square kilometers of land did he purchase?

___________ km^2

If 1 km^2 equals 100 ha, how many hectares did he purchase?

___________ ha

ID: 3.4.42

---

43. A swimming pool is 17 m long and 11 m wide, and has an average depth of 2.6 m. Find the volume of the water in the pool in cubic meters and kiloliters.

V = ___________ m^3
(Type an integer or a decimal.)

V = ___________ kL
(Type an integer or a decimal.)

ID: 3.4.43

---

44. A rectangular fish tank is 60 cm long, 30 cm wide, and 20 cm high.

a) How many cubic centimeters of water will the tank hold?
b) How many milliliters of water will the tank hold?
c) How many liters of water will the tank hold?

a) The tank will hold ___________ cubic centimeters of water.

b) The tank will hold ___________ milliliters of water.

c) The tank will hold ___________ liters of water.

ID: 3.4.44

---

45. Replace the question mark with the appropriate value.

539 cm^2 = ? mm^2

539 cm^2 = ___________ mm^2
(Simplify your answer. Type an integer or a decimal.)

ID: 3.4.45

---

46. Complete.

900.5 cm^2 = ? m^2

900.5 cm^2 = ___________ m^2
(Simplify your answer. Type an integer or a decimal.)

ID: 3.4.46

---

47. Complete the following.

6 m^3 = ? mm^3

6 m^3 = ___________ mm^3

ID: 3.4.47

---

48. Complete.

67.4 L = ? cm^3

67.4 L = ___________ cm^3
(Type an integer or a decimal.)

ID: 3.4.48

!* 49. You conduct a random survey of a representative sample of 150 college students on your campus and find the mean amount of money in a student's bank account is $228 with a standard deviation of $16.87. Complete parts (a) through (b) below.

(a) Compute the standard error using the formula from the definition of the standard error of the mean, $SE \approx \frac{SD}{\sqrt{N}}$, where N is the number of values in the sample.

$________ (Round to the nearest cent as needed.)

(b) Complete the following sentence.

There is a 99.7% probability that the average (1) ________ on your campus is $________ ± $________, which gives the interval from $________ to $________.
(Round to the nearest cent as needed.)

(1) ○ amount of money in a student's back account
○ value of a student's education
○ price of tuition
○ student's income

ID: 3.5.1

---

* 50. In order to gauge public opinion about how to handle Iran's growing nuclear program, a research group surveyed 1006 American women by telephone and asked them to rate the threat Iran's nuclear program poses to the world on a scale of 1 to 10. Describe the population, sample, population parameters, and sample statistics.

Identify the population in the given problem. Choose the correct answer below.

○ **A.** Some of the 1006 American women surveyed by telephone
○ **B.** Half of all American women
○ **C.** All American women
○ **D.** The 1006 American women surveyed by telephone

Identify the sample for the given problem. Choose the correct answer below.

○ **A.** All American women
○ **B.** Half of all American women
○ **C.** The 1006 American women surveyed by telephone
○ **D.** Some of the 1006 American women surveyed by telephone

Identify the population parameter in the given study. Choose the correct answer below.

○ **A.** The total number of all American women
○ **B.** The opinions of all American women on Iran
○ **C.** The number of American women selected
○ **D.** The opinions on Iran of the 1006 American women surveyed by telephone

Identify the sample statistic. Choose the correct answer below.

○ **A.** The opinions of all American women on Iran
○ **B.** The number of American women selected
○ **C.** The total number of American women
○ **D.** The opinions on Iran of the 1006 American women surveyed by telephone

ID: 3.5.2

---

* 51. A recent telephone poll of 1000 randomly selected men revealed that 3 in 10 men believe there has been progress in finding a cure for cancer in the last 28 years. Describe the population, sample, population parameters, and sample statistics.

Identify the population in the given problem. Choose the correct answer below.

○ **A.** The 1000 men selected
○ **B.** 3 out of 10 men in the country
○ **C.** All men in the country
○ **D.** 3 out of 10 of the 1000 men selected

* 51. (cont.) Identify the sample for the given problem. Choose the correct answer below.

- ○ **A.** 3 out of 10 men in the country
- ○ **B.** All men in the country
- ○ **C.** The 1000 men selected
- ○ **D.** 3 out of 10 of the 1000 men selected

Identify the population parameter in the given study. Choose the correct answer below.

- ○ **A.** The percentage of all men in the country who believe there has been progress
- ○ **B.** The number of men selected
- ○ **C.** The total number of all men in the country
- ○ **D.** The percentage of the 1000 men selected who believe there has been progress

Identify the sample statistic. Choose the correct answer below.

- ○ **A.** The proportion of all men in the country who believe there has been progress
- ○ **B.** The total number of all men in the country
- ○ **C.** 3 out of 10
- ○ **D.** 1000

ID: 3.5.3

---

* 52. In a poll, 1,002 women in a country were asked whether they favor or oppose the use of "federal tax dollars to fund medical research using stem cells obtained from human embryos." Among the respondents, 48% said that they were in favor. Describe the statistical study.

What is the population in the given problem? Choose the correct answer below.

- ○ **A.** 48% of all women in the country
- ○ **B.** 48% of the 1,002 women selected
- ○ **C.** All women in the country
- ○ **D.** The 1,002 women selected

Identify the sample for the given problem. Choose the correct answer below.

- ○ **A.** 48% of all women in the country
- ○ **B.** 48% of the 1,002 women selected
- ○ **C.** The 1,002 women selected
- ○ **D.** All women in the country

What is the population parameter in the given study? Choose the correct answer below.

- ○ **A.** The percentage of the 1,002 women selected who say that they are in favor
- ○ **B.** The percentage of all women in the country who say that they are in favor
- ○ **C.** The number of women selected
- ○ **D.** The total number of all women in the country

Identify the sample statistic. Choose the correct answer below.

- ○ **A.** 1,002
- ○ **B.** The total number of all women in the country
- ○ **C.** 48%
- ○ **D.** 52%

ID: 3.5.4

---

* 53. A poll is conducted the day before a state election for Senator. There are only two candidates running for this office. The poll results show that 58% of the voters favor the Republican candidate, with a margin of error of 3 percentage points. Should the Republican expect to win? Why or why not?

Choose the correct answer below.

- ○ **A.** The results suggest that the Republican is not likely to win a solid majority because, when the margin of error is taken into account, he or she will most likely not get the majority of the vote.
- ○ **B.** The results suggest that the Republican is likely to win a solid majority because he or she will most likely get between 55% and 61% of the vote.
- ○ **C.** The results suggest that the Republican is just as likely to win or lose the election because 58% is very close to 50%.

ID: 3.5.5

---

*54. The following statistical study gives a sample statistic and a margin of error. Find the confidence interval and answer any additional questions.

A national survey of 1520 respondents reached on land lines and cell phones found that the percentage of adults who favor legalized abortion has dropped from 53% a year ago to 43%. The study claimed that the error attributable to sampling is ±6 percentage points. Would you claim that a majority of people oppose legalized abortion?

The confidence interval for the study is ________% to ________%.
(Type integer or decimals. Use ascending order.)

Would you claim that a majority of people oppose legalized abortion?

- ○ **A.** Yes, the majority of people oppose legalized abortion because the confidence interval for those in favor of legalized abortion is below 50%.
- ○ **B.** No, the majority of people do not oppose legalized abortion because the confidence interval for those in favor of legalized abortion is below 50%.
- ○ **C.** No, the majority of people do not oppose legalized abortion because the confidence interval for those against legalized abortion is below 50%.
- ○ **D.** The claim cannot be determined from the information given.

ID: 3.5.6

---

*55. In a survey of 1,001 people, 701 (or 70%) said that they voted in a particular presidential election. The margin of error for this survey was 3 percentage points. However, actual voting records show that only 59% of all eligible voters actually did vote. Does this imply that people lied when they responded in the survey? Explain.

Choose the correct answer below.

- ○ **A.** Based on the survey, the actual percentage of voters is expected to be between 67% and 73%, which does not include the 59% value based on actual voter results. If the survey was conducted properly, it is unlikely that its results would be so different from the actual results, implying either that respondents intentionally lied to appear favorable to the pollsters or that their memories were inaccurate.
- ○ **B.** Based on the survey, when the margin of error is taken into account, the actual voter results are not unusual. Thus, the survey was conducted properly, and it does not imply that people lied when they responded to the survey.

ID: 3.5.7

CHAPTER 4
Percentages
MyMathLab Homework Problems*

* Problems with an asterisk are included in the pre-assigned homework assignment.
! Problems with an exclamation point are new to the Update edition.
To find the problems in MyMathLab online, please refer to the ID code listed below each problem.

!* 1. You take out a $22,500 car loan at 4.8% APR.
(a) What is the monthly or periodic interest rate?
(b) Your monthly rate can be expressed as a ratio x : 100. What quantity does the x represent?
(c) How much interest is charged in the first month?

(a) The monthly or periodic interest rate is ________%.
(Type an integer or a decimal.)

(b) What quantity does the x represent?

- ○ Balance at end of month, if the principal is $100
- ○ Interest charged per month, if the principal is $100
- ○ Amount owed per month, if the principal is $100

(c) The interest charged in the first month is $________.
(Round to the nearest cent as needed.)

ID: 4.1.1

---

2. Find the unknown value in the percent proportion $\frac{\text{part}}{\text{whole}} = \frac{\text{percent}}{100}$.

part = 15, percent = 10

whole = ________

ID: 4.1.2

---

*3. Find the unknown value in the percent proportion $\frac{\text{part}}{\text{whole}} = \frac{\text{percent}}{100}$.
part = 30, whole = 60

The answer is ________%.

ID: 4.1.3

---

4. Find the unknown value in the percent proportion $\frac{\text{part}}{\text{whole}} = \frac{\text{percent}}{100}$.
part = 84, whole = 24

The answer is ________%.

ID: 4.1.4

---

5. Find the unknown value in the percent proportion $\frac{\text{part}}{\text{whole}} = \frac{\text{percent}}{100}$.
part = 6.25, whole = 25.25

The answer is ________%.
(Round to the nearest tenth.)

ID: 4.1.5

---

*6. Find the unknown value in the percent proportion $\frac{\text{part}}{\text{whole}} = \frac{\text{percent}}{100}$.

whole = 40, percent = 30

part = ________

ID: 4.1.6

---

7. Find the unknown value in the percent proportion $\frac{\text{part}}{\text{whole}} = \frac{\text{percent}}{100}$.

whole = 56, percent = 33

part = __________
(Round to the nearest tenth.)

ID: 4.1.7

---

8. Find the unknown value in the percent proportion $\frac{\text{part}}{\text{whole}} = \frac{\text{percent}}{100}$.

part = 38, whole = 70.6

The answer is __________ %.
(Round to the nearest tenth.)

ID: 4.1.8

---

9. Find the whole if the part is 44 and the percent is 40.

The whole is __________.

ID: 4.1.9

---

10. The whole is 8000 and the part is 40. Find the percent.

The answer is __________ %.

ID: 4.1.10

---

11. Find the percent if the whole is 2600 and the part is $135\frac{3}{5}$.

The percent is __________ %.
(Round to the nearest tenth.)

ID: 4.1.11

---

12. The whole is 7050 and the part is 19.69. Find the percent.

The answer is __________ %.
(Round to the nearest tenth.)

ID: 4.1.12

---

* 13. Set up the percent proportion, and write "unknown" for the value that is not given. Recall that the percent proportion is $\frac{\text{part}}{\text{whole}} = \frac{\text{percent}}{100}$. Do not try to solve for any unknowns.

25% of how many bicycles is 15 bicycles?

Set up the percent proportion.

$$\frac{(1)}{(3)} = \frac{(2)}{100}$$

(1) ○ unknown ○ 25 ○ 15

(2) ○ 25 ○ unknown ○ 15

(3) ○ unknown ○ 15 ○ 25

ID: 4.1.13

---

* 14. Set up the percent proportion, and write "unknown" for the value that is not given. Recall that the percent proportion is $\frac{\text{part}}{\text{whole}} = \frac{\text{percent}}{100}$. Do not try to solve for any unknowns.

30% of \$710 is \$213.

Set up the percent proportion.

$$\frac{(1)}{(3)} = \frac{(2)}{100}$$

(1) ○ 710 ○ 213 ○ 30 ○ unknown

(2) ○ 30 ○ unknown ○ 710 ○ 213

(3) ○ 213 ○ 30 ○ 710 ○ unknown

ID: 4.1.14

---

15. Set up the percent proportion, and write "unknown" for the value that is not given. Recall that the percent proportion is $\frac{\text{part}}{\text{whole}} = \frac{\text{percent}}{100}$. Do not try to solve for any unknowns.

What is 39% of $980?

Set up the percent proportion.

$$\frac{(1)}{(3)} = \frac{(2)}{100}$$

(1) ○ unknown ○ 39 ○ 980

(2) ○ 980 ○ unknown ○ 39

(3) ○ 39 ○ 980 ○ unknown

ID: 4.1.15

16. Set up the percent proportion, and write "unknown" for the value that is not given. Recall that the percent proportion is $\frac{\text{part}}{\text{whole}} = \frac{\text{percent}}{100}$. Do not try to solve for any unknowns.

13 injections is 4% of what number of injections?

Set up the percent proportion.

$$\frac{(1)}{(3)} = \frac{(2)}{100}$$

(1) ○ 4 ○ 13 ○ unknown

(2) ○ 4 ○ unknown ○ 13

(3) ○ 4 ○ 13 ○ unknown

ID: 4.1.16

17. Set up the percent proportion, and write "unknown" for the value that is not given. Recall that the percent proportion is $\frac{\text{part}}{\text{whole}} = \frac{\text{percent}}{100}$. Do not try to solve for any unknowns.

413 trophies is 70% of 590 trophies.

Set up the percent proportion.

$$\frac{(1)}{(3)} = \frac{(2)}{100}$$

(1) ○ 413 ○ 590 ○ unknown ○ 70

(2) ○ 70 ○ unknown ○ 413 ○ 590

(3) ○ unknown ○ 70 ○ 413 ○ 590

ID: 4.1.17

18. Set up the percent proportion, and write "unknown" for the value that is not given. Recall that the percent proportion is $\frac{\text{part}}{\text{whole}} = \frac{\text{percent}}{100}$. Do not try to solve for any unknowns.

What percent of $355 is $142.00?

Set up the percent proportion.

$$\frac{(1)}{(3)} = \frac{(2)}{100}$$

(1) ○ 142.00 ○ unknown ○ 355

(2) ○ unknown ○ 355 ○ 142.00

(3) ○ 142.00 ○ 355 ○ unknown

ID: 4.1.18

19. Set up the percent proportion, and write "unknown" for the value that is not given. Recall that the percent proportion is $\frac{\text{part}}{\text{whole}} = \frac{\text{percent}}{100}$. Do not try to solve for any unknowns.

54.34 is 3.25% of what number?

Set up the percent proportion.

$$\frac{(1)}{(3)} = \frac{(2)}{100}$$

(1) ○ 54.34 ○ 3.25 ○ unknown

(2) ○ 3.25 ○ unknown ○ 54.34

(3) ○ 3.25 ○ 54.34 ○ unknown

ID: 4.1.19

20. Set up the percent proportion, and write "unknown" for the value that is not given. Recall that the percent proportion is $\frac{\text{part}}{\text{whole}} = \frac{\text{percent}}{100}$. Do not try to solve for any unknowns.

0.25% of 761 is what number?

Set up the percent proportion.

$$\frac{(1)}{(3)} = \frac{(2)}{100}$$

(1) ○ 0.25 ○ 761 ○ unknown

(2) ○ 0.25 ○ unknown ○ 761

(3) ○ unknown ○ 0.25 ○ 761

ID: 4.1.20

21. Set up the percent proportion for the following application problem. Do not try to solve for any unknowns.

In a tree-planting project, 380 of the 650 trees planted were still living one year later. What percent of the trees were still living?

Set up the percent proportion.

$$\frac{(1)}{(3)} = \frac{(2)}{100}$$

(1) ○ 650 ○ unknown ○ 380

(2) ○ unknown ○ 650 ○ 380

(3) ○ 380 ○ unknown ○ 650

ID: 4.1.21

* 22. Set up the percent proportion for the following application problem. Do not try to solve for any unknowns.

Of the 152 people attending a movie theater, 122 bought buttered popcorn. What percent bought buttered popcorn?

Set up the percent proportion.

$$\frac{(1)}{(3)} = \frac{(2)}{100}$$

(1) ○ unknown ○ 122 ○ 152

(2) ○ 122 ○ unknown ○ 152

(3) ○ 122 ○ 152 ○ unknown

ID: 4.1.22

23. Set up the percent proportion for the following application problem. Do not try to solve for any unknowns.

Of the lunch and dinner customers, 61% prefer a fat-free salad dressing. If the total number of customers is 425, find the number of customers who prefer fat-free dressing.

Set up the percent proportion.

$$\frac{(1)}{(3)} = \frac{(2)}{100}$$

(1) ○ 425 ○ 61 ○ unknown

(2) ○ unknown ○ 425 ○ 61

(3) ○ 425 ○ 61 ○ unknown

ID: 4.1.23

24. Set up the percent proportion for the following application problem. Do not try to solve for any unknowns.

Of the total candy bars contained in a vending machine, 81 bars have been sold. If 18% of the bars have been sold, find the total number of candy bars that were in the machine.

Set up the percent proportion.

$$\frac{(1)}{(3)} = \frac{(2)}{100}$$

(1) ○ unknown ○ 81 ○ 18

(2) ○ unknown ○ 81 ○ 18

(3) ○ unknown ○ 81 ○ 18

ID: 4.1.24

25. Set up the percent proportion for the following application problem. Do not try to solve for any unknowns.

In a poll of 250 people, 36.5% said that they get their news from television. Find the number of people who said they get their news from television.

Set up the percent proportion.

$$\frac{(1)}{(3)} = \frac{(2)}{100}$$

(1) ○ unknown ○ 250 ○ 36.5

(2) ○ 36.5 ○ unknown ○ 250

(3) ○ unknown ○ 250 ○ 36.5

ID: 4.1.25

26. Set up the percent proportion for the following application problem. Do not try to solve for any unknowns.

A medical clinic found that 16.46% of the patients were late for their appointments. The number of patients who were late was 176. Find the total numbers of patients.

Set up the percent proportion.

$$\frac{(1)}{(3)} = \frac{(2)}{100}$$

(1) ○ 16.46 ○ 176 ○ unknown

(2) ○ 16.46 ○ unknown ○ 176

(3) ○ 176 ○ unknown ○ 16.46

ID: 4.1.26

27. Set up the percent proportion for the following application problem. Do not try to solve for any unknowns.

A survey of 300 students found that 30% of them considered a detachable-face CD player a high priority for their car.

Set up the percent proportion.

$$\frac{(1)}{(3)} = \frac{(2)}{100}$$

(1) ○ 30 ○ unknown ○ 300

(2) ○ 30 ○ 300 ○ unknown

(3) ○ 300 ○ unknown ○ 30

ID: 4.1.27

28. Solve for part.

25% of 780 guests = _____ guests

__________ guests
(Type an integer.)

ID: 4.1.28

29. Solve for the part.

9% of 520 ft = _____ ft

__________ ft
(Type an integer or a decimal.)

ID: 4.1.29

30. Solve for part.

170% of 200 miles = ____ miles

__________ miles
(Type an integer.)

ID: 4.1.30

31. Solve for part.

14.5% of 8600 feet = ____ feet

__________ feet
(Type an integer or a decimal.)

ID: 4.1.31

32. Solve for the part.

140% of 900 miles = ____ miles

__________ miles

ID: 4.1.32

33. Find the part using the multiplication shortcut.

0.4% of $1700

The part is $ __________.
(Round your answer to the nearest cent.)

ID: 4.1.33

34. 56 students is 70% of how many students?

__________ students

ID: 4.1.34

35. Find the whole using the percent proportion.

42 successful students is 70% of what number of students?

The number of students is ________.

ID: 4.1.35

---

36. $12\frac{1}{2}$% of what amount is $28.00?

$12\frac{1}{2}$% of $________ is $28.00.

ID: 4.1.36

---

37. Find the percent using the percent proportion.

192 meals is what percent of 480 meals?

The percent is ________%.

ID: 4.1.37

---

38. Find the percent using the percent proportion.

24 patients is what percent of 600 patients?

The percent is ________%.

ID: 4.1.38

---

39. Find the percent using the percent proportion.

44 rolls is what percent of 800 rolls?

The percent is ________%.
(Type an integer or a decimal.)

ID: 4.1.39

---

40. What percent of $520 is $130?

________%.

ID: 4.1.40

---

41. Mary earns $460 per week and has 19% of this amount withheld for taxes, Social Security, and Medicare. Find the amount withheld.

The amount withheld is $________.
(Type a whole number or a decimal.)

ID: 4.1.41

---

*42. Of all the people that attend movies, 67% are in the 12 – 29 age group. At one theater, 600 people attended a showing of a certain movie. How many were in the 12 – 29 age group?

The number of people in the 12 – 29 age group was ________.

ID: 4.1.42

---

43. A local little league has a total of 85 players, of whom 20% are left-handed. How many left-handed players are there?

There are ________ left-handed players.

ID: 4.1.43

---

44. On average, a family of two adults and two children pays $94 per night for lodging and $102 a day for food while on vacation this year. If this increases by 4% over the next year, find the total cost per day for lodging and meals for such a family after the increase.

The cost per day will be $________.
(Type a whole number or a decimal.)

ID: 4.1.44

---

45. Of the 8760 hours in a year, one television was on for 2190 hours. What percent is this?

The percent is ________%
(Type a whole number or a decimal.)

ID: 4.1.45

✻ 46. Mary has 7.5% of her earnings deposited into her retirement plan. If $150 per month is deposited in the plan, find her monthly and yearly earnings.

Her monthly earnings are $ ________. (Type a whole number or a decimal.)

Her yearly earnings are $ ________. (Type a whole number or a decimal.)

ID: 4.1.46

47. What is 3.5% of 5800 runners?

________ runners

ID: 4.1.47

48. What percent of 560 employees is 112 employees?

The solution is ________%.

ID: 4.1.48

✻ 49. Record sales

- Pop/rock 58%
- Soul 12%
- Country 8%
- Classical 5%
- Other 17%

This circle graph shows music preferences of customers on the basis of music store sales.

A music store sells 2000 recordings a month. How many are Soul?

The answer is ________ recordings.
(Type a whole number or a decimal.)

ID: 4.1.49

50. Gas budget

- Gas produced 1%
- Taxes 15%
- Salaries 11%
- Other 14%
- Gas bought 59%

This circle graph shows how each customer's dollar is spent annually by the Indiana Gas Company.

On which category is the most money spent?

Choose the correct answer below.

- A. Other
- B. Gas produced
- C. Gas bought
- D. Taxes
- E. Salaries

ID: 4.1.50

51. A collection agency, specializing in collecting past-due child support, charges $20 as an application fee plus 9% of the amount collected. What is the total charge for collecting $3900 in past-due child support?

The total charge is $ ________.
(Type a whole number or a decimal.)

ID: 4.1.51

52. There were 13,355 new products introduced last year. If 86% of the products introduced last year failed to reach their business objectives, find the number of products that were successful.

How many products were successful?

________ products
(Round to the nearest whole number as needed.)

ID: 4.1.52

!✻ 53. Fill in the missing values in the table. Represent fractions with denominator equal to 100.

Percentages	Fractions over 100	Decimals
41.5%		
		0.0075
	$\frac{0.17}{100}$	
643.4%		
		0.606

Percentages	Fractions over 100	Decimals
41.5%	________	________
________%	________	0.0075
________%	$\frac{0.17}{100}$	________
643.4%	________	________
________%	________	0.606

ID: 4.1.53

54. Express the following number as a decimal and as a percentage.

$\frac{5}{8}$

The decimal equivalent of $\frac{5}{8}$ is ________.

The percentage equivalent of $\frac{5}{8}$ is ________%.

(Type integers or decimals.)

ID: 4.1.54

55. Express the given decimal as a percentage and a reduced fraction.

0.75

What is the percentage form of 0.75?

________%

(Simplify your answer. Type a whole number.)

What is the reduced fraction form of 0.75?

____

(Simplify your answer. Type an integer or a simplified fraction.)

ID: 4.1.55

* 56. Express the given percentage as a reduced fraction and a decimal.

225%

What is the reduced fraction form of 225%?

____

(Simplify your answer. Type an integer or a simplified fraction.)

What is the decimal form of 225%?

____

(Simplify your answer. Type an integer or a decimal.)

ID: 4.1.56

* 57. Express the following fraction as a decimal and as a percentage.

$\frac{1}{8}$

Fraction	Decimal	Percentage
$\frac{1}{8}$	________	________%

(Type an integer or decimal rounded to two decimal places as needed.)

ID: 4.1.57

58. Express the given percentage as a reduced fraction and a decimal.

53%

What is the reduced fraction form of 53%?

____

(Simplify your answer. Type an integer or a simplified fraction.)

What is the decimal form of 53%?

____

(Simplify your answer. Type an integer or a decimal.)

ID: 4.1.58

59. Express the given fraction as a decimal and a percentage.

$\frac{7}{8}$

What is the decimal form of $\frac{7}{8}$?

____
(Simplify your answer. Type an integer or a decimal.)

What is the percentage form of $\frac{7}{8}$?

__________ %
(Simplify your answer. Type an integer or a decimal.)

ID: 4.1.59

---

60. Express the first number as a percentage of the second number.
24 pounds of recyclable trash in a barrel of 56 pounds of trash

The 24 pounds of recyclable trash is __________ % of the barrel of 56 pounds of trash.
(Round to the nearest tenth as needed.)

ID: 4.1.60

---

*61. In the following statement, express the first number as a percentage of the second number.
The full-time year-round median salary for U.S. men in 2010 was $42,700, and the full-time year-round salary for U.S. women in 2010 was $34,300.

The full-time year-round median salary for U.S. men in 2010 was __________ % of the full-time year-round median salary for U.S. women in 2010.
(Round to the nearest tenth as needed.)

ID: 4.1.61

---

62. Express the first number as a percentage of the second number.
1182 people per square mile in New Jersey and a national average of 90.6 Americans per square mile in 2012

1182 people per square mile in New Jersey is __________ % of the national average of 90.6 Americans per square mile in 2012.
(Round to the nearest tenth as needed.)

ID: 4.1.62

---

63. Find fractional notation.

45%

Written in fractional notation, 45% = __________ .
(Simplify your answer. Type an integer or a fraction.)

ID: 4.1.63

---

64. Find fractional notation.

62.5%

62.5% = __________
(Simplify your answer. Type an integer or a fraction.)

ID: 4.1.64

---

65. Find fractional notation.

9.25%

9.25% = __________
(Simplify your answer. Type an integer or a fraction.)

ID: 4.1.65

---

66. Find fractional notation.

$15\frac{1}{3}\%$

$15\frac{1}{3}\% =$ ________

(Simplify your answer. Type an integer or a fraction.)

ID: 4.1.66

---

67. Find fractional notation. Simplify.

$47\frac{7}{8}\%$

$47\frac{7}{8}\% =$ ________

ID: 4.1.67

---

68. Find fractional notation. Simplify.

0.0325%

0.0325% = ________

ID: 4.1.68

---

69. Find fractional notation. Simplify.

150%

150% = ________

ID: 4.1.69

---

70. Write $\frac{1}{4}$ as a percent.

$\frac{1}{4} =$ ________ %

(Round to the nearest tenth.)

ID: 4.1.70

---

71. Find percent notation.

$\frac{1}{2}$

$\frac{1}{2} =$ ________ %

ID: 4.1.71

---

72. Find percent notation.

$\frac{3}{10}$

$\frac{3}{10} =$ ________ % (Simplify your answer.)

ID: 4.1.72

---

73. Write $\frac{99}{100}$ as a percent.

$\frac{99}{100} =$ ________ %

ID: 4.1.73

---

74. Write $\frac{5}{8}$ as a percent.

$\frac{5}{8}$ = ________ %

ID: 4.1.74

75. Find percent notation.

$\frac{5}{8}$

$\frac{5}{8}$ = ________ % (Simplify your answer.)

ID: 4.1.75

76. Find percent notation.

$\frac{8}{25}$

$\frac{8}{25}$ = ________ % (Simplify your answer.)

ID: 4.1.76

77. Find percent notation.

$\frac{11}{50}$

$\frac{11}{50}$ = ________ % (Simplify your answer.)

ID: 4.1.77

78. Find percent notation.

$\frac{4}{20}$

$\frac{4}{20}$ = ________ % (Simplify your answer.)

ID: 4.1.78

79. Write $\frac{5}{6}$ as a percent.

$\frac{5}{6}$ = ________ %

(Round to the nearest tenth.)

ID: 4.1.79

80. Find percent notation.

$\frac{1}{9}$

$\frac{1}{9}$ = ________ %

(Type an integer or a decimal. Round to the nearest tenth of a percent if needed.)

ID: 4.1.80

* 81. Complete the table.

Fractional Notation	Decimal Notation	Percent Notation
$\frac{5}{8}$		
	0.2	
		375%

Fractional Notation	Decimal Notation	Percent Notation
$\frac{5}{8}$	________	________ %
________	0.2	________ %
________	________	375%

(Simplify your answers. Type an integer, fraction, or decimal as needed.)

ID: 4.1.81

82. Complete the table. Round decimals to the nearest thousandth and percents to the nearest tenth of a percent.

Fraction	Decimal	Percent
$\frac{1}{9}$	______	______ %

ID: 4.1.82

83. Complete the table.

Fraction	Decimal	Percent
	2.1	
$5\frac{3}{5}$		

Fraction	Decimal	Percent
______	2.1	______ %
$5\frac{3}{5}$	______	______ %

(Simplify your answer.)

ID: 4.1.83

84. Of 500 people who used the Internet to find pet information, 230 said they used it when buying a pet. What portion used the Internet when buying a pet?

______ % used the Internet when buying a pet.
(Type a whole number or a decimal.)

ID: 4.1.84

85. Only 61 out of every 100 adults consume the recommended 1000 milligrams of calcium daily. What portion consumes the recommended daily amount?

______ % consume the recommended amount.
(Type a whole number or a decimal.)

ID: 4.1.85

86. Sharon needs 64 credits to graduate from her community college. So far she has earned 24 credits. What percent of the required credits does she have?

Sharon has earned ______ % of the required credits.
(Type a whole number or a decimal.)

ID: 4.1.86

87. An insurance office has 110 employees. If 99 of the employees have cellular phones, what portion of the employees do not have cellular phones?

The portion of employees who do not have cellular phones is ______.
(Type a whole number or a simplified fraction.)

ID: 4.1.87

88. The circle graph shows the number of students at Rockford College who are enrolled in various majors. Find the portion of students who are computer science majors.

______ % of the students are computer science majors.
(Round to the nearest tenth as needed.)

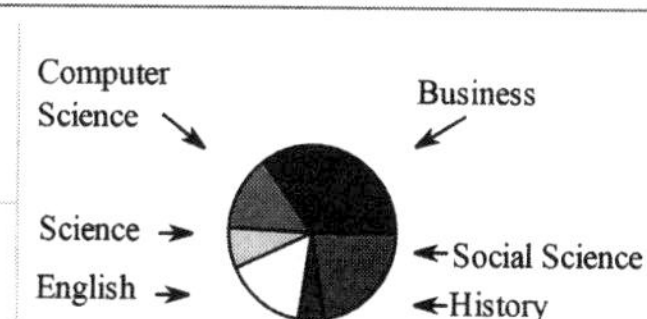

Major	# of students
Business	4200
Computer Sci	1700
Science	900
English	1900
History	600
Social Sci	2700

ID: 4.1.88

!* 89. The annual carbon dioxide (CO_2) emissions in 2012 by country is given in the table. Complete parts (a) through (d) below.

[1] Click the icon to view the table of the carbon dioxide emissions in 2012.

(a) Compute the part-to-part ratio of Japan to Russia and scale the second quantity to 100.

__________ : 100
(Round to one decimal place as needed.)

(b) Interpret the part-to-part ratio of Japan to Russia.

Select the correct choice below and fill in the answer box to complete your choice.
(Round to one decimal place as needed.)

○ **A.** __________ % of Japan is in Russia.

○ **B.** The CO_2 emissions of Japan were __________ % of the amount Russia emitted in 2012.

○ **C.** __________ % of the CO_2 emissions of Japan in 2012 were produced by Russia.

(c) Compute the part-to-whole ratio of Japan to the world and scale the second quantity to 100.

__________ : 100
(Round to one decimal place as needed.)

(d) Interpret the part-to-whole ratio of Japan to the world.

Select the correct choice below and fill in the answer box to complete your choice.
(Round to one decimal place as needed.)

○ **A.** The CO_2 emissions of Japan were __________ % of the world's total emissions in 2012.

○ **B.** __________ % of the CO_2 emissions of Japan in 2012 were produced in the world.

○ **C.** Japan is __________ % of the world.

1: Carbon Dioxide Emissions in 2012

	Region	CO_2 Emissions 2012 (million metric tons)
1	China	8,106.4
2	United States	5,270.4
3	India	1,830.9
4	Russia	1,781.7
5	Japan	1,259.1
6	Germany	788.3
7	S. Korea	657.1
8	Iran	603.6
9	Saudi Arabia	582.7
10	Canada	550.8
	World	32,310.3

ID: 4.2.1

!* 90. A store is having a clearance sale on winter gear due to global warming, with everything marked down 65%. The boots you have been wanting to buy are now $55. Fill in the table to find their original price and the mark-down in dollars.

Mark-down (part)	New Price (part)	Original Price (whole)
	$55	
$65		$100

Mark-down (part)	New Price (part)	Original Price (whole)
$ __________	$55	$ __________
$65	$ __________	$100

(Round to two decimal places as needed.)

ID: 4.2.2

* 91. Compute the total cost per year of the following pair of expenses. Then complete the sentence: On an *annual* basis, the first set of expenses is ______% of the second set of expenses.

Maria spends $12 on lottery tickets every week and spends $140 per month on food.

On an annual basis, the money spent on lottery tickets is __________ % of the money spent to buy food.
(Round to the nearest percent as needed.)

ID: 4.2.3

* 92. Compute the total cost per year of the following pair of expenses. Then complete the sentence: On an *annual* basis, the first set of expenses is _______% of the second set of expenses.

Suzanne's cell phone bill is $88 per month, and she spends $239 per year on student health insurance.

On an annual basis, the money spent on her cell phone bill is ___________% of the money spent on student health insurance.
(Round to the nearest percent as needed.)

ID: 4.2.4

* 93. Compute the total cost per year of the following pair of expenses. Then complete the sentence: On an *annual* basis, the first set of expenses is _______% of the second set of expenses.

Sheryl spends $16 every week on cigarettes and spends $37 a month on dry cleaning.

On an annual basis, the money spent on cigarettes is ___________% of the money spent on dry cleaning.
(Round to the nearest percent as needed.)

ID: 4.2.5

* 94. Compute the total cost per year of the following pair of expenses. Then complete the sentence: On an *annual* basis, the first set of expenses is _______% of the second set of expenses.

Vern buys fourteen lottery tickets each week at a cost of $2 each and spends $900 per year on his textbooks.

On an annual basis, the money spent on lottery tickets is ___________% of the money spent to buy textbooks.
(Round to the nearest percent as needed.)

ID: 4.2.6

!* 95. Your veterinarian is administering a sedative to your 50 pound dog. The sedative is mixed in saline solution. Unfortunately the solution is pre-mixed at 10% for a horse and it needs to be a 3.5% concentration to be administered at 0.3 ml per pound for your dog. How much saline water needs to be added to the current solution to reduce the concentration to 3.5% and have the correct dosage for the dog? Complete parts (a) through (d) below.
[2] Click the icon to view a ratio table for the sedative solutions.

a. How many ml (N) of the new solution (3.5%) should be administered to the dog?

___________ ml

b. How many ml (S) of the sedative are contained in the dosage of the new solution (3.5%) that should be administered to the dog?

___________ ml

c. How many ml (O) of the original solution (10%) contain the sedative in the dosage that should be administered to the dog?

___________ ml

d. How many ml of saline solution should be added to the amount (O) of the original solution (10%) to get the amount (N) of the new solution that should be administered?

___________ ml

2: Ratio Table for the Sedative Solutions

Part	Whole #1 (10%)	Whole #2 (3.5%)	
Sedative (ml)	**Original Solution (ml)**	**New Solution (ml)**	**Dog (lb)**
10	100		
3.5		100	
		0.3	1
S	O	N	50

ID: 4.2.7

!* 96. In Biology class you have 16% chemical solution that needs to be diluted to 3%. Complete parts (a) through (c) below.
[3] Click the icon to view a ratio table for the chemical solution.

a. If you have 90 ml of the 16% solution and add 10 ml of water, what is the concentration of the new solution?

___________ %

b. If you have 90 ml of the 16% solution and add 30 ml of water, what is the concentration of the new solution?

___________ %

c. How many ml of water should you add to 90 ml of the original solution to get a 3% solution?

___________ ml

3: Ratio Table for the Chemical Solution

Part	Whole #1 (16%)	Whole #2 (??%)
Chemical (ml)	**Original Solution (ml)**	**New Solution (ml)**
16	100	
x	90	100

ID: 4.2.8

!* 97. The table shows how crime has been decreasing in a certain country.

(a) What was the total change in murders from 1995 to 2012?
(b) What was the percent change of murders from 1995 to 2012?
(c) Which crime rate experienced the largest % change from 1995 to 2012?

[4] Click the icon to view the table.

(a) The total change in murders from 1995 to 2012 was ____________.
(Type an integer or a decimal.)

(b) The percent change of murders from 1995 to 2012 was ____________%.
(Type an integer or decimal rounded to the nearest tenth as needed.)

(c) Choose the correct answer below.

- ○ Violent Crime Rate
- ○ Murder Rate
- ○ Property Crime Rate
- ○ Motor Vehicle Theft Rate

4: Data Table

Crime in a certain country
by Volume and Rate per 100,000 inhabitants, 1990-2012

Year	Population	Violent Crime	Violent Crime Rate	Murder	Murder Rate	Property Crime	Property Crime Rate	Motor Vehicle Theft	Motor Vehicle Theft Rate
1990	248,877,036	1,800,980	723.6	23,342	9.4	12,888,409	5,178.6	1,694,040	680.7
1995	265,788,082	1,782,443	670.6	21,901	8.2	12,149,004	4,570.9	1,402,809	527.8
2000	281,796,917	1,624,569	576.5	15,852	5.6	10,699,194	3,796.8	1,057,631	375.3
2005	293,239,252	1,396,539	476.2	16,822	5.7	10,392,311	3,544.0	1,293,113	441.0
2009	303,948,550	1,342,777	441.8	15,718	5.2	9,639,943	3,171.6	771,142	253.7
2012	315,507,525	1,275,880	404.4	14,828	4.7	8,067,919	2,557.1	718,226	227.6

ID: 4.3.1

98. Compute the total and annual returns on the described investment.

Five years after buying 100 shares of XYZ stock for $60 per share, you sell the stock for $9000.

The total return is ____________%.
(Do not round until the final answer. Then round to one decimal place as needed.)

The annual return is ____________%.
(Do not round until the final answer. Then round to one decimal place as needed.)

ID: 4.3.2

99. Compute the total and annual returns on the following investment.

Sixteen years after purchasing shares in a mutual fund for $5700, the shares are sold for $11,400.

The the total return is ____________%.
(Do not round until the final answer. Then round to one decimal place as needed.)

The annual return is ____________%.
(Do not round until the final answer. Then round to one decimal place as needed.)

ID: 4.3.3

100. Compute the total and annual return on the following investment.

Four years after paying $2400 for shares in a startup company, you sell the shares for $2200 (at a loss).

The total return is ____________%.
(Do not round until the final answer. Then round to the nearest tenth as needed.)

The annual return is ____________%.
(Do not round until the final answer. Then round to the nearest tenth as needed.)

ID: 4.3.4

101. Compute the total and annual returns on the following investment.

Six years after purchasing shares in a mutual fund for $7400, the shares are sold for $11,400.

The the total return is ________ %.
(Do not round until the final answer. Then round to one decimal place as needed.)

The annual return is ________ %.
(Do not round until the final answer. Then round to one decimal place as needed.)

ID: 4.3.5

---

102. Suppose a man invested $250 at the end of 1900 in each of three funds that tracked the averages of stocks, bonds, and cash, respectively. Assuming that his investments grew at the rates given in the table to the right, approximately how much would each investment have been worth at the end of 2009?

Category	Average Annual Return
Stocks	6.7%
Bonds	2.3%
Cash	0.8%

His investment in the fund tracking stocks would be worth approximately $________.
(Do not round until the final answer. Then round to two decimal places as needed.)

His investment in the fund tracking bonds would be worth approximately $________.
(Do not round until the final answer. Then round to two decimal places as needed.)

His investment in the fund tracking cash would be worth approximately $________.
(Do not round until the final answer. Then round to two decimal places as needed.)

ID: 4.3.6

!* 103. For men born in a certain year, the predicted years of receiving Social Security benefits is 17.2 for the bottom decile of income earners versus 22.3 years for the top decile.
(a) What was the total difference between the top decile and bottom decile?
(b) What was the percent difference between the top decile and bottom decile?
(c) Now flip the order and complete the following sentence using percent difference: The bottom decile of income earners can expect to receive ______ less years of Social Security benefits than the top decile.

(a) The top decile of income earners can expect to receive ________ more years of Social Security benefits than the bottom decile.
(Type an integer or decimal rounded to the nearest tenth as needed.)

(b) The top decile of income earners can expect to receive ________ % more years of Social Security benefits than the bottom decile.
(Type an integer or decimal rounded to the nearest tenth as needed.)

(c) The bottom decile of income earners can expect to receive ________ % less years of Social Security benefits than the top decile.
(Type an integer or decimal rounded to the nearest tenth as needed.)

ID: 4.3.7

---

104. Decide whether the following statement makes sense (or is clearly true) or does not make sense (or is clearly false). Explain.

In many European countries, the percentage change in population has been negative in recent decades.

Choose the correct answer below.

- ○ **A.** The statement makes sense. A percentage change in population can be negative if the data reflects that.
- ○ **B.** The statement does not make sense. The phrase "percent points" should be used instead of "percentage."
- ○ **C.** The statement does not make sense. Percentages should not be used in this situation.
- ○ **D.** The statement makes sense. A percentage change in population can only be negative.

ID: 4.3.8

---

*105. Decide whether the following statement makes sense (or is clearly true) or does not make sense (or is clearly false). Explain your reasoning.

My older child weighs 25% more than my younger child.

Choose the correct answer below.

- ○ **A.** The statement does not make sense because if the older child weighs 25% more than the younger child, then his weight is -1.25 times the younger child's weight. This cannot be true because the weight is never negative.
- ○ **B.** The statement makes sense because if the older child weighs 25% more than the younger child, then his weight is 1.25 times the younger child's weight, which is possible.
- ○ **C.** The statement does not make sense because if the older child weighs 25% more than the younger child, then his weight is -0.75 times the younger child's weight. This cannot be true because the weight is never negative.
- ○ **D.** The statement makes sense because if the older child weighs 25% more than the younger child, then his weight is 0.75 times the younger child's weight, which is possible.

ID: 4.3.9

106. Decide whether the following statement makes sense (or is clearly true) or does not make sense (or is clearly false). Explain your reasoning.

If John earns 20% more than Mary does, then Mary must earn 20% less than John does.

Choose the correct answer below.

- ○ **A.** The statement does not make sense because if John earns 20% more than Mary, then Mary must earn 80% less than John does.
- ○ **B.** The statement makes sense because 20% is the absolute difference between John and Mary.
- ○ **C.** The statement does not make sense because if John earns 20% more than Mary, then Mary must earn approximately 16.7% less than John does.
- ○ **D.** The statement makes sense because the relative difference is 20% and it does not change by switching the reference value and the compared value.

ID: 4.3.10

*107. Decide whether the following statement makes sense (or is clearly true) or does not make sense (or is clearly false). Explain your reasoning.

We found that these rare cancers were 700% more common in children living near the toxic landfill than in the general population.

Choose the correct answer below.

- ○ **A.** The statement makes sense because the number of rare cancers found in children living near the toxic landfill is 8 times the number of rare cancers found in the general population, which is possible.
- ○ **B.** The statement does not make sense because the number of rare cancers found in the general population is 7 times the number of rare cancers found in children living near the toxic landfill, which does not make sense.
- ○ **C.** The statement makes sense because the number of rare cancers found in children living near the toxic landfill is 7 times the number of rare cancers found in the general population, which is possible.
- ○ **D.** The statement does not make sense because the number of rare cancers found in the general population is 8 times the number of rare cancers found in children living near the toxic landfill, which does not make sense.

ID: 4.3.11

*108. Decide whether the following statement makes sense (or is clearly true) or does not make sense (or is clearly false). Explain your reasoning.

The rate of return on our fund increased by 50%, to 15%.

Choose the correct answer below.

- ○ **A.** The statement does not make sense because if the rate of return on our fund increased by 50%, to 15%, then the previous rate is 65%, which does not make sense.
- ○ **B.** The statement makes sense because if the rate of return on our fund increased by 50%, to 15%, then the previous rate is 7.5%, which makes sense.
- ○ **C.** The statement does not make sense because if the rate of return on our fund increased by 50%, to 15%, then the previous rate is -35%, which does not make sense.
- ○ **D.** The statement makes sense because if the rate of return on our fund increased by 50%, to 15%, then the previous rate is 10%, which makes sense.

ID: 4.3.12

*109. Find the absolute change and the percentage change in the following case.

The average sale of a house decreased from $334,000 in February 2008 to $167,000 in February 2013.

The absolute change is ____________.
(Simplify your answer. Type a whole number.)

The relative change is ____________%.
(Type an integer or decimal rounded to the nearest tenth as needed.)

ID: 4.3.13

---

110. Find the absolute change and the percentage change in the following case.

The number of daily news paper in a country was 2454 in 1900 and 1333 in 2010.

The absolute change is ____________.
(Simplify your answer. Type a whole number.)

The relative change is ____________%.
(Round the final answer to the nearest integer as needed. Round all intermediate values to the nearest hundredth as needed.)

ID: 4.3.14

---

*111. Complete the following sentence.

The gestation period of humans (266 days) is _____ percent longer than the gestation period of cats (62 days).

The gestation period of humans (266 days) is ____________ percent longer than the gestation period of cats (62 days).
(Round the final answer to one decimal place as needed. Round all intermediate values to three decimal places as needed.)

ID: 4.3.15

---

112. Complete the following sentence.

The main span of Bridge A (2800 feet) is _____ percent shorter than the main span of Bridge B (4300 feet).

The main span of Bridge A (2800 feet) is ____________ percent shorter than the main span of Bridge B (4300 feet).
(Round the final answer to one decimal place as needed.)

ID: 4.3.16

---

113. Complete the following sentence.

The number of deaths due to poisoning in country A in a year (25,100) is _____ percent greater than the number of deaths due to falls (21,300).

The number of deaths due to poisoning in country A in a year (25,100) is ____________ percent greater than the number of deaths due to falls (21,300).
(Round the final answer to one decimal place as needed. Round all intermediate values to three decimal places as needed.)

ID: 4.3.17

---

*114. State whether the following statement is true or false, and explain why. If the statement is false, state the true change.

If the national economy shrank at an annual rate of 6% per year for four consecutive years, then the economy shrank by 24% over the four-year period.

Choose the correct answer below and, if necessary, fill in the answer box to complete your choice.

○ **A.** The statement is false because each year there is a different reference value. The economy actually shrank by ____________% over the four-year period.
(Type an integer or decimal rounded to the nearest tenth as needed.)

○ **B.** The statement is true because $4 \times 6\%$ is 24%.

ID: 4.3.18

---

115. State whether the following statement is true or false, and explain why. If the statement is false, state the true change.

If the profits in your consulting business increase by 8% one year and decrease by 2% the following year, your profits are up by 6% over two years.

Select the correct choice below and, if necessary, fill in the answer box within your choice.

- A. True
- B. False; If the profits in your consulting business increase by 8% one year and decrease by 2% the following year, your profits are up by ____________ % over two years.
  (Simplify your answer. Type an integer or a decimal.)

ID: 4.3.19

---

116. Determine whether the following claim could be true. Explain your answer.

By turning off her lights and closing her windows at night, Maria saved 112% on her monthly energy bill.

Choose the correct answer below.

- A. The claim could be true because her new monthly energy bill would be 88% of the previous monthly energy bill, which makes sense.
- B. The claim could not be true because her new monthly energy bill would be − 88% of the previous monthly energy bill. This is impossible since the bill cannot be negative.
- C. The claim could not be true because her new monthly energy bill would be − 12% of the previous monthly energy bill. This is impossible since the bill cannot be negative.
- D. The claim could be true because her new monthly energy bill would be 12% of the previous monthly energy bill, which makes sense.

ID: 4.3.20

---

117. Determine whether the following claim could be true. Explain your answer.

Restaurant prices have increased 105% in the last 20 years.

Choose the correct answer below.

- A. The claim could be true because an increase of 105% would more than double the original prices, which is possible.
- B. The claim could not be true because the resulting prices would be negative, and restaurants do not pay their customers to eat.
- C. The claim could be true because an increase of 105% would be 5% of the original prices, which is possible.
- D. The claim could not be true because amounts cannot be increased by 100% or more.

ID: 4.3.21

---

118. Determine whether the following claim could be true. Explain your answer.

George's computer is 1300% faster than Nancy's.

Choose the correct answer below.

- A. The claim could be true because if George's computer is 1300% faster than Nancy's, then it is 12 times Nancy's computer speed, which makes sense.
- B. The claim could not be true because if George's computer is 1300% faster than Nancy's, then it is − 12 times Nancy's computer speed. This cannot be true because the speed cannot be negative.
- C. The claim could be true because if George's computer is 1300% faster than Nancy's, then it is 14 times Nancy's computer speed, which makes sense.
- D. The claim could not be true because if George's computer is 1300% faster than Nancy's, then it is − 14 times Nancy's computer speed. This cannot be true because the speed cannot be negative.

ID: 4.3.22

---

119. You are a teacher. Your first-period class, with 25 students, had a mean score of 89% on the midterm exam. Your second-period class, with 30 students, had a mean score of 91% on the same exam. Does it follow that the mean score for both classes combined is 90%? Explain.

Choose the correct answer below.

- A. No, because it is impossible for a 25 student class to get a mean score of 89%.
- B. Yes, because 89% of 25 plus 91% of 30 is 90% of 55, the total number of students.
- C. Yes, because the average of 89% and 91% is 90%.
- D. No, because it is a general rule to never average percentages.

ID: 4.3.23

!* 120. Fill in the provided table for associated growth/decay rates and growth/decay factors. Recall that Factor = 1 + Rate.

Complete the table below.

Rate	Factor
2.02%	______
______ %	0.96
0.06%	______
− 11.8%	______
______ %	1.507
______ %	0.06

(Type integers or decimals.)

ID: 4.3.24

!* 121. To complete parts (a) through (c) below, use the following table (arrow diagram) indicating an unknown original value has decreased by 15% to arrive at the new value.

	(c)	
(b)	→	$133.11
original	− 15%	new

(a) What is the factor associated to the rate given in the diagram?

The factor associated to the rate given in the diagram is ______.
(Type an integer or a decimal. Round to the nearest cent as needed.)

(b) Use the factor to find the original value.

The original value is $ ______.
(Type an integer or a decimal. Round to the nearest cent as needed.)

(c) Determine the total change.

The total change is a(n) (1) ______ of $ ______.
(Type an integer or a decimal. Round to the nearest cent as needed.)

(1) ○ decrease
○ increase

ID: 4.3.25

122. The recomended daily allowance of niacin for adults is 20 mg. One serving of a certain breakfast cereal provides 15 mg of niacin. What percent of the recomended daily allowance of niacin does one serving of this cereal provide?

One serving of this cereal provides ______% of the recomended daily allowance of niacin.

ID: 4.3.26

* 123. The graph shows the percent of employees who take time off during one year because of colds. A company has 9910 employees. Use the graph to find the number of them who miss work because of colds for 1 to 2 days each year.

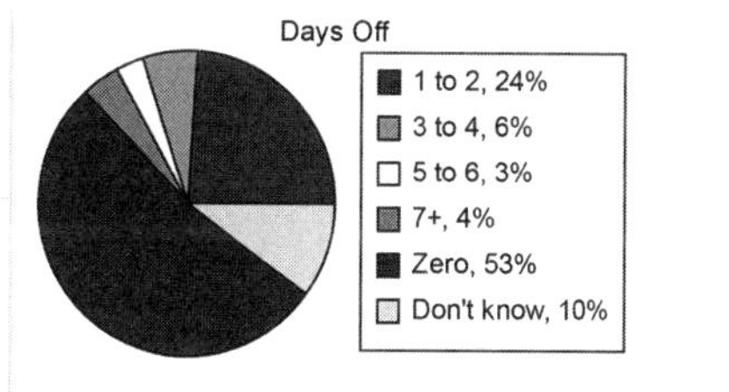

How many employees miss work 1 to 2 days per year because of colds?

______
(Simplify your answer. Round to the nearest whole number.)

ID: 4.3.27

124. The elements that compose seawater, along with the corresponding percents, are shown in the table.

If a sample of seawater contains 80 ml, how many ml of oxygen are in the sample?

Seawater Elements	
Chemical	Percent
Oxygen	85.84%
Hydrogen	10.82%
Chlorine	1.94%
Sodium	1.08%
Magnesium	0.13%
Other elements	0.19%

There are ______ ml of oxygen in the sample.
(Type an integer or a decimal rounded to two decimal places.)

ID: 4.3.28

125. Students at a high school were polled to determine the type of music they preferred. There were 1940 students who completed the poll. Their responses are represented in the circle graph.

What percent of students preferred country music?

Music Preferences

- Rap 899
- Alternative 470
- Rock and Roll 272
- Country 178
- Jazz 27
- Other 94

About ___________ % of the students who completed the poll preferred country music.
(Round to one decimal place as needed.)

ID: 4.3.29

---

126. The population of a country has been decreasing for several decades. In 1990, the population was about 136 million people. In 2010, the population was about 133 million people. Determine the percent decrease in the country's population during this time period.

The country's population decreased by about ___________ % during this time period.
(Round to one decimal place as needed.)

ID: 4.3.30

---

127. What is 13% of $45.00?

$ ___________ is 13% of $45.00.
(Type an integer or a decimal.)

ID: 4.3.31

---

128. What percent of 98 is 49?

___________ % of 98 is 49.

ID: 4.3.32

---

129. Determine the answer to the question.

36% of what number is 216?

The answer is ___________.

ID: 4.3.33

---

130. In a mathematics class, 28 students received an A on the third test, which is 175% of the students who received an A on the second test. How many students received an A on the second test?

On the second test, ___________ students received an A.

ID: 4.3.34

---

* 131. A person earns $18,200 one year and gets a 5% raise in salary. What is the new salary?

The new salary is $ ___________.

ID: 4.3.35

---

132. A vacuum cleaner dealership sold 460 units in 2011 and 491 units in 2012. Find the percent increase or decrease in the number of units sold.

The number of units sold (1) ___________ by about ___________ %.
(Round to one decimal place as needed.)

(1) ○ decreased
 ○ increased

ID: 4.3.36

---

133. A farmer recently purchased her neighbor's farm. Before the purchase, the farmer owned a total of 362 acres of land. After the purchase, she owned a total of 515 acres of land. Determine the percent increase in the number of acres of land owned by the farmer.

The number of acres of land owned by the farmer increased by about ____________%.
(Round to one decimal place as needed.)

ID: 4.3.37

---

134. During a sale, a dress decreased in price from $499.52 to $429.59. Find the percent decrease in the price of the dress.

The percent decrease was ____________%.
(Round to the nearest percent.)

ID: 4.3.38

---

135. A man purchased a used car for $6000. He decided to sell the car for 10% above his purchase price. He could not sell the car so he reduced his asking price by 10%. If he sells the car at the reduced price, will he have a profit or a loss or will he break even?

Select the correct choice below and fill in any answer box to complete your answer.

○ **A.** The man will break even.

○ **B.** The man will have a profit of $____________.

○ **C.** The man will have a loss of $____________.

ID: 4.3.39

!* 1. Going into the quarterfinals of a hockey tournament, a certain team led the league in power play conversions. A power play occurs when one team gets a penalty so that they lose a player (typically for 2 minutes), this results in a 5 on 4 situation. Converting on a power play means the team with the player advantage scores a goal in these 2 minutes. Answer parts (a) through (d).

a. The team had 144 power play opportunities and converted on 46 of them. What was their conversion rate (what percentage of power plays did they convert)?

____________%
(Type an integer or a decimal. Round to the nearest tenth as needed.)

b. Their opponents had 133 power play opportunities and the team "killed" 115 of them, meaning their opponents failed to score on 115 of these opportunities. What was the opponents' power play conversion rate?

____________%
(Type an integer or a decimal. Round to the nearest tenth as needed.)

c. What is the total difference between the conversion rate and their opponents' conversion rate?

The team's conversion rate was ____________ (1) ____________ more than their opponents' rate.
(Type an integer or a decimal. Round to the nearest tenth as needed.)

d. What is the percentage difference between the conversion rate and their opponents' conversion rate?

The team's conversion rate was ____________% more than their opponents' rate.
(Type an integer or a decimal. Round to the nearest tenth as needed.)

(1) ○ goals ○ pp ○ power plays ○ %

ID: 4.4.1

!* 2. The accompanying table shows projected populations for different demographic groups.

a. Compute the total change in the 65 years and over group from 2015 to 2060, and give proper units.

b. Compute the percent change in the 65 years and over group from 2015 to 2060, and give proper units.

[1] Click the icon to view the table.

a. The total change in the 65 years and over group from 2015 to 2060 was ____________ (1) ____________
(Type an integer or a decimal. Round to the nearest hundredth as needed.)

b. The percent change in the 65 years and over group from 2015 to 2060 was ____________ (2) ____________
(Type an integer or a decimal. Round to the nearest hundredth as needed.)

!* 2. (cont.) 1: Projected Population Distribution by Age Groups and Sex

Percent Distribution of the Projected Population by Selected Age Groups and Sex for a particular country: 2015 to 2060		
Sex and age	(Percent of total resident population as of July 1)	
	2015	2060
BOTH SEXES	**100.00**	**100.00**
Under 18 years	22.44	20.55
Under 5 years	6.19	5.52
5 to 13 years	10.97	10.22
14 to 17 years	5.28	4.81
18 to 64 years	63.74	58.65
18 to 24 years	9.25	7.92
25 to 44 years	23.44	22.49
45 to 64 years	31.05	28.24
65 years and over	13.82	20.8
85 years and over	1.76	4.05
100 years and over	0.01	0.15
16 years and over	80.20	81.85
18 years and over	77.56	79.45
15 to 44 years	36.65	34.02

(1) ○ people. ○ pp. ○ %. (2) ○ %. ○ pp. ○ people.

ID: 4.4.2

3. Clint's salary increased from $23,000 to $36,800 over a three-year period. Helen's salary increased from $29,000 to $46,400 over the same period. Whose salary increased more in absolute terms? In relative terms? Explain.

Whose salary increased more in absolute terms? Select the correct choice below and fill in the answer box(es) to complete your choice.

○ **A.** Clint's salary increased more, because his salary increased by $__________. This is more than $__________, the amount that Helen's salary increased.

○ **B.** Helen's salary increased more, because her salary increased by $__________. This is more than $__________, the amount that Clint's salary increased.

○ **C.** Neither person's salary increased more, because both of their salaries increased by $__________.

Whose salary increased more in relative terms? Select the correct choice below and fill in the answer box(es) to complete your choice.

○ **A.** Helen's salary increased more, because her salary increased by __________%. This is more than the percent increase of Clint's salary, which is __________%.

○ **B.** Clint's salary increased more, because his salary increased by __________%. This is more than the percent increase of Helen's salary, which is __________%.

○ **C.** Neither person's salary increased more, because both of their salaries increased by __________%.

ID: 4.4.3

4. Fill in the blank.

Will is 22% taller than Wanda, so Will's height is ____% of Wanda's height.

Will's height is __________% of Wanda's height.

ID: 4.4.4

5. Fill in the blank in the following statement.

The population of city A is 28% less than the population of city B, so city A's population is _____% of city B's.

City A's population is __________% of city B's.

ID: 4.4.5

6. Fill in the blank in the following statement.

The wholesale price of a TV is 40% less than retail price. Therefore, the wholesale price is _____ times the retail price.

The wholesale price is __________ times the retail price.
(Type an integer or a decimal.)

ID: 4.4.6

7. Fill in the blank.

The retail cost of a TV is 65% more than its wholesale cost. Therefore, the retail cost is ____ times the wholesale cost.

The retail cost is ____________ times the wholesale cost. (Type an integer or a decimal.)

ID: 4.4.7

---

8. The annual interest rate for Jack's savings account increased from 1.2% to 2.0%. Complete parts (a) and (b) below.

a. Describe the change as an absolute change in terms of percentage points.

The annual interest rate increased by ____________ percentage points.
(Type an integer or decimal rounded to the nearest tenth as needed.)

b. Describe the change as a relative change in terms of a percentage.

The annual interest rate increased by ____________%.
(Type an integer or decimal rounded to the nearest tenth as needed.)

ID: 4.4.8

---

* 9. The percentage of people accessing the Internet increased from 66% in 2000 to 88% in 2012. Complete parts (a) and (b) below.

a. Describe the change as an absolute change in terms of percentage points.

The percentage of people accessing the Internet increased by ____________ percentage points.
(Type an integer or a decimal.)

b. Describe the change as a relative change in terms of a percentage.

The percentage of people accessing the Internet increased by ____________%.
(Type an integer or decimal rounded to the nearest tenth as needed.)

ID: 4.4.9

---

10. The sales tax rate in a city is 8.7%. Find the tax charged on a purchase of $220, and the total cost.

How much tax is charged on a purchase of $220?
$ ____________
(Simplify your answer. Type an integer or a decimal. Round to the nearest cent if needed.)

What is the total price?
$ ____________
(Simplify your answer. Type an integer or a decimal. Round to the nearest cent if needed.)

ID: 4.4.10

---

* 11. Between 2000 and 2010, the percentage of households with cordless phones increased by 14.2% to 77%. What percentage of households had cordless phones in 2000?

About ____________% of households had cordless phones in 2000.
(Round to the nearest integer as needed.)

ID: 4.4.11

---

12. Assuming the given information is accurate, determine whether the following statement is true. Provide an explanation.

The class is 40% women and 20% of the women have blond hair, so blond women comprise 40% × 20% = 8% of the class.

Choose the correct answer below.

○ **A.** The statement is not true because blond women comprise 20% of women in the class and women comprise 40% of the class. Hence, blond women comprise 20% + 40% = 60% of the class.

○ **B.** The statement is true because blond women comprise 20% of women in the class and women comprise 40% of the class. Hence, blond women comprise 20% × 40% = 8% of the class.

○ **C.** The statement is not true because blond women comprise 20% of women in the class and women comprise 40% of the class. Hence, blond women comprise 20% + 40% = 0.6% of the class.

○ **D.** The statement is not true because blond women comprise 20% of women in the class and women comprise 40% of the class. Hence, blond women comprise 20% × 40% = 80% of the class.

ID: 4.4.12

---

*13. Assuming the given information is accurate, determine whether the following statement is true. Provide an explanation.

60% of the hotels have a restaurant, and 20% have a swimming pool, so 80% of the hotels in town have a restaurant or a pool.

Choose the correct answer below.

- ○ **A.** The statement is not true because some of the hotels with a restaurant may also have a pool.
- ○ **B.** The statement is not true because 20% × 60% = 12% of the hotels have a restaurant or a pool.
- ○ **C.** The statement is true because all hotels with a restaurant do not have a pool.
- ○ **D.** The statement is true because 20% + 60% = 80% of the hotels have a restaurant or a pool.

ID: 4.4.13

---

14. At a particular college, 90% of the undergraduates are female. If 3330 women attend the college, how many total undergraduates attend the college?

The total number of undergraduates is ________.
(Round to the nearest whole number as needed.)

ID: 4.4.14

---

15. Diners frequently add a 15% tip when charging a meal to a credit card. What is the price of the meal without the tip if the amount charged is $31.05? How much was the tip?

The price of the meal without tip is $________.

The amount of the tip is $________.

ID: 4.4.15

---

16. Simon's monthly take-home pay (after taxes) is $2400. If he pays 18% of his gross pay (before taxes) in tax, what is his gross pay?

Simon's gross pay is $________.
(Round to the nearest dollar as needed.)

ID: 4.4.16

---

17. Answer the question about the following quote from a news source.

"Some 68% of the estimated $54 trillion in credit default swaps outstanding in 2008 were speculative." What was the value of the speculative credit default swaps?

The value of the speculative credit default swaps was $________ trillion.
(Type an integer or decimal rounded to the nearest tenth as needed.)

ID: 4.4.17

---

*18. Answer the question about the following quote from a news source.

"The unemployment rate has risen more than a percentage point to 8.5% in February from 7.3% last November." What is the relative change in the unemployment rate expressed as a percentage?

The unemployment rate has risen ________%.
(Type an integer or decimal rounded to the nearest tenth as needed.)

ID: 4.4.18

---

19. Answer the question about the following quote from a news source.

"At $1.31 million, they closed last month for...30 percent above what they paid in 2007." How much did they pay in 2007?

They paid $________ million.
(Type an integer or decimal rounded to the nearest thousandth as needed.)

ID: 4.4.19

---

20. Decide whether the following statement makes sense or does not make sense.

My share of the federal government's debt is greater than the cost of a new car.

Choose the correct answer below.

- ○ Does not make sense
- ○ Makes sense

ID: 4.4.20

---

21. Decide whether the following statement makes sense or does not make sense.

Because Social Security is off-budget, we could cut Social Security taxes with no impact on the rest of the federal government.

Choose the correct answer below.

- ○ Makes sense
- ○ Does not make sense

ID: 4.4.21

---

22. Decide whether the following statement makes sense (or is clearly true) or does not make sense (or is clearly false). Explain your reasoning.

Because social security is an entitlement program and is funded by mandatory government spending, I know it will be there when I retire in 40 years.

Choose the correct answer below.

- ○ **A.** This makes sense because the Treasury bills in the Social Security trust fund represent a publicly held debt, which is money that the government must repay to individuals and institutions that bought Treasury issues.
- ○ **B.** This does not make sense because the gross debt is constantly increasing each year. Eventually the government may not have the resources to repay the Treasury bills, plus interest, in the Social Security trust fund.
- ○ **C.** This does not make sense because Social Security is not funded by mandatory government spending. It is a discretionary project.
- ○ **D.** This makes sense because all of the Social Security taxes collected are put into a trust fund that goes out to future retirees.

ID: 4.4.22

!* 23. The following table shows projected populations for different demographic groups. Answer parts (a) through (d).

	Cold got better	Cold got worse	Totals
Used zinc tablets	331	184	
Did not use zinc tablets	150	66	
Totals			

a. Fill in the totals for each row and column.

	Cold got better	Cold got worse	Totals
Used zinc tablets	331	184	____
Did not use zinc tablets	150	66	____
Totals	____	____	____

(Type integers or decimals.)

b. Compute the percentages in the columns.

	Cold got better	Cold got worse	Totals
Used zinc tablets	331 (____%)	184 (____%)	
Did not use zinc tablets	150 (____%)	66 (____%)	
Totals	____%	____%	

(Type integers or decimals. Round to the nearest tenth as needed.)

c. Compute the percentages in the rows.

	Cold got better	Cold got worse	Totals
Used zinc tablets	331 (____%)	184 (____%)	____%
Did not use zinc tablets	150 (____%)	66 (____%)	____%
Totals			

(Type integers or decimals. Round to the nearest tenth as needed.)

d. Does the table indicate that zinc tablets help cure the cold?

- ○ **A.** No, because the percentage of people whose cold got better given that they used zinc tablets is less than the percentage of people that used zinc tablets given that their cold got better.
- ○ **B.** Yes, because a greater percentage of the people whose cold got better used zinc tablets.
- ○ **C.** No, because the percentage of people whose cold got better given that they used zinc tablets is less than the percentage of people whose cold got better given that they did not use zinc tablets.
- ○ **D.** Yes, because the number of people who used zinc tablets and whose colds got better is greater than the number of people in the other three categories.

ID: 4.4.23

---

24. Fill in the remaining entries in the two-way table shown to the right.

A survey of 120 patrons at a restaurant gave the preferences for entrees and drinks shown to the right.

	Vegetarian	Meat / Fish	Total
Wine	34		50
No Wine		49	
Total			120

Fill in the missing entries in the table.

	Vegetarian	Meat / Fish	Total
Wine	34		50
No Wine		49	
Total			120

ID: 4.4.24

25. Describe the three basic uses of percentages. Give a sample statement that uses percentages in each of the three ways.

What is one way to use percentages?

- ○ **A.** Percentages can be used to describe a change in something. For example, out of 3,000 employees, 15% got raises.
- ○ **B.** Percentages can be used to express a fraction of something. For example, a company started with 15,000 employees and has grown 3% within the past year.
- ○ **C.** Percentages can be used to express a fraction of something. For example, out of 15,000 employees, 3% lost their jobs.
- ○ **D.** Percentages can be used to describe a change in something. For example, the shoes are 50% lighter, but are 17% more expensive.

What is a second way to use percentages?

- ○ **A.** Percentages can be used to compare two things. For example, the stock dropped 1.5% this past week.
- ○ **B.** Percentages can be used to describe a change in something. For example, out of 34 students, 50% passed the test.
- ○ **C.** Percentages can be used to compare two things. For example, out of 945 residents, 80% voted in the last election .
- ○ **D.** Percentages can be used to describe a change in something. For example, the cost of milk rose 5% within the past month.

What is the third way to use percentages?

- ○ **A.** Percentages can be used to express a fraction of something. For example, this class scored 10% better, but took 50% longer.
- ○ **B.** Percentages can be used to express a fraction of something. For example, the average test score dropped 5% from last year.
- ○ **C.** Percentages can be used to compare two things. For example, out of 250 cars, 30% are green.
- ○ **D.** Percentages can be used to compare two things. For example, the car costs 25% more but gets 10% more miles per gallon.

ID: 4.4.25

26. Distinguish between absolute and relative difference. Give an example that illustrates how to calculate a relative difference.

Distinguish between absolute and relative difference. Choose the correct answer below.

- ○ **A.** Absolute difference is the actual difference between the compared value and the reference value. Relative difference describes the size of the absolute difference in comparison to the reference value and can be expressed as a percentage.
- ○ **B.** Absolute difference describes the size of the relative difference in comparison to the reference value and can be expressed as a percentage. Relative difference is the actual difference between the compared value and the reference value.
- ○ **C.** Absolute difference describes the actual increase or decrease from a reference value to a new value. Relative difference is the size of the absolute difference in comparison to the reference value and can be expressed as a percentage.
- ○ **D.** Absolute difference is the size of the relative difference in comparison to the reference value and can be expressed as a percentage. Relative difference describes the actual increase or decrease from a reference value to a new value.

Give an example that illustrates how to calculate a relative difference. Choose the correct answer below.

- ○ **A.** If the new value is 60 and the reference value is 55, then relative difference $= 60 - 55 = 5$.
- ○ **B.** If the compared value is 50 and the reference value is 45, then relative difference $= \frac{50-45}{45} \times 100\% = 11.\bar{1}\%$.
- ○ **C.** If the compared value is 50 and the reference value is 45, then relative difference $= 50 - 45 = 5$.
- ○ **D.** If the new value is 60 and the reference value is 55, then relative difference $= \frac{60-55}{60} \times 100\% = 8.\bar{3}\%$.

ID: 4.4.26

27. Explain the difference between the key words 'of' and 'more than' when dealing with percentages. How are their meanings related?

Explain the difference. Choose the correct answer below.

- ○ **A.** The key word 'more than' is used to express the ratio of the compared value to the relative value. The key word 'of' is used to express the absolute change between the referenced value and the compared value.
- ○ **B.** The key word 'more than' is used to express the ratio of the compared value to the relative value. The key word 'of' is used to express the relative change between the referenced value and the compared value.
- ○ **C.** The key word 'more than' is used to express the absolute change between the referenced value and the compared value. The key word 'of' is used to express the ratio of the compared value to the referenced value.
- ○ **D.** The key word 'more than' is used to express the relative change between the referenced value and the compared value. The key word 'of' is used to express the ratio of the compared value to the referenced value.

How are their meanings related?

- ○ **A.** If the compared value is P% more than the reference value, it is (100 − P)% of the reference value.
- ○ **B.** If the compared value is P% of the reference value, it is (100 + P)% more than the reference value.
- ○ **C.** If the compared value is P% of the reference value, it is (100 − P)% more than the reference value.
- ○ **D.** If the compared value is P% more than the reference value, it is (100 + P)% of the reference value.

ID: 4.4.27

28. Explain the difference between the terms "percent" (%) and "percentage points." Give an example of how they can differ for the same situation.

What is the difference between the terms "percent" (%) and "percentage points"?

- ○ **A.** Percent is used to describe an absolute change or difference. Percentage points are used to describe a relative change or difference.
- ○ **B.** Percent is used to express fractions. Percentage points are used to describe a change.
- ○ **C.** Percent is used to describe a relative change or difference. Percentage points are used to describe an absolute change or difference.
- ○ **D.** Percent is used to describe increases. Percentage points are used to describe decreases.

Give an example of how "percent" (%) and "percentage points" can differ for the same situation. Choose the correct answer below.

- ○ **A.** Consider a savings account that previously offered 2% interest and now offers 6% interest. The percent increase is 300% and the percentage point decrease is 4.
- ○ **B.** Consider a savings account that previously offered 2% interest and now offers 6% interest. The percent increase is 4% and the percentage point increase is 200.
- ○ **C.** If a savings account that previously offered 2% interest now offers 6% interest, then the percent increase is 200% and the percentage point increase is 4.
- ○ **D.** Consider a savings account that previously offered 2% interest and now offers 6% interest. The percent increase is 300% and the percentage point increase is 4.

ID: 4.4.28

*29. The table to the right is based on the assumption that 1% of breast tumors are malignant. It also assumes that mammogram screening is 85% accurate. Complete parts (a) through (c) below.

	Tumor is Malignant	Tumor is Benign	Total
Positive Mammogram	85	1202	1287
Negative Mammogram	15	8698	8713
Total	100	9900	10,000

a. Suppose a patient has a positive mammogram. What is the chance that she really has cancer?

________ %

(Type an integer or decimal rounded to the nearest tenth as needed.)

b. What is the chance of a positive mammogram, given that the patient has cancer?

________ %

(Type an integer or decimal rounded to the nearest tenth as needed.)

c. Suppose a patient has a negative mammogram. What is the chance that she actually does have cancer?

________ %

(Type an integer or decimal rounded to the nearest hundredth as needed.)

ID: 4.4.29

✻ 30. Suppose a test for a disease is 90% accurate for those who have the disease (true positives) and 90% accurate for those who do not have the disease (true negatives). Within a sample of 4000 patients, the incidence rate of the disease is the national average. Complete parts (a) through (c) below.

	Disease	No Disease	Total
Test Positive	72	509	581
Test Negative	8	3411	3419
Total	80	3920	4000

a. Use the entries in the table to determine the overall incident rate of the disease.

The incident rate is ___________%.
(Type an integer or decimal rounded to the nearest tenth as needed.)

b. Of those with the disease, what percentage test positive?

___________%
(Type an integer or decimal rounded to the nearest tenth as needed.)

c. Of those who test positive, what percentage have the disease?

___________%
(Type an integer or decimal rounded to the nearest tenth as needed.)
Compare this result to the one in part (b) and explain why they are different.

In part (b), the comparison is to (1) ___________ and here the comparison is to (2) ___________

d. Suppose a patient tests positive for the disease. As a doctor using this table, how would you describe the patient's chance of actually having the disease? Compare this figure to the overall incidence rate of the disease. Choose the correct answer below.

○ **A.** The chance of having the disease decreases to ___________% given that the test was positive, compared to the ___________% incidence rate without the test.

○ **B.** The chance of having the disease increases to ___________% given that the test was positive, compared to the ___________% incidence rate without the test.

(1) ○ those who have the disease,
○ those who test positive,

(2) ○ all those who test positive.
○ all those who have the disease.

ID: 4.4.30

31. Consider the following hypothetical basketball records for college A and college B. Answer parts a through c.

	College A	College B
Home Games	10 wins, 19 losses	9 wins, 19 losses
Away Games	12 wins, 4 losses	56 wins, 20 losses

a. Give numerical evidence to support the claim that college A has a better team than college B. Choose the correct answer below.

○ **A.** College A won about 34.5% of their home games and about 75% of their away games, whereas college B only won about 32.1% of their home games and about 73.7% of their away games.

○ **B.** College A lost only 23 games, whereas college B lost 39 games.

○ **C.** College A won 10 of their home games, whereas college B won 9 of their home games.

b. Give numerical evidence to support the claim that college B has a better team than college A. Choose the correct answer below.

○ **A.** College B won 56 away games, whereas college A only won 12 away games.

○ **B.** College B won 65 games, whereas college A only won 22 games.

○ **C.** College B won about 62.5% of the games they played, whereas college A only won about 48.9% of the games they played.

c. Which claim do you think makes more sense? Why?

The claim in part (1) ___________ makes more sense because it is based (2) ___________

(1) ○ A
○ B

(2) ○ only on the home games.
○ on the total number of games played.
○ only on the away games.
○ separately on home games and away games.

ID: 4.4.31

32. The Department of Health of a certain state estimates a 10% rate of HIV for the "at risk" population and a 0.3% rate for the general population. Tests for HIV are 95% accurate in detecting both true negatives and true positives. Random selection of 5000 "at risk" people and 20,000 people from the general population results in the following table. Use the table below to complete parts (a) through (e).

	"At Risk" Population		General Population	
	Test Positive	Test Negative	Test Positive	Test Negative
Infected	484	16	51	9
Not Infected	218	4282	976	18,964

a. Verify that incidence rates for the general and "at risk" populations are 0.3% and 10%, respectively. Also, verify that detection rates for the general and "at risk" populations are 95%. How would you verify the incidence rates?

- ○ **A.** Divide the number of uninfected patients by the total number of patients.
- ○ **B.** Divide the number of infected patients by the total number of patients.
- ○ **C.** Divide the number of uninfected patients by the number of infected patients.
- ○ **D.** Divide the number of infected patients by the number of uninfected patients.

How would you verify the detection rates?

- ○ **A.** Divide the total number of false positives by the total number of patients.
- ○ **B.** Divide the total number of false negatives by the total number of patients.
- ○ **C.** Divide the total number of true negatives by the total number of patients.
- ○ **D.** Divide the total number of true positives by the total number of patients.

b. Consider a patient in the "at risk" category. Of those with HIV, what percentage test positive? Of those who test positive, what percentage have HIV? Explain why these two percentages are different.

Of the patients in the "at risk" category, ________ % test positive and, of these, ________ % have HIV.
(Type an integer or decimal rounded to the nearest tenth as needed.)

Why are these two percentages different?

- ○ **A.** The percentages are different because people who test positive don't always have HIV and people who have HIV don't always test positive.
- ○ **B.** The percentages are different because the people are in two different categories.
- ○ **C.** The percentages are different because the first test includes everyone who tested positive.
- ○ **D.** The percentages are different because there are people being accounted for that don't have HIV in the second calculation.

c. Suppose a patient in the "at risk" category tests positive for the disease. As a doctor using this table, how would you describe the patient's chance of actually having the disease? Compare this figure to the overall rate of the disease in the "at risk" category.

A patient in the "at risk" category who tests positive has a ________ % chance of having the disease which is

(1) ________ the overall "at risk" incidence rate of 10%.
(Type an integer or decimal rounded to the nearest tenth as needed.)

d. Consider a patient in the general population. Of those with HIV, what percentage test positive? Of those who test positive, what percentage have HIV? Explain why these two percentages are different.

Of the patients in the general population with HIV, ________ % test positive. Of the patients in the general population who test positive, ________ % have HIV.
(Type an integer or decimal rounded to the nearest tenth as needed.)

Why are these two percentages different?

- ○ **A.** The percentages are different because people who test positive don't always have HIV and people who have HIV don't always test positive.
- ○ **B.** The percentages are different because there are people being accounted for that don't have HIV in the second calculation.
- ○ **C.** The percentages are different because the people are in two different categories.
- ○ **D.** The percentages are different because the first test includes everyone who tested positive.

e. Suppose a patient in the general population tests positive for the disease. As a doctor using this table, how would you describe the patient's chance of actually having the disease? Compare this figure with the overall incidence rate of the disease.

The chance of the patient having HIV is ________ %, compared to the overall incidence rate of 0.3%.
(Type an integer or decimal rounded to the nearest tenth as needed.)

(1) ○ less than
○ greater than

ID: 4.4.32

*33. In the Senate of a particular Congress, there were 51 Democrats, 47 Republicans, and 2 Independents. Of the 24 women in the Senate, 16 are Democrats and 8 are Republicans. Complete parts (a) through (e) below.

a. Given this information, complete the following table.

	Democrats	Republicans	Totals
Women	______	______	______
Men	______	______	______
Totals	______	______	98

(Type whole numbers.)

b. What percentage of the Democratic and Republican senators are Republican women?

______ %

(Type an integer or decimal rounded to the nearest tenth as needed.)

c. Among the women in the Senate, what is the percentage of Republicans?

______ %

(Type an integer or decimal rounded to the nearest tenth as needed.)

d. Among the Republicans in the Senate, what is the percentage of women?

______ %

(Type an integer or decimal rounded to the nearest tenth as needed.)

e. Why is the percentage of women who are Republicans (part c) not equal to the percentage of Republicans who are women (part d)?

○ **A.** In part c, the percentage is of ______ women, while in part d, the percentage is of ______ Republicans.

○ **B.** In part c, the percentage is of ______ Republicans, while in part d, the percentage is of ______ women.

(Type whole numbers.)

f. Which is more prevalent, women among all 100 senators or women among Democrats?

The percentage of women among all senators is ______ % and the percentage of women among Democrats is ______ %. Therefore, (1) ______ are more prevalent.

(Type an integer or decimal rounded to the nearest tenth as needed.)

(1) ○ women among all 100 senators ○ women among Democrats

ID: 4.4.33

34. According to an analysis of a proposed federal tax cut by an accounting firm, a single person with a household income of $47,000 would save $256 in income taxes, while a single person with a household income of $580,000 would save $12,463 in taxes. A married couple with two children and a household income of $47,000 would save $1967 in income taxes, while a married couple with two children and a household income of $580,000 would save $13,922 in taxes. Complete parts (a) through (c) below.

a. Find the absolute difference in tax savings between a single person earning $47,000 and a single person earning $580,000.

The absolute difference is $ ______ . (Type a whole number.)

Express the tax savings as a percentage of earnings for each person.

For a single person earning $47,000, the tax savings is ______ % of their income.

For a single person earning $580,000, the tax savings is ______ % of their income.

(Type integers or decimals rounded to the nearest tenth as needed.)

b. Find the absolute difference in tax savings between a married couple with two children earning $47,000 and a married couple with two children earning $580,000.

The absolute difference is $ ______ . (Type a whole number.)

Express the tax savings as a percentage of earnings for each couple.

For a married couple with two children earning $47,000, the tax savings is ______ % of their income. For a married couple with two children earning $580,000, the tax savings is ______ % of their income.

(Type integers or decimals rounded to the nearest tenth as needed.)

c. Do the proposed tax cuts help lower-income people? Explain your reasoning.

For a single person, the tax cuts (1) ______ they help a higher-income single person. For a married couple with two children, the tax cuts (2) ______ they help a higher-income married couple.

(1) ○ help just as much as
○ do not help as much as
○ help more than

(2) ○ help just as much as
○ do not help as much as
○ help more than

ID: 4.4.34

!* 35. The accompanying table shows projected populations for different demographic groups.
a. For males 40-49 years old, what height is in the 95th percentile?
b. Five percent of all men 20 years and older are above what height?
c. What percentage of men 80 years and older are between 62.7 inches and 71.3 inches tall?
d. What percentage of all men 20 years and older are under 65.6 inches?
[2] Click the icon to view the table.

a. ___________ inch(es)
(Type an integer or a decimal.)

b. ___________ inch(es)
(Type an integer or a decimal.)

c. ___________ %
(Type an integer or a decimal.)

d. ___________ %
(Type an integer or a decimal.)

2: Height in Inches for Males 20 Years of Age and Older

Height in inches for males 20 years of age or older by race and ethnicity and age, by mean, standard error of mean selected percentiles: United States 2003-2006

Race and ethnicity and age	Number examined	Mean	Standard error	Percentile							
				5th	10th	15th	25th	50th	75th	85th	90th
				Inches							
All races and ethnicity groups											
20 years and over	4,482	69.4	0.07	64.4	65.6	66.3	67.4	69.4	71.5	72.6	73.2
20-29 years	808	69.9	0.13	64.7	65.8	66.6	67.8	70.0	72.0	73.0	73.5
30-39 years	742	69.4	0.13	64.1	65.3	66.1	67.5	69.5	71.5	72.7	73.4
40-49 years	769	69.7	0.11	65.2	66.2	66.8	67.9	69.7	71.6	72.7	73.3
50-59 years	591	69.5	0.15	65.0	65.8	66.5	67.5	69.5	71.5	72.7	73.4
60-69 years	668	69.0	0.11	64.2	65.4	66.1	67.1	69.0	71.1	71.9	72.7
70-79 years	555	68.4	0.16	63.8	64.6	65.5	66.4	68.5	70.3	71.0	72.0
80 years and over	349	67.2	0.14	62.7	63.6	64.3	65.5	67.2	68.9	70.0	70.5

ID: 4.5.1

* 36. For any set of data, what must be done to the data before percentiles can be determined?

Choose the correct answer below.

- ○ **A.** The data must be ranked.
- ○ **B.** The frequency of each piece of data must be found.
- ○ **C.** The data must be summed.
- ○ **D.** The quartiles of the data set must be found.

ID: 4.5.2

* 37. When a national sample of heights of kindergarten children was taken, a student was told that she was in the 65th percentile. Explain what that means.

Choose the correct interpretation below.

- ○ **A.** She is taller than 65 percent of all kindergarten children.
- ○ **B.** She is shorter than 65 percent of all kindergarten children.
- ○ **C.** She is taller than 65 kindergarten children.
- ○ **D.** She is taller than 35 percent of all kindergarten children.

ID: 4.5.3

* 38. The prices of the 21 top-rated 28-inch direct view television sets are as follows.

$230	$290	$420	$440	$510	$570	$650
270	330	420	470	550	580	650
280	370	440	500	570	620	650

Determine Q_2, Q_1, and Q_3.

Q_2 = ___________

Q_1 = ___________

Q_3 = ___________

ID: 4.5.4

*39. Give the names of two other statistics that have the same value as the 50th percentile.

Choose the correct answer below.

- ◯ **A.** Third quartile; mode
- ◯ **B.** Second quartile; median
- ◯ **C.** Second quartile; mean
- ◯ **D.** First quartile; midrange

ID: 4.5.5

---

*40. The following statistics represent weekly salaries at a construction company.

Mean	$605	First quartile	$465
Median	$520	Third quartile	$585
Mode	$490	89th percentile	$631

The most common salary is $__________.

The salary that half the employees' salaries surpass is $__________.

The percent of employees' salaries that surpassed $585 is __________%.

The percent of employees' salaries that were less than $465 is __________%.

The percent of employees' salaries that surpassed $631 is __________%.

If the company has 100 employees, the total weekly salary of all employees is $__________.

ID: 4.5.6

---

*41. A professor records the following final grades in one course. Construct a frequency table for the grades.

A	A	A	B	B	B	B	B	B	B	B	C
C	C	C	C	C	C	C	C	D	D	D	F

Complete the table.
(Type an integer or decimal rounded to the nearest tenth as needed.)

Grade	Frequency	Relative frequency	Cumulative frequency
A	_____	_____ %	_____
B	_____	_____ %	_____
C	_____	_____ %	_____
D	_____	_____ %	_____
F	_____	_____ %	_____
Total	_____	1 = 100%	_____

ID: 4.5.7

---

*42. Use 5-point bins (95 to 99, 90 to 94, etc.) to make a frequency table for the set of exam scores shown below. Include columns for relative frequency and cumulative frequency.

91 80 98 73 84 75 99 88 78 93 92 85 73 90 80 89 83 73 84 88

Complete the frequency table below.

Scores	Frequency	Relative Frequency	Cumulative Frequency
95 to 99	_____	_____ %	_____
90 to 94	_____	_____ %	_____
85 to 89	_____	_____ %	_____
80 to 84	_____	_____ %	_____
75 to 79	_____	_____ %	_____
70 to 74	_____	_____ %	_____
Total	_____	_____ %	_____

ID: 4.5.8

CHAPTER 5
Linear Functions
MyMathLab Homework Problems*

* Problems with an asterisk are included in the pre-assigned homework assignment.
! Problems with an exclamation point are new to the Update edition.
To find the problems in MyMathLab online, please refer to the ID code listed below each problem.

!* 1. The distance you drive is proportional to the amount of gas used. Driving 140 miles uses 4 gallons of gas. Complete parts (a) through (c).

(a) Fill in the following table.

Gas (gal)	Distance (mi)
0	________
4	________
8	________
12	________

(Type integers or decimals.)

(b) Represent the relationship between distance driven, D, and gas used, G, with an equation.

D = __________ • G
(Type an integer or a decimal.)

(c) Use the graphing tool to graph this equation. Use the origin and another point when drawing the line. Choose the correct graph below.

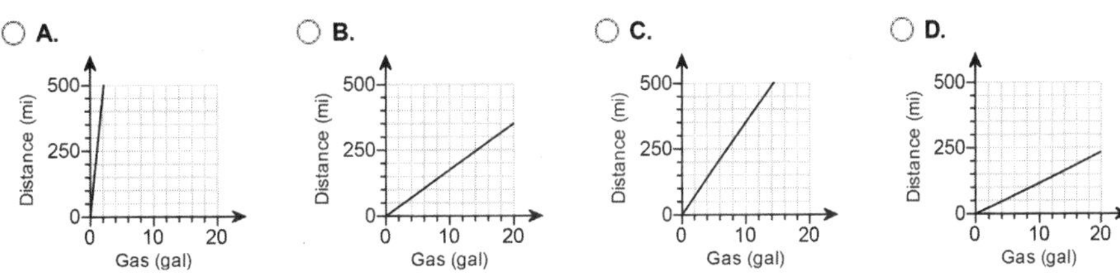

ID: 5.1.1

!* 2. The cost of an airline ticket is proportional to the distance traveled at a rate of $36 per 150 miles flown. Complete parts (a) through (c).

(a) Fill in the following table.

Distance (mi)	Cost ($)
0	________
50	________
100	________
150	________

(Type integers or decimals. Do not include the $ symbol in your answers.)

(b) Represent the relationship between cost, C, and distance flown, D, with an equation.

C = __________ • D
(Type an integer or a decimal. Do not include the $ symbol in your answer.)

(c) Use the graphing tool to graph this equation. Use the origin and another point when drawing the line. Choose the correct graph below.

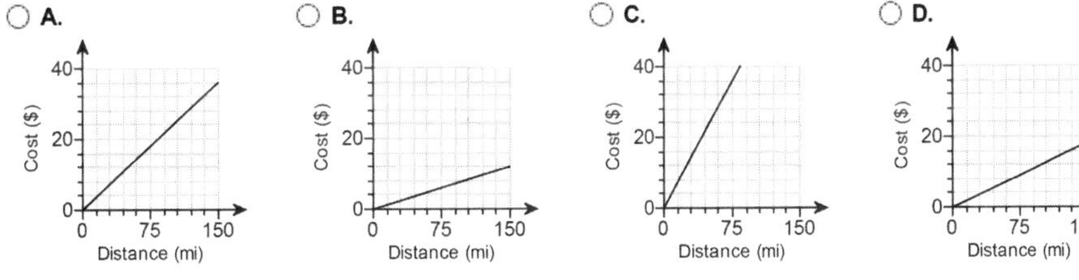

ID: 5.1.2

!* 3. Your monthly electric bill is proportional to the number of kilowatt-hours (kwh) of energy used at a rate of 5.6 cents per kwh. Complete parts (a) through (c).

(a) Fill in the following table.

Energy (kwh)	Cost ($)
0	______
400	______
800	______
1,200	______

(Type integers or decimals rounded to the nearest hundredth as needed. Do not include the $ symbol in your answers.)

(b) Represent the relationship between cost ($), C, and energy used (kwh), E, with an equation.

C = ________ • E

(Type an integer or a decimal. Do not include the $ symbol in your answer.)

(c) Use the graphing tool to graph this equation. Use the origin and another point when drawing the line. Choose the correct graph below.

○ **A.**

100
50
0
Cost ($)
0 1000 2000
Energy (kwh)

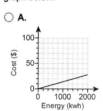

○ **B.**

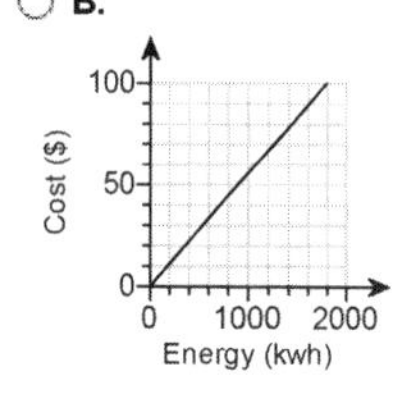

○ **C.**

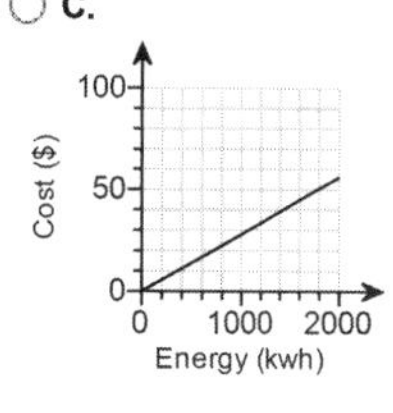

○ **D.**

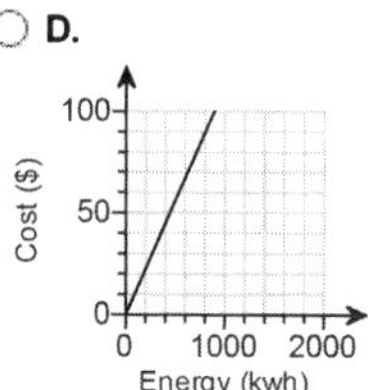

ID: 5.1.3

* 4. Plot the ordered pair (7,8) on the rectangular coordinate plane.

Plot (7,8).

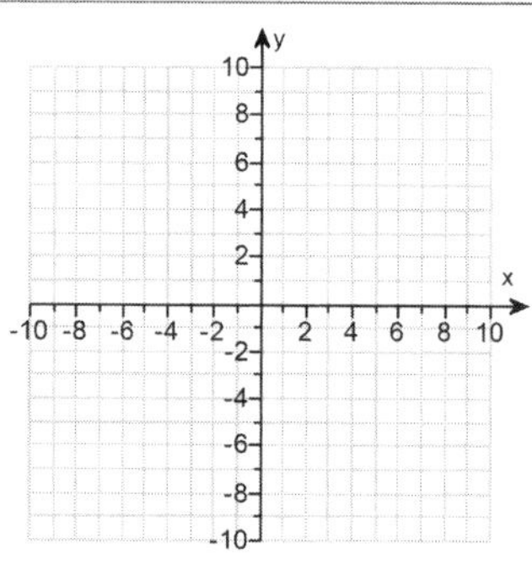

ID: 5.1.4

* 5. Plot the point (− 3, − 2) in the rectangular coordinate system.

Plot (− 3, − 2).

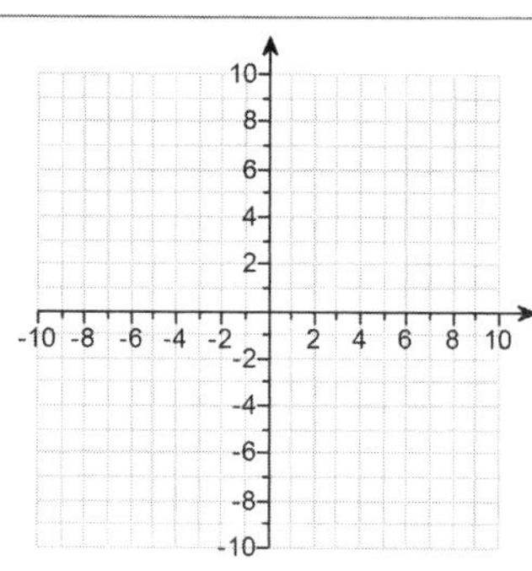

ID: 5.1.5

6. Plot the ordered pair (0,8) in the rectangular coordinate system.

Plot (0,8).

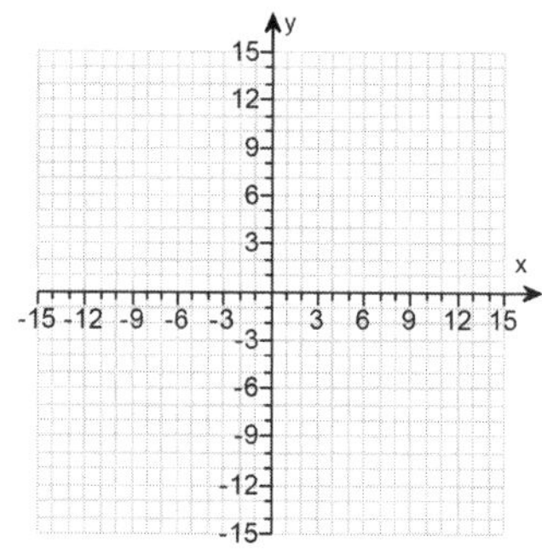

ID: 5.1.6

7. Plot the ordered pair (0, − 7) in the rectangular coordinate system.

   Plot (0, − 7).

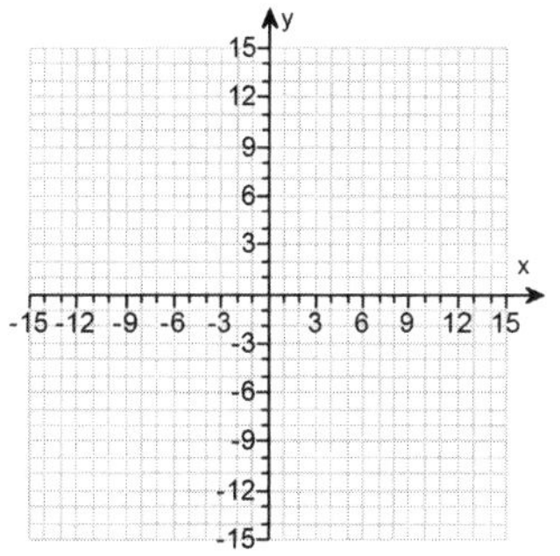

   ID: 5.1.7

8. Plot the point (− 3, 0) in the rectangular coordinate system.

   Plot (− 3, 0).

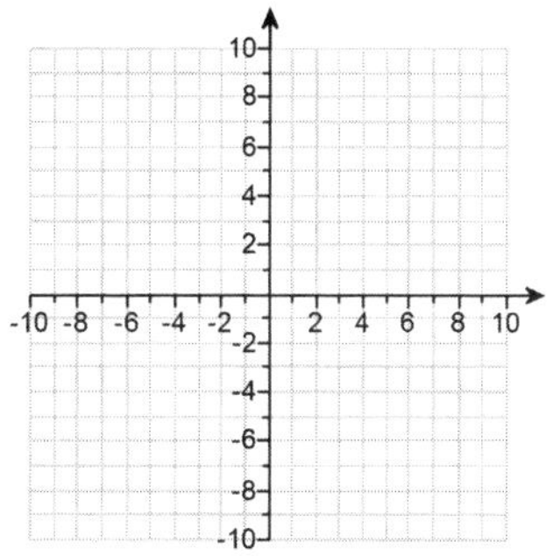

   ID: 5.1.8

9. Plot the ordered pair (− 8,5) on the rectangular coordinate plane.

   Plot (− 8,5).

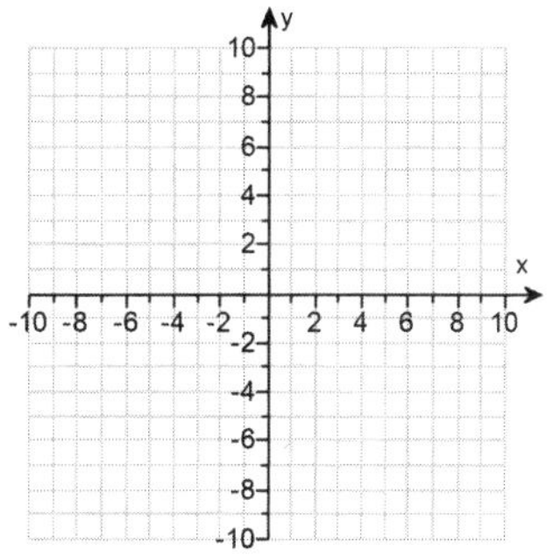

   ID: 5.1.9

10. Plot the point (2.5, 9.5) in the rectangular coordinate system.

    Plot (2.5, 9.5).

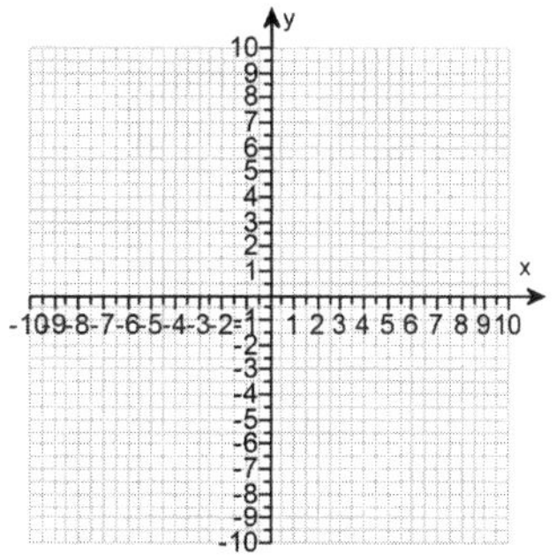

    ID: 5.1.10

11. Write the coordinates of the point shown on the graph.

    The coordinates of point A are __________.
    (Type an ordered pair.)

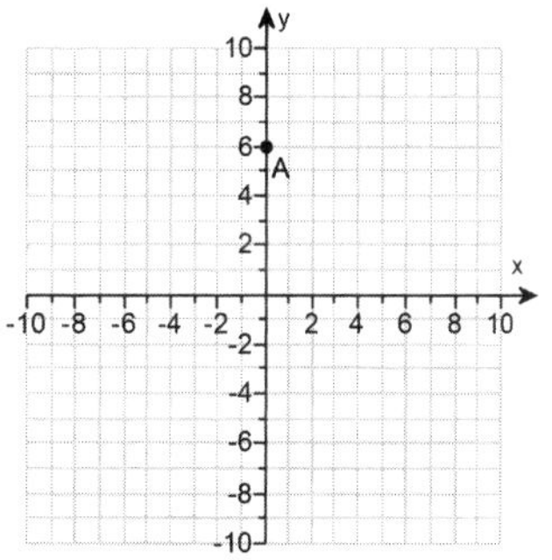

    ID: 5.1.11

12. Write the coordinates of the point shown on the graph.

The coordinates of point A are ___________.
(Type an ordered pair.)

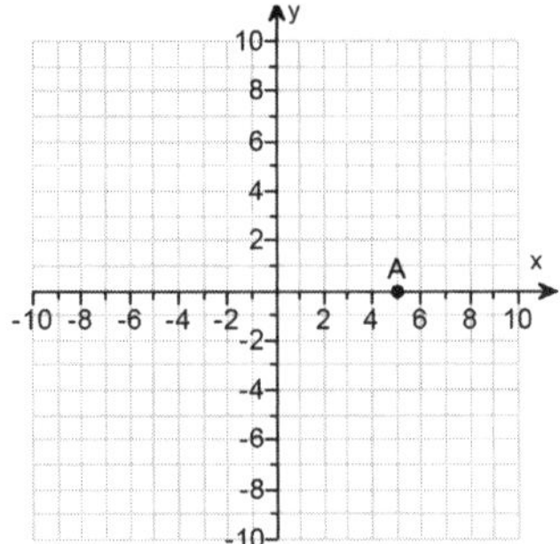

ID: 5.1.12

13. Write the coordinates of the point shown on the graph.

The coordinates of point A are ___________.
(Type an ordered pair.)

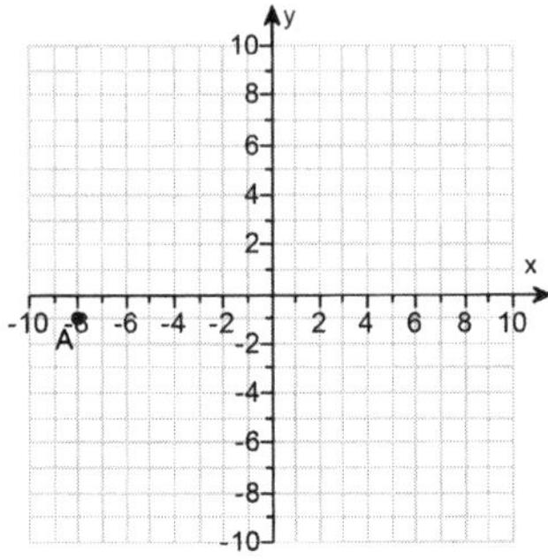

ID: 5.1.13

14. Write the coordinates of the point shown on the graph.

The coordinates of point A are ___________.
(Type an ordered pair.)

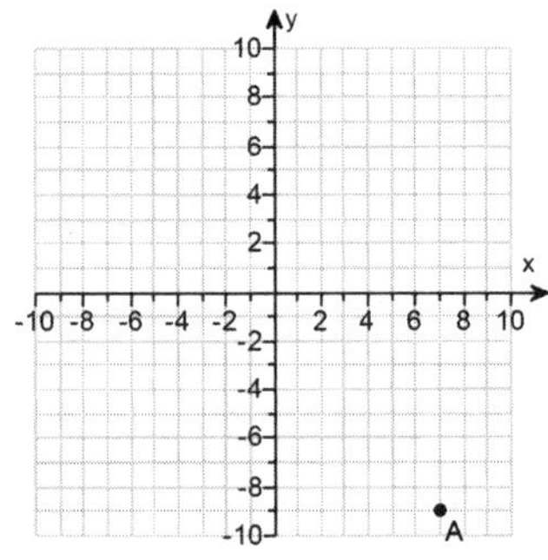

ID: 5.1.14

!*15. The distance you drive is proportional to the amount of gas used. Driving 180 miles uses 5 gallons of gas. Assume you have already driven 100 miles. Complete parts (a) through (c).

(a) Fill in the following table for total distance driven.

Gas (gal)	Distance (mi)
0	________
5	________
10	________
15	________

(Type integers or decimals.)

(b) Represent the relationship between distance driven, D, and gas used, G, with an equation.

D = ___________ • G + ___________
(Type integers or decimals.)

(c) Use the graphing tool to graph this equation. Use the initial value and another point when drawing the line. Choose the correct graph below.

○ **A.**

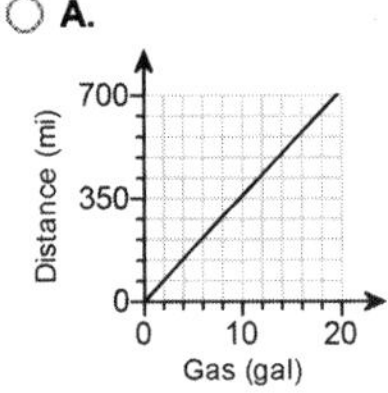

○ **B.**

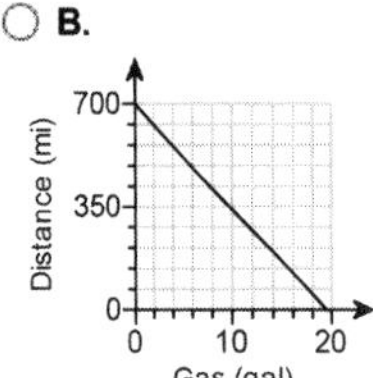

○ **C.**

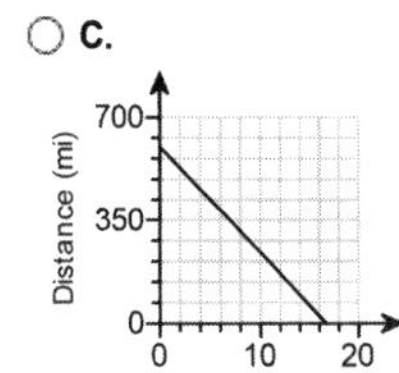

○ **D.**

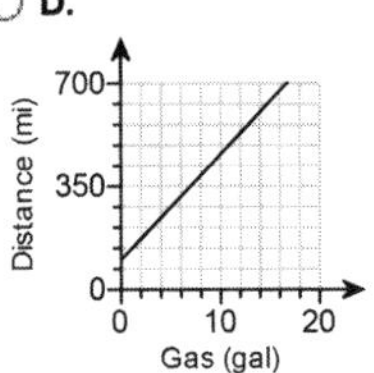

ID: 5.1.15

!* 16. The cost of an airline ticket is proportional to the distance traveled at a rate of $11 per 50 miles flown. Assume that there is a base charge of $25. Complete parts (a) through (c).

(a) Fill in the following table for total cost.

Distance (mi)	Cost ($)
0	______
50	______
100	______
150	______

(Type integers or decimals. Do not include the $ symbol in your answers.)

(b) Represent the relationship between cost, C, and distance flown, D, with an equation.

C = ________ • D + ________

(Type integers or decimals. Do not include the $ symbol in your answers.)

(c) Use the graphing tool to graph this equation. Use the initial value and another point when drawing the line. Choose the correct graph below.

○ **A.**

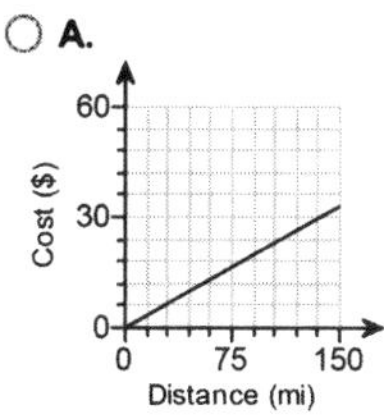

○ **B.**

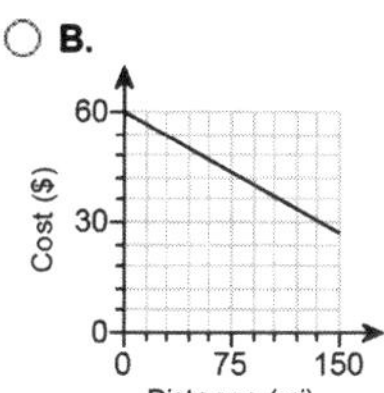

○ **C.**

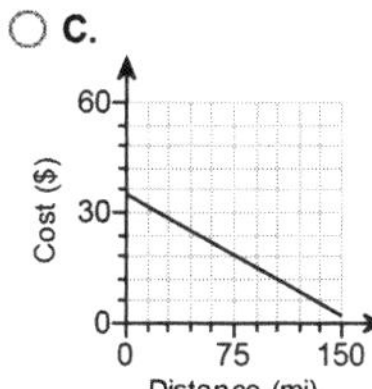

○ **D.**

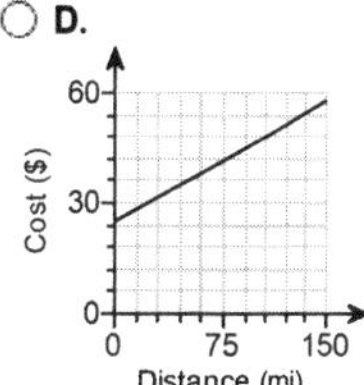

ID: 5.1.16

!* 17. Your monthly electric bill is proportional to the number of kilowatt-hours (kwh) of energy used at a rate of 4.4 cents per kwh. There is a monthly base charge of $17.50. Complete parts (a) through (c).

(a) Fill in the following table for total monthly cost.

Energy (kwh)	Cost ($)
0	______
500	______
1000	______
1500	______

(Type integers or decimals. Do not include the $ symbol in your answers.)

(b) Represent the relationship between cost ($), C, and energy used (kwh), E, with an equation.

C = ________ • E + ________

(Type integers or decimals. Do not include the $ symbol in your answers.)

(c) Use the graphing tool to graph this equation. Use the initial value and another point when drawing the line. Choose the correct graph below.

○ **A.**

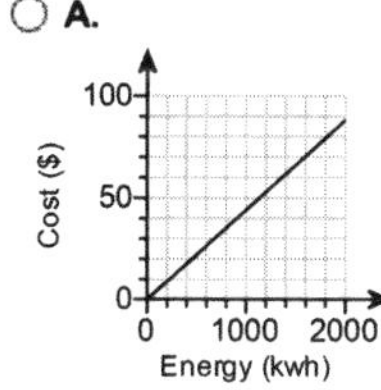

○ **B.**

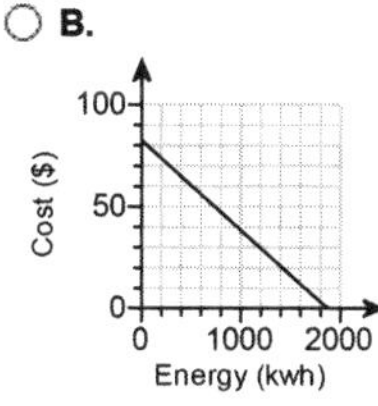

○ **C.**

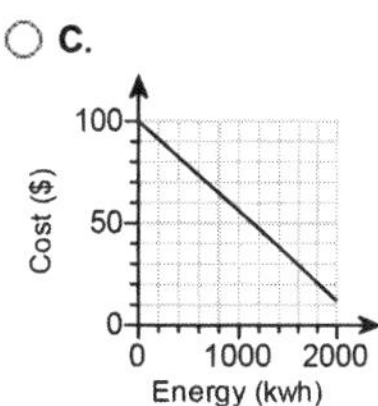

○ **D.**

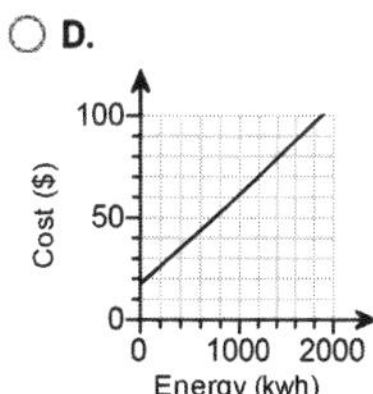

ID: 5.1.17

* 18. Determine which ordered pairs satisfy the given equation.

$x + 5y = 19$ (4,3) (−1,4) (0,−3)

Select all ordered pairs that satisfy the given equation.

☐ **A.** (4,3)
☐ **B.** (0, −3)
☐ **C.** (−1,4)
☐ **D.** None of the ordered pairs satisfy the equation.

ID: 5.1.18

∗19. Determine which ordered pairs satisfy the given equation.

$2x - 3y = -7$ $\left(-\frac{7}{2},0\right)$ (4,5) (0, − 4)

Select all ordered pairs that satisfy the given equation.

☐ **A.** (0, − 4)
☐ **B.** $\left(-\frac{7}{2},0\right)$
☐ **C.** (4,5)
☐ **D.** None of the ordered pairs satisfy the equation.

ID: 5.1.19

---

20. Determine which ordered pairs satisfy the given equation.

$2y = 3x + 7$ (1,5) (6, − 27) (0,27)

Select all ordered pairs that satisfy the given equation.

☐ **A.** (0,27)
☐ **B.** (6, − 27)
☐ **C.** (1,5)
☐ **D.** None of the ordered pairs satisfy the equation.

ID: 5.1.20

---

21. Determine which ordered pair does not satisfy the equation.

$\frac{x}{4} + \frac{7y}{8} = 5$

Choose the ordered pair that does not satisfy the equation.

○ **A.** (20, 0)
○ **B.** $\left(0, \frac{7}{40}\right)$
○ **C.** $\left(12, \frac{16}{7}\right)$

ID: 5.1.21

!∗ 22. The decline in per capita beer consumption is shown in the scatter plot.
(a) What is the slope of the linear trendline?
(b) Interpret the slope in real world terms by filling in the blanks.

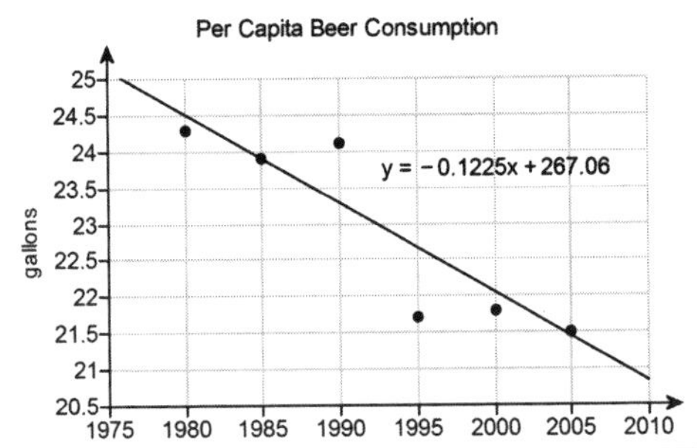

(a) The slope of the linear trendline is __________.
(Type an integer or a decimal.)

(b) The (1) __________ is changing by (2) __________ (3) __________ per (4) __________

(1) ○ number of years
○ number of gallons
○ Per Capita Beer Consumption

(2) ○ years
○ − 0.1225
○ 267.06

(3) ○ gallons
○ Per Capita Beer Consumption
○ years

(4) ○ gallons.
○ five years.
○ year.

ID: 5.2.1

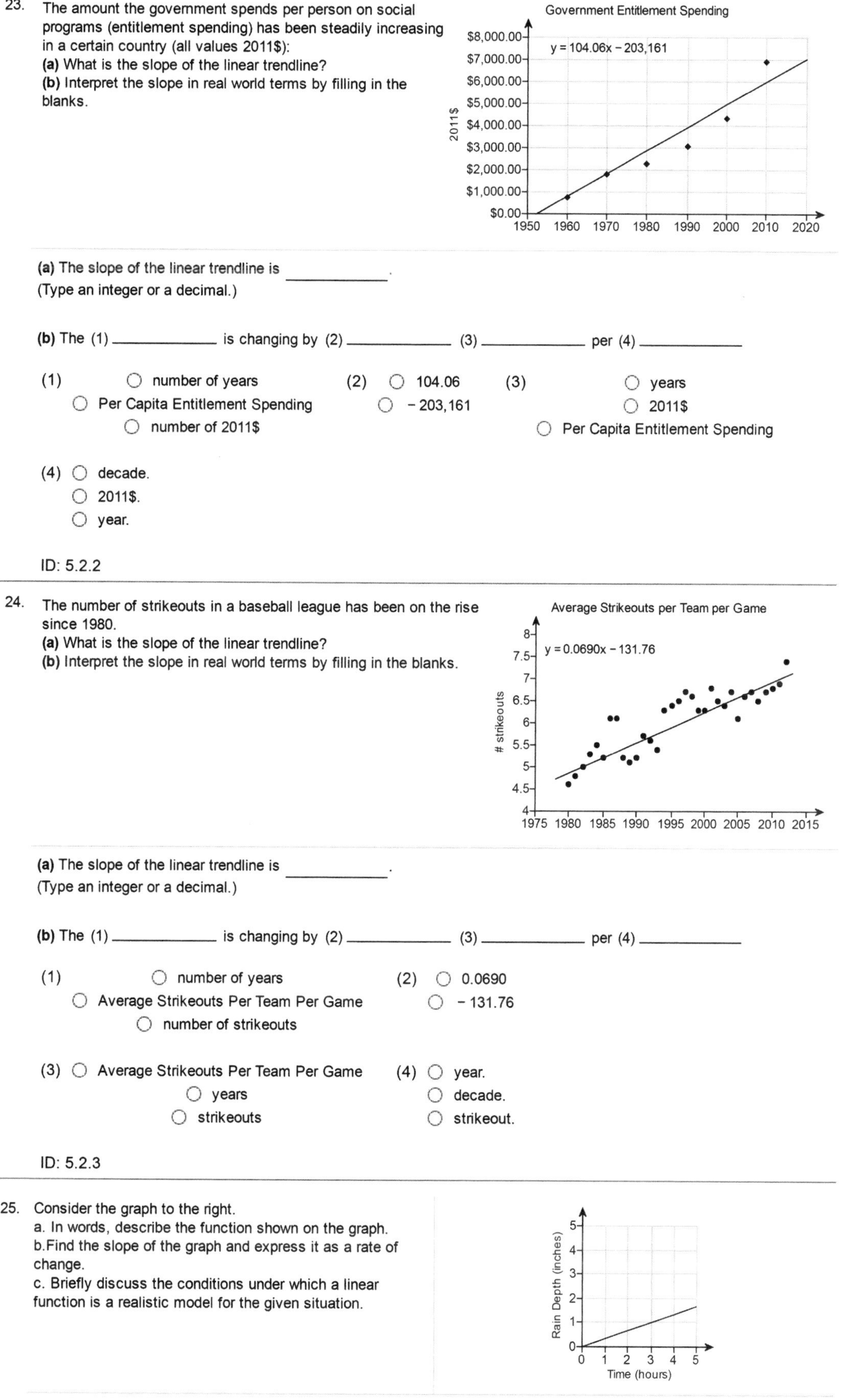

!* 23. The amount the government spends per person on social programs (entitlement spending) has been steadily increasing in a certain country (all values 2011$):
(a) What is the slope of the linear trendline?
(b) Interpret the slope in real world terms by filling in the blanks.

Government Entitlement Spending

y = 104.06x − 203,161

2011$: $8,000.00, $7,000.00, $6,000.00, $5,000.00, $4,000.00, $3,000.00, $2,000.00, $1,000.00, $0.00

1950 1960 1970 1980 1990 2000 2010 2020

(a) The slope of the linear trendline is __________.
(Type an integer or a decimal.)

(b) The (1) __________ is changing by (2) __________ (3) __________ per (4) __________

(1) ○ number of years
○ Per Capita Entitlement Spending
○ number of 2011$

(2) ○ 104.06
○ − 203,161

(3) ○ years
○ 2011$
○ Per Capita Entitlement Spending

(4) ○ decade.
○ 2011$.
○ year.

ID: 5.2.2

!* 24. The number of strikeouts in a baseball league has been on the rise since 1980.
(a) What is the slope of the linear trendline?
(b) Interpret the slope in real world terms by filling in the blanks.

Average Strikeouts per Team per Game

y = 0.0690x − 131.76

strikeouts: 8, 7.5, 7, 6.5, 6, 5.5, 5, 4.5, 4

1975 1980 1985 1990 1995 2000 2005 2010 2015

(a) The slope of the linear trendline is __________.
(Type an integer or a decimal.)

(b) The (1) __________ is changing by (2) __________ (3) __________ per (4) __________

(1) ○ number of years
○ Average Strikeouts Per Team Per Game
○ number of strikeouts

(2) ○ 0.0690
○ − 131.76

(3) ○ Average Strikeouts Per Team Per Game
○ years
○ strikeouts

(4) ○ year.
○ decade.
○ strikeout.

ID: 5.2.3

* 25. Consider the graph to the right.
a. In words, describe the function shown on the graph.
b. Find the slope of the graph and express it as a rate of change.
c. Briefly discuss the conditions under which a linear function is a realistic model for the given situation.

Rain Depth (inches): 0 1 2 3 4 5

Time (hours): 0 1 2 3 4 5

*25. (cont.) a. Select the correct answer below.

- ○ **A.** According to the function, the rain depth decreases by 1 inch every 3 hours.
- ○ **B.** According to the function, the rain depth increases by 1 inch every 3 hours.
- ○ **C.** According to the function, the rain depth decreases by 3 inches every 1 hour.
- ○ **D.** According to the function, the rain depth increases by 3 inches every 1 hour.

b. Calculate the slope and represent it as a rate of change.

rate of change = ___________ (1) ___________
(Type an integer or a fraction.)

c. Select the correct answer below.

- ○ **A.** It is a good model if the rainfall is not constant four hours.
- ○ **B.** It is a good model if the rainfall is constant for two hours and then changing for two hours.
- ○ **C.** It is a good model if the rainfall is constant for four hours.
- ○ **D.** It is a good model if the rainfall is changing for two hours, then constant for two hours.

(1) ○ inch(es) per hour
○ hour(s) per inch

ID: 5.2.4

---

26. Consider the graph to the right.
a. In words, describe the function shown on the graph.
b. Find the slope of the graph and express it as a rate of change.
c. Briefly discuss the conditions under which a linear function is a realistic model for the given situation.

a. Select the correct answer below.

- ○ **A.** According to the function, the distance from home decreases by 700 miles every 9 hours.
- ○ **B.** According to the function, the distance from home decreases by 9 miles every 700 hours.
- ○ **C.** According to the function, the distance from home increases by 700 miles every 9 hours.
- ○ **D.** According to the function, the distance from home increases by 9 miles every 700 hours.

b. Calculate the slope and represent it as a rate of change.

rate of change = ___________ (1) ___________
(Round to the tenths place as needed.)

c. Select the correct answer below.

- ○ **A.** It is a good model if speed is constant for 9 hours.
- ○ **B.** It is a good model if speed is constant for two hours and afterwards is changing.
- ○ **C.** It is a good model if speed is not constant for 9 hours.
- ○ **D.** It is a good model if speed is changing for two hours, then afterwards is constant.

(1) ○ miles per hour
○ hours per mile

ID: 5.2.5

---

27. Consider the graph to the right.
a. In words, describe the function shown on the graph.
b. Find the slope of the graph and express it as a rate of change.
c. Briefly discuss the conditions under which a linear function is a realistic model for the given situation.

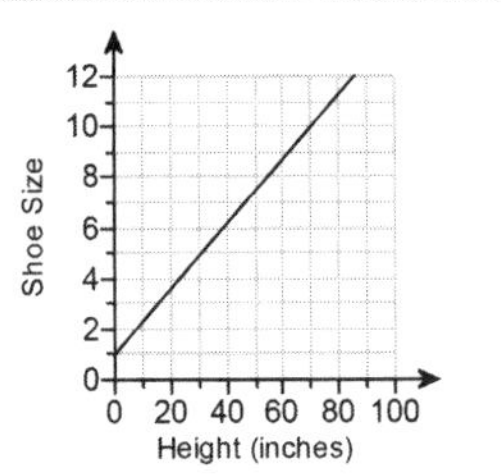

* 27. (cont.) a. Select the correct answer below.

○ **A.** According to the function, shoe size decreases by 9 every 70 inches.
○ **B.** According to the function, shoe size decreases by 70 every 9 inches.
○ **C.** According to the function, shoe size increases by 9 every 70 inches.
○ **D.** According to the function, shoe size increases by 70 every 9 inches.

b. Calculate the slope and represent it as a rate of change.

rate of change = ____________ (1) ____________
(Round to four decimal places as needed.)

c. Select the correct answer below.

○ **A.** This model is very accurate.
○ **B.** This model is accurate if no one wears a shoe above size 12.
○ **C.** This model is a rough approximation at best.
○ **D.** This model is completely inaccurate.

(1) ○ size per inch
○ inch per size

ID: 5.2.6

---

28. Determine the slope of the line through the given points.

$(-3, -4)$ and $(-1, 4)$

Select the correct choice below and, if necessary, fill in the answer box to complete your choice.

○ **A.** The slope is ____________. (Type an integer or a simplified fraction.)
○ **B.** The slope is undefined.

ID: 5.2.7

---

29. Determine the slope of the line through the given points.

$(4,3)$ and $(9, -7)$

Select the correct choice below and, if necessary, fill in the answer box to complete your choice.

○ **A.** The slope m = ____________. (Simplify your answer. Type an integer or a fraction.)
○ **B.** The slope is undefined.

ID: 5.2.8

---

30. Using the slope formula, find the slope of the line through the given points.

$(-5,6)$ and $(3,6)$

What is the slope of the line? Select the correct choice below and, if necessary, fill in the answer box to complete your choice.

○ **A.** The slope of the line is ____________. (Type an integer or a simplified fraction.)
○ **B.** The slope of the line is undefined.

ID: 5.2.9

---

31. Determine the slope of the line through the given points.

$(10, -2)$ and $(10, -9)$

Select the correct choice below and, if necessary, fill in the answer box to complete your choice.

○ **A.** The slope is ____________. (Simplify your answer. Type an integer or a fraction.)
○ **B.** The slope is undefined.

ID: 5.2.10

---

32. A portion of road A climbs steadily for 195 feet over a horizontal distance of 2600 feet. A portion of road B climbs steadily for 160 feet over a horizontal distance of 3200 feet.
Which road is steeper?

Which road is steeper?

○ road A
○ road B

ID: 5.2.11

33. Ski run A declines steadily for 30 yards over a horizontal distance of 700 yards. Ski run B declines steadily for 40 yards over a horizontal distance of 800 yards. Which ski run is steeper? Explain.

Which ski run is steeper? Choose the correct answer below.

○ Ski run A
○ Ski run B

Explain. Choose the correct answer below.

○ **A.** Ski run B's ratio of vertical distance to horizontal distance is greater than Ski run A's.
○ **B.** Ski run A's ratio of vertical distance to horizontal distance is greater than Ski run B's.

ID: 5.2.12

34. Plot the two given points and then sketch the line that contains the two points. Find the run and rise in going from the first point listed to the second point listed. Find the slope of the line.

(1,4) and (3,9)

Which graph contains the points (1,4) and (3,9)?

○ **A.**

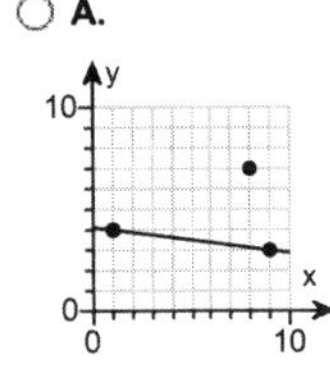

○ **B.**

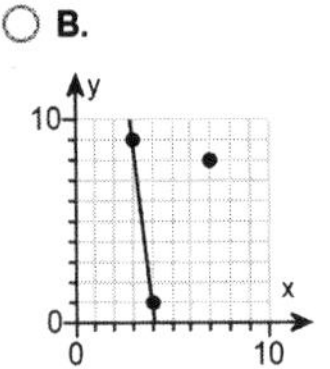

○ **C.**

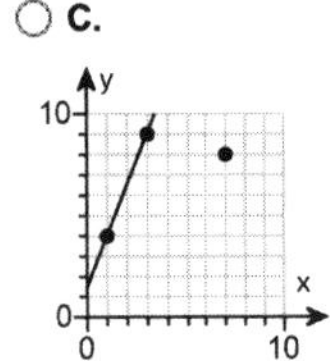

○ **D.**

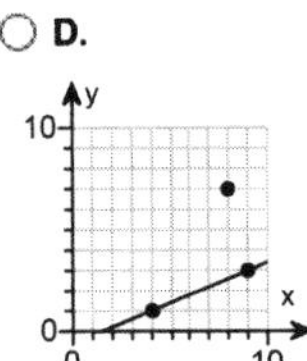

Find the rise of the line.

rise = ____________

Find the run of the line.

run = ____________

Find the slope of the line. Select the correct choice below and fill in any answer boxes within your choice.

○ **A.** slope = ____________
(Type an integer or a simplified fraction.)

○ **B.** The slope is undefined.

ID: 5.2.13

*35. Plot the two given points and then sketch the line that contains the points. Find the run and rise in going from the first point listed to the second point listed. Find the slope of the line.

(− 8, − 3) and (− 3, − 18)

Choose the correct graph below.

○ A.
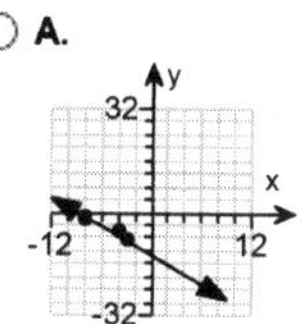

○ B.
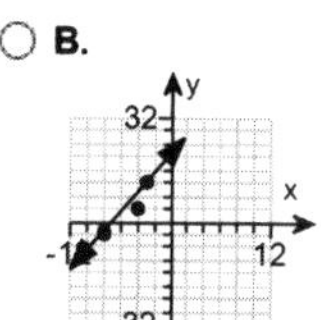

○ C.
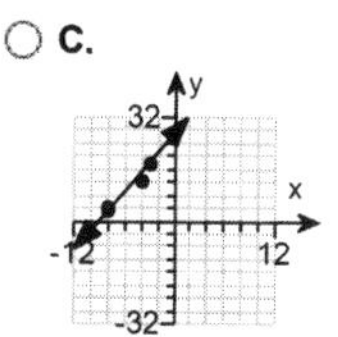

○ D.
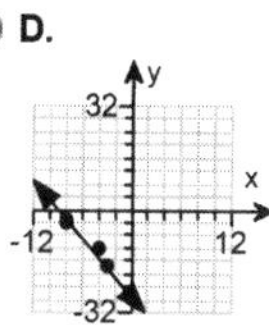

The run of the line is __________. (Type an integer or a simplified fraction.)

The rise of the line is __________. (Type an integer or a simplified fraction.)

The slope of the line is __________. (Type an integer or a simplified fraction.)

ID: 5.2.14

---

36. Use the slope formula to find the slope of the line that passes through the two given points. State whether the line is increasing, decreasing, horizontal, or vertical.

(3,5) and (4,4)

Select the correct choice below and, if necessary, fill in the answer box to complete your choice.

○ A. The slope is m = __________. (Type an integer or a simplified fraction.)

○ B. The slope is undefined.

Is the line increasing, decreasing, horizontal, or vertical?

○ A. horizontal

○ B. decreasing

○ C. vertical

○ D. increasing

ID: 5.2.15

---

37. Find the slope of the line passing through the given points. State whether the line is increasing, decreasing, horizontal, or vertical.

(− 1,2) and (3, − 2)

Select the correct choice below and fill in any answer boxes present in your choice.

○ A. The slope of the line is __________. (Type an integer or a simplified fraction.)

○ B. The slope of the line is undefined.

State whether the line is increasing, decreasing, horizontal, or vertical. Choose the correct answer below.

○ A. The line is decreasing.

○ B. The line is vertical.

○ C. The line is horizontal.

○ D. The line is increasing.

ID: 5.2.16

---

38. Find the slope of the line passing through the given points. State whether the line is increasing, decreasing, horizontal, or vertical.

(− 8, − 5) and (− 5, − 7)

Select the correct choice below and fill in any answer boxes present in your choice.

○ A. The slope of the line is __________. (Type an integer or a simplified fraction.)

○ B. The slope of the line is undefined.

State whether the line is increasing, decreasing, horizontal, or vertical. Choose the correct answer below.

○ A. The line is decreasing.

○ B. The line is vertical.

○ C. The line is horizontal.

○ D. The line is increasing.

ID: 5.2.17

---

39. Use the slope formula to find the slope of the line that passes through the two given points. State whether the line is increasing, decreasing, horizontal, or vertical.

(9,2) and (1,2)

Select the correct choice below and, if necessary, fill in the answer box to complete your choice.

○ **A.** The slope is m = __________. (Type an integer or a simplified fraction.)

○ **B.** The slope is undefined.

Is the line increasing, decreasing, horizontal, or vertical?

○ **A.** decreasing
○ **B.** horizontal
○ **C.** vertical
○ **D.** increasing

ID: 5.2.18

---

40. Find the approximate slope of the line that contains the points (− 4.7,5.1) and (− 4.3,1.8). State whether the line is increasing, decreasing, horizontal, or vertical.

Select the correct choice below and, if necessary, fill in the answer box to complete your choice.

○ **A.** The slope is __________.
(Type an integer or decimal rounded to two decimal places as needed.)

○ **B.** The slope is undefined.

Is the line increasing, decreasing, horizontal, or vertical?

○ Increasing
○ Decreasing
○ Vertical
○ Horizontal

ID: 5.2.19

---

41. Find the approximate slope of the line that contains the points (4.6, − 2.2) and (5.9, − 0.5). State whether the line is increasing, decreasing, horizontal, or vertical.

Select the correct choice below and, if necessary, fill in the answer box to complete your choice.

○ **A.** The slope is __________.
(Type an integer or decimal rounded to two decimal places as needed.)

○ **B.** The slope is undefined.

Is the line increasing, decreasing, horizontal, or vertical?

○ Decreasing
○ Horizontal
○ Vertical
○ Increasing

ID: 5.2.20

---

42. Find the approximate slope of the line that contains the points (− 4.98, − 3.27) and (− 9.63, − 2.11). State whether the line is increasing, decreasing, horizontal, or vertical.

Select the correct choice below and, if necessary, fill in the answer box to complete your choice.

○ **A.** The slope is approximately __________.
(Type an integer or decimal rounded to two decimal places as needed.)

○ **B.** The slope is undefined.

Is the line increasing, decreasing, horizontal, or vertical?

○ Vertical
○ Increasing
○ Horizontal
○ Decreasing

ID: 5.2.21

---

43. Find the slope of the line.

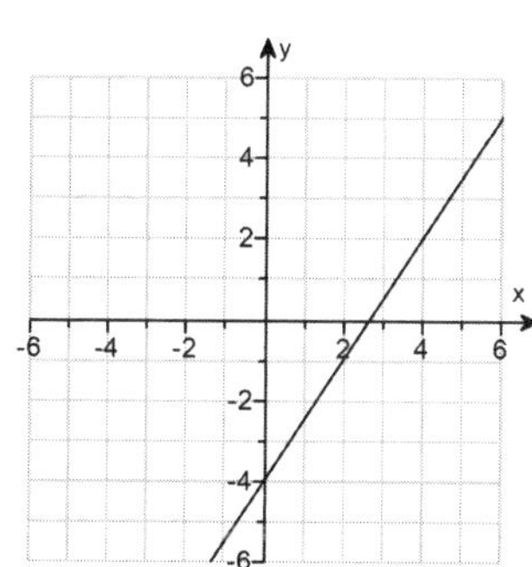

Select the correct choice below and, if necessary, fill in the answer box to complete your choice.

○ **A.** m = ________
(Type an integer or a simplified fraction.)

○ **B.** The slope is undefined.

ID: 5.2.22

---

44. Find the slope of the line shown on the graph to the right.

Select the correct choice below and, if necessary, fill in the answer box to complete your choice.

○ **A.** The slope of the line is ________.
(Simplify your answer. Type an integer or a fraction.)

○ **B.** The slope is undefined.

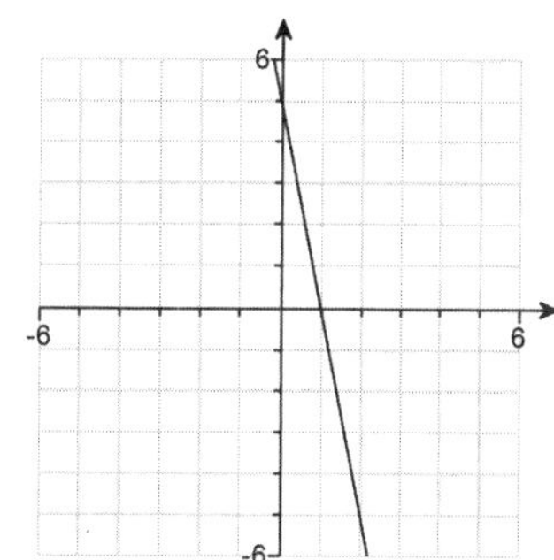

ID: 5.2.23

---

45. For the line sketched on the right, determine whether the line's slope is positive, negative, zero, or undefined.

Is the slope of the line positive, negative, zero, or undefined?

○ Undefined
○ Negative
○ Zero
○ Positive

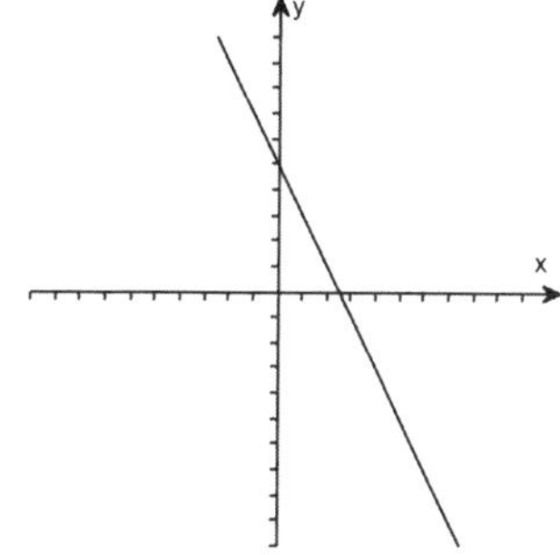

ID: 5.2.24

---

46. Sketch a line that meets the description.

The slope is a positive number near zero.

Choose the correct graph on the right.

○ **A.**

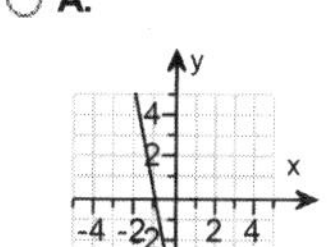

○ **B.**

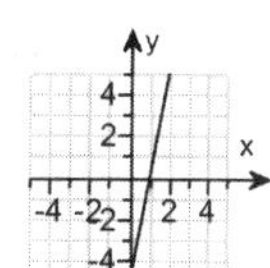

○ **C.**

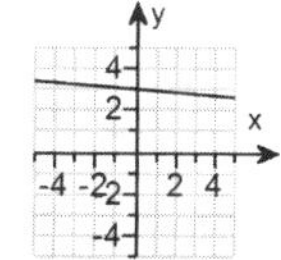

○ **D.**

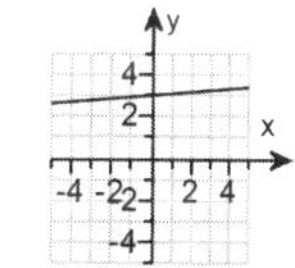

ID: 5.2.25

---

*47. A person's annual salary increases by $12,300 over a 12-year period. Find the average rate of change of the salary per year.

The average rate of change is $ ____________ per year.

ID: 5.2.26

48. An airplane's altitude declines steadily by 22,425 feet over a 13-minute period. Find the rate of change of the airplane's altitude per minute.

The average rate of change is ____________ feet per minute.

ID: 5.2.27

*49. In response to rising concerns about identity theft, the number of models of paper shredders a company manufactures increased approximately steadily from 2 models in 1990 to 33 models in 2006. Find the average rate of change of the number of shredder models manufactured per year between 1990 and 2006.

The average rate of change of the number of paper shredders manufactured per year between 1990 and 2006 was

____________.
(Type an integer or decimal rounded to two decimal places as needed.)

ID: 5.2.28

50. The number of trips from country A to country B has declined approximately linearly from 41.0 million in 2001 to 26.5 million in 2005. Find the average rate of change of the number of trips per year.

The average rate of change of the number of trips per year was ____________ million.
(Type an integer or decimal rounded to two decimal places as needed.)

ID: 5.2.29

51. The percentage of citizens who have trust in newspapers declined approximately linearly from 34% in 2000 to 25% in 2002. Find the average rate of change per year of the percentage of citizens who have trust in newspapers.

The average rate of change per year of the percentage of citizens who have trust in newspapers was ____________%.
(Type an integer or decimal rounded to two decimal places as needed.)

ID: 5.2.30

52. In a city, the average price of a three-bedroom condominium is $1,176,526, and that of a five-bedroom condominium is $3,599,340. Find the average rate of change of price with respect to the number of bedrooms.

The average rate of change of price with respect to the number of bedrooms is $ ____________.
(Type an integer or a decimal.)

ID: 5.2.31

*53. The number of country households that paid bills online was 28 million in 2006 and has increased by about 7 million per year. Let n be the number of households (in millions) that paid bills online at t years since 2006. Complete parts **a.** and **b.**

a. Is there a linear relationship between t and n? Explain. If the relationship is linear, find the slope and describe what it means in this situation.

Choose the correct answer below, and if necessary, fill in the answer box.

- ○ **A.** Yes. Since the rate of change of the number of country households that paid bills online per year is a constant 7 million per year, the variables t and n are linearly related. The slope is ____________. The number of households that pay bills online has increased by ____________ million per year.
- ○ **B.** Yes. Since the rate of change of the number of country households that paid bills online per year is a constant 7 million per year, the variables t and n are linearly related. The slope is ____________. The number of households that pay bills online has decreased by ____________ million per year.
- ○ **C.** No. Since the rate of change of the number of country households that paid bills online per year varries per year, the variables t and n are not linearly related.

b. Describe the Rule of Four as it applies to this situation.

i. Use an equation to describe the number of households (in millions) that paid bills online t years since 2006.

n = ____________ (Type an expression using t as the variable.)

* 53. (cont.) **ii.** Use a table of values of t and n to describe the situation.

Years since 2006 t	Number of households (millions) n
0	______
1	______
2	______
3	______
4	______

(Type integers or decimals.)

iii. Use a graph to describe the situation. Choose the correct graph below.

○ **A.**
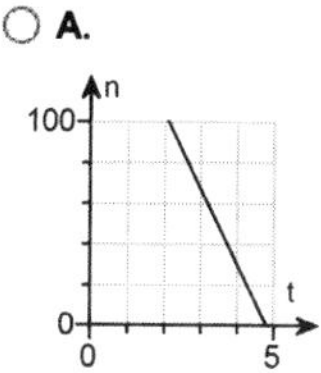

○ **B.**
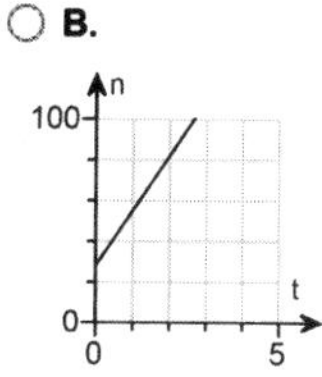

○ **C.**
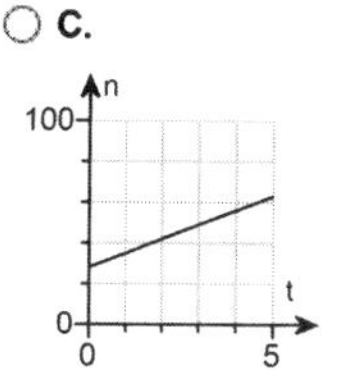

○ **D.**
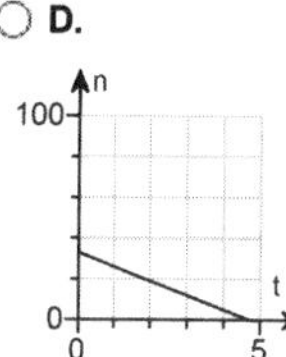

ID: 5.2.32

---

54. A student's savings account has a balance of $4800 on September 1. Each month, the balance declines by $450. Let B be the balance (in dollars) at t months since September 1.
Complete parts **a.** through **e.**

a. Find the slope of the linear model that describes this situation. What does it mean in this situation?

The slope is ______. The balance declines by $______ per month.

b. Find the B-intercept of the model. What does it mean in this situation?

The B-intercept is ______. (Type an ordered pair.)

The balance is $______ on September 1.

c. Find an equation of the model.

B = ______ (Type an expression using t as the variable.)

d. Perform a unit analysis of the equation found in part **c.**

Choose the correct answer below.

○ **A.** The unit of the expression on the left side of the equation is dollars, but the unit of the expression on the right side of the equation is months, which suggests that the equation is incorrect.

○ **B.** The unit of the expression on the left side of the equation is months, but the unit of the expression on the right side of the equation is dollars, which suggests that the equation is incorrect.

○ **C.** The units of the expressions on both sides of the equation are dollars, which suggests that the equation is correct.

○ **D.** The units of the expressions on both sides of the equation are months, which suggests that the equation is correct.

e. Find the balance on February 1 (5 months after September 1).

$______

ID: 5.2.33

---

55. For the spring semester 2009, part-time students at a college paid $433 per credit (unit or hour) for tuition and paid a mandatory part-time student fee of $30 per semester. Let T be the total one-semester cost (in dollars) of tuition plus part-time student fee for c credits of classes.
Complete parts **a.** through **d.**

a. Find the slope of the linear model that describes this situation. What does it mean in this situation?

The slope is ______. The tuition increases by $______ per credit.

b. Find an equation of the model.

T = ______ (Type an expression using c as the variable.)

*55. (cont.) **c.** Perform a unit analysis of the equation found in part **b.**

Choose the correct choice below.

- ◯ **A.** The unit of the expression on the left side of the equation is credits, but the unit of the expression on the right side of the equation is dollars, which suggests that the equation is incorrect.
- ◯ **B.** The unit of the expression on the left side of the equation is dollars, but the unit of the expression on the right side of the equation is credits, which suggests that the equation is incorrect.
- ◯ **C.** The units of the expressions on both sides of the equation are credits, which suggests that the equation is correct.
- ◯ **D.** The units of the expressions on both sides of the equation are dollars, which suggests that the equation is correct.

d. What was the total one-semester cost of tuition plus part-time student fee for 5 credits of classes?

$ __________

ID: 5.2.34

---

*56. Let n be the number of oil refineries at t years since 2003. A reasonable model of the number of oil refineries is $n = -4.61t + 174.68$.
a. What is the slope? What does it mean in this situation?
b. What is the n-intercept? What does it mean in this situation?
c. Predict the number of refineries in 2016.

a. What is the slope?

m = __________

What does the slope mean in this situation?

- ◯ **A.** It means that the number of refineries are decreasing by about 4.61 per year.
- ◯ **B.** It means that the number of refineries are decreasing by about 174.68 per year.
- ◯ **C.** It means the number of refineries in 2003 was about 174.68.
- ◯ **D.** It means the number of refineries in 2003 was about 4.61.

b. What is the n-intercept?

__________ (Type an ordered pair.)

What does the n-intercept mean in this situation?

- ◯ **A.** It means the number of refineries in 2003 was about 4.61.
- ◯ **B.** It means that the number of refineries are decreasing by about 174.68 per year.
- ◯ **C.** It means the number of refineries in 2003 was about 174.68.
- ◯ **D.** It means that the number of refineries are decreasing by about 4.61 per year.

c. Predict the number of refineries in 2016.

The number of refineries will be about __________.
(Round to the nearest whole number as needed.)

ID: 5.2.35

---

57. Let s be the sales of frozen-food bowls (in millions) in the year that is t years since 2000. A reasonable model of frozen-food bowl sales is $s = 32t + 397$.
Complete parts **a.** through **c.**

a. What is the slope? What does it mean in this situation?
Select the correct choice below and fill in the answer boxes within your choice.

- ◯ **A.** The slope is __________. The sales of frozen-food bowls are increasing by __________ million per year.
- ◯ **B.** The slope is __________. The sales of frozen-food bowls are decreasing by __________ million per year.

b. What is the s-intercept? What does it mean in this situation?

The s-intercept is __________. (Type an ordered pair.)

There were __________ million frozen-food bowls sold in 2000.

c. Estimate the sales in 2005.

The sales of frozen-food bowls in 2005 were about __________ million.

ID: 5.2.36

58. The number of Internet users in a country for various years are shown in the table below.
Let n be the number (in millions) of Internet users in the country at t years since 1995. A model of the situation is $n = 21.7t + 17.6$.

Internet users in the country

Year	Number of users (millions)
1996	39
1997	62
1998	84
1999	104
2000	121
2001	143
2002	165
2003	181
2004	209

Complete parts **a.** through **e.**

a. Use a graphing calculator to draw a scattergram and the model in the same viewing window.
Choose the correct graph below.

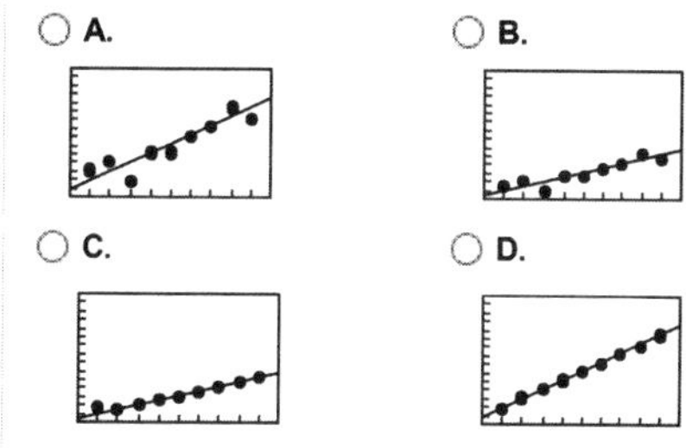

○ **A.** ○ **B.**
○ **C.** ○ **D.**

[0, 10] by [0, 300]

Does the line come close to the data points?

○ Yes
○ No

b. What is the slope? What does it mean in this situation?

The slope is ________. The number of internet users is increasing by ________ million per year.

c. Find the rates of change of the number of users (in millions) per year from each year to the next.

Internet users in the country

Year	Number of users (millions)	Rates of change of the number of users per year from each year to the next (millions)
1996	39	--------
1997	62	________
1998	84	________
1999	104	________
2000	121	________
2001	143	________
2002	165	________
2003	181	________
2004	209	________

Compare the rates of change with your result in part **b.** Choose the correct answer below.

○ **A.** All of the rates of change are fairly close to 17.6 mill
○ **B.** All of the rates of change are fairly close to 21.7 mill
○ **C.** All of the rates of change are not close to 21.7 millio
○ **D.** All of the rates of change are not close to 17.6 millio

d. What is the n-intercept? What does it mean in this situation?
The n-intercept is ________.
(Type an ordered pair.)

There were ________ million Internet users in 1995.

e. Predict the number of users in 2010.

________ million users
(Type an integer or a decimal.)

If the prediction that the country's population will be about 309 million in 2010 is correct, has model breakdown occurred?

○ **A.** Model breakdown has not occurred.
○ **B.** Model breakdown has occurred.

ID: 5.2.37

59. A person is on a car trip. Let d be the distance (in miles) traveled in t hours of driving. The line in the figure describes the relationship between t and d.
a. Is the car traveling at a constant speed?
b. What is the speed of the car?

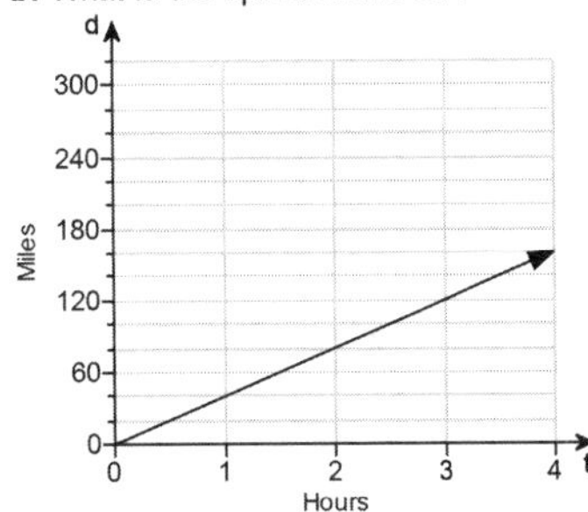

a. Is the car traveling at a constant speed?

○ Yes
○ No

b. What is the speed of the car?

The speed of the car is ________ mph.

ID: 5.2.38

---

*60. Let F be the temperature (in degrees Fahrenheit) at t hours after noon. The line in the figure shown below describes the relationship between t and F.

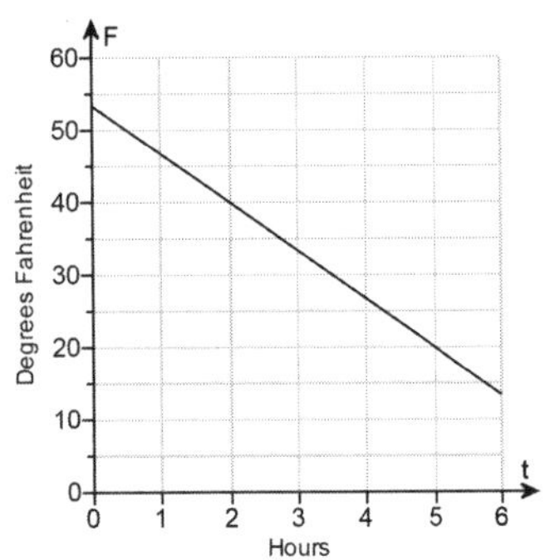

Complete parts **a.** and **b.**

a. Is the rate of change of temperature per hour constant? Explain.

○ **A.** Yes because there is a linear relationship between t and F.
○ **B.** No because there is no linear relationship between t and F.

b. What is the rate of change of temperature per hour?

________ °F
(Type an integer or decimal rounded to two decimal places as needed.)

ID: 5.2.39

---

61. A math tutor charges $55 per hour. Let c be the total charge (in dollars) for t hours of tutoring. Are t and c linearly related? If so, find the slope and describe what it means in this situation.

Choose the correct answer below and, if necessary, fill in the answer box to complete your choice.

○ **A.** Yes. The slope is ________. The total charge decreases by $ ________ per hour.
○ **B.** Yes. The slope is ________. The total charge increases by $ ________ per hour.
○ **C.** No

ID: 5.2.40

---

62. Two sets of points are described in the table. For each set, find an equation of a line that contains the points.

Set 1		Set 2	
x	y	x	y
0	7	0	9
1	9	1	2
2	11	2	−5
3	13	3	−12
4	15	4	−19

The equation of the line that describes set 1 is y = ________. (Simplify your answer.)

The equation of the line that describes set 2 is y = ________. (Simplify your answer.)

ID: 5.2.41

!* 63. The number of strikeouts in a baseball league has been on the rise since 1980.
(a) What is the y-intercept of the linear trendline?
(b) Interpret the y-intercept in real world terms.

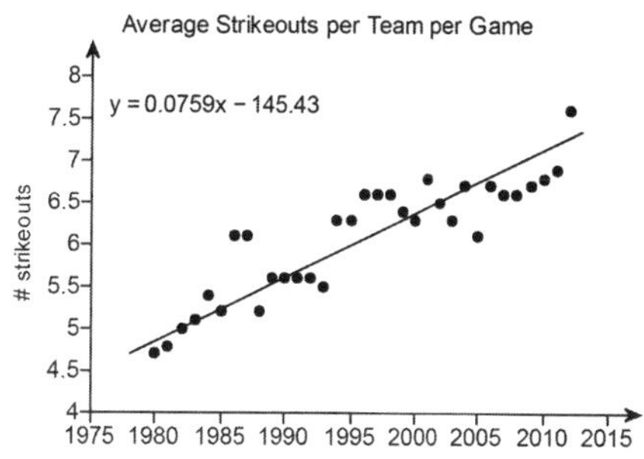

(a) The y-intercept of the linear trendline is ________.
(Type an integer or a decimal.)

(b) Choose the correct answer below.

○ **A.** The Average Strikeouts Per Team Per Game in 0 CE was about 4.5, which makes no sense in real world terms.

○ **B.** The Average Strikeouts Per Team Per Game in 1975 was − 145.43, which makes no sense in real world terms.

○ **C.** The Average Strikeouts Per Team Per Game in 0 CE was − 145.43, which makes no sense in real world terms.

○ **D.** The Average Strikeouts Per Team Per Game in 1975 was about 4.5.

ID: 5.2.42

!* 64. The amount the government spends per person on social programs (entitlement spending) has been steadily increasing in a certain country (all values 2011$):
(a) What is the y-intercept of the linear trendline?
(b) Interpret the y-intercept in real world terms.

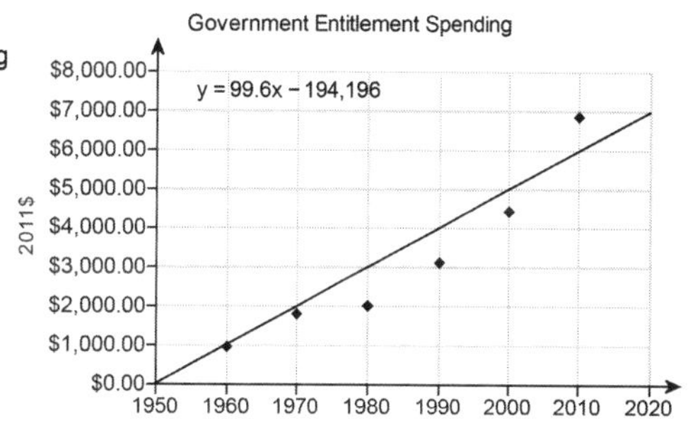

(a) The y-intercept of the linear trendline is ________.
(Type an integer or a decimal.)

(b) Choose the correct answer below.

○ **A.** The Per Capita Entitlement Spending was − $194,196 (2011$) in 1950, which makes no sense in real world terms.

○ **B.** The Per Capita Entitlement Spending was − $1,000 (2011$) in 1950, which makes no sense in real world terms.

○ **C.** The Per Capita Entitlement Spending was $194,196 (2011$) in 0 CE, which makes no sense in real world terms.

○ **D.** The Per Capita Entitlement Spending was − $194,196 (2011$) in 0 CE, which makes no sense in real world terms.

ID: 5.2.43

65. Use the following graph to find y when x = − 2.

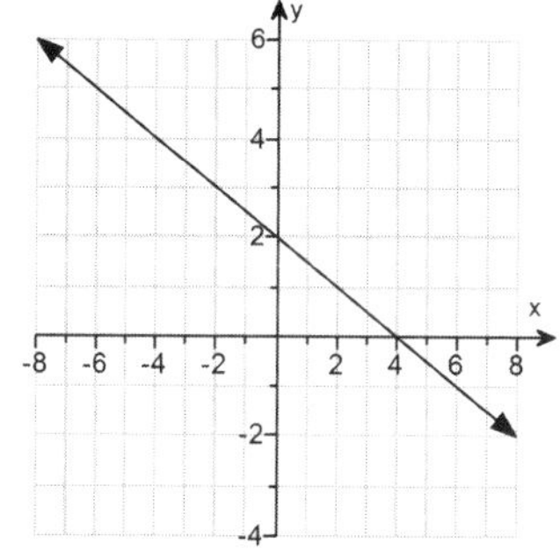

When x = − 2, y = ________.

ID: 5.2.44

66. Use the following graph to find x when y = − 2.

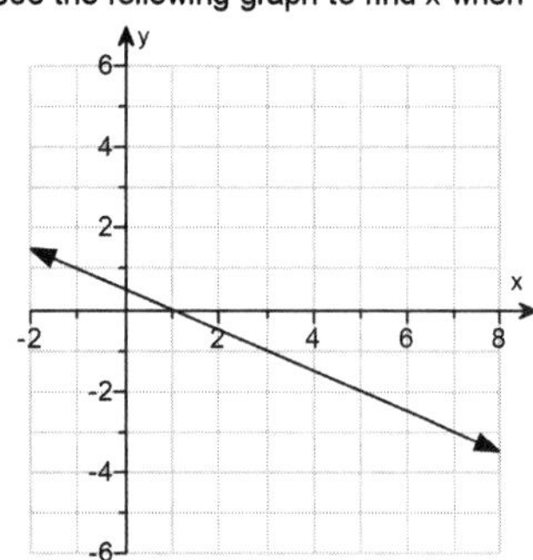

When y = − 2, x = ____________.

ID: 5.2.45

67. What is the y-intercept of the line shown in the graph below?

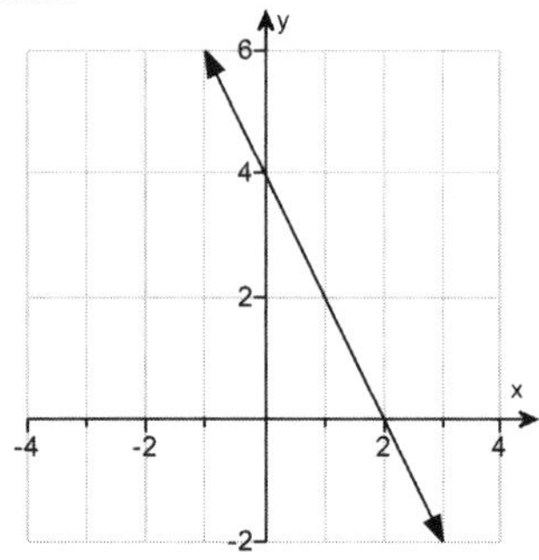

The y-intercept is ____________.
(Type an ordered pair.)

ID: 5.2.46

68. What is the y-intercept of the line displayed on the right?

What are the coordinates of the y-intercept?

____
(Type an ordered pair.)

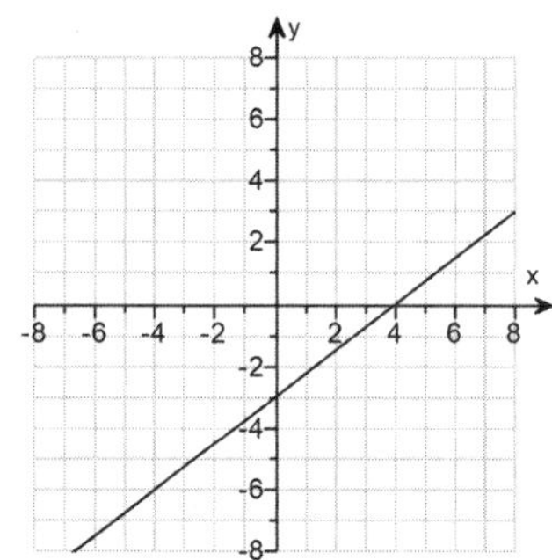

ID: 5.2.47

* 69. Water is steadily pumped out of a flooded basement. Let v be the volume of water (in thousands of gallons) that remains in the basement t hours after the water began to be pumped. A linear model is shown below.

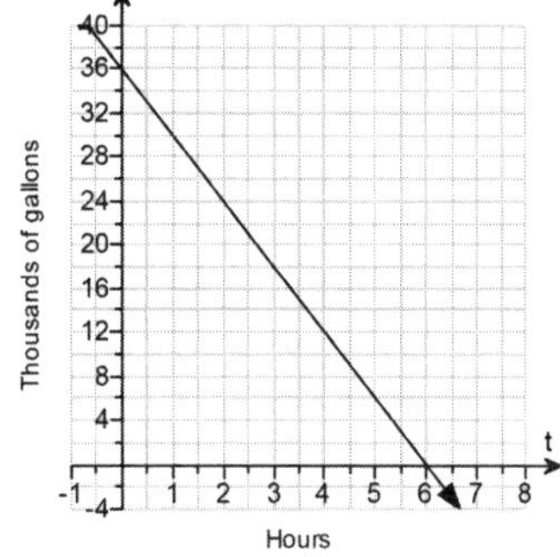

Complete parts **a)** through **d)**.

a) How much water is in the basement after 4 hours of pumping?

____________ thousand gallons

b) After how many hours of pumping will 3 thousand gallons remain in the basement?

____________ hours

c) How much water was in the basement before any water was pumped out?

____________ thousand gallons

d) After how many hours of pumping will all the water be pumped out of the basement?

____________ hours

ID: 5.2.48

70. Some ordered pairs are listed in the table below. Complete parts **a)** and **b)** below.

x	0	5	8	10	12	13	14
y	10	4	2	1	2	4	10

a) Create a scattergram of the data shown in the table.

Choose the correct graph on the right.

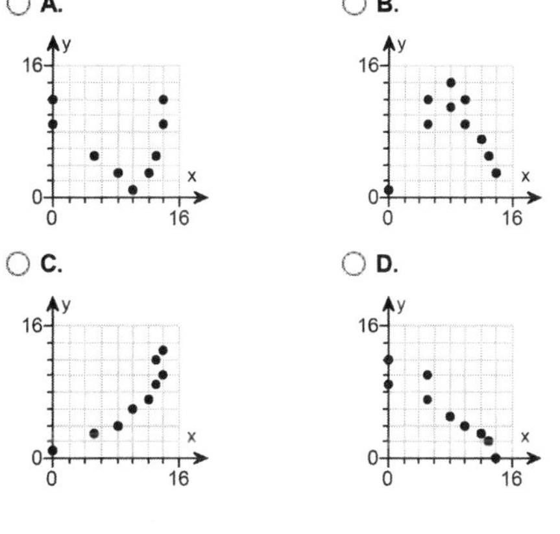

b) Is there a linear relationship between x and y? Explain.

◯ **A.** Yes, because x and y are described accurately by a

◯ **B.** No, because x and y are not described accurately by

ID: 5.2.49

71. Let d be the distance traveled (in miles) after a student has driven for t hours (not counting pit stops). Some pairs of values of t and d are shown in the following table. Complete parts **a** to **c**.

t (hours)	d (miles)
0	0
1	70
2	140
3	210
4	280

a. Create a scattergram of the data. Then draw a linear model.

Choose the correct scattergram below.

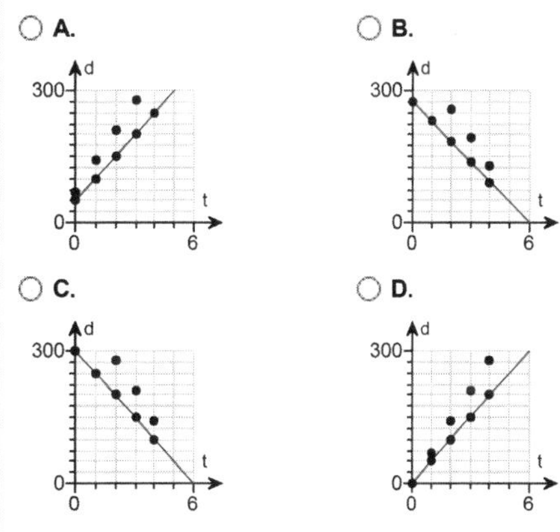

b. Estimate how far the student has traveled in 3.5 hours.

The student has traveled ____________ miles in 3.5 hours.
(Type an integer or a decimal.)

c. Estimate how long it took the student to travel 175 miles.

It took ____________ hours for the student to travel 175 miles.
(Type an integer or a decimal.)

ID: 5.2.50

72. Let E be a college's enrollment (in thousands of students) at t years since the college began. Some pairs of values of t and E are shown in the table to the right.

t (years)	E (thousands of students)
0	3
1	5
2	7
3	9
4	11

a. Create a scattergram of the data. Then draw a linear model.

Choose the correct scattergram below.

◯ **A.**

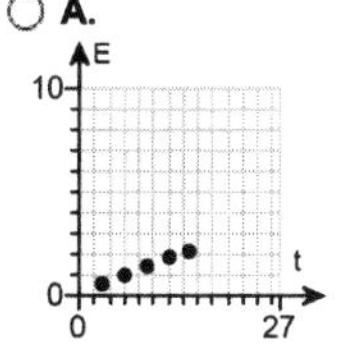

◯ **B.**

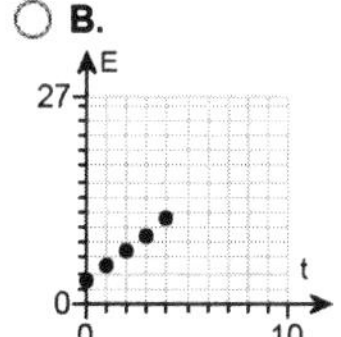

◯ **C.**

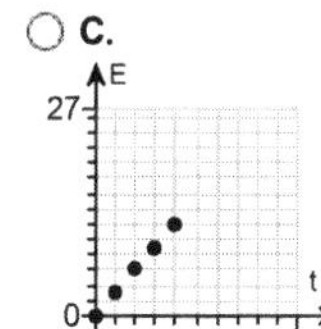

◯ **D.**

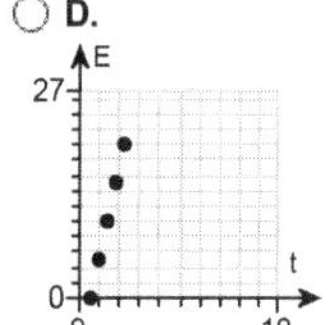

72. (cont.) Choose the correct linear model below.

A.

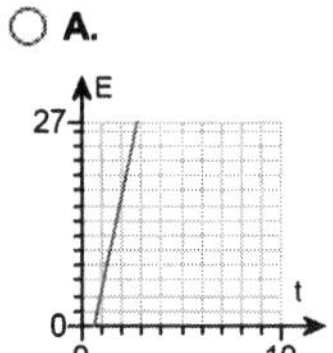

B.

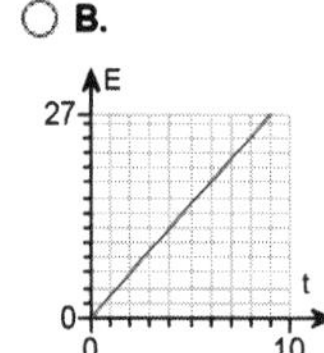

C.

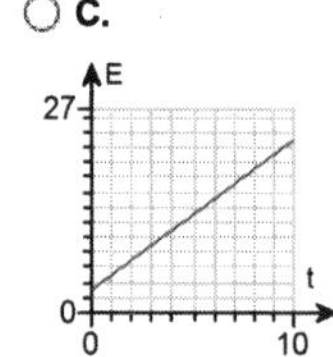

D.

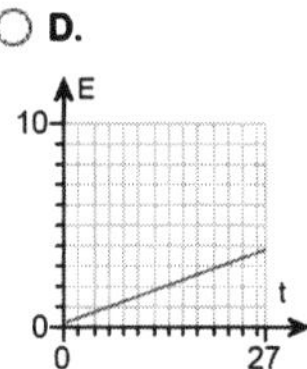

b. Predict the enrollment when it has been 8 years since the college opened.

__________ thousand students
(Type a whole number.)

c. Predict when the enrollment will reach 23 thousand students.

__________ years
(Type a whole number.)

ID: 5.2.51

---

73. Let s be a person's salary (in thousands of dollars) after he has worked for t years at a company. Some pairs of values of t and s are shown in the following table. Complete parts **a** to **d**.

t (years)	s (thousands of dollars)
0	40
2	48
4	56
6	64
8	72

a. Create a scattergram of the data. Then draw a linear model.

Choose the correct scattergram below.

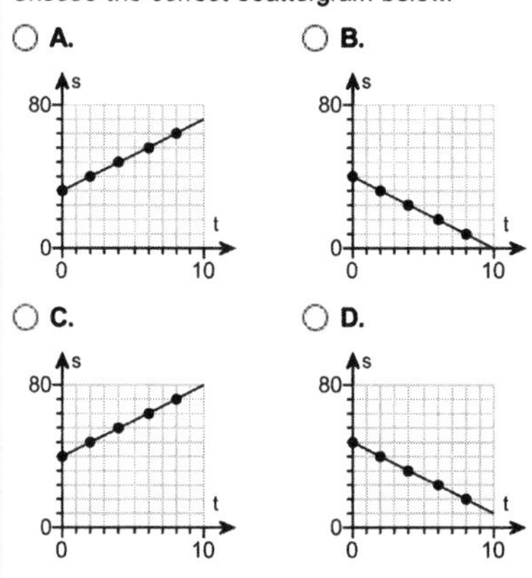

b. Estimate the person's salary after he has worked for 3 years at the company.

The person's salary is $__________ thousand after he has worked for 3 years at the company.
(Type an integer or a decimal.)

c. Estimate when the person's salary will be $60 thousand.

The person's salary will be $60 thousand after he has worked for __________ years at the company.
(Type an integer or a decimal.)

d. What is the s-intercept of the model? What does it mean in this situation?

Select the correct choice below and fill in the answer box to complete your choice.

(Type an ordered pair.)

A. The s-intercept of the model is __________. The s-intercept estimates the person's salary when he quits the job.

B. The s-intercept of the model is __________. The s-intercept joined the company.

ID: 5.2.52

74. Let v be the value (in dollars) of a company's stock at t years since 2000. Some pairs of values of t and v are shown in the following table. Complete parts **a** to **d**.

t (years)	v (dollars)
1	18
2	15
3	12
5	6
6	3

a. Create a scattergram of the data. Then draw a linear model.

Choose the correct scattergram below.

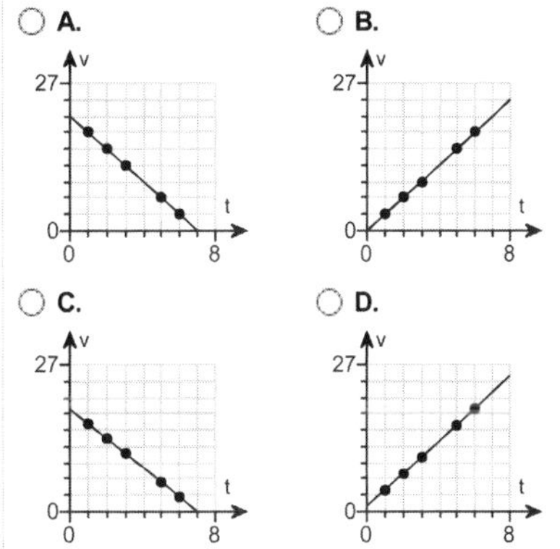

b. Estimate when the value of the stock was $9.

The value of the stock was $9 in __________.
(Round to the nearest year as needed.)

c. What is the t-intercept of the model? What does it mean in this situation?

Select the correct choice below and fill in the answer box to complete your choice.

(Type an ordered pair.)

- **A.** The t-intercept of the model is __________. The t-intercept estimates the value of the stock in 2000.
- **B.** The t-intercept of the model is __________. The t-intercept estimates the year for which the stock will have no value.

d. What is the v-intercept of the model? What does it mean in this situation?

Select the correct choice below and fill in the answer box to complete your choice.

(Type an ordered pair.)

- **A.** The v-intercept of the model is __________. The v-intercept estimates the value of the stock in 2000.
- **B.** The v-intercept of the model is __________. The v-intercept estimates the year for which the stock will have no value.

ID: 5.2.53

---

75. Let p be the profit (in millions of dollars) of a company for the year that is t years since 2000. Some pairs of values of t and p are shown in the following table.

t (years)	p (millions of dollars)
1	32
2	28
3	24
5	16
6	12

Complete parts **a.** to **d.**

a. Create a scattergram of the data. Then draw a linear model.

Choose the correct scattergram below.

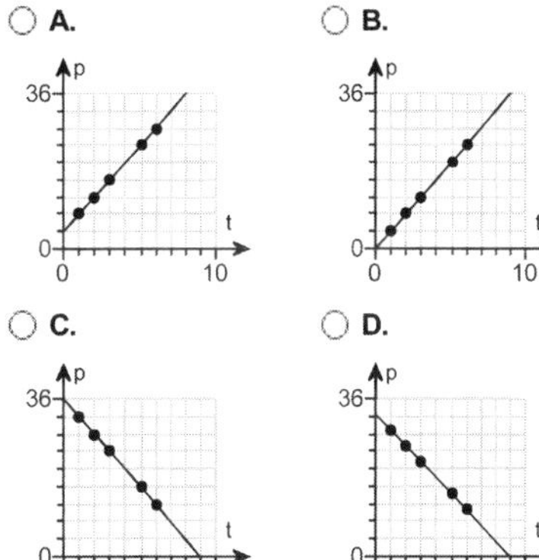

75. (cont.)

b. Predict when the profit will be $8 million.

The profit will be $8 million in the year ___________.

c. What is the p-intercept of the model? What does it mean in this situation?

Select the correct choice below and, if necessary, fill in the answer box to complete your choice.

(Type an ordered pair.)

- A. The p-intercept of the model is ___________. The p-intercept estimates the profit (in millions of dollars) of a company for the year 2000.
- B. The p-intercept of the model is ___________. The p-intercept estimates the year for which the company has no profit.

d. What is the t-intercept of the model? What does it mean in this situation?

Select the correct choice below and, if necessary, fill in the answer box to complete your choice.

(Type an ordered pair.)

- A. The t-intercept of the model is ___________. The t-intercept estimates the profit (in millions of dollars) of a company for the year 2000.
- B. The t-intercept of the model is ___________. The t-intercept estimates the year for which the company has no profit.

ID: 5.2.54

---

*76. Let g be the number of gallons of gasoline that remain in a car's gasoline tank after the car has been driven d miles since the tank was filled. Some pairs of values of d and g are shown in the following table.

d (miles)	g (gallons)
20	11
40	9
60	7
80	5
100	3
120	1

Complete parts **a.** to **e.**

a. Create a scattergram of the data. Then draw a linear model.

Choose the correct scattergram below.

A.

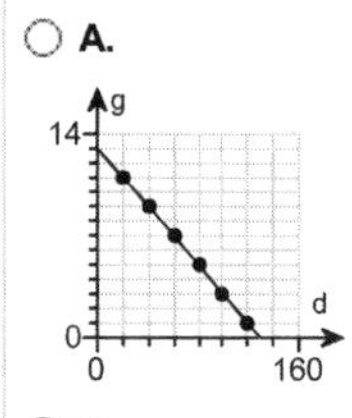

B.

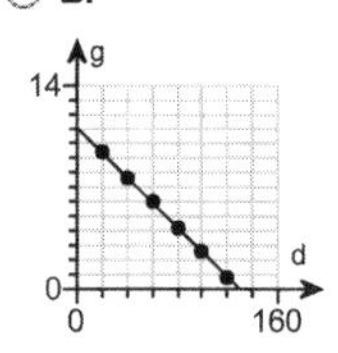

C.

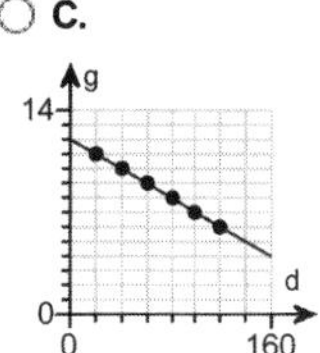

D.

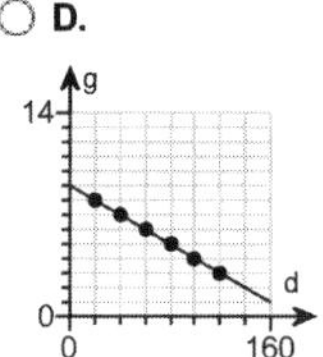

b. Estimate how much gasoline is in the tank after the driver has gone 70 miles since last filling up.

After the driver has gone 70 miles since last filling up, there will be ___________ gallons of gasoline in the tank.

c. Estimate the number of miles driven since the tank was last filled if 2 gallons of gasoline remain in the tank.

The driver drove ___________ miles since the tank was last filled if 2 gallons of gasoline are in the tank.

d. Find the d-intercept of the model. What does it mean in this situation?

d. Find the d-intercept of the model. What does it mean in this situation?

***76.** (cont.)

Select the correct choice below and, if necessary, fill in the answer box to complete your choice.

(Type an ordered pair.)

○ **A.** The d-intercept of the model is ________. The which the gasoline tank will be empty.

○ **B.** The d-intercept of the model is ________. The gasoline in the tank at the start of the trip.

e. Find the g-intercept of the model. What does it mean in this situation?

Select the correct choice below and, if necessary, fill in the answer box to complete your choice.

(Type an ordered pair.)

○ **A.** The g-intercept of the model is ________. The gasoline in the tank at the start of the trip.

○ **B.** The g-intercept of the model is ________. The which the gasoline tank will be empty.

ID: 5.2.55

---

77. Let v be the value (in thousands of dollars) of a car when it is t years old. Some pairs of values of t and v are listed in the following table.

t years	1	2	3	4	5
v thousands of dollars	12	10	8	6	4

Complete parts a to e.

a. Create a scattergram of the data. Then draw a linear model.

Choose the correct scattergram below.

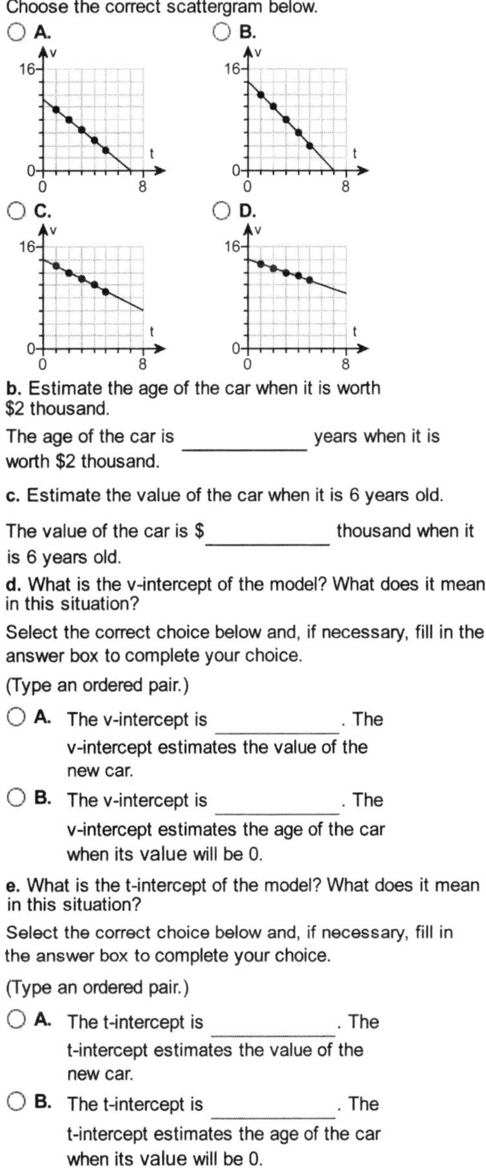

b. Estimate the age of the car when it is worth $2 thousand.

The age of the car is ________ years when it is worth $2 thousand.

c. Estimate the value of the car when it is 6 years old.

The value of the car is $________ thousand when it is 6 years old.

d. What is the v-intercept of the model? What does it mean in this situation?

Select the correct choice below and, if necessary, fill in the answer box to complete your choice.

(Type an ordered pair.)

○ **A.** The v-intercept is ________. The v-intercept estimates the value of the new car.

○ **B.** The v-intercept is ________. The v-intercept estimates the age of the car when its value will be 0.

e. What is the t-intercept of the model? What does it mean in this situation?

Select the correct choice below and, if necessary, fill in the answer box to complete your choice.

(Type an ordered pair.)

○ **A.** The t-intercept is ________. The t-intercept estimates the value of the new car.

○ **B.** The t-intercept is ________. The t-intercept estimates the age of the car when its value will be 0.

ID: 5.2.56

78. Let a be the altitude (in thousands of feet) of an airplane at t minutes since the airplane began its descent. Some pairs of values of t and a are shown in the following table.

t	0	3	6	9	12
a	25	20	15	10	5

a. Create a scattergram of the data. Then draw a linear model.

Choose the correct graph below.

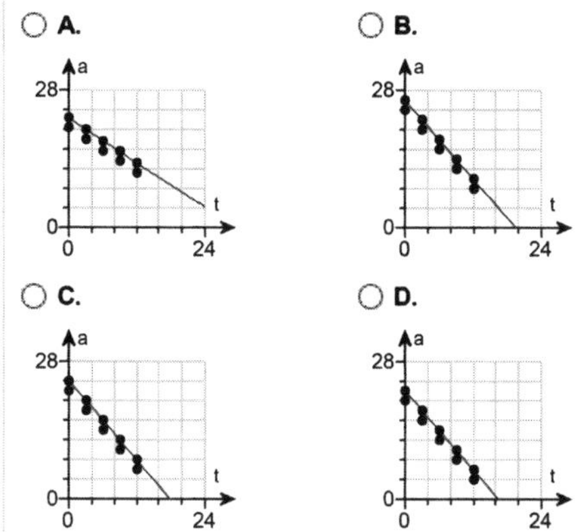

b. Use the model to estimate the airplane's altitude.

The airplane's altitude 7 minutes after it began its descent is ____________ thousand feet.
(Round to the nearest integer as needed.)

c. Use the model to estimate the time until touchdown.

The airplane will reach the ground in ____________ minutes.
(Round to the nearest integer as needed.)

ID: 5.2.57

79. Let p be the percentage of major firms that perform drug tests on employees and/or job applicants at t years since 1980. Some pairs of values of t and p are shown in the table to the right.

(a) Create a scattergram of the data.
(b) Are the variables t and p linearly related? Explain.

t (years)	p (percent)
6	21
9	50
11	70
14	78
17	74
20	68
24	63
26	71

(a) Choose the correct graph below.

○ **A.**

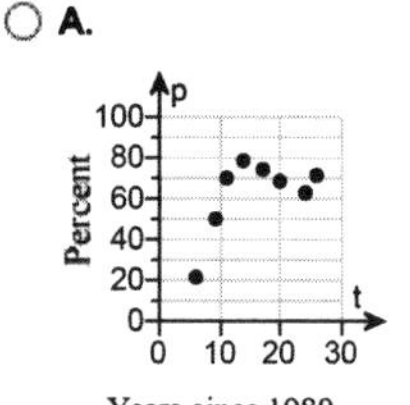

○ **B.**

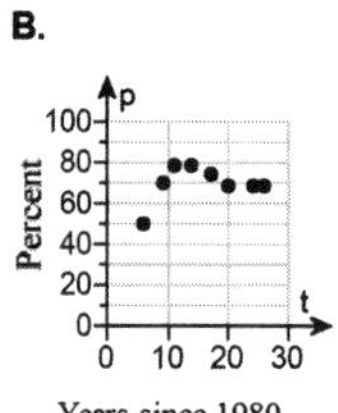

○ **C.**

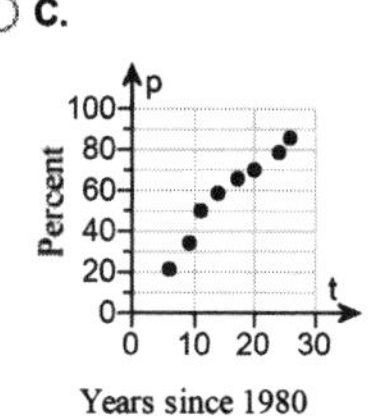

○ **D.**

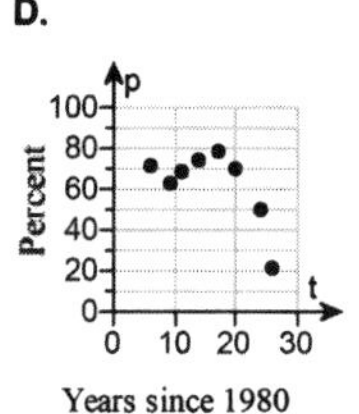

(b) Are the variables t and p linearly related? Explain.

○ **A.** Yes because the percentages of firms that perform drug tests over a span of years are described accurately by a nonvertical line.

○ **B.** No because the percentages of firms that perform drug tests over a span of years are not described accurately by a nonvertical line.

ID: 5.2.58

80. A person pays an $8 cover charge to hear a hip-hop band. Let T be the total cost (in dollars) of the cover charge plus d dollars spent on drinks. Complete parts (a) through (e).

a) Complete the table to help find an equation that describes the relationship between d and T. Show the arithmetic to help you see a pattern.

Drink Cost (dollars) d	Total Cost (dollars) T
2	________ (Do not simplify.)
3	________ (Do not simplify.)
4	________ (Do not simplify.)
5	________ (Do not simplify.)
d	________ (Do not simplify.)

What is the equation describing the relationship between d and T?

T = ________

b) Perform a unit analysis of the equation found in the previous step.

The units of the expressions on both sides of the equation are (1) ________.

c) Graph the equation. Choose the correct answer below.

○ **A.**

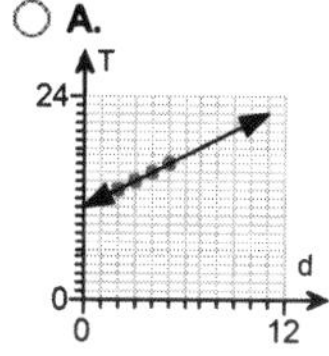

○ **B.**

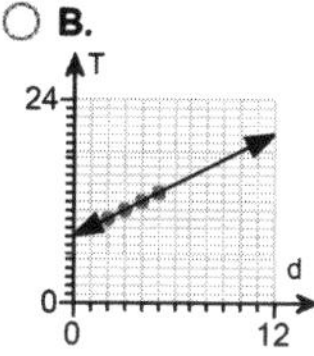

○ **C.**

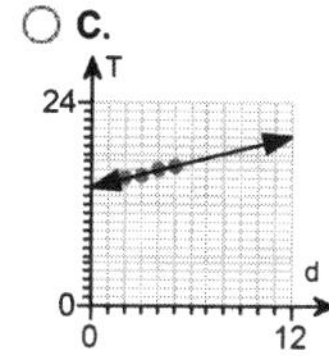

○ **D.**

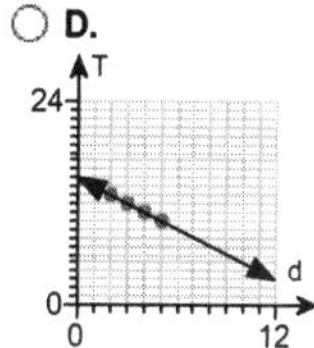

d) What is the T-intercept of the linear model?

________ (Type an ordered pair.)

What does the T-intercept mean in this situation? Choose the correct answer below.

○ **A.** The total cost if the person does not pay the cover charge.
○ **B.** The amount of money the person spends on each drink.
○ **C.** The total cost if the person does not spend any money on drinks.
○ **D.** The amount of money the person spends on drinks.

e) If $10 is spent on drinks, find the total cost of the cover charge and drinks.

The total cost of the cover charge and drinks is $________.

(1) ○ drinks
○ dollars per drink
○ drinks per dollar
○ dollars

ID: 5.2.59

81. A certain community college charged $65.50 per credit (unit or hour) for tuition in spring semester 2009. Let T be the total cost (in dollars) of tuition for enrolling in c credits of classes. Answer through **(a)** to **(d)**.

a. Complete the table to help find an equation that describes the relationship between c and T. Show the arithmetic that helps to identify the pattern.

Number of Credits c	Total Cost (in dollars) T
3	(65.50 • ________) + ________
6	(65.50 • ________) + ________
9	(65.50 • ________) + ________
12	(65.50 • ________) + ________

T = ________ (Type an expression using c as the variable.)

81. (cont.) **b.** Perform a unit analysis of the equation found in part **(a)**.

Choose the correct answer below.

- ◯ **A.** In the equation, the units on both sides are credits, so the equation is correct.
- ◯ **B.** In the equation, the units on both sides are dollars, so the equation is correct.
- ◯ **C.** In the equation, the units on one side are dollars and the units on the other side are credits, so the equation is correct.

c. Graph the equation by hand.

Choose the correct graph below.

◯ **A.**

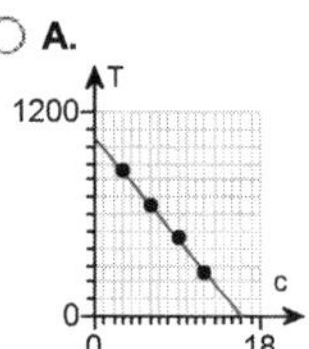

◯ **B.**

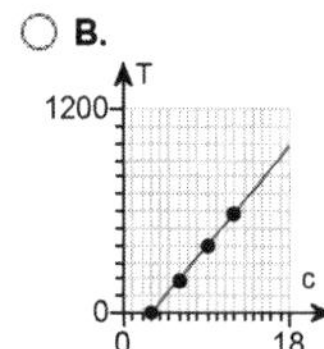

◯ **C.**

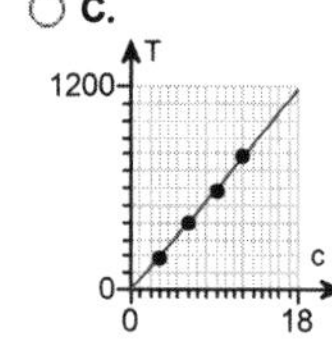

◯ **D.**

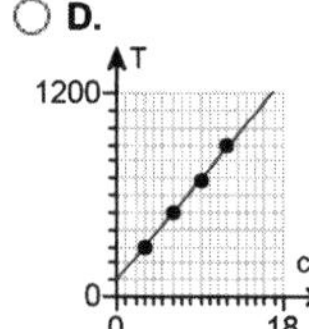

d. What is the total cost of tuition for 15 credits of classes?

The total cost of tuition for 15 credits of classes is $ ________.
(Round to the nearest cent as needed.)

ID: 5.2.60

---

*82. A person earns a starting salary of $16 thousand at a company. Each year, he receives a $2 thousand raise. Let s be the salary (in thousands of dollars) after he has worked at the company for t years. Complete parts **(a)** through **(e)**.

a. Complete the table to help find an equation for t and s. Show the arithmetic that helps to identify the pattern.
(Do not include the $ symbol in your answers.)

Time at Company (years) t	Salary (thousands of dollars) s
0	(2 • ______) + ______
1	(2 • ______) + ______
2	(2 • ______) + ______
3	(2 • ______) + ______
4	(2 • ______) + ______

s = ________ (Type an expression using t as the variable.)

b. Perform a unit analysis of the equation found in part **(a)**. Choose the correct answer below.

- ◯ **A.** In the equation, the units on both sides are years, so the equation is correct.
- ◯ **B.** In the equation, the units on both sides are thousands of dollars, so the equation is correct.
- ◯ **C.** In the equation, the units on one side are thousands of dollars and the units on the other side are years, so the equation is correct.

c. Graph the equation by hand.

Choose the correct graph below.

◯ **A.**

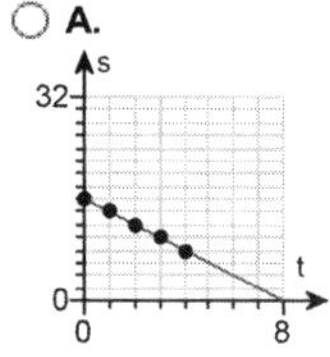

◯ **B.**

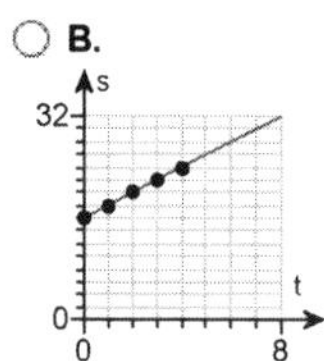

◯ **C.**

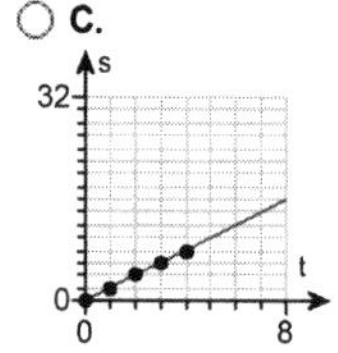

◯ **D.**

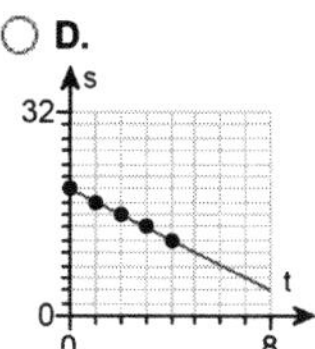

d. What is the s-intercept? What does it mean in this situation?

Select the correct choice below and fill in the answer box to complete your choice.

(Type an ordered pair.)

- ◯ **A.** The s-intercept of the model is ________, and it represents the person's salary when he quits the job.
- ◯ **B.** The s-intercept of the model is ________, and it represents the person's salary when he joined the company.

e. When will the person's salary be $28 thousand?

The person's salary will be $28 thousand after ________ years.
(Type an integer or a decimal.)

ID: 5.2.61

83. The number of hate crime convictions was 15 convictions in 2006 and has declined by about 2 convictions each year since then. Let n be the number of hate crime convictions in the year that is t years since 2006. Complete parts **(a)** through **(e)**.

(a) Complete the following table to help find an equation for t and n. Show the arithmetic that helps to identify the pattern.

Years since 2006 t	Number of Convictions n
0	_____ − _____ • 0
1	_____ − _____ • 1
2	_____ − _____ • 2
3	_____ − _____ • 3
4	_____ − _____ • 4

n = ________ − ________ t

(b) Perform a unit analysis of the equation found in part **(a)**.

Choose the correct answer below.

○ **A.** In the equation, the units on both sides are years, so the equation is correct.

○ **B.** In the equation, the units on both sides are the number of convictions, so the equation is correct.

○ **C.** In the equation, the units on one side are the number of convictions and the units on the other side are years, so the equation is correct.

(c) Graph the equation by hand found in part **(a)**.

Choose the correct graph below.

○ **A.** 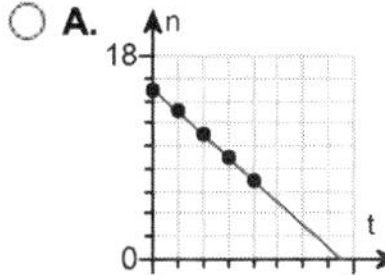

○ **B.** 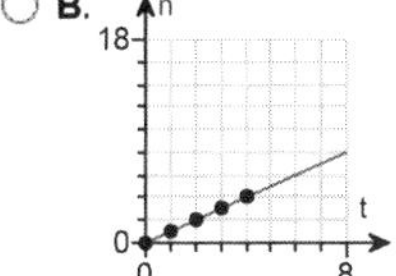

○ **C.** 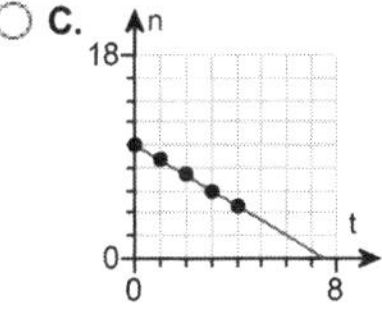

○ **D.** 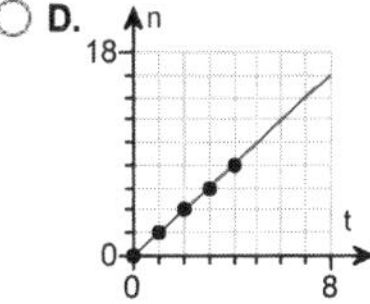

(d) Predict the number of hate crime convictions in 2011.

The number of hate crime convictions in 2011 will be ________.
(Type an integer or a decimal.)

(e) What is the t-intercept? What does it mean in this situation?

Select the correct choice below, and fill in the answer box to complete your choice.
(Type an ordered pair. Type an integer or a decimal.)

○ **A.** The t-intercept of the model is ________. The t-intercept estimates the number of hate crime convictions in 2006.

○ **B.** The t-intercept of the model is ________. The t-intercept estimates the number of years after 2006 when the number of hate crimes is zero.

ID: 5.2.62

84. To make fudgelike brownies, a person bakes a brownie mix for 8 minutes less than the baking time suggested on the box. Let r be the suggested baking time (in minutes) and a be the actual baking time (in minutes). Complete parts **(a)** through **(d)**.

a. Find an equation that describes the relationship between r and a. Assume that a is the dependent variable. [Hint: Find the equation by creating a table of values for r and a.]

An equation that describes the relationship between r and a is a = ________.
(Type an expression using r as the variable.)

b. Perform a unit analysis of the equation found in part **(a)**.

Choose the correct answer below.

○ **A.** In the equation, the units on both sides are the same, so the equation is correct.

○ **B.** In the equation, the units on both sides are not the same, so the equation is correct.

c. Graph the equation by hand. Choose the correct graph below.

○ **A.** 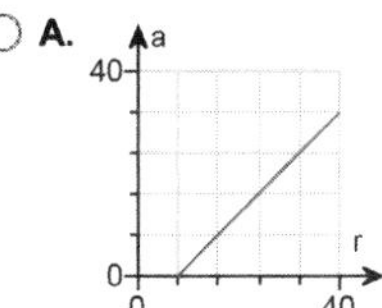

○ **B.** 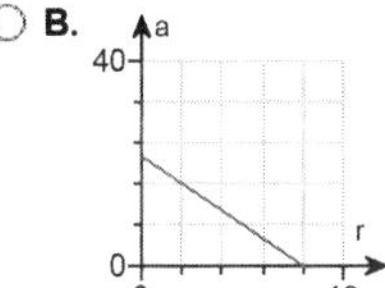

○ **C.** 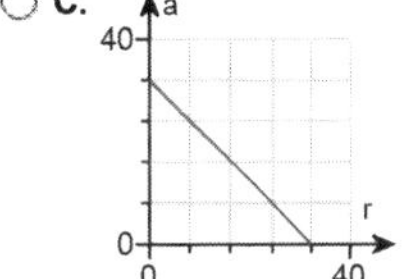

○ **D.** 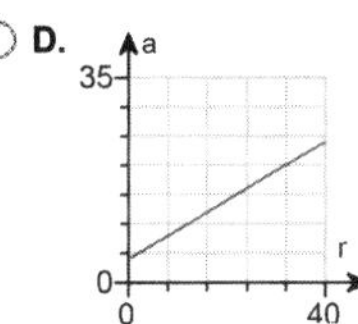

d. If the actual baking time is 22 minutes, what is the baking time suggested on the box?

If the actual baking time is 22 minutes, then the suggested baking time is ________ minutes.
(Type a whole number.)

ID: 5.2.63

85. For spring semester 2009, a college charged $40 per unit (credit or hour) for tuition. All students paid a $2 student representation fee each semester. Students who drove to school paid a $50 parking fee each semester. Let T be the total one-semester cost (in dollars) of tuition and fees for a student who drove to school and took u units of classes. Answer parts **(a)**, **(b)**, and **(c)**.

a. Find an equation for u and T. [Hint: If there is trouble finding the equation, try creating a table of values for u and T.]

The equation that describes the relationship between T and u is T = ___________.
(Simplify your answer. Type an expression using u as the variable.)

b. Perform a unit analysis of the equation found in part **(a)**. Choose the correct answer below.

- ○ **A.** In the equation, the units on both sides are hours, so the equation is correct.
- ○ **B.** In the equation, the units on both sides are dollars, so the equation is correct.
- ○ **C.** In the equation, the units on one side are hours and the units on the other side are dollars, so the equation is correct.

c. What is the total one-semester cost of tuition and fees for a student who drove to school and took 35 units of classes?

$___________ (Type an integer or a decimal.)

ID: 5.2.64

86. The average number of daily domestic flights on wide-body jets was 230 flights in 2007 and has decreased by 47 flights per year since then. Let n be the average number of daily domestic flights on wide-body jets at t years since 2007. Describe the rule of four as applied to this situation.
a. Use a table of values of t and n to describe the situation.
b. Use an equation to describe the situation.
c. Use a graph to describe the situation.

a. Complete the following table.

Years since 2007 t	Average Number of Daily Domestic Flights on Wide-Body Jets n
0	___________
1	___________
2	___________
3	___________
4	___________

(Simplify your answers.)

b. An equation that describes the authentic situation is n = ___________.
(Simplify your answer. Type an expression using t as the variable.)

c. Choose the correct graph below.

○ **A.**

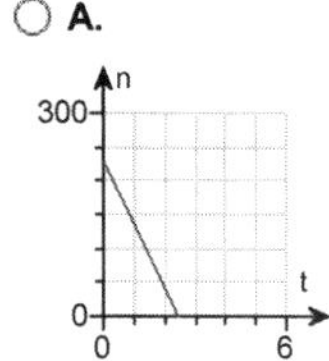

○ **B.**

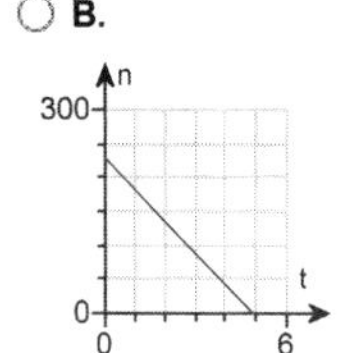

○ **C.**

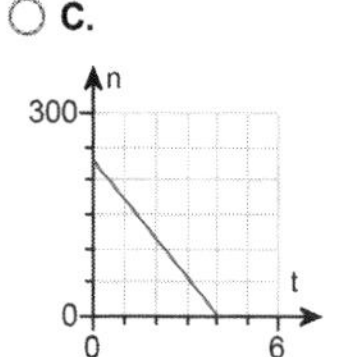

○ **D.**

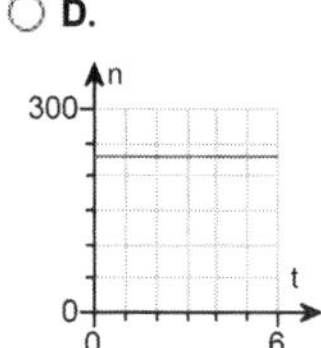

ID: 5.2.65

87. Graph the equation x = 1 by hand.

Use the graphing tool to graph the line.

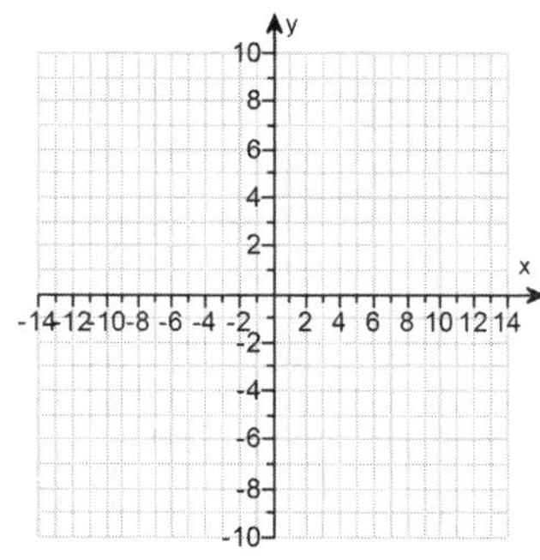

ID: 5.2.66

88. Graph the equation.

$y = -2$

Use the graphing tool to graph the line.

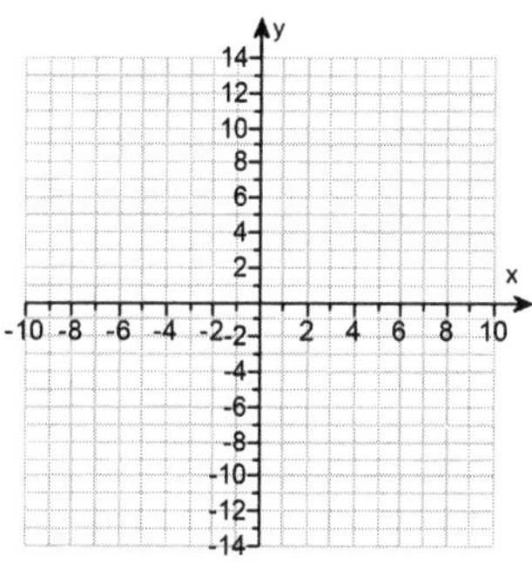

ID: 5.2.67

89. Graph the equation.

$x = -9$

Use the graphing tool to graph the line.

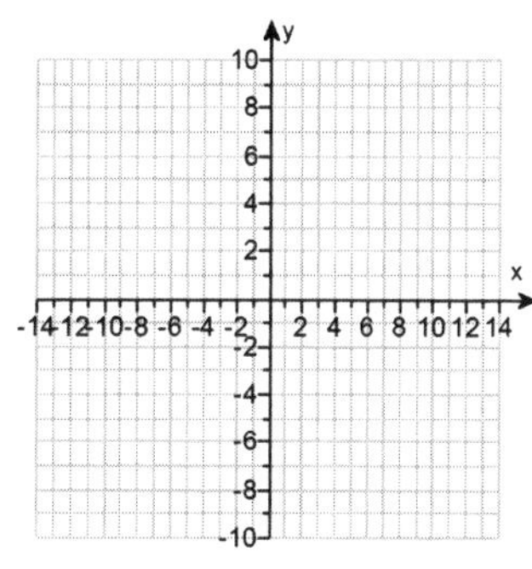

ID: 5.2.68

90. Graph the equation by plotting points.

$y = x - 4$

Use the graphing tool on the right to graph the equation.

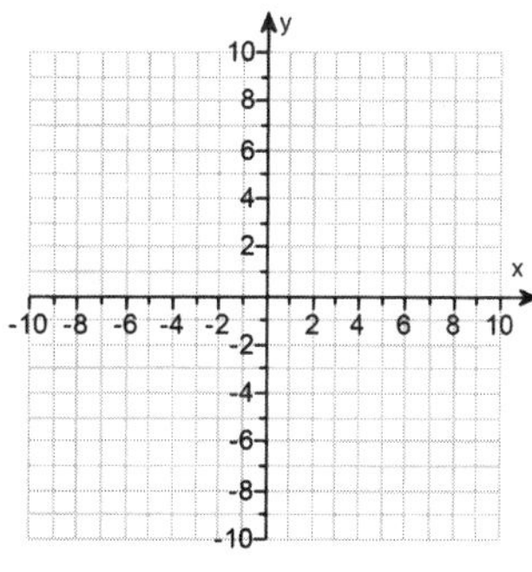

ID: 5.2.69

91. Graph the equation.

$y = \frac{2}{5}x$

Use the graphing tool on the right to graph the equation.

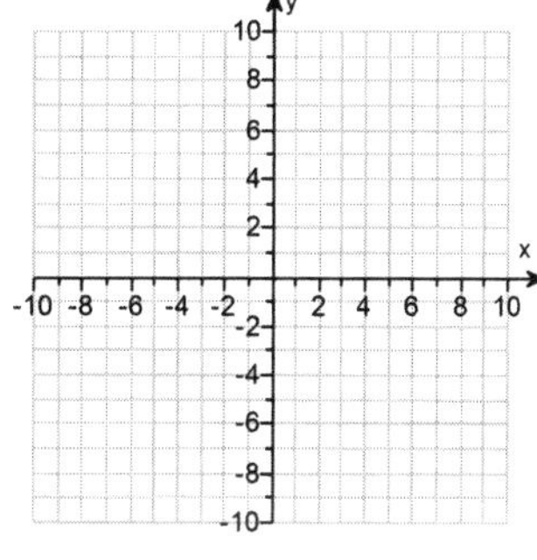

ID: 5.2.70

92. Graph the equation.

$y = 2x - 3$

Use the graphing tool to graph the line.

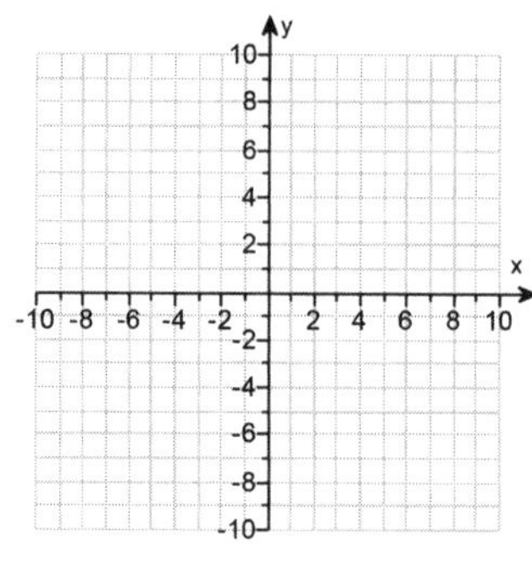

ID: 5.2.71

---

93. Find an equation of the line sketched in the figure.

An equation of the line is ________.

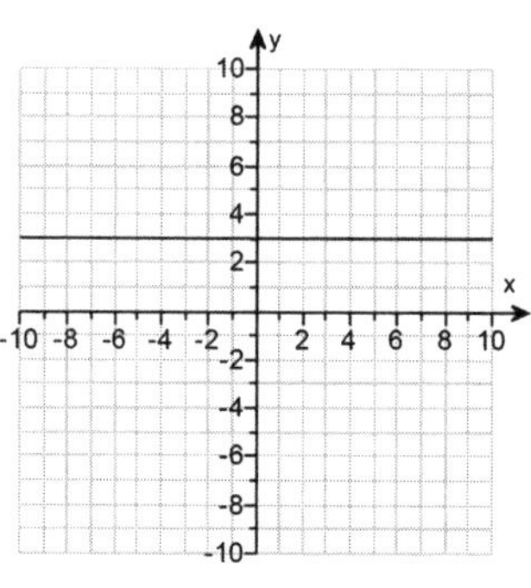

ID: 5.2.72

---

94. The points (2,7) and (7,7) are plotted to the right.

a. In going from point (2,7) to point (7,7), find the change
i. in the x-coordinate. **ii.** in the y-coordinate.

b. In going from point (7,7) to point (2,7), find the change
i. in the x-coordinate. **ii.** in the y-coordinate.

a. In going from point (2,7) to point (7,7)

i. the change in the x-coordinate is ________.

ii. the change in the y-coordinate is ________.

b. In going from point (7,7) to point (2,7)

i. the change in the x-coordinate is ________.

ii. the change in the y-coordinate is ________.

ID: 5.2.73

---

1. What does it mean to say that a function is linear?

Select all that apply.

☐ **A.** The function has a straight-line graph.
☐ **B.** The function has a rate of change that increases.
☐ **C.** The function can be described by an equation of the form $y = mx + b$.
☐ **D.** The function has a graph that includes the point (0,0).
☐ **E.** The function has a constant rate of change.

ID: 5.3.1

92. Graph the equation.

$y = 2x - 3$

Use the graphing tool to graph the line.

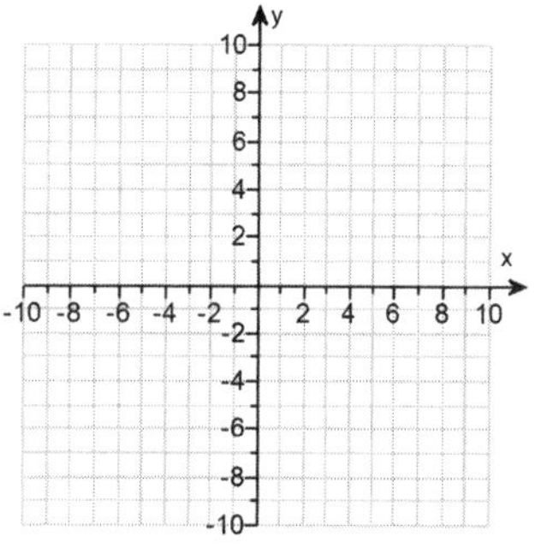

ID: 5.2.71

---

93. Find an equation of the line sketched in the figure.

An equation of the line is ________.

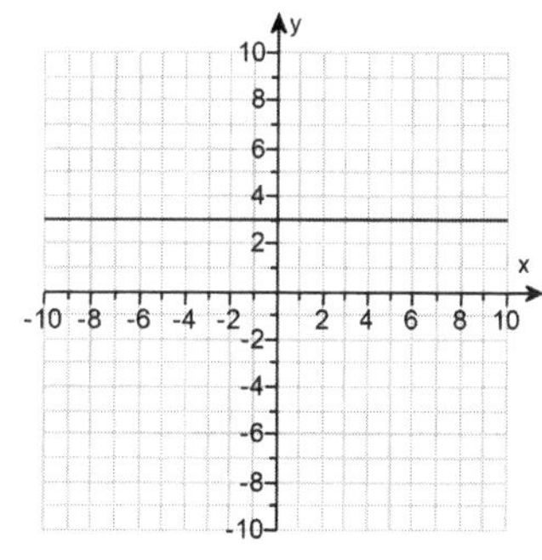

ID: 5.2.72

---

94. The points (2,7) and (7,7) are plotted to the right.

a. In going from point (2,7) to point (7,7), find the change

i. in the x-coordinate. **ii.** in the y-coordinate.

b. In going from point (7,7) to point (2,7), find the change

i. in the x-coordinate. **ii.** in the y-coordinate.

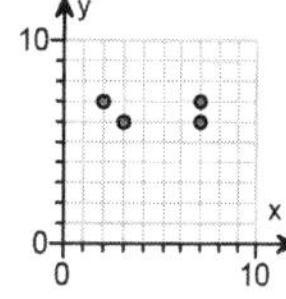

a. In going from point (2,7) to point (7,7)

i. the change in the x-coordinate is ________.

ii. the change in the y-coordinate is ________.

b. In going from point (7,7) to point (2,7)

i. the change in the x-coordinate is ________.

ii. the change in the y-coordinate is ________.

ID: 5.2.73

---

1. What does it mean to say that a function is linear?

Select all that apply.

- ☐ **A.** The function has a straight-line graph.
- ☐ **B.** The function has a rate of change that increases.
- ☐ **C.** The function can be described by an equation of the form $y = mx + b$.
- ☐ **D.** The function has a graph that includes the point (0,0).
- ☐ **E.** The function has a constant rate of change.

ID: 5.3.1

---

2. How is the rate of change of a linear function related to the slope of its graph?

Select all that apply.

- ☐ **A.** The smaller the rate of change, the shallower the graph.
- ☐ **B.** The greater the rate of change, the shallower the graph.
- ☐ **C.** The smaller the rate of change, the steeper the graph.
- ☐ **D.** The greater the rate of change, the steeper the graph.

ID: 5.3.2

---

3. Describe the general equation for a linear function. How is it related to the standard algebraic form y = mx + b?

Choose the correct answer below.

- ○ **A.** The general equation for a linear function is dependent variable = initial value + (rate of change × independent variable). In the standard algebraic form of a linear function, y is the dependent variable, x is the independent variable, m is the rate of change, and b is the initial value.
- ○ **B.** The general equation for a linear function is independent variable = initial value + (rate of change × dependent variable). In the standard algebraic form of a linear function, y is the dependent variable, x is the independent variable, m is the rate of change, and b is the initial value.
- ○ **C.** The general equation for a linear function is dependent variable = initial value + (rate of change × independent variable). In the standard algebraic form of a linear function, y is the independent variable, x is the dependent variable, m is the initial value, and b is the rate of change.
- ○ **D.** The general equation for a linear function is dependent variable = rate of change + (initial value × independent variable). In the standard algebraic form of a linear function, y is the dependent variable, x is the independent variable, m is the rate of change, and b is the initial value.

ID: 5.3.3

---

4. Decide whether the following statement makes sense (or is clearly true) or does not make sense (or is clearly false). Explain your reasoning.

When I graphed the linear function, it turned out to be a wavy curve.

Choose the correct answer below.

- ○ **A.** The statement does not make sense because a linear function has a straight-line graph.
- ○ **B.** The statement makes sense because linear functions can have graphs with any shape.
- ○ **C.** The statement does not make sense because a linear function can have a rate of change that increases or decreases.
- ○ **D.** The statement makes sense because a linear function can have a rate of change that increases or decreases.

ID: 5.3.4

---

5. Decide whether the following statement makes sense (or is clearly true) or does not make sense (or is clearly false). Explain your reasoning.

I graphed two linear functions, and the one with the greater rate of change had the greater slope.

Choose the correct answer below.

- ○ **A.** This does not make sense. According to the definition of linear functions, the slope of all linear functions must be the same.
- ○ **B.** This makes sense. According to the definition of linear functions, the initial value is equal to the slope of the graph. Thus, the rate of change does not relate to the slope.
- ○ **C.** This does not make sense. According to the definition of linear functions, the initial value is equal to the slope of the graph. Thus, the rate of change does not relate to the slope.
- ○ **D.** This makes sense. According to the definition of linear functions, the rate of change is equal to the slope of the graph and the greater the rate of change, the greater the slope.

ID: 5.3.5

---

6. Decide whether the following statement makes sense (or is clearly true) or does not make sense (or is clearly false). Explain your reasoning.

My freeway speed is the rate of change in my distance with respect to time.

Choose the correct answer below.

- A. The statement makes sense because the slope of a linear function is the change in the independent variable divided by the change in the dependent variable.
- B. The statement makes sense because the slope of a linear function is the change in the dependent variable divided by the change in the independent variable.
- C. The statement does not make sense because the slope of a linear function is the change in the dependent variable divided by the change in the independent variable.
- D. The statement does not make sense because the slope of a linear function is the change in the independent variable divided by the change in the dependent variable.

ID: 5.3.6

---

* 7. The following situation involves a rate of change that is constant. Write a statement that describes how one variable changes with respect to the other, give the rate of change numerically (with units), and use the rate of change rule to answer any questions.

You run along a path at a constant speed of 2.3 miles per hour. How far do you travel in 1.7 hours? in 3.2 hours?

Which statement describes this situation?

- A. Time varies with respect to distance traveled with a rate of change of 2.3 mi/h.
- B. The distance traveled varies with respect to time with a rate of change of 2.3 h/mi.
- C. Time varies with respect to distance traveled with a rate of change of 2.3 h/mi.
- D. The distance traveled varies with respect to time with a rate of change of 2.3 mi/h.

What is the distance traveled after 1.7 hours?

__________ miles
(Type an integer or a decimal.)

What is the distance traveled after 3.2 hours?

__________ miles
(Type an integer or a decimal.)

ID: 5.3.7

---

8. The following situation involves a rate of change that is constant. Write a statement that describes how one variable changes with respect to the other, give the rate of change numerically (with units), and use the rate of change rule to answer any questions.

A 1-degree change (increase or decrease) on the Celsius temperature scale is equivalent to a $\frac{9}{5}$-degree change on the Fahrenheit temperature scale. How much does the Fahrenheit temperature increase if the Celsius temperature increases 5 degrees? How much does the Fahrenheit temperature decrease if the Celsius temperature decreases 26 degrees?

Which statement describes this situation?

- A. The Fahrenheit temperature varies with respect to the Celsius temperature with a rate of change of $9/5^\circ$ F per degree C.
- B. The Celsius temperature varies with respect to the Fahrenheit temperature with a rate of change of $9/5^\circ$ F per degree C.
- C. The Fahrenheit temperature varies with respect to the Celsius temperature with a rate of change of $9/5^\circ$ C per degree F.
- D. The Celsius temperature varies with respect to the Fahrenheit temperature with a rate of change of $9/5^\circ$ C per degree F.

What is the increase in Fahrenheit temperature if the Celsius temperature increases by 5°?

__________ $^\circ$F
(Type an integer or a decimal.)

What is the decrease in Fahrenheit temperature if the Celsius temperature decreases by 26°?

__________ $^\circ$F
(Type an integer or a decimal.)

ID: 5.3.8

---

9. The following situation involves a rate of change that is constant. Write a statement that describes how one variable changes with respect to the other, give the rate of change numerically (with units), and use the rate of change rule to answer any questions.

Snow accumulates during a storm at a constant rate of 5.4 inches per hour. How much snow accumulates in the first 6.2 hours? in the first 9.6 hours?

Which statement describes this situation?

○ **A.** Time varies with respect to the snow accumulated with a rate of change of 5.4 h/in.
○ **B.** Time varies with respect to the snow accumulated with a rate of change of 5.4 in/h.
○ **C.** The snow accumulated varies with respect to time with a rate of change of 5.4 h/in.
○ **D.** The snow accumulated varies with respect to time with a rate of change of 5.4 in/h.

How much snow has accumulated after the first 6.2 hours?

__________ inches
(Type an integer or a decimal.)

How much snow has accumulated after the first 9.6 hours?

__________ inches
(Type an integer or a decimal.)

ID: 5.3.9

---

* 10. The following situation can be modeled by a linear function. Write an equation for the linear function and use it to answer the given question.

The price of a particular model car is $15,000 today and rises with time at a constant rate of $830 per year. How much will a new car cost in 3.9 years?

The equation used to model this situation is __________, where p is the price of a car in dollars and t is time in years.

The price of a car after 3.9 years will be $ __________.

ID: 5.3.10

---

11. The following situation can be modeled by a linear function. Write an equation for the linear function and use it to answer the given question.

A snowplow has maximum speed of 55 miles per hour on a dry highway. Its maximum speed decreases by 0.9 miles per hour for every inch of snow on the highway. According to this model, at what snow depth will the snow plow be unable to move?

The equation used to model this situation is __________, where s is the maximum speed of the snowplow in miles per hour and d is the snow depth in inches.

The snowplow will be unable to move when the snow is __________ inches deep.
(Round to the nearest inch as needed.)

ID: 5.3.11

---

12. The following situation can be modeled by a linear function. Write an equation for the linear function and use it to answer the given question. Be sure you clearly identify the independent and dependent variables. Is a linear model reasonable for the situation described?

You can rent time on computers at the local copy center for a $6 setup charge and an additional $1.75 for every 5 minutes. How much time can be rented for $22?

Select the correct choice below and fill in the answer box to complete your choice.

○ **A.** The independent variable is rental cost (r), in dollars, and the dependent variable is time (t), in minutes.
The linear function that models this situation is t = __________.
(Simplify your answer. Do not include the $ symbol in your answer.)

○ **B.** The independent variable is time (t), in minutes, and the dependent variable is rental cost (r), in dollars.
The linear function that models this situation is r = __________.
(Simplify your answer. Do not include the $ symbol in your answer.)

__________ minutes can be rented for $22.
(Round to the nearest minute as needed.)

A linear model (1) __________ reasonable for this situation.

(1) ○ is
○ is not

ID: 5.3.12

---

13. Suppose your dog weighed 2.1 pounds at birth and weighed 15.6 pounds one year later. Based on these two data points, find a linear function that describes how weight varies with age. Use this function to predict your dog's weight at 4 and 10 years of age. Comment on the validity of this model.

The equation used to model this situation is ___________, where w is the weight of the dog in pounds and t is time in years.

According to this model, the weight of the dog after 4 years will be ___________ pounds.
(Round to the nearest tenth as needed.)

According to this model, the weight of the dog after 10 years will be ___________ pounds.
(Round to the nearest tenth as needed.)

Which statement best describes the validity of this model?

- ○ **A.** The model is only accurate for small ages because the dog will eventually stop growing.
- ○ **B.** The model is always accurate because the dog will continue to grow as it gets older.
- ○ **C.** The model is only accurate for large ages because when the dog is young it grows faster than when it is older.
- ○ **D.** The model is never accurate because the dog's weight and age are not related.

ID: 5.3.13

---

14. A Campus Republicans fundraiser offers raffle tickets for $8 each. The prize for the raffle is a $425 television set, which must be purchased with the proceeds from the ticket sales. Find a function that gives the profit/loss for the raffle as it varies with the number of tickets sold. How many tickets must be sold for the raffle sales to equal the cost of the prize?

The equation used to model this situation is ___________, where p is the profit in dollars and t is the number of tickets sold.

___________ tickets must be sold for the raffle sales to equal the cost of the prize.
(Round up to the nearest whole number as needed.)

ID: 5.3.14

---

* 15. A $1170 washing machine in a laundromat is depreciated for tax purposes at a rate of $90 per year. Find a function for the depreciated value of the washing machine as it varies with time. When does the depreciated value reach $0?

The equation of the line in slope-intercept form is V = ___________.
(Type your answer in slope-intercept form. Type an expression using t as the variable. Do not include the $ symbol in your answer.)

It takes ___________ years for the machine to depreciate to $0.

ID: 5.3.15

---

16. For the following function, find the slope of the graph and the y-intercept. Then sketch the graph.

$y = 4x + 5$

The slope is ___________.
(Simplify your answer.)

The y-intercept is ___________.
(Simplify your answer.)

Use the graphing tool to graph the equation.

y
12
10
8
6
4
2
x
-12 -10 -8 -6 -4 -2 2 4 6 8 10 12
-2
-4
-6
-8
-10
-12

ID: 5.3.16

---

* 17. Find the slope and the y-intercept. Then graph the equation.

$y = -8x - 9$

What is the slope?
___________ (Type an integer or a fraction.)

What is the y-intercept?
___________ (Type an ordered pair.)

Use the graphing tool to graph the line. Use the slope and y-intercept when drawing the line.

y
20
16
12
8
4
x
-20 -16 -12 -8 -4 4 8 12 16 20
-4
-8
-12
-16
-20

ID: 5.3.17

---

*18. Use the slope and the y-intercept to graph the line.

$y = 9x - 5$

What is the slope?

__________ (Type an integer or a fraction.)

What is the y-intercept?

__________ (Type an ordered pair.)

Use the graphing tool to graph the line. Use the slope and y-intercept when drawing the line.

ID: 5.3.18

19. Give the slope and y-intercept of the line whose equation is given below. Then graph the linear function.

$y = -6x + 7$

The slope of the line is __________.
(Simplify your answer.)

The y-intercept is __________.
(Simplify your answer.)

Use the graphing tool to graph the linear equation. Use the slope and y-intercept when drawing the line.

ID: 5.3.19

*20. A group of climbers begin climbing at an elevation of 4000 feet and ascend at a steady rate of 500 vertical feet per hour. This situation can be modeled by a linear function. Identify the independent and dependent variables. Draw a graph of the function, then use the graph to find their elevation after 4 hours. Is a linear model reasonable for this situation?

The number of hours is the (1) __________ variable.

The elevation in feet is the (2) __________ variable.

Use the graphing tool to graph the line.

The elevation after 4 hours is __________ feet.

A linear model (3) __________ reasonable.

(1) ○ independent ○ dependent (2) ○ dependent ○ independent (3) ○ is ○ is not

ID: 5.3.20

21. The cost of publishing a poster is $1000 for setting up the printing equipment, plus $2 per poster printed. This situation can be modeled by a linear function. Identify the independent and dependent variables. Draw a graph of the function, then use the graph to find the total cost to produce 2500 posters. Is a linear model reasonable for this situation?

The number of posters is the (1) __________ variable.

The cost is the (2) __________ variable.

Use the graphing tool to graph the line.

The cost to produce 2500 posters is $__________.

A linear model (3) __________ reasonable.

(1) ○ independent ○ dependent (2) ○ dependent ○ independent (3) ○ is ○ is not

ID: 5.3.21

22. The cost of a particular private school begins with a one-time initiation fee of $1000, plus annual tuition of $4,000. This situation can be modeled by a linear function. Identify the independent and dependent variables. Draw a graph of the function, then use the graph to find the cost to attend this school for 2 years. Is a linear model reasonable for this situation?

Cost (dollars): 40000, 36000, 32000, 28000, 24000, 20000, 16000, 12000, 8000, 4000, 0
Number of Years: 0, 1, 2, 3, 4, 5, 6, 7

The number of years is the (1) ____________ variable.

The cost is the (2) ____________ variable.

Use the graphing tool to graph the line.

The cost for 2 years is $ ____________.

A linear model (3) ____________ reasonable.

(1) ○ independent ○ dependent
(2) ○ dependent ○ independent
(3) ○ is ○ is not

ID: 5.3.22

---

23. Which of the given ordered pairs satisfy the equation $y = 2x - 4$?

$(-1, -6)$, $(2,0)$, $(5,5)$

The ordered pair(s) ____________ satisfy the equation $y = 2x - 4$.
(Type an ordered pair. Use a comma to separate answers as needed.)

ID: 5.3.23

---

24. Determine if the ordered pair $(1, -2)$ satisfies the equation $y = -4x + 6$.

Does the ordered pair $(1, -2)$ satisfy the equation $y = -4x + 6$?

○ Yes
○ No

ID: 5.3.24

---

25. Find the y-intercept and graph the equation $y = -3x$ by hand. Use a graphing calculator to verify your answer.

Use the graphing tool to graph the line. Use the y-intercept and another point when drawing the line.

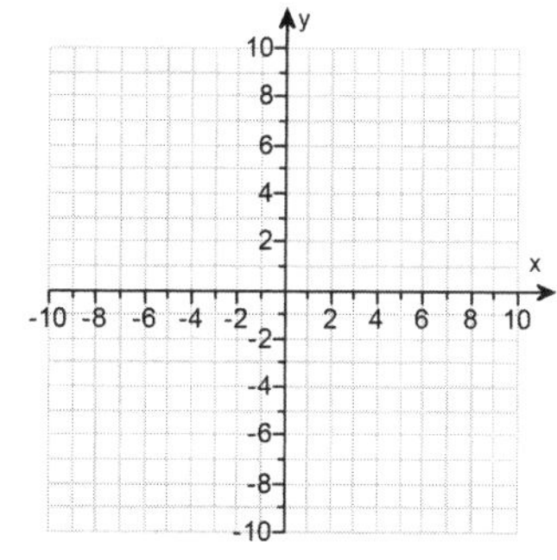

ID: 5.3.25

---

26. Find the y-intercept, and graph the equation by hand.

$$y = \frac{1}{2}x$$

Use the graphing tool to graph the line. Use the y-intercept and another point when drawing the line.

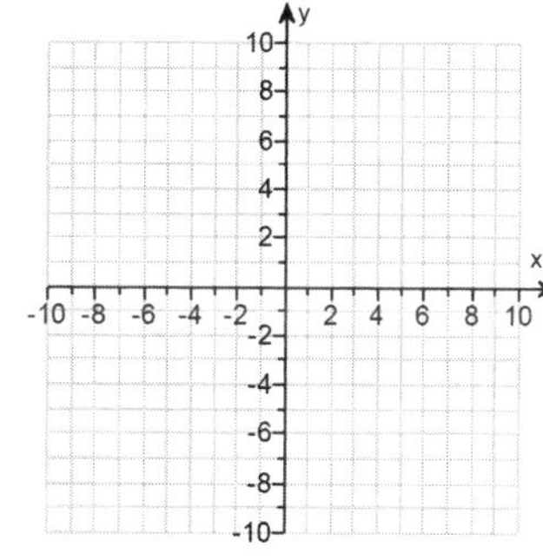

ID: 5.3.26

27. Find the y-intercept and graph the equation $y = 3x + 2$ by hand. Use a graphing calculator to verify your answer.

Use the graphing tool to graph the line. Use the y-intercept and another point when drawing the line.

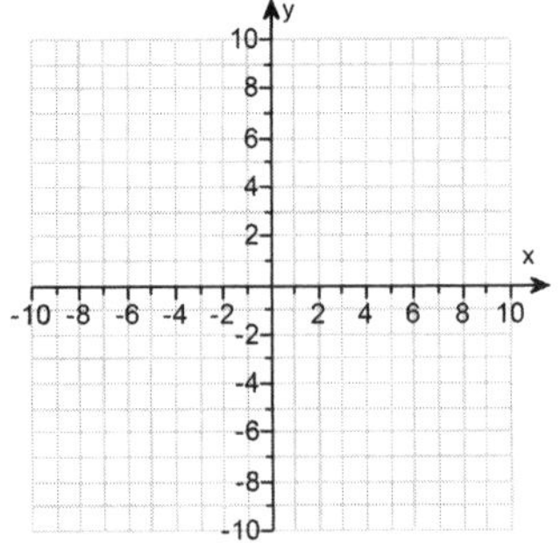

ID: 5.3.27

---

* 28. Find the y-intercept and graph the equation $y = 4x - 3$ by hand. Use a graphing calculator to verify your answer.

Use the graphing tool to graph the line. Use the y-intercept and another point when drawing the line.

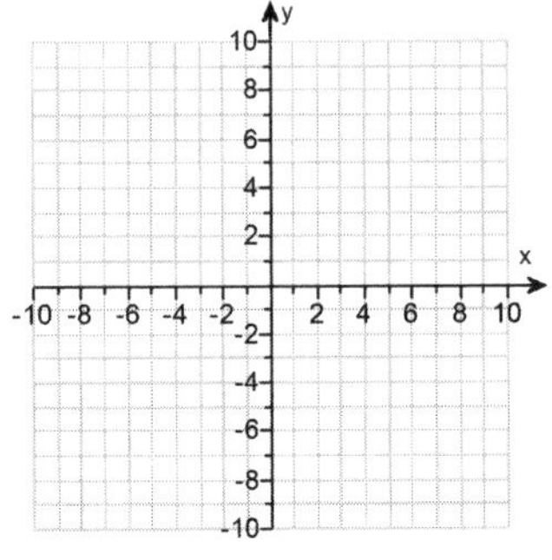

ID: 5.3.28

---

29. Find the y-intercept and graph the equation $y = \frac{1}{4}x - 1$ by hand. Use a graphing calculator to verify your answer.

Use the graphing tool to graph the line. Use the y-intercept and another point when drawing the line.

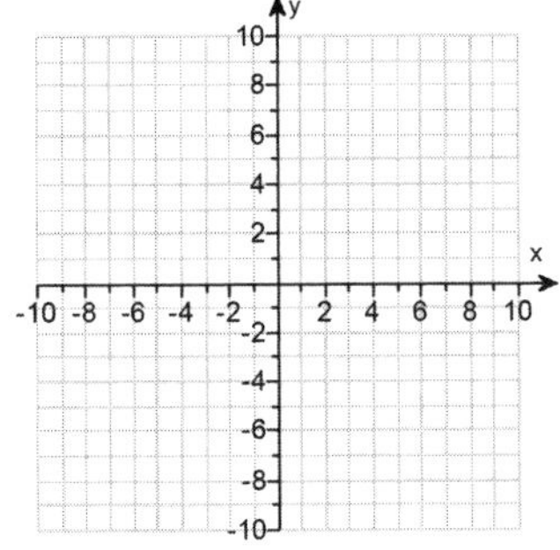

ID: 5.3.29

---

30. Find the y-intercept and graph the equation $y = -\frac{1}{6}x + 3$ by hand. Use a graphing calculator to verify your answer.

Use the graphing tool to graph the line. Use the y-intercept and another point when drawing the line.

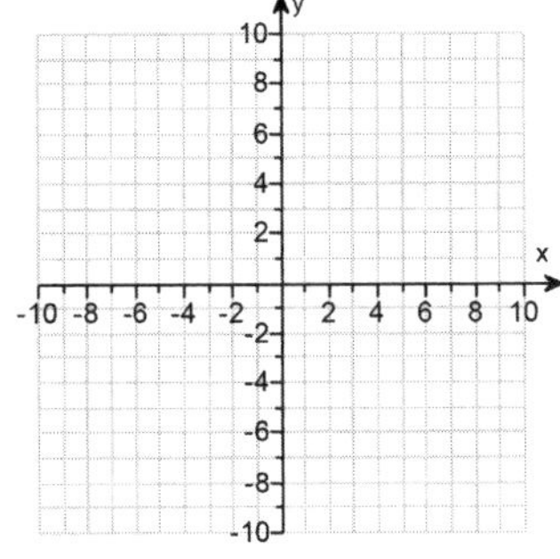

ID: 5.3.30

---

31. **a.** Graph the equations by hand. Find all x-intercepts and y-intercepts.

i. $y = 2x$ **ii.** $y = -3x$ **iii.** $y = \frac{2}{5}x$

b. What are the intercepts of the graph of an equation of the form $y = mx$, where $m \neq 0$?

a. i. The x-intercept of the line $y = 2x$ is __________. (Type an ordered pair.)

The y-intercept of the line $y = 2x$ is __________. (Type an ordered pair.)

Choose the correct graph of the line $y = 2x$ below.

○ **A.**

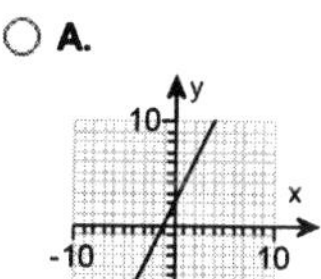

○ **B.**

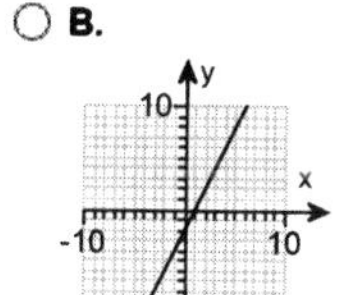

○ **C.**

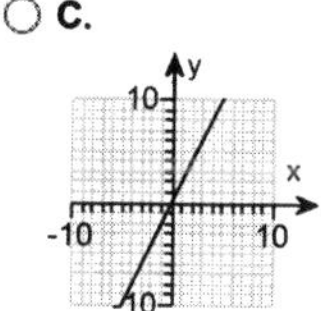

○ **D.**

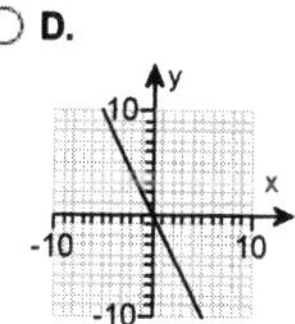

ii. The x-intercept of the line $y = -3x$ is __________. (Type an ordered pair.)

The y-intercept of the line $y = -3x$ is __________. (Type an ordered pair.)

Choose the correct graph of the line $y = -3x$ below.

○ **A.**

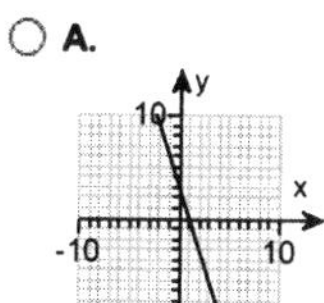

○ **B.**

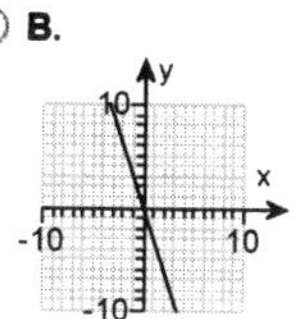

○ **C.**

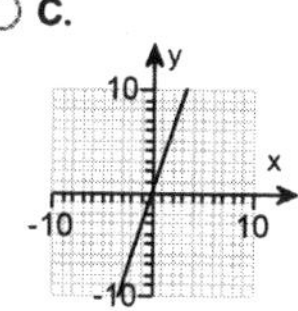

○ **D.**

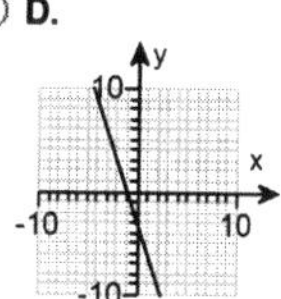

iii. The x-intercept of the line $y = \frac{2}{5}x$ is __________. (Type an ordered pair.)

The y-intercept of the line $y = \frac{2}{5}x$ is __________. (Type an ordered pair.)

Choose the correct graph of the line $y = \frac{2}{5}x$ below.

○ **A.**

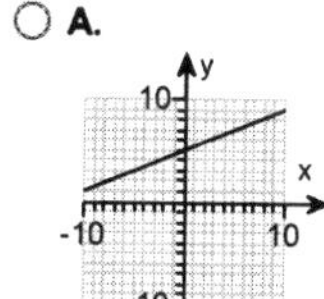

○ **B.**

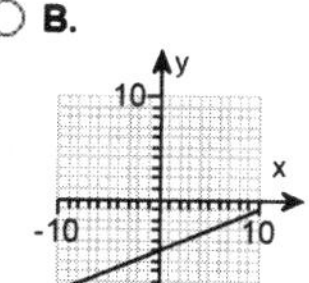

○ **C.**

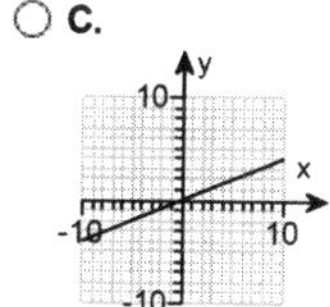

○ **D.**

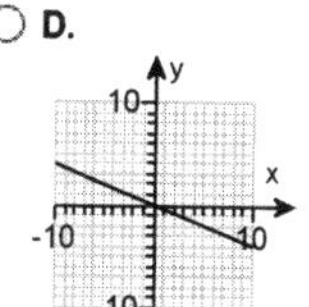

b. The x-intercept of the graph of an equation of the form $y = mx$ is __________.
(Type an ordered pair.)

The y-intercept of the graph of an equation of the form $y = mx$ is __________.

(Type an ordered pair.)

ID: 5.3.31

32. The graph of an equation is sketched in the figure. Describe five ordered-pair solutions of this equation by using a table.

x	y
−6	__________
−3	__________
0	__________
3	__________
6	__________

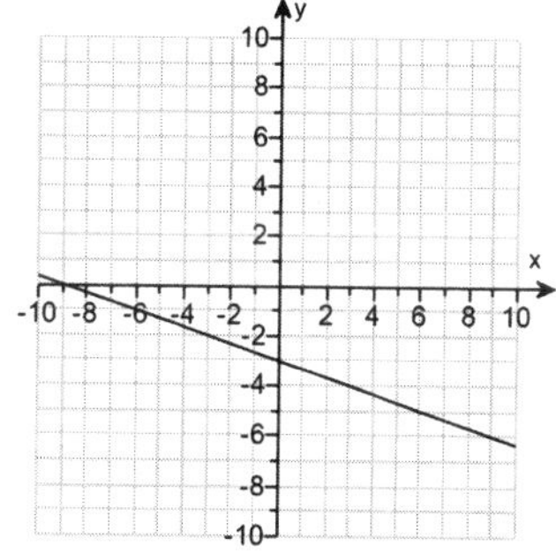

ID: 5.3.32

33. Refer to the graph sketched to the right. Find y when x = 4.

y = ___________ (Type an integer or a decimal.)

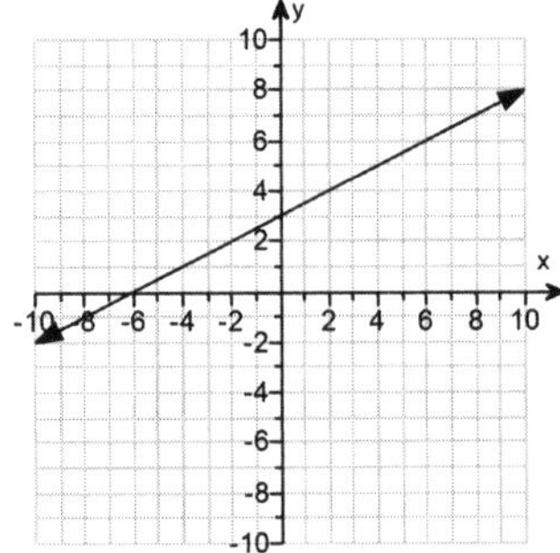

ID: 5.3.33

34. Use the graph sketched to the right to find x when y = 0.

x = ___________

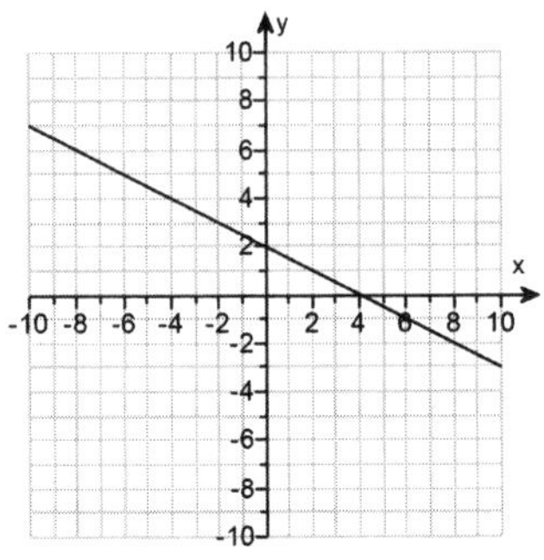

ID: 5.3.34

35. The graph of an equation is sketched to the right. Which of the points A, B, C, D, E, and F represent ordered pairs that satisfy the equation?

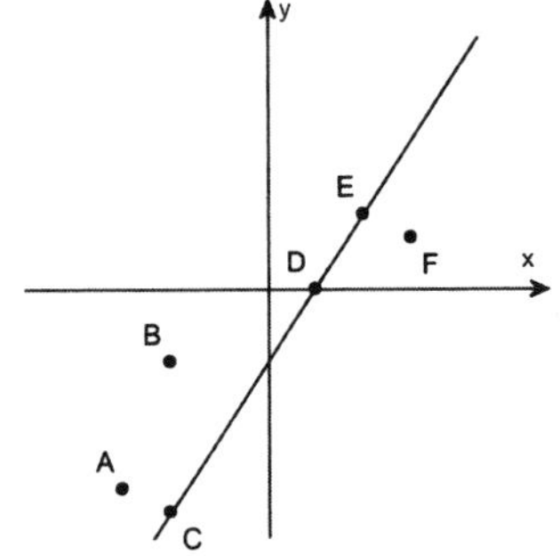

Does the point A represent an ordered pair that satisfies the equation?

- ○ Yes
- ○ No

Does the point B represent an ordered pair that satisfies the equation?

- ○ No
- ○ Yes

Does the point C represent an ordered pair that satisfies the equation?

- ○ Yes
- ○ No

Does the point D represent an ordered pair that satisfies the equation?

- ○ Yes
- ○ No

Does the point E represent an ordered pair that satisfies the equation?

- ○ Yes
- ○ No

Does the point F represent an ordered pair that satisfies the equation?

- ○ No
- ○ Yes

ID: 5.3.35

36. Find an equation of a line that contains the points listed in the table to the right. [**Hint:** For each point, what number can be added to the x-coordinate to get the y-coordinate?]

x	y
0	6
1	7
2	8
3	9
4	10

What is an equation of this line?

y = ___________ (Simplify your answer.)

ID: 5.3.36

* 37. Find an equation of the line that contains the points listed in the following table.

x	y
0	0
1	5
2	10
3	15
4	20

The equation of the line is y = ___________.
(Use integers or fractions for any numbers in the equation.)

ID: 5.3.37

* 38. The graph of an equation is shown to the right.
a. Create a table of ordered-pair solutions of this equation.
b. Find an equation of the line. [**Hint:** Recognize a pattern from the table you created in part (a).]

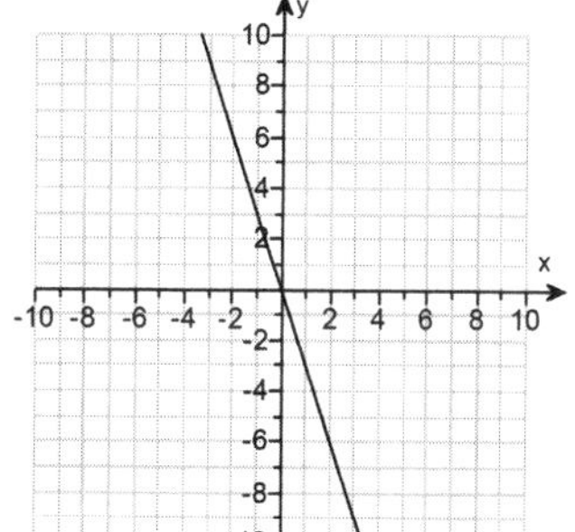

a.

x	y
−2	________
−1	________
0	________
1	________
2	________

b. What is an equation of this line?

y = ___________ (Simplify your answer.)

ID: 5.3.38

39. Graph x + y = 5 by hand. [**Hint:** Assume that the graph is a line. Think of pairs of numbers whose sum is 5.]

Use the graphing tool to graph the line.

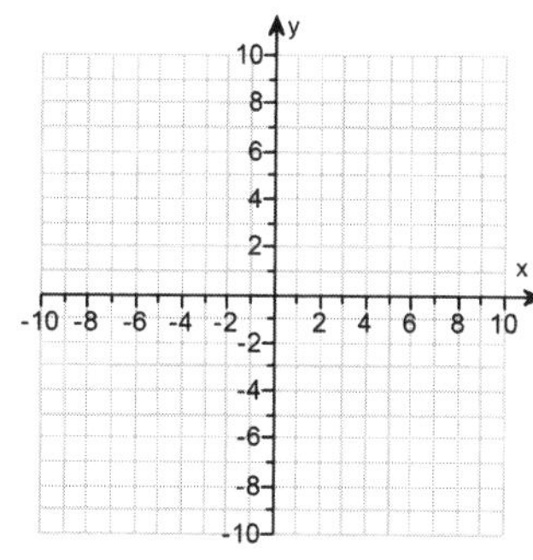

ID: 5.3.39

40. Determine whether 8 is a solution of the equation.

5x + 3 = 42; x = 8

Is x = 8 a solution of the equation 5x + 3 = 42?

○ No
○ Yes

ID: 5.3.40

41. Determine whether 3 is a solution of the equation.

$39 - x = 4(4x - 3)$

Is $x = 3$ a solution of the equation $39 - x = 4(4x - 3)$?

○ No
○ Yes

ID: 5.3.41

---

42. Solve. Verify that your result satisfies the equation.

$x + 2 = -8$

x = ___________

ID: 5.3.42

---

43. Solve. Verify that your result satisfies the equation.

$t - 7 = 16$

t = ___________

ID: 5.3.43

---

44. Solve. Verify that your result satisfies the equation.

$-11 = x - 9$

x = ___________

ID: 5.3.44

---

45. Solve the equation for x.

$-2x = 12$

x = ___________

ID: 5.3.45

---

46. Solve the following equation. Verify that your result satisfies the equation.

$-7x = 0$

x = ___________ (Type an integer or a simplified fraction.)

ID: 5.3.46

---

47. Solve. Verify that your result satisfies the equation.

$\frac{1}{4}t = 5$

t = ___________

ID: 5.3.47

---

48. Solve. Verify that your result satisfies the equation.

$-16 = \frac{4x}{5}$

x = ___________

ID: 5.3.48

---

49. Solve. Verify that your result satisfies the equation.

$$\frac{2}{7}p = -\frac{6}{5}$$

p = ____________
(Type an integer or a simplified fraction.)

ID: 5.3.49

---

50. Solve. Verify that your result satisfies the equation.

$$x + 9.1 = -10.6$$

x = ____________

ID: 5.3.50

---

51. Solve. Verify that your result satisfies the equation.

$$-3.6r = -9.00$$

r = ____________

ID: 5.3.51

---

52. Use the intersection feature on a graphing calculator to solve the following equation.

$$6x - 25 = 5$$

x = ____________ (Type an integer or a simplified fraction.)

ID: 5.3.52

---

53. Use the intersection feature on a graphing calculator to solve the following equation.

$$-4(x - 3) = -16$$

x = ____________ (Type an integer or a simplified fraction.)

ID: 5.3.53

---

54. Solve the equation $7x - 5 = 16$ by referring to the solutions of $y = 7x - 5$ shown in the table.

x	y
−3	−26
−2	−19
−1	−12
0	−5
1	2
2	9
3	16

x = ____________ (Type an integer or a fraction.)

ID: 5.3.54

---

55. Solve. (Hint: Combine like terms on the left side.)

$$6x + 2x = 16$$

x = ____________

ID: 5.3.55

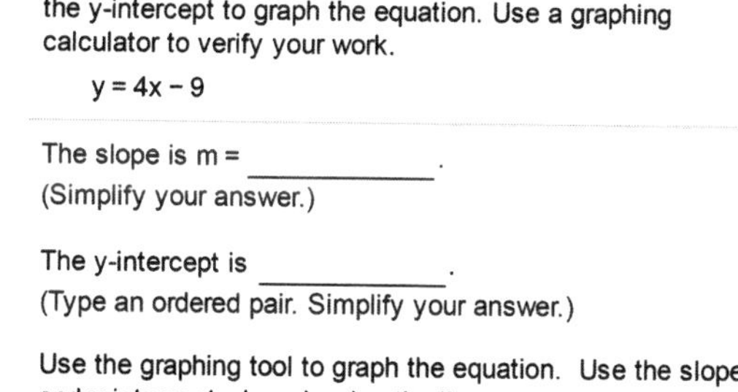

*56. Determine the slope and the y-intercept. Use the slope and the y-intercept to graph the equation. Use a graphing calculator to verify your work.

$$y = 4x - 9$$

The slope is m = ____________.
(Simplify your answer.)

The y-intercept is ____________.
(Type an ordered pair. Simplify your answer.)

Use the graphing tool to graph the equation. Use the slope and y-intercept when drawing the line.

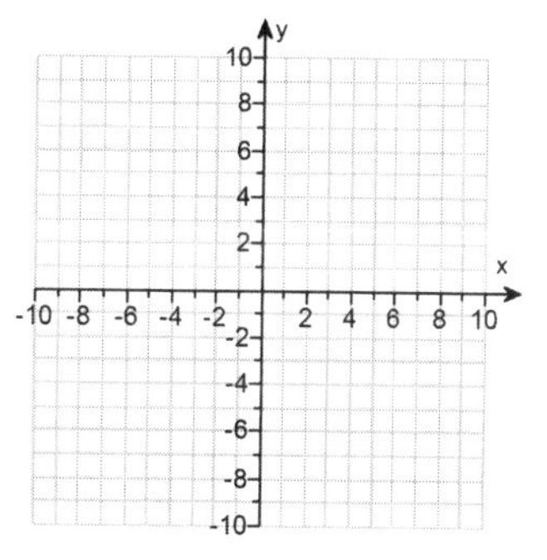

ID: 5.3.56

---

57. Determine the slope and the y-intercept. Use the slope and the y-intercept to graph the equation.

$y = 7$

The slope is m = ____________.
(Simplify your answer.)

The y-intercept is ____________.
(Type an ordered pair. Simplify your answer.)

Use the graphing tool to graph the equation. Use the slope and y-intercept when drawing the line.

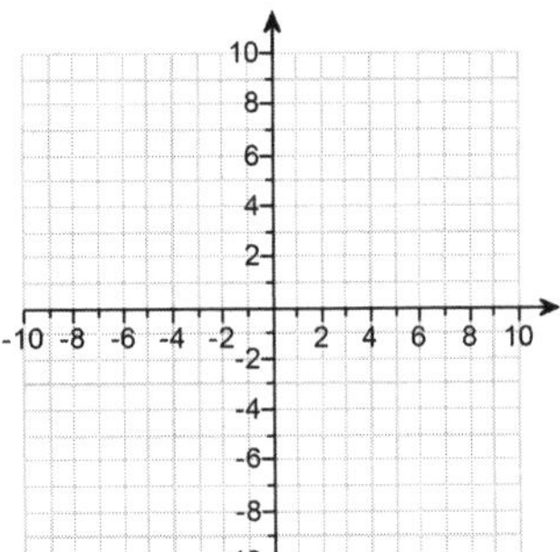

ID: 5.3.57

---

58. Determine the slope and the y-intercept. Use the slope and the y-intercept to graph the equation. Use a graphing calculator to verify your work.

$y - 3x = -9$

The slope is m = ____________.
(Simplify your answer.)

The y-intercept is ____________.
(Type an ordered pair. Simplify your answer.)

Use the graphing tool to graph the equation. Use the slope and y-intercept when drawing the line.

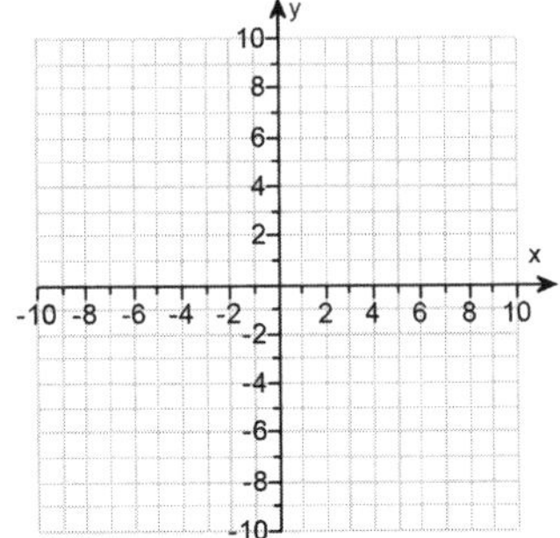

ID: 5.3.58

---

59. Determine the slope and the y-intercept. Use the slope and the y-intercept to graph the equation. Use a graphing calculator to verify your work.

$3y = 2x - 15$

The slope is ____________.
(Type an integer or a simplified fraction.)

The y-intercept is ____________.
(Type an ordered pair. Type integers or simplified fractions.)

Use the graphing tool to graph the equation. Use the slope and y-intercept when drawing the line.

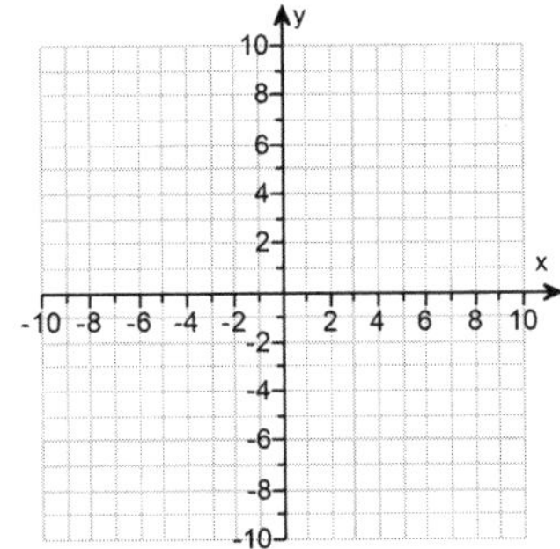

ID: 5.3.59

---

60. Determine the slope and the y-intercept. Use the slope and the y-intercept to graph the equation. Use a graphing calculator to verify your work.

$2x - 5y = 5$

The slope is m = ____________.
(Simplify your answer.)

The y-intercept is ____________.
(Type an ordered pair. Simplify your answer.)

Use the graphing tool to graph the equation. Use the slope and y-intercept when drawing the line.

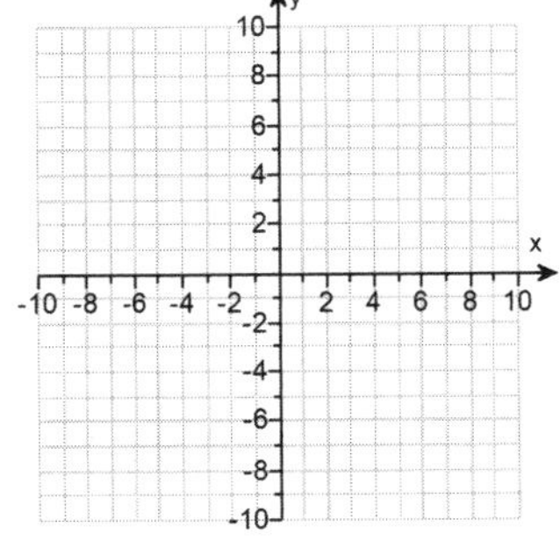

ID: 5.3.60

61. Determine the slope and the y-intercept. Use the slope and the y-intercept to graph the equation. Use a graphing calculator to verify your work.

$7x + 3y = 0$

The slope is ___________.
(Simplify your answer.)

The y-intercept is ___________.
(Type an ordered pair. Simplify your answer.)

Use the graphing tool to graph the equation. Use the slope and y-intercept when drawing the line.

ID: 5.3.61

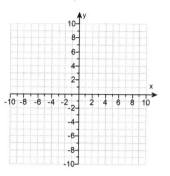

62. Determine the slope and y-intercept of the graph of the linear equation. Use the slope and y-intercept to graph the equation by hand. Verify your graph by using ZStandard followed by ZSquare on a graphing calculator.

$6(x - 2y) = 30$

The slope is m = ___________.
(Type an integer or a fraction.)

Use the graphing tool to graph the linear equation. Use the slope and y-intercept when drawing the line.

ID: 5.3.62

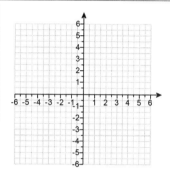

63. Determine the slope and the y-intercept of the graph of the equation below, where w, z, and a are nonzero constants.

$wx - zy = a$

The slope of the graph of the given equation is ___________.

The y-intercept of the graph of the given equation is ___________.
(Type an ordered pair.)

ID: 5.3.63

---

64. Determine the slope and the y-intercept of the graph of the equation below, where c and d are nonzero constants.

$\frac{x}{c} + \frac{y}{d} = 6$

The slope of the graph of the given equation is ___________.

The y-intercept of the graph of the given equation is ___________.
(Type an ordered pair.)

ID: 5.3.64

---

65. Find the x-intercept and y-intercept. Then graph the equation.

$12 = 4x + 3y$

Use the graphing tool to graph the equation. Use the intercepts when drawing the line. If only one intercept exists, use it and another point to draw the line.

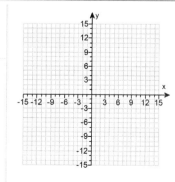

ID: 5.3.65

66. Find the x-intercept and y-intercept. Then graph the equation.

$5x - 7y + 35 = 0$

Use the graphing tool to graph the equation. Use the intercepts when drawing the line. If only one intercept exists, use it and another point to draw the line.

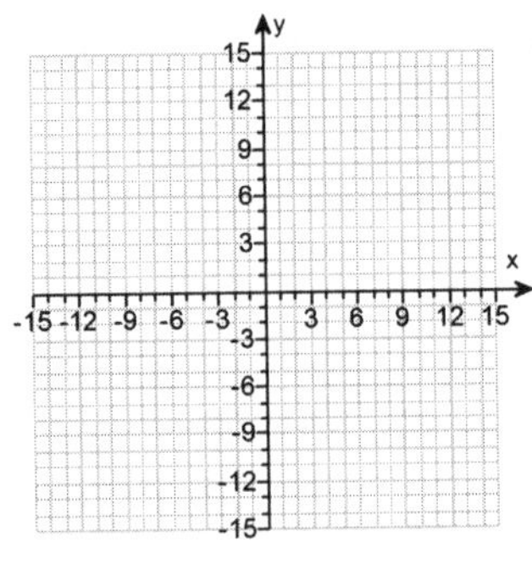

ID: 5.3.66

67. Find the x-intercept and y-intercept. Then graph the equation.

$\frac{x}{7} + \frac{y}{2} = 1$

Use the graphing tool to graph the equation. Use the intercepts when drawing the line. If only one intercept exists, use it and another point to draw the line.

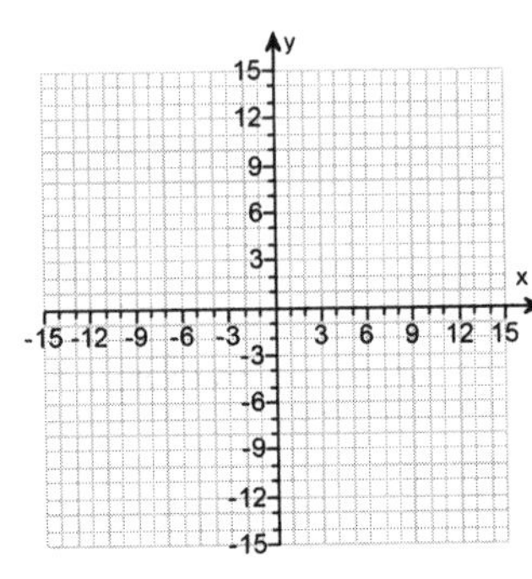

ID: 5.3.67

68. Find the approximate x-intercept and the approximate y-intercept of the equation below.

$8.4x + 3.1y = 7.6$

The x-intercept of the graph of the given equation is ____________.
(Type an ordered pair. Type integers or decimals rounded to two decimal places as needed.)

The y-intercept of the graph of the given equation is ____________.
(Type an ordered pair. Type integers or decimals rounded to two decimal places as needed.)

ID: 5.3.68

69. Find the approximate x-intercept and the approximate y-intercept.

$5.73x - 3.26y = -12.69$

The x-intercept is ____________.
(Round to two decimal places as needed. Type an ordered pair.)

The y-intercept is ____________.
(Round to two decimal places as needed. Type an ordered pair.)

ID: 5.3.69

70. Find the approximate x-intercept and the approximate y-intercept of the equation below.

$y = -3.9x + 8.88$

The x-intercept of the graph of the given equation is ____________.
(Type an ordered pair. Type integers or decimals rounded to two decimal places as needed.)

The y-intercept of the graph of the given equation is ____________.
(Type an ordered pair. Type integers or decimals rounded to two decimal places as needed.)

ID: 5.3.70

71. Find the approximate x-intercept and the approximate y-intercept of the equation below.

$y = -2.82x - 24.65$

The x-intercept of the graph of the given equation is ________.
(Type an ordered pair. Type integers or decimals rounded to two decimal places as needed.)

The y-intercept of the graph of the given equation is ________.
(Type an ordered pair. Type integers or decimals rounded to two decimal places as needed.)

ID: 5.3.71

72. Assuming that the graph of the equation below has an x-intercept and a y-intercept, find both intercepts.

$\frac{x}{w} + \frac{y}{z} = 4$

The x-intercept of the graph of the given equation is ________.
(Type an ordered pair.)

The y-intercept of the graph of the given equation is ________.
(Type an ordered pair.)

ID: 5.3.72

73. Graph the equation below using any method.

$5x - y = 4$

Use the graphing tool to graph the equation.

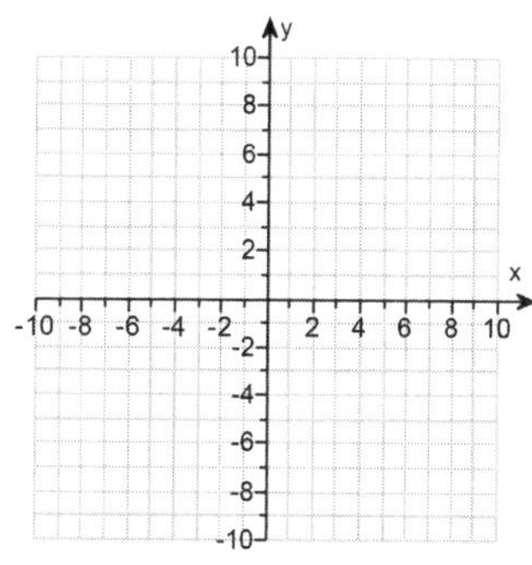

ID: 5.3.73

74. Graph by plotting points.

$-3x + 4y = 0$

Use the graphing tool to graph the linear equation.

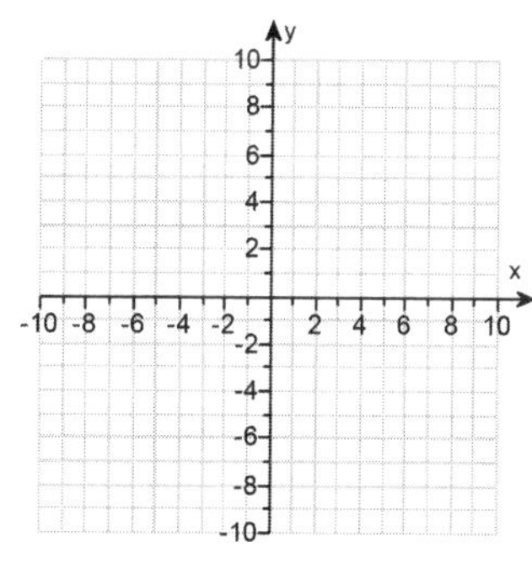

ID: 5.3.74

75. Graph by plotting points.

$12x + 4y - 20 = 0$

Use the graphing tool on the right to graph the equation.

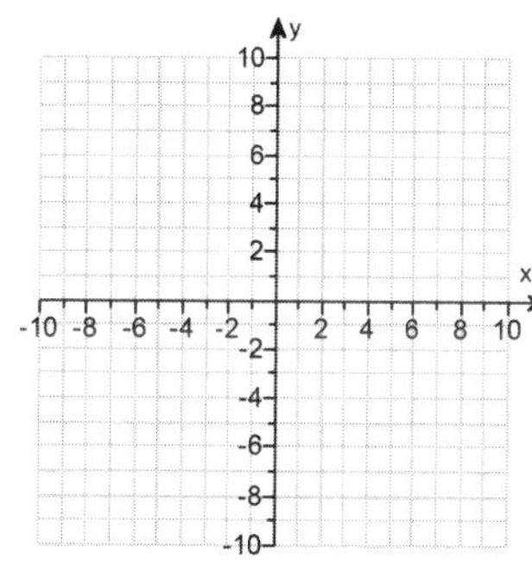

ID: 5.3.75

76. Find the equation of the line that has the given slope and contains the given point. If possible write the equation in slope-intercept form.

(1,1); slope = 6

The equation of the line is ___________.
(Type your answer in slope-intercept form.)

ID: 5.3.76

---

77. Find the equation of the line that fits the description.

Passes through (− 9,1) and has undefined slope.

The equation of the line is ___________.

ID: 5.3.77

---

78. Write an equation of the line passing through the given points.

(3,11) and (− 4, − 38)

y = ___________

ID: 5.3.78

---

79. Find an equation of the line that passes through the two given points.

(7,9) and (6,9)

The equation of the line is y = ___________.
(Simplify your answer.)

ID: 5.3.79

---

80. Find an equation of the line passing through the given points. Express your answer in slope-intercept form.

(7,3) and (7, − 8)

The equation of the line is ___________.
(Type an expression using x as the variable.)

ID: 5.3.80

---

81. Write a linear equation for a line containing the given ordered pairs. Graph the equation to check that it is correct.

(− 2,6) and (1, − 9)

y = ___________
(Type an equation using x as the variable. Simplify your answer. Type your answer in slope-intercept form.)

ID: 5.3.81

---

82. Find an approximate equation of the line that passes through the two given points. Round the slope and the constant term to two decimal places.

(− 2.4, − 1.6) and (7.4,0.3)

The equation of the line is y = ___________.
(Simplify your answer.)

ID: 5.3.82

---

83. Find an equation of the line that contains (4,4) and is parallel to y = 2x + 4. Use a graphing calculator to verify the result.

y = ___________ (Simplify your answer. Do not factor.)

ID: 5.3.83

---

84. Find an equation of the line that contains the given point and is parallel to the given line. Use a graphing calculator to verify your result.

$(6,13)$, $4x - 5y = 12$

The equation of the line is y = ____________.
(Simplify your answer. Use integers or fractions for any numbers in the expression. Type your answer in slope-intercept form.)

ID: 5.3.84

---

85. Find an equation of the line that contains the given point and is parallel to the given line.

$(12,5)$, $y = 3$

The equation of the line is y = ____________.

ID: 5.3.85

---

86. Find an equation of the line that contains the given point and is parallel to the given line.

$(-7,9)$, $x = 10$

Determine the equation of the line.

- **A.** The equation of the line is $x = -7$.
- **B.** The equation of the line is $y = 9$.
- **C.** The equation of the line is $x = 9$.
- **D.** The equation of the line is $y = -7x + 9$.

ID: 5.3.86

---

87. Write an equation of the line that contains $(7,9)$ and is perpendicular to $y = -9x + 3$. Use a graphing calculator to verify the result.

The equation of the line is y = ____________.
(Simplify your answer. Use integers or fractions for any numbers in the expression. Do not factor.)

ID: 5.3.87

---

88. Find an equation of the line that contains the given point and is perpendicular to the given line.

$(-8,4)$, $y = -9x + 7$

The equation of the line is y = ____________.
(Simplify your answer. Use integers or fractions for any numbers in the expression. Type your answer in slope-intercept form.)

ID: 5.3.88

---

89. Find an equation of the line that contains the given point and is perpendicular to the given line.

$(11,3)$, $7x - 12y = 5$

The equation of the line is y = ____________.
(Simplify your answer. Use integers or fractions for any numbers in the expression. Type your answer in slope-intercept form.)

ID: 5.3.89

---

90. Write an equation of the line containing the given point and perpendicular to the given line.

$(4,-5)$; $4x + 9y = 5$

The equation of the line is y = ____________.
(Simplify your answer. Type your answer in slope-intercept form. Use integers or fractions for any numbers in the expression.)

ID: 5.3.90

---

91. Find an equation of the line sketched in the figure.

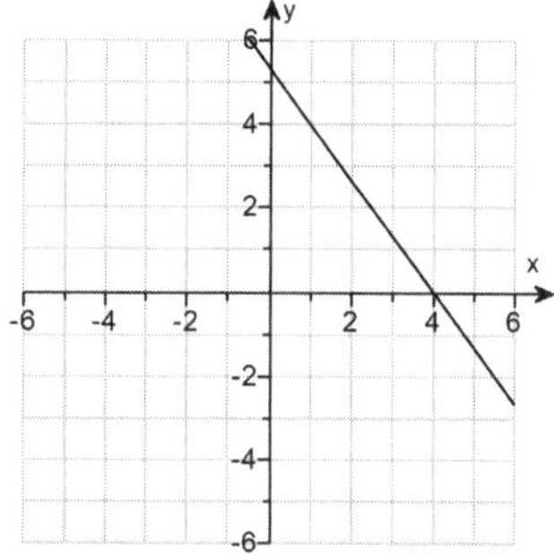

The equation of the line is y = ____________.
(Simplify your answer. Use integers or fractions for any numbers in the expression. Type your answer in slope-intercept form.)

ID: 5.3.91

---

*92. Let y be the value (in thousands of dollars) of a car when it is x years old. Some pairs of values of x and y are listed in the table. Find an equation that describes the relationship between x and y.

Age (years), x	Value (thousands of dollars), y
0	51
1	48
2	45
3	42
4	39

The equation that describes the relationship between x and y is y = ____________.
(Do not factor.)

ID: 5.3.92

---

93. Some ordered pairs are listed in the table to the right.
a. Create a scattergram of the points shown in the table.
b. Are the variables x and y linearly related, approximately linearly related, or neither?
c. Draw a line that comes close to the points in your scattergram.
d. Which point on your line has x-coordinate 6?
e. Which point on your line has y-coordinate 4?
f. What is the y-intercept of your line?
g. What is the x-intercept of your line?

x	y
1	19
3	13
5	10
7	5
9	3

a. Create a scattergram of the points shown in the table. Choose the correct graph below.

○ **A.**

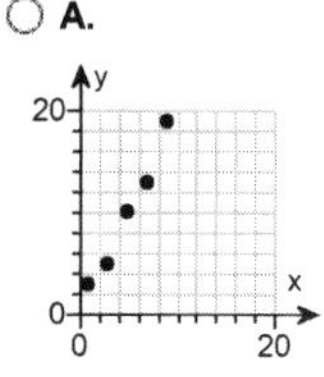

○ **B.**

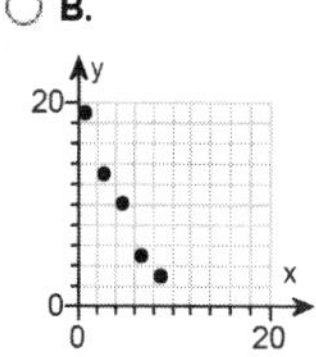

○ **C.**

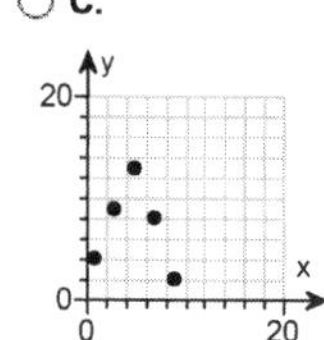

○ **D.**

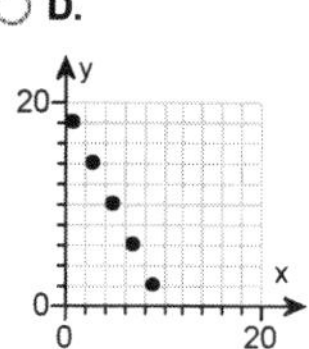

b. Are the variables x and y linearly related, approximately linearly related, or neither?

○ **A.** The variables x and y are linearly related.
○ **B.** The variables x and y are approximately linearly related.
○ **C.** The variables x and y are not related linearly.

c. Draw a line that comes close to the points in your scattergram.

○ **A.**

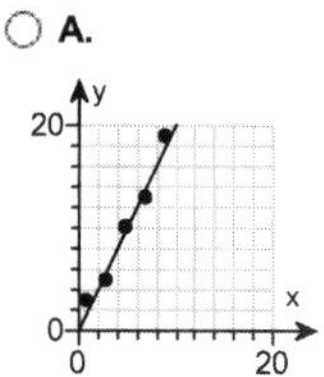

○ **B.**

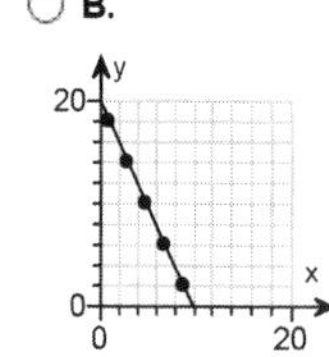

○ **C.**

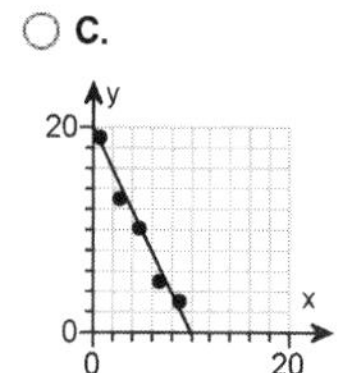

○ **D.** The variables x and y are not related linearly.

d. Which point on the line in part **c.** has x-coordinate 6?

93. (cont.) Select the correct choice below and, if necessary, fill in the answer box to complete your choice.

○ **A.** The point is ____________. (Type an ordered pair, using integers or decimals.)

○ **B.** The variables x and y are not related linearly.

e. Which point on the line in part **c.** has y-coordinate 4?

Select the correct choice below and, if necessary, fill in the answer box to complete your choice.

○ **A.** The point is ____________. (Type an ordered pair, using integers or decimals.)

○ **B.** The variables x and y are not related linearly.

f. What is the y-intercept of the line in part **c.**?

Select the correct choice below and, if necessary, fill in the answer box to complete your choice.

○ **A.** The y-intercept is ____________. (Type an ordered pair, using integers or decimals.)

○ **B.** The variables x and y are not related linearly.

g. What is the x-intercept of the line in part **c.**?

Select the correct choice below and, if necessary, fill in the answer box to complete your choice.

○ **A.** The x-intercept is ____________. (Type an ordered pair, using integers or decimals.)

○ **B.** The variables x and y are not related linearly.

ID: 5.4.1

---

*94. The percentages of dentistry degrees earned by women are shown in the table for various years.

Year	Percent
1970	4
1980	14
1990	25
2000	37
2002	36

Let p be the percentage of dentistry degrees earned by women at t years since 1970. For example, t = 0 represents 1970 and t = 10 represents 1980.

a. Create a scattergram of the data. Choose the correct scattergram below.

○ **A.** ○ **B.** 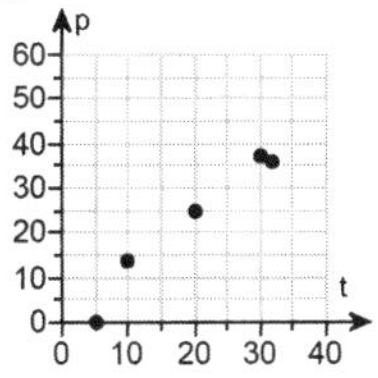 ○ **C.** 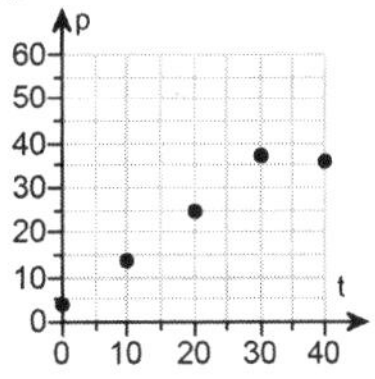 ○ **D.**

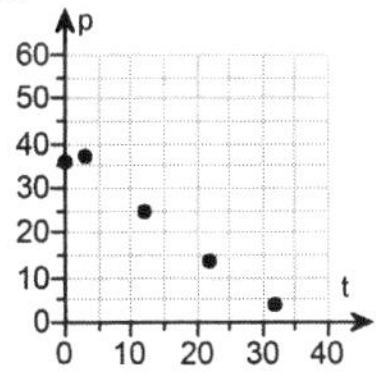

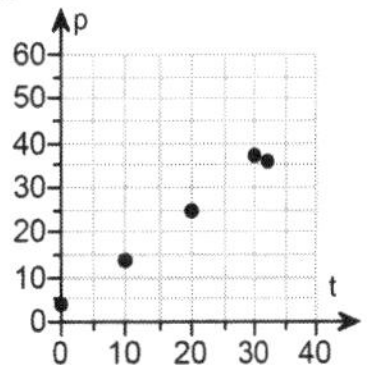

b. Draw a line that comes close to the points in your scattergram. Choose the correct scattergram below.

○ **A.** ○ **B.** 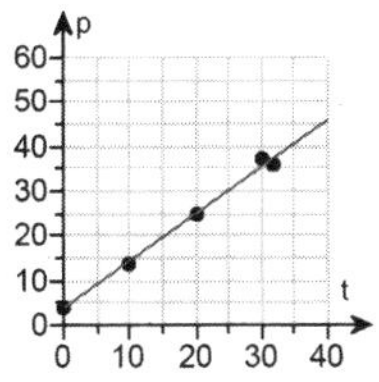 ○ **C.** 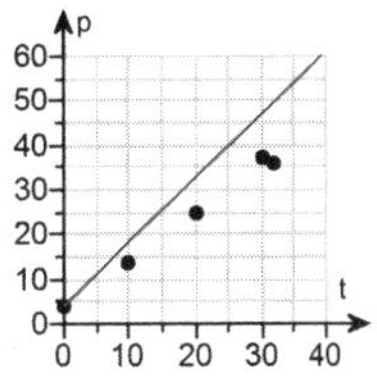 ○ **D.**

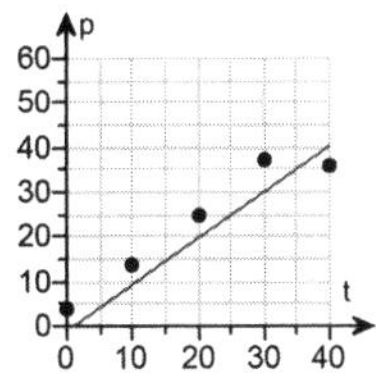

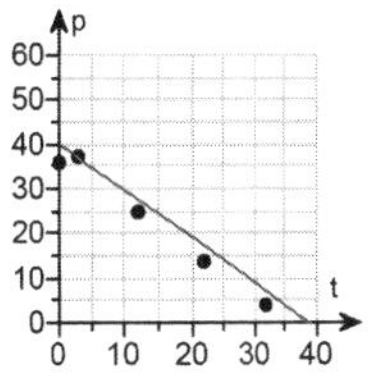

c. Predict the percentage of dentistry degrees that will be earned by women in 2010.

The percentage of dentistry degrees earned by women in 2010 will be about ____________%.

d. Estimate when women earned 20% of dentistry degrees.

Women earned 20% of dentistry degrees in ____________.

ID: 5.4.2

* 95. If there are too many ticketed passengers for a flight, a person can volunteer to be "bumped" onto another flight. The voluntary bumping rates for large U.S. airlines (number of bumps per 10,000 passengers, January through September) are shown in the table for various years. Let r be the voluntary bumping rate (number of bumps per 10,000 passengers) at t years since 2000.

Year	Bumping Rate
2000	22
2001	17
2002	16
2003	13
2004	12
2005	10

a. Create a scattergram of the data. Choose the correct graph below.

○ **A.**

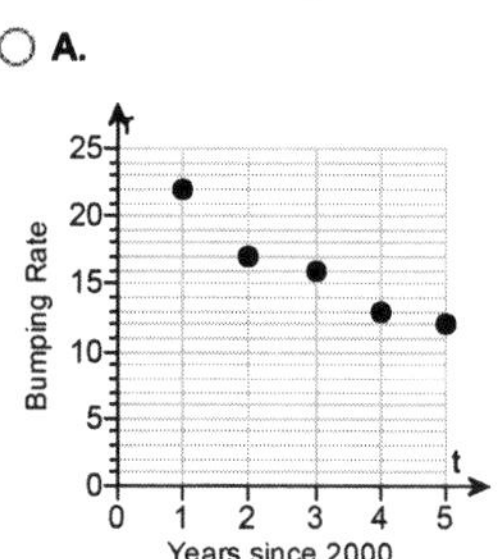

○ **B.**

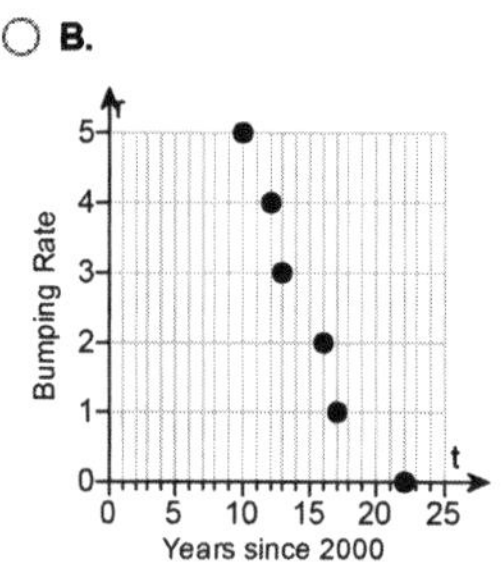

○ **C.**

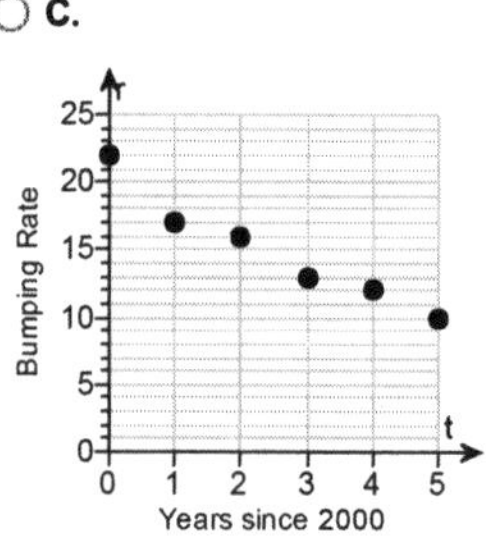

b. Draw a line that comes close to the points in your scattergram.

Choose the correct graph below.

○ **A.**

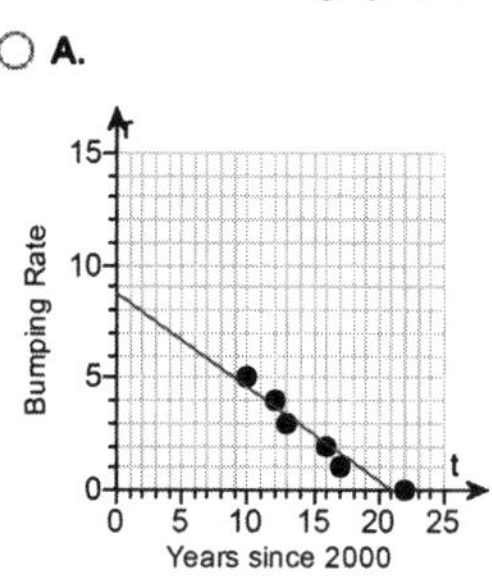

○ **B.**

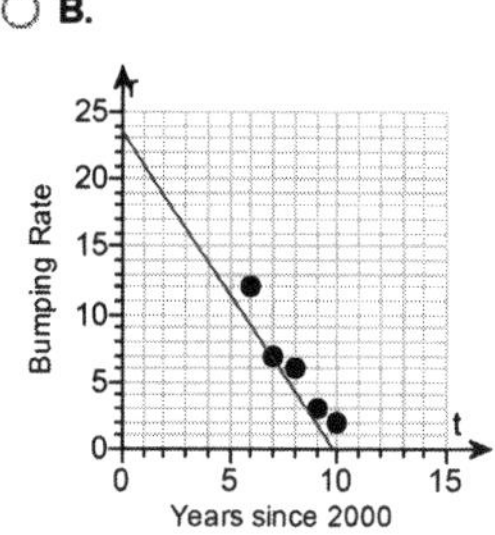

○ **C.**

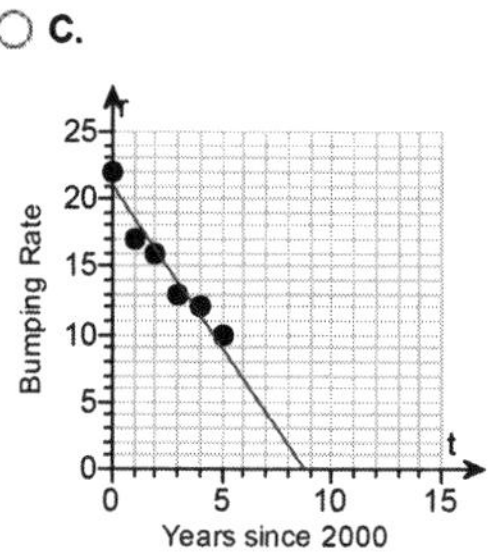

c. What is the r-intercept of the model?

____________ (Round to the nearest integer. Type an ordered pair.)

What does it mean in this situation?

○ **A.** According to the model, the average bumping rate was 21 per 10,000 passengers in the year 2000.

○ **B.** According to the model, the average bumping rate per 10,000 passengers was decreasing by 21 in the year 2000.

○ **C.** According to the model, the average bumping rate will be 0 per 10,000 passengers in the year 2021.

d. Predict when the voluntary bumping rate will be 5 bumps per 10,000 passengers.

____________ (Round to the nearest year.)

e. What is the t-intercept of the model?

____________ (Round to the nearest integer. Type an ordered pair.)

What does it mean in this situation?

○ **A.** According to the model, the average bumping rate will be 0 per 10,000 passengers in the year 2009. Since this prediction implies that the airlines will eliminate bumping completely, it is not plausible, and therefore model breakdown has occurred.

○ **B.** According to the model, the average bumping rate will be 0 per 9 passengers in the year 2009. Since this prediction implies that the airlines will eliminate bumping completely, it is not plausible, and therefore model breakdown has occurred.

○ **C.** According to the model, the average bumping rate was 9 per 10,000 passengers in the year 2000. This seems reasonable, since the airlines cannot eliminate bumping completely.

ID: 5.4.3

96. Due to improved technology and public service campaigns, the number of collisions at highway-railroad crossings per year has declined since 1986 (see table on the right).

Year	Number of collisions (in thousands)	Year	Number of collisions (in thousands)
1986	6.9	1998	3.3
1990	6.1	2002	2.9
1994	4.8	2003	2.8

Let n be the number of collisions (in thousands) for the year that is t years since 1980.

a. Create a scattergram of the data. Choose the correct scattergram below.

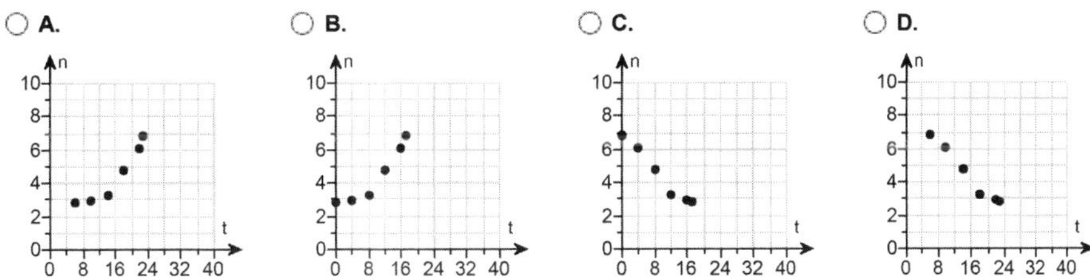

b. Draw a line that comes close to the data points in your scattergram. Choose the correct scattergram below.

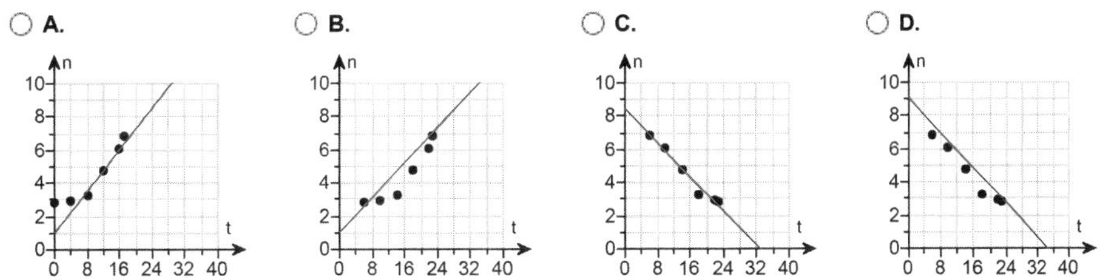

c. Use your linear model to estimate the number of collisions in 1997.

In 1997 there were about ____________ thousand collisions.

Did you perform interpolation or extrapolation?

○ interpolation
○ extrapolation

d. Use your linear model to predict in which year there will be 1.0 thousand collisions.

There will be 1.0 thousand collisions in ____________.

Did you perform interpolation or extrapolation?

○ extrapolation
○ interpolation

e. Find the n-intercept of your linear model. Choose the correct answer below.

○ **A.** (0,8.4)
○ **B.** (8.4,0)
○ **C.** (33,0)
○ **D.** (0,12.4)

f. Find the t-intercept of your linear model. Choose the correct answer below.

○ **A.** (8.4,0)
○ **B.** (33,0)
○ **C.** (28,0)
○ **D.** (0,33)

ID: 5.4.4

97. The loudness of sound can be measured by using a decibel scale. Some examples of sounds at various sound levels are listed in the adjacent table.
Let S be the sound level (in decibels) for a volume number n.
The sound levels of music for various volume numbers are shown in the table below. Complete parts **a.** through **d.**

Sound Level	Example
0	Faintest sound heard by humans
20	Leaves rustling
45	Background noise in a city home
75	Noisy office
100	Inside New York subway
115	Very loud rock music
130	Cannon

Volume Number	6	8	10	12	14	16	18	20
Sound Level	61	65	69	73	77	80	84	88

a. Create a scattergram of the data in the given table. Choose the correct graph below.

○ **A.** ○ **B.** ○ **C.** ○ **D.**

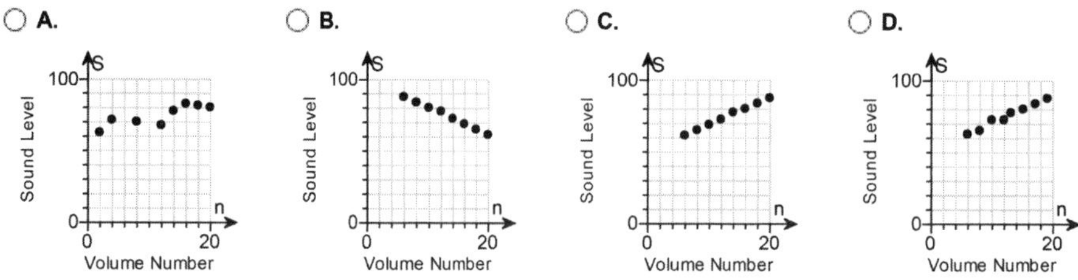

b. Draw a line that comes close to the points in your scattergram.

○ **A.** ○ **B.** ○ **C.** ○ **D.** The variables n and S are not related linearly.

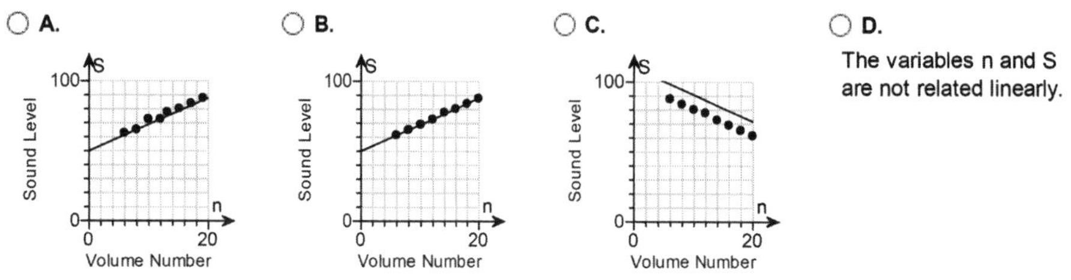

c. Use your model to estimate the sound level when the volume number is 19.

Select the correct choice below and, if necessary, fill in the answer box to complete your choice.

○ **A.** Sound level = ____________ (Type an integer or a decimal.)

○ **B.** The variables n and S are not related linearly.

d. Use your model to estimate for what volume number the sound level is comparable to that of a noisy office.

Select the correct choice below and, if necessary, fill in the answer box to complete your choice.

○ **A.** Volume number = ____________ (Type an integer or a decimal.)

○ **B.** The variables n and S are not related linearly.

ID: 5.4.5

---

* 98. The percentages of people who are satisfied with the way things are in their country are shown in the table on the right for various years.

Year	Percent
1992	25
1993	32
1994	37
1995	43

Year	Percent
1996	45
1997	50
1998	57
1999	56

Let p be the percentage of people at t years since 1990 who are satisfied with the way things are.

a. Create a scattergram of the data. Choose the correct answer below.

○ **A.** ○ **B.** ○ **C.** ○ **D.**

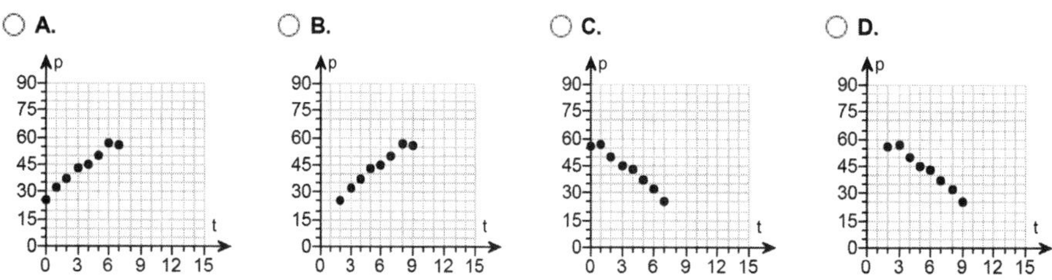

***98.** (cont.)

○ **A.** ○ **B.** ○ **C.** ○ **D.**

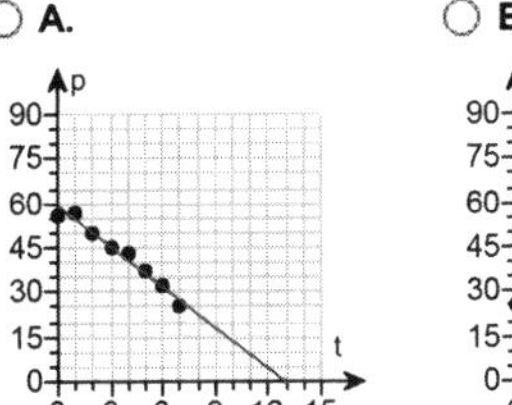

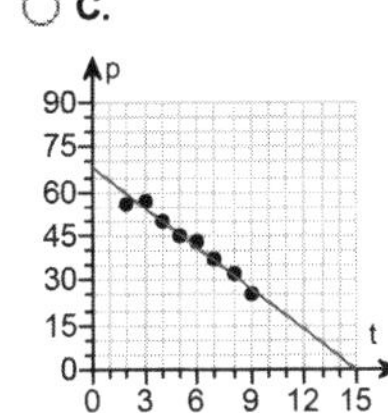

c. Use your line to estimate the percentage of people who were satisfied in 2004.

The percentage of people who were satisfied in 2004 is ___________%.

d. Data for the years 2000-2004 are shown in the table on the right.

Year	Percent	Year	Percent
2000	57	2003	45
2001	54	2004	42
2002	48		

Create a scattergram of the data for the years 1992-2004. Choose the correct answer below.

○ **A.** ○ **B.** ○ **C.** ○ **D.**

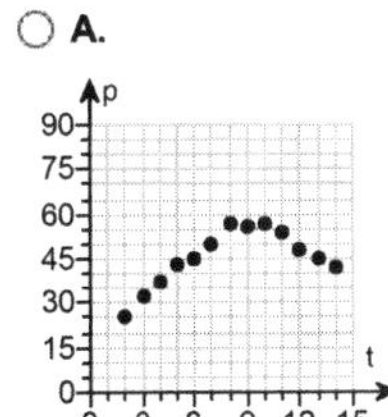

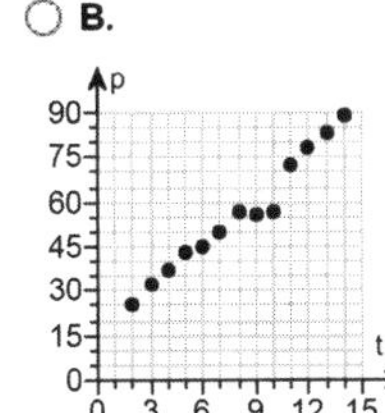

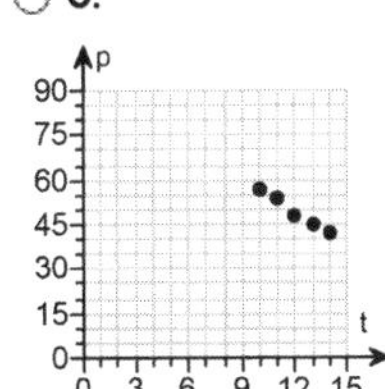

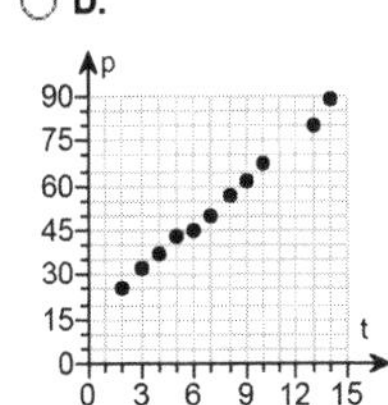

e. Compute the error in the estimation for 2004 that you made in part (c). (The error is the difference between the estimated percentage and the actual percentage.)

The error in the estimation for 2004 is ___________%.

ID: 5.4.6

---

99. The percentages of people living below the poverty level are shown in the table below for various years.

Year	Percent
1993	15.3
1994	14.8
1995	13.8
1996	13.5
1997	13.3
1998	12.7
1999	11.7
2000	11.4

Let p be the percentage of people living below the poverty level at t years since 1990.

Year	Percent
2001	11.6
2002	12.2
2003	12.6
2004	12.8

(a) Create a scattergram of the data for years 1993-2000. Choose the correct scattergram below.

○ **A.** ○ **B.** ○ **C.** ○ **D.**

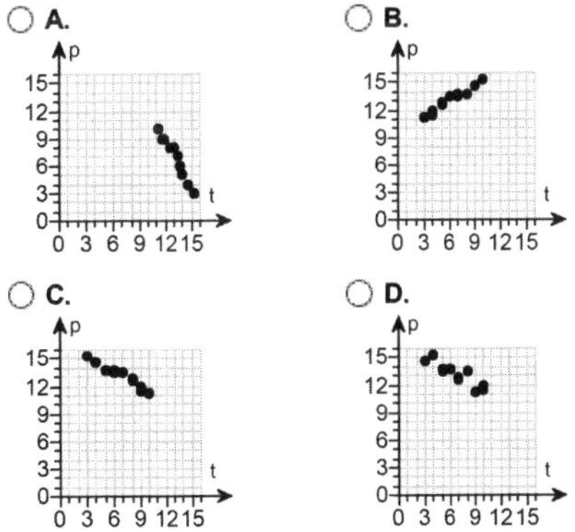

(b) Draw a line that comes close to the data points. Choose the correct answer below.

○ **A.** ○ **B.** ○ **C.** ○ **D.**

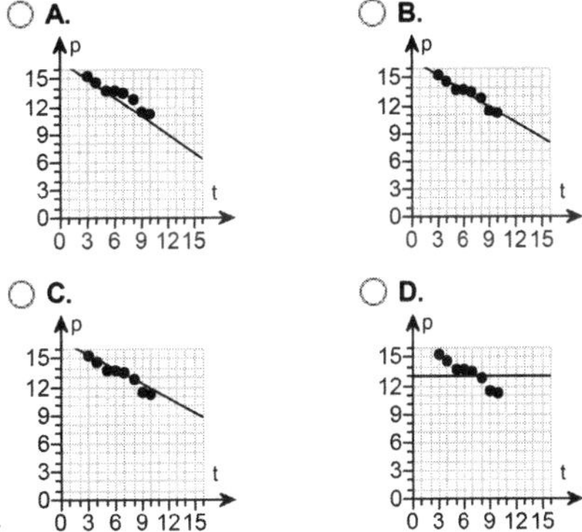

99.
(cont.)

(c) Use your line to estimate the percentage in 2004. Choose the correct answer below.

○ 7.7
○ 9.2
○ 10.2
○ 8.2

(d) Data for the years 2001-2004 are shown in the second table on the left. Create a scattergram of the data for the years 1993-2004. Choose the correct scattergram bellow.

○ **A.** ○ **B.**

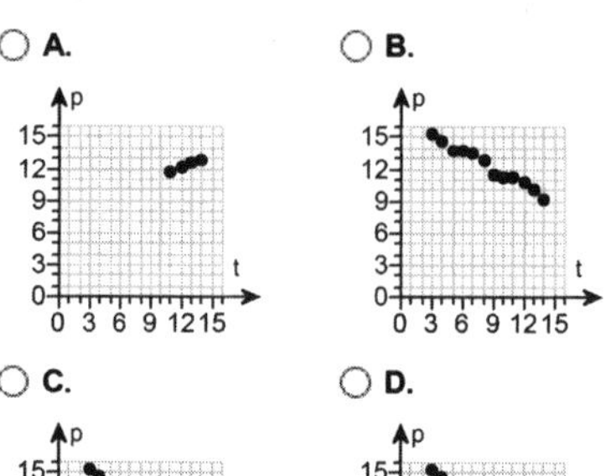

○ **C.** ○ **D.**

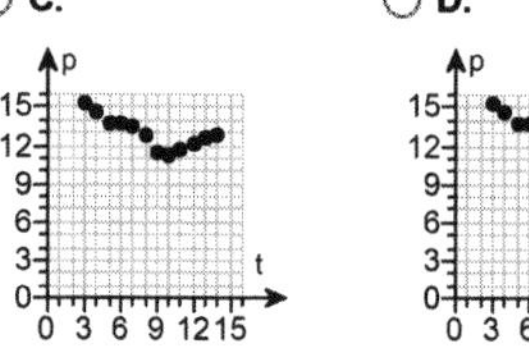

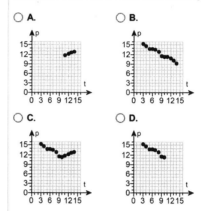

(e) Compute the error in the estimation for 2004 that you made in part (c). The error is the difference between the estimated
percentage and the actual percentage.

error = ________

ID: 5.4.7

---

* 100. The windchill is a measure of how cold you feel as a result of being exposed to wind. The table below provides some data on windchills for various temperatures for a certain wind speed.

Temperature (°F)	Windchill (°F)
−15	−31
−11	−25
−4	−19
3	−12
10	−4
13	6
21	8
23	12

Let w be the windchill (in degrees Fahrenheit) corresponding to a temperature of t degrees Fahrenheit.

(a) Without graphing, estimate the coordinates of the t-intercept for a line that comes close to the data points. Choose the correct answer below.

○ (−14,0)
○ (13,0)
○ (12,0)
○ (10,0)

(b) Without graphing, estimate the coordinates of the w-intercept for a line that comes close to the data points. Choose the correct answer below.

○ (0,−12)
○ (0,12)
○ (0,−19)
○ (0,−14)

ID: 5.4.8

---

101. Due to a crackdown on fraudulent corporate reports, the number of restatements of facts in such reports has increased approximately linearly from 298 restatements in 2004 to 1967 restatements in 2008. Let n be the number of restatements in the year that is t years since 2000. Find an equation of a linear model to describe the data.

Choose the correct answer below.

○ **A.** $n = -417.25t + 1371$
○ **B.** $n = 417.25t - 1371$
○ **C.** $t = 417.25n + 1371$
○ **D.** $n = 1371t + 417.25$

ID: 5.4.9

---

102. The number of rushing yards per year by a running back of a team has decreased approximately linearly from 1847 yards in 2004 to 28 yards in 2008. Let r be a player's number of rushing yards in the year that is t years since 2000. Find an equation of a linear model to describe the data.

Choose the correct answer below.

- A. $r = -454.75t + 3666$
- B. $r = 3666t - 454.75$
- C. $r = -227.38t + 3686$
- D. $r = 454.75t + 3666$

ID: 5.4.10

---

103. The number of flag desecrations (intentionally defacing or dishonoring the flag) has declined approximately linearly from 11 in 2001 to 5 in 2004 in some country. Let n be the number of flag desecrations in the year that is t years since 2000. Find an equation of a linear model to describe the data.

An equation that describes the data is n = ________.
(Type an expression using t as the variable. Type your answer in slope-intercept form.)

ID: 5.4.11

---

104. The average length of a 6-year-old fish is 25 inches, and that of a 19-year-old fish is 54.5 inches. A fish's age and average length are approximately linearly related. Let L be the average length (in inches) of the fish at age a years. Find an equation of a linear model to describe the data.

Choose the correct answer below.

- A. $L = 11.38a + 2.27$
- B. $L = 2.27a + 11.38$
- C. $a = 11.38L + 2.27$
- D. $a = 2.27L + 11.38$

ID: 5.4.12

---

*105. Consider the scattergram of data and the graph of the model y = mx + b in the indicated figure. Sketch the graph of a linear model that describes the data better.

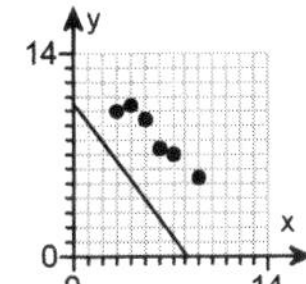

Choose the correct answer below.

A.
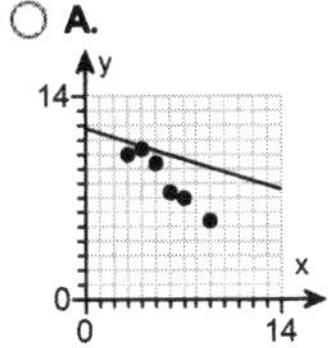

B.
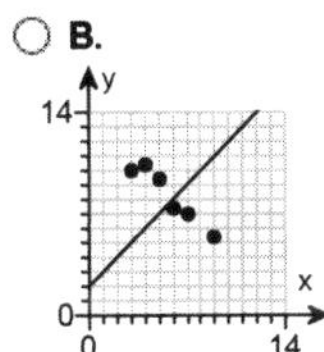

C.
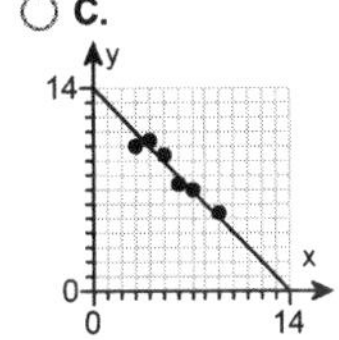

D.
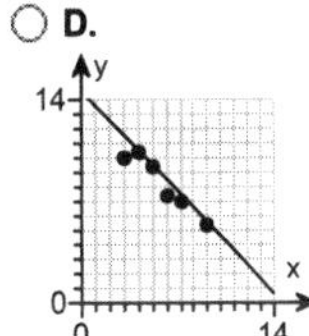

ID: 5.4.13

---

106. Find an equation of a line that comes close to the points listed in the table. Then use a graphing calculator to check that your line comes close to the points.

x	y
3	12
4	13
5	10
6	11
8	8

Choose the equation below that best represents the data.

- A. $y = -x + 16$
- B. $y = -x + 17$
- C. $y = -0.3x + 14$
- D. $y = x + 2$

ID: 5.4.14

---

107. The percentages of births outside marriage in a particular country are shown in the table to the right for various years. Let p be the percentage of births outside marriage in the country at t years since 1900. Complete parts (a) through (c).

aa aa

Year	Percent of Births Outside Marriage
1970	9.8
1975	15.3
1980	18.9
1985	22.9
1990	25.6
1995	31.9
2000	34.3
2005	42.0

a. Use a graphing calculator to draw a scattergram of the data. Choose the correct scattergram below.

 A. ○ B. ○ C. ○ D.

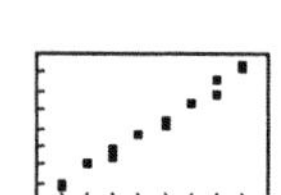
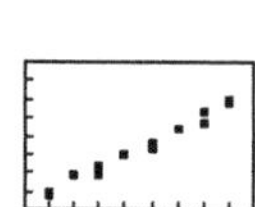
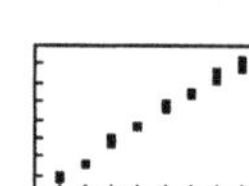
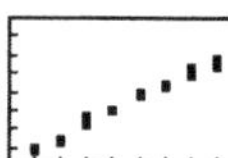

All graphs are [65,110,5] by [5,45,5].

b. Find an equation of a linear model to describe the data. Choose the correct answer below.

○ **A.** $p = 1.20t + 79.01$
○ **B.** $p = 0.87t - 51.05$
○ **C.** $p = 0.83t + 53.56$
○ **D.** $p = 1.15t - 74.85$

c. Draw the line and the scattergram in the same viewing window. Verify that the line passes through the two chosen points and that it comes close to all of the data points. Choose the correct graph below.

 A. ○ B. ○ C. ○ D.

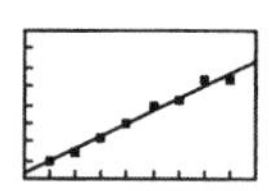
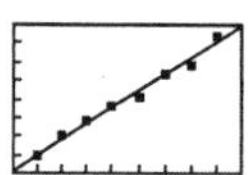
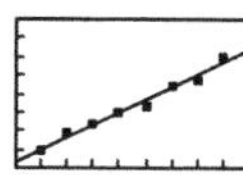
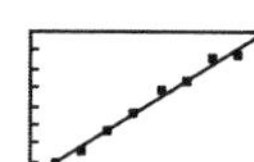

All graphs are [65,110,5] by [5,45,5].

ID: 5.4.15

108. The percentages of the peoples who have been diagnosed with diabetes are shown in the table for various age groups.

Age Group (years)	Age Used to Represent Age Group (years)	Percent
35 – 39	37	2
40 – 44	42	4
45 – 49	47	7
50 – 54	52	8
55 – 59	57	10
60 – 64	62	11
65 – 69	67	14

a. Let p be the percentage of people at age a years who have been diagnosed with diabetes at some point in their lives. Use a graphing calculator to draw a scattergram of the data. Choose the correct answer below.

 A. ○ B.

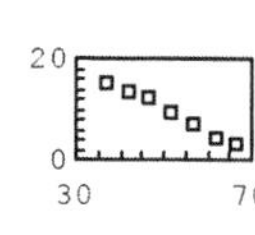
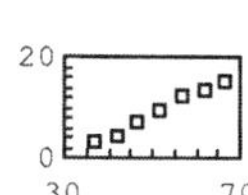

○ C. ○ D.

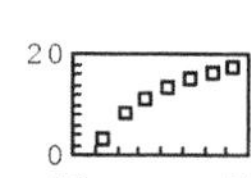
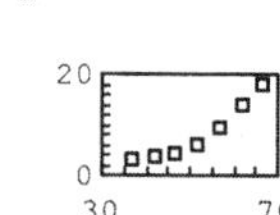

b. Find an equation of a linear model to describe the data. Do not use calculator or other software. Choose the equation below that best represents the data.

○ **A.** $p = 0.4a - 12.8$
○ **B.** $a = 0.4p - 12.8$
○ **C.** $p = -0.4a - 12.8$
○ **D.** $p = 0.6a - 23.2$

c. Draw your line and the scattergram in the same viewing window. Verify that the line passes through the two points you chose in finding the equation in part (b) and that it comes close to all of the data points. Choose the correct answer below.

108.
(cont.)

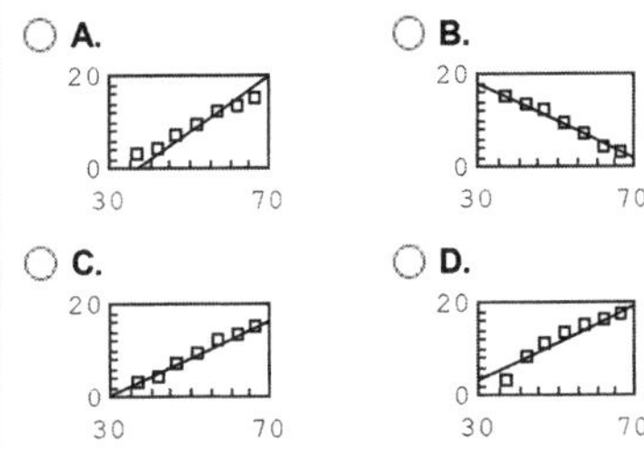

d. Find the regression equation to describe the data. Use a graphing calculator. Choose the equation below that best represents the data.

- A. $a = 0.40p - 11.74$
- B. $p = -0.43a - 11.60$
- C. $p = 0.38a - 11.69$
- D. $p = 0.6a - 23.2$

e. Use a graphing calculator to graph the equations you found in parts (b) and (d) in the same viewing window. Choose the correct answer below.

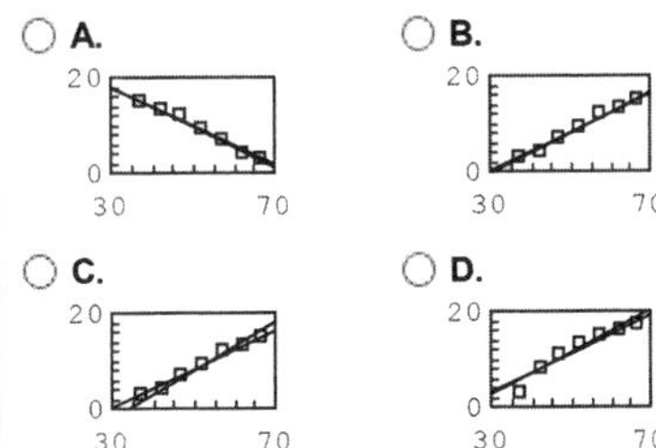

ID: 5.4.16

---

109. To enroll in a certain math class, a student must score at least 21 points (out of 50) on a placement test. Using four semesters of data, the math department computed the percentages of students who succeeded in the class (grade of A, B, or C) for various groups of scores on the placement test. Let p be the percentage of students succeeding in the course who scored x points on the placement test. Complete parts (a) through (c).

Placement Score Group	Score Used to Represent Score Group	Percentage Who Succeeded in Math Class
21-25	23	36
26-30	28	52
31-35	33	60
36-40	38	71
41-45	43	79
46-50	48	*

* There were not enough students in this group to give useful data.

a. Use a graphing calculator to draw a scattergram of the data. Choose the correct scattergram below.

A. 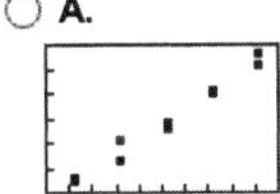
B. 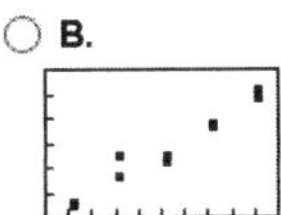
C. 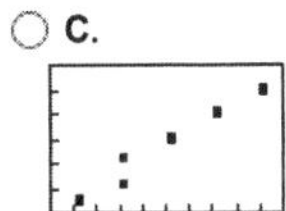
D. 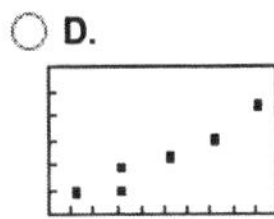

All graphs are [20,45,2.5] by [30,90,10].

b. Find an equation of a line that you think comes close to the points in the scattergram. Choose the equation below which best represents the data.

- A. $p = 2.33x - 17.59$
- B. $p = 3.56x - 18.47$
- C. $p = 0.43x + 26.11$
- D. $p = 0.28x + 29.56$

c. Draw the line and the scattergram in the same viewing window. Verify that the line contains the two points chosen in finding the equation in part (b) and that it comes close to all of the data points. Choose the correct graph below.

A. 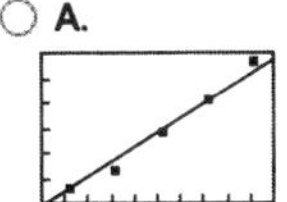
B. 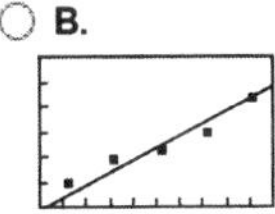
C. 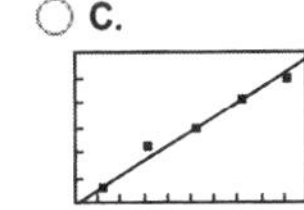
D. 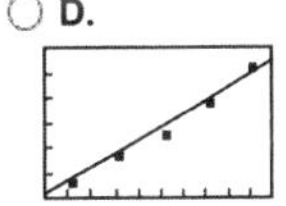

All graphs are [20,45,2.5] by [30,90,10].

ID: 5.4.17

* 110. The table lists College record times for the men's 400-meter run.

Year	1900	1916	1929	1931	1941	1950	1959	1968	1988	1999
Record Time (seconds)	49.5	49.0	48.8	47.7	47.6	47.5	46.5	45.55	44.89	44.85

a. Let r be the record time (in seconds) at t years since 1900. Use a graphing calculator to draw a scattergram of the data. Choose the correct answer below.

○ **A.** ○ **B.** ○ **C.** ○ **D.**

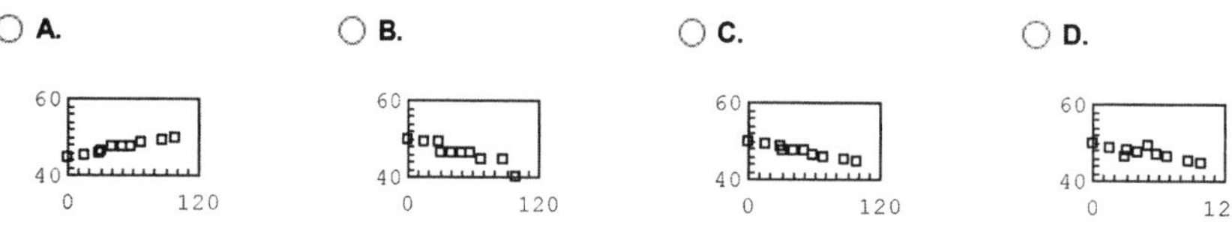

b. Find an equation of a linear model to describe the data. Choose the equation below that best represents the data.

○ **A.** $t = -0.057r + 49.912$
○ **B.** $r = -0.047t + 51.545$
○ **C.** $r = 0.057t + 49.912$
○ **D.** $r = -0.057t + 49.912$

c. Draw your line and the scattergram in the same viewing window. Verify that the line passes through the two points you chose in finding the equation in part (b) and that it comes close to all of the data points. Choose the correct answer below.

○ **A.** ○ **B.** ○ **C.** ○ **D.**

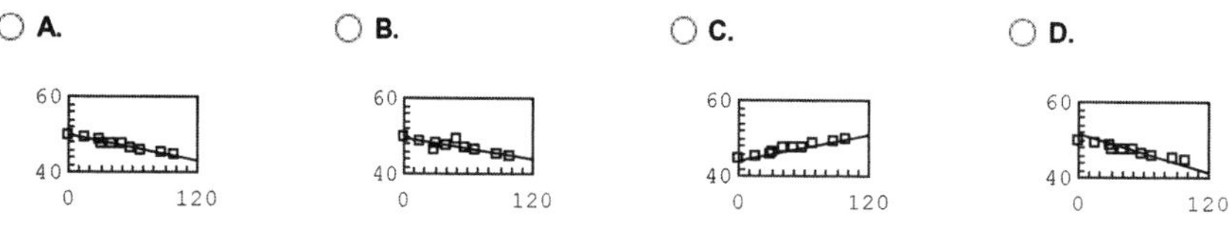

ID: 5.4.18

---

* 111. The market shares (percentages of vehicle sales) of an automobile company are shown in the table to the right for various years. Use the table to answer parts **(a)** through **(e)**.

Year	Market Share (%)
1998	26
2000	23
2002	20
2004	19
2006	15
2008	14

a. Let $s = f(t)$ be the company's market share (in percent) at t years since 1995. Find an equation of f using the data points for the years 2000 and 2008. Does the model fit the data well?

$f(t) =$ __________
(Round to three decimal places as needed.)

Does the model fit the data well?

○ Yes
○ No

b. Find f(12). What does it mean in this situation?

$f(12) =$ __________
(Round to three decimal places as needed.)

Intepret the result.

According to the model, __________ % of the market share belongs to the automobile company in the year __________.
(Round to the nearest year as needed.)

c. Find t when $f(t) = 4$. What does it mean in this situation?

$t =$ __________
(Round to two decimal places as needed.)

*111. (cont.) Interpret the result.

According to the model, ___________% of the market share belongs to the automobile company in the year ___________.

(Round to the nearest year as needed.)

d. Find the t-intercept. What does it mean in this situation?

The t-intercept is ___________.

(Type an ordered pair. Round to two decimal places as needed.)

Interpret the t-intercept.

According to the model, ___________% of the market share belongs to the automobile company in the year ___________.

(Round to the nearest year as needed.)

e. Find the s-intercept. What does it mean in this situation?

The s-intercept is ___________.

(Type an ordered pair. Round to three decimal places as needed.)

Intepret the s-intercept.

According to the model, ___________% of the market share belongs to the automobile company in the year ___________.

(Round to the nearest year as needed.)

ID: 5.4.19

*112. An equation $p = 0.77t - 43.18$ models the percentage p of births outside marriage in a country at t years since 1900 (see table on the right.) Use the equation to answer parts **(a)** through **(e)**.

Year	Percent of Births Outside Marriage
1970	10.7
1975	14.6
1980	18.4
1985	22.3
1990	26.1
1995	30.0
2000	33.8
2005	37.7

a. Rewrite the equation $p = 0.77t - 43.18$ with the function name f. Choose the correct answer below.

○ **A.** $f(p) = 0.77p - 43.18$
○ **B.** $f(t) = 0.77p - 43.18$
○ **C.** $f(p) = t$
○ **D.** $f(t) = 0.77t - 43.18$

b. Find f(110). What does the result mean in this situation?

$f(110) =$ ___________ (Type an integer or a decimal.)

Interpret the result.

According to the model, about ___________% of births in the year ___________ will be outside marriage.

(Round to the nearest year as needed.)

c. Find the value of t so that $f(t) = 51$. What does the result mean in this situation?

$t =$ ___________ (Round to two decimal places as needed.)

Interpret the result.

According to the model, ___________% of births around the year ___________ will be outside marriage.

(Round to the nearest year as needed.)

d. According to the model, in what year will all births be outside marriage?

All births will be outside marriage in the year ___________.

(Round to the nearest year as needed.)

e. Estimate the percentage of births outside marriage in 1997. The actual percentage is 32.4%. What is the error in the estimate? (The error is the difference between the estimated value and the actual value.)

According to the model, ___________% of births were outside of marriage in 1997.

(Round to one decimal place as needed.)

Find the error.

The error is ___________ percentage point(s).

(Type an integer or a decimal. Use the answer from the previous step to find this answer.)

ID: 5.4.20

113. The equation $p = 0.42a - 13.91$ models p, the percentage of people at age a years who have been diagnosed with diabetes at some point in their lives (see the table below).Use this information to answer parts **(a)** through **(e)**.

Age Group	35-39	40-44	45-49	50-54	55-59	60-64	65-69
Age Used to Represent Age Group	37	42	47	52	57	62	67
Percent	2	4	5	8	10	13	14

a. Rewrite the equation $p = 0.42a - 13.91$ with the function name f. Choose the correct answer below.

- ○ **A.** $f(a) = p$
- ○ **B.** $f(a) = 0.42a - 13.91$
- ○ **C.** $f(p) = a$
- ○ **D.** $f(p) = 0.42p - 13.91$

b. Estimate the percentage of 39-year-old people who have been diagnosed with diabetes.

__________ %
(Type an integer or a decimal.)

c. Estimate at what age 9% of people have been diagnosed with diabetes.

__________ years
(Round to two decimal places as needed.)

d. Find the a-intercept. What does it mean in this situation?

The a-intercept is __________.
(Type an ordered pair. Round to two decimal places as needed.)

Interpret the a-intercept.

According to the model, __________ % of __________ -year-old people have been diagnosed with diabetes.
(Type integers or decimals rounded to two decimal places as needed.)

e. The chance of any one person being diagnosed increases as the person grows older. However, 13% of all people over the age of 70 have been diagnosed at some point in their lives. This is less than the percentage for ages 65-69 years. How is this possible?

- ○ **A.** The data collection methods could be flawed. Thus, the model might not be accurate.
- ○ **B.** The data might not fit a linear model. Thus, the model might not be accurate.
- ○ **C.** The model does not come close enough to the given data points to be accurate for ages over 69.

ID: 5.4.21

---

114. The rate at which a cricket chirps depends on the temperature of the surrounding air. It is possible to estimate the air temperature by counting chirps. Examine the table to the right. Use the table to answer parts **(a)** through **(d)**.

Temperature (°F)	Rate (chirps per minute)
50	43
60	86
70	129
80	172
90	215

a. Let g(F) be the number of chirps per minute a cricket makes when the temperature is F degrees Fahrenheit. Find an equation of g. Verify that the graph of the equation comes close to the points in the scattergram of the data.

$g(F) =$ __________ (Type your answer in slope-intercept form.)

Does the graph of the equation come close to the scattergram of the data?

- ○ No
- ○ Yes

b. Find g(73). What does it mean in this situation?

$g(73) =$ __________ (Type an integer or a decimal.)

Intepret the result.

According to the model, when the temperature is __________ °F, the crickets will chirp approximately __________ times per minute.

c. Find F when $g(F) = 106$. What does it mean in this situation?

$F =$ __________ (Round to two decimal places as needed.)

114. (cont.) Interpret the result.

According to the model, when the temperature is approximately ________ °F, the crickets will chirp ________ times per minute.

d. What are the possible air temperatures at a field where the crickets are not chirping?

- ○ **A.** - 171°F and below
- ○ **B.** - 171°F and above
- ○ **C.** - 172°F
- ○ **D.** - 171°F
- ○ **E.** - 172°F and above
- ○ **F.** - 172°F and below
- ○ **G.** 40°F and below
- ○ **H.** 42°F and above
- ○ **I.** 40°F
- ○ **J.** 42°F and below
- ○ **K.** 42°F
- ○ **L.** 40°F and above

ID: 5.4.22

* 115. The number of commercial airline boardings on domestic flights increased steadily during the 1990s. Let f(t) be the number of commercial airline boardings on domestic flights (in millions) for the year that is t years since 1990.

Year	Number of Boardings (millions)
1991	452
1993	481
1995	548
1997	597
1999	634
2000	667

a. Use a graphing calculator to draw a scattergram of the data. Choose the correct graph below.

○ **A.** ○ **B.**

○ **C.** ○ **D.**

The viewing window for all graphs is Xmin = 0, Xmax = 11, Xscl = 1, Ymin = 430, Ymax = 680, Yscl = 25.

b. Find an equation of f. Does your model fit the data well? Choose the correct answer below.

- ○ **A.** f(t) = 24.32f − 421.33
- ○ **B.** f(t) = 24.32t + 421.33
- ○ **C.** f(t) = 421.33f − 24.32
- ○ **D.** f(t) = 421.33t + 24.32

Does your model fit the data well?

- ○ yes
- ○ no

c. Use your model f to estimate the number of boardings in 2004.

The model predicts that the number of boardings in 2004 is ________ million.
(Round to the nearest integer as needed.)

The actual number was 694 million. What is the error in your estimate?

The error is ________ million.
(Round to the nearest integer as needed.)

ID: 5.4.23

116. The percentage of mothers who smoke cigarettes during pregnancy has declined approximately linearly from 13.4% in 1997 to 11.6% in 2000. Predict the percentage in 2014.

The percentage of mothers who will smoke cigarettes during pregnancy in 2014 will be ________ %.
(Round to one decimal place as needed.)

ID: 5.4.24

117. The number of words in some code increased approximately linearly from 1.4 million words in 1955 to 9.6 million words in 2005. Predict the number of words in the code in 2025.

The number of words in the code in 2025 will be ______ million.
(Round to one decimal place as needed.)

ID: 5.4.25

---

118. The percentage of male workers who prefer a female boss over a male boss increased approximately linearly from 4% in 1974 to 15% in 1996. Predict when 18% of male workers will prefer a female boss.

In the year ______, 18% of male workers will prefer a female boss.
(Round to the nearest year as needed.)

ID: 5.4.26

---

* 119. The percentage of female workers who prefer a female boss over a male boss increased approximately linearly from 14% in 1975 to 25% in 2006. Predict when 30% of female workers will prefer a female boss.

30% of female workers will prefer a female boss in year ______.
(Round to the nearest whole number as needed.)

ID: 5.4.27

---

120. The percentage of automobile consumers who are under 50 years of age decreased approximately linearly from 54.1% in 1980 to 50.9% in 1995.

a. Predict when the percentage will be 48%.
b. Predict the percentage in 2000.

a. The percentage will be 48% around the year ______.
(Simplify your answer. Round to the nearest year as needed.)

b. The percentage in 2000 will be ______%.
(Simplify your answer. Round the final answer to two decimal places as needed. Round all intermediate values to two decimal places as needed.)

ID: 5.4.28

---

121. A basement is flooded with 640 cubic feet of water. It takes 4 hours to pump out the water. Let f(t) be the number of cubic feet of water that remains in the basement after t hours of pumping.

a. Find a linear equation of f.

f(t) = ______

b. Graph f. Choose the correct graph below.

○ **A.** ○ **B.** 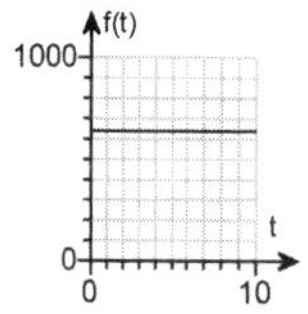 ○ **C.** 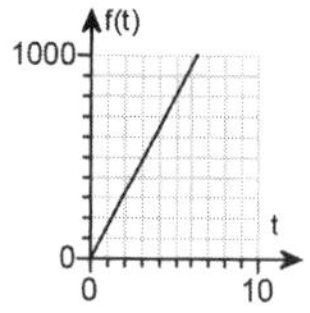 ○ **D.**

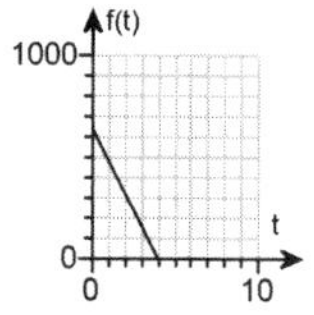

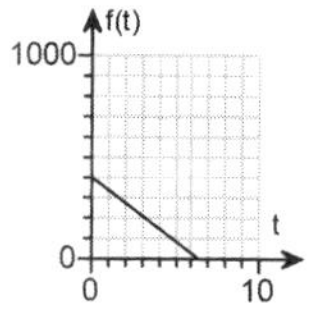

c. What is the domain of the function? Explain.

______
(Type an inequality or a compound inequality.)

Choose the correct answer below.

○ **A.** Time is the output. The pumping took 4 hours, starting from 0. Thus, the domain is the set of all numbers between 0 and 4 inclusive.

○ **B.** Time is the input. The pumping took 4 hours, starting from 0. Thus, the domain is the set of all numbers smaller than 0 and greater than 4 inclusive.

○ **C.** Time is the input. The pumping took 4 hours, starting from 0. Thus, the domain is the set of all numbers between 0 and 4 inclusive.

121. (cont.) What is the range of the function?

____

(Type an inequality or a compound inequality.)

Choose the correct answer below.

- ○ **A.** The amount of water pumped is the output. Since the volume of water is 640 cubic feet, and the pumping lasted until all of the water was pumped, the range is the set of all numbers greater than 640 inclusive.
- ○ **B.** The amount of water pumped is the input. Since the volume of water is 640 cubic feet, and the process lasted until all of the water was pumped, the range is the set of all numbers between 0 and 640 inclusive.
- ○ **C.** The amount of water pumped is the output. Since the volume of water is 640 cubic feet, and the process lasted until all of the water was pumped, the range is the set of all numbers between 0 and 640 inclusive.

ID: 5.4.29

CHAPTER 6
Exponential Functions
MyMathLab Homework Problems*

* Problems with an asterisk are included in the pre-assigned homework assignment.
! Problems with an exclamation point are new to the Update edition.
To find the problems in MyMathLab online, please refer to the ID code listed below each problem.

!* 1. You deposit $3000 into a savings account with an APR of 5.3%. Complete parts (a) through (c) below.

(a) Compute the amount of interest you gain after 1 year.

$________ (Round to the nearest dollar as needed.)

(b) To compute the amount of money in the savings account at the end of 1 year, take the original value and add interest: $3000 + 5.3% • $3000. This is equivalent to multiplying $3000 by what factor?

________ (Round to three decimal places as needed.)

(c) Fill in the following table, one year at a time:

(Round to the nearest cent as needed.)

Year	Beginning	Interest	End
1	$3000	$____	$____
2	$____	$____	$____
3	$____	$____	$____
4	$____	$____	$____
5	$____	$____	$____

ID: 6.1.1

2. Calculate the amount of money you'll have at the end of the indicated time period.
You invest $2000 in an account that pays simple interest of 2% for 20 years.

The amount of money you'll have at the end of 20 years is $________.

ID: 6.1.2

* 3. Calculate the amount of money you'll have at the end of the indicated time period, assuming that you earn simple interest.
You deposit $3400 in an account with an annual interest of 5.1% for 20 years.

The amount of money you'll have at the end of 20 years is $________.
(Type an integer or a decimal.)

ID: 6.1.3

* 4. Complete the table, for the following investments, which shows the performance (interest and balance) over a 5-year period.

Suzanne deposits $5000 in an account that earns simple interest at an annual rate of 3.3%. Derek deposits $5000 in an account that earns compound interest at an annual rate of 3.3% and is compounded annually.

Year	Suzanne's Annual Interest	Suzanne's Balance	Derek's Annual Interest	Derek's Balance
1	$___	$___	$___	$___
2	$___	$___	$___	$___
3	$___	$___	$___	$___
4	$___	$___	$___	$___
5	$___	$___	$___	$___

Complete the following table.

(Round to the nearest dollar as needed.)

Year	Suzanne's Annual Interest	Suzanne's Balance	Derek's Annual Interest	Derek's Balance
1	$____	$____	$____	$____
2	$____	$____	$____	$____
3	$____	$____	$____	$____
4	$____	$____	$____	$____
5	$____	$____	$____	$____

ID: 6.1.4

* 5. Use the compound interest formula to determine the accumulated balance after the stated period.

$5000 invested at an APR of 9% for 7 years.

If interest is compounded annually, what is the amount of money after 7 years?

$ ____________
(Do not round until the final answer. Then round to the nearest cent as needed.)

ID: 6.1.5

---

* 6. Use the compound interest formula to compute the balance in the following account after the stated period of time, assuming interest is compounded annually.

$7000 invested at an APR of 2.1% for 12 years.

The balance in the account after 12 years is $ ____________.
(Round to the nearest cent as needed.)

ID: 6.1.6

---

7. Use the appropriate compound interest formula to compute the balance in the account after the stated period of time

$13,000 is invested for 9 years with an APR of 5% and quarterly compounding.

The balance in the account after 9 years is $ ____________.
(Round to the nearest cent as needed.)

ID: 6.1.7

---

8. Use the appropriate compound interest formula to compute the balance in the account after the stated period of time

$23,000 is invested for 2 years with an APR of 5% and daily compounding.

The balance in the account after 2 years is $ ____________.
(Round to the nearest cent as needed.)

ID: 6.1.8

---

9. Use the appropriate compound interest formula to compute the balance in the account after the stated period of time

$6,000 is invested for 14 years with an APR of 5% and monthly compounding.

The balance in the account after 14 years is $ ____________.
(Round to the nearest cent as needed.)

ID: 6.1.9

---

10. Use the compound interest formula for compounding more than once a year to determine the accumulated balance after the stated period.

A $25,000 deposit at an APR of 6.3% with quarterly compounding for 35 years.

The amount after 35 years will be $ ____________.
(Round to the nearest cent as needed.)

ID: 6.1.10

!* 11. You deposit $2500 into a savings account with an APR of 1.4%. Complete parts (a) through (c) below.

(a) Compute the amount of interest you gain after 1 year.

$ ____________ (Round to the nearest dollar as needed.)

(b) To compute the amount of money in the savings account at the end of 1 year, take the original value and add interest: $2500 + 1.4% • $2500. This is equivalent to multiplying $2500 by what factor?

____________ (Round to three decimal places as needed.)

(c) To compute the amount of money in the account after 6 years you would multiply $2500 by what factor?

____________ (Round to three decimal places as needed.)

ID: 6.1.11

!* 12. You deposit $450 into a savings account with an APR of 3.2%. Use the table to complete parts (a) through (b) below.

	A	B
1	Year	Amount
2	0	$450
3	1	$464.40
4	2	$479.26
5	3	$494.60
6	4	$510.42

(a) What **recursive** formula would you enter in cell B3 that could be filled down?

- ○ = **B$2** * 1.032^**A3**
- ○ = **B2** * 0.032
- ○ = **B$2** * 1.032
- ○ = **B2** * 1.032

(b) What **closed** formula would you enter in cell B3 that could be filled down?

- ○ = **B$2** * 1.032^**A$3**
- ○ = **B$2** * 0.032
- ○ = **B$2** * 1.032^**A3**
- ○ = **B$2** * 1.032

ID: 6.1.12

---

* 13. Describe the basic differences between linear growth and exponential growth.

Choose the correct answer below.

○ **A.** Linear growth occurs when a quantity grows by the same absolute amount in each unit of time, and exponential growth occurs when a quantity grows by the same relative amount, that is, by the same percentage, in each unit of time.

○ **B.** Linear growth occurs when a quantity grows by random amounts in each unit of time, and exponential growth occurs when a quantity grows by different, but proportional amounts, in each unit of time.

○ **C.** Linear growth occurs when a quantity grows by different, but proportional amounts, in each unit of time, and exponential growth occurs when a quantity grows by random amounts in each unit of time.

○ **D.** Linear growth occurs when a quantity grows by the same relative amount, that is, by the same percentage, in each unit of time, and exponential growth occurs when a quantity grows by the same absolute amount in each unit of time.

ID: 6.1.13

---

14. Briefly summarize the story of the bacteria in the bottle. Explain the answers to the four questions in the text.

Briefly summarize the story of the bacteria in a bottle. Choose the correct answer below.

○ **A.** The number of bacteria in a bottle increases by 2 every minute. There is one bacteria at 11:00 and the bottle is full at 12:00, so the colony is doomed.

○ **B.** The number of bacteria in a bottle doubles every minute. There is one bacteria at 11:00 and the bottle is full at 12:00, so the colony is doomed.

○ **C.** The number of bacteria in a bottle increases by 1 every minute. There is one bacteria at 11:00 and the bottle is full at 12:00, so the colony is doomed.

○ **D.** The number of bacteria in a bottle triples every minute. There is one bacteria at 11:00 and the bottle is full at 12:00, so the colony is doomed.

Why was the bottle half-full at 11:59?

○ **A.** The bottle was half-full at 11:59 because the volume of bacteria exceeds the volume of the bottle at 12:00.

○ **B.** The bottle was half-full at 11:59 because the bacteria stop dividing before the bottle becomes completely full.

○ **C.** The bottle was half-full at 11:59 because the number of bacteria doubles during the last minute.

○ **D.** The bottle was half-full at 11:59 because the bottle is half-full at 11:30, and 11:59 is after 11:30.

14. (cont.) Why won't the other bacteria believe you about the impending disaster?

- A. The other bacteria won't believe you because the rate at which the bacteria are dividing will cause less than 10% of the bottle to be occupied by 11:59.
- B. The other bacteria won't believe you because $\frac{3}{4}$ of the bottle is still unoccupied at 11:56.
- C. The other bacteria won't believe you because the rate at which the bacteria are dividing will cause less than 1% of the bottle to be occupied by 11:59.
- D. The other bacteria won't believe you because $\frac{15}{16}$ of the bottle is still unoccupied at 11:56.

Why does the discovery of the 3 new bottles give the bacteria only 2 additional minutes?

- A. The discovery gives only 2 additional minutes because each of the 3 new bottles takes 40 seconds to fill, and the first bottle is already full.
- B. The discovery gives only 2 additional minutes because the bacteria consistently fill 2 bottles per minute.
- C. The discovery gives only 2 additional minutes because the bacteria will fill 2 bottles by 12:01 and 4 bottles by 12:02.
- D. The discovery gives only 2 additional minutes because it will take half of a minute to fill each bottle, for a total of 2 minutes.

Why is there no hope that any future discoveries will allow the colony to continue its exponential growth?

- A. There is no hope because the 4 bottles found have already been filled completely, so there is no time to look for others.
- B. There is no hope because the volume of bacteria would exceed the volume of the entire universe after only $5\frac{1}{2}$ hours.
- C. There is no hope because the bacteria are unlikely to build enough spaceships to support future mass migrations.
- D. There is no hope because the number of bottles in the lab is finite and they will eventually run out of

ID: 6.1.14

---

15. Decide whether the following statement makes sense (or is clearly true) or does not make sense (or is clearly false). Explain your reasoning.

Money in a bank account earning compound interest at an annual percentage rate of 3% is an example of exponential growth.

Choose the correct answer below.

- A. The statement makes sense because the money in the account grows by the same percentage, which is an example of exponential growth.
- B. The statement makes sense because the money in the account grows by the same absolute amount, which is an example of exponential growth.
- C. The statement does not makes sense because the money in the account grows by the same absolute amount, which is an example of linear growth.
- D. The statement does not make sense because the money in the account grows by the same percentage, which is an example of linear growth.

ID: 6.1.15

---

16. Decide whether the following statement makes sense (or is clearly true) or does not make sense (or is clearly false). Explain your reasoning.

A small town that grows exponentially can become a large city in just a few decades.

Choose the correct answer below.

- A. The statement makes sense because exponential growth leads to repeated doublings, making the population increase slowly.
- B. The statement makes sense because exponential growth leads to repeated doublings, making the population increase rapidly.
- C. The statement does not makes sense because exponential growth leads to repeated halvings, making the population decrease rapidly.
- D. The statement does not make sense because exponential growth cannot continue indefinitely, so the population will not get large enough for the town to be considered a city.

ID: 6.1.16

---

17. Decide whether the following statement makes sense (or is clearly true) or does not make sense (or is clearly false). Explain your reasoning.

Human population has been growing exponentially for a few centuries, and this trend can be expected to continue forever in the future.

Choose the correct answer below.

○ **A.** The statement does not make sense because the human population rises and falls cyclically throughout history.

○ **B.** The statement makes sense because there will always be humans around.

○ **C.** The statement makes sense because the human population will grow by the same relative amount in each unit of time.

○ **D.** The statement does not make sense because exponential growth cannot continue indefinitely.

ID: 6.1.17

---

*18. The population of a town is increasing by 630 people per year. State whether this growth is linear or exponential. If the population is 1700 today, what will the population be in three years?

Is the population growth linear or exponential?

○ exponential

○ linear

What will the population be in three years?

____

ID: 6.1.18

---

19. During the worst periods of hyperinflation in a certain country, the price of food increased at a rate of 20% per month. State whether this increase was linear or exponential. If your food bill was $100 in one month during this period, what was it three months later?

Was the growth in inflation linear or exponential?

○ linear

○ exponential

What was the monthly food bill after three months?

$__________

(Round to the nearest dollar as needed.)

ID: 6.1.19

---

*20. The price of a computer component is decreasing at a rate of 11% per year. State whether this decrease is linear or exponential. If the component costs $110 today, what will it cost in three years?

Is the decline in price linear or exponential?

○ linear

○ exponential

What will the component cost in three years?

$__________

(Round to the nearest cent as needed.)

ID: 6.1.20

---

21. State whether the growth (or decay) is linear or exponential, and answer the associated question.

The value of a house is increasing by $2400 per year. If it is worth $180,000 today, what will it be worth in three years?

Is the increase in value linear or exponential?

○ exponential

○ linear

What will the house be worth in three years?

$__________

ID: 6.1.21

!* 22. Given the exponential equation $y = 550 \cdot e^{0.0945 \cdot x}$, complete parts (a) through (b) below.

(a) Represent $e^{0.0945}$ as a decimal to 4 decimal places.

__________ (Round to four decimal places as needed.)

(b) Rewrite the equation in the form $P = P_0 \cdot (1 + r)^x$.

○ $P = 550 \cdot (1.0945)^x$

○ $P = 550 \cdot (1 + 9.45\%)^x$

○ $P = 550 \cdot (1 + 9.91\%)^x$

○ $P = 550 \cdot (0.0991)^x$

ID: 6.2.1

!* 23. A population can be modeled by the exponential equation $y = 260{,}000 \cdot e^{-0.0758 \cdot t}$, where t = years since 1990 and y = population. Complete parts (a) through (d) below.

(a) What is the continuous decay rate per year? (Hint: If the rate k is a negative number, this implies a continuous decay rate with the opposite sign of k.)

The population is decreasing at a continuous rate of __________ % per year.
(Round to two decimal places as needed.)

(b) What is the annual decay rate (not continuous)? (Hint: If the rate r is a negative number, this implies an annual decay rate with the opposite sign of r.)

The population is decreasing at an annual rate of __________ % per year.
(Round to two decimal places as needed.)

(c) Rewrite the equation in the form $P = P_0 \cdot (1 + r)^t$.

○ **A.** $P = 260{,}000 \cdot (-0.730)^t$

○ **B.** $P = 260{,}000 \cdot (1 - 7.58\%)^t$

○ **C.** $P = 260{,}000 \cdot (0.9270)^t$

○ **D.** $P = 260{,}000 \cdot (0.9242)^t$

(d) How many people will there be after 8 years?

__________ people
(Round to the nearest whole number as needed.)

ID: 6.2.2

!* 24. A population can be modeled by the exponential equation $y = 14{,}000 \cdot e^{0.2123 \cdot t}$, where t = years since 2010 and y = population. Complete parts (a) through (d) below.

(a) What is the continuous growth rate per year?

__________ % (Round to two decimal places as needed.)

(b) What is the annual growth rate (not continuous)?

__________ % (Round to two decimal places as needed.)

(c) Rewrite the equation in the form $P = P_0 \cdot (1 + r)^t$.

○ **A.** $P = 14{,}000 \cdot (1 + 23.65\%)^t$

○ **B.** $P = 14{,}000 \cdot (0.2365)^t$

○ **C.** $P = 14{,}000 \cdot (1 + 21.23\%)^t$

○ **D.** $P = 14{,}000 \cdot (1.2123)^t$

(d) How many people will there be after 8 years?

__________ people (Round to the nearest whole number as needed.)

ID: 6.2.3

---

*25. Consider the following case of exponential growth. Complete parts a through c below.

The population of a town with an initial population of 49,000 grows at a rate of 3.5% per year.

a. Create an exponential function of the form $Q = Q_0 \times (1 + r)^t$, (where $r > 0$ for growth and $r < 0$ for decay) to model the situation described.

$Q =$ ______ $\times($______$)^t$

(Type integers or decimals.)

b. Create a table showing the value of the quantity Q for the first 10 years of growth.

Year = t	Population	Year = t	Population
0	49,000	6	______
1	______	7	______
2	______	8	______
3	______	9	______
4	______	10	______
5	______		

(Round to the nearest whole number as needed.)

c. Make a graph of the exponential function. Choose the correct graph below.

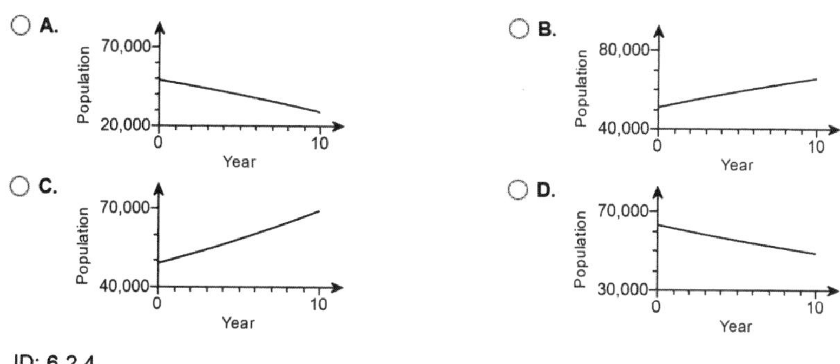

ID: 6.2.4

*26. Consider the following case of exponential decay. Complete parts (a) through (c) below.

A privately owned forest that had 2,000,000 acres of old growth is being clear cut at a rate of 6% per year.

a. Create an exponential function of the form $Q = Q_0 \times (1 + r)^t$, (where $r > 0$ for growth and $r < 0$ for decay) to model the situation described.

$Q =$ ______ $\times($______$)^t$

(Type integers or decimals.)

b. Create a table showing the value of the quantity Q for the first 10 years of growth.

Year = t	Acres	Year = t	Acres
0	2,000,000	6	______
1	______	7	______
2	______	8	______
3	______	9	______
4	______	10	______
5	______		

(Round to the nearest whole number as needed.)

c. Make a graph of the exponential function. Choose the correct graph below.

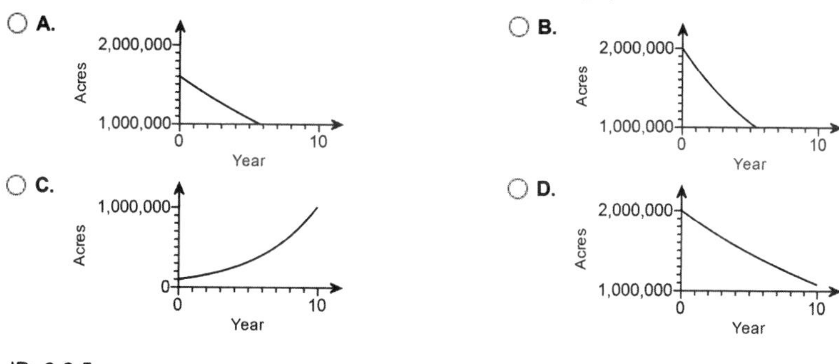

ID: 6.2.5

* 27. Answer the questions for the problem given below.
The average price of a home in a town was $175,000 in 2007 but home prices are rising by 6% per year.

a. Find an exponential function of the form $Q = Q_0 \times (1 + r)^t$ (where $r > 0$) for growth to model the situation described.

$Q = \$$ ________ $\times (1 +$ ________ $)^t$
(Type an integer or a decimal.)

b. Fill the table showing the value of the average price of a home for the following five years.

Year = t	Average price
0	$175,000
1	$ ________
2	$ ________
3	$ ________
4	$ ________
5	$ ________

(Do not round until the final answer. Then round to the nearest dollar as needed.)

ID: 6.2.6

* 28. Consider the following case of exponential growth. Complete parts (a) through (c) below.
Your starting salary at a new job is $1600 per month, and you get annual raises of 6% per year.

a. Create an exponential function of the form $Q = Q_0 \times (1 + r)^t$, (where $r > 0$ for growth and $r < 0$ for decay) to model the situation described.

$Q =$ ________ $\times ($ ________ $)^t$
(Type integers or decimals.)

b. Create a table showing the value of the quantity Q for the first 10 years of growth.

Year = t	Salary	Year = t	Salary
0	$1600	6	$ ________
1	$ ________	7	$ ________
2	$ ________	8	$ ________
3	$ ________	9	$ ________
4	$ ________	10	$ ________
5	$ ________		

(Round to two decimal places as needed.)

c. Make a graph of the exponential function. Choose the correct graph below.

○ A.
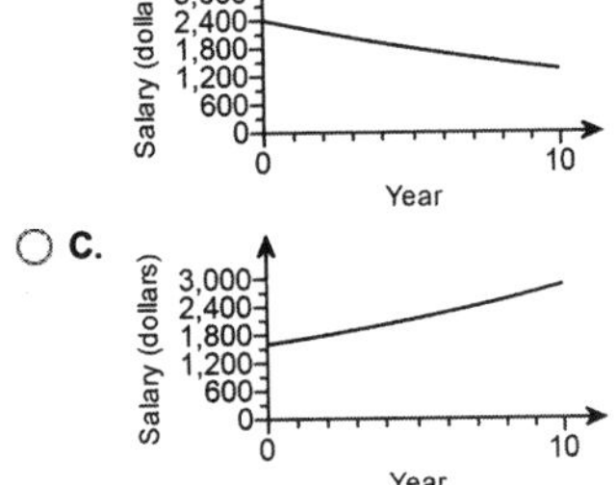

○ B.
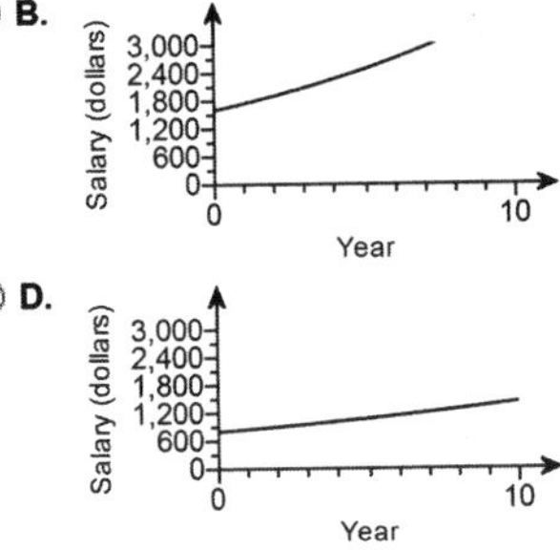

○ C.

Salary (dollars) 3,000 2,400 1,800 1,200 600 0; 0 10 Year

○ D.

Salary (dollars) 3,000 2,400 1,800 1,200 600 0; 0 10 Year

ID: 6.2.7

!* 29. Air pressure can be modeled by the exponential equation $y = 14.5 \cdot e^{-0.0423 \cdot x}$, where x = altitude in 1000's of feet and y = air pressure in psi. Complete parts (a) through (e) below.

(a) What is the continuous decay rate per 1000 feet? (Hint: If the rate k is a negative number, this implies a continuous decay rate with the opposite sign of k.)

The air pressure is decreasing at a continuous rate of ________ % per 1000 feet.
(Round to two decimal places as needed.)

(b) What is the decay rate every 1000 feet (not continuous)? (Hint: If the rate r is a negative number, this implies an annual decay rate with the opposite sign of r.)

The air pressure is decreasing at a rate of ________ % per 1000 feet.
(Round to two decimal places as needed.)

!* 29. (cont.) (c) Rewrite the equation in the form $P = P_0 \cdot (1 + r)^x$.

○ A. $P = 14.5 \cdot (0.9586)^x$

○ B. $P = 14.5 \cdot (1.0414)^x$

○ C. $P = 14.5 \cdot (1 - 4.23\%)^x$

○ D. $P = 14.5 \cdot (0.9577)^x$

(d) What is the air pressure at 35,000 feet?

__________ psi (Round to two decimal places as needed.)

(e) What is the air pressure at sea level?

__________ psi (Round to one decimal place as needed.)

ID: 6.2.8

!* 30. Your mutual fund goes up 11.6% in the first year, then down 2.8% in the 2nd year, and finally up again 6.8% in the 3rd year. Complete parts **a** and **b**.

a) What is the average rate of return per year?

__________ % (Do not round until the final answer. Then round to two decimal places as needed.)

b) If the fund plummets 26.9% in the 4th year, what is the average rate of return per year for the 4 years?

__________ % (Do not round until the final answer. Then round to two decimal places as needed.)

ID: 6.3.1

!* 31. You average 46 mph for the first 30 miles of a trip and then 65 mph for the next 30 miles. Complete parts **a** and **b**.

a) What is the average speed over the 60 miles?

__________ mph (Type an integer or a decimal rounded to one decimal place.)

b) If you then average 70 mph over the next 30 miles what is the average speed over the 90 miles?

__________ mph (Type an integer or a decimal rounded to one decimal place.)

ID: 6.3.2

!* 32. Determine whether to use the arithmetic mean, the geometric mean, or the harmonic mean to complete parts **a** and **b**.
[1]Click the icon to view the three types of means.

a) You mix equal weights of Steel (7850 kg/m^3), Zinc (7135 kg/m^3), and Copper (8940 kg/m^3) together. What is the density of the resulting alloy? (Hint: Density is the rate of weight to volume, kg/m^3.)

To find the density of the resulting alloy, the (1) __________ mean should be used and the density is __________ kg/m^3.
(Type an integer or a decimal rounded to one decimal place.)

b) If your veggie hot dog stand generates revenues of \$7850, \$7135, and \$8940 at 3 events, what is your average revenue per event?

To find the average revenue per event, the (2) __________ mean should be used and the average revenue is \$__________.
(Round to the nearest cent as needed.)

1: Types of means.

The **arithmetic mean**, $\frac{a_1 + a_2 + \cdots + a_n}{n}$, is an average of n numbers.

The **geometric mean**, $\sqrt[n]{a_1 \cdot a_2 \cdot \cdots \cdot a_n}$, is the average of change in growth where the rate of growth and/or decay changes over time.

The **harmonic mean**, $\frac{n}{\frac{1}{a_1} + \frac{1}{a_2} + \cdots + \frac{1}{a_n}}$, is the average of rates, as in travelling n miles at one rate and n miles at another rate.

(1) ○ arithmetic ○ geometric ○ harmonic

(2) ○ arithmetic ○ geometric ○ harmonic

ID: 6.3.3

---

*33. Suppose the rate of return for a particular stock during the past two years was 15% and 45%. Compute the geometric mean rate of return. (Note: A rate of return of 15% is recorded as 0.15, and a rate of return of 45% is recorded as 0.45.)

The geometric mean rate of return is ____________%.
(Round to one decimal place as needed.)

ID: 6.3.4

*34. Suppose the rate of return for a particular stock during the past two years was 15% and − 50%. Compute the geometric mean rate of return.

The geometric mean rate of return is ____________%.
(Round to one decimal place as needed.)

ID: 6.3.5

*35. A company's stock price rose 0.7% in 2011, and in 2012, it increased 18.6%.

a. Compute the geometric mean rate of return for the two-year period 2011 − 2012. (Hint: Denote an increase of 18.6% by 0.186.)
b. If someone purchased $1,000 of the company's stock at the start of 2011, what was its value at the end of 2012?
c. Over the same period, another company had a geometric mean rate of return of 32.95%. If someone purchased $1,000 of the other company's stock, how would its value compare to the value found in part (b)?

a. The geometric mean rate of return for the two-year period 2011 − 2012 was ____________%.
(Type an integer or decimal rounded to two decimal places as needed.)

b. If someone purchased $1,000 of the company's stock at the start of 2011, its value at the end of 2012 was
$____________.
(Round to the nearest cent as needed.)

c. If someone purchased $1,000 of the other company's stock at the start of 2011, its value at the end of 2012 was

$____________, which is (1) ____________ than the value from part (b).
(Round to the nearest cent as needed.)

(1) ○ less
○ more

ID: 6.3.6

*36. A company's stock price rose 3.8% in 2011, and in 2012, it increased 77.2%.

a. Compute the geometric mean rate of return for the two-year period 2011 − 2012. (Hint: Denote an increase of 77.2% by 0.772.)
b. If someone purchased $1,000 of the company's stock at the start of 2011, what was its value at the end of 2012?
c. Over the same period, another company had a geometric mean rate of return of 9.9%. If someone purchased $1,000 of the other company's stock, how would its value compare to the value found in part (b)?

a. The geometric mean rate of return for the two-year period 2011 − 2012 was ____________%.
(Type an integer or decimal rounded to two decimal places as needed.)

b. If someone purchased $1,000 of the company's stock at the start of 2011, its value at the end of 2012 was
$____________.
(Round to the nearest cent as needed.)

c. If someone purchased $1,000 of the other company's stock at the start of 2011, its value at the end of 2012 was

$____________, which is (1) ____________ than the value from part (b).
(Round to the nearest cent as needed.)

(1) ○ more
○ less

ID: 6.3.7

* 37. The data in the accompanying table represent the total rates of return (in percentages) for three stock exchanges over the four-year period from 2009 to 2012. Calculate the geometric mean rate of return for each of the three stock exchanges.

[2] Click the icon to view data table for total rate of return for stock market indices.
[3]Click the icon to view data table for total rate of return for platinum, gold, and silver.

a. Compute the geometric mean rate of return per year for the stock indices from 2009 through 2012.

For stock exchange A, the geometric mean rate of return for the four-year period 2009-2012 was ________ %.
(Type an integer or decimal rounded to two decimal places as needed.)

For stock exchange B, the geometric mean rate of return for the four-year period 2009-2012 was ________ %.
(Type an integer or decimal rounded to two decimal places as needed.)

For stock exchange C, the geometric mean rate of return for the four-year period 2009-2012 was ________ %.
(Type an integer or decimal rounded to two decimal places as needed.)

b. What conclusions can you reach concerning the geometric mean rates of return per year of the three market indices?

- ○ **A.** Stock exchange B had a higher return than exchange C and a much higher return than exchange A.
- ○ **B.** Stock exchange A had a much higher return than exchanges B or C.
- ○ **C.** Stock exchange A had a higher return than exchange C and a much higher return than exchange B.
- ○ **D.** Stock exchange C had a much higher return than exchanges A or B.

c. Compare the results of (b) to those of the results of the precious metals. Choose the correct answer below.

- ○ **A.** All three stock indices had lower returns than any of the precious metals.
- ○ **B.** Silver had a much higher return than any of the three stock indices. Both gold and platinum had a worse return than stock index C, but a better return than indices A and B.
- ○ **C.** Silver had a worse return than stock index C, but a better return than indices A and B. Gold had a better return than index B, but a worse return than indices A and C. Platinum had a worse return than all three stock indices.
- ○ **D.** All three stock indices had higher returns than any of the precious metals.

2: Data table for total rate of return

Year	A	B	C
2012	7.36	13.49	15.63
2011	5.37	0.00	− 1.97
2010	10.00	11.68	16.51
2009	18.64	23.37	43.69

3: Geometric mean rate of return for stock market indices

Metal	Geometric mean rate of return
Platinum	15.38%
Gold	15.88%
Silver	22.25%

ID: 6.3.8

* 38. In 2009–2012, the value of precious metals changed rapidly. The data in the accompanying table represents the total rate of return (in percentage) for platinum, gold, and silver from 2009 through 2012. Complete parts (a) through (c) below.

[4] Click the icon to view data table for total rate of return for platinum, gold, and silver.
[5]Click the icon to view the geometric mean rate of return for stock market indices.

a. Compute the geometric mean rate of return per year for platinum, gold, and silver from 2009 through 2012.

The geometric mean rate of return for platinum during this time period was ________ %.
(Type an integer or decimal rounded to two decimal places as needed.)

The geometric mean rate of return for gold during this time period was ________ %.
(Type an integer or decimal rounded to two decimal places as needed.)

The geometric mean rate of return for silver during this time period was ________ %.
(Type an integer or decimal rounded to two decimal places as needed.)

b. What conclusions can you reach concerning the geometric mean rates of return of the three precious metals?

- ○ **A.** Gold had a higher return than silver and a much higher return than platinum.
- ○ **B.** Platinum had a much higher return than silver and gold.
- ○ **C.** Platinum had a higher return than silver and a much higher return than gold.
- ○ **D.** Silver had a much higher return than gold and platinum.

* 38. (cont.) c. Compare the results of (b) to those of the results of the stock indices. Choose the correct answer below.

- ○ **A.** All three metals had higher returns than any of the stock indices.
- ○ **B.** All three metals had lower returns than any of the stock indices.
- ○ **C.** Silver had a much higher return than any of the three stock indices. Both gold and platinum had a worse return than stock index C, but a better return than indices A and B.
- ○ **D.** Silver had a worse return than stock index C, but a better return than indices A and B. Gold had a better return than index B, but a worse return than indices A and C. Platinum had a worse return than all three stock indices.

4: Data table for total rate of return

Year	Platinum	Gold	Silver
2012	6.3	0.5	56.5
2011	− 24.5	8.9	− 8.7
2010	19.9	28.9	14.5
2009	55.8	23.3	46.4

5: Geometric mean rate of return for stock market indices

Stock indices	Geometric mean rate of return
A	8.85%
B	9.51%
C	20.99%

ID: 6.3.9

!* 39. The half-life of a certain element is 16.2 days, meaning every 16.2 days the amount is cut in half. Complete parts (a) through (d) below.

(a) Fill in the following table.

Days	Grams
0	40
16.2	______
32.4	______
48.6	______

(Round to two decimal places as needed.)

(b) What is the average percent change per day over the first 16.2 days?

______ % (Round to two decimal places as needed.)

(c) Write down an equation for the amount of the element left after d days in the form: $A = A_0 \cdot (1 + r)^d$

- ○ $A = 40 \cdot (1 - 4.19\%)^d$
- ○ $A = 40 \cdot (1 + 4.19\%)^d$
- ○ $A = 40 \cdot (0.0419)^d$
- ○ $A = 40 \cdot (1.0419)^d$

(d) How much is left after 3 days?

______ grams (Round to one decimal place as needed.)

ID: 6.3.10

!* 40. The average cost of gas dropped from a high of $2.84 per gallon on June 1, 2015 to a low of $1.64 on February 1, 2016. Complete parts (a) through (c) below.

(a) What is the average percent change in gas price per month?

______ % (Round to one decimal place as needed.)

(b) What is the decay factor associated to this rate?

______ (Round to three decimal places as needed.)

(c) Write down an equation for the price of gas m months after June 1, 2015 in the form: $P = P_0 \cdot (1 + r)^m$

- ○ **A.** $P = 2.84 \cdot (0.066)^m$
- ○ **B.** $P = 2.84 \cdot (1.066)^m$
- ○ **C.** $P = 2.84 \cdot (0.934)^m$
- ○ **D.** $P = 2.84 \cdot (1 - 0.934)^m$

ID: 6.3.11

CHAPTER 7
Logical Arithmetic
MyMathLab Homework Problems*

* Problems with an asterisk are included in the pre-assigned homework assignment.
! Problems with an exclamation point are new to the Update edition.
To find the problems in MyMathLab online, please refer to the ID code listed below each problem.

!* 1. A certain town's population is growing according to the following equation. Answer parts (a) through (c).

$P = 7{,}500 \cdot (1.069)^t$

(a) To find how long it will take for the population, P, to triple, substitute ________ for P.
(Type an integer or a decimal.)

(b) We are looking at the time, t, which solves the equation: $3 = (1.069)^t$. Fill in the following table.

t	1.069^t
14	
15	
16	
17	
18	
19	

(Type integers or decimals rounded to four decimal places as needed.)

(c) The time it takes to triple is closest to what integer value of t in the table above?

The time it takes to triple is closest to t = ________.

ID: 7.1.1

* 2. Solve for x.

$7^x = 49$

The solution is x = ________.
(Simplify your answer. Type an integer or a fraction. Use a comma to separate answers as needed.)

ID: 7.1.2

3. Solve the following equation for the unknown quantity x.

$3^x = 53$

x = ________
(Round to the nearest hundredth as needed. Use a comma to separate answers as needed.)

ID: 7.1.3

4. Solve for x.

$4^{2x} = 18$

What is the solution?

x = ________
(Round to two decimal places as needed. Use a comma to separate answers as needed.)

ID: 7.1.4

* 5. Solve for x.

$\log_{10} x = 4$

x = ________

ID: 7.1.5

* 6. Solve for x.

$\log_{10} x = 2.9$

x = ________
(Round to two decimal places as needed.)

ID: 7.1.6

7. Solve for x.

$3 \log_{10} x = 1.2$

x = ____________
(Round to two decimal places as needed.)

ID: 7.1.7

8. Solve the following equation for the unknown quantity x.

$\log_{10}(3 + x) = 2.7$

x = ____________
(Round to two decimal places as needed. Use a comma to separate answers as needed.)

ID: 7.1.8

!*9. Evaluate logarithms without using a calculator by rewriting them in exponential form. Answer parts (a) through (d).

(a) Rewrite $\log_7 49 = y$ as an exponential. Select the correct choice below and fill in the answer box within your choice.

- ○ **A.** 7^{49} = ____________
- ○ **B.** 7____________ = 49
- ○ **C.** 49____________ = 7

(b) Solve the equation $\log_7 49 = y$.

$\log_7 49$ = ____________
(Type an integer or a decimal rounded to two decimal places as needed.)

(c) Rewrite $\log_7 1 = y$ as an exponential. Select the correct choice below and fill in the answer box within your choice.

- ○ **A.** 1____________ = 7
- ○ **B.** 7^1 = ____________
- ○ **C.** 7____________ = 1

(d) Solve the equation $\log_7 1 = y$.

$\log_7 1$ = ____________
(Type an integer or a decimal rounded to two decimal places as needed.)

ID: 7.1.9

!*10. Evaluate logarithms without using a calculator by rewriting them in exponential form. Answer parts (a) through (d).

(a) Rewrite $\ln e^{-7} = y$ as an exponential. Select the correct choice below and fill in the answer box within your choice.

- ○ **A.** 2____________ $= e^{-7}$
- ○ **B.** e____________ $= e^{-7}$
- ○ **C.** -7^{e} = ____________

(b) Solve the equation $\ln e^{-7} = y$.

$\ln e^{-7}$ = ____________
(Type an integer or a decimal.)

(c) Rewrite $\ln e^{14} = y$ as an exponential. Select the correct choice below and fill in the answer box within your choice.

- ○ **A.** 2____________ $= e^{14}$
- ○ **B.** 14^{e} = ____________
- ○ **C.** e____________ $= e^{14}$

(d) Solve the equation $\ln e^{14} = y$.

$\ln e^{14}$ = ____________
(Type an integer or a decimal.)

ID: 7.1.10

!* 11. Evaluate logarithms without using a calculator by rewriting them in exponential form. Answer parts (a) through (d).

(a) Rewrite **log** 0.01 = y as an exponential. Select the correct choice below and fill in the answer box within your choice.

○ **A.** $10^3 =$ ________

○ **B.** $10^{\_\_\_\_} = 0.01$

○ **C.** $0.01^{\_\_\_\_} = 10$

(b) Solve the equation **log** 0.01 = y.

log 0.01 = ________
(Type an integer or a decimal.)

(c) Rewrite **log** 100,000 = y as an exponential. Select the correct choice below and fill in the answer box within your choice.

○ **A.** $10^{\_\_\_\_} = 100{,}000$

○ **B.** $100{,}000^{\_\_\_\_} = 10$

○ **C.** $10^{100{,}000} =$ ________

(d) Solve the equation **log** 100,000 = y.

log 100,000 = ________
(Type an integer or a decimal.)

ID: 7.1.11

!*12. Evaluate logarithms using properties of logarithms. Answer parts (a) through (f).

(a) Rewrite the following as a power of 10.

$10^2 \cdot 10^6 = 10^{\_\_\_\_}$
(Simplify your answer.)

(b) Solve the equation **log** $[10^2 \cdot 10^6] = y$.

log $[10^2 \cdot 10^6] =$ ________
(Simplify your answer.)

(c) Rewrite the following as a power of 10.

$10^2 \div 10^6 = 10^{\_\_\_\_}$
(Simplify your answer.)

(d) Solve the equation **log** $[10^2 \div 10^6] = y$.

log $[10^2 \div 10^6] =$ ________
(Simplify your answer.)

(e) Rewrite the following as a power of 10.

$[10^2]^6 = 10^{\_\_\_\_}$
(Simplify your answer.)

(f) Solve the equation **log** $[10^2]^6 = y$.

log $[10^2]^6 =$ ________
(Simplify your answer.)

ID: 7.1.12

13. Determine whether the following statement is true or false without doing any calculations.

$10^{1.235}$ is between 1 and 10

Is the statement true or false?

○ True
○ False

ID: 7.1.13

14. Determine whether the following statement is true or false without doing any calculations. Explain your reasoning.

$10^{-2.2}$ is between 0.001 and 0.01

Is the statement true or false?

- ○ True, because $10^{-3} = 0.001$ and $10^{-2} = 0.01$.
- ○ False, because $10^{-3} = 0.001$ and $10^{-2} = 0.01$.
- ○ True, because $10^{-2} = -10^2 = -100$ and $10^{-3} = -10^3 = -1{,}000$.
- ○ False, because $10^{-2} = -10^2 = -100$ and $10^{-3} = -10^3 = -1{,}000$.

ID: 7.1.14

15. Determine whether the statement is true or false without doing any calculations. Explain your reasoning.

$\log_{10}\pi$ is between 3 and 4

Choose the correct answer below.

- ○ **A.** The statement is false because π is between 1 and 10. Thus, $\log_{10}\pi$ should be between 0 and 1.
- ○ **B.** The statement is false because π is between 0.1 and 1. Thus, $\log_{10}\pi$ should be between -1 and 0.
- ○ **C.** The statement is true because π is between 3 and 4. Thus, $\log_{10}\pi$ should be between 3 and 4.
- ○ **D.** The statement is true because π is less than 10^3. Thus, $\log_{10}\pi$ should be between 3 and 4.

ID: 7.1.15

16. Determine whether the following statement is true or false without doing any calculations.

$\log_{10} 15{,}000{,}000$ is between 15 and 16

Is the statement true or false?

- ○ False
- ○ True

ID: 7.1.16

17. Determine whether the following statement is true or false without doing any calculations.

$\log_{10}\left(\frac{1}{2}\right)$ is between 1 and 10

Is the statement true or false?

- ○ True
- ○ False

ID: 7.1.17

*18. Using the approximation $\log_{10} 4 \approx 0.602$, find each of the following without a calculator.

a. $\log_{10} 16$ **b.** $\log_{10} 4000$ **c.** $\log_{10} \frac{1}{16}$ **d.** $\log_{10} 0.4$

a. $\log_{10} 16 =$ ____________
(Simplify your answer. Type an integer or decimal rounded to three decimal places as needed.)

b. $\log_{10} 4000 =$ ____________
(Simplify your answer. Type an integer or decimal rounded to three decimal places as needed.)

c. $\log_{10} \frac{1}{16} =$ ____________
(Simplify your answer. Type an integer or decimal rounded to three decimal places as needed.)

d. $\log_{10} 0.4 =$ ____________
(Simplify your answer. Type an integer or decimal rounded to three decimal places as needed.)

ID: 7.1.18

*19. Evaluate the following expressions.

a. $10^8 \times 10^6$ b. $10^4 \times 10^{-2}$ c. $\frac{10^6}{10^3}$ d. $\frac{10^8}{10^{-4}}$

a. $10^8 \times 10^6 =$ ________ (Simplify your answer. Type your answer using exponential notation.)

b. $10^4 \times 10^{-2} =$ ________ (Simplify your answer. Type your answer using exponential notation.)

c. $\frac{10^6}{10^3} =$ ________ (Simplify your answer. Type your answer using exponential notation.)

d. $\frac{10^8}{10^{-4}} =$ ________ (Simplify your answer. Type your answer using exponential notation.)

ID: 7.1.19

20. Evaluate the following expressions.

a. $\frac{10^{40}}{10^{30}}$ b. $10^0 + 10^1$ c. $10^5 + 10^{-3}$ d. $10^5 - 10^3$

a. $\frac{10^{40}}{10^{30}} =$ ________ (Simplify your answer. Type your answer using exponential notation.)

b. $10^0 + 10^1 =$ ________ (Simplify your answer. Type an integer or a decimal.)

c. $10^5 + 10^{-3} =$ ________ (Simplify your answer. Type an integer or a decimal.)

d. $10^5 - 10^3 =$ ________ (Simplify your answer. Type an integer or a decimal.)

ID: 7.1.20

!*21. A population is growing by 6.1% per year.

(a) What is the associated growth factor?
(b) To solve for the doubling time we must solve what equation?
(c) What is the doubling time?

(a) The associated growth factor is ________.
(Type an integer or a decimal.)

(b) Choose the correct answer below.

○ **A.** $2 = 1.061^t$

○ **B.** $1.061 = 2^t$

○ **C.** $t = 1.061^2$

(c) The doubling time is ________ years.
(Do not round until the final answer. Then round to two decimal places as needed.)

ID: 7.2.1

!*22. A radioactive substance is decaying by 6.9% per day.

(a) What is the associated decay factor?
(b) To solve for the half-life we must solve what equation?
(c) What is the half-life?

(a) The associated decay factor is ________.
(Type an integer or a decimal.)

(b) Choose the correct answer below.

○ **A.** $0.931 = 2^t$

○ **B.** $0.5 = 0.931^t$

○ **C.** $t = 0.931^{0.5}$

(c) The half-life is ________ days.
(Do not round until the final answer. Then round to two decimal places as needed.)

ID: 7.2.2

23. What is a doubling time? Suppose a population has a doubling time of 30 years. By what factor will it grow in 120 years?

Choose the correct definition of a doubling time below.

- A. The time required for each doubling in exponential growth.
- B. The time required for each halving in exponential growth.
- C. The time required for each halving in linear growth.
- D. The time required for each doubling in linear growth.

By what factor will population grow in 120 years?

____________ (Type exponential notation with positive exponents.)

ID: 7.2.3

---

24. State the approximate doubling time formula and the conditions under which it works well. Give an example.

Choose the correct approximate doubling time formula for a quantity growing exponentially at a rate of P% per time period.

- A. $T_{double} \approx 70 + P$
- B. $T_{double} \approx \frac{P}{70}$
- C. $T_{double} \approx 70 \cdot P$
- D. $T_{double} \approx \frac{70}{P}$

Under which conditions does the approximate doubling formula work well?

- A. The approximation works best for growth rates over 100%.
- B. The approximation works best for positive growth rates.
- C. The approximation works best for large growth rates.
- D. The approximation works best for small growth rates.

Choose the best example of the use of the approximate doubling formula.

- A. The compound interest of a bank account grows by 20% each year.
- B. The population of flies is increasing at a rate of 55% per month.
- C. The population of a certain community of raccoons is increasing at a rate of 6% per month.
- D. A certain bacteria is growing at a rate of 102% per day.

ID: 7.2.4

---

25. Given a half-life, explain how you calculate the value of an exponentially decaying quantity at any time t.

Choose the correct answer below.

- A. Let t be the amount of time that has passed. The quantity after time t is the original quantity times this factor of $\left(\frac{1}{2}\right)^t$.
- B. Let t be the amount of time that has passed and T_{half} be the half-life. The quantity after time t is the original quantity times this factor of $t \times \left(\frac{1}{2}\right)^{T_{half}}$.
- C. Let t be the amount of time that has passed. The quantity after time t is the original quantity times this factor of $\left(\frac{1}{2}\right)^{T_{half}/t}$.
- D. Let t be the amount of time that has passed and T_{half} be the half-life. The quantity after time t is the original quantity times this factor of $\left(\frac{1}{2}\right)^{t/T_{half}}$.

ID: 7.2.5

---

26. Briefly describe exact doubling time and half-life formulas. Explain all their terms.

Briefly describe the exact doubling time formula and explain all of its terms. Choose the correct answer below.

- A. The formula is $T_{double} = -\dfrac{\log_{10}2}{\log_{10}(1+r)}$ where T_{double} is the time it takes for the quantity to double, and r is the fractional decay rate.
- B. The formula is $T_{double} = -\dfrac{\log_{10}2}{\log_{10}(1+r)}$ where T_{double} is the time it takes for the quantity to double, and r is the fractional growth rate.
- C. The formula is $T_{double} = \dfrac{\log_{10}2}{\log_{10}(1+r)}$ where T_{double} is the time it takes for the quantity to double, and r is the fractional decay rate.
- D. The formula is $T_{double} = \dfrac{\log_{10}2}{\log_{10}(1+r)}$ where T_{double} is the time it takes for the quantity to double, and r is the fractional growth rate.

Briefly describe the exact half-life formula and explain all of its terms. Choose the correct answer below.

- A. The formula is $T_{half} = -\dfrac{\log_{10}2}{\log_{10}(1+r)}$ where T_{half} is the time it takes for there to be half of the quantity remaining, and r is the fractional growth rate.
- B. The formula is $T_{half} = -\dfrac{\log_{10}2}{\log_{10}(1+r)}$ where T_{half} is the time it takes for there to be **log** $_{10}2$ of the quantity remaining, and r is the fractional growth rate.
- C. The formula is $T_{half} = -\dfrac{\log_{10}2}{\log_{10}(1+r)}$ where T_{half} is the time it takes for there to be **log** $_{10}2$ of the quantity remaining, and r is the fractional decay rate.
- D. The formula is $T_{half} = -\dfrac{\log_{10}2}{\log_{10}(1+r)}$ where T_{half} is the time it takes for there to be half of the quantity remaining, and r is the fractional decay rate.

ID: 7.2.6

---

27. Decide whether each of the following statements makes sense (or is clearly true) or does not make sense (or is clearly false). Explain your reasoning.

Our town is growing with a doubling time of 15 years, so its population will double in 15 years.

The statement (1) ________ because the population increases by a factor of (2) ________ in 15 years.

(1) ○ makes sense
○ does not make sense

(2) ○ 3^2
○ 2^2
○ 2
○ 2^3

ID: 7.2.7

---

* 28. Decide whether the following statement makes sense (or is clearly true) or does not make sense (or is clearly false). Explain your reasoning.

Our town is growing at a rate of 7% per year, so it will double in population every 10 years.

Choose the correct answer below.

- A. This does not make sense because $T_{double} < 10$ when substituting 7 for r into the exact doubling time formula.
- B. This does not make sense because $T_{double} > 10$ when substituting 0.07 for r into the exact doubling time formula.
- C. This makes sense because $T_{double} \approx 10.2$ when substituting 0.07 for r into the exact doubling time formula.
- D. This makes sense because $T_{double} \approx 10.2$ when substituting 7 for r into the exact doubling time formula.

ID: 7.2.8

29. Decide whether each of the following statements makes sense (or is clearly true) or does not make sense (or is clearly false). Explain your reasoning.
A toxic chemical decays with a half-life of 11 years, so half of it will be gone 11 years from now and then half of what remains will be gone 11 years after that.

The statement (1) ____________ because after 22 years, the toxic chemical will decay by a factor of (2) ____________

(1) ○ makes sense
○ does not make sense

(2) ○ 0.5.
○ 0.25.
○ 2.

ID: 7.2.9

30. The doubling time of a population of flies is 5 hours. By what factor does the population increase in 32 hours? By what factor does the population increase in 1 week?

By what factor does the population increase in 32 hours?

____
(Type exponential notation with positive exponents. Use integers or decimals for any numbers in the expression.)

By what factor does the population increase in 1 week?

____
(Type exponential notation with positive exponents. Use integers or decimals for any numbers in the expression.)

ID: 7.2.10

31. The initial population of a town is 4000, and it grows with a doubling time of 7 years. Determine how long it will take for the population to quadruple.

It will take the population ____________ years to quadruple.
(Round to the nearest whole number as needed.)

ID: 7.2.11

* 32. The initial population of a town is 4400, and it grows with a doubling time of 10 years. What will the population be in 12 years?

What will the population be in 12 years?

____
(Round to the nearest whole number as needed.)

ID: 7.2.12

33. The number of cells in a tumor doubles every 4.5 months. If the tumor begins with a single cell, how many cells will there be after 3 years? after 4 years?

How may cells will there be after 3 years?

____
(Do not round until the final answer. Then round to the nearest whole number as needed.)

How many cells will there be after 4 years?

____
(Do not round until the final answer. Then round to the nearest whole number as needed.)

ID: 7.2.13

34. In 2013, the estimated world population was 7.1 billion. Use a doubling time of 65 years to predict the population in 2027, 2061, and 2105.

What will the population be in 2027?

The population will be ____________ billion.
(Round to one decimal place as needed.)

What will the population be in 2061?

The population will be ____________ billion.
(Round to one decimal place as needed.)

What will the population be in 2105?

The population will be ____________ billion
(Round to one decimal place as needed.)

ID: 7.2.14

35. A community of rabbits begins with an initial population of 93 and grows 7% per month. Make a table that shows the population for each of the next 15 months. Based on the table, find the doubling time of the population and briefly discuss how well the approximate doubling time formula works for this case.

Complete the table below for months 0 through 7.

(Do not round until the final answer. Then round to the nearest integer as needed.)

Month	Population
0	93
1	
2	
3	
4	
5	
6	
7	

Complete the table below for months 8 through 15.

(Do not round until the final answer. Then round to the nearest integer as needed.)

Month	Population
8	
9	
10	
11	
12	
13	
14	
15	

Based on previously calculated data, determine the doubling time of the population.

The doubling time of the population is between ___________ and ___________ months.

(Type a whole number. Use ascending order.)

Briefly discuss how well the approximate doubling time formula works for this case. Choose the correct answer below.

- **A.** The doubling time formula does not work well to approximate the doubling time because the growth rates are too large.
- **B.** The doubling time formula works well to approximate the doubling time because it is accurate to the computed values.
- **C.** The doubling time formula does not work well to approximate the doubling time because the growth rates are too small.
- **D.** The doubling time formula works well to approximate the doubling time because the formula always works correctly.

ID: 7.2.15

---

* 36. Use the approximate doubling time formula (rule of 70) for the case described below. Discuss whether the formula is valid for the case described.

An economic indicator is increasing at the rate of 5% per year. What is its doubling time? By what factor will the indicator increase in 3 years?

What is its doubling time?

___________ years

(Type an integer or decimal rounded to the nearest tenth as needed.)

By what factor will the indicator increase in 3 years?

____

(Type an integer or decimal rounded to the nearest hundredth as needed.)

Is this formula valid in the case described?

- No
- Yes

ID: 7.2.16

37. Use the approximate doubling time formula (rule of 70) for the case described below. Discuss whether the formula is valid for the case described.

Gasoline prices are rising at a rate of 0.7% per month. What is their doubling time? By what factor will prices increase in 1 year? in 9 years?

What is its doubling time?

__________ months
(Type an integer or decimal rounded to the nearest hundredth as needed.)

By what factor will the prices increase in 1 years?

____
(Type an integer or decimal rounded to the nearest hundredth as needed.)

By what factor will the prices increase in 9 years?

____
(Type an integer or decimal rounded to the nearest hundredth as needed.)

Is this formula valid in the case described?

- ○ Yes, the given growth rate is above 15%
- ○ Yes, the given growth rate is below 15%
- ○ No, the given growth rate is above 15%
- ○ No, the given growth rate is below 15%

ID: 7.2.17

---

38. The half-life of a radioactive substance is 50 years. If you start with some amount of this substance, what fraction will remain in 150 years? What fraction will remain in 200 years?

The fraction that will remain in in 150 years is the following.

__________ (Simplify your answer.)

The fraction that will remain in in 200 years is the following.

__________ (Simplify your answer.)

ID: 7.2.18

---

39. The half-life of a drug in the bloodstream is 18 hours. What fraction of the original drug dose remains in 48 hours? in 60 hours?

What fraction of the original drug dose remains in 48 hours?

____
(Do not round until the final answer. Then round to the nearest hundredth as needed.)

What fraction of the original drug dose remains in 60 hours?

____
(Do not round until the final answer. Then round to the nearest hundredth as needed.)

ID: 7.2.19

---

40. The current population of a threatened animal species is 1.9 million, but it is declining with a half-life of 20 years. How many animals will be left in 25 years? in 60 years?

The population after 25 years will be __________ animals.
(Round to the nearest whole number as needed.)

The population after 60 years will be __________ animals.
(Round to the nearest whole number as needed.)

ID: 7.2.20

---

41. A particular isotope has a half-life of 56 days. If you start with 1 kilogram of this isotope, how much will remain after 120 days? after 240 days?

The remaining amount after 120 days will be __________ kilogram(s).
(Round to three decimal places as needed.)

The remaining amount after 240 days will be __________ kilogram(s).
(Round to three decimal places as needed.)

ID: 7.2.21

---

42. Use the approximate half-life formula for the case described below. Discuss whether the formula is valid for the case described.

Urban encroachment is causing the area of a forest to decline at the rate of 8% per year. What is the half-life of the forest? What fraction of the forest will remain in 10 years?

What is the half-life of the forest?

__________ years
(Type an integer or decimal rounded to the nearest hundredth as needed.)

What fraction of the forest will remain in 10 years?

____
(Type an integer or decimal rounded to the nearest thousandth as needed.)

Is this formula valid in the case described?

○ No
○ Yes

ID: 7.2.22

---

43. Use the approximate half-life formula for the case described below. Discuss whether the formula is valid for the case described.

Poaching is causing a population of elephants to decline by 10% per year. What is the half-life for the population? If there are 10,000 elephants today, how many will remain in 40 years?

What is the half-life for the population?

__________ years (Type an integer or a decimal.)

If there are 10,000 elephants today, how many will remain in 40 years?

__________ (Round to the nearest whole number as needed.)

Does the approximate half-life formula give a valid approximation in the case described?

○ No
○ Yes

ID: 7.2.23

---

44. Compare the doubling times found with the approximate and exact doubling time formulas. Then use the exact doubling time formula to answer the given question.

Inflation is causing prices to rise at a rate of 6% per year. For an item that costs $900 today, what will the price be in 4 years?

Calculate the doubling times found with the approximate and exact doubling time.

The approximate doubling time is __________ years and the exact doubling time is __________ years.
(Round to two decimal places as needed.)

Compare the doubling times found with the approximate and exact doubling time. Choose the correct answer below.

○ **A.** The approximate doubling time is less than the exact doubling time.
○ **B.** The approximate doubling time is greater than the exact doubling time.
○ **C.** The approximate doubling time is more than a year greater than the exact doubling time.
○ **D.** The approximate doubling time is more than a year less than the exact doubling time.

For an item that costs $900 today, what will the price be in 4 years?

$__________
(Round to two decimal places as needed.)

ID: 7.2.24

---

45. Compare the doubling times found with the approximate and exact doubling time formulas. Then use the exact doubling time formula to answer the given question.

A nation of 200 million people is growing at a rate of 5% per year. What will its population be in 20 years?

Calculate the doubling times found with the approximate and exact doubling time.

The approximate doubling time is ___________ years and the exact doubling time is ___________ years.
(Round to two decimal places as needed.)

Compare the doubling times found with the approximate and exact doubling time. Choose the correct answer below.

- ○ **A.** The approximate doubling time is less than the exact doubling time.
- ○ **B.** The approximate doubling time is greater than the exact doubling time.
- ○ **C.** The approximate doubling time is more than a year less than the exact doubling time.
- ○ **D.** The approximate doubling time is more than a year greater than the exact doubling time.

What will its population be in 20 years?

The population would be ___________ million people
(Round to the nearest integer as needed.)

ID: 7.2.25

---

*46. Scientists believe that Earth once had 10 trillion tons of a naturally existing plutonium isotope (back when the Earth was formed). Given a half-life of 25,000 years for that specific plutonium isotope and the Earth's current age of 4.6 billion years, how much would remain today? Use your answer to explain why this isotope is not found naturally on Earth today.

The remaining amount after 4.6 billion years will be ___________ ton(s).
(Round to three decimal places as needed.)

Explain why this isotope is not found naturally on Earth today.

- ○ **A.** The age of the Earth is approximately 184,000 half-lives, so the amount of this isotope remaining today is negligible.
- ○ **B.** The age of the Earth is more than twice the half-life of the isotope. All decaying elements reduce to zero after two half-lives.
- ○ **C.** The age of the Earth is more than ten times the half-life of the isotope. All decaying elements reduce to zero after ten half-lives.
- ○ **D.** The age of the Earth is more than 284,000 half-lives, so the amount of this isotope remaining today is negligible.

ID: 7.2.26

---

47. Total emissions of carbon dioxide from the burning of fossil fuels have been increasing at about 6% per year (data from 2010 to 2011). If emissions continue to increase at this rate, about how much higher will total emissions be in 2050 than in 2010?

Using the approximate formula, emissions will increase by a factor of ___________ between 2010 and 2050.
Using the exact formula, emissions will increase by a factor of ___________ between 2010 and 2050.
(Round to two decimal places as needed.)

ID: 7.2.27

---

*48. The homicide rate decreases at a rate of 10% per year in a city that had 200 homicides in the most recent year. At this rate, in how many years will the number of homicides reach 100 in a year? Complete parts (a) and (b) below.

a. Give an approximate answer using the formula $T_{half} \approx \frac{70}{P}$.

___________ years (Round to two decimal places as needed.)

b. Give an exact answer.

___________ years (Round to two decimal places as needed.)

ID: 7.2.28

---

49. The pressure of Earth's atmosphere at sea level is approximately 1000 millibars, and it decreases by a factor of 2 every 7 km as you go up in altitude.

a. If you live at an elevation of 1 km (roughly 3300 ft), what is the atmospheric pressure?
b. What is the atmospheric pressure at the top of a mountain that is 8819 meters?
c. By approximately what percentage does atmospheric pressure decrease every kilometer?

a. The atmospheric pressure would be ___________ millibars.
(Round to the nearest integer as needed.)

b. The atmospheric pressure would be ___________ millibars.
(Round to the nearest integer as needed.)

c. By approximately what percentage does atmospheric pressure decrease every kilometer?

The atmospheric pressure decreases by approximately ___________ % every kilometer.
(Round up to the nearest percent.)

ID: 7.2.29

*50. If prices increase at a monthly rate of 3%, by what percentage do they increase in a year?

The annual inflation rate is ___________ %.
(Round to the nearest tenth as needed.)

ID: 7.2.30

51. If prices increase at a monthly rate of 11,000%, by what percentage do they increase in a year? In a day? (Assume 30 days per month.)

The annual inflation rate is about ___________ × 10 ___________ %.
(Type whole numbers.)

The daily inflation rate is ___________ %.
(Round to the nearest whole number as needed.)

ID: 7.2.31

52. Suppose that poaching reduces the population of an endangered animal by 4% per year. Further suppose that when the population of this animal falls below 40, its extinction is inevitable (owing to the lack of reproductive options without severe in-breeding). If the current population of the animal is 1500, when will it face extinction? Comment on the validity of this exponential model.

It will take about ___________ years for the animal to face extinction.
(Do not round until the final answer. Then round to the nearest whole number as needed.)

Comment on the validity of this exponential model.

The model is (1) ___________ because the initial population is (2) ___________ and at this rate of decaying, the number of years predicted by the model is (3) ___________ for the population to face extinction due to the lack of reproductive options.

(1) ○ valid
○ not valid

(2) ○ not very high
○ very high

(3) ○ reasonable
○ not reasonable

ID: 7.2.32

53. The drug Valium is eliminated from the bloodstream exponentially with a half-life of 36 hours. Suppose that a patient receives an initial dose of 20 milligrams of Valium at midnight.
a. How much Valium is in the patient's blood at noon on the first day?
b. Estimate when the Valium concentration will reach 20% of its initial level.

a. How much Valium is in the patient's blood at noon on the first day?

There is approximately ___________ mg of Valium in the patient's blood at noon on the first day.
(Round to the nearest tenth as needed.)

b. Estimate when the Valium concentration will reach 20% of its initial level.

After approximately ___________ hours the Valium concentration will reach 20% of its initial level.
(Round to the nearest hour.)

ID: 7.2.33

*54. A certain element has a half life of 3.5 billion years.

a. You find a rock containing a mixture of the element and lead. You determine that 40% of the original element remains; the other 60% decayed into lead. How old is the rock?
b. Analysis of another rock shows that it contains 5% of its original element; the other 95% decayed into lead. How old is the rock?

a. The rock is approximately ________ billion years old.
(Round to one decimal place as needed.)

b. The rock is approximately ________ billion years old.
(Round to one decimal place as needed.)

ID: 7.2.34

---

55. A toxic radioactive substance with a density of 2 milligrams per square centimeter is detected in the ventilating ducts of a nuclear processing building that was used 45 years ago. If the half- life of the substance is 20 years, what was the density of the substance when it was deposited 45 years ago?

The density of the radioactive substance when it was deposited 45 years ago was approximately ________ mg/cm^2.
(Round to the nearest tenth as needed.)

ID: 7.2.35

---

56. Between 2005 and 2010, the average rate of inflation was about 2.2% per year. If a cart of groceries cost $150 in 2005, what did it cost in 2010?

A cart of groceries cost approximately $________ in 2010.
(Round to two decimal places as needed.)

ID: 7.2.36

---

*57. Between 1858 and 1996, carbon dioxide (CO_2) concentration in the atmosphere rose from roughly 284 parts per million to 371 parts per million. Assume that this growth can be modeled with an exponential function $Q = Q_0 \times (1 + r)^t$. Complete parts (a) and (b) below.

a. By experimenting with various values of the growth rate r, find an exponential function that fits the data for 1858 and 1996.

$r \approx$ ________
(Round to five decimal places as needed.)

b. Use this exponential model to predict when the CO_2 concentration will double its 1858 level.

According to this model, the CO_2 concentration will double its 1858 level in ________.
(Type a whole number.)

ID: 7.2.37

!*58. You invest $6,000 with a 5.3% APR, compounded monthly.

(a) Complete the equation $P = ? \cdot (1 + ?)^m$ where m = months.

(b) Complete the equation $P = ? \cdot \left(1 + \frac{?}{?}\right)^{? \cdot t}$ where t = years.

(c) What is the value of the investment after 48 months? Note: To avoid round-off error use the equation which has no decimals that have been rounded off.

(a) Complete the equation.

$P = \_\_\_\_ \cdot (1 + \_\_\_\_)^m$
(Type integers or decimals rounded to four decimal places as needed.)

(b) Complete the equation.

$P = \_\_\_\_ \cdot \left(1 + \frac{\_\_\_\_}{\_\_\_\_}\right)^{\_\_\_\_ \cdot t}$
(Type integers or decimals.)

(c) The value of the investment after 48 months is $________.
(Do not round until the final answer. Then round to the nearest cent as needed.)

ID: 7.3.1

!* 59. You invest $6,000 with a 7% APR, compounded daily.

(a) Complete the equation $P = ? \cdot (1 + ?)^{d}$ where d = days.

(b) Complete the equation $P = ? \cdot \left(1 + \frac{?}{?}\right)^{? \cdot t}$ where t = years.

(c) What is the value of the investment after 22 days? Note: To avoid round-off error use the equation which has no decimals that have been rounded off.

(a) Complete the equation.

P = ________ • (1 + ________)^{d}
(Type integers or decimals rounded to five decimal places as needed.)

(b) Complete the equation.

$P = \_\_\_\_ \cdot \left(1 + \frac{\_\_\_\_}{\_\_\_\_}\right)^{\_\_\_\_ \cdot t}$
(Type integers or decimals.)

(c) The value of the investment after 22 days is $________.
(Do not round until the final answer. Then round to the nearest cent as needed.)

ID: 7.3.2

---

60. Use the compound interest formula to compute the total amount accumulated and the interest earned.

$2500 for 2 years at 1.6% compounded monthly

The total amount accumulated after 2 years is $________.
(Round to the nearest cent as needed.)

The amount of interest earned is $________.
(Round to the nearest cent as needed.)

ID: 7.3.3

---

*61. Use the compound interest formula to compute the total amount accumulated and the interest earned.

$2500 for 3 years at 2% compounded quarterly

The total amount accumulated after 3 years is $________.
(Round to the nearest cent as needed.)

The amount of interest earned is $________.
(Round to the nearest cent as needed.)

ID: 7.3.4

---

62. Use the compound interest formula to compute the total amount accumulated and the interest earned.

$5500 for 4 years at 5.5% compounded monthly

The total amount accumulated after 4 years is $________.
(Round to the nearest cent as needed.)

The amount of interest earned is $________.
(Round to the nearest cent as needed.)

ID: 7.3.5

---

63. Interest is compounded semianually. Find the amount in the account and the interest earned after the given time.

Principal	Rate of Interest	Time
$4000	4%	3 years

The amount in the account is $________.
(Do not round until the final answer. Then round to the nearest cent as needed.)

The interest earned is $________.
(Do not round until the final answer. Then round to the nearest cent as needed.)

ID: 7.3.6

---

64. Use the compound interest formula to compute the total amount accumulated and the interest earned.

$6500 for 2 years at 3% compounded daily (use n = 360)

The total amount accumulated after 2 years is $___________.
(Round to the nearest cent as needed.)

The amount of interest earned is $___________.
(Round to the nearest cent as needed.)

ID: 7.3.7

---

65. Use the present value formula to determine the amount to be invested now, or the present value needed.

The desired accumulated amount is $50,000 after 11 years invested in an account with 7% interest compounded annually.

The amount to be invested now, or the present value needed, is $___________.
(Round to the nearest cent as needed.)

ID: 7.3.8

---

66. Use the present value formula to determine the amount to be invested now, or the present value needed.

The desired accumulated amount is $100,000 after 2 years invested in an account with 5% interest compounded quarterly.

The amount to be invested now, or the present value needed, is $___________.
(Round to the nearest cent as needed.)

ID: 7.3.9

---

67. A youth sports league receives a $80,000 donation for building a new snack bar and office building. The league decides to invest this money in a money market account that pays 5% interest compounded quarterly. How much will the league have in this account after 4 years?

The league will have $___________ in this account after 4 years.
(Round to the nearest cent as needed.)

ID: 7.3.10

---

*68. To help pay for a class trip at the end of their senior year, the sophomore class at a high school invests $1300 from fund-raisers in a 30-month CD paying 3.2% interest compounded monthly. Determine the amount the class will receive when it cashes in the CD after 30 months.

The sophomore class will receive $___________ when it cashes in the CD.
(Round to the nearest cent as needed.)

ID: 7.3.11

---

69. A recent high school graduate received $900 in gifts of cash from friends and relatives. In addition, she received three scholarships in the amounts of $250, $800, and $1500. If she takes all her gift and scholarship money and invests it in a 36-month CD paying 2% interest compounded daily, how much will the graduate have when she cashes in the CD at the end of the 36-months?

The graduate will have $___________ when she cashes in the CD.
(Round to the nearest cent as needed.)

ID: 7.3.12

---

*70. At the time of her grandson's birth, a grandmother deposited $9,000 in an account. The account was paying 2.5% interest compounded monthly.

a. If the rate did not change, what was the value of the account after 19 years?
b. If the money had been invested at 2.5% compounded quarterly, what would the value of the account have been after 19 years?

a. The value of the account will be $___________.
(Round to the nearest cent.)

b. The value of the account will be $___________
(Round to the nearest cent.)

ID: 7.3.13

---

71. Brent Pickett borrowed $5000 from his brother Dave. He agreed to repay the money at the end of 2 years, giving Dave the same amount of interest that he would have received if the money had been invested at 2.25% compounded quarterly. How much money did Brent repay his brother?

Brent repaid his brother $___________.
(Round to the nearest cent as needed.)

ID: 7.3.14

---

72. Karen Gaines invested $10,000 in a money market account with an interest rate of 1.75% compounded semiannually. Four years later, Karen withdrew the full amount to put toward the down payment on a new house. How much did Karen withdraw from the account?

Karen withdrew $___________.
(Round to the nearest cent as needed.)

ID: 7.3.15

---

73. Determine the effective annual yield for $1 invested for 1 year at 3.6% compounded quarterly.

The effective annual yield is ___________%.
(Round to the nearest hundredth.)

ID: 7.3.16

---

74. Dave Dudley won a photography contest and received a $1400 cash prize. Will he earn more interest in 1 year if he invests his winnings in a simple interest account that pays 6% or in an account that pays 5.75% interest compounded monthly?

In which account will he earn more interest?

○ Simple interest account

○ Compound interest account

ID: 7.3.17

---

*75. Jane Roznowski wants to invest some money now to buy a new tractor in the future. If she wants to have $325,000 available in 4 years, how much does she need to invest now in a CD paying 5.25% interest compounded monthly?

Jane needs to invest $___________ now.
(Round to the nearest cent as needed.)

ID: 7.3.18

---

76. Determine the total amount and the interest paid on $2000 with interest compounded monthly for 5 years at

a) 3%. **b)** 6%. **c)** 12%.
d) Is there a predictable outcome in either the amount or the interest when the rate is doubled?

a) The total amount accumulated at 3% is $___________.
(Round to the nearest cent as needed.)

The interest paid at 3% is $___________.
(Round to the nearest cent as needed.)

b) The total amount accumulated at 6% is $___________.
(Round to the nearest cent as needed.)

The interest paid at 6% is $___________.
(Round to the nearest cent as needed.)

c) The total amount accumulated at 12% is $___________.
(Round to the nearest cent as needed.)

The interest paid at 12% is $___________.
(Round to the nearest cent as needed.)

d) Is the outcome predictable?

○ **A.** Yes, the total amount increases by half if the interest rate doubles.

○ **B.** Yes, the total amount doubles if the interest rate doubles.

○ **C.** Yes, the interest increases by half if the interest rate doubles.

○ **D.** Yes, the interest doubles if the interest rate doubles.

○ **E.** No, neither the total amount nor the interest is predictable.

ID: 7.3.19

---

77. You are given a choice of taking the simple interest on $100,000 invested for 4 years at a rate of 3% or the interest on $100,000 invested for 4 years at an interest rate of 3% compounded daily. Which investment earns the greater amount of interest? Give the difference between the amounts of interest earned by the two investments.

The investment with (1) ___________ interest earns $ ___________ more in interest.
(Round to the nearest cent as needed.)

(1) ○ compound
○ simple

ID: 7.3.20

!* 78. You invest $4,000 with a 5% APR, compounded daily.

(a) Complete the equation $P = ? \cdot \left(1 + \frac{?}{?}\right)^{? \cdot t}$ where t = years.

(b) Complete the equation $P = ? \cdot (1 + ?)^t$ where t = years.
(c) What is the APY?

(a) Complete the equation.

$P = \_\_\_\_ \cdot \left(1 + \frac{\_\_\_\_}{\_\_\_\_}\right)^{\_\_\_\_ \cdot t}$

(Type integers or decimals.)

(b) Complete the equation.

$P = \_\_\_\_ \cdot (1 + \_\_\_\_)^t$
(Type integers or decimals rounded to four decimal places as needed.)

(d) The APY is ___________ %.
(Round to two decimal places as needed.)

ID: 7.3.21

79. What is the difference between simple interest and compound interest? Why do you end up with more money with compound interest?

Choose the correct answer below.

○ **A.** Simple interest is interest paid both on the original investment and on all interest that has been added to the original investment whereas compound interest is interest paid only on the original investment. Since compound interest is calculated based on a smaller amount, it results in a larger amount of money over time.

○ **B.** Simple interest is interest paid at a fixed rate over time whereas compound interest fluctuates over time. Since the rates for compound interest are always increasing, it results in a larger amount of money over time compared to simple interest.

○ **C.** Simple interest is interest paid only on the original investment whereas compound interest is interest paid both on the original investment and on all interest that has been added to the original investment. Since compound interest is calculated based on a larger amount than simple interest, it results in a larger amount of money over time.

○ **D.** Simple interest is interest paid only on 50% of the original investment whereas compound interest is interest paid only on 100% of the original investment. Since compound interest is calculated based on a larger amount than simple interest, it results in a larger amount of money over time.

ID: 7.3.22

80. Explain why the term APR/n appears in the compound interest formula for interest paid n times a year.

Choose the correct answer below.

○ **A.** APR represents the annual principle rate. The APR represents the original investment and must be divided by the number of compounding periods per year, n, in order to determine the yearly compounded interest rate.

○ **B.** APR represents the annual percentage rate (as a decimal). To account for the interest paid n times a year, this annual (yearly) rate needs to be divided by the number of compounding periods per year, n.

○ **C.** APR represents the annual principle rate. Since the APR is the total amount of interest earned in a year, it needs to be divided by the number of compounding periods per year, n.

○ **D.** APR represents the annual percentage rate (as a decimal). Since the APR represents a yearlong rate, to account for fluctuation, the rate needs to be divided by the number of compounding periods per year, n.

ID: 7.3.23

*81. State the compound interest formula for interest paid more than once a year. Define all the variables.

What is the compound interest formula for interest paid more than once a year?

○ **A.** $A = P \times (1 + APR)^{y}$

○ **B.** $A = P \times e^{(APR \times Y)}$

○ **C.** $A = P\left(1 + \frac{APR}{n}\right)^{(nY)}$

Define the variables in the compound interest formula for interest paid more than once a year. Choose the correct answer below.

○ **A.** A is the accumulated balance after Y years, P is the starting principal, APR is the annual percentage rate (as a decimal), and Y is the number of years.

○ **B.** A is the accumulated balance after Y years, P is the starting principal, APR is the annual percentage rate (as a decimal), n is the number of compounding periods per year, and Y is the number of years.

○ **C.** A is the accumulated balance after Y years, P is the starting principal, APR is the annual percentage rate (as a decimal), Y is the number of years, and e is a special irrational number with a value of $e \approx 2.71828$.

ID: 7.3.24

---

*82. What is continuous compounding? How does the APY for continuous compounding compare to the APY for, say, daily compounding? Explain the formula for continuous compounding.

Choose the correct answer below.

○ **A.** Compounding daily is also known as continuous compounding. The APY for continuous compounding is equivalent to the APY for daily compounding. The formula for continuous compounding is also known as the compound interest formula.

○ **B.** Compounding at least once per year is called continuous compounding. The APY for continuous compounding is smaller than the APY for daily compounding. The formula for continuous compounding is also known as the compound interest formula.

○ **C.** Compounding twice daily is called continuous compounding. The APY for continuous compounding is only slightly larger than the APY for daily compounding. The formula for continuous compounding is a special form of the simple interest formula.

○ **D.** Compounding infinitely many times per year is called continuous compounding. The APY for continuous compounding is only slightly larger than the APY for daily compounding. The formula for continuous compounding is a special form of the compound interest formula.

ID: 7.3.25

---

83. Decide if the following statement makes sense (or is clearly true) or does not make sense (or is clearly false).

Bank A was offering simple interest at 5.5% per year, which was clearly a better deal than the 5.5% compound interest rate at Bank B.

Choose the correct answer below.

○ **A.** The statement makes sense, because the simple interest pays more than the compound interest.

○ **B.** The statement does not make sense, because the simple interest pays the same amount as the compound interest at the same interest rate.

○ **C.** The statement does not make sense, because the compound interest pays more than the simple interest.

ID: 7.3.26

---

84. Decide whether the following statement makes sense (or is clearly true) or does not make sense (or is clearly false). Explain your reasoning.

Both banks were paying the same annual percentage rate (APR), but one had a higher annual percentage yield than the other (APY).

Choose the correct answer below.

○ **A.** This statement makes sense because the banks can have a different number of compounding periods, which results in different annual percentage yields.

○ **B.** This statement does not make sense because if the annual percentage rates are the same, then the annual percentage yields will be the same as well.

○ **C.** This statement makes sense because the banks can have different starting principal, which results in different annual percentage yields.

○ **D.** This statement does not make sense because two banks will never have the same annual percentage rate.

ID: 7.3.27

---

85. Decide if the following statement makes sense (or is clearly true) or does not make sense (or is clearly false).

The bank that pays the highest annual percentage rate (APR) is always the best deal.

Choose the correct answer below.

- A. The statement makes sense because a higher APR always results in a higher annual percentage yield than an interest rate with a lower APR.
- B. The statement does not make sense because, depending on how often the interest is compounded, a lower APR could result in a higher annual percentage yield.
- C. The statement does not make sense because a higher APR always results in a lower annual percentage yield than an interest rate with a lower APR.

ID: 7.3.28

---

86. Decide if the following statement makes sense (or is clearly true) or does not make sense (or is clearly false).

My bank paid an annual interest rate (APR) of 3.0% but at the end of the year my account balance had grown by 3.1%.

Choose the correct answer below.

- A. This does not make sense, the annual interest rate (APR) is always greater than the annual percentage yield (APY) and the interest rate paid on the balance.
- B. This does not make sense, the annual interest rate (APR) is always the annual percentage yield (APY) and the interest rate paid on the balance.
- C. This makes sense, because the annual interest rate (APR) does not always match the annual percentage yield (APY).

ID: 7.3.29

---

*87. Find the annual percentage yield (APY) in the following situation.

A bank offers an APR of 6.4% compounded daily.

The annual percentage yield is ________%.
(Do not round until the final answer. Then round to two decimal places as needed.)

ID: 7.3.30

---

88. Find the annual percentage yield (APY) in the following situation.

A bank offers an APR of 3.46% compounded monthly.

The annual percentage yield is ________%.
(Do not round until the final answer. Then round to two decimal places as needed.)

ID: 7.3.31

!*89. For each of the following functions, find the APR and state the compounding period (annually, quarterly, monthly, daily, continuously).

(a) $P = [6{,}500] \cdot \left(1 + \left[\frac{0.027}{365}\right]\right)^{365 \cdot t}$

(b) $P = [6{,}500] \cdot (1.027)^{t}$

(c) $P = [6{,}500] \cdot (1.027)^{12t}$

(d) $P = [6{,}500] \cdot (e)^{0.027t}$

(a) The APR is ________%.
(Type an integer or a decimal.)

The compounding period is (1) ________

(b) The APR is ________%.
(Type an integer or a decimal.)

The compounding period is (2) ________

(c) The APR is ________%.
(Type an integer or a decimal.)

The compounding period is (3) ________

!* 89. (cont.) **(d)** The APR is ____________%.
(Type an integer or a decimal.)

The compounding period is (4) ____________

(1) ○ annually. ○ monthly. ○ continuously. ○ quarterly. ○ daily.

(2) ○ continuously. ○ quarterly. ○ annually. ○ monthly. ○ daily.

(3) ○ monthly. ○ annually. ○ quarterly. ○ daily. ○ continuously.

(4) ○ monthly. ○ quarterly. ○ daily. ○ continuously. ○ annually.

ID: 7.4.1

!*90. For each of the following functions, find the yield and doubling time.

(a) $P = [2{,}000] \cdot \left(1 + \left[\frac{0.023}{4}\right]\right)^{4 \cdot t}$

(b) $P = [2{,}000] \cdot (1.023)^t$

(c) $P = [2{,}000] \cdot (1.023)^{12t}$

(d) $P = [2{,}000] \cdot (e)^{0.023t}$

(a) The yield is ____________%.
(Round to three decimal places as needed.)

The doubling time is ____________ years.
(Round to two decimal places as needed.)

(b) The yield is ____________%.
(Round to three decimal places as needed.)

The doubling time is ____________ years.
(Round to two decimal places as needed.)

(c) The yield is ____________%.
(Round to three decimal places as needed.)

The doubling time is ____________ years.
(Round to two decimal places as needed.)

(d) The yield is ____________%.
(Round to three decimal places as needed.)

The doubling time is ____________ years.
(Round to two decimal places as needed.)

ID: 7.4.2

!*91. For each of the following functions, rewrite as $y = 3{,}000 \cdot e^{k \cdot x}$, and find the continuous rate k.

(a) $P = [3{,}000] \cdot (1.053)^t$

(b) $P = [3{,}000] \cdot (1.24)^t$

(c) $P = [3{,}000] \cdot (0.94)^t$

(d) $P = [3{,}000] \cdot (e)^{0.024t}$

(a) Select the correct choice below and, if necessary, fill in the answer box to complete your choice.

○ **A.** y = ____________
(Type an expression using x as the variable. Use integers or decimals for any numbers in the expression. Round to five decimal places as needed.)

○ **B.** The function is already in the form $y = 3{,}000 \cdot e^{k \cdot x}$.

k = ____________%
(Round to three decimal places as needed.)

!* 91. (cont.) **(b)** Select the correct choice below and, if necessary, fill in the answer box to complete your choice.

○ **A.** y = ___________
(Type an expression using x as the variable. Use integers or decimals for any numbers in the expression. Round to five decimal places as needed.)

○ **B.** The function is already in the form $y = 3{,}000 \cdot e^{k \cdot x}$.

k = ___________ %
(Round to three decimal places as needed.)

(c) Select the correct choice below and, if necessary, fill in the answer box to complete your choice.

○ **A.** y = ___________
(Type an expression using x as the variable. Use integers or decimals for any numbers in the expression. Round to five decimal places as needed.)

○ **B.** The function is already in the form $y = 3{,}000 \cdot e^{k \cdot x}$.

k = ___________ %
(Round to three decimal places as needed.)

(d) Select the correct choice below and, if necessary, fill in the answer box to complete your choice.

○ **A.** y = ___________
(Type an expression using x as the variable. Use integers or decimals for any numbers in the expression. Round to five decimal places as needed.)

○ **B.** The function is already in the form $y = 3{,}000 \cdot e^{k \cdot x}$.

k = ___________ %
(Round to three decimal places as needed.)

ID: 7.4.3

!* 92. Fill in the following table.

Annual Growth/ Decay Rate	Doubling Time/ Half-Life	Growth / Decay Factor Per Year	Continuous Rate Per Year	Growth / Decay Factor Per Decade	Growth / Decay Rate Per Decade
32%		1.32		16.06	
	35.00 years	1.02	1.98%		
				0.279	

Fill in the table.

(Type integers or decimals rounded to two decimal places as needed.)

Annual Growth/ Decay Rate	Doubling Time/ Half-Life	Growth / Decay Factor Per Year	Continuous Rate Per Year	Growth / Decay Factor Per Decade	Growth / Decay Rate Per Decade
32%	________ years	1.32	________ %	16.06	________ %
________ %	35.00 years	1.02	1.98%	________	________ %
________ %	________ years	________	________ %	0.279	________ %

ID: 7.4.4

---

*93. Use the formula for continuous compounding to compute the balance in the account after 1, 5, and 20 years. Also, find the APY for the account.

A $12,000 deposit in an account with an APR of 3.5%.

The balance in the account after 1 year is approximately $ ___________.
(Round to the nearest cent as needed.)

The balance in the account after 5 years is approximately $ ___________.
(Round to the nearest cent as needed.)

The balance in the account after 20 years is approximately $ ___________.
(Round to the nearest cent as needed.)

The APY for the account is approximately ___________ %
(Round to two decimal places as needed.)

ID: 7.4.5

*94. Use the formula for continuous compounding to compute the balance in the account after 1, 5, and 20 years. Also, find the APY for the account.

A $6000 deposit in an account with an APR of 3.1%.

The balance in the account after 1 year is approximately $ ________.
(Round to the nearest cent as needed.)

The balance in the account after 5 years is approximately $ ________.
(Round to the nearest cent as needed.)

The balance in the account after 20 years is approximately $ ________.
(Round to the nearest cent as needed.)

The APY for the account is approximately ________ %
(Round to two decimal places as needed.)

ID: 7.4.6

*95. Use the formula for continuous compounding to compute the balance in the account after 1, 5, and 20 years. Also, find the APY for the account.

A $6000 deposit in an account with an APR of 7%.

The balance in the account after 1 year is approximately $ ________.
(Round to the nearest cent as needed.)

The balance in the account after 5 years is approximately $ ________.
(Round to the nearest cent as needed.)

The balance in the account after 20 years is approximately $ ________.
(Round to the nearest cent as needed.)

The APY for the account is approximately ________ %
(Round to two decimal places as needed.)

ID: 7.4.7

CHAPTER 8
Curve Fitting and Correlation
MyMathLab Homework Problems*

* Problems with an asterisk are included in the pre-assigned homework assignment.
! Problems with an exclamation point are new to the Update edition.
To find the problems in MyMathLab online, please refer to the ID code listed below each problem.

*1. What is a correlation? Give three examples of pairs of variables that are correlated.

Select the correct answer below.

- A. A correlation is only when two variables tend to change in opposite directions, with one increasing and one decreasing.
- B. A correlation is only when two variables tend to increase or decrease together.
- C. A correlation exists between two variables when higher values of one variable consistently go with higher or lower values of another variable.
- D. A correlation is when one variable causes another variable.

Give three examples of pairs of variables that are correlated. Select the correct answer below.

- A. production cost of movies and gross receipts of movies, inflation and unemployment, the Superbowl winner and the performance of the stock market
- B. amount of smoking and lung cancer, height and weight of people, price of a good and demand of the good
- C. the Superbowl winner and the performance of the stock market, amount of smoking and lung cancer, per capita personal income and the percent of the population below the poverty level
- D. production cost of movies and gross receipts of movies, per capita personal income and the percent of the population below the poverty level, height and weight of people

ID: 8.1.1

---

*2. Define and distinguish among positive correlation, negative correlation, and no correlation. How do we determine the strength of a correlation?

Define positive correlation. Choose the correct answer below.

- A. Positive correlation means that there is no apparent relationship between the two variables.
- B. Positive correlation means that there is a good relationship between the two variables.
- C. Positive correlation means that both variables tend to increase (or decrease) together.
- D. Positive correlation means that two variables tend to change in opposite directions, with one increasing while the other decreases.

Define negative correlation. Choose the correct answer below.

- A. Negative correlation means that two variables tend to change in opposite directions, with one increasing while the other decreases.
- B. Negative correlation means that there is no apparent relationship between the two variables.
- C. Negative correlation means that there is a bad relationship between the two variables.
- D. Negative correlation means that both variables tend to increase (or decrease) together.

Define no correlation. Choose the correct answer below.

- A. No correlation means that both variables tend to increase (or decrease) together.
- B. No correlation means that there is no apparent relationship between the two variables.
- C. No correlation means that the two variables are always zero.
- D. No correlation means that two variables tend to change in opposite directions, with one increasing while the other decreases.

How do we determine the strength of a correlation?

- A. No correlation is stronger than negative correlation. Positive correlation is stronger than no correlation.
- B. Negative correlation is stronger than no correlation. Positive correlation is stronger than negative correlation.
- C. The more closely two variables follow the general trend, the weaker the correlation (which may be positive or negative).
- D. The more closely two variables follow the general trend, the stronger the correlation (which may be positive or negative).

ID: 8.1.2

---

3. Briefly describe each of the six guidelines for establishing causality. Give an example of the application of each guideline.

Select the correct answer below.

- A. The first guideline states that the suspected cause should be tested with an experiment.
- B. The first guideline states that among groups that differ only in the presence or absence of the suspected cause, one should check that the effect is similarly present or absent.
- C. The first guideline states that the physical mechanism by which the suspected cause produces the effect should be determined.
- D. The first guideline states to look for evidence that larger amounts of the suspected cause produce larger amounts of the effect.
- E. The first guideline states that if the effect might be produced by other potential causes, make sure the effect still remains after accounting for these other potential causes.
- F. The first guideline states that one should look for situations where the effect is correlated with the suspected cause, even when other factors vary.

Give an example of the first guideline. Select the correct answer below.

- A. When checking to see if smoking causes cancer, let the group of smokers vary between people of different ethnicities and genetic background to see if lung cancer is still more prevalent among smokers than non-smokers.
- B. When checking to see if smoking causes cancer, look at two groups as identical as possible, with one group being smokers and the other group being non-smokers.
- C. When checking to see if smoking causes cancer, let groups of smokers and non-smokers be completely random to see if lung cancer occurs more in the smoking group than the non-smoking group.
- D. When checking to see if smoking causes cancer, try to find what it is in cigarettes that causes cells to mutate and cause cancer.
- E. When checking to see if smoking causes cancer, look at those who smoke a lot and those who only smoke a little and compare the incidents of lung cancer.
- F. When checking to see if smoking causes cancer, test the effects of cigarettes on lung tissue or animals.

Select the correct answer below.

- A. The second guideline states that the suspected cause should be tested with an experiment.
- B. The second guideline states that among groups that differ only in the presence or absence of the suspected cause, one should check that the effect is similarly present or absent.
- C. The second guideline states that one should look for situations where the effect is correlated with the suspected cause, even when other factors vary.
- D. The second guideline states that if the effect might be produced by other potential causes, make sure the effect still remains after accounting for these other potential causes.
- E. The second guideline states to look for evidence that larger amounts of the suspected cause produce larger amounts of the effect.
- F. The second guideline states that the physical mechanism by which the suspected cause produces the effect should be determined.

Give an example of the second guideline. Select the correct answer below.

- A. When checking to see if smoking causes cancer, look at those who smoke a lot and those who only smoke a little and compare the incidents of lung cancer.
- B. When checking to see if smoking causes cancer, test the effects of cigarettes on lung tissue or animals.
- C. When checking to see if smoking causes cancer, look at two groups as identical as possible, with one group being smokers and the other group being non-smokers.
- D. When checking to see if smoking causes cancer, let the group of smokers vary between people of different ethnicities and genetic background to see if lung cancer is still more prevalent among smokers than non-smokers.
- E. When checking to see if smoking causes cancer, let groups of smokers and non-smokers be completely random to see if lung cancer occurs more in the smoking group than the non-smoking group.
- F. When checking to see if smoking causes cancer, try to find what it is in cigarettes that causes cells to mutate and cause cancer.

Select the correct answer below.

- A. The third guideline states that if the effect might be produced by other potential causes, make sure the effect still remains after accounting for these other potential causes.
- B. The third guideline states that one should look for situations where the effect is correlated with the suspected cause, even when other factors vary.
- C. The third guideline states to look for evidence that larger amounts of the suspected cause produce larger amounts of the effect.
- D. The third guideline states that the suspected cause should be tested with an experiment.
- E. The third guideline states that among groups that differ only in the presence or absence of the suspected cause, one should check that the effect is similarly present or absent.
- F. The third guideline states that the physical mechanism by which the suspected cause produces the effect should be determined.

3. (cont.) Give an example of the third guideline. Select the correct answer below.

- A. When checking to see if smoking causes cancer, test the effects of cigarettes on lung tissue or animals.
- B. When checking to see if smoking causes cancer, look at those who smoke a lot and those who only smoke a little and compare the incidents of lung cancer.
- C. When checking to see if smoking causes cancer, let groups of smokers and non-smokers be completely random to see if lung cancer occurs more in the smoking group than the non-smoking group.
- D. When checking to see if smoking causes cancer, look at two groups as identical as possible, with one group being smokers and the other group being non-smokers.
- E. When checking to see if smoking causes cancer, let the group of smokers vary between people of different ethnicities and genetic background to see if lung cancer is still more prevalent among smokers than non-smokers.
- F. When checking to see if smoking causes cancer, try to find what it is in cigarettes that causes cells to mutate and cause cancer.

Select the correct answer below.

- A. The fourth guideline states that one should look for situations where the effect is correlated with the suspected cause, even when other factors vary.
- B. The fourth guideline states that if the effect might be produced by other potential causes, make sure the effect still remains after accounting for these other potential causes.
- C. The fourth guideline states to look for evidence that larger amounts of the suspected cause produce larger amounts of the effect.
- D. The fourth guideline states that the physical mechanism by which the suspected cause produces the effect should be determined.
- E. The fourth guideline states that the suspected cause should be tested with an experiment.
- F. The fourth guideline states that among groups that differ only in the presence or absence of the suspected cause, one should check that the effect is similarly present or absent.

Give an example of the fourth guideline. Select the correct answer below.

- A. When checking to see if smoking causes cancer, let groups of smokers and non-smokers be completely random to see if lung cancer occurs more in the smoking group than the non-smoking group.
- B. When checking to see if smoking causes cancer, try to find what it is in cigarettes that causes cells to mutate and cause cancer.
- C. When checking to see if smoking causes cancer, test the effects of cigarettes on lung tissue or animals.
- D. When checking to see if smoking causes cancer, look at two groups as identical as possible, with one group being smokers and the other group being non-smokers.
- E. When checking to see if smoking causes cancer, let the group of smokers vary between people of different ethnicities and genetic background to see if lung cancer is still more prevalent among smokers than non-smokers.
- F. When checking to see if smoking causes cancer, look at those who smoke a lot and those who only smoke a little and compare the incidents of lung cancer.

Select the correct answer below.

- A. The fifth guideline states that if the effect might be produced by other potential causes, make sure the effect still remains after accounting for these other potential causes.
- B. The fifth guideline states that the suspected cause should be tested with an experiment.
- C. The fifth guideline states to look for evidence that larger amounts of the suspected cause produce larger amounts of the effect.
- D. The fifth guideline states that the physical mechanism by which the suspected cause produces the effect should be determined.
- E. The fifth guideline states that among groups that differ only in the presence or absence of the suspected cause, one should check that the effect is similarly present or absent.
- F. The fifth guideline states that one should look for situations where the effect is correlated with the suspected cause, even when other factors vary.

Give an example of the fifth guideline. Select the correct answer below.

- A. When checking to see if smoking causes cancer, let the group of smokers vary between people of different ethnicities and genetic background to see if lung cancer is still more prevalent among smokers than non-smokers.
- B. When checking to see if smoking causes cancer, look at those who smoke a lot and those who only smoke a little and compare the incidents of lung cancer.
- C. When checking to see if smoking causes cancer, let groups of smokers and non-smokers be completely random to see if lung cancer occurs more in the smoking group than the non-smoking group.
- D. When checking to see if smoking causes cancer, test the effects of cigarettes on lung tissue or animals.
- E. When checking to see if smoking causes cancer, try to find what it is in cigarettes that causes cells to mutate and cause cancer.
- F. When checking to see if smoking causes cancer, look at two groups as identical as possible, with one group being smokers and the other group being non-smokers.

3. (cont.) Select the correct answer below.

- ○ **A.** The sixth guideline states that the suspected cause should be tested with an experiment.
- ○ **B.** The sixth guideline states that one should look for situations where the effect is correlated with the suspected cause, even when other factors vary.
- ○ **C.** The sixth guideline states that among groups that differ only in the presence or absence of the suspected cause, one should check that the effect is similarly present or absent.
- ○ **D.** The sixth guideline states that the physical mechanism by which the suspected cause produces the effect should be determined.
- ○ **E.** The sixth guideline states that if the effect might be produced by other potential causes, make sure the effect still remains after accounting for these other potential causes.
- ○ **F.** The sixth guideline states to look for evidence that larger amounts of the suspected cause produce larger amounts of the effect.

Give an example of the sixth guideline. Select the correct answer below.

- ○ **A.** When checking to see if smoking causes cancer, test the effects of cigarettes on lung tissue or animals.
- ○ **B.** When checking to see if smoking causes cancer, look at two groups as identical as possible, with one group being smokers and the other group being non-smokers.
- ○ **C.** When checking to see if smoking causes cancer, try to find what it is in cigarettes that causes cells to mutate and cause cancer.
- ○ **D.** When checking to see if smoking causes cancer, let groups of smokers and non-smokers be completely random to see if lung cancer occurs more in the smoking group than the non-smoking group.
- ○ **E.** When checking to see if smoking causes cancer, let the group of smokers vary between people of different ethnicities and genetic background to see if lung cancer is still more prevalent among smokers than non-smokers.
- ○ **F.** When checking to see if smoking causes cancer, look at those who smoke a lot and those who only smoke a little and compare the incidents of lung cancer.

ID: 8.1.3

---

*4. Determine whether the statement makes sense or does not make sense, and explain your reasoning.

I found a strong negative correlation for data relating the percentage of people in various countries who are literate and the percentage who are undernourished. I concluded that an increase in literacy causes a decrease in undernourishment.

Choose the correct answer below.

- ○ **A.** The statement makes sense. If a correlation exists between two variables, it can be concluded that an increase or decrease in one variable causes an increase or decrease in the other.
- ○ **B.** The statement does not make sense. There is no way for an increase in literacy to cause a decrease in undernourishment.
- ○ **C.** The statement does not make sense. Correlation is not necessarily causation.
- ○ **D.** The statement makes sense. The correlation between increased literacy and decreased undernourishment is simply a coincidence.

ID: 8.1.4

---

5. Decide whether the following statement makes sense (or is clearly true) or does not make sense (or is clearly false). Explain your reasoning.

I found a nearly perfect positive correlation between variable A and variable B and therefore was able to conclude that an increase in variable A causes an increase in variable B.

Select the correct answer below.

- ○ **A.** The statement does make sense because a negative correlation implies that an increase in variable A causes an increase in variable B.
- ○ **B.** The statement does make sense because a correlation alone is enough evidence to establish causality.
- ○ **C.** The statement does not make sense because a correlation alone is not enough evidence to establish causality.
- ○ **D.** The statement does not make sense because a negative correlation would imply that an increase in variable A causes an increase in variable B.

ID: 8.1.5

---

6. Decide whether the following statement makes sense (or is clearly true) or does not make sense (or is clearly false). Explain your reasoning.

I had originally suspected that an increase in variable E would cause a decrease in variable F, but I no longer believe this because I found no correlation between the two variables.

The statement (1) ________ Originally, (2) ________ correlation was suspected. Since no correlation was found, there is apparently (3) ________ relationship between the variables.

(1) ○ makes sense.
○ does not make sense.

(2) ○ a positive
○ a negative
○ no

(3) ○ a negative
○ no
○ a positive

ID: 8.1.6

---

7. For the following pair of variables, state the units that might be used to measure each variable. Then state whether you believe that they are correlated. If you believe they are correlated, state whether the correlation is positive or negative. Explain your reasoning.

Price of gasoline and sport utility vehicle (SUV) sales

To measure price of gas, the unit (1) ________ might be used.

To measure SUV sales, the unit (2) ________ might be used.

What correlation, if any, is there between the variables?

○ **A.** There is a positive correlation because SUV sales tend to increase when price of gas increases.
○ **B.** There is a negative correlation because SUV sales tend to increase when price of gas decreases.
○ **C.** The variables are not correlated.

(1) ○ pounds
○ dollars per gallon
○ billions of dollars
○ miles per gallon

(2) ○ miles per gallon
○ pounds
○ dollars per gallon
○ billions of dollars

ID: 8.1.7

---

* 8. For the following pair of variables, state the units that might be used to measure each variable. Then state whether you believe that the two variables are correlated. If you believe they are correlated, state whether the correlation is positive or negative. Explain your reasoning.

Altitude on a mountain hike and air pressure

To measure altitude, the unit (1) ________ might be used.

To measure air pressure, the unit (2) ________ might be used.

What correlation, if any, is there between the variables?

○ **A.** There is a negative correlation because air pressure tends to increase when altitude decreases.
○ **B.** There is a negative correlation because air pressure tends to increase when altitude increases.
○ **C.** There is a positive correlation because air pressure tends to increase when altitude increases.
○ **D.** There is a positive correlation because air pressure tends to increase when altitude decreases.
○ **E.** The variables are not correlated.

(1) ○ square inches
○ feet above sea level
○ billions of dollars
○ pounds per square inch

(2) ○ pounds per square inch
○ square inches
○ feet above sea level
○ billions of dollars

ID: 8.1.8

---

9. For the following pair of variables, state the units that might be used to measure each variable. Then state whether you believe that the two variables are correlated. If you believe they are correlated, state whether the correlation is positive or negative. Explain your reasoning.

Altitude on a mountain hike and air pressure

To measure altitude, the unit (1) ___________ might be used.

To measure air pressure, the unit (2) ___________ might be used.

What correlation, if any, is there between the variables?

- ○ **A.** There is a negative correlation because air pressure tends to increase when altitude increases.
- ○ **B.** There is a positive correlation because air pressure tends to increase when altitude increases.
- ○ **C.** There is a positive correlation because air pressure tends to increase when altitude decreases.
- ○ **D.** There is a negative correlation because air pressure tends to increase when altitude decreases.
- ○ **E.** The variables are not correlated.

(1) ○ feet above sea level
○ pounds per square inch
○ pounds
○ dollars per gallon

(2) ○ pounds per square inch
○ dollars per gallon
○ pounds
○ feet above sea level

ID: 8.1.9

---

10. For the following pair of variables, state the units that might be used to measure each variable. Then state whether you believe that the two variables are correlated. If you believe they are correlated, state whether the correlation is positive or negative. Explain your reasoning.

Latitude north of the equator and the average high temperature in June

---

To measure latitude, the unit (1) ___________ might be used.

To measure temperature, the unit (2) ___________ might be used.

What correlation, if any, is there between the variables?

- ○ **A.** There is a positive correlation because the average high temperature in June tends to increase when latitude increases.
- ○ **B.** There is a negative correlation because the average high temperature in June tends to increase when latitude decreases.
- ○ **C.** There is a positive correlation because the average high temperature in June tends to increase when latitude decreases.
- ○ **D.** There is a negative correlation because the average high temperature in June tends to increase when latitude increases.
- ○ **E.** The variables are not correlated.

(1) ○ degrees Fahrenheit
○ degrees of latitude
○ births per year
○ pounds

(2) ○ degrees of latitude
○ degrees Fahrenheit
○ births per year
○ pounds

ID: 8.1.10

---

*11. Consider the following statement about a correlation. State the correlation clearly (for example, there is a positive correlation between variable A and variable B). Then state whether the correlation is most likely due to coincidence, a common underlying cause, or a direct cause. Explain your answer.

In a large resort city, the crime rate increased as the number of taxi cabs increased.

There is (1) ___________ correlation between the crime rate and the number of taxi cabs.

Determine the possible explanation for the correlation. Choose the correct answer below.

- ○ **A.** This correlation is due to a possible direct cause because criminals need cabs.
- ○ **B.** This correlation is due to a common underlying cause because there is no link between crime and cabs.

*11. (cont.)

○ **C.** This correlation is due to a coincidence because criminals need cabs.

○ **D.** This correlation is due to coincidence because no link exists between crime and cabs.

○ **E.** This correlation is due to a common underlying cause because it is possible that, with an increase in tourism, both the crime rate and the number of cabs increase.

○ **F.** There is no correlation because there is no link between crime and cabs.

(1) ○ a negative
○ no
○ a positive

ID: 8.1.11

---

12. Consider the following statement about a correlation. State the correlation clearly. Then state whether the correlation is most likely due to a coincidence, a common underlying cause, or a direct cause. Explain your answer.

Over the past three decades, the number of miles of freeways in Los Angeles has grown, and traffic congestion has worsened.

Select the correct answer below.

○ **A.** There is no correlation between the number of miles of freeways and the traffic congestion in Los Angeles.

○ **B.** There is a negative correlation between the number of miles of freeways and the traffic congestion in Los Angeles.

○ **C.** There is a positive correlation between the number of miles of freeways and the traffic congestion in Los Angeles.

Is the correlation most likely due to a coincidence, a common underlying cause, or a direct cause? Explain.

○ **A.** There is no correlation between the number of miles of freeways and the traffic congestion in Los Angeles.

○ **B.** The correlation is most likely due to a coincidence because the number of miles of freeways and the traffic congestion is not related.

○ **C.** The correlation is most likely due to the common underlying cause of Los Angeles having a very large population.

○ **D.** The correlation is most likely due to a direct cause because increasing the number of miles of freeways made the traffic congestion worse.

ID: 8.1.12

---

*13. Consider the following statement about a correlation. State the correlation clearly (for example, there is a positive correlation between variable A and variable B). Then state whether the correlation is most likely due to coincidence, a common underlying cause, or a direct cause. Explain your answer.

When gasoline prices rise, sales of sport utility vehicles decline.

There is (1) __________ correlation between gasoline prices and sport utility vehicle sales.

Determine the possible explanation for the correlation. Choose the correct answer below.

○ **A.** This correlation is due to coincidence because there is no link between gas prices and sales of sport utility vehicles.

○ **B.** This correlation is due to a possible direct cause because sport utility vehicles require more gasoline than a smaller type of vehicle.

○ **C.** This correlation is due to a common underlying cause because sport utility vehicles require more gasoline than a smaller type of vehicle.

○ **D.** This correlation is due to a possible direct cause because there is no link between gas prices and sales of sport utility vehicles.

○ **E.** This correlation is due to a common underlying cause because the price of gas increases the purchase price of only sports utility vehicles.

○ **F.** There is no correlation because there is no link between gas prices and sales of sport utility vehicles.

(1) ○ a negative
○ a positive
○ no

ID: 8.1.13

---

14. Consider the following statement about a correlation. State the correlation clearly. Then state whether the correlation is most likely due to a coincidence, a common underlying cause, or a direct cause. Explain your answer.

Sales of ice cream increase whenever the sales of swimming suits increase.

Select the correct answer below.

- ○ **A.** There is no correlation between the number of sales of ice cream and the sales of swimming suits.
- ○ **B.** There is a positive correlation between the sales of ice cream and the sales of swimming suits.
- ○ **C.** There is a negative correlation between the sales of ice cream and the sales of swimming suits.

Is the correlation most likely due to a coincidence, a common underlying cause, or a direct cause? Explain.

- ○ **A.** The correlation is most likely due to the common underlying cause that people eat more ice cream and people do more swimming in the summer time.
- ○ **B.** The correlation is most likely due to a coincidence because ice cream sales and swimming suit sales share nothing in common.
- ○ **C.** The correlation is most likely due to a direct cause because increasing the sales ice cream increased the sales of swimming suits.
- ○ **D.** There is no correlation between the number of sales of ice cream and the sales of swimming suits.

ID: 8.1.14

---

15. Consider the following statement about a correlation. State the correlation clearly (for example, there is a positive correlation between variable A and variable B). Then state whether the correlation is most likely due to coincidence, a common underlying cause, or a direct cause. Explain your answer.

Automobile gas mileage decreases with tire pressure.

There is (1) ____________ correlation between gas mileage and tire pressure.

Determine the possible explanation for the correlation. Choose the correct answer below.

- ○ **A.** This correlation is due to a direct cause because more gasoline is needed to roll a tire with lower pressure.
- ○ **B.** This correlation is due to a direct cause because there is no link between gas mileage and tire pressure.
- ○ **C.** This correlation is due to coincidence because there is no link between gas mileage and tire pressure.
- ○ **D.** This correlation is due to a common underlying cause because as temperature decreases, both gas mileage and tire pressure decrease.
- ○ **E.** This correlation is due to a common underlying cause because more gasoline is needed to roll a tire with lower pressure.
- ○ **F.** There is no correlation because there is no link between gas mileage and tire pressure.

(1) ○ no
○ a positive
○ a negative

ID: 8.1.15

---

16. Consider the following statement about a correlation. State the correlation clearly. Then state whether the correlation is most likely due to a coincidence, a common underlying cause, or a direct cause. Explain your answer.

Over a period of twenty years, the number of ministers and priests in a city increased, as did attendance at movies.

Select the correct answer below.

- ○ **A.** There is a negative correlation between the number of ministers and priests and the attendance at movies.
- ○ **B.** There is a positive correlation between the the number of ministers and priests and the attendance at movies.
- ○ **C.** There is no correlation between the number of ministers and priests and the attendance at movies.

Is the correlation most likely due to a coincidence, a common underlying cause, or a direct cause? Explain.

- ○ **A.** There is no correlation between the number of ministers and priests and the attendance at movies.
- ○ **B.** The correlation is most likely due to a direct cause because increasing the number of ministers and priests increased the attendance at movies.
- ○ **C.** The correlation is most likely due to a coincidence because the number of ministers and priests and the attendance at movies are not related.
- ○ **D.** The correlation is most likely due to the common underlying cause that the city's entire population grew over twenty years.

ID: 8.1.16

---

*17. There is a strong correlation between tobacco smoking and incidence of lung cancer, and most physicians believe that tobacco smoking causes lung cancer. However, not everyone who smokes gets lung cancer. Briefly describe how smoking could cause cancer when not all smokers get cancer.

Select the correct answer below.

○ **A.** Smoking can cause cancer even though not all smokers get cancer because most smokers stop smoking before they get cancer.

○ **B.** Not all smokers get cancer because many people smoke tobacco products that do not cause cancer.

○ **C.** Not all smokers get cancer because smoking only makes cancer worse and many smokers did not have cancer before they started smoking.

○ **D.** Not all smokers get cancer because cancer is caused by cell mutation, and while smoking increases the chances of such a mutuation occuring, the mutation does not occure in every smoker.

ID: 8.1.17

---

18. Suppose that people living near a particular high-voltage power line have a higher incidence of cancer than people living farther from the power line. Can you conclude that the high-voltage power line is the cause of the elevated cancer rate? If not, what other explanations might there be for it? What other types of research would you like to see before you conclude that high-voltage power lines cause cancer?

Select the correct answer below.

○ **A.** You cannot conclude that the power line is the cause of the elevated cancer rate because cause cannot be established until a mechanism is confirmed.

○ **B.** You can conclude that the power line is the cause of the elevated cancer rate because elevated cancer rates are correlated with the cause even though other factors vary.

○ **C.** You can conclude that the power line is the cause of the elevated cancer rate because a correlation is enough to establish cause.

○ **D.** You cannot conclude that the power line is the cause of the elevated cancer rate because it is not known if the correlation is strong or weak.

What other types of research would you like to see before you conclude that high-voltage power lines cause cancer?

○ **A.** A study that determines the overall health of the city where the power line is located.

○ **B.** A study that determines the genetic background of the people living close to the power line.

○ **C.** A study that determines the effect of electricity on a cell's growth mechanism.

○ **D.** No further research is needed.

ID: 8.1.18

---

19. Identify at least two hidden assumptions in the following argument.

Buying a house today makes good sense. The rent money you save can be put into a long-term investment.

Which of the following are hidden assumptions for this argument? Select all that apply.

☐ **A.** A long-term investment will help pay for a house.

☐ **B.** People should make long-term investments with their money.

☐ **C.** Buying a house later does not make good sense.

☐ **D.** You will spend less out-of-pocket on your home payments than you would on rent.

ID: 8.1.19

---

20. Identify at least two hidden assumptions in the following argument.

I recommend giving to the Charity A because it supports so many worthwhile causes.

Which of the following are hidden assumptions for this argument? Select all that apply.

☐ **A.** Giving to Charity A is better than giving to Charity B.

☐ **B.** The money you give is spent on worthwhile causes.

☐ **C.** Charity A supports worthwhile causes.

☐ **D.** Charity A does not support unworthy causes.

ID: 8.1.20

---

21. Identify at least two hidden assumptions in the following argument.

The current governer has campaigned for tax cuts. He gets my vote.

Which of the following are hidden assumptions for this argument? Select all that apply.

- ☐ **A.** Tax cuts are more important than other issues.
- ☐ **B.** The governer will keep his promise on tax cuts.
- ☐ **C.** Campaigning for tax cuts is important.
- ☐ **D.** Voting for the current governer will put him in office.

ID: 8.1.21

---

*22. Identify at least two hidden assumptions in the following argument.

I support increased military spending because we need a strong country.

Which of the following are hidden assumptions for this argument? Select all that apply.

- ☐ **A.** A stronger country means a stronger military.
- ☐ **B.** More military spending will mean a better military.
- ☐ **C.** Military spending is important.
- ☐ **D.** A stronger military means a stronger country.

ID: 8.1.22

---

23. The following argument gives several reasons for a particular political position. Identify at least one unstated issue that may be the real issue of concern.

I oppose the President's spending proposal. Taxpayer money should not be used for programs that many taxpayers do not support. Excessive spending also risks increasing budget deficits. Greater deficits increase the federal debt, which in turn increases our reliance on foreign investors.

Choose the correct answer below.

- ○ **A.** The speaker may have an ideological opposition to paying taxes.
- ○ **B.** The speaker may be opposed to the government spending money.
- ○ **C.** The President's spending proposal is significantly under budget.
- ○ **D.** The speaker may want the country to depend more on foreign investors.

ID: 8.1.23

---

24. When must a single person who is claimed as a dependent by someone else file a tax return? Assuming a single person is not age 65 or older and not blind, that person must file a return if any of the following apply.

(i) unearned income was more than $900; or

(ii) earned income was more than $5450; or

(iii) gross income was more than the larger of $900 or your earned income (up to $5150) plus $300

Determine whether the following dependents (under age 65 and not blind) must file a return.

a. Maria had unearned income of $750, earned income of $5700, and gross income of $6450. Does Maria have to file a tax return?

- ○ Yes
- ○ No

b. Van had unearned income of $200, earned income of $3000, and gross income of $3500. Does Van have to file a tax return?

- ○ Yes
- ○ No

c. Walt had no unearned income and had earned and gross income of $5400. Does Walt have to file a tax return?

- ○ No
- ○ Yes

d. Helena had unearned income of $200, earned income of $5200, and gross income of $5500. Does Helena have to file a tax return?

- ○ No
- ○ Yes

ID: 8.1.24

---

25. Consider the following excerpt from the contract for the lease of an apartment.

> Landlord shall return the security deposit to resident within one month after termination of this lease or surrender and acceptance of the premises, whichever occurs first.

Suppose the lease terminates on July 31, and the resident moves out of the apartment on July 6. Answer parts **a** through **c**.

a. Has the landlord complied with the terms of the lease if the resident receives the security deposit back on July 29?

- ○ No
- ○ Yes

b. Has the landlord complied with the terms of the lease if the resident receives the security deposit back on August 3?

- ○ No
- ○ Yes

c. Has the landlord complied with the terms of the lease if the resident receives the security deposit back on August 9?

- ○ No
- ○ Yes

ID: 8.1.25

---

26. You are deciding whether to buy a car for $18,000 or to accept a lease agreement. The lease entails a $900 fee plus monthly payments of $260 for 36 months. Under the lease agreement, you are responsible for service on the car and insurance. At the end of the lease, you may purchase the car for $8000. Complete parts **a** through **c** below.

a. Should the cost of service and insurance determine which option you choose?

- ○ **A.** Yes, because you probably don't have to pay for services when you buy the car.
- ○ **B.** No, because it is cheaper to lease the car than to buy it.
- ○ **C.** No, because you will probably have to pay for service and insurance with either plan.
- ○ **D.** Yes, because you get a discount on your insurance when you lease the car.

b. Does the total cost of purchasing the car at the end of the lease agreement exceed the cost of purchasing the car at the outset?

- ○ **A.** Yes, the total cost of the car at the end of the lease is $ ________.
- ○ **B.** No, the total cost of the car at the end of the lease is $ ________

c. What are some possible advantages of leasing the car?

- ○ **A.** You can give the car back whenever you want and you can get a new car whenever you want.
- ○ **B.** You can sell the car whenever you want and you can make money on the car when you sell it.
- ○ **C.** Not all of the money is needed up front and you have years to decide if you want to buy the car.
- ○ **D.** The insurance costs less and you get a service discount.

ID: 8.1.26

---

27. You receive the following e-mail notification.

> "Through a random selection from more than 20 million e-mail addresses, you've been selected as the winner of our grand prize–a two-week vacation in the Bahamas. To claim your prize, please call our toll-free number. Have your credit card ready for identification and a small processing fee."

Does this sound like a deal worth taking? Explain.

Choose the correct answer below.

- ○ **A.** No, because a legitimate sweepstakes would not ask you to pay a processing fee in order to claim your prize. Note also that the notice never says that your vacation will be fully paid for. The notification is most likely spam.
- ○ **B.** Yes, because a two-week vacation in the Bahamas is something worth taking. There is no reason not to call the toll-free number.
- ○ **C.** Yes, because most legitimate sweepstakes ask you to pay a processing fee in order to claim your prize. There is no reason not to call the toll-free number.
- ○ **D.** No, because out of 20 million e-mail addresses it is unlikely that yours has been chosen as the winner. The notification is most likely spam.

ID: 8.1.27

✻ 28. Consider the scatterplot to the right.
a. State whether the diagram shows a positive correlation, a negative correlation, or no correlation. If there is a positive or negative correlation, is it strong or weak?
b. Summarize any conclusions that can be drawn from the diagram.

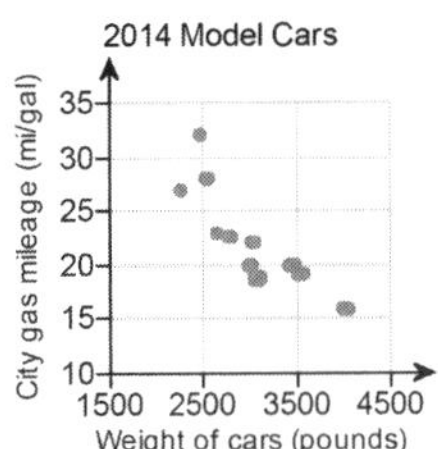

a. Select the correct answer below.

- ○ **A.** There is a weak positive correlation.
- ○ **B.** There is a strong negative correlation.
- ○ **C.** There is a weak negative correlation.
- ○ **D.** There is a strong positive correlation.
- ○ **E.** There is no correlation.

b. Select the correct answer below.

- ○ **A.** Heavier cars get the same gas mileage as lighter cars.
- ○ **B.** Heavier cars generally get lower gas mileage.
- ○ **C.** Heavier cars generally get higher gas mileage.
- ○ **D.** No conclusion can be drawn.

ID: 8.1.28

✻ 29. Consider the scatterplot to the right.
a. State whether the diagram shows a positive correlation, a negative correlation, or no correlation. If there is a positive or negative correlation, is it strong or weak?
b. Summarize any conclusions that can be drawn from the diagram.

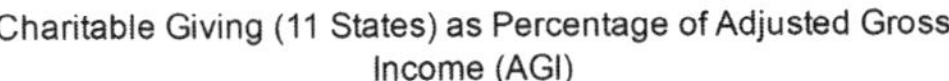

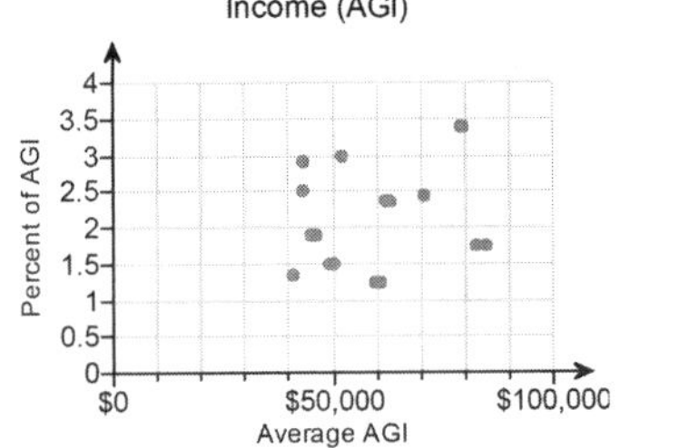

a. Select the correct answer below.

- ○ **A.** There is a weak positive correlation.
- ○ **B.** There is a strong negative correlation.
- ○ **C.** There is a weak negative correlation.
- ○ **D.** There is a strong positive correlation.
- ○ **E.** There is no correlation.

b. Select the correct answer below.

- ○ **A.** Higher AGI may imply slightly lower charitable giving as a percentage of AGI.
- ○ **B.** Higher AGI may imply slightly higher charitable giving as a percentage of AGI.
- ○ **C.** Higher AGI implies much higher charitable giving as a percentage of AGI.
- ○ **D.** No conclusion can be drawn.

ID: 8.1.29

---

30. Discuss the statement and tell what possible misuse or misinterpretation may exist.

In a study of patients with flu symptoms, each patient was found to have improved symptoms after taking vitamin C. Therefore, vitamin C cures the flu.

Discuss the statement and tell what possible misuse or misinterpretation may exist. Choose the correct answer below.

- ○ **A.** The statement is not valid because having improved symptoms does not necessarily translate to the patients being cured of the flu.
- ○ **B.** The statement is not valid because the patients may have improved on their own without taking vitamin C and having improved symptoms does not necessarily translate to the patients being cured of the flu.
- ○ **C.** The statement is valid because each patient had improved symptoms which translates to the patients being cured of the flu.
- ○ **D.** The statement is valid because the patients may have improved on their own without taking vitamin C and having improved symptoms translates to the patients being cured of the flu.

ID: 8.1.30

---

31. Discuss the statement and tell what possible misuse or misinterpretation may exist.

There are more empty spaces in the parking lot of an Italian restaurant than at a Mexican restaurant. Therefore, more people prefer Mexican food than Italian food.

Discuss the statement and tell what possible misuse or misinterpretation may exist. Choose the correct answer below.

- ○ **A.** The statement is not valid because more people may walk to the Italian restaurant than the Mexican restaurant.
- ○ **B.** The statement is not valid because the Italian restaurant might be closed on Sundays and the Mexican restaurant might be open on Sundays.
- ○ **C.** The statement is not valid because Italian food is always more popular than Mexican food.
- ○ **D.** The statement is valid because there are more empty spaces in the parking lot of the Italian restaurant than at the Mexican restaurant.

ID: 8.1.31

---

32. Discuss the statement and tell what possible misuse or misinterpretation may exist.

Suppose more accidents occur on Sunday. Therefore, people do not drive carefully on Sunday.

Discuss the statement and tell what possible misuse or misinterpretation may exist. Choose the correct answer below.

- ○ **A.** The statement is valid because more people may drive on Sunday.
- ○ **B.** The statement is valid because most accidents occur on Sunday.
- ○ **C.** The statement is not valid because more people may drive on Sunday.
- ○ **D.** The statement is not valid because most accidents occur on Sunday.

ID: 8.1.32

---

*33. Discuss the statement and tell what possible misuse or misinterpretation may exist.

Suppose ninety percent of accidents occur within 12 miles of home. Therefore, it is safer not to drive within 12 miles of home.

Discuss the statement and tell what possible misuse or misinterpretation may exist. Choose the correct answer below.

- ○ **A.** The statement is not valid because people may drive within 12 miles of home more often.
- ○ **B.** The statement is not valid because most accidents occur within 12 miles of home.
- ○ **C.** The statement is valid because people may drive within 12 miles of home more often.
- ○ **D.** The statement is valid because most accidents occur within 12 miles of home.

ID: 8.1.33

---

34. Discuss the statement and tell what possible misuse or misinterpretation may exist.

Sixty students said that they would recommend Professor Wilson to a friend. Fifty students said that they would recommend Professor Lowenthal to a friend. Therefore, Professor Wilson is a better teacher than Professor Lowenthal.

Discuss the statement and tell what possible misuse or misinterpretation may exist. Choose the correct answer below.

- ○ **A.** The statement is valid because if more students prefer a teacher it means that teacher is better and student opinion determines the quality of a professor's teaching abilities.
- ○ **B.** The statement is not valid because we don't know how many of each professor's students were surveyed and student opinion does not necessarily determine the quality of a professor's teaching abilities.
- ○ **C.** The statement is not valid because if more students prefer a teacher it means that teacher is better and student opinion does not matter to determining the quality of a professor's teaching abilities.
- ○ **D.** The statement is valid because we don't know how many of each professor's students were surveyed and student opinion determines the quality of a professor's teaching abilities.

ID: 8.1.34

---

35. Determine what possible misuse or misinterpretation may exist in the given statement.

A chocolate bar is less expensive at Dino's grocery store than at Rick's grocery store. Therefore, the quality of a chocolate bar is better at Dino's grocery store than at Rick's grocery store. Assume both chocolate bars are the same size.

Choose the answer that best applies to the given statement.

- ○ **A.** The statement is not valid because it uses vague wording.
- ○ **B.** The statement is not valid because of an unknown sample size.
- ○ **C.** The statement is not valid because important information is missing.
- ○ **D.** The statement is not valid because the conclusion does not relate to the given information.
- ○ **E.** There is no misuse of information. The statement is valid.

ID: 8.1.35

---

36. Discuss the statement and tell what possible misuse or misinterpretation may exist.
The average depth of the pond is 8 ft, so it is deep enough to dive into.

Discuss the statement and tell what possible misuse or misinterpretation may exist. Choose the correct answer below.

- ○ **A.** The statement is valid because there may be shallow sections in the pond, so it may not be deep enough to dive into.
- ○ **B.** The statement is not valid because there may be shallow sections in the pond, so it may not be deep enough to dive into.
- ○ **C.** The statement is valid because the average depth of the pond is deep enough to dive into.
- ○ **D.** The statement is not valid because the average depth of the pond is deep enough to dive into.

ID: 8.1.36

!* 37. The average attendance at baseball stadiums over a given season is correlated with the maximum capacity (maximum number of seats available). Use the data and the graph of the correlation available below to complete parts (a) through (d).
Click here to view the data.[1] Click here to view the graph.[2]

a. The best-fit line is called the "least-squares" line because it minimizes the sum of the squared vertical distances

between each data point and (1) ________

b. A stadium has a max capacity of 42,405 and an average attendance of 28,765. Compute the associated y-value for the maximum capacity using the equation of the best-fit line from the scatterplot. Use this to compute the squared distance between the average attendance and the line.

The y-value using the equation is y = ________.
(Round to the nearest whole number as needed.)

The squared distance is ________.
(Round to the nearest whole number as needed.)

c. Interpret the slope in real world terms.

(2) ________ increases by (3) ________ people per additional 100 seats of capacity.

d. Use the line of best-fit to predict the average attendance of a new stadium that seats 40,000 people.

The predicted average attendance is ________ people.
(Round to the nearest whole number as needed.)

1: Baseball Stadium Attendance Data

Capacity	Average Attendance
36,265	36,204
36,392	14,351
38,371	23,304
40,025	31,948
40,575	36,606
40,813	17,164
40,929	37,348
41,096	39,050
41,538	38,586
41,950	26,339
42,405	28,765
42,513	32,807
43,402	24,619
43,560	34,212
43,716	24,500
43,765	16,903
45,105	41,987
45,265	26,624
46,887	42,489
47,854	30,675
48,130	26,587
48,581	28,200
49,023	25,754
49,193	29,557
50,157	31,830
50,524	28,344
50,480	25,904
55,913	46,316
57,340	43,376
57,493	51,927
Capacity	**Average Attendance**

!* 37. (cont.) 2: Graph Showing the Correlation

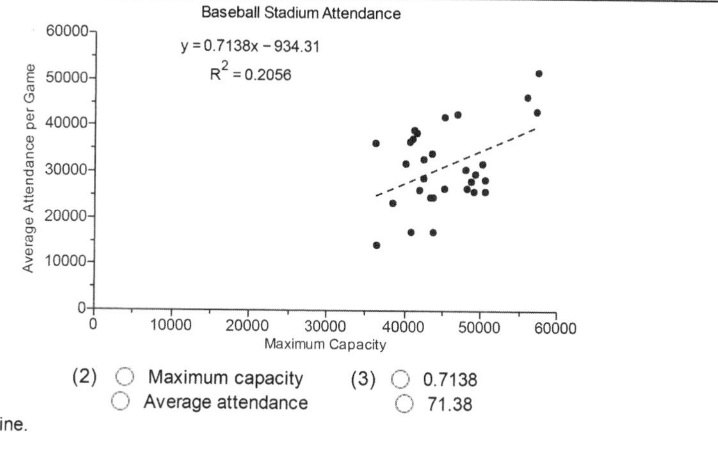

(1) ○ the y-axis.
○ the mean.
○ any linear trendline.
○ the x-axis.

(2) ○ Maximum capacity
○ Average attendance

(3) ○ 0.7138
○ 71.38

ID: 8.2.1

!* 38. The median weekly earnings is correlated with education level (years of schooling estimated). Use the data and the graph of the correlation available below to complete parts (a) through (d).
Click here to view the data.[3] Click here to view the graph.[4]

a. The best-fit line is called the "least-squares" line because it minimizes the sum of the squared vertical distances between each data point and (1) ________

b. A person with a Master's degree has 18 years of schooling and median weekly earnings of $1,336. Compute the associated y-value for their years of schooling using the equation of the best-fit line from the scatterplot. Use this to compute the squared distance between the actual median weekly earnings and the line.

The y-value using the equation is y = $ ________.
(Round to two decimal places as needed.)

The squared distance is ________.
(Round to two decimal places as needed.)

c. Interpret the slope in real world terms.

(2) ________ increases by (3) ________ per additional (4) ________

d. Use the line of best-fit to predict the median weekly earnings for a person with 11 years of schooling.

The predicted median weekly earnings is $ ________.
(Round to two decimal places as needed.)

3: Earnings and Education Data

Years Schooling	Median Weekly Earnings in 2015
22	1,630
19	1,735
18	1,336
16	1,142
14	797
13	738
12	680
8	485

4: Graph Showing the Correlation

Median Weekly Earnings in 2015

y = 99.32x − 446.73

$R^2 = 0.8977$

$2,000 $1,800 $1,600 $1,400 $1,200 $1,000 $800 $600 $400 $200 $0

0 5 10 15 20 25

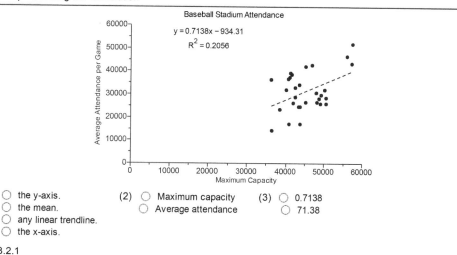

Years of Schooling

!*38. (cont.) (1) ○ the x-axis.
○ any linear trendline.
○ the y-axis.
○ the mean.

(2) ○ Median weekly earnings
○ Cost of 1 year of schooling

(3) ○ $446.73
○ $89.77
○ $99.32

(4) ○ year of schooling.
○ dollar.

ID: 8.2.2

!*39. The following two graphics below show hip fracture incidence rates (fractures per 100,000 person-years), HFI, for women aged 50 years and older in 33 countries and animal/vegetable protein consumption per capita. Use the data and the graphs of the correlations available below to complete parts (a) through (d).
Click here to view the data.[5] Click here to view the graphs.[6]

a. The best-fit line is called the "least-squares" line because it minimizes the sum of the squared vertical distances between each data point and (1) ____________

b. One country has an HFI of 119.8 and an animal protein intake of 68.4 g/day. Compute the associated y-value for their animal protein intake using the equation of the best-fit line from the scatterplot. Use this to compute the squared distance between the actual HFI and the line.

The y-value using the equation is y = ____________.
(Round to one decimal place as needed.)

The squared distance is ____________.
(Round to one decimal place as needed.)

c. Interpret the slope of the HFI versus animal protein intake in real world terms.

(2) ____________ increase(s) by (3) ____________ (4) ____________ per additional (5) ____________

d. Use the line of best-fit to predict the hip fracture incidence rate for a country with an average animal protein intake of 50 g/day.

The predicted rate is ____________ per 100,000 person-years.
(Round to one decimal place as needed.)

5: Hip Fracture Incidence Data

HFI per 100,000 Person-Years	Animal Protein (AP) Intake (g/day)	Vegetable Protein (VP) Intake (g/day)
1.1	6.8	38.5
3.5	11.7	49.3
2.7	17.4	29.4
4.9	16.3	33.4
8.3	27.2	46.6
11.9	16.2	67.7
23.4	26.4	29.1
26.6	25.4	33.8
33.1	24.3	66.4
45.3	35.8	50.9
57.4	23.1	43.7
55.9	51.9	53.1
59.7	53.4	33.2
63.4	51.5	42.2
66.5	45.9	42.3
69.5	43.8	35.9
75.5	41.1	51.4
76.9	59.8	42.2
77.2	74.9	35.3
93.9	53.8	35.2
108.5	59.3	33.5
112.1	52.3	56.9
116.3	55.1	36.7
121.2	39.6	49.3
119.8	68.4	31.6
126.5	65.6	31.6
128.4	61.9	35.8
140.7	69.4	35.7
147.2	67.5	35.2
167.1	57.5	28.9
171.3	59.9	29.8
185.4	57.3	33.9
198.1	63.8	34.5
HFI per 100,000 Person-Years	Animal Protein (AP) Intake (g/day)	Vegetable Protein (VP) Intake (g/day)

!* 39. (cont.) 6: Graphs Showing the Correlations

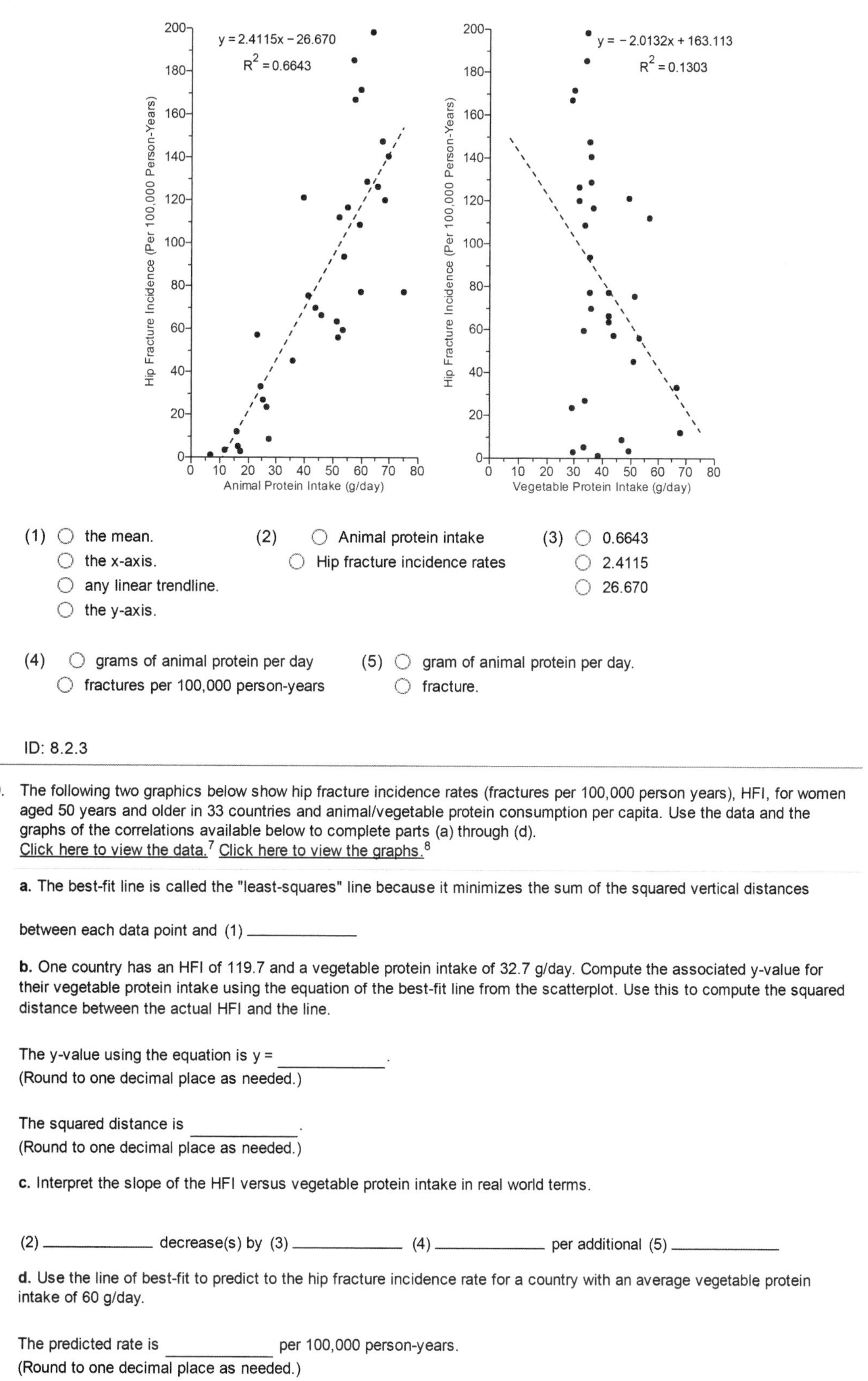

(1)
- ○ the mean.
- ○ the x-axis.
- ○ any linear trendline.
- ○ the y-axis.

(2)
- ○ Animal protein intake
- ○ Hip fracture incidence rates

(3)
- ○ 0.6643
- ○ 2.4115
- ○ 26.670

(4)
- ○ grams of animal protein per day
- ○ fractures per 100,000 person-years

(5)
- ○ gram of animal protein per day.
- ○ fracture.

ID: 8.2.3

!* 40. The following two graphics below show hip fracture incidence rates (fractures per 100,000 person years), HFI, for women aged 50 years and older in 33 countries and animal/vegetable protein consumption per capita. Use the data and the graphs of the correlations available below to complete parts (a) through (d).
Click here to view the data.[7] Click here to view the graphs.[8]

a. The best-fit line is called the "least-squares" line because it minimizes the sum of the squared vertical distances between each data point and (1) ____________

b. One country has an HFI of 119.7 and a vegetable protein intake of 32.7 g/day. Compute the associated y-value for their vegetable protein intake using the equation of the best-fit line from the scatterplot. Use this to compute the squared distance between the actual HFI and the line.

The y-value using the equation is y = ____________.
(Round to one decimal place as needed.)

The squared distance is ____________.
(Round to one decimal place as needed.)

c. Interpret the slope of the HFI versus vegetable protein intake in real world terms.

(2) ____________ decrease(s) by (3) ____________ (4) ____________ per additional (5) ____________

d. Use the line of best-fit to predict to the hip fracture incidence rate for a country with an average vegetable protein intake of 60 g/day.

The predicted rate is ____________ per 100,000 person-years.
(Round to one decimal place as needed.)

!* 40. (cont.)

7: Hip Fracture Incidence Data

HFI per 100,000 Person-Years	Animal Protein (AP) Intake (g/day)	Vegetable Protein (VP) Intake (g/day)
2.7	8.8	38.6
1.2	11.4	51.8
4.9	15.6	27.8
6.9	16.6	34.2
6.8	27.8	43.9
12.2	17.5	67.1
20.3	25.1	28.5
25.2	22.9	31.7
31.7	24.6	66.3
46.1	35.9	47.5
56.7	25.6	43.7
56.3	52.5	53.9
61.6	51.6	31.8
66.7	50.7	45.1
68.6	45.1	43.4
68.4	44.8	36.8
76.8	38.9	49.6
74.5	61.1	43.3
76.4	72.6	38.1
93.5	55.2	38.2
111.5	59.7	34.7
111.7	51.9	57.2
115.7	53.1	35.7
118.2	40.9	50.9
119.7	70.2	34.6
125.6	66.1	34.6
128.2	60.6	34.1
138.8	68.8	34.7
147.8	67.4	36.4
166.1	57.2	31.3
170.9	61.3	27.9
188.5	60.5	34.8
197.8	61.2	35.2
HFI per 100,000 Person-Years	Animal Protein (AP) Intake (g/day)	Vegetable Protein (VP) Intake (g/day)

8: Graphs Showing the Correlations

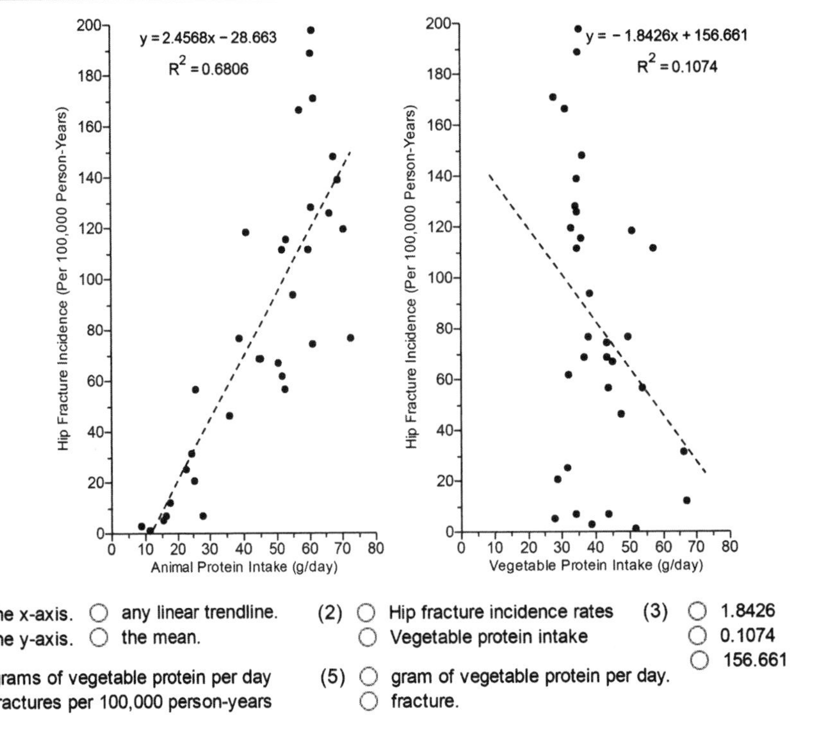

(1) ○ the x-axis. ○ any linear trendline.
○ the y-axis. ○ the mean.

(2) ○ Hip fracture incidence rates
○ Vegetable protein intake

(3) ○ 1.8426
○ 0.1074
○ 156.661

(4) ○ grams of vegetable protein per day
○ fractures per 100,000 person-years

(5) ○ gram of vegetable protein per day.
○ fracture.

ID: 8.2.4

!* 41. The scatterplot shows the CO_2 emissions (millions metric tons) for 30 countries around the world in 2008 and 2012. Use the data and the graph of the correlation available below to complete parts (a) through (d).
Click here to view the data.[9] Click here to view the graph.[10]

a. The best-fit line is called the "least-squares" line because it minimizes the sum of the squared vertical distances between each data point and (1) ____________

b. One country emitted 5,839.1 million metric tons of CO_2 in 2008 and 5,268.8 in 2012. Compute the associated y-value for their 2008 emissions using the equation of the best-fit line from the scatterplot. Use this to compute the squared distance between the actual 2012 emissions and the line.

The y-value using the equation is y = ____________.
(Round to one decimal place as needed.)

The squared distance is ____________.
(Round to one decimal place as needed.)

c. Interpret the slope in real world terms.

Emissions of CO_2 in (2) ____________ increased by (3) ____________ million metric tons per additional (4) ____________ in (5) ____________

d. Use the line of best-fit to predict the CO_2 emissions in 2012 for a country emitting 500 million metric tons in 2008.

The predicted emissions are ____________ million metric tons.
(Round to one decimal place as needed.)

9: Emissions Data

2008	2012
9.4	13.3
28.4	31.1
2.1	1.7
4.5	3.5
428.3	501.8
51.7	48.3
5.2	8.4
9.2	9.1
18.4	20.5
5.2	9.5
5.1	3.6
3.8	2.4
6.8	11.2
1,449.1	1,829.3
104.8	129.5
522.9	655.4
7.9	8.8
11.3	12.2
0.9	3.9
7.5	10.6
4.1	6.1
45.5	63.7
2.1	3.5
295.1	289.9
4.1	4.3
1,630.6	1,781.9
355.1	313.2
55.6	51.8
61.1	65.9
5,839.1	5,268.8
2008	**2012**

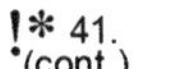
41. (cont.) 10: Graph Showing the Correlation

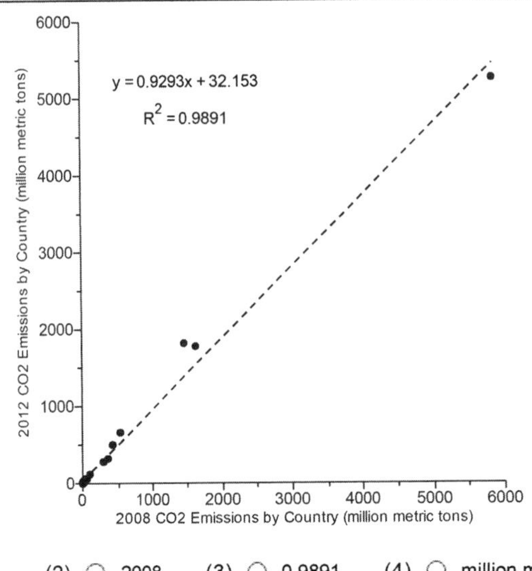

(1) ○ the y-axis.
○ any linear trendline.
○ the mean.
○ the x-axis.

(2) ○ 2008
○ 2012

(3) ○ 0.9891
○ 32.153
○ 0.9293

(4) ○ million metric tons
○ metric ton

(5) ○ 2008.
○ 2012.

ID: 8.2.5

!* 42. You correlate data on average number of emergency room visits per month and percentage of ER patient deaths per month at hospitals around the country.

(a) The coefficient of linear determination is 0.76. Use this statistic in a meaningful sentence.
(b) Compute the associated correlation coefficient.

(a) (1) ________ of the variability in (2) ________ can be attributed to variability in (3) ________

(b) Compute the associated correlation coefficient.

________ (Round to two decimal places as needed.)

(1) ○ 0.76%
○ 76%

(2) ○ the percentage of ER patient deaths
○ the average number of emergency room visits

(3) ○ the percentage of ER patient deaths.
○ average number of emergency room visits.

ID: 8.3.1

* 43. The table to the right gives the per capita gross national product and the per capita expenditure on defense for eight developed countries. Gross domestic product (GDP) is a measure of the total economic output of a country in monetary terms. Per capita GDP is the GDP averaged over every person in the country. Complete parts a though c.

Country	Per Capita GDP ($)	Per Capita Defense ($)
A	36,671	930
B	33,470	812
C	34,321	524
D	35,059	1344
E	33,618	344
F	47,136	1238
G	35,121	1024
H	45,719	1736

a. Make a scatter diagram for the data.

○ **A.**

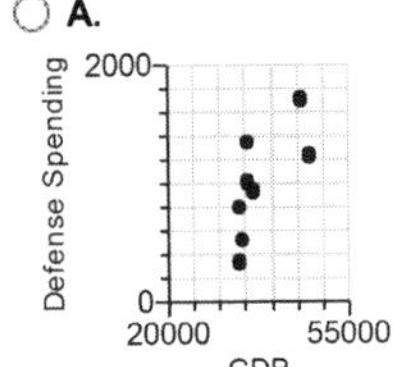

○ **B.**

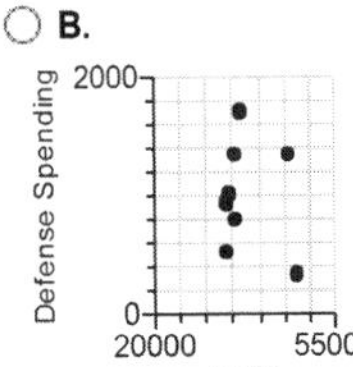

○ **C.**

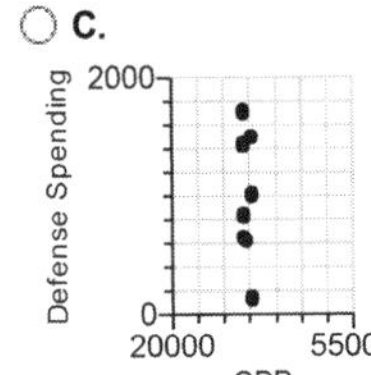

○ **D.**

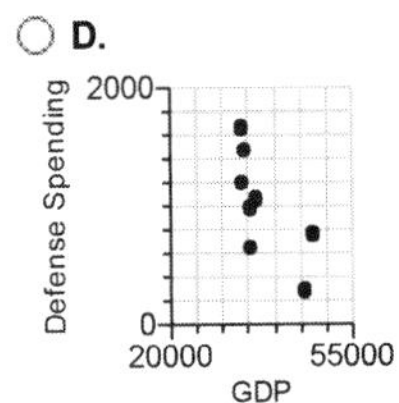

***43. (cont.)** b. State whether the two variables appear to be correlated, and if so, state whether the correlation is positive, negative, strong, or weak.

- ○ **A.** The two variables appear to be correlated and the correlation is strong and positive.
- ○ **B.** The two variables appear to be correlated and the correlation is weak and positive.
- ○ **C.** The two variables appear to be correlated and the correlation is strong and negative.
- ○ **D.** The two variables appear to be correlated and the correlation is weak and negative.
- ○ **E.** The two variables do not appear to be correlated.

c. Suggest a reason for the correlation or lack of correlation.

- ○ **A.** The higher a country's per capita GDP, the less it can spend on per capita national defense.
- ○ **B.** The higher a country's per capita GDP, the more it can spend on per capita national defense.
- ○ **C.** There is no correlation between a country's per capita GDP and spending on per capita national defense.

ID: 8.3.2

***44.** The following table gives per capita personal income and percent of the population below the poverty level for ten states. Complete parts a though c.

State	Per Capita Income ($)	Percent Below Poverty Level
A	43,790	16.3
B	44,154	12.5
C	43,717	14.1
D	41,537	10.5
E	44,269	10.5
F	36,746	14.5
F	36,165	16.2
H	45,755	6.3
I	33,482	10.3
J	33,810	16.7

a. Make a scatter diagram for the data.

○ **A.**

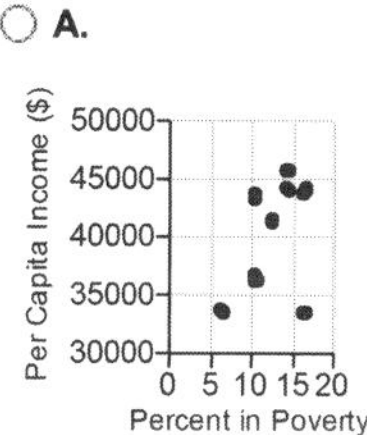

○ **B.**

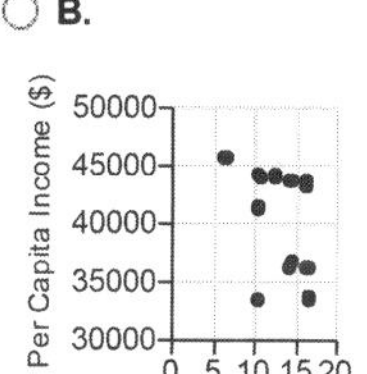

○ **C.**

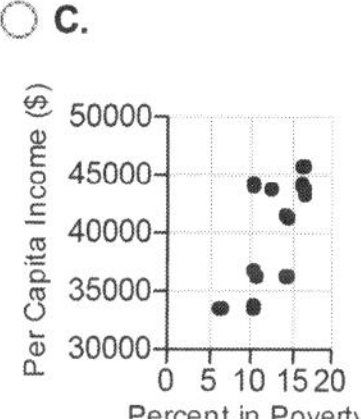

○ **D.**

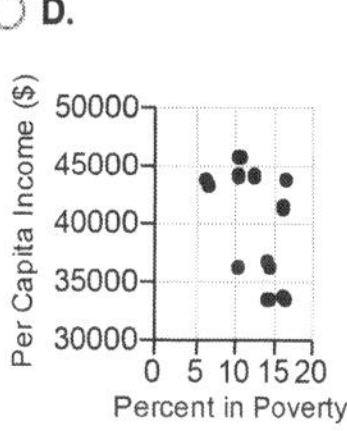

b. State whether the two variables appear to be correlated, and if so, state whether the correlation is positive, negative, strong, or weak.

- ○ **A.** The two variables appear to have weak negative correlation.
- ○ **B.** The two variables appear to have strong positive correlation.
- ○ **C.** The two variables appear to have strong negative correlation.
- ○ **D.** The two variables appear to have weak positive correlation.
- ○ **E.** The two variables do not appear to be correlated.

c. Suggest a reason for the correlation or lack of correlation.

- ○ **A.** Per capita personal income reflects the general income of the people in the state, so a higher per capita personal income implies there are more people living under the poverty line.
- ○ **B.** States with a higher per capita personal income are more likely to have welfare programs meant to reduce the number of people living in poverty.
- ○ **C.** Per capita personal income reflects the general income of the people in the state, so a higher per capita personal income implies there are fewer people living under the poverty line.
- ○ **D.** Since per capita income is an average, it would be affected by extremely high or low income values. This might make it a poor variable to pair with percent below the poverty line.

ID: 8.3.3

---

*45. The following table gives the average teacher salary and the expenditure on public education per pupil for ten places. Complete parts a though c.

State	Teacher Salary ($)	Per-Pupil Expenditure ($)
A	47,901	9031
B	59,438	11,135
C	46,529	6104
D	64,387	14,495
E	69,177	14,745
F	42,071	8558
G	55,083	10,440
H	48,168	9251
I	45,313	6844
J	55,401	15,373

a. Make a scatter diagram for the data.

○ A.

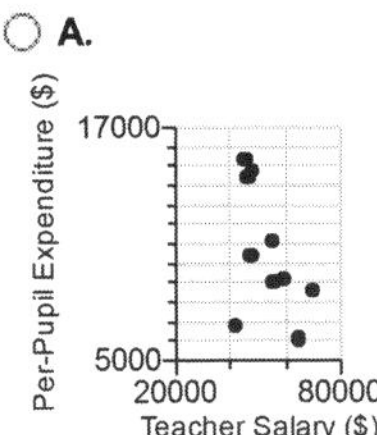

○ B.

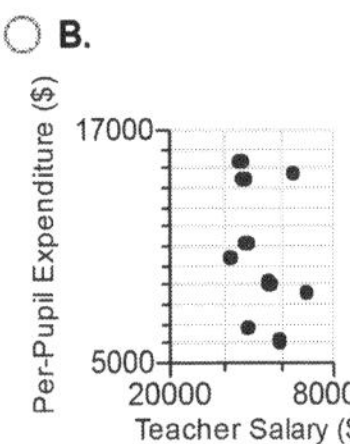

○ C.

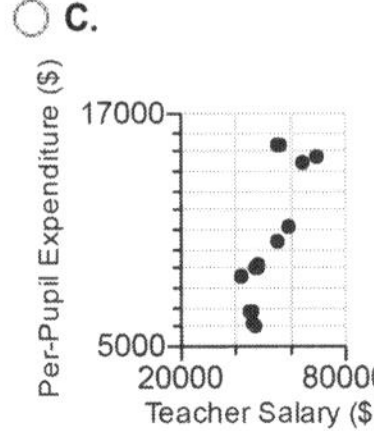

○ D.

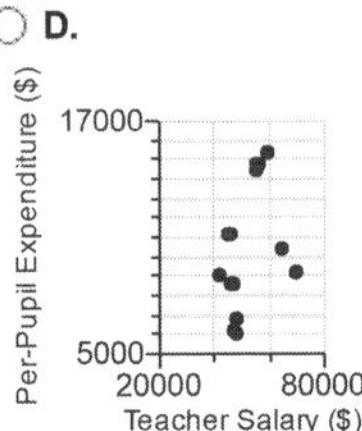

b. State whether the two variables appear to be correlated, and if so, state whether the correlation is positive, negative, strong, or weak.

○ **A.** The two variables appear to have strong negative correlation.
○ **B.** The two variables appear to have strong positive correlation.
○ **C.** The two variables appear to have weak positive correlation.
○ **D.** The two variables appear to have weak negative correlation.
○ **E.** The two variables do not appear to be correlated.

c. Suggest a reason for the correlation or lack of correlation.

○ **A.** States more focused on education are more likely to pay teachers more and spend more per-pupil.
○ **B.** States more focused on education are likely to pay teachers more and less likely to spend more per-pupil.
○ **C.** States more focused on education are less likely to pay teachers more and more likely to spend more per-pupil.
○ **D.** Teacher salary and per-pupil expenditure are not related.

ID: 8.3.4

---

*46. Fill in the blank with an appropriate word, phrase, or symbol.

A unitless measure that describes the strength of the linear relationship between two variables is called the linear correlation ________.

A unitless measure that describes the strength of the linear relationship between two variables is called the linear correlation (1) ________

(1) ○ number.
○ value.
○ variable.
○ coefficient.

ID: 8.3.5

---

*47. Fill in the blank with an appropriate word, phrase, or symbol.

The value of r, the linear correlation coefficient, that represents the strongest positive correlation is ____.

The value of r, the linear correlation coefficient, that represents the strongest positive correlation is (1) ________

(1) ○ 1.
○ − 1.
○ 0.

ID: 8.3.6

*48. Fill in the blank with an appropriate word, phrase, or symbol(s).

The value of r, the linear correlation coefficient, that represents no correlation between two variables is _____.

The value of r, the linear correlation coefficient, that represents no correlation between two variables is

(1) ____________

(1) ○ 0.
○ 1.
○ − 1.

ID: 8.3.7

---

*49. Fill in the blank with an appropriate word, phrase, or symbol.

If one quantity increases as the other quantity decreases, the two variables are said to have a ________ correlation.

If one quantity increases as the other quantity decreases, the two variables are said to have a

(1) ____________ correlation.

(1) ○ negative
○ positive

ID: 8.3.8

---

*50. Fill in the blank with an appropriate word, phrase, or symbol.

The line such that the sum of the squares of the vertical distances between the data points in the scatter diagram and the line is a minimum is called the line of best __________.

The line such that the sum of the squares of the vertical distances between the data points in the scatter diagram and the line is a minimum is called the line of best (1) ____________

(1) ○ fit.
○ correlation.
○ regression.
○ squares.

ID: 8.3.9

---

*51. How do you interpret a coefficient of determination, r^2, equal to 0.14?

Choose the correct answer below.

○ **A.** The interpretation is that 0.14% of the variation in the independent variable can be explained by the variation in the dependent variable.
○ **B.** The interpretation is that 0.86% of the variation in the dependent variable can be explained by the variation in the independent variable.
○ **C.** The interpretation is that 14% of the variation in the dependent variable can be explained by the variation in the independent variable.
○ **D.** The interpretation is that 86% of the variation in the independent variable can be explained by the variation in the dependent variable.

ID: 8.3.10

---

*52. If SSR = 120, why is it impossible for SST to equal 110?

Choose the correct answer below.

○ **A.** It is impossible because SST = SSR + SSE and a sum of squares cannot be negative.
○ **B.** It is impossible because SST cannot be less than − 100 or greater than 100.
○ **C.** It is impossible because SST = 2(SSR).
○ **D.** It is impossible because SSE = SSR + SST and a sum of squares cannot be negative.

ID: 8.3.11

!* 53. The table gives hypothetical data on the number of a certain store per 100,000 people in various regions of the country and the associated obesity rates for those regions. Complete parts (a) and (b) below.

	A	B
1	Stores per 100,000 people	Obesity Rates (%)
2	2	12
3	3.2	15
4	4	10
5	7	15
6	2.3	6.3
7	3.7	2.3

(a) Use the appropriate functions in Excel (AVERAGE, STDEV.S, COVARIANCE.S, and CORREL) to compute the statistics for the bivariate data listed in the table below.

	D	E	F
1		**Stores**	**Obesity**
2	**Mean**	____	____
3	**StDev**	____	____
4	**Covar.S**	____	
5	**Correl**	____	

(Type integers or decimals rounded to the nearest thousandth as needed.)

(b) Dividing the covariance by the product of the standard deviations gives what value?

Dividing the covariance by the product of the standard deviations gives a value of ________.
(Type an integer or decimal rounded to the nearest thousandth as needed.)

ID: 8.4.1

!* 54. The table gives hypothetical data on the final exam grade and course grade. Answer parts (a) through (c) below.
[11] Click the icon to view the table.

(a) Use the appropriate functions in Excel (AVERAGE, STDEV.S, COVARIANCE.S, and CORREL) to compute the statistics for the bivariate data listed in the table below.

	D	E	F
1		**Final**	**Course**
2	**Mean**	____	____
3	**StDev**	____	____
4	**Covar.S**	____	
5	**Correl**	____	

(Type integers or decimals rounded to the nearest thousandth as needed.)

(b) Dividing the covariance by the product of the standard deviations dives what value?

Dividing the covariance by the product of the standard deviations gives a value of ________.
(Type an integer or decimal rounded to the nearest thousandth as needed.)

(c) What percentage of the variability in course grades can be attributed to variability in the final exam grades?

________%
(Type an integer or decimal rounded to the nearest tenth as needed.)

11: Data Table

	A	B
1	Final Exam	Course Grade
2	73	78
3	52	64
4	93	94
5	54	57
6	81	76
7	98	77
8	93	92
9	26	49
10	72	72
11	78	79
12	32	36
13	62	52
14	23	49
15	89	91
16	51	64
17	89	91

ID: 8.4.2

55. The following is a set of data from a sample of n = 11 items. Complete parts (a) through (c).

X	60	36	57	60	12	21	24	42	51	54	27
Y	20	12	19	20	4	7	8	14	17	18	9

a. Compute the sample covariance.

________ (Round to three decimal places as needed.)

b. Compute the coefficient of correlation.

____

(Do not round until the final answer. Then round to three decimal places as needed.)

c. How strong is the relationship between X and Y? Explain.

○ **A.** X and Y have a perfect positive correlation because all points fall on a straight line with a positive slope.

○ **B.** X and Y have a strong positive correlation because as X increases, Y tends to increase also.

○ **C.** X and Y have no correlation.

○ **D.** X and Y have a perfect negative correlation because all points fall on a straight line with a negative slope.

ID: 8.4.3

---

56. A study of 218 students at a major state university suggests a link between time spent on social networking websites and grade point average. Students who rarely or never used social networking websites had higher grade point averages than students who use social networking websites.

Does the study suggest that time spent on social networking websites and grade point average are positively correlated or negatively correlated?

○ **A.** The study suggests a positive correlation because the study shows that as time spent on social networking websites increases, grade point average tends to decrease.

○ **B.** The study suggests a negative correlation because the study shows that as time spent on social networking websites decreases, grade point average tends to decrease.

○ **C.** The study suggests a negative correlation because the study shows that as time spent on social networking websites increases, grade point average tends to decrease.

○ **D.** The study suggests a positive correlation because the study shows that as time spent on social networking websites decreases, grade point average tends to increase.

Do you think that there might be a cause-and-effect relationship between time spent on social networking websites and grade point average?

○ **A.** It is not possible that there is a cause-and-effect relationship.

○ **B.** While it is possible that there is a cause-and-effect relationship, it is not necessarily the case.

○ **C.** The study shows that there is a cause-and-effect relationship.

ID: 8.4.4

---

*57. The following data represent the calories and fat, in grams, of various 16-ounce iced coffee drinks.

Product	Calories	Fat
A	220	7.3
B	230	4.1
C	240	18.1
D	260	16.9
E	420	17.0
F	520	20.4
G	540	22.4

Use the data above to complete parts (a) through (d).

a. Compute the covariance.

____

(Round to three decimal places as needed.)

b. Compute the coefficient of correlation.

____

(Round to three decimal places as needed.)

c. Which do you think is more valuable in expressing the relationship between calories and fat—the covariance or the coefficient of correlation? Explain.

○ **A.** The covariance is more valuable. It is an exact measure of the strength of a linear relationship.

○ **B.** The correlation is more valuable. It is the better measure for positive relationships.

○ **C.** The covariance is more valuable. It is not susceptible to the negative effects of lurking variables.

○ **D.** The correlation is more valuable. It can be used to determine the relative strength of a linear relationship.

d. What conclusions can you reach about the relationship between calories and fat?

○ **A.** The correlation shows a nearly perfect positive relationship.

○ **B.** The correlation indicates a moderate positive relationship. As calories increase, fat tends to increase.

○ **C.** The covariance shows a very strong negative relationship. If calories increase, fat will decrease.

○ **D.** The covariance indicates a large variance in both calories and fat.

ID: 8.4.5

* 58. Movie companies need to predict the gross receipts of individual movies after a movie has debuted. The accompanying results are the first weekend gross, the national gross, and the worldwide gross (in millions of dollars) of six movies. Complete parts (a) through (d) below.

[12] Click the icon to view the gross receipts of the six movies.

a. Compute the covariance between first weekend gross and national gross, first weekend gross and worldwide gross, and national gross and worldwide gross.

Find the covariance between first weekend gross and national gross.

___________ (Round to four decimal places as needed.)

Find the covariance between first weekend gross and worldwide gross.

___________ (Round to four decimal places as needed.)

Find the covariance between national gross and worldwide gross.

___________ (Round to four decimal places as needed.)

b. Compute the coefficient of correlation between first weekend gross and national gross, first weekend gross and worldwide gross, and national gross and worldwide gross.

Find the coefficient of correlation between first weekend gross and national gross.

___________ (Round to three decimal places as needed.)

Find the coefficient of correlation between first weekend gross and worldwide gross.

___________ (Round to three decimal places as needed.)

Find the coefficient of correlation between national gross and worldwide gross.

___________ (Round to three decimal places as needed.)

c. Which is more valuable in expressing the relationship between first weekend gross, national gross, and wordwide gross, the covariance or the coefficient of correlation? Explain.

○ **A.** The coefficient of correlation, because it measures the relative strength of a linear relationship between each pair of variables.

○ **B.** The coefficient of correlation, because it can prove that there is a causation effect between each pair of variables.

○ **C.** The covariance, because it reflects the differences between each pair of variables.

○ **D.** The covariance, because it measures the relative strength of a linear relationship between each pair of variables.

d. Based on (a) and (b), what conclusions can be reached about the relationship between first weekend gross, national gross, and worldwide gross?

○ **A.** There is a weak negative linear relationship between first weekend gross and both national gross and worldwide gross. There is a strong positive linear relationship between national gross and worldwide gross.

○ **B.** There is a weak positive linear relationship between first weekend gross and national gross. There is no relationship between first weekend gross and worldwide gross. There is a strong positive linear relationship between national gross and worldwide gross.

○ **C.** There is a strong negative linear relationship between first weekend gross and both national gross and worldwide gross. There is a strong positive linear relationship between national gross and worldwide gross.

○ **D.** There is a weak positive linear relationship between first weekend gross and both national gross and worldwide gross. There is a strong negative linear relationship between national gross and worldwide gross.

12: Gross receipts of six movies

Title	First Weekend	National Gross	Worldwide Gross
Movie A	90.255	317.438	976.513
Movie B	88.152	261.487	878.416
Movie C	93.096	249.113	795.546
Movie D	102.021	290.372	896.311
Movie E	77.174	292.563	938.491
Movie F	77.548	301.339	934.816

ID: 8.4.6

59. The following data contains coaches' salaries and team revenues (in millions of dollars) for ten college basketball teams. Use these data to complete parts (a) through (c).

Salary	1.2	1.5	0.8	1.6	0.3	1.1	0.4	1.4	0.5	1.7
Revenue	7.4	10.7	5.7	11.5	1.7	6.7	2.8	11.0	3.3	12.8

a. Compute the covariance.

__________ (Round to three decimal places as needed.)

b. Compute the coefficient of correlation.

__________ (Round to three decimal places as needed.)

c. What conclusions can you reach about the relationship between a coach's salary and revenue?

○ **A.** There is a slight relationship between a coach's salary and revenue. Increases in a coach's salary cause increases in revenue.

○ **B.** There is a strong positive relationship between a coach's salary and revenue. As a coach's salary increases, revenue always increases.

○ **C.** There is no relationship between a coach's salary and revenue.

○ **D.** There is a strong positive relationship between a coach's salary and revenue. As a coach's salary increases, revenue tends to increase.

ID: 8.4.7

60. College football players trying out for a semi-professional league are given a standardized intelligence test. The data below contains the average score on this exam and the graduation rate for football players at 10 different schools. Use these data to complete parts (a) through (c).

Test Score	27.6	27.3	25.4	25.4	24.2	23.9	20.4	19.5	16.4	16.1
Graduation %	43.1	63.1	51.2	47.5	76.3	32.1	40.9	57.5	57.1	37.9

a. Compute the covariance.

__________ (Round to three decimal places as needed.)

b. Compute the coefficient of correlation.

__________ (Round to three decimal places as needed.)

c. What conclusions can you reach about the relationship between test scores and graduation rate?

○ **A.** There is a weak linear relationship between the variables. Correlations this low can be caused by random variations.

○ **B.** The covariance is too small to draw any significant conclusions.

○ **C.** There is a weak relationship between test scores and graduation rates. Increases in scores cause relatively small increases in graduation rates.

○ **D.** There is no relationship between the variables.

ID: 8.4.8

!* 61. The scatterplot gives hypothetical data on final exam grades and course grades.
(a) Use the statistics for the bivariate data listed in the table below to compute the equation of the line of best fit. Use the equation

$$y = \overline{Y} + R \cdot \frac{SD_Y}{SD_X} \cdot (x - \overline{X}).$$

(b) What is the z-score of a student's final exam grade of 83?
(c) What is the z-score of the associated course grade for the student who got an 83 on the final exam?

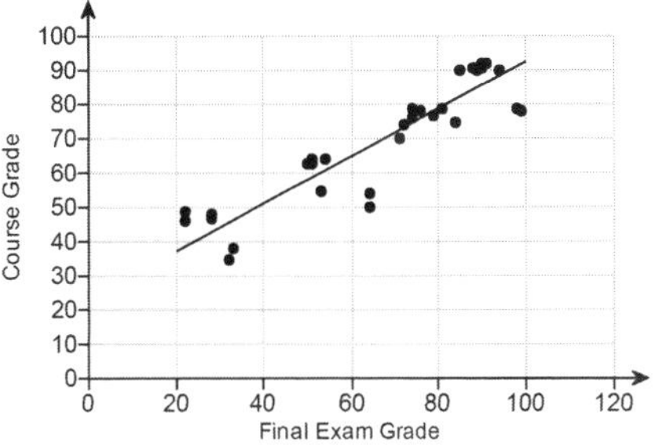

(a) Compute the equation of the line of best fit.

y = __________ x + __________
(Type integers or decimals rounded to four decimal places as needed.)

	D	E	F
1		**Final**	**Course**
2	**Mean**	66.125	69.125
3	**StDev**	24.025	18.406
4	**Covar.S**	399.183	
5	**Correl**	0.903	

(b) The z-score is __________.
(Type an integer or decimal rounded to the nearest thousandth as needed.)

(c) The z-score of the associated course grade for the student who got an 83 on the final exam is __________.
(Type an integer or decimal rounded to the nearest thousandth as needed.)

ID: 8.4.9

!* 62. The scatterplot gives hypothetical data on the number of a certain store per 100,000 people in various regions of the country and the associated obesity rates for those regions.
(a) Use the statistics for the bivariate data listed in the table below to compute the equation of the line of best fit. Use the equation

$$y = \bar{Y} + R \cdot \frac{SD_Y}{SD_X} \cdot (x - \bar{X}).$$

(b) What is the z-score of a region with 1 of these stores?
(c) What is the z-score of the associated obesity rate for a region with 1 of these stores?

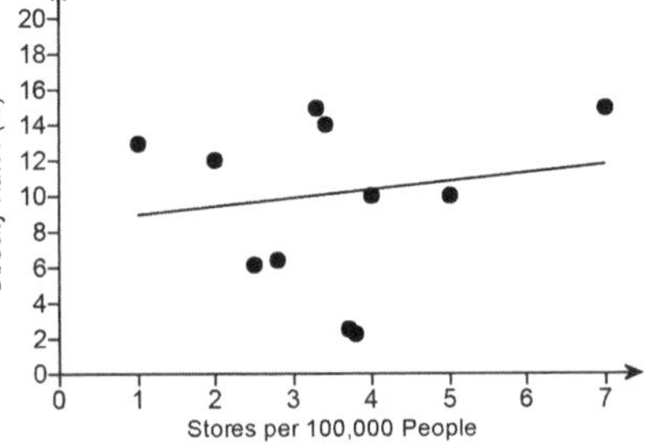

(a) Compute the equation of the line of best fit.

y = ___________ x + ___________
(Type integers or decimals rounded to four decimal places as needed.)

	D	E	F
1		**Stores**	**Obesity**
2	**Mean**	3.767	10.250
3	**StDev**	2.071	5.145
4	**Covar.S**	2.018	
5	**Correl**	0.189	

(b) The z-score is ___________.
(Type an integer or decimal rounded to the nearest thousandth as needed.)

(c) The z-score of the associated obesity rate for a region with 1 of these stores is ___________.
(Type an integer or decimal rounded to the nearest thousandth as needed.)

ID: 8.4.10

!* 63. The scatterplot gives the median weekly earnings in 2015 with years of schooling.
(a) Use the statistics for the bivariate data listed in the table below to compute the equation of the line of best fit. Use the equation $y = \bar{Y} + R \cdot \frac{SD_Y}{SD_X} \cdot (x - \bar{X})$.
(b) What is the z-score of a person with 13 years of schooling?
(c) What is the z-score of the associated median weekly earnings of a person with 13 years of schooling?

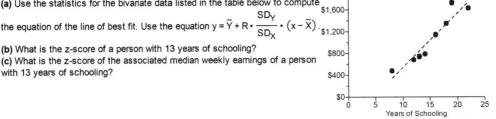

Median Weekly Earnings in 2015

$2,000 $1,600 $1,200 $800 $400 $0

0 5 10 15 20 25

Years of Schooling

(a) Use the statistics for the bivariate data listed in the table below to compute the equation of the line of best fit.

y = ___________ x + (___________)
(Round to three decimal places as needed.)

	D	E	F
1		**Schooling**	**Earnings**
2	**Mean**	15.250	1065.500
3	**StDev**	4.432	465.137
4	**Covar.S**	1954.714	
5	**Correl**	0.948	

(b) The z-score is ___________.
(Round to three decimal places as needed.)

(c) The z-score of the associated median weekly earnings of a person with 13 years of schooling is ___________.
(Round to three decimal places as needed.)

ID: 8.4.11

!* 64. The following scatterplots show hip fracture incidence (HFI) rates (fractures per 100,000 person-years) for women aged 50 years and older in 33 countries and animal/vegetable protein consumption per capita. Answer parts (a) through (c).[13] Click the icon to view the scatterplots.

	Animal Protein	**HFI**
Mean	45.091	81.485
StDev	20.212	57.040
Covar.S	901.517	
Correl	0.782	

a. Use the statistics for the bivariate data on listed in the table in the problem statement to compute the equation of the line of best fit, y = __ • x + __. Use the equation $y = \bar{Y} + R \cdot \frac{SD_Y}{SD_X} \cdot (x - \bar{X})$.

y = ___________ • x + (___________)
(Round to the nearest thousandth as needed.)

b. What is the z-score of a country with an animal protein intake of 22 g/day?

___________ (Round to the nearest thousandth as needed.)

!* 64. (cont.) **c.** What is the z-score of the associated hip fracture incidence rate for a country with an animal protein intake of 22 g/day? ________ (Round to the nearest thousandth as needed.)

13: Hip fracture rates per animal/vegetable protein intake

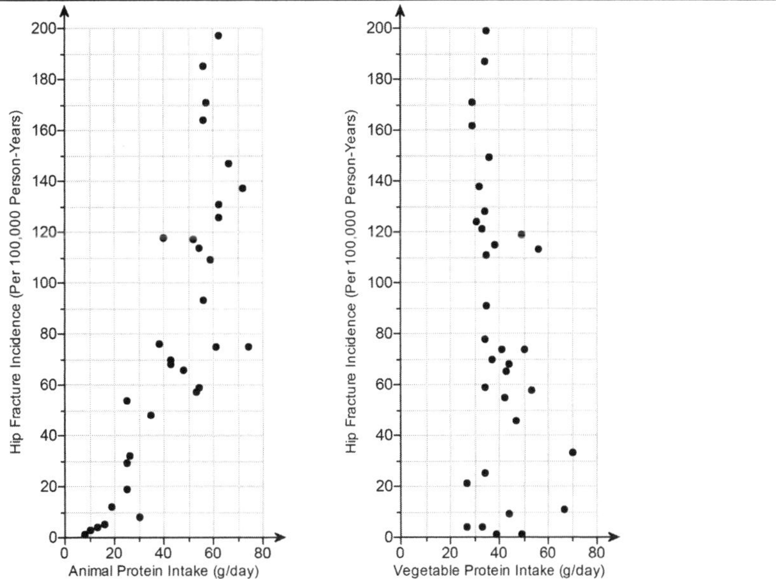

ID: 8.4.12

!* 65. The following scatterplots show hip fracture incidence (HFI) rates (fractures per 100,000 person-years) for women aged 50 years and older in 33 countries and animal/vegetable protein consumption per capita. Answer parts (a) through (c).
[14] Click the icon to view the scatterplots.

	Vegetable Protein	HFI
Mean	40.030	81.515
StDev	10.406	57.367
Covar.S	− 201.141	
Correl	− 0.337	

a. Use the statistics for the bivariate data on listed in the table in the problem statement to compute the equation of the line of best fit, y = __ • x + __. Use the equation $y = \bar{Y} + R \cdot \frac{SD_Y}{SD_X} \cdot (x - \bar{X})$.

y = ________ • x + (________)
(Round to the nearest thousandth as needed.)

b. What is the z-score of a country with a vegetable protein intake of 52 g/day?

________ (Round to the nearest thousandth as needed.)

c. What is the z-score of the associated hip fracture incidence rate for a country with a vegetable protein intake of 52 g/day?

________ (Round to the nearest thousandth as needed.)

14: Hip fracture rates per animal/vegetable protein intake

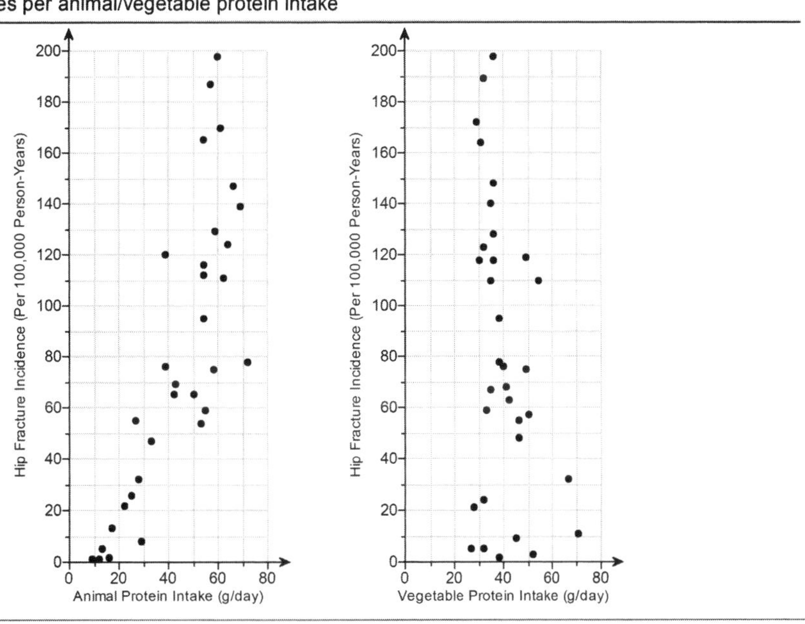

ID: 8.4.13

66. Fitting a straight line to a set of data yields the following prediction line. Complete (a) through (c) below.

$\hat{Y}_i = 9 + 2X_i$

a. Interpret the meaning of the Y-intercept, b_0. Choose the correct answer below.

- A. The Y-intercept, $b_0 = 9$, implies that for each increase of 1 unit in X, the value of Y is expected to increase by 9 units.
- B. The Y-intercept, $b_0 = 9$, implies that when the value of X is 0, the mean value of Y is 9.
- C. The Y-intercept, $b_0 = 2$, implies that when the value of X is 0, the mean value of Y is 2.
- D. The Y-intercept, $b_0 = 9$, implies that the average value of Y is 9.

b. Interpret the meaning of the slope, b_1. Choose the correct answer below.

- A. The slope, $b_1 = 2$, implies that for each increase of 1 unit in X, the value of Y is expected to decrease by 2 units.
- B. The slope, $b_1 = 9$, implies that for each increase of 1 unit in X, the value of Y is expected to increase by 9 units.
- C. The slope, $b_1 = 2$, implies that for each increase of 1 unit in X, the value of Y is expected to increase by 2 units.
- D. The slope, $b_1 = 2$, implies that the average value of Y is 2.

c. Predict the mean value of Y for X = 4.

$\hat{Y}_i =$ ________ (Simplify your answer.)

ID: 8.4.14

---

67. Fitting a straight line to a set of data yields the prediction line $\hat{Y}_i = 6 + 4X_i$. The values of X used to find the prediction line range from 6 to 35.
a. Should this model be used to predict the mean value of Y when X equals 7?
b. Should this model be used to predict the mean value of Y when X equals − 7?
c. Should this model be used to predict the mean value of Y when X equals 0?
d. Should this model be used to predict the mean value of Y when X equals 34?

a. Should this model be used to predict the mean value of Y when X equals 7?

- Yes
- No
- Not enough information

b. Should this model be used to predict the mean value of Y when X equals − 7?

- Yes
- No
- Not enough information

c. Should this model be used to predict the mean value of Y when X equals 0?

- Yes
- No
- Not enough information

d. Should this model be used to predict the mean value of Y when X equals 34?

- Yes
- No
- Not enough information

ID: 8.4.15

---

68. Fitting a straight line to a set of data yields the following prediction line. Complete (a) through (c) below.

$\hat{Y}_i = 12 - 0.4X_i$

a. Interpret the meaning of the Y-intercept, b_0. Choose the correct answer below.

- A. The Y-intercept, $b_0 = 12$, implies that for each increase of 1 unit in X, the value of Y is expected to increase by 12 units.
- B. The Y-intercept, $b_0 = 12$, implies that the average value of Y is 12.
- C. The Y-intercept, $b_0 = 12$, implies that when the value of X is 0, the mean value of Y is 12.
- D. The Y-intercept, $b_0 = -0.4$, implies that when the value of X is 0, the mean value of Y is − 0.4.

b. Interpret the meaning of the slope, b_1. Choose the correct answer below.

- A. The slope, $b_1 = 0.4$, implies that for each increase of 1 unit in X, the value of Y is expected to increase by 0.4 units.
- B. The slope, $b_1 = -0.4$, implies that the average value of Y is − 0.4.
- C. The slope, $b_1 = 12$, implies that for each increase of 1 unit in X, the value of Y is expected to increase by 12 units.
- D. The slope, $b_1 = -0.4$, implies that for each increase of 1 unit in X, the value of Y is estimated to decrease by 0.4 units.

c. Predict the mean value of Y for X = 4.

$\hat{Y}_i =$ ________ (Type an integer or a decimal.)

ID: 8.4.16

---

* 69. The production of wine is a multibillion-dollar worldwide industry. In an attempt to develop a model of wine quality as judged by wine experts, data was collected from red wine variants of a certain type of wine. A sample of 12 wines is given. Develop a simple linear regression model to predict wine quality, measured on a scale from 0 (very bad) to 10 (excellent), based on alcohol content (%). Complete parts (a) through (d) below.
[15] Click the icon to view the data of wine quality and alcohol content.

a. Construct a scatter plot. Choose the correct graph below.

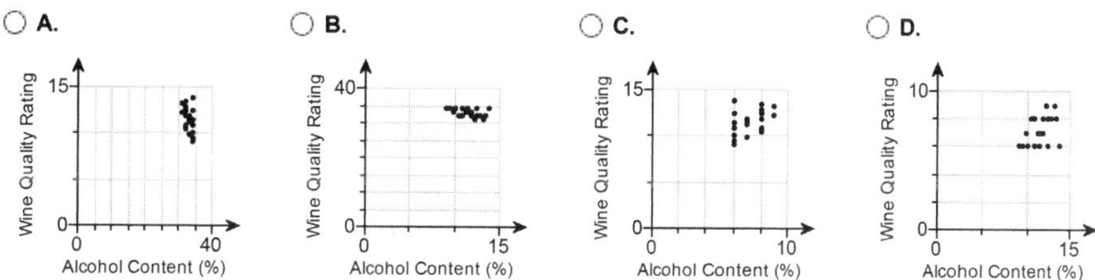

b. For these data, $b_0 = 6.3$ and $b_1 = 0.1$. Interpret the meaning of the slope, b_1, in this problem. Choose the correct answer below.

- **A.** The slope, b_1, implies that the alcohol content is equal to the value of b_1, in percentages.
- **B.** The slope, b_1, implies that for each increase of 1 wine quality rating, the alcohol content is expected to increase by the value of b_1, in percentages.
- **C.** The slope, b_1, implies that for each 0.1 percentage decrease in alcohol content, the wine should have an increase in its rating by 1.
- **D.** The slope, b_1, implies that for each increase of alcohol percentage of 1.0, the wine quality rating is expected to increase by the value of b_1.

c. Predict the mean wine quality for wines with an 4% alcohol content.

$\hat{Y}_i =$ ____________ (Round to two decimal places as needed.)

d. What conclusion can you reach based on the results of (a)-(c)?

- **A.** Alcohol percentage appears to be affected by the wine quality. Each increase of 1 in quality leads to a mean increase in alcohol of about 6.3.
- **B.** Wine quality appears to be affected by the alcohol percentage. Each increase of 1% in alcohol leads to a mean increase in wine quality of about 6.3.
- **C.** Alcohol percentage appears to be affected by the wine quality. Each increase of 1 in quality leads to a mean increase in alcohol of about 0.1.
- **D.** Wine quality appears to be affected by the alcohol percentage. Each increase of 1% in alcohol leads to a mean increase in wine quality of about 0.1.

15: Alcohol Content and Quality Rating

Wine	Alcohol Content (%)	Quality Rating
1	10.0	6
2	10.8	8
3	10.4	8
4	11.9	8
5	11.7	7
6	11.8	7
7	12.5	6
8	12.3	9
9	12.4	8
10	13.2	9
11	13.5	8
12	13.8	6

ID: 8.4.17

CHAPTER 9
Financial Health
MyMathLab Homework Problems*

* Problems with an asterisk are included in the pre-assigned homework assignment.
! Problems with an exclamation point are new to the Update edition.
To find the problems in MyMathLab online, please refer to the ID code listed below each problem.

*1. Decide whether the following statement makes sense (or is clearly true) or does not make sense (or is clearly false). Explain your reasoning.

If interest rates stay at 6% APR and I continue to make my monthly $25 deposits into my retirement plan, I should have at least $30,000 saved when I retire in 20 years.

The statement (1) ________ because I will have $ ________ in my retirement account when I retire in 20 years.
(Round to the nearest cent as needed.)

(1) ◯ does not make sense ◯ does make sense

ID: 9.1.1

---

*2. Decide whether the following statement makes sense (or is clearly true) or does not make sense (or is clearly false). Explain.

My financial advisor showed me that I could reach my retirement goal with deposits of $157 per month and an average return of 8%. But I don't want to deposit that much of my paycheck, so I'm going to reach the same goal by getting an average annual return of 17% instead.

Choose the correct answer below.

◯ **A.** This makes sense because an average annual return of 17% is greater than 8%.

◯ **B.** This makes sense because 17% of $157 is greater than 8% of $157.

◯ **C.** This does not make sense because you cannot choose your own annual rate of return.

◯ **D.** This does not make sense because $157 is not a lot of money to earn interest off of.

ID: 9.1.2

---

*3. Decide whether the following statement makes sense (or is clearly true) or does not make sense (or is clearly false). Explain your reasoning.

I'm putting all my savings into stocks because stocks always outperform other types of investments over the long term.

Choose the correct answer below.

◯ **A.** The statement does not make sense because although stocks historically outperform bonds and cash over the long term, investing in stocks is high-risk and there is no guarantee that the investment will yield a high return.

◯ **B.** The statement does make sense because stocks historically outperform bonds and cash over the long term and investing in stocks is high-risk, which offers higher returns.

◯ **C.** The statement does make sense because stocks are a low-risk investment, offering predictable low returns.

◯ **D.** The statement does not make sense because stocks never outperform bonds and cash over the long term.

ID: 9.1.3

---

*4. Decide whether the following statement makes sense (or is clearly true) or does not make sense (or is clearly false). Explain your reasoning.

I bought a fund advertised on the web that says it uses a secret investment strategy to get an annual return twice that of stocks, with no risk at all.

Choose the correct answer below.

◯ **A.** The statement does make sense because this secret investing strategy must be a new financial planning strategy that does not incorporate the three traditional investment considerations: liquidity, risk, and return.

◯ **B.** The statement does not make sense because investing in stocks is high-risk to get high returns, thus getting higher returns than stocks with this secret strategy must mean the fund advertised on the web is high-risk, not no risk.

◯ **C.** The statement does not make sense because investing in stocks is low-risk to get high returns, thus getting higher returns than stocks with this secret strategy must mean the fund advertised on the web is low-risk, not no risk.

◯ **D.** The statement does make sense because the strategy indicates that the return is a predictable amount, thus the fund advertised on the web is a no-risk investment.

ID: 9.1.4

*5. Decide whether the following statement makes sense (or is clearly true) or does not make sense (or is clearly false). Explain. I'm already retired, so I need low-risk investments. That's why I put most of my money in U.S. Treasury bills, notes, and bonds.

Choose the correct answer below.

- ○ **A.** This makes sense because low-risk is a smart choice for a retired person with limited monthly income.
- ○ **B.** This does not make sense because U.S Treasury bills are different than notes and bonds. The U.S Treasury bills are low-risk while the notes and bonds are high-risk.
- ○ **C.** This makes sense because the safest investments are federally insured bank accounts and U.S. Treasury bills; there's virtually no risk of losing the principal invested.
- ○ **D.** This does not make sense because U.S. Treasury bills, notes, and bonds are high-risk investments that offer prospects of higher returns, along with the possibility of losing the principal.

ID: 9.1.5

!*6. Suppose that $6,000 is invested in a 6-month CD with an APY of 1.2%. Complete parts (a) through (d) below.

(a) What is the corresponding APR?

The corresponding APR is ________%.
(Simplify your answer. Round to three decimal places as needed.)

(b) How much is the investment worth after 6 months?

After 6 months, the investment is worth $________
(Simplify your answer. Round to two decimal places as needed.)

(c) How much is the investment worth after 1 year? Assume that the entire amount is left in the CD to be compounded.

After 1 year, the investment is worth $________
(Simplify your answer. Round to two decimal places as needed.)

(d) How much is the investment worth after 5 years? Assume that the entire amount is left in the CD to be compounded.

After 5 years, the investment is worth $________
(Simplify your answer. Round to two decimal places as needed.)

ID: 9.2.1

!*7. Suppose that $5,500 is invested in a 3-year CD with an APY of 2.3%. Recall that this means the money must be left with the bank for 3 years, and they will guarantee an annual rate of return of 2.3% with compounding interest. Complete parts (a) through (c) below.

(a) What is the corresponding APR?

The corresponding APR is ________%.
(Simplify your answer. Round to three decimal places as needed.)

(b) How much is the investment worth after 2 years?

After 2 years, the investment is worth $________
(Simplify your answer. Round to two decimal places as needed.)

(c) How much is the investment worth after 5 years?

After 5 years, the investment is worth $________
(Simplify your answer. Round to two decimal places as needed.)

ID: 9.2.2

---

8. Why is it so important to understand your personal finances? What types of problems are more common among people who do not have their finances under control?

Why is it so important to understand your personal finances?

- ○ **A.** It is important to understand your personal finances because understanding your personal finances will prevent divorce and other difficulties in personal relationships.
- ○ **B.** It is important to understand your personal finances because you need to know what your credit card interest is so that you can pay the balance off quicker. Once the balance is paid off, you can then invest in the stock market.
- ○ **C.** It is important to understand your personal finances because you need to know how much money you have and how much money you spend in order to find a way to live within your means.
- ○ **D.** It is important to understand your personal finances because there will be an exam at the end of the term.

What types of problems are more common among people who do not have their finances under control?

- ○ **A.** People who do not have their finances under control have higher marriage rates, and no difficulty in personal relationships. However, they tend to suffer from higher rates of depression among a variety of other ailments.
- ○ **B.** People who do not have their finances under control suffer from financial stress, higher divorce rates, and other difficulties in personal relationships. They also suffer from higher rates of depression among a variety of other ailments.
- ○ **C.** People who do not have their finances under control suffer from financial stress, and have less friends. They also suffer from higher interest rates.
- ○ **D.** People who do not have their finances under control suffer from financial stress because they usually have to pay an accountant to balance their checkbooks.

ID: 9.2.3

9. What is a budget? Describe the four-step process of figuring out your monthly budget.

What is a budget?

- ○ **A.** A budget is the value obtained from subtracting your monthly expenses from your monthly income.
- ○ **B.** A budget is a list of your monthly income, including wages, bank interest, and any other income such as once-per-year payments.
- ○ **C.** A budget keeps track of how much money you are spending on your credit cards and any interest you are being charged and helps to determine how much interest you can afford to pay.
- ○ **D.** A budget keeps track of how much money you have coming in and how much you have going out and helps to determine what adjustments need to be made.

Describe the four-step process of figuring out your monthly budget. Choose the correct answer below.

- ○ **A.** First, list all your monthly income. Next, list all your monthly credit card debt. Then subtract your total credit card debt from your total income to determine the amount of interest being paid each month. Finally, make adjustments as needed.
- ○ **B.** First, list all your monthly income. Next, list all your monthly expenses. Then subtract your total income from your total expenses to determine your net monthly cash flow. Finally, make adjustments as needed.
- ○ **C.** First, list all your monthly income. Next, list all your monthly expenses. Then subtract your total expenses from your total income to determine your net monthly cash flow. Finally, make adjustments as needed.
- ○ **D.** First, list all your monthly income. Next, list all your monthly expenses. Then add your total expenses to your total income to determine your net monthly cash flow. Finally, make adjustments as needed.

ID: 9.2.4

---

10. Summarize how average spending patterns change with age. How can comparing your own spending to average spending patterns help you evaluate your budget?

Summarize how average spending patterns change with age. Choose the correct answer below.

- ○ **A.** As people get older, they tend to spend more on health care and donations to charity than younger people. They also tend to spend less on personal insurance, pensions, clothing, and services than younger people.
- ○ **B.** As people get older, they tend to spend more on transportation and housing than younger people. They also tend to spend less on health care.
- ○ **C.** As people get older, they tend to spend more on clothing and services than younger people. They also tend to spend less on food and housing than younger people.
- ○ **D.** As people get older, they tend to spend more on food and entertainment than younger people. They also tend to spend less on housing than younger people.

How can comparing your own spending to average spending patterns help you evaluate your budget?

- ○ **A.** If you are spending a higher percentage of your money on an item in your budget than the average person, you might want to consider finding lower-cost options or adjusting your budget.
- ○ **B.** It is a good idea to check how you compare to the rest of the population. If you find that people spend more than you on gas, you can give others advice on how to spend less.
- ○ **C.** If you are spending a higher percentage of your money on entertainment than the average person, you might be able to find cheaper ticket prices if you ask around.
- ○ **D.** It can be useful to check how you compare to the rest of the population. If you notice that most people donate less than you do to charity, it might be time to stop giving away so much.

ID: 9.2.5

---

11. Decide whether the following statement makes sense (or is clearly true) or does not make sense (or is clearly false). Explain your reasoning.

When I figured out my monthly budget, I included only my rent and my spending on gasoline, because nothing else could possibly add up to much.

Choose the correct answer below.

- ○ **A.** This statement makes sense because everything else she buys is so inexpensive that her monthly cash flow will not be affected.
- ○ **B.** This statement makes sense because rent and gas are the only expensive items on her list.
- ○ **C.** This statement does not make sense because rent and gas prices are constantly on the rise.
- ○ **D.** This statement does not make sense because everything she buys during the month will affect her monthly costs and overall cash flow.

ID: 9.2.6

---

12. Decide whether the following statement makes sense (or is clearly true) or does not make sense (or is clearly false). Explain your reasoning.

My monthly cash flow was − $177, which explained why my credit card debt kept rising.

Choose the correct answer below.

- A. This statement makes sense because a cash flow of − $177 means that if he doesn't have any money saved, then any money he spends must be borrowed from a credit card.
- B. This statement makes sense if the credit card balance is $177.
- C. This statement does not make sense because he incorrectly calculated his monthly cash flow.
- D. This statement does not make sense because − $177 is not a real dollar amount.

ID: 9.2.7

---

13. Decide whether the following statement makes sense (or is clearly true) or does not make sense (or is clearly false). Explain your reasoning.

My vacation travel cost a total of $2880, which I entered into my monthly budget as $240 per month.

Choose the correct answer below.

- A. This statement does not make sense because when making a monthly budget, expenses such as vacations should be ignored since they are a small expense compared to other monthly expenses.
- B. This statement does not make sense because the value entered into the monthly budget should be $288.
- C. This statement does not make sense because when making a monthly budget, expenses such as vacations should only be included for the month in which they are taken.
- D. This statement makes sense because when making a monthly budget, a prorated amount for expenses that don't recur monthly, such as vacations, should be included.

ID: 9.2.8

---

14. Decide whether the following statement makes sense (or is clearly true) or does not make sense (or is clearly false). Explain your reasoning.

Emma and Emily are good friends who do everything together, spending the same amount on eating out, entertainment, and other leisure activities. Yet Emma has a negative monthly cash flow while Emily's is positive, because Emily has more income.

Choose the correct answer below.

- A. The statement makes sense because even though Emma and Emily spend the same amount on entertainment expenses, they may spend different amounts on other expenses. Regardless of income, Emma's and Emily's cash flows could be positive or negative.
- B. This statement makes sense because Emily makes more money than Emma, so she has a greater cash flow at the end of the month.
- C. This statement does not make sense because Emma uses a credit card for her expenses and Emily uses cash for her expenses.
- D. This statement does not make sense because Emily's rent could be lower than Emma's, which means that she will have a greater monthly cash flow.

ID: 9.2.9

---

15. Decide whether the following statement makes sense (or is clearly true) or does not make sense (or is clearly false). Explain your reasoning.

Brandon discovered that his daily routine of buying a slice of pizza and a soda at lunch was costing him more than $14,000 per year.

Choose the correct answer below.

- A. This statement does not make sense because this would mean that a slice of pizza and a soda costs him about $38 a day.
- B. This statement makes sense because this would mean that a slice of pizza and a soda costs him about $4 a day.
- C. This statement makes sense because this would mean that a slice of pizza and a soda costs him about $38 a day.
- D. This statement does not make sense because this would mean that a slice of pizza and a soda costs him about $4 a day.

ID: 9.2.10

---

16. Decide whether the following statement makes sense (or is clearly true) or does not make sense (or is clearly false). Explain your reasoning.

I bought the cheapest health insurance I could find, because that's sure to be the best option for my long-term financial success.

Choose the correct answer below.

○ **A.** This statement does not make sense because the cheapest health insurance plans do not cover as much as the more expensive insurance plans. If he gets sick, he might end up paying more money than he would if he had a more expensive plan.

○ **B.** This statement makes sense because if he gets sick, the overall cost will be a lot less because he has an inexpensive health insurance plan.

○ **C.** This statement does not make sense because health insurance is very expensive. If he really wants to save money, he should drop the insurance plan and hold on to his money.

○ **D.** This statement makes sense because there is no need to buy expensive health insurance. The cheapest plan is good enough, and it will save you money in the long run.

ID: 9.2.11

!* 17. Suppose that a 5-year T-note is purchased with a face value of $10,000 and a coupon rate of 3.5%.

(a) What is the total return of this investment?

(b) What is the average rate of return?

(a) The total return is $__________.
(Simplify your answer.)

(b) The average rate of return is __________%.
(Simplify your answer. Round to two decimal places as needed.)

ID: 9.2.12

!* 18. A town wants to build a park for $1,000,000 and issues 500 bonds for $2,000 each, with a term of 7 years and a coupon rate of 6%. Consider the purchase of one such bond.

(a) What is the total return of this investment? **(b)** What is the average rate of return?

(a) The total return is $__________.
(Simplify your answer.)

(b) The average rate of return is __________%.
(Simplify your answer. Round to two decimal places as needed.)

ID: 9.2.13

!* 19. Suppose that someone owns a 30-year $18,000 T-bond with a rate of 6%. After 7 years the bond is sold for cash, but interest rates have risen to 8.5%.

(a) How much has the bond paid in total for the first 7 years?

(b) How much will the bond pay the person buying it over the next 23 years?

(c) How much is the bond currently worth?

(a) Over the first 7 years, the bond has paid $__________.
(Simplify your answer.)

(b) Over the next 23 years, the bond will pay the buyer $__________.
(Simplify your answer.)

(c) The bond is currently worth $__________.
(Simplify your answer. Round to two decimal places as needed.)

ID: 9.2.14

!* 20. Suppose that someone owns a 30-year $24,000 T-bond with a rate of 4%. After 7 years the bond is sold for cash, but interest rates have fallen to 2.5%.

(a) How much has the bond paid in total for the first 7 years?

(b) How much will the bond pay the person buying it over the next 23 years?

(c) How much is the bond currently worth?

(a) Over the first 7 years, the bond has paid $__________.
(Simplify your answer.)

(b) Over the next 23 years, the bond will pay the buyer $__________.
(Simplify your answer.)

(c) The bond is currently worth $__________.
(Simplify your answer. Round to two decimal places as needed.)

ID: 9.2.15

---

21. Calculate the current yield on the described bond.

A $500 Treasury bond with a coupon rate of 2.2% that has a market value of $400

The current yield is ___________%. (Round to two decimal places as needed.)

ID: 9.2.16

---

22. Calculate the annual interest that you will receive on the described bond.

A $1500 Treasury bond with a current yield of 5.0% that is quoted at 106 points

The annual interest is $___________. (Round to the nearest cent as needed.)

ID: 9.2.17

---

23. Compute the annual interest that would be earned on the following bond.

A $2000 Treasury bond with a current yield of 6.5% that is quoted at 118.8 points

The annual interest is $___________.
(Round to the nearest cent as needed.)

ID: 9.2.18

!*24. A small company is started up that makes blankets. The company sells a total of 5,000 shares at $20 each to raise money to start the business. At the end of the year, the company makes $27,000 in profits and pays out $12,000 in dividends. Complete parts (a) through (f) below.

(a) What is the market capitalization of the company?

The market capitalization is $___________.
(Simplify your answer. Do not include the $ symbol in your answer.)

(b) What is the share price?

The share price is $___________.
(Simplify your answer. Do not include the $ symbol in your answer.)

(c) What is the earnings per share?

The earnings per share is $___________.
(Simplify your answer. Do not include the $ symbol in your answer. Round to two decimal places as needed.)

(d) What is the PE ratio?

The PE ratio is ___________.
(Simplify your answer. Round to three decimal places as needed.)

(e) What is the dividend in dollars per share?

The dividend per share is $___________
(Simplify your answer. Do not include the $ symbol in your answer. Round to two decimal places as needed.)

(f) What is the dividend as a percentage of the share price?

The dividend per share is ___________% of the share price.
(Simplify your answer. Round to one decimal place as needed.)

ID: 9.2.19

!*25. A small company is started up that makes yarn. The company sells a total of 3,000 shares at $50 each to raise money to start the business. At the end of the year, the company makes $30,000 in profits and pays out $5,000 in dividends. Complete parts (a) through (f) below.

(a) What is the market capitalization of the company?

The market capitalization is $___________.
(Simplify your answer. Do not include the $ symbol in your answer.)

(b) What is the share price?

The share price is $___________.
(Simplify your answer. Do not include the $ symbol in your answer.)

! * 25. (cont.) **(c)** What is the earnings per share?

The earnings per share is $ ___________.
(Simplify your answer. Do not include the $ symbol in your answer. Round to two decimal places as needed.)

(d) What is the PE ratio?

The PE ratio is ___________.
(Simplify your answer. Round to three decimal places as needed.)

(e) What is the dividend in dollars per share?

The dividend per share is $ ___________
(Simplify your answer. Do not include the $ symbol in your answer. Round to two decimal places as needed.)

(f) What is the dividend as a percentage of the share price?

The dividend per share is ___________ % of the share price.
(Simplify your answer. Round to one decimal place as needed.)

ID: 9.2.20

! * 26. A consumer invests $22,000 in a mutual fund with a 2% front end load and a 3.5% annual expense fee, which is charged as a percentage of the consumer's balance at the end of the year. The fund increases in value by 19.8% over the first year. Complete parts (a) through (e) below.

(a) What is the amount of money charged up front just for investing in the mutual fund?

The charge up front is $ ___________.
(Simplify your answer. Do not include the $ symbol in your answer. Round to two decimal places as needed.)

(b) After subtracting the front end load, the remainder of the money grows by 19.8% over the first year. What is the ending balance before the expense fee?

The ending balance before the expense fee is $ ___________.
(Simplify your answer. Do not include the $ symbol in your answer. Round to two decimal places as needed.)

(c) What is the expense fee charged on this balance?

The expense fee is $ ___________.
(Simplify your answer. Do not include the $ symbol in your answer. Round to two decimal places as needed.)

(d) What is the final ending balance after the expense fee is deducted?

The final ending balance after the expense fee is $ ___________.
(Simplify your answer. Do not include the $ symbol in your answer. Round to two decimal places as needed.)

(e) What is the total rate of return for this first year?

The total rate of return is ___________ %.
(Simplify your answer. Round to two decimal places as needed.)

ID: 9.2.21

---

27. Compute the total and annual returns on the described investment.
Four years after buying 200 shares of XYZ stock for $80 per share, you sell the stock for $24,500.

The total return is ___________ %.
(Do not round until the final answer. Then round to one decimal place as needed.)

The annual return is ___________ %.
(Do not round until the final answer. Then round to one decimal place as needed.)

ID: 9.2.22

---

28. Compute the total and annual returns on the following investment.
Seventeen years after purchasing shares in a mutual fund for $6500, the shares are sold for $11,900.

The the total return is ___________ %.
(Do not round until the final answer. Then round to one decimal place as needed.)

The annual return is ___________ %.
(Do not round until the final answer. Then round to one decimal place as needed.)

ID: 9.2.23

---

29. Compute the total and annual return on the following investment.
Four years after paying $2500 for shares in a startup company, you sell the shares for $1600 (at a loss).

The total return is __________%.
(Do not round until the final answer. Then round to the nearest tenth as needed.)

The annual return is __________%.
(Do not round until the final answer. Then round to the nearest tenth as needed.)

ID: 9.2.24

30. Compute the total and annual returns on the following investment.
Eight years after purchasing shares in a mutual fund for $7100, the shares are sold for $11,200.

The the total return is __________%.
(Do not round until the final answer. Then round to one decimal place as needed.)

The annual return is __________%.
(Do not round until the final answer. Then round to one decimal place as needed.)

ID: 9.2.25

31. Suppose a man invested $300 at the end of 1900 in each of three funds that tracked the averages of stocks, bonds, and cash, respectively. Assuming that his investments grew at the rates given in the table to the right, approximately how much would each investment have been worth at the end of 2010?

Category	Average Annual Return
Stocks	6.4%
Bonds	1.9%
Cash	0.9%

His investment in the fund tracking stocks would be worth approximately $__________.
(Do not round until the final answer. Then round to two decimal places as needed.)

His investment in the fund tracking bonds would be worth approximately $__________.
(Do not round until the final answer. Then round to two decimal places as needed.)

His investment in the fund tracking cash would be worth approximately $__________.
(Do not round until the final answer. Then round to two decimal places as needed.)

ID: 9.2.26

*32. Use the stock table below to answer parts **a** through **g**. Assume that the data for Company XYZ stock came from an online quote you looked at during lunch.

Company XYZ (XYZ)

Last	Change	%Change	Volume
15.68	+0.45	2.95	58,000,000
Open	High	Low	
14.29	16.35	12.79	
52-Week High		52-Week Low	
23.27		11.09	

Market Cap ($ millions)	82,320
P/E ratio	17.66
Dividend (latest quarter)	0.28
Dividend Yield	7.14%
Shares Outstanding (millions)	5250

a. What is the symbol for Company XYZ stock?

The symbol is (1) __________

b. What was the price per share at the end of the day yesterday?

$__________ (Round to the nearest cent as needed.)

c. Based on the current price, what is the total value of the shares that have been traded so far today?

$__________ million (Round to the nearest whole number as needed.)

d. What percentage of all Company XYZ shares have been traded so far today?

__________% (Round to the nearest hundredth as needed.)

e. Suppose you own 100 shares of Company XYZ. Based on the current price and dividend yield, what total dividend should you expect to receive this year?

$__________ (Round to the nearest cent as needed.)

f. What were the earnings per share for Company XYZ?

$__________ (Round to the nearest cent as needed.)

g. How much total profit did Company XYZ earn in the past year?

$__________ million (Round to the nearest tenth as needed.)

(1) ○ Company XYZ. ○ XYZ.

ID: 9.2.27

33. Answer the following questions, assuming that the mutual fund quote below is one that you found online today. Complete parts (a) through (c) below.

A certain Limited-Term Tax-Exempt Fund (CMLTX)

		1-Day Net Change	1-Day Return
NAV.	$9.32	$0.00	0.0%

Total Returns (%) 3, 5 and 10 year returns are annualized.

	YTD	1-Yr	5-Yr	10-Yr
Fund	2.58%	3.89%	3.48%	3.08%

a. Suppose you invest $4000 in this fund today. How many shares will you buy?

__________ shares
(Round to two decimal places as needed.)

b. Suppose you had invested $4000 in this fund 5 years ago. How much would your investment be worth now?

$ __________
(Round to two decimal places as needed.)

c. Suppose you had invested $4000 in this fund 10 years ago. How much would your investment be worth now?

$ __________
(Round to two decimal places as needed.)

ID: 9.2.28

!* 34. You make $65,000 per year and your company matches 50 cents for every dollar you deposit into your 401k plan, up to 4% of your salary. Complete parts (a) through (c) below.

(a) If you contribute $200 every month to your 401k, what will your company contribute each month?

The company will contribute $ __________ .
(Type an integer or a decimal rounded to two decimal places as needed.)

(b) If you contribute $750 every month to your 401k, what will your company contribute each month?

The company will contribute $ __________ .
(Type an integer or a decimal rounded to two decimal places as needed.)

(c) What is the maximum amount of money the company will contribute to your 401k each year?

The maximum amount that the company will contribute each year is $ __________ .
(Type an integer or a decimal rounded to two decimal places as needed.)

ID: 9.3.1

!* 35. Sal and Cal both work for the same company making $70,000 each in annual salary. Sal deposits 7% of her salary to her 401k plan and the company matches 25 cents for each dollar contributed to the 401k up to the 7%. Cal deposits nothing into his 401k. Complete parts (a) through (c) below.

(a) If they are both in the 30% income tax bracket, how much more in taxes will Cal pay than Sal, assuming that all other factors are equal?

Cal will pay $ __________ more than Sal will pay in income taxes.
(Simplify your answer. Do not include the $ symbol in your answer.)

(b) How much will the company contribute to Sal's 401k plan?

The company will contribute $ __________ to Sal's 401k plan.
(Simplify your answer. Do not include the $ symbol in your answer.)

(c) What is the total amount contributed to Sal's 401k at the end of the first year?

The total amount contributed to Sal's 401k at the end of the first year is $ __________ .
(Simplify your answer. Do not include the $ symbol in your answer.)

ID: 9.3.2

---

* 36. Consider the two savings plans below. Compare the balances in each plan after 5 years. Which person deposited more money in the plan? Which of the two investment strategies is better?

Yolanda deposits $50 per month in an account with an APR of 5%, while Zach deposits $600 at the end of each year in an account with an APR of 5%.

The balance in Yolanda's saving plan after 5 years was $ ___________.
(Round the final answer to the nearest cent as needed. Round all intermediate values to seven decimal places as needed.)

The balance in Zach's saving plan after 5 years was $ ___________.
(Round the final answer to the nearest cent as needed. Round all intermediate values to seven decimal places as needed.)

Which person deposited more money in the plan?

- **A.** They deposited the same amount of money in their savings plans.
- **B.** Zach deposited more money in his savings plan.
- **C.** Yolanda deposited more money in her savings plan.

Which of the two investment strategies was better?

- **A.** Neither plan was better than the other because both plans yield the same accumulated savings plan balance after 5 years.
- **B.** Yolanda's investment strategy was better because she had a larger accumulated savings plan balance after 5 years.
- **C.** Zach's investment strategy was better because he had a larger accumulated savings plan balance after 5 years.

ID: 9.3.3

---

* 37. Consider the two savings plans below. Compare the balances in each plan after 13 years. Which person deposited more money in the plan? Which of the two investment strategies is better?

Yolanda deposits $350 per month in an account with an APR of 4%, while Zach deposits $4000 at the end of each year in an account with an APR of 4.5%.

The balance in Yolanda's saving plan after 13 years was $ ___________.
(Round the final answer to the nearest cent as needed. Round all intermediate values to seven decimal places as needed.)

The balance in Zach's saving plan after 13 years was $ ___________.
(Round the final answer to the nearest cent as needed. Round all intermediate values to seven decimal places as needed.)

Which person deposited more money in the plan?

- **A.** Yolanda deposited more money in her savings plan.
- **B.** Zach deposited more money in his savings plan.
- **C.** Neither, they deposited the same amount of money in their savings plans.

Which of the two investment strategies was better?

- **A.** Yolanda's investment strategy was better because she had a larger total return after 13 years.
- **B.** Neither plan was better than the other because both plans yield the same total return after 13 years.
- **C.** Zach's investment strategy was better because he had a larger total return after 13 years.

ID: 9.3.4

---

* 38. Suppose someone wants to accumulate $75,000 for a college fund over the next 15 years. Determine whether the following investment plans will allow the person to reach the goal. Assume the compounding and payment periods are the same.

The person deposits $125 per month into an account with an APR of 6%.

Will the person meet the goal? Select the correct choice below and fill in the answer box to complete your choice.
(Round the final answer to the nearest cent as needed. Round all intermediate values to six decimal places as needed.)

- **A.** No, because the amount that will be in the college fund, $ ___________, is less than the goal of $75,000.
- **B.** Yes, because the amount that will be in the college fund, $ ___________, is more than the goal of $75,000.

ID: 9.3.5

*39. Suppose you bought XYZ stock 1 year ago for $5.68 per share and sell it at $9.44. You also pay a commission of $0.35 per share on your sale. What is the total return on your investment?

The total return is ________%.
(Round to the nearest tenth as needed.)

ID: 9.3.6

---

*40. One December, a 101-year-old woman died and left $23 million to a university. This fortune was accumulated through shrewd and patient investment of a $8000 nest egg over the course of 45 years. In turning $8000 into $23 million, what were the total and annual returns? How did her annual return compare to the 6.3% average annual return for stocks?

Her total return on the investment was ________%.
(Type a whole number.)

Her annual return was ________%, which is (1) ________ the 6.3% average annual return for stocks.
(Round to two decimal places as needed.)

(1) ○ lower than
○ the same as
○ higher than

ID: 9.3.7

---

*41. Mitch and Bill are both age 75. When Mitch was 23 years old, he began depositing $1000 per year into a savings account. He made deposits for the first 10 years, at which point he was forced to stop making deposits. However, he left his money in the account, where it continued to earn interest for the next 42 years. Bill didn't start saving until he was 48 years old, but for the next 27 years he made annual deposits of $1000. Assume that both accounts earned an average annual return of 7% (compounded once a year). Complete parts (a) through (d) below.

a. How much money does Mitch have in his account at age 75?

At age 75, Mitch has $________ in his account.
(Round to the nearest cent as needed.)

b. How much money does Bill have in his account at age 75?

At age 75, Bill has $________ in his account.
(Round to the nearest cent as needed.)

c. Compare the amounts of money that Mitch and Bill deposit into their accounts.

Mitch deposits $________ in his account and Bill deposits $________ in his account.

d. Draw a conclusion about this parable. Choose the correct answer below.

○ **A.** Bill ends up with more money in his account than Mitch because he make more deposits than Mitch, and each additional deposit will accrue interest each year.

○ **B.** Both Bill and Mitch end with the same amount of money in their accounts, but Mitch had to deposit less money using his method. It is better to start saving as early as possible.

○ **C.** Mitch ends up with more money in his account despite not having deposited as much money as Bill because the interest that is initially accumulated accrues interest throughout the life of the account.

○ **D.** Both Bill and Mitch have the same return on their investments despite using different methods of saving.

ID: 9.3.8

!*42. Choose the correct function you would type into Excel to calculate the following.
(a) You earn 11% a year for 3 years on a $100,000 investment. How much is it worth after two years?
(b) What is the monthly payment on a $20,000 car loan at 9.5% annual interest for 6 years?
(c) How much money will you have after depositing $300 a month for 30 years into an account that returns 11.3% APR compounded monthly?
(d) You are buying a $22,650 car with a 8 year loan. What APR do you need to get a $500 monthly payment?

(a) Choose the correct answer below.

○ **A.** = FV(11%, 3, 0, − 100000)
○ **B.** = FV(11%/12, 36, 0, − 100000)
○ **C.** = FV(11%, 3, 0, 100000)
○ **D.** = FV(11%/12, 36, 0, 100000)

(b) Choose the correct answer below.

○ **A.** = PMT(9.5%/12, 6, 20000, 0)
○ **B.** = PMT(9.5%/12, 72, − 20000, 0)
○ **C.** = PMT(9.5%/12, 72, 20000, 0)
○ **D.** = PMT(9.5%, 72, 20000, 0)

(c) Choose the correct answer below.

○ **A.** = FV(11.3%/12, 30, − 300, 0)
○ **B.** = FV(11.3%, 30, 0, 300)
○ **C.** = FV(11.3%/12, 360, − 300, 0)
○ **D.** = FV(11.3%/12, 360, 0, − 300)

(d) Choose the correct answer below.

○ **A.** = RATE(96, − 500, 22650, 0)*12
○ **B.** = RATE(8, − 500, 22650, 0)*12
○ **C.** = RATE(96, − 500, 22650, 0)
○ **D.** = RATE(96, 500, − 22650, 0)*12

ID: 9.4.1

!* 43. Compute the values of the following Excel functions without typing them into Excel.

(a) = FV(10%, 2, 0, 800)
(b) = NPER(10%, 0, 1000, 1100)
(c) = RATE(2, − 500, 0, 1030) Note: Payments are made at the END of each period.
(d) = PV(14%, 1, 0, 114)
(e) = FV(6%, 2, − 200, − 1000)

(a) The value of the Excel function = FV(10%, 2, 0, 800) is $__________.
(Type an integer or a decimal.)

(b) The value of the Excel function = NPER(10%, 0, 1000, 1100) is __________.
(Type an integer or a decimal.)

(c) The value of the Excel function = RATE(2, − 500, 0, 1030) is __________%.
(Type an integer or a decimal.)

(d) The value of the Excel function = PV(14%, 1, 0, 114) is $__________.
(Type an integer or a decimal.)

(e) The value of the Excel function = FV(6%, 2, − 200, − 1000) is $__________.
(Type an integer or a decimal.)

ID: 9.4.2

---

44. How much must be deposited today into the following account in order to have $45,000 in 7 years for a down payment on a house? Assume no additional deposits are made.

An account with annual compounding and an APR of 5%

$__________ should be deposited today.
(Do not round until the final answer. Then round to the nearest cent as needed.)

ID: 9.4.3

---

*45. How much must be deposited today into the following account in order to have $75,000 in 5 years for a down payment on a house? Assume no additional deposits are made.

An account with monthly compounding and an APR of 5%

$__________ should be deposited today.
(Do not round until the final answer. Then round to the nearest cent as needed.)

ID: 9.4.4

---

46. Suppose you start saving today for a $75,000 down payment that you plan to make on a house in 7 years. Assume that you make no deposits into the account after the initial deposit. For the account described below, how much would you have to deposit now to reach your $75,000 goal in 7 years.

An account with daily compounding and an APR of 5%

You should invest $__________.
(Do not round until the final answer. Then round to two decimal places as needed.)

ID: 9.4.5

---

47. You want to have a $75,000 college fund in 16 years. How much will you have to deposit now under the scenario below. Assume that you make no deposits into the account after the initial deposit.

An APR of 8% compounded daily.

You should invest $__________.
(Do not round until the final answer. Then round to two decimal places as needed.)

ID: 9.4.6

---

48. How much must be deposited today into the following account in order to have a $145,000 college fund in 15 years? Assume no additional deposits are made.

An account with quarterly compounding and an APR of 7.9%

$__________ should be deposited today.
(Do not round until the final answer. Then round to the nearest cent as needed.)

ID: 9.4.7

---

* 49. The following pair of investment plans are identical except for a small difference in interest rates. Compute the balance in the accounts after 10 and 30 years. Discuss the difference.

Chang invests $700 in a savings account that earns 4.0% compounded annually. Kio invests $700 in a different savings account that earns 4.25% compounded annually.

After 10 years Chang will have a balance of approximately $ ________. After 30 years Chang will have a balance of approximately $ ________.
(Round to the nearest cent as needed.)

After 10 years Kio will have a balance of approximately $ ________. After 30 years Kio will have a balance of approximately $ ________.
(Round to the nearest cent as needed.)

After 10 years Kio will have $ ________ or ________ % (1) ________ than Chang.

After 30 years Kio will have $ ________ or ________ % (2) ________ than Chang.
(Round to two decimal places as needed.)

(1) ○ less (2) ○ less
○ more ○ more

ID: 9.4.8

* 50. Consider an account with an APR of 5.3%. Find the APY with quarterly compounding, monthly compounding, and daily compounding. Comment on how changing the compounding period affects the annual yield.

When interest is compounded quarterly, the APY is ________ %.
(Do not round until the final answer. Then round to two decimal places as needed.)

When interest is compounded monthly, the APY is ________ %.
(Do not round until the final answer. Then round to two decimal places as needed.)

When interest is compounded daily, the APY is ________ %.
(Do not round until the final answer. Then round to two decimal places as needed.)

How does changing the number of compounding periods affect the annual yield?

○ **A.** Increasing the number of compounding periods decreases the annual yield.
○ **B.** Increasing the number of compounding periods does not affect the annual yield.
○ **C.** Increasing the number of compounding periods increases the annual yield.
○ **D.** The effect from changing the number of compounding periods on the annual yield cannot be determined.

ID: 9.4.9

51. Compare the accumulated balance in two accounts that both start with an initial deposit of $1000. Both accounts have an APR of 4.6%, but one account compounds interest annually while the other account compounds interest daily. Make a table that shows the interest earned each year and the accumulated balance in both accounts for the first 10 years. Compare the balance in the accounts, in percentage terms, after 10 years.

Fill out the table below.

	Account 1 (Annual Compounding)		Account 2 (Daily Compounding)	
Year	Interest	Balance	Interest	Balance
1	$ ________	$ ________	$ ________	$ ________

(Round to the nearest dollar as needed.)

Fill out the table below.

	Account 1 (Annual Compounding)		Account 2 (Daily Compounding)	
Year	Interest	Balance	Interest	Balance
2	$ ________	$ ________	$ ________	$ ________

(Round to the nearest dollar as needed.)

Fill out the table below.

	Account 1 (Annual Compounding)		Account 2 (Daily Compounding)	
Year	Interest	Balance	Interest	Balance
3	$ ________	$ ________	$ ________	$ ________

(Round to the nearest dollar as needed.)

51. (cont.) Fill out the table below.

	Account 1 (Annual Compounding)		Account 2 (Daily Compounding)	
Year	Interest	Balance	Interest	Balance
4	$ ____	$ ____	$ ____	$ ____

(Round to the nearest dollar as needed.)

Fill out the table below.

	Account 1 (Annual Compounding)		Account 2 (Daily Compounding)	
Year	Interest	Balance	Interest	Balance
5	$ ____	$ ____	$ ____	$ ____

(Round to the nearest dollar as needed.)

Fill out the table below.

	Account 1 (Annual Compounding)		Account 2 (Daily Compounding)	
Year	Interest	Balance	Interest	Balance
6	$ ____	$ ____	$ ____	$ ____

(Round to the nearest dollar as needed.)

Fill out the table below.

	Account 1 (Annual Compounding)		Account 2 (Daily Compounding)	
Year	Interest	Balance	Interest	Balance
7	$ ____	$ ____	$ ____	$ ____

(Round to the nearest dollar as needed.)

Fill out the table below.

	Account 1 (Annual Compounding)		Account 2 (Daily Compounding)	
Year	Interest	Balance	Interest	Balance
8	$ ____	$ ____	$ ____	$ ____

(Round to the nearest dollar as needed.)

Fill out the table below.

	Account 1 (Annual Compounding)		Account 2 (Daily Compounding)	
Year	Interest	Balance	Interest	Balance
9	$ ____	$ ____	$ ____	$ ____

(Round to the nearest dollar as needed.)

Fill out the table below.

	Account 1 (Annual Compounding)		Account 2 (Daily Compounding)	
Year	Interest	Balance	Interest	Balance
10	$ ____	$ ____	$ ____	$ ____

(Round to the nearest dollar as needed.)

In ten years, the amount in Account 1 has increased by ____ %.
In ten years, the amount in Account 2 has increased by ____ %.
(Round to the one decimal place as needed.)

ID: 9.4.10

52. Rosa invests $3400 in an account with an APR of 3% and annual compounding. Julian invests $2900 in an account with an APR of 4% and annual compounding. Complete parts a through c.

a. Compute the balance in each account after 5 and 20 years.

After 5 years Rosa will have a balance of approximately $ ____. After 20 years Rosa will have a balance of approximately $ ____.
(Round to the nearest cent as needed.)

After 5 years Julian will have a balance of approximately $ ____. After 20 years Julian will have a balance of approximately $ ____.
(Round to the nearest cent as needed.)

b. Determine, for each account and for 5 and 20 years, the percentage of balance that is interest.

After 5 years approximately ____ % of Rosa's balance is interest. After 20 years approximately ____ % of Rosa's balance is interest.
(Round to the nearest percent as needed.)

After 5 years approximately ____ % of Julian's balance is interest. After 20 years approximately ____ % of Julian's balance is interest.
(Round to the nearest percent as needed.)

c. Comment on the effect of interest rates and patience.

Choose the correct answer below.

- ○ **A.** A lower initial principal with a higher APR will always have a lower balance than a higher initial principal with a lower APR.
- ○ **B.** A lower initial principal with a higher APR over a long enough time period can result in a higher balance than a higher initial principal with a lower APR.
- ○ **C.** The percent of the balance that is interest is the same after 5 years and after 20 years.

ID: 9.4.11

*53. Suppose someone wants to accumulate $115,000 for retirement in 30 years. The person has two choices. Plan A is a single deposit into an account with annual compounding and an APR of 6%. Plan B is a single deposit into an account with continuous compounding and an APR of 5.7%. How much does the person need to deposit in each account in order to reach the goal?

The person must deposit $________ into the account for Plan A to reach the goal of $115,000.
(Round to the nearest cent as needed.)

The person must deposit $________ into the account for Plan B to reach the goal of $115,000.
(Round to the nearest cent as needed.)

ID: 9.4.12

---

54. How long will it take money to triple at an APR of 6.6% compounded annually?

It will take about ________ years to triple an amount of money earning 6.6% compounded annually.
(Round to one decimal place as needed.)

ID: 9.4.13

---

55. $4000 is deposited in an account that pays an APR of 7.1% compounded annually. How long will it take for the balance to reach $100,000?

It will take about ________ years for the balance to reach $100,000.
(Round to one decimal place as needed.)

ID: 9.4.14

---

*56. Many organizations use endowments to provide operating expenses or benefits. An endowment is established when a (usually large) principal is established in an account, at which point only the interest is withdrawn for expenses without depleting the principal. Suppose a scholarship endowment is established with a generous gift of $60,000. Complete parts (a)-(c) below.

a. If interest is compounded monthly at an annual rate of 7.9%, does the account generate enough interest to provide a $4750 scholarship every year? Select the correct choice below and fill in the answer box to complete your choice.

(Do not round until the final answer. Then round to the nearest cent as needed.)

○ **A.** The endowment will generate enough for the scholarship because the interest earned, $________, is more than $4750.

○ **B.** The endowment will not generate enough for the scholarship because the interest earned, $________, is less than $4750.

b. If the annual interest rate drops to 7.2%, does the account generate enough interest to provide a $4750 scholarship every year? Select the correct choice below and fill in the answer box to complete your choice.

(Do not round until the final answer. Then round to the nearest cent as needed.)

○ **A.** The endowment will generate enough for the scholarship because the interest earned, $________, is more than $4750.

○ **B.** The endowment will not generate enough for the scholarship because the interest earned, $________, is less than $4750.

c. Estimate (a little trial and error is needed) the minimum interest rate that will allow the fund to payout a $4750 scholarship per year.

The minimum APR is ________%.
(Round to one decimal place as needed.)

ID: 9.4.15

---

57. Find the savings plan balance after 15 months with an APR of 9% and monthly payments of $100.

The balance is $________.
(Do not round until the final answer. Then round to the nearest cent as needed.)

ID: 9.4.16

---

*58. Find the savings plan balance after 4 years with an APR of 7% and monthly payments of $250.

The balance is $________.
(Do not round until the final answer. Then round to the nearest cent as needed.)

ID: 9.4.17

---

*59. At age 24, someone sets up an IRA (individual retirement account) with an APR of 6%. At the end of each month he deposits $50 in the account. How much will the IRA contain when he retires at age 65? Compare that amount to the total deposits made over the time period.

After retirement the IRA will contain $__________.
(Do not round until the final answer. Then round to the nearest cent as needed.)

The total deposits made over the time period is $__________.
(Type a whole number.)

ID: 9.4.18

---

60. Deposits of $300 per month are put into an investment plan that pays an APR of 4.1%. How much money will be in the plan after 25 years?

A total of $__________ will have been paid into the account over 25 years and after the 25 years, the account will have a balance of $__________.
(Do not round until the final answer. Then round to two decimal places as needed.)

ID: 9.4.19

---

61. Use the savings plan formula to answer the following question.

Your goal is to create a college fund for your child. Suppose you find a fund that offers an APR of 6%. How much should you deposit monthly to accumulate $80,000 in 13 years?

You should invest $__________ each month.
(Do not round until the final answer. Then round to two decimal places as needed.)

ID: 9.4.20

---

62. You want to purchase a new car in 6 years and expect the car to cost $30,000. Your bank offers a plan with a guaranteed APR of 6.5% if you make regular monthly deposits. How much should you deposit each month to end up with $30,000 in 6 years?

You should invest $__________ each month.
(Round the final answer to the nearest cent as needed. Round all intermediate values to seven decimal places as needed.)

ID: 9.4.21

---

*63. Suppose a man is 25 years old and would like to retire at age 60. Furthermore, he would like to have a retirement fund from which he can draw an income of $125,000 per year—forever! How can he do it? Assume a constant APR of 8%.

He can have a retirement fund from which he can draw $125,000 per year by having $__________ in his savings account when he retires.
(Do not round until the final answer. Then round to the nearest integer as needed.)

He can reach his goal by making monthly deposits of $__________.
(Do not round until the final answer. Then round to two decimal places as needed.)

ID: 9.4.22

!*64. You owe $3,667 on your credit card which has a 17.5% APR.

(a) How much interest do you get charged this month on your balance of $3,667?
(b) You make a payment of $850. What is your new balance for the next month?
(c) How many total months will it take you to pay off the debt if you continue to make $850 payments each month (the last month you would pay just what you owe)?

(a) The interest is $__________.
(Round to the nearest cent as needed.)

(b) The new balance for the next month is $__________.
(Round to the nearest cent as needed.)

(c) It would take __________ payments to pay off the debt.
(Round up to the nearest whole number as needed.)

ID: 9.5.1

---

* 65. Suppose that on January 1 you have a balance of $5000 on a credit card whose APR is 12%, which you want to pay off in 1 year. Assume that you make no additional charges to the card after January 1.

a. Calculate your monthly payments.
b. When the card is paid off, how much will you have paid since January 1?
c. What percentage of your total payment from part (b) is interest?

---

a. The monthly payment is $ ______.
(Do not round until the final answer. Then round to the nearest cent as needed.)

b. The total paid since January 1 is $ ______.
(Use the answer from part (a) to find this answer. Round to the nearest cent as needed.)

c. The percentage of the total paid that is interest is ______ %.
(Use the answer from part (b) to find this answer. Round to one decimal place as needed.)

ID: 9.5.2

---

66. Suppose that on January 1 you have a balance of $3600 on a credit card whose APR is 12%, which you want to pay off in 5 years. Assume that you make no additional charges to the card after January 1.

a. Calculate your monthly payments.
b. When the card is paid off, how much will you have paid since January 1?
c. What percentage of your total payment (part b) is interest?

---

a. The monthly payment is $ ______.
(Do not round until the final answer. Then round to the nearest cent as needed.)

b. The total paid since January 1 is $ ______.
(Use the answer from part a to find this answer. Round to the nearest cent as needed.)

c. The percentage of the total paid that is interest is ______ %.
(Use the answer from part b to find this answer. Round to one decimal place as needed.)

ID: 9.5.3

---

* 67. Assume you have a balance of $1100 on a credit card with an APR of 18%, or 1.5% per month. You start making monthly payments of $200, but at the same time you charge an additional $90 per month to the credit card. Assume that interest for a given month is based on the balance for the previous month. The following table shows how you can calculate your monthly balance. Complete and extend the table to show the balance at the end of each month until the debt is paid off. How long does it take to pay off the credit card debt?

Fill out the table row by row, and continue until the last full payment.
(Round to the nearest cent as needed.)

Month	Payment	Expenses	Interest	New Balance
0	-	-	-	$1100
1	$200	$90	$0.015 \times \$1100 = \$16.50$	$\$1100 - \$200 + \$90 + \$16.50 = \$1006.50$
2	$200	$90	$ ______	$ ______
3	$200	$90	$ ______	$ ______
4	$200	$90	$ ______	$ ______

Continue until the last full payment.

⋮	⋮	⋮	⋮	⋮
______	$200	$90	$ ______	$ ______

Therefore, a(n) ______ th partial payment will pay off the loan, which means the loan will be paid off in ______ months.

ID: 9.5.4

---

* 68. The table below shows the expenses and payments for 8 months on a credit card account with an initial balance of $250. Assume that the interest rate is 2.0% per month (24% APR) and that interest for a given month is charged on the balance for the previous month. Complete the table. After 8 months, what is the balance on the credit card?

[1] Click the icon to view the table of expenses and payments.

Complete the table below.
(Round to the nearest cent as needed.)

Month	Payment	Expenses	Interest	Balance
0	---	---	---	$250
1	$250	$200	$5.00	$205.00
2	$225	$225	$ ______	$ ______
3	$370	$350	$ ______	$ ______
4	$400	$350	$ ______	$ ______
5	$0	$80	$ ______	$ ______
6	$70	$110	$ ______	$ ______
7	$225	$200	$ ______	$ ______
8	$90	$70	$ ______	$ ______

After 8 months, what is the balance on the credit card?

$ ______ (Round to the nearest cent as needed.)

1: Table of expenses and payments

Month	Payment	Expenses	Interest	Balance
0	---	---	---	$250
1	$250	$200	2.0% × $250 = $5.00	205.00
2	$225	$225		
3	$370	$350		
4	$400	$350		
5	0	$80		
6	$70	$110		
7	$225	$200		
8	$90	$70		

ID: 9.5.5

69. How do credit card loans differ from ordinary installment loans? Why are credit card loans particularly dangerous?

How do credit card loans differ from ordinary installment loans?

- ○ **A.** Credit card loans differ from installment loans in that credit cards charge an annual fee, and often raise the interest rate.
- ○ **B.** Credit card loans differ from installment loans in that you are required to pay off your balance at the end of each 25 to 30 day grace period.
- ○ **C.** Credit card loans differ from installment loans in that you are not required to pay off your balance in any set period of time.
- ○ **D.** Credit card loans differ from installment loans in that you are required to pay off your balance at the end of each month.

Why are credit card loans particularly dangerous?

- ○ **A.** Credit card loans are particularly dangerous because they have very high interest rates compared to other types of loans, so it is easy to get into financial trouble.
- ○ **B.** Credit card loans are particularly dangerous because they can be used as identification to rent a car.
- ○ **C.** Credit card loans are particularly dangerous because they charge an annual fee, and often raise the interest rate.
- ○ **D.** Credit card loans are particularly dangerous because they don't require equal monthly payments, so many people never pay off their balance.

ID: 9.5.6

70. Decide whether the following statement makes sense (or is clearly true) or does not make sense (or is clearly false). Explain your reasoning.

The interest rate on my student loan is only 7%, yet more than half of my payments are currently going toward interest rather than principal.

Choose the correct answer below.

- ○ **A.** The statement makes sense. A much larger portion of every payment goes towards interest, regardless of the interest rate.
- ○ **B.** The statement does not make sense. For every payment, 7% goes towards interest and 93% goes towards principal.
- ○ **C.** The statement does not make sense. Principal is always paid off entirely before any payments go toward interest.
- ○ **D.** The statement makes sense. The portions of installment loan payments going towards principal and toward interest vary as the loan is paid down.

ID: 9.5.7

* 71. Decide whether the following statement makes sense (or is clearly true) or does not make sense (or is clearly false). Explain your reasoning.

My student loans were all 20-year loans at interest rates of 5% or above, so when my bank offered me a 20-year loan at 2%, I took it and used it to pay off the student loans.

Choose the correct answer below.

- **A.** This does not make sense because the interest rates of the other student loans are not given.
- **B.** This does not make sense because the student loans have different loan terms with varying interest rates.
- **C.** This makes sense because the bank loan has a lower loan term with a lower interest rate.
- **D.** This makes sense because the bank loan has the same loan term with a lower interest rate.

ID: 9.5.8

* 72. Decide whether the following statement makes sense (or is clearly true) or does not make sense (or is clearly false). Explain your reasoning.

I make only the minimum required payments on my credit card balance each month, because that way I'll have more of my own money to keep.

Choose the correct answer below.

- **A.** The statement does not make sense. It takes a very long time to pay off a credit card loan if only the minimum payments are made. This results in much more interest being paid.
- **B.** The statement makes sense. If you spend less money on a credit card loan, then you will have much more spending money every month.
- **C.** The statement makes sense. Minimum payments go entirely towards principal.
- **D.** The statement does not make sense. The same amount of money is paid in the long term, regardless of how much is paid each month.

ID: 9.5.9

73. Decide whether the following statement makes sense (or is clearly true) or does not make sense (or is clearly false). Explain your reasoning.

I had a choice between a fixed rate mortgage at 6% and an adjustable rate mortgage that started at 3% for the first year with a maximum increase of 1.5 percentage points a year. I took the adjustable rate, because I'm planning to move within three years.

Choose the correct answer below.

- **A.** The statement does not make sense. The average monthly payment for the adjustable rate mortgage will be higher over the first three years than the fixed rate mortgage.
- **B.** The statement makes sense. For adjustable rate mortgages, the first three years worth of payments go almost entirely toward principal.
- **C.** The statement makes sense. The monthly payment for the adjustable rate mortgage is guaranteed to be lower for the first three years of the loan term.
- **D.** The statement does not make sense. Adjustable rate mortages usually have higher monthly payments at the beginning of the term than at the end of the term.

ID: 9.5.10

74. Decide whether the following statement makes sense (or is clearly true) or does not make sense (or is clearly false). Explain your reasoning.

Fixed rate loans with 15-year terms have lower interest rates than loans with 30-year terms, so it always makes sense to take the 15-year loan.

Choose the correct answer below.

- **A.** This makes sense because it is always better to have loans with short loan terms. A borrower could pay off the loan in 15 years, and then spend the next 15 years saving money.
- **B.** This does not make sense because 15-year loans don't usually have lower interest rates. The lenders would never be able to profit if the interest rates of these loans were less than those of 30-year loans.
- **C.** This does not make sense because the monthly payments for the 15-year loan are much greater than a 30-year loan, even at a lower interest rate. Even though the interest is higher for 30-year loans, the borrower could pay more toward the principal each month with the option of paying the lower monthly payment if finances are poor one month.
- **D.** This makes sense because paying a lower interest rate for a short period of time is not as costly as paying a higher interest rate for a long period of time.

ID: 9.5.11

* 75. Compare the monthly payments and total loan costs for the following pairs of loan options. Assume that both loans are fixed rate and have the same closing costs.

You need a $130,000 loan.
Option 1: a 30-year loan at an APR of 10%.
Option 2: a 15-year loan at an APR of 9.5%.

Find the monthly payment for each option.

The monthly payment for option 1 is $__________.
The monthly payment for option 2 is $__________.
(Do not round until the final answer. Then round to the nearest dollar as needed.)

Find the total amount paid for each option.

The total payment for option 1 is $__________.
The total payment for option 2 is $__________.
(Use the answers from the previous step to find this answer.)

Compare the two options. Which appears to be the better option?

○ **A.** Option 2 is the better option, but only if the borrower can afford the higher monthly payments over the entire term of the loan.
○ **B.** Option 1 will always be the better option.
○ **C.** Option 2 will always be the better option
○ **D.** Option 1 is the better option, but only if the borrower plans to stay in the same home for the entire term of the loan.

ID: 9.5.12

76. Compare the monthly payments and total loan costs for the following pairs of loan options. Assume that both loans are fixed rate and have the same closing costs.

You need a $30,000 loan.
Option 1: a 30-year loan at an APR of 7.15%.
Option 2: a 15-year loan at an APR of 6.75%.

Find the monthly payment for each option.

The monthly payment for option 1 is $__________.
The monthly payment for option 2 is $__________.
(Do not round until the final answer. Then round to the nearest cent as needed.)

Find the total amount paid for each option.

The total payment for option 1 is $__________.
The total payment for option 2 is $__________.
(Use the answers from the previous step. Round to the nearest cent as needed.)

Compare the two options to determine which is the better economic option. Which appears to be the better option?

○ **A.** Option 1 is the better option, but only if the borrower needs the lower monthly payment.
○ **B.** Option 2 is the better option, but only if the borrower can afford the higher monthly payments over the entire term of the loan.
○ **C.** Option 1 will always be the better option.
○ **D.** Option 2 will always be the better option.

ID: 9.5.13

* 77. You need a loan of $185,000 to buy a home. Calculate your monthly payments and total closing costs for each choice below. Briefly discuss how you would decide between the two choices.

Choice 1: 30-year fixed rate at 6% with closing costs of $1100 and no points.
Choice 2: 30-year fixed rate at 5.5% with closing costs of $1100 and 3 points.

What is the monthly payment for choice 1?

$__________
(Do not round until the final answer. Then round to the nearest cent as needed.)

What is the monthly payment for choice 2?

$__________
(Do not round until the final answer. Then round to the nearest cent as needed.)

What is the total closing cost for choice 1?

$__________

What is the total closing cost for choice 2?

$__________

* 77. (cont.) Why might choice 1 be the better choice?

- ○ **A.** The closing costs are lower.
- ○ **B.** The monthly payment is higher.
- ○ **C.** The closing costs are higher.
- ○ **D.** The monthly payment is lower.

Why might choice 2 be the better choice?

- ○ **A.** The monthly payment is lower.
- ○ **B.** The closing costs are lower.
- ○ **C.** The closing costs are higher.
- ○ **D.** The monthly payment is higher.

ID: 9.5.14

---

78. Consider the following pair of loan options for a $150,000 mortgage. Calculate the monthly payment and total closing costs for each option. Explain which is the better option and why.

Choice 1: 30-year fixed rate at 4.5% with closing costs of $2300 and 1 point.
Choice 2: 30-year fixed rate at 4.25% with closing costs of $2300 and 5 points.

What is the monthly payment for choice 1?

$__________
(Do not round until the final answer. Then round to the nearest cent as needed.)

What is the monthly payment for choice 2?

$__________
(Do not round until the final answer. Then round to the nearest cent as needed.)

What is the total closing cost for choice 1?

$__________

What is the total closing cost for choice 2?

$__________

Why might choice 1 be the better choice?

- ○ **A.** The closing costs are lower.
- ○ **B.** The monthly payment is higher.
- ○ **C.** The closing costs are higher.
- ○ **D.** The monthly payment is lower.

Why might choice 2 be the better choice?

- ○ **A.** The monthly payment is higher.
- ○ **B.** The monthly payment is lower.
- ○ **C.** The closing costs are higher.
- ○ **D.** The closing costs are lower.

ID: 9.5.15

---

* 79. Suppose you have a student loan of $35,000 with an APR of 12% for 40 years. Complete parts (a) through (c) below.

a. What are your required monthly payments?

The required monthly payment is $__________.
(Do not round until the final answer. Then round to the nearest cent as needed.)

b. Suppose you would like to pay the loan off in 20 years instead of 40. What monthly payments will you need to make?

The monthly payment required to pay off the loan in 20 years instead of 40 is $__________.
(Do not round until the final answer. Then round to the nearest cent as needed.)

c. Compare the total amount you'll pay over the loan term if you pay the loan off in 20 years versus 40 years.

Total payments for the 40-year loan = $__________.
Total payments for the 20-year loan = $__________.

ID: 9.5.16

80. You have a choice between a 30-year fixed rate loan at 5.5% and an adjustable rate mortgage (ARM) with a first year rate of 2%. Neglecting compounding and changes in principal, estimate your monthly savings with the ARM during the first year on a $200,000 loan. Suppose that the ARM rate rises to 7.5% at the start of the third year. Approximately how much extra will you then be paying over what you would have paid if you had taken the fixed rate loan?

What is the approximate monthly savings with the ARM during the first year?

$ ________ (Round to the nearest dollar as needed.)

Approximately how much extra will be paid per month with the ARM during the third year?

$ ________ (Round to the nearest dollar as needed.)

ID: 9.5.17

81. You can afford monthly payments of $400. If current mortgage rates are 3.52% for a 30-year fixed rate loan, how much can you afford to borrow? If you are required to make a 10% down payment and you have the cash on hand to do it, how expensive a home can you afford? (Hint: You will need to solve the loan payment formula for P.)

How much can you afford to borrow?

$ ________ (Round to the nearest dollar as needed.)

How expensive a home can you afford?

$ ________ (Round to the nearest dollar as needed.)

ID: 9.5.18

* 82. Suppose you have the following three student loans: $10,000 with an APR of 7.5% for 17 years, $18,000 with an APR of 8% for 22 years, and $11,500 with an APR of 9% for 12 years.

a. Calculate the monthly payment for each loan individually.
b. Calculate the total you'll pay in payments during the life of all three loans.
c. A bank offers to consolidate your three loans into a single loan with an APR of 8% and a loan term of 22 years. What will your monthly payments be in that case? What will your total payments be over the 22 years?

a. The monthly payment of the $10,000 loan is $ ________.
(Do not round until the final answer. Then round to the nearest cent as needed.)

The monthly payment of the $18,000 loan is $ ________.
(Do not round until the final answer. Then round to the nearest cent as needed.)

The monthly payment of the $11,500 loan is $ ________.
(Do not round until the final answer. Then round to the nearest cent as needed.)

b. The total you'll pay in payments during the life of all three loans is $ ________.
(Round to the nearest cent as needed.)

c. The monthly payment of the consolidated loan is $ ________.
(Do not round until the final answer. Then round to the nearest cent as needed.)

The total you'll pay in payments during the life of the consolidated loan is $ ________.
(Round to the nearest cent as needed.)

ID: 9.5.19

83. Suppose you want to borrow $105,000 and you find a bank offering a 20-year loan with an APR of 6%.
a. Find your regular payments if you pay n = 1, 12, 26, 52 times a year.
b. Compute the total payout for each of the loans in part (a).
c. Compare the total payouts computed in part (b).

a. The payment for n = 1 would be $ ________.
The payment for n = 12 would be $ ________.
The payment for n = 26 would be $ ________.
The payment for n = 52 would be $ ________.
(Do not round until the final answer. Then round to the nearest cent as needed.)

b. For n = 1, the total amount paid is $ ________, for n = 12, the total amount paid is $ ________, for n = 26, the total amount paid is $ ________, and for n = 52, the total amount paid is $ ________.
(Round to the nearest dollar.)

c. What can be said about the frequency of payment and the total amount paid?

○ **A.** More frequent payments result in a larger total amount paid.
○ **B.** Less frequent payments result in a smaller total amount paid.
○ **C.** More frequent payments result in a smaller total amount paid.
○ **D.** There is no relationship between the payment frequency and total amount paid.

ID: 9.5.20

84. A person wants to buy a house with a selling price of \$170,000 and has determined that monthly payments of \$1500 are affordable. This person has \$12,000 in savings that can be used for a down payment. The bank offers a 10-year loan at a fixed 6% APR, a 20-year loan at a fixed 9%, or a 15-year loan with an adjustable rate mortgage (ARM) with a first-year rate of 3% and a rate cap of 9%. Analyze the offerings, along with the pros and cons of each option.

What is the monthly payment with the first option?

The monthly payment amount is \$__________.
(Round the final answer to the nearest cent as needed. Round all intermediate values to six decimal places as needed.)

Decide whether each feature of the first loan option is a pro or a con.

The monthly payment will never increase. (1) __________

The monthly payment will never decrease. (2) __________

The interest rate is certain. (3) __________

The mortgage is paid off in 10 years. (4) __________

The payment is more than what the person can afford per month. (5) __________

What is the monthly payment with the second option?

The monthly payment amount is \$__________.
(Round the final answer to the nearest cent as needed. Round all intermediate values to six decimal places as needed.)

Decide whether each feature of the second loan option is a pro or a con.

The monthly payment will never increase. (6) __________

The monthly payment will never decrease. (7) __________

The interest rate is certain. (8) __________

The total amount paid is much more than the first option. (9) __________

The person can afford the monthly payments. (10) __________

If the rate for the third option remains at the introductory rate, what is the monthly payment?

The monthly payment is \$__________.
(Round the final answer to the nearest cent as needed. Round all intermediate values to six decimal places as needed.)

Over-estimate the monthly payment for the third option by calculating the monthly payment at the maximum rate.

The monthly payment is \$__________.
(Round the final answer to the nearest cent as needed. Round all intermediate values to six decimal places as needed.)

The monthly payments for the third option may vary as interest rates vary. However, the pros and cons can still be identified.

The monthly payment is uncertain. (11) __________

The rate for the first year is the lowest of all the options. (12) __________

There is the possibility that the rate will remain low throughout the loan term. (13) __________

There is the possibility that the rate will go up after the first year and remain high throughout the loan term. (14) __________

The person would most likely be able to afford the monthly payments since the over-estimated value is close to the affordable amount. (15) __________

(1) ○ Pro ○ Con (2) ○ Pro ○ Con (3) ○ Pro ○ Con (4) ○ Pro ○ Con (5) ○ Pro ○ Con (6) ○ Pro ○ Con

(7) ○ Pro ○ Con (8) ○ Pro ○ Con (9) ○ Pro ○ Con (10) ○ Pro ○ Con (11) ○ Pro ○ Con (12) ○ Pro ○ Con

(13) ○ Pro ○ Con (14) ○ Pro ○ Con (15) ○ Pro ○ Con

ID: 9.5.21

CHAPTER 10
Logically!
MyMathLab Homework Problems*

* Problems with an asterisk are included in the pre-assigned homework assignment.
! Problems with an exclamation point are new to the Update edition.
To find the problems in MyMathLab online, please refer to the ID code listed below each problem.

!* 1. Answer parts (a) through (d) using the conditional statement.

If I shovel your driveway then you pay me $20.

(a) Identify the following statement's relationship to the given conditional.

If you pay me $20 then I will shovel your driveway.

Choose the correct answer below.

○ **A.** Negation
○ **B.** Contrapositive
○ **C.** Converse
○ **D.** Inverse

(b) Identify the following statement's relationship to the given conditional.

If you don't pay me $20 then I will not shovel your driveway.

Choose the correct answer below.

○ **A.** Inverse
○ **B.** Contrapositive
○ **C.** Converse
○ **D.** Negation

(c) Identify the following statement's relationship to the given conditional.

If I don't shovel your driveway then you don't pay me $20.

Choose the correct answer below.

○ **A.** Contrapositive
○ **B.** Negation
○ **C.** Converse
○ **D.** Inverse

(d) Identify the following statement's relationship to the given conditional.

I shovel your driveway and you don't pay me $20.

Choose the correct answer below.

○ **A.** Contrapositive
○ **B.** Converse
○ **C.** Inverse
○ **D.** Negation

ID: 10.1.1

!* 2. Answer parts (a) through (d) using the conditional statement.

I spend what I earn.

(a) Identify the following statement's relationship to the given conditional.

If I spent it then I earned it.

Choose the correct answer below.

○ **A.** Inverse
○ **B.** Negation
○ **C.** Contrapositive
○ **D.** Converse

!* 2. (cont.) **(b)** Identify the following statement's relationship to the given conditional.

I don't spend what I don't earn.

Choose the correct answer below.

- ◯ **A.** Contrapositive
- ◯ **B.** Inverse
- ◯ **C.** Converse
- ◯ **D.** Negation

(c) Identify the following statement's relationship to the given conditional.

If I did not earn it then I don't spend it.

Choose the correct answer below.

- ◯ **A.** Negation
- ◯ **B.** Contrapositive
- ◯ **C.** Converse
- ◯ **D.** Inverse

(d) Identify the following statement's relationship to the given conditional.

I earned it and I did not spend it.

Choose the correct answer below.

- ◯ **A.** Converse
- ◯ **B.** Inverse
- ◯ **C.** Negation
- ◯ **D.** Contrapositive

ID: 10.1.2

!* 3. A teacher tells her class that students who get an A in the course always get an A on the final exam. Identify the converse error.

Choose the correct answer below.

- ◯ **A.** Assuming that this means if you get an A in the course then you got an A on the final exam.
- ◯ **B.** Assuming that this means if you don't get an A on the final then you do get an A in the course.
- ◯ **C.** Assuming that this means if you get an A on the final then you get an A in the class.
- ◯ **D.** Assuming that this means if you don't get an A on the final exam then you won't get an A in the course.

ID: 10.1.3

!* 4. A friend tells you that they always call people they would like to date. Identify the converse error.

Choose the correct answer below.

- ◯ **A.** Assuming that this means if they don't call you then they don't want to date you.
- ◯ **B.** Assuming that this means if they don't call you then they would like to date you.
- ◯ **C.** Assuming that this means if they call you they would like to date you.
- ◯ **D.** Assuming that this means if they would like to date you then they will call you.

ID: 10.1.4

---

5. Consider the following example of the logical fallacy of appeal to popularity. Complete parts (a) and (b) below.

Apple's iPhone outsells all other smart phones, so it must be the best smart phone on the market.

a. What is the premise? Choose the correct answer below.

- ◯ **A.** Apple's iPhone outsells all other smart phones.
- ◯ **B.** Apple's iPhone.
- ◯ **C.** All other smart phones.
- ◯ **D.** Apple's iPhone is the best smart phone on the market.

5. (cont.) What is the conclusion? Choose the correct answer below.

○ **A.** It is the best smart phone on the market.
○ **B.** It outsells all other smart phones.
○ **C.** All other smart phones.
○ **D.** Apple's iPhone.

b. Briefly explain how appeal to popularity occurs in the argument. Choose the correct answer below.

○ **A.** This conclusion was drawn from an inadequate number of cases that have not been sufficiently analyzed.
○ **B.** If you read carefully, you'll recognize that the premise and the conclusion both say essentially the same thing.
○ **C.** The fact that many people buy the iPhone does not necessarily mean it is the best smart phone on the market.
○ **D.** We cannot conclude that the popularity of the iPhone caused it to be the best smart phone on the market.

ID: 10.1.5

---

6. Consider the following example of a fallacy. Complete parts **a** and **b** below.

Fifty years of searching has not revealed life on other planets, so life in the universe must be confined to Earth.

a. Identify the premise and conclusion of the argument. Choose the correct answer below.

○ **A.** Premise: Fifty years of searching has not revealed life on other planets. Conclusion: Life in the universe may not be confined to Earth.
○ **B.** Premise: Life in the universe must be confined to Earth. Conclusion: Fifty years of searching has not revealed life on other planets.
○ **C.** Premise: Fifty years of searching has not revealed life on other planets. Conclusion: Life in the universe must be confined to Earth.
○ **D.** Premise: Life in the universe may not be confined to Earth. Conclusion: Fifty years of searching has not revealed life on other planets.

b. Briefly describe how the stated fallacy occurs in the argument.

○ **A.** The conclusion is stated as if it were caused by the premise
○ **B.** The premise is stated according to a lack of evidence of the opposite of the conclusion.
○ **C.** The premise directs attention away from the conclusion.
○ **D.** The conclusion is stated as if it were the only possible conclusion.

ID: 10.1.6

---

7. Consider the following example of a fallacy. Complete parts **a** and **b** below.

He refused to testify by invoking his Fifth Amendment rights, so he must be guilty.

a. Identify the premise and conclusion of the argument. Choose the correct answer below.

○ **A.** Premise: He refused to testify by invoking his Fifth Amendment rights. Conclusion: He may not be guilty.
○ **B.** Premise: He may not be guilty. Conclusion: He refused to testify by invoking his Fifth Amendment rights.
○ **C.** Premise: He refused to testify by invoking his Fifth Amendment rights. Conclusion: He must be guilty.
○ **D.** Premise: He must be guilty. Conclusion: He refused to testify by invoking his Fifth Amendment rights.

b. Briefly describe how the stated fallacy occurs in the argument. Choose the correct answer below.

○ **A.** The conclusion is stated as the opposite as the premise.
○ **B.** The conclusion is stated to invoke an emotional response.
○ **C.** The conclusion is stated as if it were the only possible conclusion.
○ **D.** The conclusion is stated as if it were caused by the premise.

ID: 10.1.7

---

8. Consider the following example of a fallacy. Complete parts **a** and **b** below.

If the Senator doesn't have any religious affiliation, then he can't have the personal values required to represent me.

a. Identify the premise and conclusion of the argument. Choose the correct answer below.

- ○ **A.** Premise: The Senator doesn't have a religious affiliation. Conclusion: He has the personal values required to represent me.
- ○ **B.** Premise: The Senator has the personal values required to represent me. Conclusion: He doesn't have a religious affiliation.
- ○ **C.** Premise: The Senator doesn't have a religious affiliation. Conclusion: He can't have the personal values required to represent me.
- ○ **D.** Premise: The Senator can't have the personal values required to represent me. Conclusion: He doesn't have a religious affiliation.

b. Briefly describe how the stated fallacy occurs in the argument. Choose the correct answer below.

- ○ **A.** The conclusion is based on a personal allegation.
- ○ **B.** The conclusion is stated as if it were the only possible conclusion.
- ○ **C.** The conclusion is based on invoking emotion.
- ○ **D.** The conclusion is stated as the opposite as the premise.

ID: 10.1.8

---

9. Consider the following example of the logical fallacy of circular reasoning. Complete parts (a) and (b) below.

Illegal immigration is against the law, so illegal immigrants are criminals.

a. What is the premise? Choose the correct answer below.

- ○ **A.** Illegal immigration.
- ○ **B.** The law.
- ○ **C.** Illegal immigration is against the law.
- ○ **D.** Illegal immigrants are criminals.

b. What is the conclusion? Choose the correct answer below.

- ○ **A.** Illegal immigration.
- ○ **B.** The law.
- ○ **C.** Illegal immigrants are criminals.
- ○ **D.** Criminals are against the law.

Briefly explain how circular reasoning occurs in the argument. Choose the correct answer below.

- ○ **A.** This argument uses ignorance about the truth of a proposition to conclude the opposite.
- ○ **B.** This argument is circular because it questions the motives of the immigrants.
- ○ **C.** This argument is based on a distortion of someone's words or beliefs.
- ○ **D.** The conclusion is a restatement of the premise.

ID: 10.1.9

---

10. Consider the following example of a fallacy. Complete parts **a** and **b** below.

Good grades are needed to get into college, and a college diploma is necessary for a good career. Therefore, attendance should count in high school grades.

a. Identify the premise and conclusion of the argument. Choose the correct answer below.

- ○ **A.** Premise: Good grades are needed to get into college. Conclusion: A college diploma is necessary for a good career.
- ○ **B.** Premise: Good grades are needed to get into college, and a college diploma is necessary for a good career. Conclusion: Attendance should count in high school grades.
- ○ **C.** Premise: A college diploma is necessary for a good career. Conclusion: Attendance should count in high school grades.
- ○ **D.** Premise: Good grades are needed to get into college. Conclusion: Attendance should count in high school grades.

10. (cont.) **b.** Briefly describe how the stated fallacy occurs in the argument. Choose the correct answer below.

- ○ **A.** The conclusion is stated as if it were the only possible conclusion.
- ○ **B.** The conclusion is stated as if it were caused by the premise.
- ○ **C.** The premise is stated as the opposite as the conclusion.
- ○ **D.** The premise directs attention away from the conclusion.

ID: 10.1.10

---

11. Consider the following example of the logical fallacy of straw man. Complete parts (a) and (b) below.

The mayor wants to raise taxes to fund social programs, so she must not believe in the value of hard work.

a. What is the premise? Choose the correct answer below.

- ○ **A.** Social programs
- ○ **B.** She must not believe in the value of hard work.
- ○ **C.** The mayor wants to raise taxes to fund social programs.
- ○ **D.** The mayor

What is the conclusion? Choose the correct answer below.

- ○ **A.** She must not believe in the value of hard work.
- ○ **B.** Social programs require a tax raise.
- ○ **C.** The mayor
- ○ **D.** Social programs

b. Briefly explain how straw man occurs in the argument. Choose the correct answer below.

- ○ **A.** This is a personal attack on the mayor, so it's called a straw man.
- ○ **B.** The conclusion is a restatement of the premise.
- ○ **C.** The mayor is characterized (perhaps wrongly) by one quality, on which the conclusion is based.
- ○ **D.** It artificially precludes choices that ought to be considered.

ID: 10.1.11

---

12. This argument involves some kind of fallacy. Identify the fallacy.

After getting new dishes, I started to sneeze. I must be allergic to the new dishes.

- ○ **A.** Personal attack (ad hominem)
- ○ **B.** Circular reasoning
- ○ **C.** False cause
- ○ **D.** Hasty generalization

ID: 10.1.12

---

13. In the following argument, identify the premise and conclusion, explain why the argument is deceptive, and, if possible, identify the type of fallacy it represents.

All the mayors in my hometown have been men, which shows that men are better qualified for high office than women.

Identify the premise. Choose the correct answer below.

- ○ **A.** Men are better qualified for high office than women.
- ○ **B.** Mayors of a certain town.
- ○ **C.** Men in high office.
- ○ **D.** All the mayors of my hometown have been men.

Identify the conclusion. Choose the correct answer below.

- ○ **A.** Men in high office.
- ○ **B.** Women need more representation in high office.
- ○ **C.** Mayors of a certain town.
- ○ **D.** Men are better qualified for high office than women.

13. (cont.) Explain why the argument is deceptive. Choose the correct answer below.

○ **A.** The argument is deceptive because it makes a generalization about men in office that is used to make a claim about women in office. The premise has nothing to do with how qualified women are in office.

○ **B.** The argument is deceptive because it appeals to the popular notion that men are more qualified than women for high office, even though the premise has nothing to do with how qualified women are in office.

○ **C.** The argument is deceptive because it restates the premise in other words to reach the conclusion.

○ **D.** The argument is deceptive because it appeals to the ignorant notion that men are more qualified than women for high office, even though the premise has nothing to do with how qualified women are in office.

Which type of fallacy does the argument represent?

○ **A.** Circular Reasoning

○ **B.** Hasty Generalization

○ **C.** Appeal to Popularity

○ **D.** Appeal to Ignorance

ID: 10.1.13

---

14. The argument involves some kind of fallacy. Identify the fallacy.

When confronted with questions from the press about alleged scandals, a congressman replies that the allegations against him should be ignored since his accuser is part of a vast right-wing conspiracy.

○ **A.** Limited choice

○ **B.** Appeal to popularity

○ **C.** Personal attack (ad hominem)

○ **D.** Circular reasoning

ID: 10.1.14

---

*15. In the following argument, identify the premise and conclusion, explain why the argument is deceptive, and, if possible, identify the type of fallacy it represents.

My baby was vaccinated and later developed autism, which is why I believe that vaccines cause autism.

Identify the premise. Choose the correct answer below.

○ **A.** I believe that vaccines cause autism.

○ **B.** Autism.

○ **C.** My baby was vaccinated and later developed autism.

○ **D.** Vaccines.

Identify the conclusion. Choose the correct answer below.

○ **A.** Vaccines aren't good.

○ **B.** Babies should not be vaccinated.

○ **C.** Autism needs more attention in the medical field.

○ **D.** I believe that vaccines cause autism.

Explain why the argument is deceptive. Choose the correct answer below.

○ **A.** The argument is deceptive because it attempts to show that because there is no proof that vaccines cause autism, vaccines cannot cause autism.

○ **B.** The argument is deceptive because it makes a generalization about vaccines based on too few cases.

○ **C.** The argument is deceptive because it claims that many people believe that vaccines cause autism, so vaccines must cause autism.

○ **D.** The argument is deceptive because it attempts to create a link between vaccines and autism. The premise of the argument does not fully support the conclusion.

Which type of fallacy does the argument represent?

○ **A.** False Cause

○ **B.** Appeal to Ignorance

○ **C.** Hasty Generalization

○ **D.** Appeal to Popularity

ID: 10.1.15

---

16. In the following argument, identify the premise and conclusion, explain why the argument is deceptive, and, if possible, identify the type of fallacy it represents.

Everyone loves Shakespeare, because his plays have been read for many centuries.

Identify the premise. Choose the correct answer below.

- ○ **A.** Shakespeare's plays have been read for many centuries.
- ○ **B.** The number of centuries.
- ○ **C.** Shakespeare's plays.
- ○ **D.** Everyone loves Shakespeare.

Identify the conclusion. Choose the correct answer below.

- ○ **A.** The number of centuries is large.
- ○ **B.** Everyone loves Shakespeare.
- ○ **C.** Shakespeare's plays are good.
- ○ **D.** His plays have been read for many centuries.

Explain why the argument is deceptive. Choose the correct answer below.

- ○ **A.** The argument is deceptive because it assumes that many people reading Shakespeare's plays is evidence that those people actually like Shakespeare.
- ○ **B.** The argument is deceptive because it makes a generalization about the people who read Shakespeare's plays based on too few cases.
- ○ **C.** The argument is deceptive because the premise and conclusion essentially say the same thing, so the argument seems logical.
- ○ **D.** The argument is deceptive because it assumes that because Shakespeare's plays have been read for centuries, Shakespeare's plays are good. This is not necessarily the case.

Which type of fallacy does the argument represent?

- ○ **A.** False Cause
- ○ **B.** Hasty Generalization
- ○ **C.** Appeal to Popularity
- ○ **D.** Circular Reasoning

ID: 10.1.16

---

17. In the following argument, identify the premise and conclusion, explain why the argument is deceptive, and identify the type of fallacy it represents.

I will not give money to the tsunami relief organization. After I last gave to a charity, an audit showed that most of the money was used to pay its administrators in the front office.

Choose the correct premise and conclusion of the argument below.

- ○ **A.** Premise: After I last gave to a charity, an audit showed that most of the money was used to pay its administrators in the front office. Conclusion: I will not give money to the tsunami relief organization.
- ○ **B.** Premise: I will give money to the tsunami relief organization. Conclusion: After I last gave to a charity, an audit showed that most of the money was used to pay its administrators in the front office.
- ○ **C.** Premise: I will not give money to the tsunami relief organization. Conclusion: After I last gave to a charity, an audit showed that most of the money was used to pay its administrators in the front office
- ○ **D.** Premise: After I last gave to a charity, an audit showed that most of the money was used to pay its administrators in the front office. Conclusion: I will give money to the tsunami relief organization.

Choose the best explanation for why the fallacy is deceptive.

- ○ **A.** The premise is stated as the opposite as the conclusion and uses ignorance about the truth to conclude the opposite.
- ○ **B.** The conclusion is based on a personal allegation and uses ignorance about the truth to conclude the opposite.
- ○ **C.** The conclusion is based on a personal allegation and stated as if it were caused by the premise.
- ○ **D.** The conclusion is stated as if it were the only possible conclusion and the premise is stated as the opposite as the conclusion.

Choose the type of fallacy the argument represents. Select all that apply.

- ☐ **A.** straw man
- ☐ **B.** limited choice
- ☐ **C.** personal attack
- ☐ **D.** appeal to ignorance
- ☐ **E.** circular reasoning

ID: 10.1.17

---

18. In the following argument, identify the premise and conclusion, explain why the argument is deceptive, and identify the type of fallacy it represents.

The Congressperson is a member of a national firearms club, so I'm sure she will not suppport a ban on rifles.

Choose the correct premise and conclusion of the argument below.

- **A.** Premise: The Congressperson is a member of a national firearms club. Conclusion: I'm sure she will not suppport a ban on rifles.
- **B.** Premise: I'm sure the Congressperson may suppport a ban on rifles. Conclusion: She is a member of a national firearms club.
- **C.** Premise: I'm sure the Congressperson will not suppport a ban on rifles. Conclusion: She is a member of a national firearms club.
- **D.** Premise: The Congressperson is a member of a national firearms club. Conclusion: I'm sure she may suppport a ban on rifles.

Choose the best explanation for why the fallacy is deceptive.

- **A.** The conclusion is based on a personal allegation and a distortion of someone's words or beliefs.
- **B.** The conclusion is stated as if it were the only possible conclusion and the premise is stated as the opposite as the conclusion.
- **C.** The conclusion is based on the distortion of someone's words or beliefs and the premise is stated as the opposite as the conclusion.
- **D.** The conclusion is based on a personal allegation and stated as if it were caused by the premise.

Choose the type of fallacy the argument represents. Select all that apply.

- **A.** circular reasoning
- **B.** personal attack
- **C.** straw man
- **D.** hasty generalization
- **E.** appeal to ignorance

ID: 10.1.18

---

19. This argument involves some kind of fallacy. Identify the fallacy.

One candidate favors eliminating affirmative action programs. The other candidate states: "My opponent doesn't think there's anything wrong with discrimination."

- **A.** Hasty generalization
- **B.** Straw man
- **C.** Limited choice
- **D.** Personal attack (ad hominem)

ID: 10.1.19

---

20. In the following argument, identify the premise(s) and conclusion, explain why the argument is deceptive, and identify the type of fallacy it represents.

My little boy loves dolls and my little girl loves trucks, so there's no truth to the claim that boys are more interested in mechanical toys while girls prefer maternal toys.

Identify the premise(s) and conclusion of the argument. Choose the correct answer below.

- **A.** Premise: It's not true that little boys are more interested in mechanical toys and girls prefer maternal toys. Conclusion: My little boy loves dolls and my little girl loves trucks.
- **B.** Premise: My little boy loves dolls. Conclusion: It's not true that little boys are more interested in mechanical toys and girls prefer maternal toys.
- **C.** Premise: My little boy loves dolls and my little girl loves trucks. Conclusion: It's not true that little boys are more interested in mechanical toys and girls prefer maternal toys.
- **D.** Premise: My little girl loves trucks. Conclusion: It's not true that little boys are more interested in mechanical toys and girls prefer maternal toys.

20. (cont.) Explain why the argument is deceptive. Choose the correct answer below.

○ **A.** The conclusion is stated as if it were the only possible conclusion and uses ignorance about the truth to conclude the opposite.

○ **B.** The conclusion is based on a personal allegation and stated as if it were caused by the premise.

○ **C.** The conclusion is drawn from an inadequate number of cases and uses ignorance about the truth to conclude the opposite.

○ **D.** The premise is stated as the opposite as the conclusion and is drawn from an inadequate number of cases.

Identify the type of fallacy the argument represents. Select all that apply.

☐ **A.** hasty generalization

☐ **B.** personal attack

☐ **C.** limited choice

☐ **D.** circular reasoning

☐ **E.** appeal to ignorance

ID: 10.1.20

---

21. Consider the following fallacy (which was not discussed in the text). Explain why the fallacy applies to the example.

Tha fallacy of division has the following form.

Premise: X has some property.
Conclusion: All things or people that belong to X must have the same property.
Example: Americans use more gasoline than Europeans, so Jake, who is American, must use more gasoline than Europeans.

Choose the correct answer below.

○ **A.** Jake is not European, so he uses a lot of gasoline.

○ **B.** X is the amount of gasoline used, and Jake uses a lot of gasoline because he is American.

○ **C.** Americans have some property, which is using more gasoline that Europeans. Therefore, Jake must have the same property of using more gasoline than Europeans.

○ **D.** An Americans uses more gasoline than Europeans, and so does every other American on Earth.

ID: 10.1.21

---

* 22. Consider the following fallacy (which was not discussed in the text). Explain why the fallacy applies to the example.

The slippery slope fallacy has the following form.

Premise: X has occurred and is related to Y.
Conclusion: Y will inevitably occur.
Example: America has sent troops to three countries recently. Before you know it, we will have troops everywhere.

Choose the correct answer below.

○ **A.** Let X be America having troops everywhere. Let Y be America sending troops to three countries recently. This is inevitable because America has troops everywhere.

○ **B.** Let X be America sending troops to three countries recently. Let Y be America having troops everywhere. The two events are related, and Y will inevitably occur.

○ **C.** Let Y be America sending troops to three countries recently. This is inevitable because soon there will be troops everywhere.

○ **D.** America will inevitably send troops to other countries because many countries send troops to other countries.

ID: 10.1.22

---

23. Consider the following fallacy (which was not discussed in the text). Explain why the fallacy applies to the example.

The middle ground fallacy has the following form.

Premise: X and Y are two extreme positions on a question.
Conclusion: Z, which lies between X and Y, must be correct.
Example: Senator Peters supports a large tax cut, and Senator Willis supports no tax cut. That means a small tax cut must be best.

23. (cont.) Choose the correct answer below.

- ○ **A.** The mayor chose a middle ground position, therefore it's a middle ground fallacy.
- ○ **B.** Let X be no tax cut and Y be a tax cut. A small tax cut lies between no tax cut and a tax cut. Let Z be a small tax cut.
- ○ **C.** Let X be no tax cut and Y be a small tax cut. There doesn't need to be a Z because it is implied.
- ○ **D.** Let Z be the Mayor's decision for no tax cut, which is not an extreme position.

ID: 10.1.23

---

24. Determine if the following statement is a proposition, and give an explanation.

December 25 was not celebrated as the birth date of Christ until the year 440 A.D.

Is the given statement a proposition?

- ○ **A.** No, because the given statement can be either true or false, but it is not a complete sentence.
- ○ **B.** Yes, because the given statement can be either true or false, and it is a complete sentence.
- ○ **C.** No, because the given statement is false.
- ○ **D.** Yes, because the given statement is true, and it is a complete sentence.

ID: 10.1.24

---

25. Determine if the following statement is a proposition, and give an explanation.

Back to the past.

Is the given statement a proposition?

- ○ **A.** No, because the statement makes a claim, but it is not a complete sentence.
- ○ **B.** Yes, because the statement makes a claim that is true.
- ○ **C.** Yes, because the statement makes a claim, and it is a complete sentence.
- ○ **D.** No, because the statement does not make a claim, and it is not a complete sentence.

ID: 10.1.25

---

26. Determine if the following statement is a proposition, and give an explanation.

Who cares?

Is the given statement a proposition?

- ○ **A.** No, because the statement does not make a claim; it is a question.
- ○ **B.** Yes, because the statement is a question, which makes a claim.
- ○ **C.** No, because the statement is not a complete sentence.
- ○ **D.** Yes, because the statement makes a claim, and it is a complete sentence.

ID: 10.1.26

---

* 27. Write the negation of the proposition. Then state the truth value of the original proposition and its negation.

China is in Europe.

Write the negation of the proposition. Choose the correct answer below.

- ○ **A.** China is never in Asia.
- ○ **B.** China is sometimes not in Europe.
- ○ **C.** China is in Asia.
- ○ **D.** China is not in Europe.

The truth value of the original proposition is (1) __________

The truth value of the negation is (2) __________

(1) ○ true. ○ false.   (2) ○ false. ○ true.

ID: 10.1.27

---

28. Write the negation of the proposition. Then state the truth value of the original proposition and its negation.

Friday does not come before Saturday.

Write the negation of the proposition. Choose the correct answer below.

- A. Saturday does come before Friday.
- B. It is not true that Friday comes before Saturday.
- C. Friday comes before Saturday.
- D. Sometimes Friday does not come before Saturday.

The truth value of the original proposition is (1) ____________

The truth value of the negation is (2) ____________

(1) ○ false. (2) ○ false.
○ true. ○ true.

ID: 10.1.28

---

29. Explain the meaning of the given statement, which contains a mulitple negation. Then answer the question that follows.
Sarah did not decline the offer to go to dinner. Did Sarah go to dinner?

Choose the correct answer below.

- A. The first negation "decline the offer" makes it seem that Sarah would not go to dinner. The statement reinforces this negation, "did not decline the offer." Therefore, Sarah declines the offer to go to dinner.
- B. The first negation "decline the offer" makes it seem that Sarah would go to dinner. But the statement negates this negation, "did not decline the offer." Therefore, Sarah declines the offer to go to dinner.
- C. The first negation "decline the offer" makes it seem that Sarah would go to dinner. The statement reinforces this negation, "did not decline the offer." Therefore, Sarah accepts the offer to go to dinner.
- D. The first negation "decline the offer" makes it seem that Sarah would not go to dinner. But the statement negates this negation, "did not decline the offer." Therefore, Sarah accepts the offer to go to dinner.

ID: 10.1.29

---

30. Explain the meaning of the given statement, which contains a multiple negation. Did the Congressman vote in favor of discrimination?

The Congressman voted against the anti-discrimination bill.

Choose the correct answer below.

- A. The statement means that the Congressman did not vote in favor of a bill that does not favor discrimination. So, the Congressman voted against discrimination.
- B. The statement means that the Congressman voted in favor of a bill that does not favor discrimination. So, the Congressman voted against discrimination.
- C. The statement means that the Congressman did not vote in favor of a bill that favors discrimination. So, the Congressman voted in favor of discrimination.
- D. The statement means that the Congressman did not vote in favor of a bill that does not favor discrimination. So, the Congressman voted in favor of discrimination.

ID: 10.1.30

---

31. Explain the meaning of the given statement, which contains a mulitple negation. Then answer the question that follows.

Paul denies that he opposes the plan to build a new dorm. Does Paul support building a new dorm?

Choose the correct answer below.

- A. The first negation "opposes the plan" makes it seem that Paul supports the new dorm. The statement reinforces this negation, "Paul denies that he opposes the plan." Therefore, it seems that Paul supports the plan for the new dorm.
- B. The first negation "opposes the plan" makes it seem that Paul would not support the new dorm. The statement reinforces this negation, "Paul denies that he opposes the plan." Therefore, it seems that Paul opposes the plan for the new dorm.
- C. The first negation "opposes the plan" makes it seem that Paul would not support the new dorm. But the statement negates this negation, "Paul denies that he opposes the plan." Therefore, it seems that Paul supports the plan for the new dorm.
- D. The first negation "opposes the plan" makes it seem that Paul supports the new dorm. But the statement negates this negation, "Paul denies that he opposes the plan." Therefore, it seems that Paul opposes the plan for the new dorm.

ID: 10.1.31

---

32. Make a truth table for the given statement. Assume that q and s represent propositions.

if q, then s

Complete the truth table.

q	s	if q, then s
T	T	(1) ____
T	F	(2) ____
F	T	(3) ____
F	F	(4) ____

(1) ○ T ○ F (2) ○ T ○ F (3) ○ F ○ T (4) ○ F ○ T

ID: 10.1.32

---

*33. Identify the hypothesis and conclusion in the following proposition, and state their truth values. Then determine whether the entire proposition is true or false.

If tigers can run, then tigers have flippers.

State the hypothesis and conclusion, and give their truth values.

The hypothesis is (1) ____ which is (2) ____ The conclusion is (3) ____ which is (4) ____

Is the entire proposition true or false? ○ False ○ True

(1) ○ tigers have flippers, ○ tigers can run, (2) ○ true. ○ false. (3) ○ tigers have flippers, ○ tigers can run, (4) ○ false. ○ true.

ID: 10.1.33

---

34. Identify the hypothesis and conclusion in the following proposition, and state their truth values. Then determine whether the entire proposition is true or false.

If Tokyo is in Japan, then New York is in Mongolia.

State the hypothesis and conclusion, and give their truth values.

The hypothesis is (1) ____ which is (2) ____ The conclusion is (3) ____ which is (4) ____

Is the entire proposition true or false? ○ False ○ True

(1) ○ Tokyo is in Japan, ○ New York is in Mongolia, (2) ○ false. ○ true. (3) ○ Tokyo is in Japan, ○ New York is in Mongolia, (4) ○ false. ○ true.

ID: 10.1.34

---

35. Identify the hypothesis and conclusion in the statement, and state their truth values. Then determine whether the entire statement is true or false and explain why.

If $14 + 6 = 8$, then America has a queen.

What is the hypothesis in the statement? ○ $14 + 6 = 8$ ○ America has a queen

What is the conclusion in the statement? ○ America has a queen ○ $14 + 6 = 8$

Is the hypothesis true or false? ○ true ○ false

Is the conclusion true or false? ○ false ○ true

Is the statement true or false?

○ **A.** The statement is false since the hypothesis is false and the conclusion is false.
○ **B.** The statement is true since the hypothesis is true and the conclusion is true.
○ **C.** The statement is true since the hypothesis is false and the conclusion is false.
○ **D.** The statement is false since the hypothesis is true and the conclusion is true.

ID: 10.1.35

* 36. Express the following statement in the form *if p, then q*. Identify p and q clearly.

Whenever it rains, I get wet.

Identify p and q. Choose the correct answer below.

- ○ **A.** p = it rains; q = I get wet
- ○ **B.** p = I get wet; q = it rains

Which statement below is a correct wording of the given statement with the form *if p, then q*?

- ○ **A.** If it is not raining, then I do not get wet.
- ○ **B.** If I get wet, then it rains.
- ○ **C.** If it rains, then I get wet.
- ○ **D.** If it does not rain, then I get wet.

ID: 10.1.36

---

37. Express the following statement in the form *if p, then q*. Identify p and q clearly.

Winning is a sufficient condition for not losing.

Identify p and q. Choose the correct answer below.

- ○ **A.** p = you are not losing; q = you are winning
- ○ **B.** p = you are winning; q = you are not losing

Which statement below is a correct wording of the given statement with the form *if p, then q*?

- ○ **A.** If you are not losing, then you are winning.
- ○ **B.** If you are not winning, then you are losing.
- ○ **C.** If you are winning, then you are not losing.
- ○ **D.** If you are winning, then you are losing.

ID: 10.1.37

---

* 38. Write the converse, inverse, and contrapositive of the following proposition. Of these four propositions, state which pairs are equivalent.

If Jose owns a computer, then he owns a PC.

Identify the converse. Choose the correct answer below.

- ○ **A.** If Jose does not own a computer, then he does not own a PC.
- ○ **B.** If Jose owns a PC, then he owns a computer.
- ○ **C.** If Jose owns a PC, then he does not own a computer.
- ○ **D.** If Jose does not own a PC, then he does not own a computer.

Identify the inverse. Choose the correct answer below.

- ○ **A.** If Jose does not own a computer, then he does not own a PC.
- ○ **B.** If Jose owns a PC, then he does not own a computer.
- ○ **C.** If Jose owns a PC, then he owns a computer.
- ○ **D.** If Jose does not own a PC, then he does not own a computer.

Identify the contrapositive. Choose the correct answer below.

- ○ **A.** If Jose does not own a PC, then he does not own a computer.
- ○ **B.** If Jose does not own a computer, then he does not own a PC.
- ○ **C.** If Jose owns a PC, then he does not own a computer.
- ○ **D.** If Jose owns a PC, then he owns a computer.

Select all pairs of propositions that are logically equivalent.

- ☐ **A.** Conditional and contrapositive
- ☐ **B.** Conditional and converse
- ☐ **C.** Inverse and contrapositive
- ☐ **D.** Conditional and inverse
- ☐ **E.** Converse and inverse
- ☐ **F.** Converse and contrapositive

ID: 10.1.38

---

39. Write the converse, inverse, and contrapositive of the following proposition. Of these four propositions, state which pairs are equivalent.

If Teresa works in Michigan, then she works in the North.

Identify the converse. Choose the correct answer below.

- ○ **A.** If Teresa works in the North, then she works in Michigan.
- ○ **B.** If Teresa does not work in Michigan, then she does not work in the North.
- ○ **C.** If Teresa works in Michigan, then she does not work in the North.
- ○ **D.** If Teresa does not work in the North, then she does not work in Michigan.

Identify the inverse. Choose the correct answer below.

- ○ **A.** If Teresa does not work in Michigan, then she does not work in the North.
- ○ **B.** If Teresa does not work in the North, then she does not work in Michigan.
- ○ **C.** If Teresa works in Michigan, then she does not work in the North.
- ○ **D.** If Teresa works in the North, then she works in Michigan.

Identify the contrapositive. Choose the correct answer below.

- ○ **A.** If Teresa works in Michigan, then she does not work in the North.
- ○ **B.** If Teresa does not work in Michigan, then she does not work in the North.
- ○ **C.** If Teresa does not work in the North, then she does not work in Michigan.
- ○ **D.** If Teresa works in the North, then she works in Michigan.

Select all pairs of propositions that are logically equivalent.

- ☐ **A.** Conditional and inverse
- ☐ **B.** Conditional and contrapositive
- ☐ **C.** Converse and inverse
- ☐ **D.** Conditional and converse
- ☐ **E.** Converse and contrapositive
- ☐ **F.** Inverse and contrapositive

ID: 10.1.39

---

40. Write the converse, inverse, and contrapositive of the following proposition. Of these four propositions, state which pairs are equivalent.

If the clouds are dark, then it is wet outside.

Identify the converse. Choose the correct answer below.

- ○ **A.** If it is not wet outside, then the clouds are not dark.
- ○ **B.** If it is wet outside, then the clouds are dark.
- ○ **C.** If the clouds are not dark, then it is not wet outside.
- ○ **D.** If the clouds are dark, then it is not wet outside.

Identify the inverse. Choose the correct answer below.

- ○ **A.** If it is not wet outside, then the clouds are not dark.
- ○ **B.** If the clouds are not dark, then it is not wet outside.
- ○ **C.** If the clouds are dark, then it is not wet outside.
- ○ **D.** If it is wet outside, then the clouds are dark.

Identify the contrapositive. Choose the correct answer below.

- ○ **A.** If the clouds are not dark, then it is not wet outside.
- ○ **B.** If the clouds are dark, then it is not wet outside.
- ○ **C.** If it is wet outside, then the clouds are dark.
- ○ **D.** If it is not wet outside, then the clouds are not dark.

Select all pairs of propositions that are logically equivalent.

- ☐ **A.** Converse and inverse
- ☐ **B.** Conditional and inverse
- ☐ **C.** Conditional and converse
- ☐ **D.** Converse and contrapositive
- ☐ **E.** Inverse and contrapositive
- ☐ **F.** Conditional and contrapositive

ID: 10.1.40

41. Rephrase the following statement using one or more conditional statements (*if p, then q*).

Only the healthy live a long life.

Rephrase the given statement. Choose the correct answer below.

- ○ **A.** If you live a long life, then you are healthy.
- ○ **B.** If you do not live a long life, then you are not healthy.
- ○ **C.** If you are healthy, then you live a long life.
- ○ **D.** If you are not healthy, then you live a long life.

ID: 10.1.41

---

42. Rephrase the following statement using one or more conditional statements (*if p, then q*).

If you cannot help the many, you cannot save the few.

Rephrase the given statement. Choose the correct answer below.

- ○ **A.** If you cannot save the few, then you cannot help the many.
- ○ **B.** If you help the many, then you save the few.
- ○ **C.** If you save the few, then you help the many.
- ○ **D.** If you cannot help the many, then you save the few.

ID: 10.1.42

---

43. Write the following conditional statement in the form (a) 'p is sufficient for q' and (b) 'q is necessary for p.'

If you believe, then you can achieve. –Tupac Shakur

a. Choose the correct answer below.

- ○ **A.** Achieving is sufficient for believing.
- ○ **B.** Believing is sufficient for achieving.

b. Choose the correct answer below.

- ○ **A.** Believing is necessary for achieving.
- ○ **B.** Achieving is necessary for believing.

ID: 10.1.43

---

44. Write the following conditional statement in the form (a) 'p is sufficient for q' and (b) 'q is necessary for p.'

If we ever forget that we are One Nation Under God, then we will be a nation gone under. –Ronald Reagan

a. Choose the correct answer below.

- ○ **A.** Being a nation gone under is sufficient for forgetting that we are One Nation Under God.
- ○ **B.** Forgetting that we are One Nation Under God is sufficient for being a nation gone under.

b. Choose the correct answer below.

- ○ **A.** Being a nation gone under is a necessary result of forgetting that we are One Nation Under God.
- ○ **B.** Forgetting that we are One Nation Under God is necessary for being a nation gone under.

ID: 10.1.44

---

45. Explain why the contrapositive is called the inverse of the converse. Is the contrapositive also the converse of the inverse?

The converse of a conditional statement 'if p, then q' is (1) ________ The inverse of a conditional statement 'if p, then q' is (2) ________ So, the inverse of the converse is (3) ________ which is known as the contrapositive. The converse of the inverse would be (4) ________ which is (5) ________ as the contrapositive.

(1)
- ○ 'if q, then p.'
- ○ 'if not p, then q.'
- ○ 'if not p, then not q.'
- ○ 'if not q, then not p.'
- ○ 'if p, then not q.'

(2)
- ○ 'if q, then p.'
- ○ 'if not q, then not p.'
- ○ 'if not p, then q.'
- ○ 'if not p, then not q.'
- ○ 'if p, then not q.'

45. (cont.)

(3) ○ 'if not p, then q.'
○ 'if not p, then not q,'
○ 'if not q, then not p,'
○ 'if p, then not q.'
○ 'if q, then p,'

(4) ○ 'if q, then p,'
○ 'if p, then not q.'
○ 'if not q, then not p,'
○ 'if not p, then not q,'
○ 'if not p, then q.'

(5) ○ the same
○ not the same

ID: 10.1.45

---

46. Describe whether the following statement makes sense (or is clearly true) or does not make sense (or is clearly false). Explain your reasoning.

Reed was relieved because his insurance company chose not to deny his claim.

Choose the correct answer below.

○ **A.** The statement does not make sense. The insurance company accepted Reed's claim, so it does not make sense that Reed is relieved.
○ **B.** The statement makes sense. The insurance company accepted Reed's claim, so it makes sense that Reed is relieved.
○ **C.** The statement does not make sense. The insurance company denied Reed's claim, so it does not make sense that Reed is relieved.
○ **D.** The statement makes sense. The insurance company denied Reed's claim, so it makes sense that Reed is relieved.

ID: 10.1.46

---

47. Decide whether the statement makes sense (or is clearly true) or does not make sense (or is clearly false).

Javier takes a shower to save time. When he gets into the shower at 6:50, he is out by 7:10. When he used to take baths, it would take him a quarter of an hour.

○ Does not make sense
○ Makes sense

ID: 10.1.47

---

48. Describe whether the following statement makes sense (or is clearly true) or does not make sense (or is clearly false). Explain your reasoning.

Alan decided to buy his ticket online for \$33 plus a 10% surcharge rather than from the box office, where it costs \$35 with no additional charges.

Choose the correct answer below.

○ **A.** The statement makes sense. \$33 is cheaper than \$35, so it makes sense that Alan would buy the ticket online.
○ **B.** The statement does not make sense. \$33 plus a 10% surcharge is more than \$35, so it does not make sense that Alan would buy the ticket online.
○ **C.** The statement makes sense. \$33 plus a 10% surcharge is less than \$35, so it makes sense that Alan would buy the ticket online.
○ **D.** The statement does not make sense. A 10% surcharge is more than no surcharge, so it doesn't make sense that Alan would buy the ticket online.

ID: 10.1.48

---

49. Decide whether the statement makes sense (or is clearly true) or does not make sense (or is clearly false).

Wayne's bank charges a \$1 service charge for every transaction. To save money, he withdraws \$100 cash every other week instead of withdrawing \$50 each week.

○ Makes sense
○ Does not make sense

ID: 10.1.49

---

50. Give an answer and explanation for the following question.

Jose had 10 bagels and ate all but 8 of them. How many bagels were left?

There were ________ bagels left because he ate ________ of them.

ID: 10.1.50

---

51. Give an answer and an explanation for the following question.

A farmer's rooster laid an egg in a neighbor's yard. Who owns the egg?

Choose the correct answer below.

- **A.** The neighbor owns the egg because it was laid in his or her yard.
- **B.** The town owns the egg because no clear ownership can be determined.
- **C.** The farmer owns the egg because it was the farmer's rooster.
- **D.** Roosters don't lay eggs.

ID: 10.1.51

---

52. Give an answer and an explanation for the following question.

A large barrel is filled with 11 different kinds of fruit. At least how many individual fruits must you remove from the barrel (without looking) to be certain that you have two of the same fruit?

Select the correct choice below and, if necessary, fill in the answer box to complete your choice.

- **A.** You must remove at least ________ individual fruits, since it is possible that you will remove a different fruit each time you remove a fruit from the barrel.
- **B.** You must remove 2 individual fruits, since it is possible that you will remove the same fruit twice in a row.

ID: 10.1.52

---

53. Suppose you go to a party with four Americans and four Canadians, none of whom you have met. How many people must you meet to be sure of meeting one Canadian and one American?

You must meet ________ people.

ID: 10.1.53

---

54. Suppose you go to a party with four Americans and four Canadians, none of whom you have met. How many people must you meet to be sure of meeting two Canadians?

You must meet ________ people.

ID: 10.1.54

---

55. Suzanne goes bowling at least one day per week, but never on two consecutive days. List all the numbers of days per week that Suzanne could go bowling.

How many days a week can Suzanne go bowling?

- **A.** 1, 2, 3, 4, or 5 days
- **B.** 1, 2, 3, or 4 days
- **C.** 1, 2, or 3 days
- **D.** 1 or 2 days

ID: 10.1.55

---

56. Half of the class consists of communication majors, and half of the class consists of men. Does it follow that one quarter of the class is male communication majors?

Choose the correct answer below.

- Yes
- No

ID: 10.1.56

---

57. Give an answer and an explanation for the following question.

Half of a country's exports consist of corn, and half of the corn is from the state of Caldonia. Does it follow that one quarter of the exports consist of corn from Caldonia?

Choose the correct answer below.

- A. No, because it is possible that half of the exports come from Caldonia and the other half of the exports consist of corn.
- B. Yes, because one half of one half is one quarter.
- C. Yes, because half of the exports come from Caldonia and the other half of the exports consist of corn.
- D. No, because there is no link between the corn the country exports and the corn that comes from Caldonia.

ID: 10.1.57

---

58. A city charter's policy on reelection states the following.

A person who has served three consecutive terms of four years shall be eligible for appointment, nomination for or election to the office of councilmember no sooner than for a term beginning eight years after completion of that councilmember's third consecutive full term.

Use this statement to answer parts **a** through **d**.

a. What is the maximum number of consecutive years that a councilmember could serve?

____________ (Type a whole number.)

b. How many years must a councilmember who has served three consecutive full terms wait before running for office again?

____________ (Type a whole number.)

c. Suppose a councilmember has served two consecutive full terms and is then defeated for reelection. According to this provision, is she or he required to wait 8 years before running for office again?

- Yes
- No

d. Suppose a councilmember serves three consecutive terms and is reelected 10 years later. According to this provision, how many consecutive terms can she or he serve at that time?

____________ (Type a whole number.)

ID: 10.1.58

---

59. Explain how the following quote is ambiguous.

Two jumbo jets with more than 350 people aboard nearly collided during a landing attempt.

What additional information is needed to remove the ambiguity?

- A. State whether or not the jets were able to land.
- B. Specify what the distance was between the two jets.
- C. Specify if there were 350 people on each jet or both jets combined.
- D. Specify the size of the jets.

ID: 10.1.59

---

60. Explain how the following quote is ambiguous. What additional information is needed to remove the ambiguity?

Last night I shot an elephant in my pajamas. –Groucho Marx

Choose the correct answer below.

- A. It is unknown whether Groucho is wearing the elephant's pajamas or the elephant is wearing his own pajamas. This information needs to be known to remove the ambiguity.
- B. The person who shot the elephant is unknown. This information needs to be known to remove the ambiguity.
- C. The time that the shooting took place is unknown. This information needs to be known to remove the ambiguity.
- D. It is unknown whether Groucho is wearing his own pajamas or the elephant is wearing Groucho's pajamas. This information needs to be known to remove the ambiguity.

ID: 10.1.60

---

61. Two assistant district attorneys, Alice and Zack, are running for the position of district attorney. The candidates make the following statements.

Zack: In the last five years, Alice has prosecuted 111 defendants charged with sexual assault on children. Of those, only eleven cases even went to trial, and of those, only five cases resulted in conviction and a prison sentence.

Alice: I have prosecuted 268 cases involving sexual assault on children. More than 55% of the 268 cases resulted in prison or jail sentences as part of the original plea agreement.

Comment on whether the two candidates' numbers for cases prosecuted by Alice are consistent.

Choose the correct answer below.

- **A.** They are not consistent because the number of cases Alice claims she has prosecuted is significantly larger than the number of cases Zack claims Alice prosecuted.
- **B.** They are not consistent because Alice does not specify the time period for her 268 cases.
- **C.** They are not consistent because 55% of 268 is more than eleven.
- **D.** They could be consistent because Alice does not specify the time period for her 268 cases.

ID: 10.1.61

---

62. An end-user license agreement (EULA) is a contract between a software manufacturer and a user that spells out the terms of use of the software. Within the many pages of the EULA for Company A's online store are the following clauses.

1. Company A reserves the right at any time to modify this Agreement and to impose new or additional terms or conditions on your use of the online store. Such modifications and additional terms and conditions will be effective immediately and incorporated into this Agreement. Your continued use of the online store will be deemed acceptance thereof.
2. Company A is not responsible for typographic errors.

Complete parts (a) through (d) below.

a. Do new conditions for the use of the online store need to be approved by the user?

- **A.** No, because new conditions are added directly to the agreement.
- **B.** Yes, because the user is responsible for checking the EULA for changes to approve them.
- **C.** No, because new conditions go into effect immediately, without user approval.
- **D.** Yes, because new conditions are approved by the user before going into effect.

b. Are users notified of changes in the EULA?

- **A.** Yes, because the user is responsible for checking the EULA for changes.
- **B.** Yes, because continued use of the service implies acceptance.
- **C.** No, because new conditions are added directly to the agreement, without user approval. Since users do not approve of the changes, they are not notified of them.
- **D.** Not necessarily, because continued use of the service implies acceptance.

c. What potential risks for the user do you see in clause (1)?

- **A.** New conditions may not affect the user.
- **B.** New conditions that affect the user could go into effect without user knowledge or approval.
- **C.** Company A may never change the EULA.
- **D.** The user could discontinue service if they do not approve of the changes.

d. What potential risks for the user do you see in clause (2)?

- **A.** Typographical errors may cause confusion in some other EULA clauses.
- **B.** Company A should be responsible for any typographical errors in their EULA.
- **C.** There is no way to distinguish a typographical error from a deliberate attempt to take advantage of users.
- **D.** Company A could deliberately make typographical errors for no reason.

ID: 10.1.62

---

63. Analyze the following situation and determine which decision would be the best decision to make. Explain your answer.

A man and his spouse are expecting a baby. Their current health insurance costs $119 per month, but doesn't cover prenatal care or delivery. They can upgrade to a policy that will cover their prenatal care and delivery, but their new premium will be $274 per month. The cost of prenatal care and delivery is approximately $3000.

Select the correct choice below and fill in any answer boxes within your choice.

○ **A.** They should upgrade to the new policy because the current policy costs $ ________ for nine months, which is significantly more than the upgrade which costs $ ________ for nine months.

○ **B.** They should keep their current policy because it costs $ ________ for nine months, which is significantly less than the upgrade which costs $ ________ for nine months.

ID: 10.1.63

---

64. Analyze the following situation, and explain what decision you would make and why.

You fly frequently between two cities 1500 miles apart. Average round-trip cost on Airline A is $325. Airline B offers the same trip for only $300. However, Airline A has a frequent flyer program in which you earn a free round-trip ticket after you fly 26,000 miles. Airline B does not have a frequent flyer program.

Select the correct answer below, and if necessary, fill in the answer boxes to complete your choice.

○ **A.** Flying round-trip under 19 times, Airline ________ is cheaper. Flying round-trip 19 times or more, Airline ________ is cheaper.

○ **B.** Flying round-trip 10 to 13, 20 to 26, or over 29 times, Airline ________ is cheaper. For any other number flights, Airline ________ is cheaper than or equal to the other airline.

○ **C.** Airline A is cheaper for any number of flights.

○ **D.** Airline B is cheaper for any number of flights.

ID: 10.1.64

---

65. Give an explanation for the following fact that is more plausible than the given explanation.

Fact: A football team in Division A has won four out of the last six championship games.
Explanation: More Division A fans attend the championship game, so Division A teams have a home team advantage.

What is a better explanation?

○ **A.** Winning four of six games is only one more win than the three wins that would be expected by pure chance.

○ **B.** The championship game is always played at a team in Division A's field, which gives Division A teams a home team advantage.

○ **C.** The league is purposefully set up to give the teams in Division A an advantage.

○ **D.** The referees favor the teams in Division A in the championship game.

ID: 10.1.65

---

66. Give an explanation for the following fact that is more plausible than the given explanation.

Fact: In the first decade of the 2000s, violent crimes decreased, while the number of inmates in custody increased.
Explanation: There was an increase in false conviction.

What is a better explanation?

○ **A.** The violent crimes in prison were not recorded.

○ **B.** Judges wanted more people to go to prison.

○ **C.** Sentencing by judges and juries became stricter.

○ **D.** The facts are incorrect, since the results are impossible.

ID: 10.1.66

---

67. Describe one way in which both of the statements in the following pair could be true.

A: In some countries, the number of deaths per year has been increasing.
B: In those same countries, the annual death rate (deaths per 100,000 people in the population) has been decreasing.

What is one reason the two statements could both be true?

- A. If the population increases fast enough, then the death rate can decrease while the number of deaths increases.
- B. The facts are incorrect, since it is impossible for the number of deaths per year to increase while the annual death rate decreases.
- C. People are moving out of the countries, so the death rate decreases while the number of deaths increases.
- D. There are not 100,000 people in the countries, so the death rate can decrease while the number of deaths increases.

ID: 10.1.67

68. Describe one way in which both of the statements in the following pair could be true.

A: The gun homicide rate is greater in country X than in country Y.
B: The gun fatality rate is greater in country Y than in country X.

What is one reason the two statements could both be true?

- A. There is a war going on in country Y.
- B. Country Y has a high gun suicide rate.
- C. Country Y has a larger population than in country X.
- D. Country X has a larger population than in country Y.

ID: 10.1.68

!* 69. Determine the output of the following IF functions.
(a) = IF(3< = 3 * 2,15,11)
(b) = IF(9 − 4 = 4 * 3 / 4,"Good","Job")
(c) = IF(9 − 1^3<>2 + 6,"SUPER","SALLY")
(d) = IF(6 * 5< = 2 * 3 * 6,"WOOO","HOOO!")

(a) The output of = IF(3< = 3 * 2,15,11) is (1) ____________

(b) The output of = IF(9 − 4 = 4 * 3 / 4,"Good","Job") is (2) ____________

(c) The output of = IF(9 − 1^3<>2 + 6,"SUPER","SALLY") is (3) ____________

(d) The output of = IF(6 * 5< = 2 * 3 * 6,"WOOO","HOOO!") is (4) ____________

(1) ○ 15. ○ 11.
(2) ○ Good. ○ Job.
(3) ○ SUPER. ○ SALLY.
(4) ○ WOOO. ○ HOOO!

ID: 10.2.1

!* 70. The owner of a mail order catalog wants to charge a shipping fee of 4% of the sub-total unless the sub-total is over $100, in which case the owner wants shipping to be free. Determine the IF function that needs to be entered in the cell B2.

	A	B
1	Sub-Total:	$ 107
2	Shipping:	

Choose the correct answer below.

- A. = IF(B1 > = 100,0,4% * B1)
- B. = IF(B1 < = 100,4%,0)
- C. = IF(B1 < = 100,4% * B1,0)
- D. = IF(B1 > 100,0,4%)
- E. = IF(B1 > 100,4% * B1,0)

ID: 10.2.2

!* 71. A person's height is entered in inches. If they are over 67 inches, then their size is "TALL", otherwise it is "REGULAR." Determine the IF function that needs to be entered in cell B2.

	A	B
1	Height (in.):	68
2	Size:	

Choose the correct answer below.

- ○ **A.** = IF(B1 < = 67,"TALL","REGULAR")
- ○ **B.** = IF(B1 > 67,"TALL","REGULAR")
- ○ **C.** = IF(B1 > 67,"REGULAR","TALL")
- ○ **D.** = IF(B1 < 67,"REGULAR","TALL")
- ○ **E.** = IF(B1 > = 67,"TALL","REGULAR")

ID: 10.2.3

!* 72. Determine the output of the following IF functions.
a. = IF(5 > = 2 * 3,12,IF(23/2 > 4 * 3,14,71))
b. = IF(7 – 4 = 5 * 4/5,"Good",IF(3^3<>27,"Ness","Job"))
c. = IF(5 – 1^3<>1 + 3,"SUPER",IF(9 < 2,"SILLY",IF(3 > 7,"WHAT",IF(8 – 2 > 30,"THE","SALLY"))))
d. = IF(6 * 2 < = 2 * 3 * 4,"WOOO",IF(58^79 < 9,"BOOOO","HOOO!"))

a. The output is (1) ________

b. The output is (2) ________

c. The output is (3) ________

d. The output is (4) ________

(1) ○ 12. ○ 71. ○ 14.

(2) ○ Ness. ○ Job. ○ Good.

(3) ○ SALLY. ○ WHAT. ○ THE. ○ SUPER. ○ SILLY.

(4) ○ WOOO. ○ HOOO! ○ BOOOO.

ID: 10.2.4

!* 73. The owner of a mail order catalog wants to charge a shipping fee of 10% of the sub-total if the sub-total is $150 or under and 4% if the sub-total is under $360. Orders with sub-totals that do not meet these criteria will have free shipping. Determine the IF function that needs to be entered in the cell B2.

	A	B
1	Sub-Total:	$ 414
2	Shipping:	

Choose the correct answer below.

- ○ **A.** = IF(B1 < = 150,10% * B1,IF(B1 < 360,4 * B1,IF(B1 > 360,0)))
- ○ **B.** = IF(B1 > = 360,0,IF(B1 > 150,10 * B1,4% * B1))
- ○ **C.** = IF(B1 > 150,4% * B1,IF(B1 > = 360,0,10 * B1))
- ○ **D.** = IF(B1 > 150,0,IF(B1 < 360,4 * B1,10% * B1))
- ○ **E.** = IF(B1 < = 150,10% * B1,IF(B1 < 360,4 * B1,0))

ID: 10.2.5

!* 74. Use the following table to determine the outputs of the VLOOKUP functions in parts (a) through (e). (Remember that the first column is where you look to determine the row, and assume the table has been named.)

0	$ 0.05	$ 0.07	$ 0.08
7	$ 0.10	$ 0.11	$ 0.12
12	$ 0.12	NA	$ 0.15
14	$ 0.15	$ 0.18	NA
21	$ 0.19	$ 0.20	$ 0.21

(a) = VLOOKUP(6,table,3)

Select the correct choice below and, if necessary, fill in the answer box to complete your choice.

- **A.** $______ (Type an integer or a decimal.)
- **B.** 12
- **C.** 0
- **D.** 14
- **E.** 21
- **F.** 7
- **G.** NA

(b) = VLOOKUP(12,table,2)

Select the correct choice below and, if necessary, fill in the answer box to complete your choice.

- **A.** $______ (Type an integer or a decimal.)
- **B.** 12
- **C.** 0
- **D.** 14
- **E.** 7
- **F.** 21
- **G.** NA

(c) = VLOOKUP(25,table,4)

Select the correct choice below and, if necessary, fill in the answer box to complete your choice.

- **A.** $______ (Type an integer or a decimal.)
- **B.** 0
- **C.** 21
- **D.** 7
- **E.** 14
- **F.** 12
- **G.** NA

(d) = VLOOKUP(20,table,2)

Select the correct choice below and, if necessary, fill in the answer box to complete your choice.

- **A.** $______ (Type an integer or a decimal.)
- **B.** 14
- **C.** 21
- **D.** 0
- **E.** 7
- **F.** 12
- **G.** NA

(e) = VLOOKUP(24,table,1)

Select the correct choice below and, if necessary, fill in the answer box to complete your choice.

- **A.** $______ (Type an integer or a decimal.)
- **B.** 12
- **C.** 0
- **D.** 7
- **E.** 14
- **F.** 21
- **G.** NA

ID: 10.3.1

!* 75. You are teaching a class where any student with an average of 92 or more does not have to take the final and gets an A. All other students must take the final which counts for 40% of their grade. Complete parts (a) and (b) below.
[1] Click the icon to view the Excel table.

(a) What IF function would you enter in cell D3 (to be filled down) for the Course Average that takes into account the two possibilities outlined above?

- **A.** = IF(B3 < 92, B3, (B3 + C3)*40%)
- **B.** = IF(B3 >= 92, B3, C3*40%)
- **C.** = IF(B3 < 92, AVERAGE(B3,C3)*40%, C3)
- **D.** = IF(B3 >= 92, D3, B3*60% + C3*40%)
- **E.** = IF(B3 >= 92, B3, B3*60% + C3*40%)

(b) What VLOOKUP function would be entered in cell E3 (to be filled down) that gives the course letter grade?

- **A.** = VLOOKUP(B3, F2:G9, 2)
- **B.** = VLOOKUP(B3, G2:G9, 2)
- **C.** = VLOOKUP(D3, F2:F9, 2)
- **D.** = VLOOKUP(D3, F2:G9, 2)
- **E.** = VLOOKUP(D3, F2:G9, 1)

1: Excel Table

	A	B	C	D	E	F	G
1	Student	Course Avg	Final Exam	Course Avg	Course Grade	Table	
2		Before Final	Grade			0	F
3	Jim	90	83	87.2	B	70	D
4	Bob	74	80	76.4	D+	74	D+
5	Sue	98		98	A	78	C
6	Kim	81	87	83.4	C+	82	C+
7	Jan	98		98	A	85	B
8						90	B+
9						92	A

ID: 10.3.2

76. The following propositions have the form *p and q*. State p and q, and give their truth values. Then determine whether the entire proposition is true or false, and explain why.

Carrots are vegetables and onions are fruit.

Identify p. Choose the correct answer below.

- **A.** Onions are fruit.
- **B.** Carrots are vegetables.
- **C.** Carrots
- **D.** Onions

Identify q. Choose the correct answer below.

- **A.** Onions are fruit.
- **B.** Carrots are vegetables.
- **C.** Onions
- **D.** Carrots

What is the truth value of p?

○ true ○ false

What is the truth value of q?

○ false ○ true

Is the entire proposition true or false?

- **A.** The entire proposition is true because p is true and q is false.
- **B.** The entire proposition is true because p is false and q is true.
- **C.** The entire proposition is false because p is true and q is false.
- **D.** The entire proposition is false because p is false and q is true.

ID: 10.3.3

* 77. The statement below connects two individual propositions with the word *and*. State the two individual propositions and, if possible, whether each is true or false. Then state whether the entire statement is true or false and explain why.

$2+6=7$ and $5\times8=40$.

What is the first proposition?

- A. $2+6$
- B. $2+6=7$
- C. 7

What is the second proposition?

- A. 5×8
- B. $5\times8=40$
- C. 40

Is the first proposition true or false?

- true
- false

Is the second proposition true or false?

- false
- true

Is the statement, $2+6=7$ and $5\times8=40$, true or false?

- A. The statement is false because the first proposition is false and the second proposition is true.
- B. The statement is false because the first proposition is true and the second proposition is false.
- C. The statement is true because the first proposition is false and the second proposition is true.
- D. The statement is true because the first proposition is false and the second proposition is true.

ID: 10.3.4

78. The following propositions have the form 'p and q.' State p and q, and give their truth values. Then determine whether the entire proposition is true or false, and explain why.

The Mississippi River flows through Louisiana and the Colorado river flows through Arizona.

Identify p. Choose the correct answer below.

- A. The Colorado river flows through Arizona.
- B. The Mississippi River flows through Louisiana.
- C. The Mississippi River
- D. The Colorado river

Identify q. Choose the correct answer below.

- A. The Colorado river
- B. The Mississippi River flows through Louisiana.
- C. The Colorado river flows through Arizona.
- D. The Mississippi River

What is the truth value of p?

- true
- false

What is the truth value of q?

- true
- false

Is the entire proposition true or false?

- A. The entire proposition is true because at least one, p or q, is true.
- B. The entire proposition is false because both p and q are false.
- C. The entire proposition is false because at least one, p or q, is false.
- D. The entire proposition is true because both p and q are true.

ID: 10.3.5

79. The following proposition has the form *p and q*. State p and q, and give their truth values. Then determine whether the entire proposition is true or false, and explain why.

Some people are awake and some people are dogs.

State p and q, and give their truth values. Choose the correct answer below.

- A. p = some people are awake; p is false
  q = some people are dogs; q is true
- B. p = all people are awake; p is true
  q = all people are dogs; q is true
- C. p = all people are awake; p is true
  q = all people are dogs; q is false
- D. p = some people are awake; p is false
  q = some people are dogs; q is false
- E. p = some people are awake; p is true
  q = some people are dogs; q is true
- F. p = all people are awake; p is false
  q = all people are dogs; q is true
- G. p = some people are awake; p is true
  q = some people are dogs; q is false
- H. p = all people are awake; p is false
  q = all people are dogs; q is false

Determine whether the entire proposition is true or false, and explain why. Choose the correct answer below.

- A. The entire proposition *p and q* is false because only q is true.
- B. The entire proposition *p and q* is true because both p and q are false.
- C. The entire proposition *p and q* is true because both p and q are true.
- D. The entire proposition *p and q* is false because both p and q are true.
- E. The entire proposition *p and q* is true because only p is true.
- F. The entire proposition *p and q* is false because only p is true.
- G. The entire proposition *p and q* is true because only q is true.
- H. The entire proposition *p and q* is false because both p and q are false.

ID: 10.3.6

---

80. State whether *or* is used in the inclusive or exclusive sense in the following proposition.

I will eat breakfast at restaurant A or restaurant B.

In the given proposition, is *or* inclusive or exclusive?

- Exclusive
- Inclusive

ID: 10.3.7

---

81. State whether *or* is used in the inclusive or exclusive sense in the following proposition.

While in the city, I would be thrilled to attend sporting events or museums.

In the given proposition, is *or* inclusive or exclusive?

- Inclusive
- Exclusive

ID: 10.3.8

---

82. The following proposition has the form *p or q*. State p and q, and give their truth value. Then determine whether the entire proposition is true or false, and explain why.

Carrots are vegetables or carrots are fruit.

Identify p. Choose the correct answer below.

- A. Carrots are fruit.
- B. Carrots
- C. vegetables
- D. Carrots are vegetables.

Identify q. Choose the correct answer below.

- A. fruit
- B. Carrots are fruit.
- C. Carrots are vegetables.
- D. Carrots

82. (cont.) What is the truth value of p?

○ true ○ false

What is the truth value of q?

○ true ○ false

Is the entire proposition true or false?

○ **A.** The entire proposition is false because both p and q are false.
○ **B.** The entire proposition is false because one truth value of p and q is false.
○ **C.** The entire proposition is true because both p and q are true.
○ **D.** The entire proposition is true because at least one truth value of p and q is true.

ID: 10.3.9

---

83. The statement below connects two individual propositions with the word *or*. State the two individual propositions and, if possible, whether each is true or false. Then state whether the entire statement is true or false and explain why.

$6 \times 7 = 84$ or $3 + 5 = 7$.

What is the first proposition?

○ **A.** 84
○ **B.** 6×7
○ **C.** $6 \times 7 = 84$

What is the second proposition?

○ **A.** 7
○ **B.** $3 + 5$
○ **C.** $3 + 5 = 7$

Is the first proposition, $6 \times 7 = 84$, true or false?

○ false ○ true

Is the second proposition, $3 + 5 = 7$, true or false?

○ true ○ false

Is the statement, $6 \times 7 = 84$ or $3 + 5 = 7$, true or false?

○ **A.** The statement is true because the first proposition is false and the second proposition is false.
○ **B.** The statement is true because the first proposition is false and the second proposition is true.
○ **C.** The statement is false because the first proposition is false and the second proposition is false.
○ **D.** The statement is false because the first proposition is true and the second proposition is false.

ID: 10.3.10

---

*84. The following proposition has the form *p or q*. State p and q, and give their truth values. Then determine whether the entire proposition is true or false, and explain why.

Planets yell or flowers jump.

State p and q, and give their truth values. Choose the correct answer below.

○ **A.** p = planets jump; p is false
q = flowers yell; q is false

○ **B.** p = planets yell; p is true
q = flowers jump; q is true

○ **C.** p = planets jump; p is true
q = flowers yell; q is false

○ **D.** p = planets jump; p is false
q = flowers yell; q is true

○ **E.** p = planets yell; p is false
q = flowers jump; q is true

○ **F.** p = planets yell; p is false
q = flowers jump; q is false

○ **G.** p = planets yell; p is true
q = flowers jump; q is false

○ **H.** p = planets jump; p is true
q = flowers yell; q is true

Determine whether the entire proposition is true or false, and explain why. Choose the correct answer below.

○ **A.** The entire proposition *p or q* is true because both p and q are true.
○ **B.** The entire proposition *p or q* is true because p is true.
○ **C.** The entire proposition *p or q* is false because q is true.
○ **D.** The entire proposition *p or q* is false because p is true.
○ **E.** The entire proposition *p or q* is false because both p and q are true.
○ **F.** The entire proposition *p or q* is true because both p and q are false.
○ **G.** The entire proposition *p or q* is true because q is true.
○ **H.** The entire proposition *p or q* is false because both p and q are false.

ID: 10.3.11

---

* 85. Use the two sets below to answer parts (a) and (b).

attorneys and men

a. Draw a Venn diagram with two circles showing the given relationship between two sets. Let A = attorneys and M = men. Choose the correct answer below.

○ A. ○ B. ○ C. ○ D.

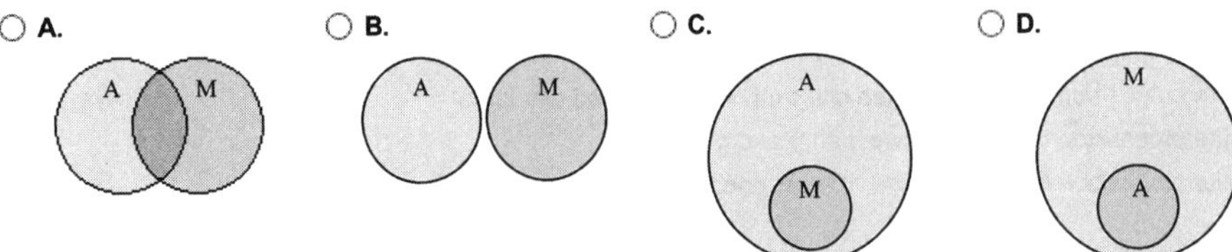

b. Provide an explanation of the diagram. Choose the correct answer below.

○ **A.** The diagram correctly shows two circles are disjoint because there are no men who are attorneys.
○ **B.** The diagram correctly shows one circle is contained in the other because all men are attorneys.
○ **C.** The diagram correctly shows the two circles overlap because some men are attorneys.
○ **D.** The diagram correctly shows one circle is contained in the other because all attorneys are men.

ID: 10.3.12

86. Draw a Venn diagram with two circles showing the given relationship between two sets.

wrenches and tools

Let A = wrenches and B = tools. Choose the correct answer below.

○ **A.**

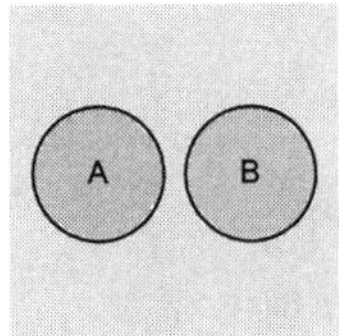

○ **B.**

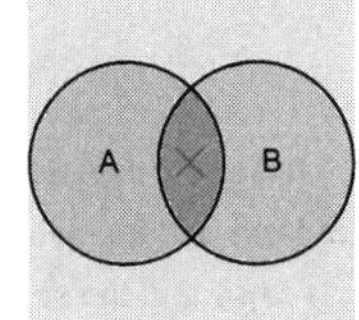

○ **C.**

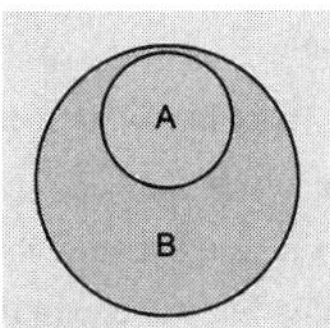

ID: 10.3.13

87. Use the two sets below to answer parts (a) and (b).

dentists and card players

a. Draw a Venn diagram with two circles showing the given relationship between two sets. Let D = dentists and C = card players. Choose the correct answer below.

○ **A.**

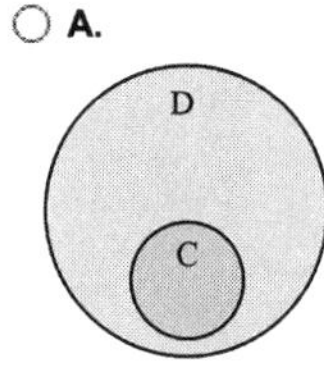

○ **B.**

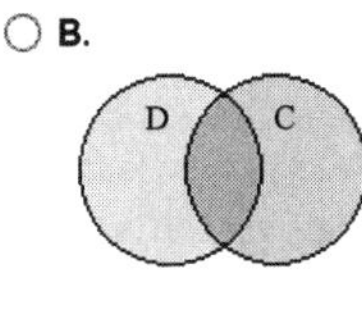

○ **C.**

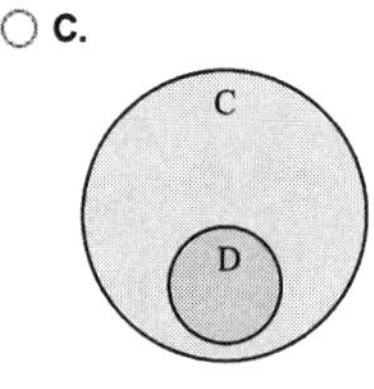

○ **D.**

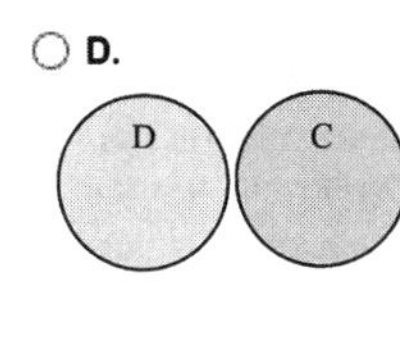

b. Provide an explanation of the diagram you chose. Choose the correct answer below.

○ **A.** The diagram correctly shows the two circles overlap because some card players are dentists.
○ **B.** The diagram correctly shows two circles are disjoint because there are no card players who are dentists.
○ **C.** The diagram correctly shows one circle is contained in the other because all card players are dentists.
○ **D.** The diagram correctly shows one circle is contained in the other because all dentists are card players.

ID: 10.3.14

88. Draw a Venn diagram with two circles showing the given relationship between two sets.

dogs and fish

Let A = dogs and B = fish. Choose the correct answer below.

○ A. ○ B. ○ C.

ID: 10.3.15

* 89. If the given categorical proposition is not already in standard form, rephrase in standard form. State the subject and predicate sets and draw a Venn diagram for the proposition. Then, based only on the Venn diagram (not on any other knowledge you have), answer the question that follows the proposition.

All U.S. presidents have been over 30 years old. Can you conclude that some people who were over 30 years old are not U.S. presidents?

Does the categorical proposition need to be rephrased?

○ **A.** No, the proposition is in standard form.
○ **B.** Yes, it should be rephrased as "Most U.S. presidents are people who were over 30 years old.
○ **C.** Yes, it should be rephrased as "No U.S. presidents are people who were over 30 years old."
○ **D.** Yes, it should be rephrased as "All U.S. presidents are people who were over 30years old."

Which set is the subject set S?

○ **A.** The set U.S. presidents is S because it is the predicate of the sentence.
○ **B.** The set people who were over 30 years old is S because it is the subject of the sentence.
○ **C.** The set U.S. presidents is S because it is the subject of the sentence.
○ **D.** The set people who were over 30 years old is S because it is the predicate of the sentence.

Which set is the predicate set P?

○ **A.** The set U.S. presidents is P because it is the subject of the sentence.
○ **B.** The set people who were over 30 years old is P because it is the subject of the sentence.
○ **C.** The set people who were over 30 years old is P because it is the predicate of the sentence.
○ **D.** The set U.S. presidents is P because it is the predicate of the sentence.

Given the above subject set S and predicate set P, which of the diagrams below is the correct Venn diagram?

○ **A.**

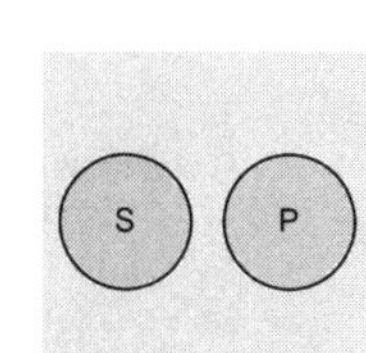

○ **B.**

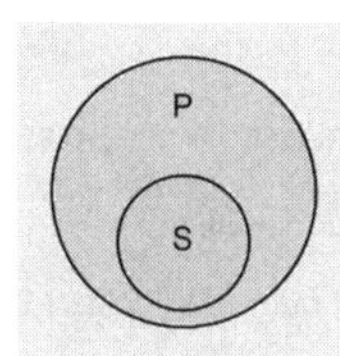

○ **C.**

Based only on the Venn diagram above and not on any other knowledge you have can you conclude that some people who were over 30 years old are not U.S. presidents.

○ **A.** Yes, because there are parts of P not in S and parts of S not in P.
○ **B.** Yes, because S could also contain P.
○ **C.** No, because S and P do not intersect.
○ **D.** No, because there are parts of P not in S and parts of S not in P.
○ **E.** No, because S could also contain P, that is, the two sets could be identical.
○ **F.** Yes, because S and P do not intersect.

ID: 10.3.16

90. If the given categorical proposition is not already in standard form, rephrase in standard form. State the subject and predicate sets and draw a Venn diagram for the proposition. Then, based only on the Venn diagram (not on any other knowledge you have), answer the question that follows the proposition.

All wheels are objects that are round. Can you conclude that no objects that are not round are wheels?

Does the categorical proposition need to be rephrased?

- A. No, the proposition is in standard form.
- B. Yes, it should be rephrased as "Most wheels are objects that are round."
- C. Yes, it should be rephrased as "No wheels are objects that are round."
- D. Yes, it should be rephrased to "All objects that are round are wheels."

Which set is the subject set S?

- A. The set objects that are round is S because it is the subject of the sentence.
- B. The set objects that are round is S because it is the predicate of the sentence.
- C. The set wheels is S because it is the subject of the sentence.
- D. The set wheels is S because it is the predicate of the sentence.

Which set is the predicate set P?

- A. The set objects that are round is P because it is the predicate of the sentence.
- B. The set wheels is P because it is the predicate of the sentence.
- C. The set wheels is P because it is the subject of the sentence.
- D. The set objects that are round is P because it is the subject of the sentence.

Given the above subject set S and predicate set P, which of the diagrams below is the correct Venn diagram?

- A.

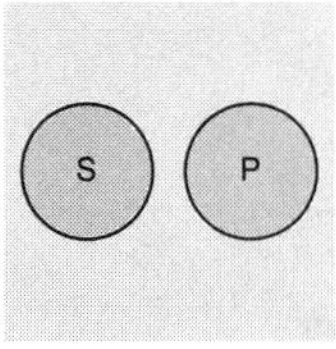

S P

- B.

S P

- C.

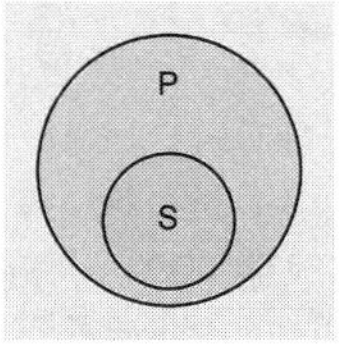

P S

Based only on the Venn diagram above and not on any other knowledge you have, can you conclude that no objects that are not round are wheels?

- A. No, because S and P do not intersect.
- B. Yes, because S and P do not intersect.
- C. Yes, because there are parts of P not in S and parts of S not in P.
- D. No, because P contains all of S.
- E. Yes, because P contains all of S.
- F. No, because there are parts of P not in S and parts of S not in P.

ID: 10.3.17

---

91. If the given categorical proposition is not already in standard form, rephrase in standard form. State the subject and predicate sets and draw a Venn diagram for the proposition. Then, based only on the Venn diagram (not on any other knowledge you have), answer the question that follows the proposition.

Donkeys don't hum. Is it possible that some things that hum are donkeys?

Does the categorical proposition need to be rephrased?

- A. Yes. The standard form is "Some donkeys are things that do not hum."
- B. Yes. The standard form is "No donkeys are things that hum."
- C. Yes. The standard form is "Some donkeys are things that hum."
- D. Yes. The standard form is "All donkeys are things that hum."
- E. No, the proposition is in standard form.

Which set is the subject set S?

- A. The set of things that hum is S because it is the subject of the sentence.
- B. The set donkeys is S because it is the predicate of the sentence.
- C. The set donkeys is S because it is the subject of the sentence.
- D. The set of things that hum is S because it is the predicate of the sentence.

91. (cont.) Which set is the predicate set P?

- ○ **A.** The set of things that hum is P because it is the predicate of the sentence.
- ○ **B.** The set donkeys is P because it is the subject of the sentence.
- ○ **C.** The set donkeys is P because it is the predicate of the sentence.
- ○ **D.** The set of things that hum is P because it is the subject of the sentence.

Given the above subject set S and predicate set P, which of the diagrams below is the correct Venn diagram?

○ **A.** S P ○ **B.** S P ○ **C.** P S

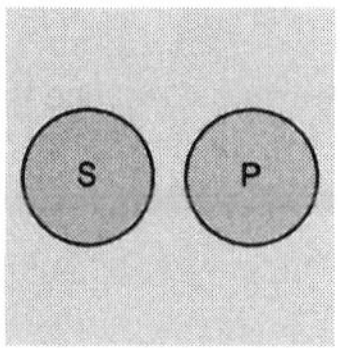

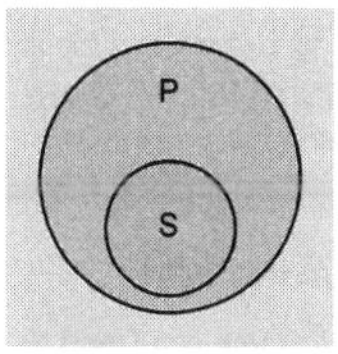

Based only on the Venn diagram above and not on any other knowledge you have is it possible that some things that hum are donkeys?

- ○ **A.** No, because S and P do not intersect.
- ○ **B.** Yes, because S and P do not intersect.
- ○ **C.** No, because P contains all of S.
- ○ **D.** Yes, because P contains all of S.
- ○ **E.** No, because there are parts of P not in S and parts of S not in P.
- ○ **F.** Yes, because there are parts of P not in S and parts of S not in P.

ID: 10.3.18

---

92. For the categorical proposition given below, do the following.

a. If necessary, rephrase the statement in standard form.
b. State the subject and predicate sets.
c. Draw a Venn diagram for the proposition and label all regions of the diagram.
d. Based only on the Venn diagram (not on any other knowledge you have), answer the question that follows each proposition.

Winners shout. Is it true that no whisperers are winners?

a. Does the categorical proposition need to be rephrased?

- ○ **A.** Yes. The standard form is "No winners are people who shout."
- ○ **B.** Yes. The standard form is "Some winners are people who shout."
- ○ **C.** Yes. The standard form is "Some winners are people who do not shout."
- ○ **D.** Yes. The standard form is "All winners are people who shout."
- ○ **E.** No. The proposition is in standard form.

b. Which set is the subject set S?

- ○ **A.** winners that shout
- ○ **B.** people who shout
- ○ **C.** people who do not shout
- ○ **D.** winners

Which set is the predicate set P?

- ○ **A.** winners that shout
- ○ **B.** people who shout
- ○ **C.** people who do not shout
- ○ **D.** winners

c. If S is the subject set and P is the predicate set, which of the diagrams below is the correct Venn diagram?

○ **A.** S P ○ **B.** P S ○ **C.** S P

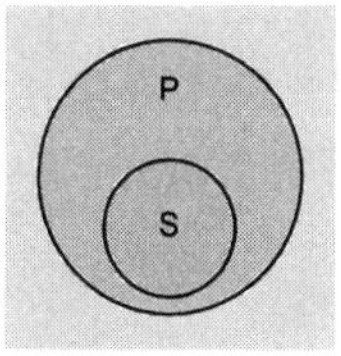

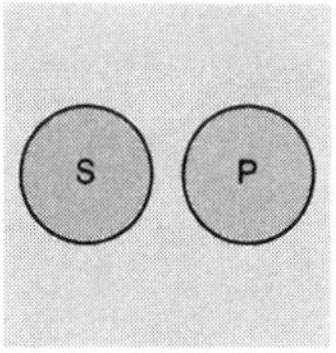

92. (cont.) d. Answer the question based only on the Venn diagrams. Is it true that no whisperers are winners?

- ○ **A.** No. Because P contains all of S. If something is in P, then it must also be in S.
- ○ **B.** Yes. Because S and P do not overlap, if a member is not in P, then it must be in S.
- ○ **C.** No. Because S and P do not overlap, the statement need not be true.
- ○ **D.** Yes. Because P and S overlap, things not in P must be in S.
- ○ **E.** Yes. Because P contains all of S. If something is not in P, then it cannot be in S.
- ○ **F.** No. Because P and S overlap, things not in P do not need to be in S.

ID: 10.3.19

---

* 93. Draw a Venn diagram with three overlapping circles (eight regions) for the following groups of three sets. Describe the members of each region, or state that a region has no members.

men, fire fighters, and nurses

Choose the correct answer below.

- ○ [2] Click the icon to view the Venn diagram b.
- ○ [3] Click the icon to view the Venn diagram c.
- ○ [4] Click the icon to view the Venn diagram a.
- ○ [5] Click the icon to view the Venn diagram d.

2: Venn diagram b

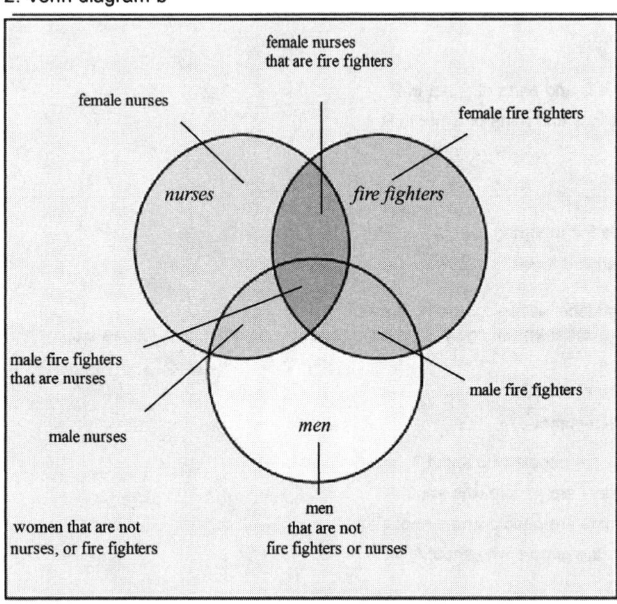

3: Venn diagram c

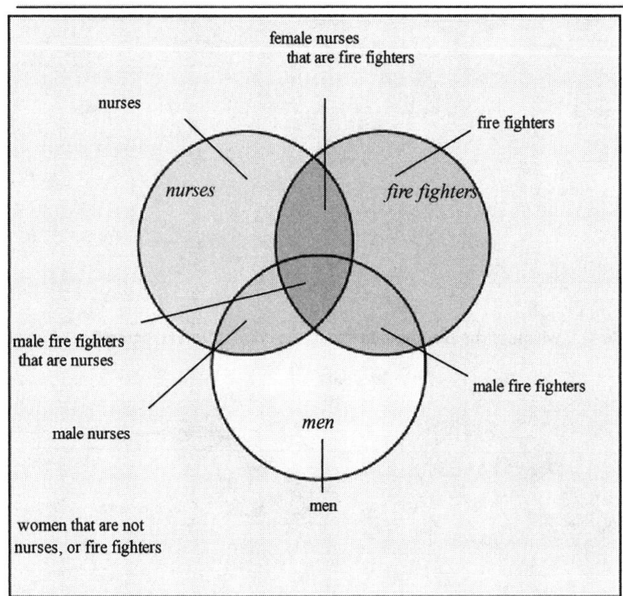

*93. (cont.) 4: Venn diagram a

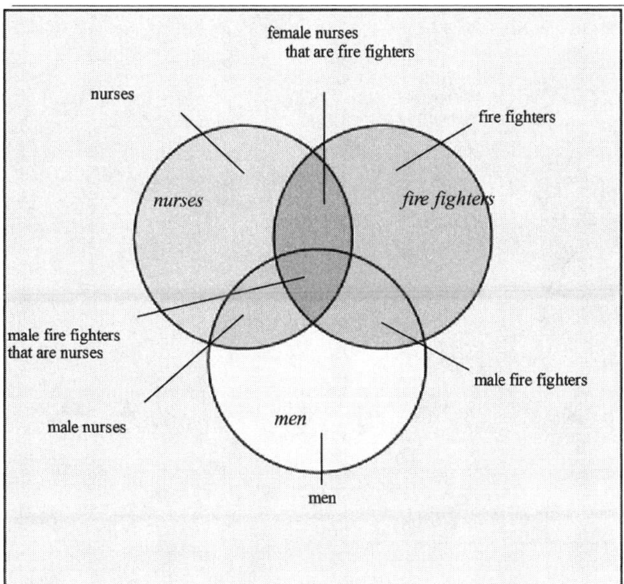

5: Venn diagram d

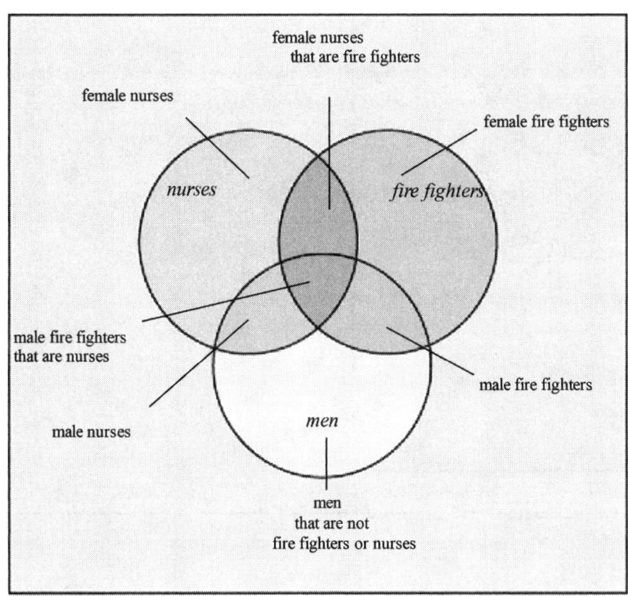

ID: 10.3.20

94. Draw a Venn diagram with three overlapping circles (eight regions) for the following groups of three sets. Describe the members of each region, or state that a region has no members.

commissioned art, pottery, and paintings

Choose the correct answer below.

- ○ [6] Click the icon to view the Venn diagram d.
- ○ [7] Click the icon to view the Venn diagram a.
- ○ [8] Click the icon to view the Venn diagram b.
- ○ [9] Click the icon to view the Venn diagram c.

94. (cont.) 6: Venn diagram d

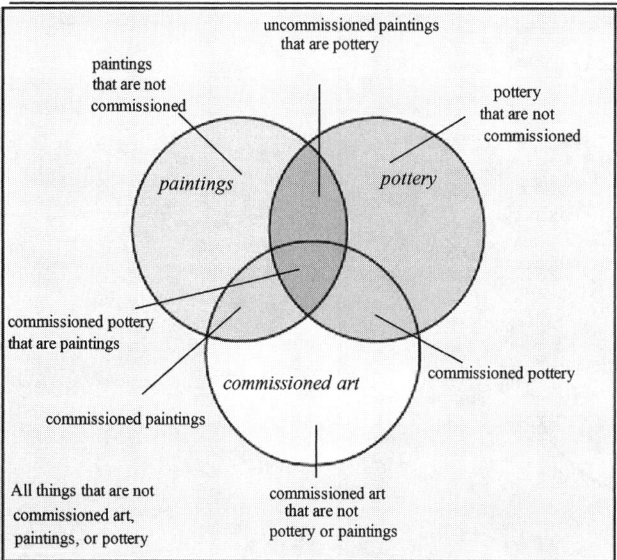

7: Venn diagram a

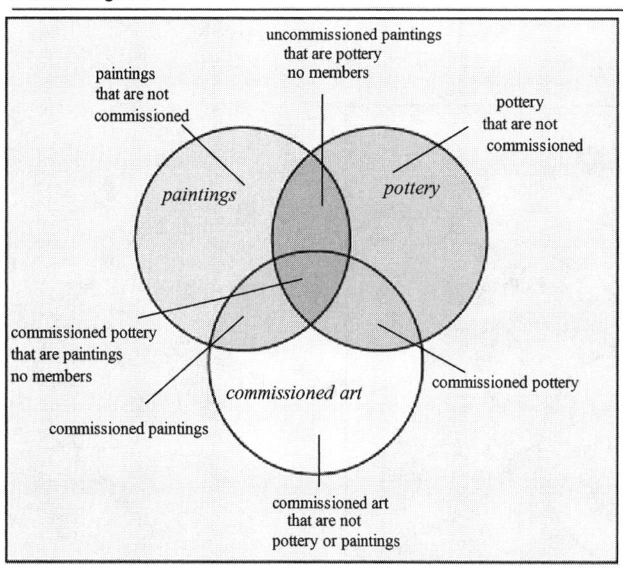

8: Venn diagram b

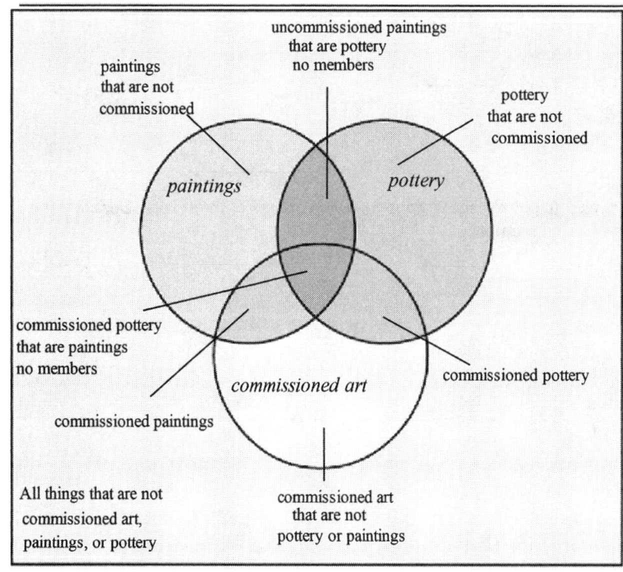

94. (cont.) 9: Venn diagram c

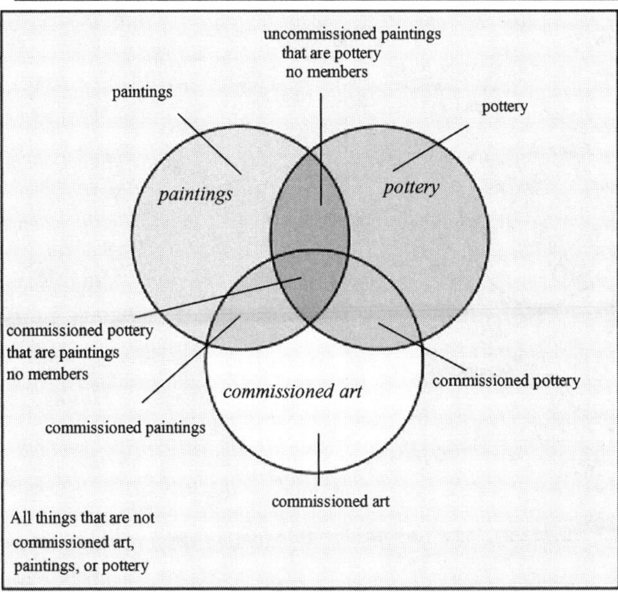

ID: 10.3.21

---

95. Draw a Venn diagram with three overlapping circles (eight regions) for the following group of three sets. Describe the members of each region, or state that a region has no members.

words that begin with i, verbs, and words with fewer than 5 letters

Choose the correct answer below.

- ○ [10] Click the icon to view the Venn diagram c.
- ○ [11] Click the icon to view the Venn diagram b.
- ○ [12] Click the icon to view the Venn diagram a.
- ○ [13] Click the icon to view the Venn diagram d.

10: Venn diagram c

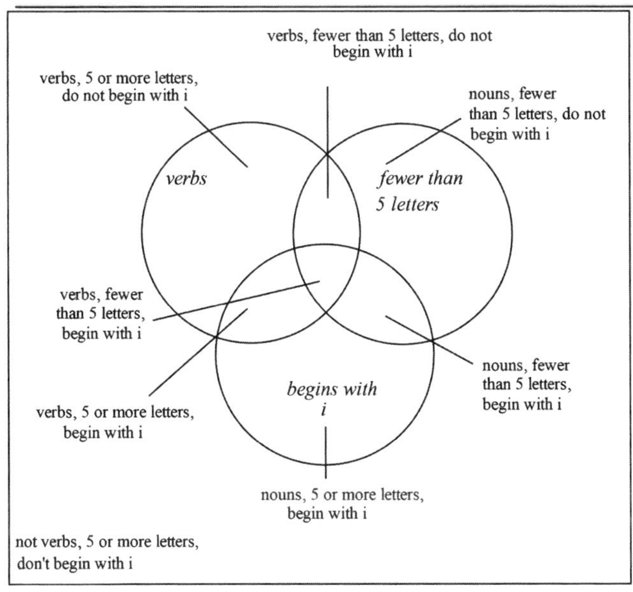

95. (cont.) 11: Venn diagram b

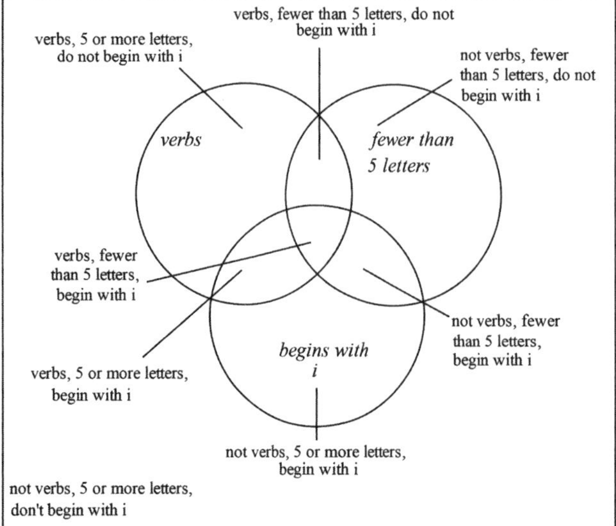

12: Venn diagram a

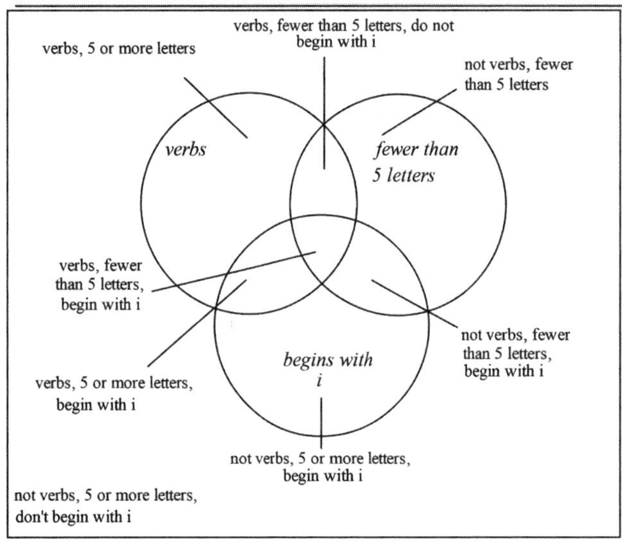

13: Venn diagram d

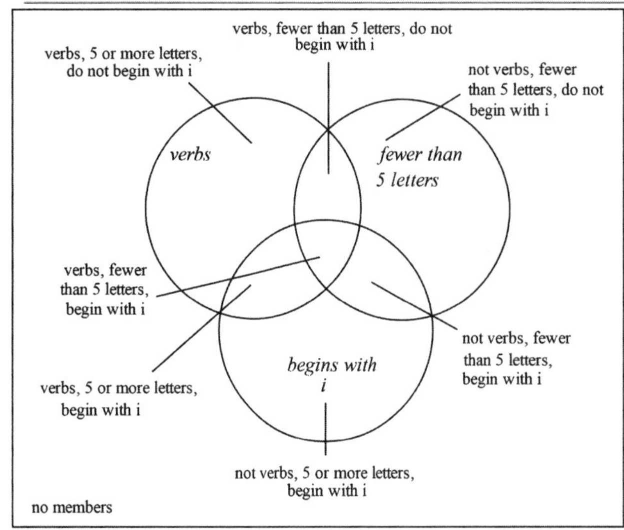

ID: 10.3.22

* 96. Use the Venn diagram to the right to answer questions **a.** through **d.** below.

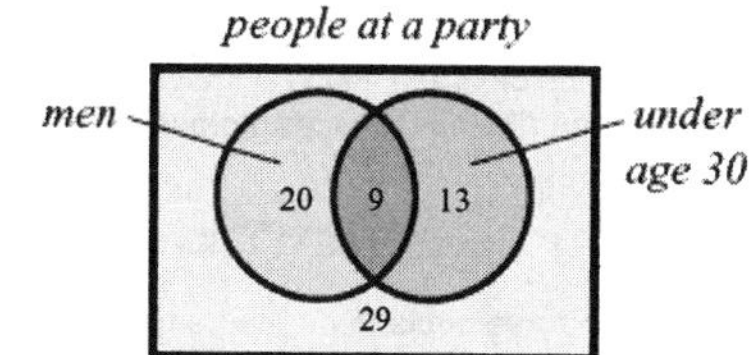

a. How many women at the party are under 30?

____

b. How many men at the party are not under 30?

____

c. How many women are at the party?

____

d. How many people are at the party?

____

ID: 10.3.23

---

97. The table to the right gives popular vote counts (in millions) for the two leading candidates in a presidential election. Draw a two-circle Venn diagram that represents the results.

	Candidate A	Candidate B
Women	37.38	26.14
Men	29.15	27.29

Choose the correct answer below.

○ **A.**

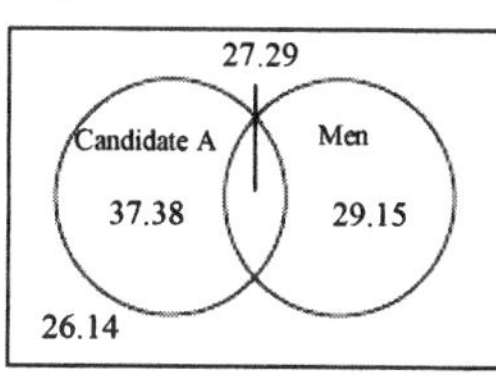

○ **B.**

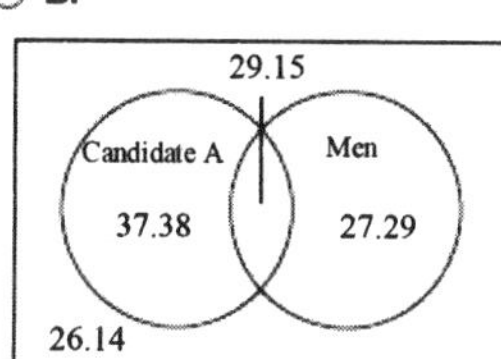

○ **C.**

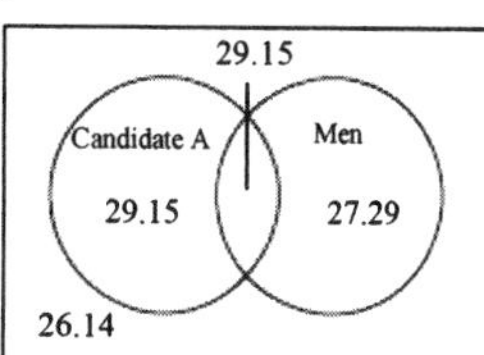

ID: 10.3.24

---

98. Use the Venn diagram to the right to answer questions **a.** through **d.** below.

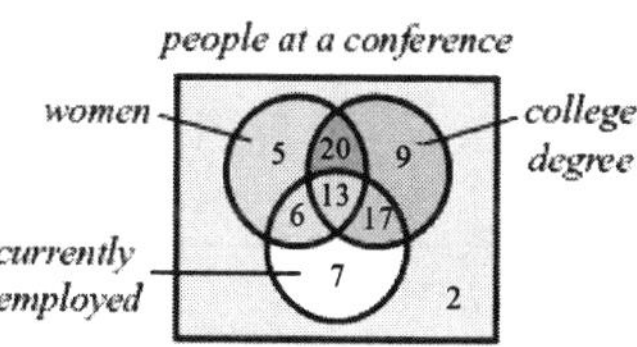

a. How many people at the conference are unemployed women with a college degree?

____

b. How many people at the conference are employed men?

____

c. How many people at the conference are employed women without a college degree?

____

d. How many men are at the conference?

____

ID: 10.3.25

---

* 99. Patients in a (hypothetical) hospital on a single day were taking antibiotics (A), blood pressure medication (BP) and pain medication (P) in numbers summarized in the table to the right.

Complete parts (a) through (f) below.

A only	10	A and BP only	18
BP only	4	A and P only	24
P only	20	BP and P only	13
None	2	All three	22

a. Draw a three-circle Venn diagram that summarizes the results in the table.

Choose the correct answer below.

- ○ **A.** [14] Click the icon to view the Venn diagram.
- ○ **B.** [15] Click the icon to view the Venn diagram.
- ○ **C.** [16] Click the icon to view the Venn diagram.
- ○ **D.** [17] Click the icon to view the Venn diagram.

b. How many patients took antibiotics or blood pressure medication?

____________ patients (Type a whole number.)

c. How many patients took blood pressure medication but not pain medication?

____________ patients (Type a whole number.)

d. How many patients took (at least) pain medication?

____________ patients (Type a whole number.)

e. How many patients took antibiotics and blood pressure medicine but not pain medication?

____________ patients (Type a whole number.)

f. How many patients took antibiotics or blood pressure medicine or pain medication?

____________ patients (Type a whole number.)

14: Figure

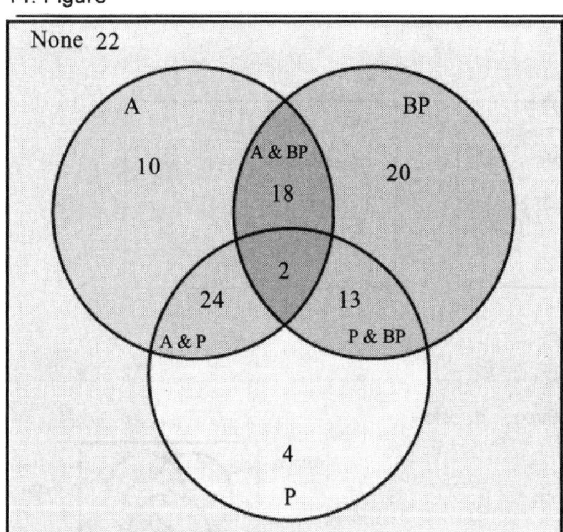

15: Figure

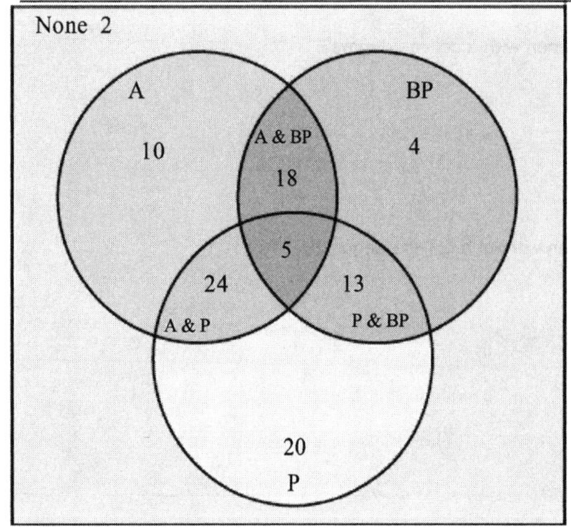

* 99. (cont.) 16: Figure

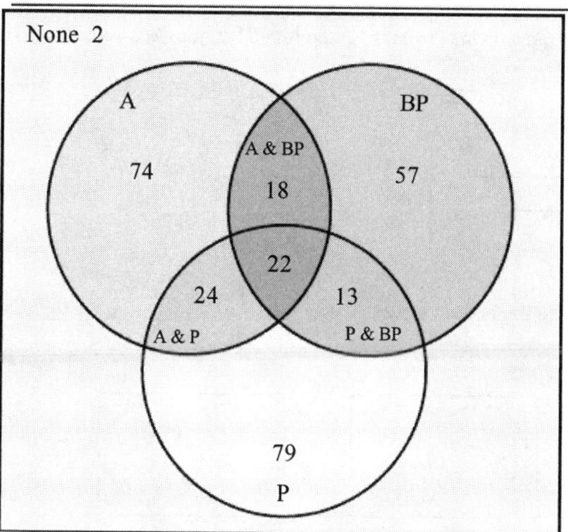

17: Figure

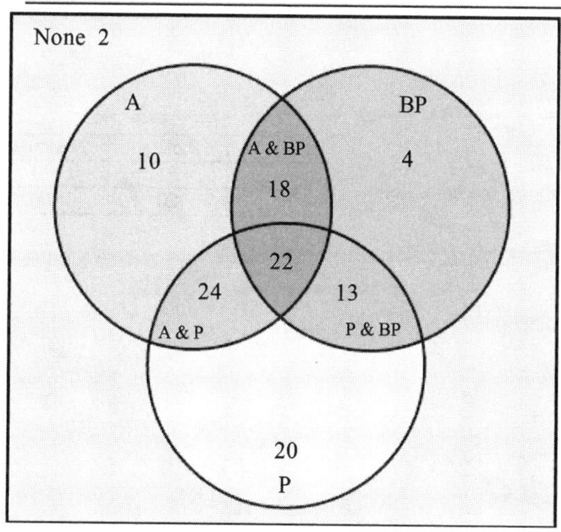

ID: 10.3.26

* 100. Of the 37 theater performances that a critic reviewed, 16 were comedies. She gave favorable reviews to 6 of the comedies and unfavorable reviews to 12 of the non-comedies. Answer parts (a)-(d) below.

a. Complete the two-way table summarizing the reviews.

	Favorable	Non-favorable
Comedy	6	____
Non-comedy	____	12

(Type whole numbers.)

b. Make a Venn diagram from the table in part (a). Choose the correct answer below.

○ A.

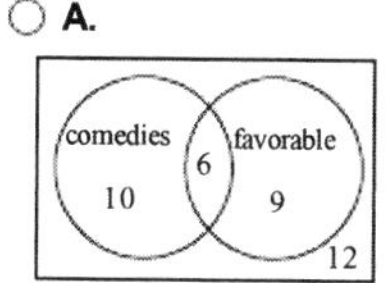

○ B.

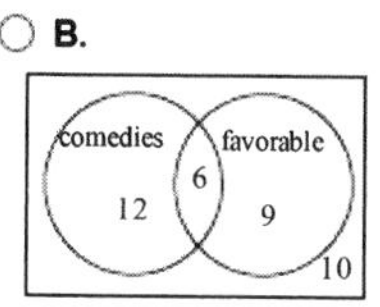

○ C.

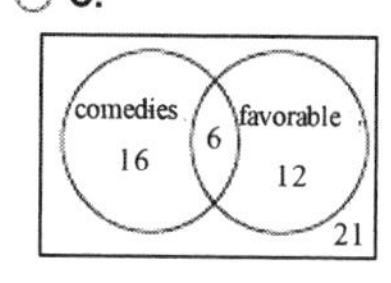

○ D.

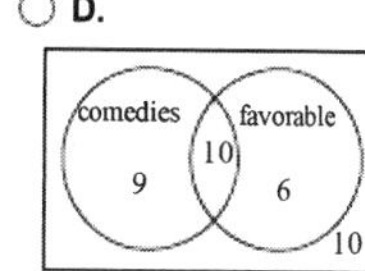

c. How many comedies received unfavorable reviews?

____ (Type a whole number.)

d. How many non-comedies received favorable reviews?

____ (Type a whole number.)

ID: 10.3.27

101. 123 people who grew up in either New York or Los Angeles were surveyed to determine whether they preferred hip-hop music or rock music (both and neither were not acceptable responses). Of those who grew up in Los Angeles, 33 preferred hip-hop and 47 prefered rock. Of those who grew up in New York, 21 preferred hip hop. Answer parts (a)-(c) below.

a. Complete the two-way table summarizing the reviews.

	Hip-hop	Rock
NY	21	______
LA	______	47

(Type whole numbers.)

b. Make a Venn diagram from the table in part (a). Choose the correct answer below.

○ A.

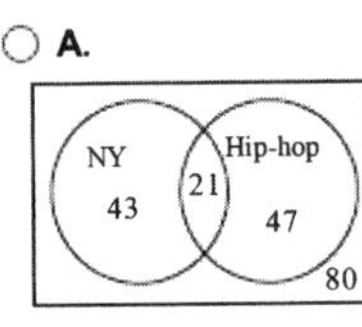

○ B.

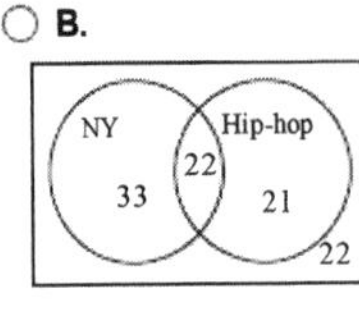

○ C.

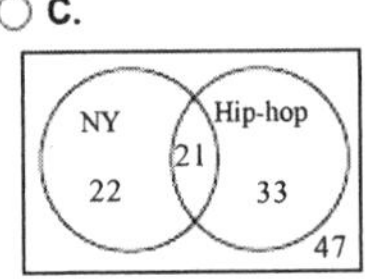

○ D.

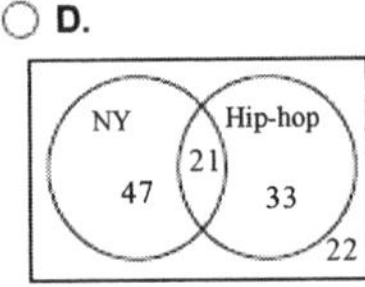

c. How many New Yorkers preferred rock?

__________ (Type a whole number.)

ID: 10.3.28

102. A scan of all biology and business majors at a college shows the accompanying breakdown by gender. Draw a Venn diagram for the data. Let set A = women and set B = business majors.

	Biology	Business
Women	31	119
Men	20	87

Choose the correct answer below.

○ A.

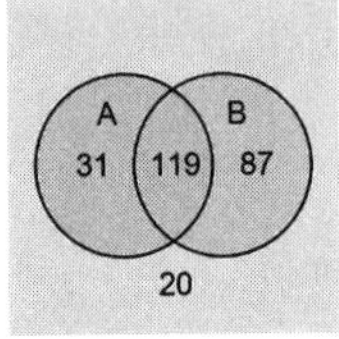

○ B.

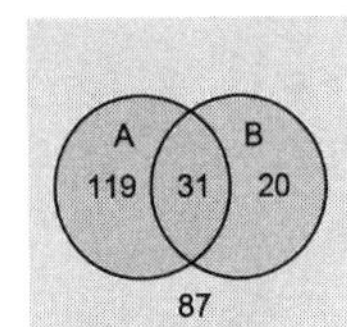

○ C.

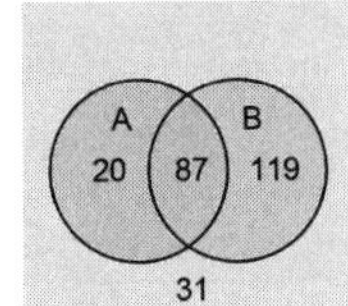

ID: 10.3.29

103. Draw a Venn diagram that illustrates the relationships among the following sets. The diagram should have one circle for each set. A circle may lie entirely inside of other circles, it may overlap other circles, or it may be completely separate from other circles.

animals, house pets, cats, canaries, fish

Choose the correct Venn diagram below.

○ A.

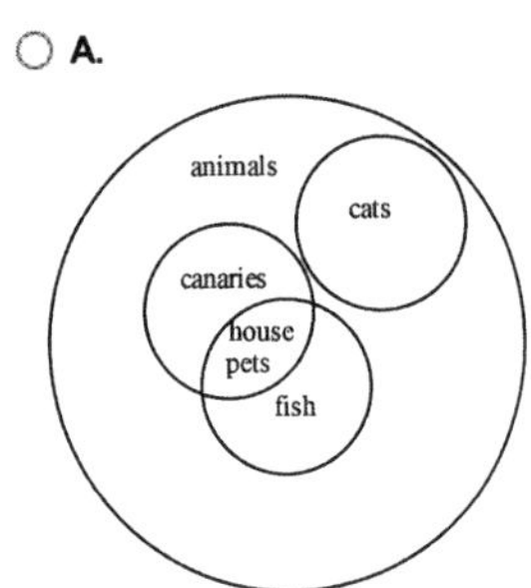

○ B.

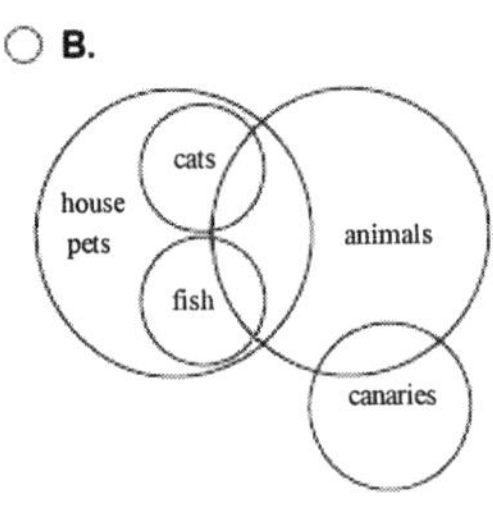

○ C.

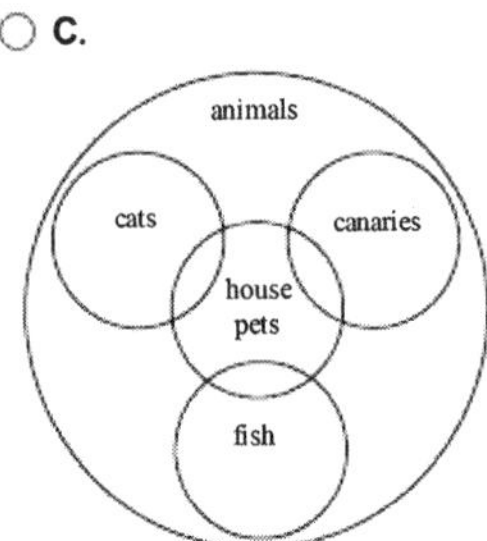

ID: 10.3.30

104. Draw a Venn diagram that illustrates the relationship among the following sets. The diagram should have one circle for each set. In this case, a circle may lie entirely inside of other circles, it may overlap other circles, or it may be completely separate from other circles.

things that fly, vehicles, blue jays, hang gliders, airplanes

Choose the correct Venn diagram below.

- ○ **A.** [18] Click the icon to view the Venn diagram.
- ○ **B.** [19] Click the icon to view the Venn diagram.
- ○ **C.** [20] Click the icon to view the Venn diagram.
- ○ **D.** [21] Click the icon to view the Venn diagram.

18: Figure

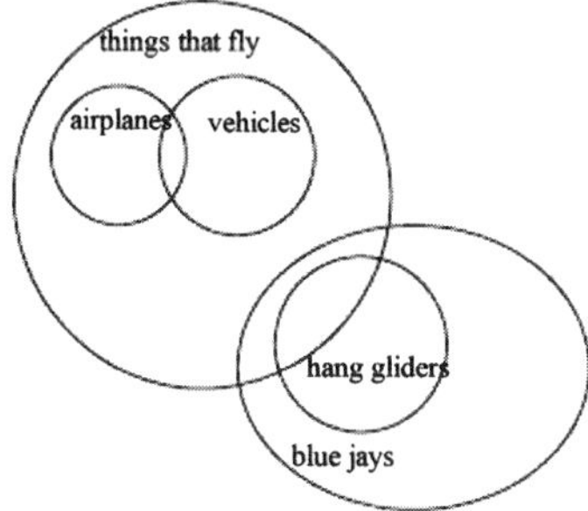

19: Figure

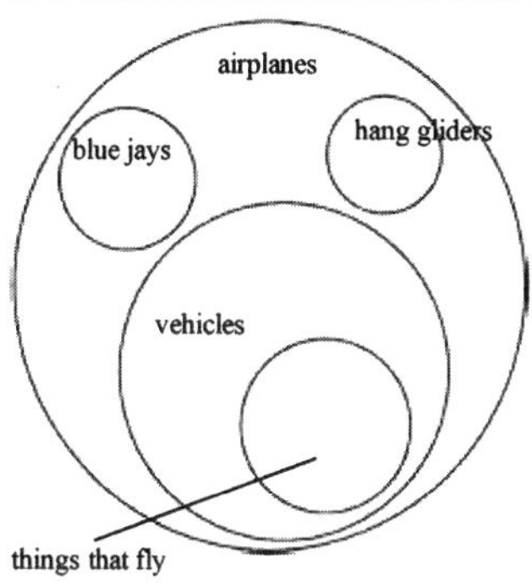

20: Figure

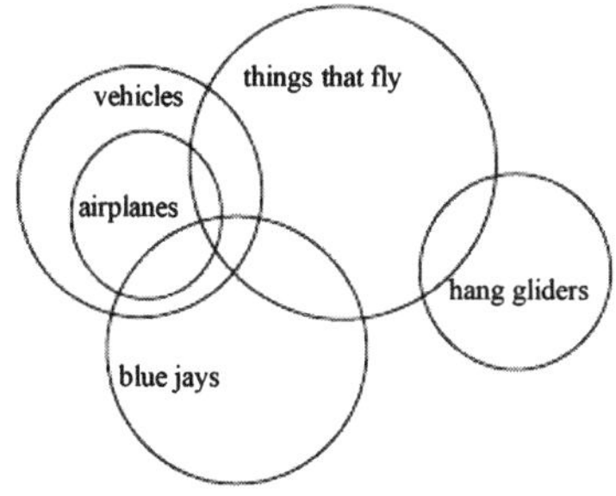

21: Figure

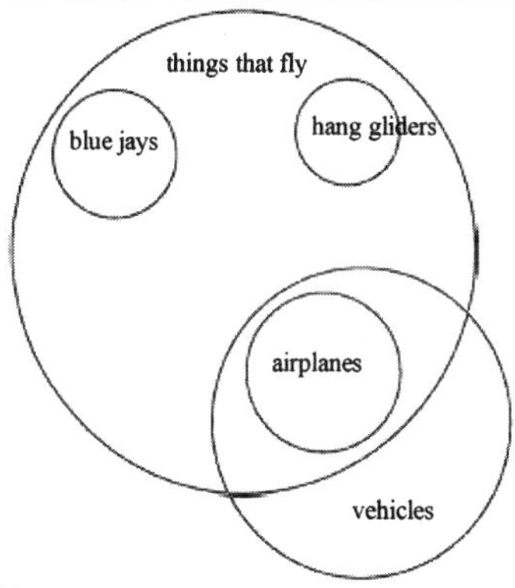

ID: 10.3.31

105. Draw a Venn diagram that represents the information in the following statement. Use the diagram (and no other information) to answer the questions that follow.

All meat has protein. All dairy products have protein. Some beans have protein. All beans, but no meat or dairy products, are plants.

Draw a Venn diagram. Choose the correct answer below.

○ A. ○ B. ○ C.

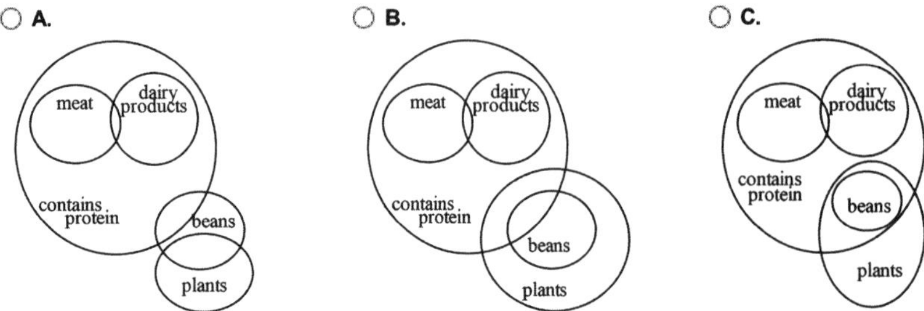

Use the diagram (and no other information) to answer the question below.

Could there be beans that are dairy products?

○ **A.** Yes. Both circles for beans and dairy products overlap with the circle for protein.
○ **B.** No. The circle for beans and the circle for dairy products do not overlap.
○ **C.** No. The circle for dairy products is not inside the circle for beans.
○ **D.** Yes. Both circles are inside the circle for protein.

Use the diagram (and no other information) to answer the question below.

Could there be meat that is a dairy product?

○ **A.** No. There are no dairy products that have meat.
○ **B.** No. The circle for meat is not inside the circle for dairy products.
○ **C.** Yes. The circle for meat and the circle for dairy products are both in the circle for protein.
○ **D.** Yes. The circle for meat overlaps the circle for dairy products.

Use the diagram (and no other information) to answer the question below.

Could there be plants with protein?

○ **A.** No. The circle for plants is not inside the circle for protein.
○ **B.** Yes. The circle for plants overlaps the circle for protein.
○ **C.** No. The circle for plants is disjoint from the circle for protein.
○ **D.** Yes. The circle for plants is inside the circle for beans, and the circle for beans overlaps the circle for protein.

ID: 10.3.32

---

106. A computer store offers a basic computer with four options A, B, C, and D, any or none of which buyers can select. Answer parts (a) through (e) below.

a. How many different sets of options can buyers choose? For example, one choice is A and C, another choice is no options, and another choice is all options.

Buyers can choose __________ sets of options.

b. Consider the four-circle Venn diagram on the right. Label the regions with the various sets of options.

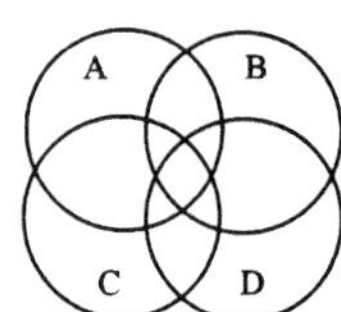

106. (cont.) Choose the correct answer below.

○ A.

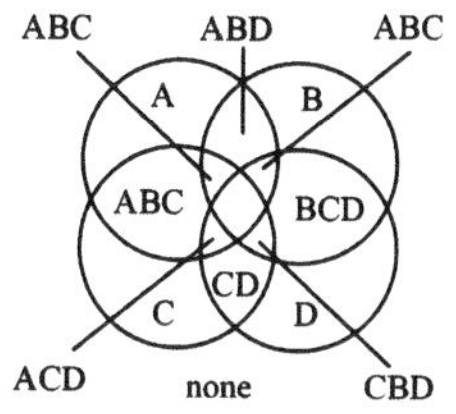

ABC ABD ABC
A B
ABC BCD
CD
C D
ACD none CBD

○ B.

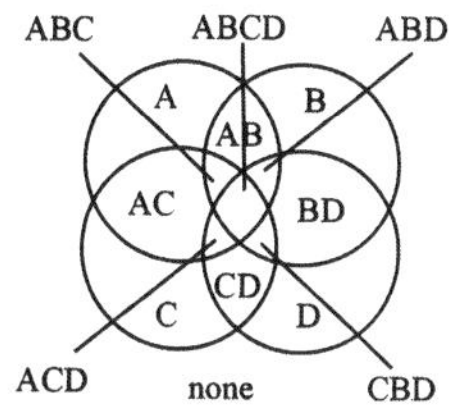

ABC ABCD ABD
A B
AB
AC BD
CD
C D
ACD none CBD

○ C.

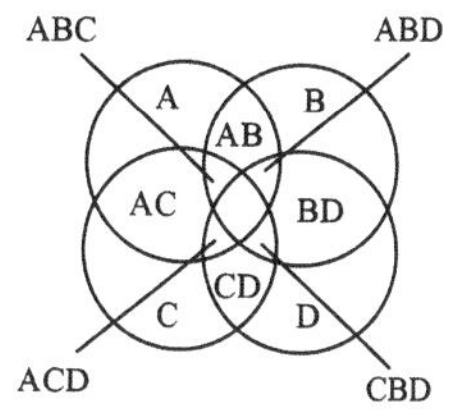

ABC ABD
A B
AB
AC BD
CD
C D
ACD CBD

c. Does the diagram in part (b) represent all the sets of option? If not, which sets of options are missing?

○ **A.** No, there is no overlapping circles that represent options B and C.

○ **B.** Yes, all sets of options are represented by overlapping circles in the Venn Diagram.

○ **C.** No, there is no overlapping circles that represent options A and D or B and C.

○ **D.** No, there is no overlapping circles that represent options A and D.

d. Suppose the computer store offered five options A, B, C, D, and E. How many different sets of options would be available?

There would be ___________ sets of options.

e. Generalizing from parts (a) through (d), how many different sets of options are available if the store offers N options, where N = 2, 3, 4,...,?

There would be ___________ sets of options. (Type an expression using N as the variable.)

ID: 10.3.33

!* 107. Use the IF function to answer the questions.

= IF(RAND() < 0.32, "H", "T")

(a) What is the probability of the function returning an H?
(b) What is the probability of the function returning a T?

(a) ___________ %

(b) ___________ %

ID: 10.4.1

!* 108. Assume cell F8 in a spreadsheet has a random number in it using the = RAND() function.

= IF(F8 < 0.20, 2003, IF(F8 < 0.45, 2004, IF(F8 < 0.75, 2005, 2006)))

(a) What is the probability of this function returning 2004?
(b) What is the probability of this function returning 2005?

(a) ___________ %
(Type an integer or a decimal.)

(b) ___________ %
(Type an integer or a decimal.)

ID: 10.4.2

!* 109. Assume cell A1 = RANDBETWEEN(1,5) and B1 = IF(A1 < 2, 2002, IF(A1 < 3, 2003, 2004)).
(a) What is the probability of this function returning 2003?
(b) What is the probability of this function returning 2004?
(c) Which IF function will return R, S, or T with equal probability? Assume cell A2 = RAND().

(a) ___________
(Type an integer or a fraction.)

(b) ___________
(Type an integer or a fraction.)

(c) Choose the correct answer below.

○ **A.** = IF(A2 < 1/3, "R", IF(A2 < 2/3, "S", "T"))

○ **B.** = IF(A2 > 2/3, "T", IF(A2 < 2/3, "S", "R"))

○ **C.** = IF(A2 < 1/3, "R", IF(A2 < 2/3, "S", IF(A2 < 3/3, "T")))

○ **D.** = IF(RAND() < 1/3, "R", IF(RAND() < 2/3, "S", "T"))

ID: 10.4.3

CHAPTER 11
Change, Risk, and Likelihood
MyMathLab Homework Problems*

* Problems with an asterisk are included in the pre-assigned homework assignment.
! Problems with an exclamation point are new to the Update edition.
To find the problems in MyMathLab online, please refer to the ID code listed below each problem.

!* 1. Use the risk charts for men and women to answer the following questions.
(a) What is the chance of a 45 year old female smoker dying from a heart attack in the next 10 years?
(b) A 65 year old male who has never smoked is at greatest risk of dying from which of the following choices over the next 10 years?
(c) A 35 year old person who has never smoked has what chance of NOT dying over the next 10 years? Assume the person is equally likely to be a male or female.
Click here to view the risk chart for men.[1]
Click here to view the risk chart for women.[2]

(a) Choose the correct answer below.

- ○ **A.** 23 out of 1,000
- ○ **B.** 2 out of 1,000
- ○ **C.** 4 out of 1,000
- ○ **D.** 6 out of 1,000

(b) Choose the correct answer below.

- ○ **A.** stroke
- ○ **B.** accident
- ○ **C.** COPD
- ○ **D.** lung cancer

(c) The person's chances of NOT dying over the next 10 years is ________.
(Type an integer or a simplified fraction.)

1: Risk chart

Risk chart for Men: The numbers in a row tell you how many out of 1,000 men in that group will die in the next 10 years from...

	Male	Vascular Disease		Cancer					Lung Disease		
Age	Smoking Status	Heart Attack	Stroke	Lung	Breast	Colon	Prostate	Ovarian	COPD	Accidents	All Causes
35	Never	1	1							5	11
	Smoker	**7**	**1**	**1**						**5**	**42**
45	Never	6	1	1		1				6	35
	Smoker	**21**	**3**	**8**		**1**			**2**	**6**	**91**
55	Never	19	3	1		3	2		1	5	74
	Smoker	**41**	**7**	**34**		**3**	**1**		**7**	**4**	**178**
65	Never	54	3	6		4	8		9	8	184
	Smoker	**74**	**16**	**89**		**7**	**6**		**26**	**5**	**365**
75	Never	137	32	8		13	19		6	11	449
	Smoker	**140**	**39**	**109**		**11**	**15**		**60**	**9**	**667**

2: Risk chart

Risk chart for Women: The numbers in a row tell you how many out of 1,000 women in that group will die in the next 10 years from...

	Female	Vascular Disease		Cancer					Lung Disease		
Age	Smoking Status	Heart Attack	Stroke	Lung	Breast	Colon	Prostate	Ovarian	COPD	Accidents	All Causes
35	Never	1			1					2	18
	Smoker	**1**	**1**	**1**	**1**					**2**	**14**
45	Never	2	1	1	3	1		1		2	25
	Smoker	**6**	**3**	**4**	**3**	**1**		**2**	**2**	**2**	**41**
55	Never	8	2	2	6	2		2	1	2	55
	Smoker	**20**	**6**	**26**	**5**	**2**		**2**	**9**	**2**	**110**
65	Never	25	7	5	8	5		4	3	3	131
	Smoker	**45**	**15**	**55**	**7**	**5**		**3**	**31**	**3**	**241**
75	Never	86	30	7	10	10		5	6	7	335
	Smoker	**99**	**34**	**58**	**10**	**9**		**4**	**61**	**7**	**463**

ID: 11.1.1

!* 2. Use the risk charts for men and women to answer the following questions.
(a) A 55 year old female smoker takes a pill that reduces her risk of heart attack by 4%. What is her new risk of heart attack?
(b) Determine if the following sentence makes sense, and choose the best explanation:
"Smoking reduces the risk of colon cancer in 65 year old men."
Click here to view the risk chart for men.[3]
Click here to view the risk chart for women.[4]

(a) Choose the correct answer below.

- **A.** 23 out of 1,000
- **B.** 21 out of 1,000
- **C.** 29 out of 1,000
- **D.** 24 out of 1,000

(b) Choose the correct answer below.

- **A.** This sentence makes sense because the risk of dying from colon cancer drops from 8 in 1,000 to 7 in 1,000.
- **B.** This sentence does not make sense. Although the risk of dying from colon cancer is lower for 65 year old male smokers than for 65 year old male non-smokers, the risk of 65 year old male smokers dying from other causes is much higher. Thus, it appears that fewer 65 year old male smokers will die from colon cancer in the next 10 years when actually they will die from other causes first.
- **C.** The sentence does not make sense. Although the risk of dying from colon cancer is lower for 65 year old male smokers than for 65 year old male non-smokers, the risk of younger male smokers dying from colon cancer is higher. Thus, it appears that fewer 65 year old male smokers will die from colon cancer in the next 10 years when actually more male smokers die from colon cancer at a younger age.
- **D.** This sentence does not make sense because the risk of dying from colon cancer drops from 8 in 1,000 to 7 in 1,000.

3: Risk chart

Risk chart for Men: The numbers in a row tell you how many out of 1,000 men in that group will die in the next 10 years from...

	Male	Vascular Disease		Cancer					Lung Disease		
Age	Smoking Status	Heart Attack	Stroke	Lung	Breast	Colon	Prostate	Ovarian	COPD	Accidents	All Causes
35	Never	1	1							5	20
	Smoker	**7**	**1**	**1**						**5**	**42**
45	Never	6	1	1		1				6	35
	Smoker	**21**	**3**	**8**		**1**			**2**	**6**	**91**
55	Never	19	3	1		3	2		1	5	74
	Smoker	**41**	**7**	**34**		**3**	**1**		**7**	**4**	**178**
65	Never	59	5	4		8	3		2	3	168
	Smoker	**74**	**16**	**89**		**7**	**6**		**26**	**5**	**365**
75	Never	137	32	8		13	19		6	11	449
	Smoker	**140**	**39**	**109**		**11**	**15**		**60**	**9**	**667**

4: Risk chart

Risk chart for Women: The numbers in a row tell you how many out of 1,000 women in that group will die in the next 10 years from...

	Female	Vascular Disease		Cancer					Lung Disease		
Age	Smoking Status	Heart Attack	Stroke	Lung	Breast	Colon	Prostate	Ovarian	COPD	Accidents	All Causes
35	Never	1			1					2	11
	Smoker	**1**	**1**	**1**	**1**					**2**	**14**
45	Never	2	1	1	3	1		1		2	25
	Smoker	**6**	**2**	**3**	**2**	**1**		**1**	**1**	**1**	**35**
55	Never	8	2	2	6	2		2	1	2	55
	Smoker	**25**	**6**	**26**	**5**	**2**		**2**	**9**	**2**	**110**
65	Never	25	7	5	8	5		4	3	3	131
	Smoker	**45**	**15**	**55**	**7**	**5**		**3**	**31**	**3**	**241**
75	Never	86	30	7	10	10		5	6	7	335
	Smoker	**99**	**34**	**58**	**10**	**9**		**4**	**61**	**7**	**463**

ID: 11.1.2

*3. Briefly explain why quantifying risk is important to decision making.

Why is risk an important to quantify risk when making a decision?

- ○ **A.** Quantifying risk is important so it can be measured against the benefits when making decisions. Ideally, the risk will outweigh the benefits.
- ○ **B.** Quantifying risk is important so it can be measured across a population and help identify why people make the decisions they do.
- ○ **C.** Quantifying risk is important so it can be measured against the benefits when making decisions. Ideally, the risk will equal the benefits.
- ○ **D.** Quantifying risk is important so it can be measured against the benefits when making decisions appropriate for our own personal circumstances.

ID: 11.1.3

---

4. What are vital statistics? How are they usually described? Give a few examples.

Choose the correct answer below.

- ○ **A.** Vital statistics are data concerning deaths of citizens. They are usually expressed in terms of deaths per person. Two examples are the rate of deaths caused by cancer and the rate of deaths caused by heart disease.
- ○ **B.** Vital statistics are data concerning life expectancy. They are usually expressed in terms of the number of years a person with a given age today can expect to live on average. Two examples are the life expectancy of a forty-year-old male in 2010 and the life expectancy of a nineteen-year-old female in 1921.
- ○ **C.** Vital statistics are data concerning risk. They are usually expressed in terms of accident rates or death rates. Two examples are the accident rate for a specific type of car and the death rate of deaths caused by cancer.
- ○ **D.** Vital statistics are data concerning births, deaths, and life expectancy of citizens. They are usually expressed in terms of deaths per person or per 100,000 people or as the number of years a person is expected to live. Two examples are the rate of deaths caused by cancer and the rate of deaths caused by heart disease.

ID: 11.1.4

---

5. Explain the meaning of "life expectancy." How does life expectancy change with age? How is it affected by changes in the overall health of a population?

Define "life expectancy." Choose the best answer below.

- ○ **A.** Life expectancy is the number of years a person of a given age has lived so far.
- ○ **B.** Life expectancy is the average age a person in a population is expected to live, only including ages of people with death due to health issues.
- ○ **C.** Life expectancy is the average age a person in a population is expected to live, including ages of people with death due to accidents.
- ○ **D.** Life expectancy is the number of additional years a person of a given age can expect to live on average.

Life expectancy (1) __________ with age.

Life expectancy (2) __________ if changes in the overall health of a population improve. It (3) __________ if changes in the overall health of a population decline.

(1)	(2)	(3)
○ decreases	○ decreases	○ decreases
○ stays the same	○ stays the same	○ increases
○ increases	○ increases	○ stays the same

ID: 11.1.5

---

6. Decide whether the following statement makes sense (or is clearly true) or does not make sense (or is clearly false). Explain your reasoning.

No one can succeed in selling a product that will kill thousands of people per year.

Choose the correct answer below.

- ○ **A.** The statement does not make sense because cars are sold every day and car accidents kill about 40,000 people per year.
- ○ **B.** The statement does not make sense because no one would buy anything that may lead to their death.
- ○ **C.** The statement makes sense because cars are sold every day and car accidents kill about 40,000 people per year.
- ○ **D.** The statement makes sense because no one would buy anything that may lead to their death.

ID: 11.1.6

---

7. Decide whether the following statement makes sense (or is clearly true) or does not make sense (or is clearly false). Explain your reasoning.

Your life expectancy is the major factor in determining how long you live.

Choose the correct answer below.

- ○ **A.** The statement does not make sense because life expectancy changes with the state of medicine and technology. Thus, it is an unreliable method of determining life spans.
- ○ **B.** The statement makes sense because life expectancy changes with the state of medicine and technology. Thus, it is a reliable method of determining life spans.
- ○ **C.** The statement makes sense because life expectancy is based on your diet and exercise habits.
- ○ **D.** The statement does not make sense because life expectancy is based on the current state of medicine and technology. If you have healthy habits and exercise each day, then you are more likely to live longer, regardless of your life expectancy.

ID: 11.1.7

---

8. Decide whether the following statment makes sense (is clearly true) or does not make sense (is clearly false). Explain your reasoning.

A 60-year-old has a shorter life expectancy than a 20-year-old.

Choose the correct answer below.

- ○ **A.** The statement makes sense because life expectancy measures the number of additional years a person of a given age can expect to live on average. Therefore, someone who is 20 has a lower life expectancy than someone who is 60.
- ○ **B.** The statement makes sense because life expectancy measures the number of additional years a person of a given age can expect to live on average. Therefore, someone who is 20 has higher life expectancy than someone who is 60.
- ○ **C.** The statement does not make sense because life expectancy measures the number of years the average person in a population will live. Therefore, the person's current age does not matter because everyone should live to be the same age.
- ○ **D.** The statement does not make sense because life expectancy measures the number of years a person of a given age has lived. Therefore, someone who is 20 has lived less years than someone who is 60.

ID: 11.1.8

---

*9. Use the table to express the 1983 fatality rate in deaths per 100 million vehicle-miles traveled.

Year	Population (millions)	Traffic fatalities	Licensed drivers (millions)	Vehicle miles (trillions)
1983	247	48,753	169	1.6
1996	288	45,238	184	2.6
2001	293	45,296	197	3.4

The 1983 fatality rate is ________ deaths per 100 million vehicle-miles.
(Round to the nearest tenth as needed.)

ID: 11.1.9

---

10. Use the table to express the 2003 fatality rate in deaths per 100,000 licensed drivers.

Year	Population (millions)	Traffic fatalities	Licensed drivers (millions)	Vehicle miles (trillions)
1980	246	48,071	163	1.2
1990	283	46,902	184	2.7
2003	308	45,006	200	3.9

The 2003 fatality rate is ________ deaths per 100,000 licensed drivers.
(Round to the nearest tenth as needed.)

ID: 11.1.10

---

* 11. The table below shows the number of accidents, fatalities, and hours flown for a country's general aviation (non-commercial, personal, corporate, and instructional flights). Compute the accident rate per 100,000 flight hours in 2002 and 2012. By this measure, has general aviation become safer?

Year	Accidents	Fatalities	Hours Flown (millions)
2002	1507	709	23.7
2008	1567	498	22.2
2012	1380	449	20.7

Select the correct choice below and fill in any answer boxes within your choice.
(Round to the nearest tenth as needed.)

○ **A.** General aviation has not become safer because the accident rate in 2002, ________ accidents per 100,000 flight hours, is lower than the accident rate in 2012, ________ accidents per 100,000 flight hours.

○ **B.** General aviation has become safer because the accident rate in 2002, ________ accidents per 100,000 flight hours, is higher than the accident rate in 2012, ________ accidents per 100,000 flight hours.

ID: 11.1.11

* 12. The table shows the leading causes of death in a certain country in a recent year. The population of the country was 313 million. What is the empirical probability of death by pneumonia or influenza during a single year? How much greater is the risk of death by pneumonia or influenza than death by kidney disease?

Cause	Deaths	Cause	Deaths
Heart disease	596,800	Alzheimer's disease	84,800
Cancer	575,600	Diabetes	73,400
Chronic respiratory diseases	143,400	Pneumonia/Influenza	53,500
Stroke	128,600	Kidney disease	45,400
Accidents	122,100	Suicide	38,300

The empirical probability of death by pneumonia or influenza during a single year is ________.
(Round to five decimal places as needed.)

The risk of death by pneumonia or influenza is about ________ times greater than risk by death of kidney disease.
(Round to one decimal place as needed.)

ID: 11.1.12

13. The table shows the leading causes of death in a certain country in a recent year. The population of the country was 317 million. What was the death rate due to diabetes in deaths per 100,000 of the population of the country?

Cause	Deaths	Cause	Deaths
Heart disease	596,800	Alzheimer's disease	84,200
Cancer	575,800	Diabetes	73,100
Chronic respiratory diseases	143,800	Pneumonia/Influenza	53,800
Stroke	128,100	Kidney disease	45,600
Accidents	122,700	Suicide	38,400

There were about ________ deaths from diabetes per 100,000 people.
(Round to the nearest tenth as needed.)

ID: 11.1.13

14. The table shows the leading causes of death in a certain country in a recent year. The population of the country was 313 million. If you lived in a typical city of 500,000, how many people would you expect to die of cancer each year?

Cause	Deaths	Cause	Deaths
Heart disease	596,500	Alzheimer's disease	84,900
Cancer	575,900	Diabetes	73,900
Chronic respiratory diseases	143,100	Pneumonia/Influenza	53,100
Stroke	128,900	Kidney disease	45,100
Accidents	122,600	Suicide	38,500

About ________ people would be expected to die of cancer each year.
(Type a whole number. Round to the nearest person as needed.)

ID: 11.1.14

* 15. Use the graph to estimate the death rate for 70-year-olds. Assuming that there were about 11.3 million 70-year-olds, how many people of this age could be expected to die in a year?

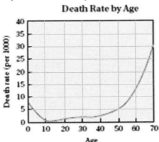

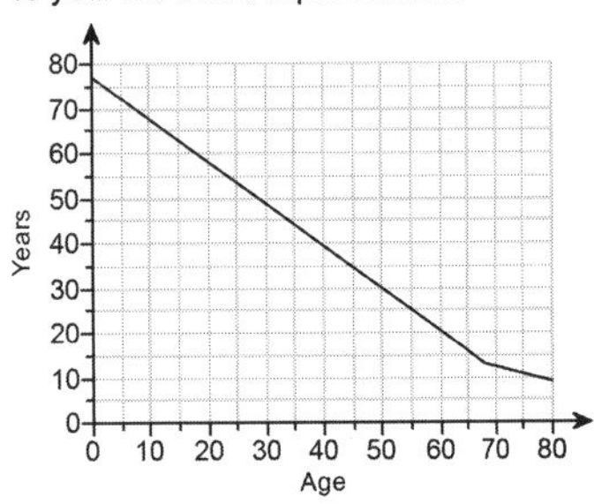

ID: 11.1.15

The estimated death rate for 70-year-olds is __________ deaths per 1000 people.
(Round to the nearest whole number as needed.)

Assuming that there were about 11.3 million 70-year-olds, __________ people of this age could be expected to die in a year.
(Simplify your answer.)

---

16. Use the graph to determine to what age the average 40-year-old could expect to live.

ID: 11.1.16

The average 40-year-old could expect to live to __________ years of age.

---

17. Suppose that a life insurance company insures 1,300,000 fifty-year-old people in a given year. (Assume a death rate of 5 per 1000 people.) The cost of the premium is $400 per year, and the death benefit is $45,000. What is the expected profit or loss for the insurance company?

The insurance company can expect a(n) $ __________ million (1) __________
(Type an integer or decimal rounded to one decimal place as needed.)

(1) ○ loss.
○ profit.

ID: 11.1.17

---

* 18. In a certain country, the life expectancy for women in 1900 was 47 years and in 2000 it was 79 years. Assuming that life expectancy between 2000 and 2100 increases by the same percentage as it did between 1900 and 2000, what will the life expectancy be for women in 2100?

Assuming the life expectancy between 2000 and 2100 will increase by the same percentage as it did between 1900 and 2000, the life expectancy for women in 2100 will be __________ years.
(Round to the nearest integer as needed.)

ID: 11.1.18

---

* 19. Country A reported 45,433 births for a year (assume 365 days) with a population of about 2.6 million people. Country B reported 18,711 births with a population of about 1.6 million people.
a. How many people were born each day of the year in Country A?
b. How many people were born each day of the year in Country B?
c. What was the birth rate in Country A in births per 1000 people?
d. What was the birth rate in Country B in births per 1000 people?

a. There were __________ people born each day of the year in Country A.
(Round to the nearest whole number as needed.)

b. There were __________ people born each day of the year in Country B.
(Round to the nearest whole number as needed.)

c. The birth rate in Country A was __________ births per 1000 people.
(Round to the nearest tenth as needed.)

d. The birth rate in Country B was __________ births per 1000 people.
(Round to the nearest tenth as needed.)

ID: 11.1.19

20. In a certain year the population of a country reached 300 million. The overall birth rate was estimated to be 13.7 births per 1,000, and the overall death rate was estimated to be 8.6 deaths per 1,000. Complete parts **a** through **d**.

a. Approximately how many births were there in the country?

__________ (Simplify your answer. Type an integer or a decimal.)

b. About how many deaths were there in the country?

__________ (Simplify your answer. Type an integer or a decimal.)

c. Based on births and deaths alone (that is, not counting immigration and emigration), about how much did the population rise during that year?

__________ (Simplify your answer. Type an integer or a decimal.)

d. Ignoring immigration and emigration, what is the rate (in decimal form) of population growth of the country in that year?

__________ (Simplify your answer. Type an integer or a decimal.)

What is the population growth rate expressed as a percentage?

__________% (Simplify your answer. Type an integer or a decimal.)

ID: 11.1.20

* 21. Each year there are approximately 5 million births in a country, of which 167,000 are twin births (that is, $2 \times 167{,}000$ babies), 6500 are triplet births, and 500 are quadruplet births. Assume that births of five or more babies in one delivery are negligible in number. Complete parts (a)–(c) below.

a. What is the approximate probability that an expectant mother will give birth to more than one baby? Assume that multiple births are randomly distributed in the population.

The probability is approximately __________.
(Do not round until the final answer. Then round to three decimal places as needed.)

b. What is the approximate probability that a randomly selected newborn is a twin? (Remember that there are two babies for each twin birth.)

The probability is approximately __________.
(Do not round until the final answer. Then round to three decimal places as needed.)

c. What is the approximate probability that a randomly selected newborn is a twin, a triplet, or a quadruplet?

The probability is approximately __________.
(Do not round until the final answer. Then round to three decimal places as needed.)

ID: 11.1.21

!* 22. Suppose 2 dice are rolled and you are interested in determining the probability of getting a 3, 8, or 11. Use the dice chart to answer parts (a) through (c).
a. What is the size of the sample space?
b. The event of rolling a 3, 8, or 11 consists of how many outcomes?
c. What is the probability of rolling a 3, 8, or 11?
[5] Click the icon to view the dice chart.

a. The size of the sample space is __________.
(Type a whole number.)

b. The event of rolling a 3, 8, or 11 consists of __________ outcomes.
(Type a whole number.)

c. The probability of rolling a 3, 8, or 11 is __________.
(Simplify your answer.)

5: Dice Chart

Dice Chart

Roll	Probability
2	1/36
3	2/36
4	3/36
5	4/36
6	5/36
7	6/36
8	5/36
9	4/36
10	3/36
11	2/36
12	1/36

ID: 11.2.1

!* 23. In a poker game, the dealer states that fours and queens are wild. Use the figure of the standard deck of cards to answer parts (a) through (c).
a. What is the size of the sample space?
b. The event of being dealt a wild card consists of how many outcomes?
c. What is the probability of being dealt a wild card?
[6] Click the icon to view the standard deck of cards.

a. The size of the sample space is ________.
(Type a whole number.)

b. The event of being dealt a wild card consists of ________ outcome(s).
(Type a whole number.)

c. The probability of being dealt a wild card is ________.
(Type an integer or a simplified fraction.)

6: Standard Deck of Cards

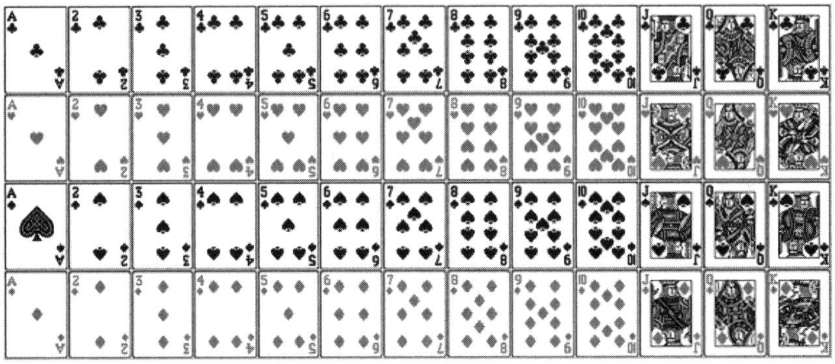

ID: 11.2.2

!* 24. A coin is flipped 3 times in a row. You want to determine the probability of getting exactly 3 tails. Answer parts (a) through (c).
a. What is the sample space? (Use "H" for heads and "T" for tails.)
b. The event of getting exactly 3 tails consists of how many outcomes?
c. What is the probability of getting exactly 3 tails?

a. Choose the correct answer below.

○ **A.** {HHH, HHT, TTH, TTT}
○ **B.** {HH, HT, TH}
○ **C.** {H, T, HT, TH, HHH, TTT}
○ **D.** {HHH, HHT, HTH, THH, HTT, THT, TTH, TTT}

b. The event of getting exactly 3 tails consists of ________ outcome(s).
(Type a whole number.)

c. The probability of getting exactly 3 tails is ________.
(Simplify your answer.)

ID: 11.2.3

25. Suppose we describe the weather as either sunny (S) or calm (C). Answer parts (a) and (b) below.

a. Using the letters S and C, list all the possible outcomes for the weather on two consecutive days.

________ (Use a comma to separate answers as needed.)

b. If we are only interested in the number of S days, what are the possible events for two consecutive days.

________ (Type a whole number. Use a comma to separate answers as needed.)

ID: 11.2.4

26. Find the odds for and the odds against the event rolling a fair die and getting a 2, a 5, or a 6.

a. The odds for the event are ________ to ________. (Simplify your answers.)

b. The odds against the event are ________ to ________. (Simplify your answers.)

ID: 11.2.5

27. Find the odds for and the odds against the event rolling a fair die and getting a 6, a 4, or a 2.

a. The odds for the event are ________ to ________.

b. The odds against the event are ________ to ________.

ID: 11.2.6

---

28. The odds on (against) your bet are 6 to 7. If you bet $56 and win, how much will you gain?

$ ________
(Type an integer or a decimal.)

ID: 11.2.7

---

29. An experiment consists of drawing 1 card from a standard 52-card deck. What is the probability of drawing a black face card?

What is the probability of drawing a black face card? ________
(Type an integer or a simplified fraction.)

ID: 11.2.8

---

30. Decide which method (theoretical, relative frequency, or subjective) is appropriate, and compute or estimate the following probability.

Drawing a red queen or ace of clubs from a standard deck of cards

The (1) ________ method should be used.

The probability of drawing a red queen or ace of clubs is ________.
(Type an integer or a simplified fraction.)

(1) ○ relative frequency
○ theoretical
○ subjective

ID: 11.2.9

---

31. Decide which method (theoretical, relative frequency, or subjective) is appropriate, and compute or estimate the following probability.

Randomly meeting someone born between 1:00 pm and 3:00 pm

The (1) ________ method should be used.

The probability of meeting someone born between 1:00 pm and 3:00 pm is ________.
(Type an integer or a simplified fraction.)

(1) ○ theoretical
○ relative frequency
○ subjective

ID: 11.2.10

---

32. Decide which method (theoretical, relative frequency, or subjective) is appropriate, and compute or estimate the following probability.

Randomly meeting someone with a phone number that ends in 6, 8 or 9

The (1) ________ method should be used.

The probability of randomly meeting someone with a phone number that ends in 6, 8 or 9 is ________.
(Type an integer or a simplified fraction.)

(1) ○ relative frequency
○ theoretical
○ subjective

ID: 11.2.11

---

33. Use the theoretical method to determine the probability of the outcome or event given below.

The next president of the United States was born on Wednesday or Thursday

The probability of the given event is ______. (Type an integer or a simplified fraction.)

ID: 11.2.12

---

34. In a family with 4 children, excluding multiple births, what is the probability of having 4 girls? Assume that a girl is as likely as a boy at each birth.

The probability of having 4 girls is ______. (Type a fraction. Simplify your answer.)

ID: 11.2.13

---

35. Suppose that an urn contains 3 white marbles, 12 black marbles, and 5 green marbles. If one marble is selected, determine the probability that it is green.

The probability that the marble is green is ______.
(Type an integer or a simplified fraction.)

ID: 11.2.14

---

36. Decide which method (theoretical, relative frequency, or subjective) is appropriate, and compute or estimate the following probability.

Randomly meeting someone whose Social Security number ends in the same digit as yours

Choose the correct answer below.

○ **A.** Using the theoretical method, the probability is 0.9.

○ **B.** Using the subjective method, the probability is $\frac{1}{10}$.

○ **C.** Using the theoretical method, the probability is $\frac{1}{10}$.

○ **D.** Using the subjective method, the probability is 0.9.

○ **E.** Using the relative frequency method, the probability is $\frac{1}{10}$.

○ **F.** Using the relative frequency method, the probability is 0.9.

ID: 11.2.15

---

37. What is the probability of not rolling a sum of 3 with two fair dice?

The probability of not rolling a sum of 3 with two fair dice is ______.
(Type an integer or a simplified fraction.)

ID: 11.2.16

---

38. Decide which method (theoretical, relative frequency, or subjective) is appropriate, and compute or estimate the following probability.

Rolling a sum of 6 when you roll two dice

The (1) ______ method should be used.

The probability of rolling a sum of 6 is ______.
(Type an integer or a simplified fraction.)

(1) ○ relative frequency
○ subjective
○ theoretical

ID: 11.2.17

---

39. Suppose there is a bag containing 15 yellow marbles (Y), 15 violet marbles (V), 15 red marbles (R), and 15 black marbles (B). Someone mixes the marbles thoroughly, draws one marble at random, puts the marble back in the bag, mixes the bag thoroughly, and draws another marble at random. Complete parts (a) and (b) below.

a. List all possible outcomes of this process. Choose the correct answer below.

- ○ **A.** YV, YR, YB, VR, VB, RB
- ○ **B.** YY, YV, YR, YB, VY, VV, VR, VB, RY, RV, RR, RB, BY, BV, BR, BB
- ○ **C.** YY, YV, YR, YB, VV, VR, VB, RR, RB, BB
- ○ **D.** Y, V, R, B

b. Make the probability distribution showing the probability of drawing 0, 1, and 2 violet marbles.

Result	Probability
0 V	______
1 V	______
2 V	______

(Simplify your answers.)

ID: 11.2.18

---

* 40. The following table gives the gender and political affiliation of 100 randomly selected voters at a voting site. Suppose you select a voter at random from that voting site. Answer the following questions **a-e**.

	Women	Men
Republicans	22	24
Democrats	29	14
Independents	5	6

a. What is the probability that you select a woman?
______ (Type an integer or a simplified fraction.)

b. What is the probability that you select an Independent?
______ (Type an integer or a simplified fraction.)

c. What is the probability that you do not select a Republican?
______ (Type an integer or a simplified fraction.)

d. What is the probability that you select a female Republican?
______ (Type an integer or a simplified fraction.)

e. What is the probability that you select someone who is not a male Independent?
______ (Type an integer or a simplified fraction.)

ID: 11.2.19

---

41. In 2010, there were 30 million people over 65 years of age out of a population of 317 million. By 2050, it is estimated that there will be 84 million people over 65 years of age out of a population of 433 million. Would your chances of meeting a person over 65 at random be greater in 2010 or 2050? Explain.

The chances are greater in (1) ______ because the relative frequency probability of meeting a person over age 65 in 2010 is ______ and the relative frequency probability of meeting a person over age 65 in 2050 is ______.

(Round to the nearest thousandth as needed.)

(1) ○ 2050 ○ 2010

ID: 11.2.20

---

42. Suppose event A has a 0.99 probability of occurring, and event B has a 0.95 probability of occurring—both high probabilities. Compute the odds for event A and the odds for event B. Comment on the relative difference between the odds for the two events compared to the relative difference between the probabilities. How are the odds deceptive in this case?

The odds for event A are ______.
(Round to three decimal places as needed.)

The odds for event B are ______.
(Round to three decimal places as needed.)

The difference between the probability for event A and the probability for event B is ______, while the difference between the odds for event A and the odds for event B is ______. The odds are deceptive because they make the difference in likelihoods look a lot (1) ______ than they actually are.
(Round to three decimal places as needed.)

(1) ○ larger ○ smaller

ID: 11.2.21

43. Decide whether each of the following statement makes sense (or is clearly true) or does not make sense (or is clearly false). Explain your reasoning.

The probability of getting heads and tails when you toss a coin is 0, but the probability of getting heads or tails is 1.

Choose the correct answer below.

- A. The statement does not make sense because the probability of getting heads and tails is greater than 0.
- B. The statement does not make sense because the probability of getting heads and tails is less than 0.
- C. The statement makes sense because heads and tails are equally likely outcomes.
- D. The statement makes sense because heads and tails are the only possible outcomes and it is impossible to get both heads and tails on a single coin toss.

ID: 11.2.22

---

44. Decide whether each of the following statement makes sense (or is clearly true) or does not make sense (or is clearly false). Explain your reasoning.

The probability of drawing an ace or a spade from a deck of cards is the same as the probability of drawing the ace of spades.

Choose the correct answer below.

- A. The statement makes sense because drawing an ace and drawing a spade are independent events.
- B. The statement does not make sense because there is one card that is the ace of spades but more than one card that is either an ace or a spade.
- C. The statement makes sense because the probability of each is $\frac{1}{52}$.
- D. The statement does not make sense because drawing an ace and drawing a spade are independent events.

ID: 11.2.23

---

45. Decide whether the following makes sense (or is clearly true) or does not make sense (or is clearly false). Explain your reasoning.

My chance of getting a 5 on the roll of one die is 1 / 6, so my chance of getting at least one 5 when I roll three dice is 3 / 6.

Choose the correct answer below.

- A. This does not make sense because this is the same logic that the Chevalier used, which was wrong. The real probability is always 1 / 6.
- B. This does not make sense because the real probability would be $1-\left(\frac{5}{6}\right)^3$, which is not equal to 3 / 6.
- C. This makes sense because the Chevalier used the same logic to win great sums of money.
- D. This makes sense because the probability of rolling at least one five in three rolls is 1 / 6 + 1 / 6 + 1 / 6.

ID: 11.2.24

---

46. A 12-sided die is rolled. The set of equally likely outcomes is {1,2,3,4,5,6,7,8,9,10,11,12}. Find the probability of rolling a 4.

The probability of rolling a 4 is ____________.
(Type an integer or a simplified fraction.)

ID: 11.2.25

---

47. An 8-sided die is rolled. Find the probability of rolling an odd number. The set of equally likely outcomes is shown below.

{1, 2, 3, 4, 5, 6, 7, 8}

The probability of rolling an odd number on an 8-sided die is ____________.
(Type an integer or a simplified fraction.)

ID: 11.2.26

---

48. A 12-sided die is rolled. The set of equally likely outcomes is {1,2,3,4,5,6,7,8,9,10,11,12}. Find the probability of rolling a number less than 4.

The probability of rolling a number less than 4 is ___________.
(Type an integer or a simplified fraction.)

ID: 11.2.27

---

49. A 12-sided die is rolled. The set of equally likely outcomes is {1,2,3,4,5,6,7,8,9,10,11,12}. Find the probability of rolling a number greater than 7.

The probability of rolling a number greater than 7 is ___________.
(Type an integer or a simplified fraction.)

ID: 11.2.28

---

50. A 12-sided die is rolled. The set of equally likely outcomes is {1,2,3,4,5,6,7,8,9,10,11,12}. Find the probability of rolling a number less than 20.

The probability of rolling a number less than 20 is ___________.
(Type an integer or a simplified fraction.)

ID: 11.2.29

---

51. A 12-sided die is rolled. The set of equally likely outcomes is {1,2,3,4,5,6,7,8,9,10,11,12}. Find the probability of rolling a number greater than 21.

The probability of rolling a number greater than 21 is ___________.
(Type an integer or a simplified fraction.)

ID: 11.2.30

---

52. You are dealt one card from a standard 52-card deck. Find the probability of being dealt a six.

The probability of being dealt a six is ___________.
(Type an integer or a simplified fraction.)

ID: 11.2.31

---

53. You are dealt one card from a standard 52-card deck. Find the probability of being dealt a club.

The probability of being dealt a club is ___________.
(Type an integer or a simplified fraction.)

ID: 11.2.32

---

54. You are dealt one card from a standard 52-card deck. Find the probability of being dealt a red card.

The probability of being dealt a red card is ___________.
(Type an integer or a simplified fraction.)

ID: 11.2.33

---

55. You are dealt one card from a standard 52-card deck. Find the probability of being dealt the ace of clubs.

The probability of being dealt the ace of clubs is ___________.
(Type an integer or a simplified fraction.)

ID: 11.2.34

---

56. You are dealt one card from a standard 52-card deck. Find the probability of being dealt a nine and a jack.

The probability of being dealt a nine and a jack is ___________.
(Type an integer or a simplified fraction.)

ID: 11.2.35

---

57. A fair coin is tossed two times in succession. The set of equally likely outcomes is {HH, HT, TH, TT}. Find the probability of getting exactly zero tails.

The probability of getting zero tails is ____________.
(Type an integer or a simplified fraction.)

ID: 11.2.36

---

58. A fair coin is tossed 3 times in succession. The set of equally likely outcomes is {HHH, HHT, HTH, THH, HTT, THT, TTH, TTT}. Find the probability of getting a tail on the first toss.

The probability of getting a tail on the first toss is ____________.
(Type an integer or a simplified fraction.)

ID: 11.2.37

---

59. You select a family with four children. If M represents a male child and F a female child, the set of equally likely outcomes for the children's genders is {FFFF, FFFM, FFMF, FMFF, MFFF, MFFM, MFMF, MMFF, FFMM, FMFM, FMMF, FMMM, MFMM, MMFM, MMMF, MMMM}. Find the probability of selecting a family with exactly two female children.

The probability of having exactly two female children is ____________.
(Type an integer or a simplified fraction.)

ID: 11.2.38

---

60. You select a family with four children. If M represents a male child and F a female child, the set of equally likely outcomes for the children's genders is {FFFF, FFFM, FFMF, FMFF, MFFF, MFFM, MFMF, MMFF, FFMM, FMFM, FMMF, FMMM, MFMM, MMFM, MMMF, MMMM}. Find the probability of selecting a family with exactly zero female children.

The probability of having exactly zero female children is ____________.
(Type an integer or a simplified fraction.)

ID: 11.2.39

---

* 61. You select a family with three children. If M represents a male child and F a female child, the set of equally likely outcomes for the children's genders is shown below. Find the probability of selecting a family with at least one female child.

{MMM, MMF, MFM, MFF, FMM, FMF, FFM, FFF}

The probability of having at least one female child is ____________.
(Type an integer or a simplified fraction.)

ID: 11.2.40

---

62. You select a family with three children. If M represents a male child, and F represents a female child, the set of equally likely outcomes for the children's genders is { MMM, MMF, MFM, MFF, FMM, FMF, FFM, FFF }. Find the probability of selecting a family with 5 female children.

P(5 female children) = ____________
(Type an integer or a simplified fraction.)

ID: 11.2.41

---

63. A single die is rolled twice. The 36 equally-likely outcomes are shown to the right.

Find the probability of getting a first number that is less than the second number.

	Second Roll: 1	2	3	4	5	6
First Roll: 1	(1,1)	(1,2)	(1,3)	(1,4)	(1,5)	(1,6)
2	(2,1)	(2,2)	(2,3)	(2,4)	(2,5)	(2,6)
3	(3,1)	(3,2)	(3,3)	(3,4)	(3,5)	(3,6)
4	(4,1)	(4,2)	(4,3)	(4,4)	(4,5)	(4,6)
5	(5,1)	(5,2)	(5,3)	(5,4)	(5,5)	(5,6)
6	(6,1)	(6,2)	(6,3)	(6,4)	(6,5)	(6,6)

The probability of getting a first number that is less than the second number is ____________.
(Type an integer or a simplified fraction.)

ID: 11.2.42

---

64. A single die is rolled twice. The 36 equally-likely outcomes are shown to the right.

Find the probability of getting two numbers whose sum is 5.

	Second Roll					
First Roll	⚀	⚁	⚂	⚃	⚄	⚅
⚀	(1,1)	(1,2)	(1,3)	(1,4)	(1,5)	(1,6)
⚁	(2,1)	(2,2)	(2,3)	(2,4)	(2,5)	(2,6)
⚂	(3,1)	(3,2)	(3,3)	(3,4)	(3,5)	(3,6)
⚃	(4,1)	(4,2)	(4,3)	(4,4)	(4,5)	(4,6)
⚄	(5,1)	(5,2)	(5,3)	(5,4)	(5,5)	(5,6)
⚅	(6,1)	(6,2)	(6,3)	(6,4)	(6,5)	(6,6)

The probability of getting two numbers whose sum is 5 is ___________.
(Type an integer or a simplified fraction.)

ID: 11.2.43

---

65. A single die is rolled twice. The 36 equally-likely outcomes are shown to the right.

Find the probability of getting two numbers whose sum exceeds 15.

	Second Roll					
First Roll	⚀	⚁	⚂	⚃	⚄	⚅
⚀	(1,1)	(1,2)	(1,3)	(1,4)	(1,5)	(1,6)
⚁	(2,1)	(2,2)	(2,3)	(2,4)	(2,5)	(2,6)
⚂	(3,1)	(3,2)	(3,3)	(3,4)	(3,5)	(3,6)
⚃	(4,1)	(4,2)	(4,3)	(4,4)	(4,5)	(4,6)
⚄	(5,1)	(5,2)	(5,3)	(5,4)	(5,5)	(5,6)
⚅	(6,1)	(6,2)	(6,3)	(6,4)	(6,5)	(6,6)

The probability of getting two numbers whose sum exceeds 15 is ___________.
(Type an integer or a simplified fraction.)

ID: 11.2.44

---

66. Use the spinner shown to answer the question. Assume that it is equally probable that the pointer will land on any one of the colored regions. If the pointer lands on a borderline, spin again.

If the spinner is spun once, find the probability that the pointer lands in a red region.

The probability that the pointer lands in a red region is ___________.
(Type an integer or a simplified fraction.)

ID: 11.2.45

---

67. Use the spinner shown to answer the question. Assume that it is equally probable that the pointer will land on any one of the colored regions. If the pointer lands on a borderline, spin again.

If the spinner is spun once, find the probability that the pointer lands in a blue region.

The probability that the pointer lands in a blue region is ___________.
(Type an integer or a simplified fraction.)

ID: 11.2.46

---

68. Use the spinner shown to answer the question. Assume that it is equally probable that the pointer will land on any one of the colored regions. If the pointer lands on a borderline, spin again.

If the spinner is spun once, find the probability that the pointer lands in a region that is green or red.

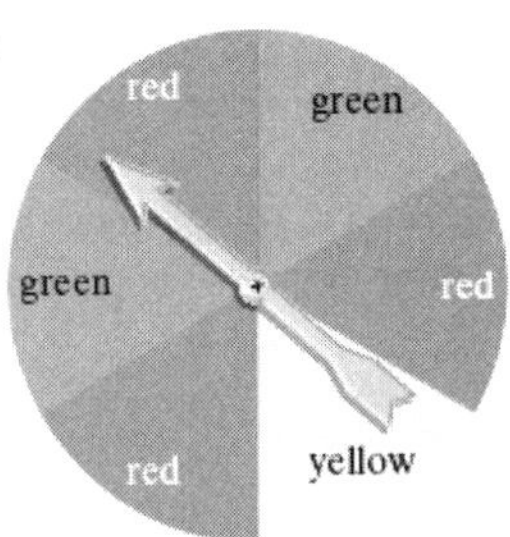

The probability that the pointer lands in a region that is green or red is ________.
(Type an integer or a simplified fraction.)

ID: 11.2.47

69. Use the spinner shown to answer the question. Assume that it is equally probable that the pointer will land on any one of the colored regions. If the pointer lands on a borderline, spin again.

If the spinner is spun once, find the probability that the pointer lands in a region that is green and yellow.

The probability that the pointer lands in a region that is green and yellow is ________.
(Type an integer or a simplified fraction.)

ID: 11.2.48

70. Sickle cell anemia is an inherited disease in which red blood cells become distorted and deprived of oxygen. A person with two sickle cell genes will have the disease, but a person with only one sickle cell gene will have a mild, non-fatal anemia called sickle cell trait. Using S to represent the sickle cell gene, and s a healthy gene, the table shows the four possibilities for the children of two Ss parents. Find the probability that these parents give birth to a child who has sickle cell anemia.

		Second Parent	
		S	**s**
First Parent	**S**	SS	Ss
	s	sS	ss

P(child has sickle cell anemia) = ________
(Type an integer or a simplified fraction.)

ID: 11.2.49

71. Sickle cell anemia is an inherited disease in which red blood cells become distorted and deprived of oxygen. A person with two sickle cell genes will have the disease, but a person with only one sickle cell gene will have a mild, non-fatal anemia called sickle cell trait. Using S to represent the sickle cell gene, and s a healthy gene, the table shows the four possibilities for the children of two Ss parents. Find the probability that these parents give birth to a child who has sickle cell trait.

		Second Parent	
		S	**s**
First Parent	**S**	SS	Ss
	s	sS	ss

P(child has sickle cell trait) = ________
(Type an integer or a simplified fraction.)

ID: 11.2.50

72. Sickle cell anemia is an inherited disease in which red blood cells become distorted and deprived of oxygen. A person with two sickle cell genes will have the disease, but a person with only one sickle cell gene will have a mild, nonfatal anemia called sickle cell trait. If we use S to represent a healthy gene, and s a sickle cell gene, the table shows the four possibilities for the children of one healthy, SS parent, and one parent with sicke cell trait, Ss. Find the probability that these parents give birth to a child who has sickle cell trait.

		Second Parent (with Sickle Cell Trait)	
		S	**s**
Healthy First Parent	**S**	SS	Ss
	S	SS	Ss

The probability that the parents give birth to a child who has sickle cell trait = ________.
(Type an integer or a simplified fraction.)

ID: 11.2.51

73. The target in the figure shown to the right contains four squares. If a dart thrown at random hits the target, find the probability that it will land in a green region.

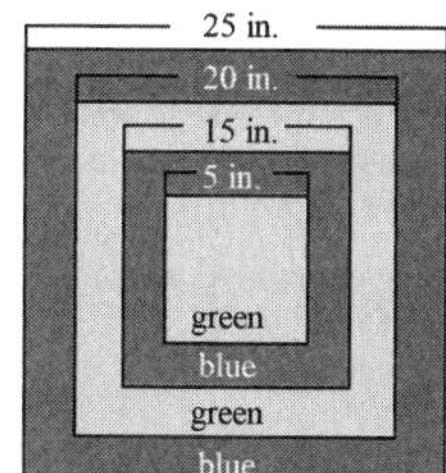

The probability that a dart will land in a green region of the square target is ________.
(Type an integer or a simplified fraction.)

ID: 11.2.52

74. Some three-digit numbers, such as 202 and 616, read the same forward and backward. If a boy selects a number from all three-digit numbers, find the probability that it will read the same forward and backward.

The probability that a number selected from all three-digit numbers will read the same forward and backward is ________.
(Type an integer or a simplified fraction.)

ID: 11.2.53

75. This problem involves empirical probability. The table shows the breakdown of 90 thousand single parents on active duty in the U.S. military in a certain year. All numbers are in thousands and rounded to the nearest thousand. Use the data in the table to find the probability that a randomly selected single parent in the U.S. military is female.

	Army	Navy	Marine Corps	Air Force	Total
Male	26	24	5	12	67
Female	10	7	1	5	23
Total	36	31	6	17	90

The probability that a randomly selected single parent in the U.S. military is female is ________.
(Type an integer or decimal rounded to the nearest hundredth as needed.)

ID: 11.2.54

76. This problem involves empirical probability. The table shows the breakdown of 91 thousand single parents on active duty in the U.S. military in a certain year. All numbers are in thousands and rounded to the nearest thousand. Use the data in the table to find the probability that a randomly selected single parent in the U.S. military is in the Army.

	Army	Navy	Marine Corps	Air Force	Total
Male	23	24	5	16	68
Female	9	7	1	6	23
Total	32	31	6	22	91

The probability that a randomly selected single parent in the U.S. military is in the Army is ________.
(Type an integer or decimal rounded to the nearest hundredth as needed.)

ID: 11.2.55

77. This problem involves empirical probability. The table shows the breakdown of 91 thousand single parents on active duty in the U.S. military in a certain year. All numbers are in thousands and rounded to the nearest thousand. Use the data in the table to find the probability that a randomly selected single parent in the U.S. military is a woman in the Air Force.

	Army	Navy	Marine Corps	Air Force	Total
Male	26	25	7	10	68
Female	10	8	1	4	23
Total	36	33	8	14	91

The probability that a randomly selected single parent in the U.S. military is a woman in the Air Force is ________.

(Type an integer or decimal rounded to the nearest hundredth as needed.)

ID: 11.2.56

78. The table shows the number, expressed in millions, of citizens who moved in 2004, categorized by where they moved and whether they were an owner or a renter.

Number of People in a Certain Country Who Moved in 2004, in Millions

	Moved to Same Region	Moved to Different Region	Moved to Different Country
Owner	11.8	2.9	0.4
Renter	18.8	4.6	1.1

Find the probability, expressed as a decimal rounded to the nearest hundredth, that a randomly selected citizen who moved in 2004 was an owner.

P(citizen was an owner) ≈ ___________
(Round to the nearest hundredth as needed.)

ID: 11.2.57

---

79. The table shows the number, expressed in millions, of citizens who moved in 2004, categorized by where they moved and whether they were an owner or a renter.

Number of People in a Certain Country Who Moved in 2004, in Millions

	Moved to Same Region	Moved to Different Region	Moved to Different Country
Owner	11.6	2.8	0.3
Renter	18.7	4.4	1.1

Find the probability, expressed as a decimal rounded to the nearest hundredth, that a randomly selected citizen who moved in 2004 was a person who moved within the same region.

P(citizen was a person who moved within the same region) ≈ ___________
(Round to the nearest hundredth as needed.)

ID: 11.2.58

---

80. The table shows the number, expressed in millions, of citizens who moved in 2004, categorized by where they moved and whether they were an owner or a renter.

Number of People in a Certain Country Who Moved in 2004, in Millions

	Moved to Same Region	Moved to Different Region	Moved to Different Country
Owner	11.6	2.9	0.4
Renter	18.7	4.4	1.1

Find the probability, expressed as a decimal rounded to the nearest hundredth, that a randomly selected citizen who moved in 2004 was an owner who moved to a different country.

P(citizen was an owner who moved to a different country) ≈ ___________
(Round to the nearest hundredth as needed.)

ID: 11.2.59

---

81. The table below shows the educational attainment of a country's population, aged 25 and over. Use the data in the table, expressed in millions, to find the probability that a randomly selected citizen, aged 25 or over, had some college (less than 4 years).

	Less Than 4 Years High School	4 Years High School Only	Some College (Less Than 4 Years)	4 Years College (or More)	Total
Male	13	21	20	25	79
Female	19	23	21	20	83
Total	32	44	41	45	162

The probability that a randomly selected citizen, aged 25 or over, had some college (less than 4 years) is ___________.
(Type an integer or a simplified fraction.)

ID: 11.2.60

---

82. The table below shows the educational attainment of a country's population, aged 25 and over. Use the data in the table, expressed in millions, to find the probability that a randomly selected citizen, aged 25 or over, was a man with 4 years of college (or more).

	Less Than 4 Years High School	4 Years High School Only	Some College (Less Than 4 Years)	4 Years College (or More)	Total
Male	11	26	18	25	80
Female	12	28	22	20	82
Total	23	54	40	45	162

The probability that a randomly selected citizen, aged 25 or over, was a man with 4 years of college (or more) is ___________.
(Type an integer or a simplified fraction.)

ID: 11.2.61

---

83. A restaurant offers 4 appetizers and 9 main courses. In how many ways can a person order a two-course meal? Use the multiplication principle with two groups of items.

There are ____________ ways a person can order a two-course meal.

ID: 11.2.62

84. Pizza House offers 2 different salads, 3 different kinds of pizza, and 4 different desserts. How many different three course meals can be ordered?

How many different meals can be ordered?

____

ID: 11.2.63

85. You are required to take five courses, one each in humanities, sociology, science, math, and music. You have a choice of 4 humanities courses, 3 sociology courses, 4 science courses, 7 math courses, and 3 music courses. How many different sets of five courses are possible?

There are ____________ different sets of five courses possible.
(Type a whole number.)

ID: 11.2.64

86. A person can order a new car with a choice of 5 possible colors, with or without air conditioning, with or without automatic transmission, with or without power windows, and with or without a CD player. In how many different ways can a new car be ordered with regard to these options?

There are ____________ different ways that a new car can be ordered.

ID: 11.2.65

87. Suppose you toss a fair coin 10,000 times. Should you expect to get exactly 5000 heads? Why or why not? What does the law of large numbers tell you about the results you are likely to get?

Should you expect to get exactly 5000 heads? Why or why not? Choose the correct answer below.

- ○ **A.** You shouldn't expect to get exactly 5000 heads, because you cannot predict precisely how many heads will occur.
- ○ **B.** You shouldn't expect to get exactly 5000 heads, because it is not easy to count precisely the number of heads that occurred.
- ○ **C.** You should expect to get exactly 5000 heads, because the proportion of heads should be 50% for such a large number of tosses.
- ○ **D.** You should expect to get exactly 5000 heads, because for a fair coin, the proportion of heads is exactly 50%.

What does the law of large numbers tell you about the results you are likely to get?

- ○ **A.** The proportion of heads should not approach 0.5 as the number of tosses increases.
- ○ **B.** The proportion of heads should approach 0.5 as the number of tosses decreases.
- ○ **C.** The proportion of heads should approach 0.5 as the number of tosses approaches an exact number.
- ○ **D.** The proportion of heads should approach 0.5 as the number of tosses increases.

ID: 11.2.66

88. What are arrangements with repetition? Give an example of a situation in which the n^r formula gives the number of possible arrangements.

What are arrangements with repetition?

- ○ **A.** If r selections were made from a group of n choices, a total of ${}_nC_r = \frac{n!}{(n-r)! \times r!}$ different arrangements would be possible.
- ○ **B.** If r selections were made from a group of n choices, a total of $\underbrace{n \times n \times \cdots \times n}_{r \text{ times}} = n^r$ different arrangements would be possible.
- ○ **C.** If r selections were made from a group of n choices, a total of ${}_nP_r = \frac{n!}{(n-r)!}$ different arrangements would be possible.
- ○ **D.** If r selections were made from a group of n choices, a total of $n! = n \times (n-1) \times \ldots \times 2 \times 1$ different arrangements would be possible.

88. (cont.) Give an example of a situation in which the n^r formula gives the number of possible arrangements. Choose the correct answer below.

- A. Suppose that a license plate can display 6 numerals. How many different 6-number license plates are possible? Note that in this case, n = 10 (the numerals 0 through 9) and r = 6 (the number of numerals that the plate can display).
- B. A school principal needs to schedule 5 different classes in 5 different time periods. How many schedules are possible? Note that in this case, n = 5 (the number of classes) and r = 5 (the time periods).
- C. Suppose Mary selects 4 different flavors of ice cream in a shop that carries 8 flavors. How many flavor combinations are possible? Note that in this case, n = 8 (the number of flavors available) and r = 4 (the number of flavors selected).
- D. Suppose John coaches a team of 10 swimmers, from which he must put together a 5-person relay team. How many possibilities does he have in this case? Note that in this case, n = 10 (the number of swimmers on the team) and r = 5 (the number of people on the relay team).

ID: 11.2.67

---

89. What do we mean by combinations? Explain the meaning of each of the terms in the combinations formula. Give an example of its use.

Choose the correct answer below.

- A. The n! represents the number of permutations, which includes different orderings. The $(n-r)! \times r!$ represents the number of different orderings of n items taken r at a time. Dividing n! by $(n-r)! \times r!$ determines the number of permutations counting each different ordering, which is a combination.
- B. The n! represents the number of permutations, which includes different orderings. The $(n-r)! \times r!$ represents the number of different orderings of n items taken r at a time. Dividing n! by $(n-r)! \times r!$ determines the number of permutations without counting each different ordering, which is a combination.
- C. The n! represents the number of combinations, which includes different orderings. The $(n-r)! \times r!$ represents the number of different orderings of n items taken r at a time. Dividing n! by $(n-r)! \times r!$ determines the number of combinations without counting each different ordering, which is a permutation.
- D. The n! represents the number of permutations, not counting different orderings. The $(n-r)! \times r!$ represents the number of different orderings of n items taken r at a time. Dividing n! by $(n-r)! \times r!$ determines the number of permutations counting each different ordering, which is a combination.

Give an example of its use. Select the correct answer below.

- A. The formula can be used when deciding how many ways someone can choose two hats from 10 options.
- B. The formula can be used when deciding how many ways someone can dial a number on a telephone.
- C. The formula can be used when deciding how many ways someone can choose a vanity license plate.
- D. The formula can be used when deciding how many ways the first five letters of the alphabet can be arranged.

ID: 11.2.68

---

90. Decide whether the following statement makes sense (or is clearly true) or does not make sense (or is clearly false). Explain your reasoning.

Linda used the permutations formula to determine how many possible relay orders could be made with the 10 girls on her swim team.

Choose the correct answer below.

- A. The statement makes sense because all selections come from the same swim team, each girl can be selected only once, and the order matters.
- B. The statement does not make sense because all selections come from the same swim team, each girl can be selected only once, and the order does not matter. Hence, combinations must be used.
- C. The statement makes sense because all selections come from the same swim team, each girl can be selected more than once, and the order matters.
- D. The statement does not make sense because all selections come from the same swim team, each girl can be selected more than once, and the order matters. Hence, arrangements with repetition must be used.

ID: 11.2.69

---

91. Determine whether the following statement makes sense (or is clearly true) or does not make sense (or is clearly false). Explain your reasoning.

The number of different possible batting orders for 9 players on a 25-person baseball team is so large that there's no hope of trying them all out.

Select the correct answer below.

- A. The statement makes sense because substituting n = 25 and r = 9 into the formula ${}_nP_r = \frac{n!}{(n-r)!}$ results in almost 4 trillion batting orders.
- B. The statement makes sense because substituting n = 25 and r = 9 into the formula ${}_nP_r = \frac{n!}{(n-r)!}$ results in more than 700 billion batting orders.
- C. The statement does not make sense because substituting n = 25 and r = 9 into the formula ${}_nC_r = \frac{n!}{(n-r)!\,r!}$ results in only 162 combinations.
- D. The statement does not make sense because substituting n = 25 and r = 9 into the formula ${}_nC_r = \frac{n!}{(n-r)!\,r!}$ results in only a little more than 1000 combinations.

ID: 11.2.70

---

92. Decide whether the following statement makes sense (or is clearly true) or does not make sense (or is clearly false). Explain your reasoning.

The probability that two people in a randomly selected group will have the same last name is much higher than the probability that someone in this group will have the same last name as you do.

Choose the correct answer below.

- A. The statement does not make sense because the coincidence that two people in a randomly selected group will have the same last name is more likely than the coincidence that someone in this group will have the same last name as you do.
- B. The statement makes sense because the coincidence that two people in a randomly selected group will have the same last name is more likely than the coincidence that someone in this group will have the same last name as you do.
- C. The statement does not make sense because the coincidence that two people in a randomly selected group will have the same last name is less likely than the coincidence that someone in this group will have the same last name as you do.
- D. The statement makes sense because the coincidence that two people in a randomly selected group will have the same last name is less likely than the coincidence that someone in this group will have the same last name as you do.

ID: 11.2.71

---

93. Simplify.

3!

3! = ____________

(Simplify your answer. Type an integer or a fraction.)

ID: 11.2.72

---

94. Evaluate.

$\frac{15!}{12!}$

The solution is ____________.

ID: 11.2.73

---

95. Evaluate the expression.

$\frac{15!}{13!2!}$

$\frac{15!}{13!2!}$ = ____________

(Simplify your answer. Type an integer or a fraction.)

ID: 11.2.74

96. Evaluate the expression.

$$\frac{17!}{4!(17-4)!}$$

$\frac{17!}{4!(17-4)!}$ = __________
(Simplify your answer.)

ID: 11.2.75

---

97. Evaluate the expression.

$$\frac{13!}{2!(13-2)!}$$

$\frac{13!}{2!(13-2)!}$ = __________
(Simplify your answer.)

ID: 11.2.76

---

98. Evaluate the expression.

$$\frac{8!\ 8!}{4!\ 7!}$$

$\frac{8!\ 8!}{4!\ 7!}$ = __________
(Simplify your answer. Type an integer or a fraction.)

ID: 11.2.77

---

99. Answer the following question using the appropriate counting technique, which may be either arrangements with repetition, permutations, or combinations. Be sure to explain why this counting technique applies to the problem.

How many different six-digit codes can be formed using digits 0 through 9?

What counting technique should be used to make this calculation?

- **A.** Arrangements with repetitions because there are r selections from a group of n choices and choices can be repeated.
- **B.** Permutations because the selections come from a single group of items, no item can be selected more than once and the order of the arrangement matters.
- **C.** Combinations because the selections come from a single group of items where no item can be selected more than once and the order of the arrangement does not matter
- **D.** Arrangements with repetitions because the selections come from a single group of items, and the order of the arrangement matters.

There are __________ possible codes.
(Type a whole number.)

ID: 11.2.78

---

100. A company's computer passwords must consist of 5 letters with no repetition of letters.

How many different passwords are possible?

____

ID: 11.2.79

---

101. Baby Caden wants to arrange 5 blocks in a row. How many different arrangements can he make?

There are __________ ways to arrange the 5 blocks.
(Simplify your answer.)

ID: 11.2.80

---

*102. An election ballot asks voters to select six city commissioners from a group of seventeen candidates. In how many ways can this be done?

Six city commissioners can be selected from a group of seventeen candidates in ____________ different ways.

ID: 11.2.81

---

103. Answer the following question using the appropriate counting technique, which may be either arrangements with repetition, permutations, or combinations. Be sure to explain why this counting technique applies to the problem.

How many possible birth orders with respect to gender are possible in a family with six children? (For example, BBBGGG and GBGBGB are different orders.)

What counting technique should be used to make this calculation?

- ○ **A.** Arrangements with repetitions because there are r selections from a group of n choices and choices can be repeated.
- ○ **B.** Arrangements with repetitions because the selections come from a single group of items, and the order of the arrangement matters.
- ○ **C.** Combinations because the selections come from a single group of items, no item can be selected more than once and the order of the arrangement does not matter.
- ○ **D.** Permutations because the selections come from a single group of items, no item can be selected more than once and the order of the arrangement matters.

There are ____________ possible birth orders for a family with six children.
(Type a whole number.)

ID: 11.2.82

---

104. Answer the following question using the appropriate counting technique, which may be either arrangements with repetition, permutations, or combinations. Be sure to explain why this counting technique applies to the problem.

How many license plates can be made of the form XXXX-YY, where X is a letter of the alphabet and Y is a numeral 0-9?

What counting technique should be used to make this calculation?

- ○ **A.** Combinations because the selections come from a single group of items, no item can be selected more than once and the order of the arrangement does not matter.
- ○ **B.** Permutations because the selections come from a single group of items, no item can be selected more than once and the order of the arrangement matters.
- ○ **C.** Arrangements with repetitions because the selections come from a single group of items, and the order of the arrangement matters.
- ○ **D.** Arrangements with repetitions because there are r selections from a group of n choices and choices can be repeated.

How many license plates can be made of the form XXXX-YY, where X is a letter of the alphabet and Y is a numeral 0-9?

- ○ **A.** There are 3,276,000 possible license plates.
- ○ **B.** There are 6,760,000 possible license plates.
- ○ **C.** There are 45,697,600 possible license plates.
- ○ **D.** There are 32,292,000 possible license plates.

ID: 11.2.83

---

105. Answer the following question using the appropriate counting technique, which may be either arrangements with repetition, permutations, or combinations. Be sure to explain why this counting technique applies to the problem.

How many different telephone numbers of the form aaa-bbb-cccc can be formed if the area code aaa cannot contain 7 and the prefix bbb cannot contain 5?

What counting technique should be used to make this calculation?

- ○ **A.** Combinations because the selections come from a single group of items, no item can be selected more than once and the order of the arrangement does not matter.
- ○ **B.** Permutations because the selections come from a single group of items, no item can be selected more than once and the order of the arrangement matters.
- ○ **C.** Arrangements with repetitions because there are *r* selections from a group of *n* choices and choices can be repeated.
- ○ **D.** Arrangements with repetitions because the selections come from a single group of items, and the order of the arrangement matters.

105. (cont.) How many different telephone numbers of the form aaa-bbb-cccc can be formed if the area code aaa cannot contain 7 and the prefix bbb cannot contain 5?

- ○ **A.** There are 4,782,969,000 different telephone numbers.
- ○ **B.** There are 387,420,489 different telephone numbers.
- ○ **C.** There are 6,561,000,000 different telephone numbers.
- ○ **D.** There are 5,314,410,000 different telephone numbers.

ID: 11.2.84

---

106. How many permutations are there of the letters in the word 'CHARGES', if all the letters are used without repetition?

The number of permutations is ________.

ID: 11.2.85

---

107. Answer the following question using the appropriate counting technique, which may be either arrangements with repetition, permutations, or combinations. Be sure to explain why this counting technique applies to the problem.

How many different two-letter "words" can be formed from the alphabet QRS?

What counting technique should be used to make this calculation?

- ○ **A.** Permutations because the selections come from a single group of items, choices can be repeated, and the order of the arrangement does not matter.
- ○ **B.** Arrangements with repetitions because there are *r* selections from a group of *n* choices and choices can be repeated.
- ○ **C.** Combinations because the selections come from a single group of items, no item can be selected more than once and the order of the arrangement does not matter.
- ○ **D.** Permutations because the selections come from a single group of items, no item can be selected more than once and the order of the arrangement matters.

The number of two-letter words that can be made is ________.
(Type a whole number.)

ID: 11.2.86

---

108. Baby Braden wants to arrange 8 blocks in a row. How many different arrangements can he make?

There are ________ ways to arrange the 8 blocks.
(Simplify your answer.)

ID: 11.2.87

---

109. Suppose you are one of 16 people at a dinner party. Find the probability that at least one of the other guests has the same birthday as you and that some pair of guests share the same birthday. Assume there are 365 days in the year.

The probability that at least one other guest shares your birthday is approximately ________.
(Round to four decimal places as needed.)

The probability that some pair of guests share the same birthday is approximately ________.
(Round to four decimal places as needed.)

ID: 11.2.88

---

*110. An ice cream shop offers 23 different flavors of ice cream and 7 different toppings. Answer questions (a) through (d) using the appropriate counting technique (multiplication principle, arrangements with repetitions, permutations, or combinations). Explain why you chose the particular technique.

a. How many different sundaes can you create using one of the ice cream flavors and one of the toppings? What counting technique will you use to make this calculation?

- ○ **A.** Combinations because the selections come from a single group of items and the order of the arrangement does not matter.
- ○ **B.** The multiplication principle because there are M possible outcomes for one group and N outcomes for the other group.
- ○ **C.** Permutations because the selections come from a single group of items and the order of the arrangement matters.
- ○ **D.** Arrangements with repetitions because there are r selections from a group of n choices and you can repeat choices.

*110. (cont.) You can create ____________ different sundaes.
(Type a whole number.)

b. How many different triple cones can you create from the 23 flavors if the same flavor may be used more than once? Assume that you specify which flavor goes on the bottom, middle and top. What counting technique will you use to make this calculation?

- ○ **A.** The multiplication principle because there are M possible outcomes for one group and N outcomes for the other group.
- ○ **B.** Permutations because the selections come from a single group of items and the order of the arrangement matters.
- ○ **C.** Combinations because the selections come from a single group of items and the order of the arrangement does not matter.
- ○ **D.** Arrangements with repetitions because there are r selections from a group of n choices and you can repeat choices.

You can create ____________ different triple cones.
(Type a whole number.)

c. Using the 23 flavors, how many different triple cones can you create with 3 different flavors if you specify which flavor goes on the bottom, middle and top? What counting technique will you use to make this calculation?

- ○ **A.** Arrangements with repetitions because there are r selections from a group of n choices and you can repeat choices.
- ○ **B.** The multiplication principle because there are M possible outcomes for one group and N outcomes for the other group.
- ○ **C.** Combinations because the selections come from a single group of items and the order of the arrangement does not matter.
- ○ **D.** Permutations because the selections come from a single group of items and the order of the arrangement matters.

You can create ____________ different triple cones without repeating a flavor.
(Type a whole number.)

d. Using the 23 flavors, how many different triple cones can you create with 3 different flavors if you don't care about the order of the flavors of the cone? What counting technique will you use to make this calculation?

- ○ **A.** Combinations because the selections come from a single group of items and the order of the arrangement does not matter.
- ○ **B.** Arrangements with repetitions because there are r selections from a group of n choices and you can repeat choices.
- ○ **C.** The multiplication principle because there are M possible outcomes for one group and N outcomes for the other group.
- ○ **D.** Permutations because the selections come from a single group of items and the order of the arrangement matters.

You can create ____________ different triple cones when order does not matter.
(Type a whole number.)

ID: 11.2.89

---

111. Pizza parlor A advertises 20 different three-topping pizzas. How many individual toppings does Pizzeria A actually use? Pizzeria B advertises 21 different two-topping pizzas. How many toppings does pizza parlor B actually use? (Hint: In these problems, you are given the total number of combinations, and you must find the number of toppings that are used.)

Pizza parlor A uses ____________ different toppings.
(Type a whole number.)

Pizza parlor B uses ____________ different toppings.
(Type a whole number.)

ID: 11.2.90

---

112. Find the probability of the given event.

Choosing five numbers that match five randomly selected balls when the balls are numbered 1 through 32.

The probability of the given event is ____________.
(Type an integer or a simplified fraction.)

ID: 11.2.91

---

113. Find the probability of being dealt 5 cards from a standard 52-card deck, and the cards are a 9, 10, jack, queen, and king, all of the same suit.

The probabilty of being dealt this hand is ___________.
(Type an integer or simplified fraction.)

ID: 11.2.92

---

114. The trifecta at most racetracks consists of selecting the first-, second-, and third-place finishers in a particular race in their proper order. If there are twelve entries in the trifecta race, how many tickets must you purchase to guarantee a win?

You must purchase ___________ tickets.

ID: 11.2.93

---

115. Find the probability of guessing the top three winners (in any order) from a group of 18 finalists in a spelling bee.

The probability that someone correctly predicts the top three winners from a group of 18 finalists is ___________.
(Type an integer or a fraction.)

ID: 11.2.94

---

116. Find the probability of being dealt 5 cards from a standard 52-card deck, and getting one pair (and not a superior poker hand, if possible).

The probabilty of being dealt one pair is ___________.
(Round to six decimal places as needed.)

ID: 11.2.95

---

117. Suppose that 1500 people are all playing a game for which the chance of winning is 46%. Complete parts (a) and (b) below.

a. Assuming everyone plays exactly four games, what is the probability of one person winning four games in a row?

P(four wins in a row) = ___________
(Round to three decimal places as needed.)

On average, how many of the 1500 people could be expected to have a "hot streak" of four games?

____
(Round to the nearest whole number as needed.)

b. Assuming everyone plays exactly eight games, what is the probability of winning eight games in a row?

P(eight wins in a row) = ___________
(Round to five decimal places as needed.)

On average, how many of the 1500 people could be expected to have a "hot streak" of eight games?

____
(Round to the nearest whole number as needed.)

ID: 11.2.96

---

118. A lottery game is played in many places and requires $1 per ticket to play. To win the jackpot, a person must correctly pick six unique numbers from balls numbered 1 through 36 (order does not matter) and correctly pick a final number, which is chosen from balls numbered 1 through 26. What is the probability of winning the jackpot?

The probability is 1 in ___________.

ID: 11.2.97

---

119. There are five performers who will present their comedy acts this weekend at a comedy club. How many different ways are there to schedule their appearances?

___________ ways

ID: 11.2.98

---

120. In an encyclopedia of language, the author presents five sentences that make a reasonable paragraph regardless of their order. The sentences are listed below.

Mark had told him about the foxes.
John looked out of the window.
Could it be a fox?
However, nobody had seen one for months.
He thought he saw a shape in the bushes.

In how many different orders can the five sentences be arranged?

The five sentences can be arranged in __________ different orders.

ID: 11.2.99

---

121. There are 7 performers who will present their comedy acts this weekend at a comedy club. One of the performers insists on being the last stand-up comic of the evening. If this performer's request is granted, how many different ways are there to schedule the appearances?

__________ ways

ID: 11.2.100

---

122. You need to arrange four of your favorite books along a small shelf. How many different ways can you arrange the books, assuming that the order of the books makes a difference to you?

__________ ways

ID: 11.2.101

---

123. Use the five sentences below to answer the question.

Mark had told him about the foxes.
John looked out of the window.
Could it be a fox?
However, nobody had seen one for months.
He thought he saw a shape in the bushes.

How many different five-sentence paragraphs can be formed if the paragraph begins with "He thought he saw a shape in the bushes" and ends with "John looked out of the window"?

There are __________ different five-sentence paragraphs that can be formed in this situation.

ID: 11.2.102

---

124. A television programmer is arranging the order that six movies will be seen between the hours of 6 P.M. and 6 A.M. Two of the movies have a G rating, and they are to be shown in the first two time blocks. One of the movies is rated NC-17, and it is to be shown in the last of the time blocks, from 4 A.M. until 6 A.M. Given these restrictions, in how many ways can the six movies be arranged during the indicated time blocks?

The number of different ways the six movies can be arranged during the indicated time blocks is __________.
(Type a whole number.)

ID: 11.2.103

---

125. A camp counselor and four campers are to be seated along a picnic bench. In how many ways can this be done if the counselor must be seated in the fourth seat and a camper who has a tendency to engage in food fights must sit to the counselor's immediate left?

There are __________ way(s) this can be done.

ID: 11.2.104

---

126. Seven horses are entered in a race. If four horses are tied for first place, and there are no ties among the other three horses, in how many ways can the seven horses cross the finish line?

There are __________ distinct ways the horses can cross the finish line.

ID: 11.2.105

---

127. Six men and six women line up at a checkout counter in a store. In how many ways can they line up if the first person in line is a woman, and the people in line alternate woman, man, woman, man, and so on?

__________ ways

ID: 11.2.106

128. In how many distinct ways can the letters of the word BELLE be arranged?

__________ ways

ID: 11.2.107

129. How many distinct permutations can be formed using the letters of the word "TALLAHASSEE"?

There are __________ distinct permutations.
(Type a whole number.)

ID: 11.2.108

130. In how many ways can the digits in the number 9,444,111 be arranged?

__________ ways

ID: 11.2.109

131. A signal can be formed by running different colored flags up a pole, one above the other. Find the number of different signals consisting of 10 flags that can be made using 4 white flags, 3 red flags, and 3 blue flags.

____

ID: 11.2.110

* 132. Determine whether the following problem involves a permutation or combination. (It is not necessary to solve the problem.)

A medical researcher needs 29 people to test the effectiveness of an experimental drug. If 100 people have volunteered for the test, in how many ways can 29 people be selected?

○ Permutation
○ Combination

ID: 11.2.111

* 133. Determine whether the following problem involves a permutation or combination. (It is not necessary to solve the problem.)

How many different 4-letter passwords can be formed from the letters A, B, C, D, E, F, and G if no repetition of letters is allowed?

○ Permutation
○ Combination

ID: 11.2.112

* 134. Dawn, Maria, Tyrone, Sergio, and Ian have all been invited to a dinner party. They arrive randomly and each person arrives at a different time.

a. In how many ways can they arrive?
b. In how many ways can Dawn arrive first and Ian last?
c. Find the probability that Dawn will arrive first and Ian last.

a. __________ (Type an integer.)

b. __________ (Type an integer.)

c. __________ (Type a fraction. Simplify your answer.)

ID: 11.2.113

135. Six stand-up comics, A, B, C, D, E, and F, are to perform on a single evening at a comedy club. The order of performance is determined by random selection. Find the probability that:
   a. Comic E will perform second.
   b. Comic B will perform third and Comic C will perform second.
   c. The comedians will perform in the following order: E, B, C, D, F, A.
   d. Comic F or Comic A will perform last.

a. ________
(Type a fraction. Simplify your answer.)

b. ________
(Type a fraction. Simplify your answer.)

c. ________
(Type a fraction. Simplify your answer.)

d. ________
(Type a fraction. Simplify your answer.)

ID: 11.2.114

136. The digits 3, 4, 5, 6, 7, and 8 are randomly arranged to form a three-digit number. (Digits are not repeated.) Find the probability that the number is even and greater than 800.

The probability that the three-digit number is even and greater than 800 is ________.
(Type an integer or a simplified fraction.)

ID: 11.2.115

!* 1. There are 100 students in your class, 80 male and 20 female. One-quarter of the males have seen a particular movie while only 20% of the females have seen it. Use the table below to complete parts (a) through (h).

	Male	**Female**	**Totals**
Seen Movie			
Not Seen Movie			
Totals			

(a) How many students are male and have seen the movie?

	Male	**Female**	**Totals**
Seen Movie	________		
Not Seen Movie			
Totals			

(b) How many students are male and have not seen the movie?

	Male	**Female**	**Totals**
Seen Movie			
Not Seen Movie	________		
Totals			

(c) How many students are female and have seen the movie?

	Male	**Female**	**Totals**
Seen Movie		________	
Not Seen Movie			
Totals			

(d) How many students are female and have not seen the movie?

	Male	**Female**	**Totals**
Seen Movie			
Not Seen Movie		________	
Totals			

!* 1. (cont.) **(e)** How many students total have seen the movie?

	Male	Female	Totals
Seen Movie			______
Not Seen Movie			
Totals			

(f) How many students total have not seen the movie?

	Male	Female	Totals
Seen Movie			
Not Seen Movie			______
Totals			

(g) What is the probability of a student being female given they have seen the movie?

______ (Simplify your answer.)

(h) What is the probability of a student not having seen the movie given they are female?

______ (Simplify your answer.)

ID: 11.3.1

!* 2. There are 36 students in your class. Use the data table available below to complete parts (a) through (d).
[1] Click the icon to view the data table.

(a) What is the probability a randomly selected student is a female?

______ (Simplify your answer.)

(b) What is the probability of a student being female given they are in the class of 2020?

______ (Simplify your answer.)

(c) What is the probability of a student being in the class of 2020 given they are female?

______ (Simplify your answer.)

(d) What is the probability of a student being male given they have a cumulative GPA over 3.0?

______ (Simplify your answer.)

1: Data Table of Student Information

Gender	Year	Cum GPA
M	2017	3.68
F	2020	3.39
M	2017	2.27
M	2020	2.41
F	2020	2.22
F	2017	3.08
M	2017	3.92
F	2020	2.72
M	2018	3.42
F	2018	3.77
F	2019	3.65
F	2020	3.21
F	2018	2.98
M	2020	2.57
F	2017	3.16
F	2020	3.92
M	2017	2.34
F	2020	2.73
F	2019	2.68
M	2019	3.44
F	2018	2.87
M	2019	2.44
F	2019	2.42
M	2019	3.73

!* 2.
(cont.)

F	2017	2.47
M	2019	3.68
M	2017	3.38
M	2018	3.71
F	2020	3.93
F	2020	3.61
M	2020	2.76
F	2020	3.95
F	2018	2.23
F	2017	3.72
F	2018	3.69
F	2019	3.54
Gender	**Year**	**Cum GPA**

ID: 11.3.2

* 3. Elizabeth brought a box of donuts to share. There are two-dozen (24) donuts in the box, all identical in size, shape, and color. Two are jelly-filled, 10 are lemon-filled, and 12 are custard-filled. You randomly select one donut, eat it, and select another donut. Find the probability of selecting two custard-filled donuts in a row.

__________ (Type an integer or a simplified fraction.)

ID: 11.3.3

4. Elizabeth brought a box of donuts to share. There are two-dozen (24) donuts in the box, all identical in size, shape, and color. Six are jelly-filled, 9 are lemon-filled, and 9 are custard-filled. You randomly select one donut, eat it, and select another donut. Find the probability of selecting a jelly-filled donut followed by a custard-filled donut.

__________ (Type an integer or a simplified fraction.)

ID: 11.3.4

5. Consider a political discussion group consisting of 10 Democrats, 7 Republicans, and 5 Independents. Suppose that two group members are randomly selected, in succession, to attend a political convention. Find the probability of selecting two Republicans.

__________ (Type an integer or a simplified fraction.)

ID: 11.3.5

6. Consider a political discussion group consisting of 8 Democrats, 8 Republicans, and 6 Independents. Suppose that two group members are randomly selected, in succession, to attend a political convention. Find the probability of selecting a Democrat and then a Republican.

__________ (Type an integer or a simplified fraction.)

ID: 11.3.6

7. Consider a political discussion group consisting of 8 Democrats, 5 Republicans, and 2 Independents. Suppose that two group members are randomly selected, in succession, to attend a political convention. Find the probability of selecting no Republicans.

__________ (Type an integer or a simplified fraction.)

ID: 11.3.7

8. An ice chest contains 7 cans of apple juice, 4 cans of grape juice, 4 cans of orange juice, and 6 cans of mango juice. Suppose that you reach into the container and randomly select three cans in succession. Find the probability of selecting three cans of mango juice.

The probability of selecting from the ice chest three cans of mango juice is __________.
(Type an integer or a simplified fraction.)

ID: 11.3.8

9. An ice chest contains six cans of apple juice, eight cans of grape juice, four cans of orange juice, and two cans of mango juice. Suppose that you reach into the container and randomly select three cans in succession. Find the probability of selecting a can of grape juice, then a can of orange juice, then a can of apple juice.

The probability of selecting from the ice chest a can of grape juice, then a can of orange juice, then a can of apple juice is __________.
(Type an integer or a simplified fraction.)

ID: 11.3.9

10. An ice chest contains six cans of apple juice, five cans of grape juice, four cans of orange juice, and eight cans of mango juice. Suppose that you reach into the container and randomly select three cans in succession. Find the probability of selecting no apple juice.

The probability of selecting no apple juice from the ice chest is ____________.
(Type an integer or a simplified fraction.)

ID: 11.3.10

---

* 11. The numbered disks shown are placed in a box and one disk is selected at random. Find the probability of selecting an 8, given that a blue disk is selected.

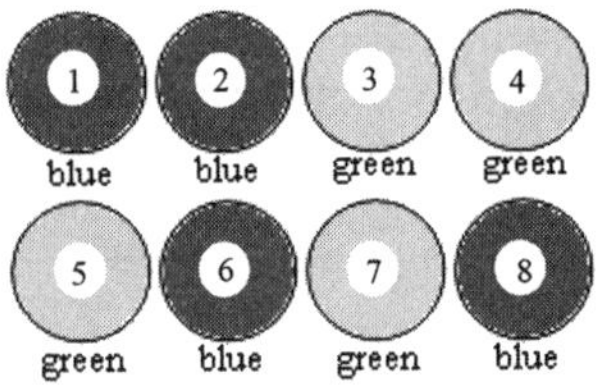

1 2 3 4
blue blue green green
5 6 7 8
green blue green blue

Find the probability of selecting an 8, given that a blue disk is selected.

____________ (Type an integer or a simplified fraction.)

ID: 11.3.11

---

12. The numbered disks shown are placed in a box and one disk is selected at random. Find the probability of selecting an even number, given that a blue disk is selected.

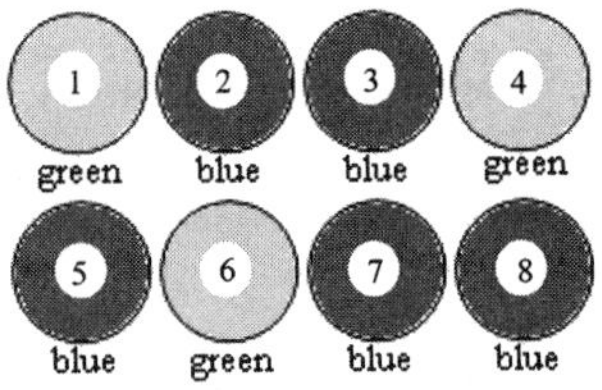

1 2 3 4
green blue blue green
5 6 7 8
blue green blue blue

Find the probability of selecting an even number, given that a blue disk is selected.

____________ (Type an integer or a simplified fraction.)

ID: 11.3.12

---

13. The numbered disks shown are placed in a box and one disk is selected at random. Find the probability of selecting a green disk, given that an even number is selected.

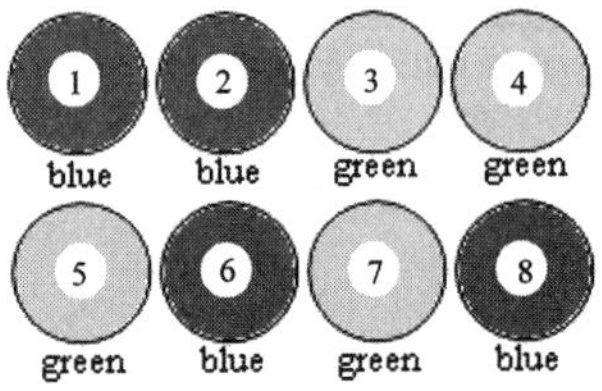

1 2 3 4
blue blue green green
5 6 7 8
green blue green blue

What is the probability of selecting a green disk, given that an even number is selected?

____________ (Type an integer or a simplified fraction.)

ID: 11.3.13

---

14. The numbered disks shown are placed in a box and one disk is selected at random. Find the probability of selecting a blue disk, given that the number selected is at least 4.

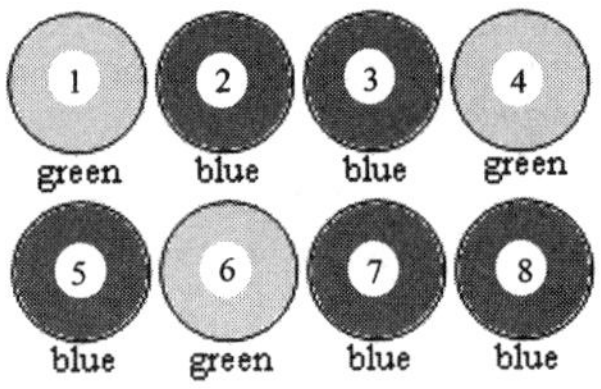

1 2 3 4
green blue blue green
5 6 7 8
blue green blue blue

What is the probability of selecting a blue disk, given that the number selected is at least 4?

____________ (Type an integer or a simplified fraction.)

ID: 11.3.14

---

15. The table shows the outcome of car accidents in a certain state for a recent year by whether or not the driver wore a seat belt.

	Wore Seat Belt	No Seat Belt	Total
Driver Survived	415,385	169,692	585,077
Driver Died	511	2211	2722
Total	415,896	171,903	587,799

Find the probability of not surviving a car accident, given that the driver did not wear a seat belt.

The probability as a decimal is ____________.
(Round to three decimal places as needed.)

The probability as a fraction is ____________.
(Type an integer or a simplified fraction.)

ID: 11.3.15

*16. The table shows the outcome of car accidents in a certain state for a recent year by whether or not the driver wore a seat belt.

	Wore Seat Belt	No Seat Belt	Total
Driver Survived	418,243	164,926	583,169
Driver Died	486	1770	2256
Total	418,729	166,696	585,425

Find the probability of not wearing a seat belt, given that the driver survived a car accident.

The probability as a decimal is ____________.
(Round to three decimal places as needed.)

The probability as a fraction is ____________.
(Type an integer or a simplified fraction.)

ID: 11.3.16

17. If one person is selected from the population described in the table, find the probability that the person is female, given that this person is married.

Marital Status of the U.S. Population, Ages 18 or Older, in Millions

	Never Married	Married	Widowed	Divorced	Total
Male	28.1	60.2	3.1	8.5	99.9
Female	22.5	63.6	11.3	12.7	110.1
Total	50.6	123.8	14.4	21.2	210.0

The probability is approximately ____________.
(Round to three decimal places as needed.)

ID: 11.3.17

18. If one person is selected from the population described in the table, find the probability that the person is married, given that this person is a man.

Marital Status of the U.S. Population, Ages 18 or Older, in Millions

	Never Married	Married	Widowed	Divorced	Total
Male	28.1	60.2	3.1	9.0	100.4
Female	23.3	61.9	10.7	12.7	108.6
Total	51.4	122.1	13.8	21.7	209.0

The probability is approximately ____________.
(Round to three decimal places as needed.)

ID: 11.3.18

19. If one person is selected from the population described in the table, find the probability that the person has never married or is married, given that this person is a woman.

Marital Status of the U.S. Population, Ages 18 or Older, in Millions

	Never Married	Married	Widowed	Divorced	Total
Male	28.1	62.1	2.7	8.5	101.4
Female	22.5	63.6	13.0	12.7	111.8
Total	50.6	125.7	15.7	21.2	213.2

The probability is approximately ____________.
(Round to three decimal places as needed.)

ID: 11.3.19

20. This exercise is on probabilities and coincidence of shared birthdays. Complete parts (a) through (e) below.

a. If two people are selected at random, the probability that they do not have the same birthday (day and month) is $\frac{365}{365} \cdot \frac{364}{365}$. Explain why this is so. (Ignore leap years and assume 365 days in a year.)

The first person can have any birthday, so they can have a birthday on ________ of the 365 days. In order for the second person to not have the same birthday they must have one of the ________ remaining birthdays.
(Type whole numbers.)

b. If four people are selected at random, find the probability that they all have different birthdays.

The probability that they all have different birthdays is ________.
(Round to three decimal places as needed.)

c. If four people are selected at random, find the probability that at least two of them have the same birthday.

The probability that at least two of them have the same birthday is ________.
(Round to three decimal places as needed.)

d. If 14 people are selected at random, find the probability that at least 2 of them have the same birthday.

The probability that at least two of them have the same birthday is ________.
(Round to three decimal places as needed.)

e. Show that if 23 people are selected at random, the probability that at least 2 of them have the same birthday is greater than $\frac{1}{2}$.

The probability that none of the 23 people share a birthday is ________. The probability that at least 2 of 23 people have the same birthday is ________. The probability that there exists people with the same birthday is

(1) ________ than the probability of all 23 not sharing a birthday.
(Round to three decimal places as needed.)

(1) ○ less
○ greater

ID: 11.3.20

---

21. Twenty nine cards numbered from 1 through 29 are placed into a box and two cards are selected without replacement. Find the probability that both numbers selected are odd, given that their sum is even.

Find the probability that both numbers selected are odd, given that their sum is even.

The probability is ________. (Type an integer or a simplified fraction.)

ID: 11.3.21

---

22. Consider the circles shown to the right. Assume one circle is selected at random and each circle is equally likely to be selected. Determine the probability of selecting the number 2, given that the circle is yellow.

1	2	3	4	5	6
orange	green	orange	yellow	green	orange

The probability of selecting the number 2, given that the circle is yellow, is ________.
(Type an integer or a simplified fraction.)

ID: 11.3.22

---

23. Consider the circles shown to the right. Assume one circle is selected at random and each circle is equally likely to be selected. Determine the probability of selecting a number less than 3, given that the number is less than 5.

1	2	3	4	5	6
yellow	green	orange	orange	orange	yellow

The probability of selecting a number less than 3, given that the number is less than 5, is ________.
(Type an integer or a simplified fraction.)

ID: 11.3.23

---

24. Consider the circles shown to the right. Assume one circle is selected at random and each circle is equally likely to be selected. Determine the probability of selecting a black number, given that the circle is green.

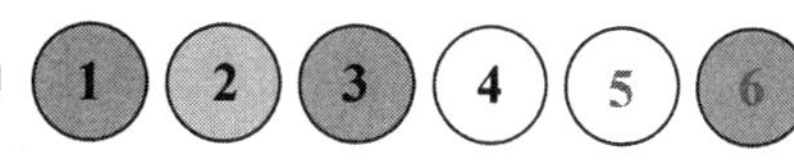

The probability of selecting a black number, given that the circle is green, is ________.
(Type an integer or a simplified fraction.)

ID: 11.3.24

---

25. Consider the figures to the right. Assume that one number from 1 to 7 is equally likely to be selected at random. Each number corresponds to one of the seven figures. Determine the probability of selecting an odd number, given that a square is selected.

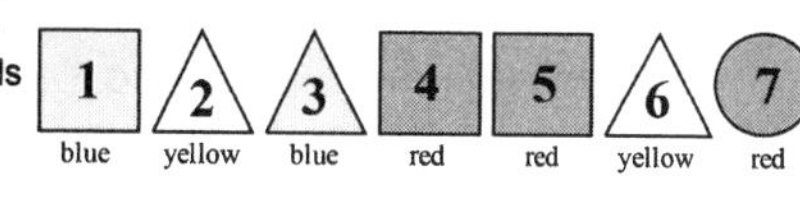

The probability of selecting an odd number, given that a square is selected, is ________.
(Type an integer or a simplified fraction.)

ID: 11.3.25

---

26. Consider the wheel to the right. If the wheel is spun and each section is equally likely to stop under the pointer, determine the probability that the pointer lands on an even number, given that the color is gold.

Note that the gold sectors are the sectors numbered 12 and 7.

The probability that the pointer lands on an even number, given that the color is gold, is ________.
(Type an integer or a simplified fraction.)

ID: 11.3.26

---

27. Consider the wheel to the right. If the wheel is spun and each section is equally likely to stop under the pointer, determine the probability that pointer lands on red, given that the number is greater than 5.

The probability that the pointer lands on red, given that the number is greater than 5, is ________.
(Type an integer or a simplified fraction.)

ID: 11.3.27

---

28. Assume that a hat contains four bills: a $1 bill, a $2 bill, a $10 bill, and a $50 bill. Each bill is equally likely to be selected. Two bills are to be selected at random with replacement. Construct a sample space and determine the probability that both bills are $2 bills.

Which of the figures illustrates the tree diagram for the sample space? Choose the correct answer on the right.

The probability that both bills are $2 bills is ___________.
(Type an integer or a simplified fraction.)

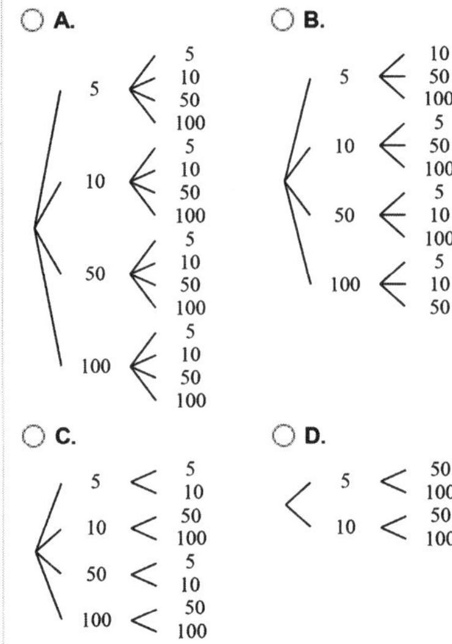

ID: 11.3.28

29. Two dice are rolled one after the other. Construct a sample space and determine the probability that the sum of the dots on the dice total 6.

The probability that the sum of the dots on the dice total 6 is ___________.
(Type an integer or a simplified fraction.)

ID: 11.3.29

30. Two dice are rolled one after another. Construct a sample space and determine the probability that the sum of the dots on the dice total a number greater than 8 if the second die is a 5.

The probability that the sum of the dots on the dice is a number greater than 8 if the second die is a 5 is ___________.
(Type an integer or a simplified fraction.)

ID: 11.3.30

31. The table shows the results of a survey of patrons of a particular restaurant chain.

Meals	Good Service	Poor Service	Total
Lunch	528	339	867
Dinner	909	693	1602
Total	1437	1032	2469

If one of these patrons is selected at random, find the probability that their service was poor, given that their meal was lunch.

The probability that their service was poor, given that their meal was lunch, is ___________.
(Round to four decimal places as needed.)

ID: 11.3.31

32. The table shows the results of a coffee taste test. If one of the individuals surveyed is selected at random, determine the probability that the individual selected is a woman, given that the person prefers Brand A.

	Brand A	Brand B	Total
Men	64	39	103
Women	51	71	122
Total	115	110	225

The probability that the individual selected is a woman, given that the person prefers Brand A, is ___________.
(Type an integer or a simplified fraction.)

ID: 11.3.32

33. The table shows the number of cars and trucks that used a certain toll road on a particular day. The number of cars and trucks that used, and did not use, an electronic toll pass on that same day was also recorded.

Toll Pass	Cars	Trucks	Total
Used	519	329	848
Did not use	911	648	1559
Total	1430	977	2407

If one of these vehicles is selected at random, determine the probability that the vehicle was a truck.

The probability that the vehicle was a truck is ________.
(Round to four decimal places as needed.)

ID: 11.3.33

34. The table shows the number of cars and trucks that used a certain toll road on a particular day. The number of cars and trucks that used, and did not use, an electronic toll pass on that same day was also recorded.

Toll Pass	Cars	Trucks	Total
Used	528	349	877
Did not use	973	670	1643
Total	1501	1019	2520

If one of these vehicles is selected at random, determine the probability that the vehicle used a toll pass given that the vehicle was a car.

The probability that the vehicle used a toll pass, given that the vehicle is a car, is ________.
(Round to four decimal places as needed.)

ID: 11.3.34

35. Sales representatives at a car dealership were split into two groups. One group used an aggressive approach to sell a customer a new automobile. The other group used a passive approach. The following table summarizes the records for 649 customers. If one of these customers is selected at random, determine the probability that the aggressive approach was used.

Approach	Sale	No Sale	Total
Aggressive	106	248	354
Passive	209	86	295
Total	315	334	649

The probability that the aggressive approach was used is ________.
(Type an integer or a simplified fraction.)

ID: 11.3.35

36. Sales representatives at a car dealership were split into two groups. One group used an aggressive approach to sell a customer a new automobile. The other group used a passive approach. The following table summarizes the records for 625 customers.

Approach	Sale	No Sale	Total
Aggressive	80	270	350
Passive	210	65	275
Total	290	335	625

If one of these customers is selected at random, determine the probability of a sale, given that the aggressive approach was used.

The probability of a sale, given that the aggressive approach was used, is ________.
(Type an integer or a simplified fraction.)

ID: 11.3.36

37. The following table shows the age distribution of residents of a certain country. The data are rounded to the nearest million people. If one of these individuals is selected at random, determine the probability that the person is male.

Age	Male	Female	Total
0-14	36	32	68
15-64	101	107	208
65 years or over	19	25	44
Total	156	164	320

The probability of the person being a male is ________.
(Type an integer or a simplified fraction.)

ID: 11.3.37

38. The following table shows the age distribution of residents of a certain country. The data are rounded to the nearest million people. If one of these individuals is selected at random, determine the probability that the person is 15-64 years old, given that the person is male.

Age	Male	Female	Total
0-14	34	32	66
15-64	102	107	209
65 years or over	17	23	40
Total	153	162	315

The probability that the person is 15-64 years old, given that the person is male, is ___________.
(Type an integer or a simplified fraction.)

ID: 11.3.38

39. The following table shows the age distribution of residents of a certain country. The data are rounded to the nearest million people. If one of these individuals is selected at random, determine the probability that the person is male, given that the person is 65 + years old.

Age	Male	Female	Total
0-14	38	30	68
15-64	103	106	209
65 years or over	17	25	42
Total	158	161	319

The probability that the person is male, given that the person is 65 + years old, is ___________.
(Type an integer or a simplified fraction.)

ID: 11.3.39

40. A quality control inspector is checking a sample of lightbulbs for defects. The table summarizes the results. If one of these lightbulbs is selected at random, find the probability that the lightbulb is good, given that it is not 50 watts.

Wattage	Good	Defective	Total
20	58	9	67
50	55	9	64
100	78	11	89
Total	191	29	220

The probability is ___________.
(Type an integer or a simplified fraction.)

ID: 11.3.40

41. Suppose that each circle is equally likely to be selected. One circle is selected at random. Determine the probability indicated.

P(− | white circle obtained)

P(− | white circle obtained) = ___________ (Type an integer or a simplified fraction.)

ID: 11.3.41

42. Suppose that each circle is equally likely to be selected. One circle is selected at random. Determine the probability indicated. Note that the symbols shown are black, white, or red.

P(black circle with white − | − obtained)

P(black circle with white − | − obtained) = ___________ (Type an integer or a simplified fraction.)

ID: 11.3.42

!* 43. The probability a basketball player makes a free throw is equal to the ratio of made shots to number of shots taken. Right now the player has made 5 out of 8 shots, so he has a $\frac{5}{8}$ chance of making the 9th shot.

(a) If he makes the 9th shot, what is the probability he makes his 10th shot?
(b) What is the probability he makes the 10th shot given he misses the 9th shot?
(c) What is the probability he will miss the 9th and 10th shots and be 5 for 10?
(d) What is the probability he will make the 9th and 10th shots and be 7 for 10?

(a) P(Makes 10th shot|Makes 9th shot) = ___________ (Simplify your answer.)

(b) P(Makes 10th shot|Misses 9th shot) = ___________ (Simplify your answer.)

(c) P(Misses 9th shot AND Misses 10th shot) = ___________ (Simplify your answer.)

(d) P(Makes 9th shot AND Makes 10th shot) = ___________ (Simplify your answer.)

ID: 11.3.43

44. Determine whether the following individual events are independent or dependent. Then find the probability of the combined event.

The next four births at a hospital all being girls.

Choose the correct answer below.
(Simplify your answer.)

- ◯ **A.** The individual events are dependent. The probability of the combined event is ________.
- ◯ **B.** The individual events are independent. The probability of the combined event is ________.

ID: 11.3.44

---

*45. Determine whether the following individual events are independent or dependent. Then find the probability of the combined event.

Rolling two 6s followed by one 4 on three tosses of a fair die.

Choose the correct answer below.
(Type an integer or a simplified fraction.)

- ◯ **A.** The individual events are dependent. The probability of the combined event is ________.
- ◯ **B.** The individual events are independent. The probability of the combined event is ________.

ID: 11.3.45

---

46. Determine whether the following individual events are independent or dependent. Then find the probability of the combined event.

Drawing three queens in a row from a standard deck of cards when the drawn card is not returned to the deck each time

The event of drawing a queen and the event of drawing a queen the next time are (1) ________

The probability of drawing three queens in a row from a standard deck of cards when the drawn card is not returned to the deck each time is ________.
(Type an integer or a simplified fraction.)

(1) ◯ independent.
◯ dependent.

ID: 11.3.46

---

*47. Determine whether the following individual events are independent or dependent. Then find the probability of the combined event.

Randomly drawing and immediately eating two red pieces of candy in a row from a bag that contains 6 red pieces of candy out of 35 pieces of candy total.

Choose the correct answer below.
(Round to three decimal places as needed.)

- ◯ **A.** The individual events are dependent. The probability of the combined event is ________.
- ◯ **B.** The individual events are independent. The probability of the combined event is ________.

ID: 11.3.47

---

48. Determine whether the following individual events are independent or dependent. Then find the probability of the combined event.

Randomly selecting a four-person committee consisting entirely of men from a pool of 16 men and 11 women

The event of selecting a man and the event of selecting a man the next time are (1) ________

The probability of randomly selecting a four-person committee consisting entirely of men from a pool of 16 men and 11 women is ________.
(Round to four decimal places as needed.)

(1) ◯ independent.
◯ dependent.

ID: 11.3.48

---

* 49. Use the spinner shown. It is equally probable that the pointer will land on any one of the six regions. If the pointer lands on a borderline, spin again. If the pointer is spun twice, find the probability that it will land on

grey and then purple

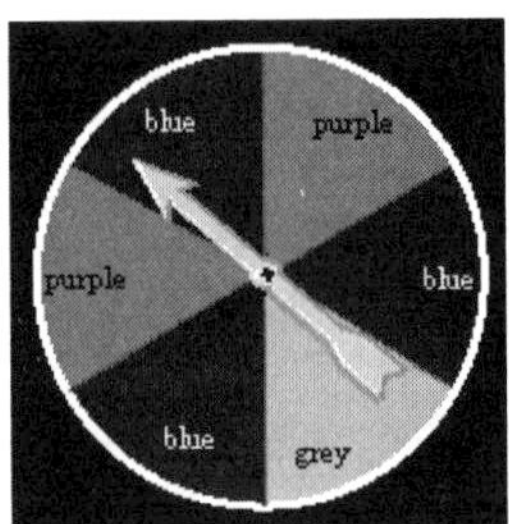

Find the probability that the spinner will land on grey and then purple.

__________ (Type an integer or a simplified fraction.)

ID: 11.3.49

50. Use the spinner shown. It is equally probable that the pointer will land on any one of the six regions. If the pointer lands on a borderline, spin again. If the pointer is spun twice, find the probability that it will land on green and then green.

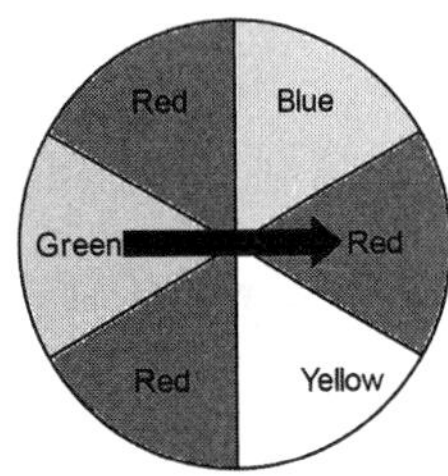

Find the probability that the spinner will land on green and then green.

The probability is __________.
(Type an integer or a simplified fraction.)

ID: 11.3.50

51. Use the spinner shown. It is equally probable that the pointer will land on any one of the regions. If the pointer lands on a borderline, spin again. If the pointer is spun twice, find the probability that it will land on a color other than brown for each spin.

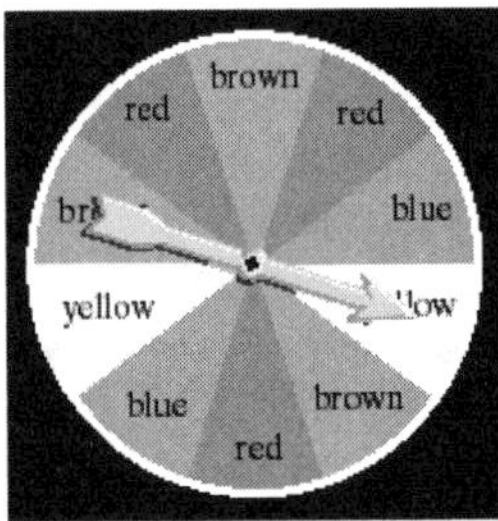

Find the probability that the spinner will land on a color other than brown for each spin.

__________ (Type an integer or a simplified fraction.)

ID: 11.3.51

52. Use the spinner shown. It is equally probable that the pointer will land on any one of the eight regions. If the pointer lands on a borderline, spin again. If the pointer is spun three times, find the probability that it will land on

green and then yellow and then blue

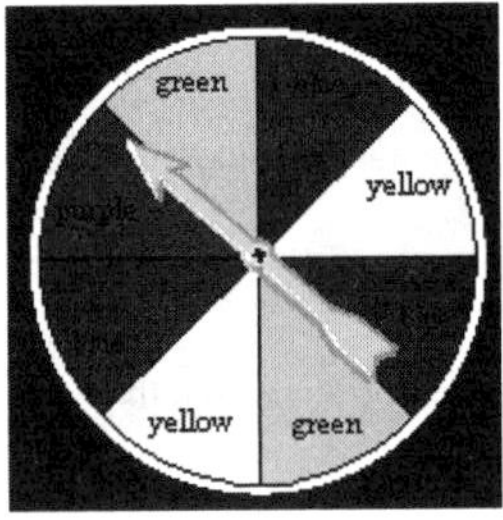

Find the probability that the spinner will land on green and then yellow and then blue.

__________ (Type an integer or a simplified fraction.)

ID: 11.3.52

53. Use the spinner shown. It is equally probable that the pointer will land on any one of the eight regions. If the pointer lands on a borderline, spin again. If the pointer is spun three times, find the probability that it will land on

green every time

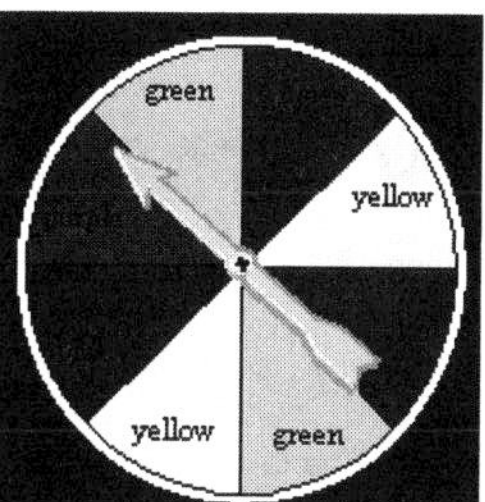

Find the probability that the spinner will land on green every time.

___________ (Type an integer or a simplified fraction.)

ID: 11.3.53

---

54. A single die is rolled twice. Find the probability of rolling a 1 the first time and a 3 the second time.

Find the probability of rolling a 1 the first time and a 3 the second time.

___________ (Type an integer or a simplified fraction.)

ID: 11.3.54

---

55. A single die is rolled twice. Find the probability of rolling an even number the first time and a number greater than 1 the second time.

Find the probability of rolling an even number the first time and a number greater than 1 the second time.

___________ (Type an integer or a simplified fraction.)

ID: 11.3.55

---

56. You draw one card from a 52-card deck. Then the card is replaced in the deck and the deck is shuffled, and you draw again. Find the probability of drawing a ten the first time and a diamond the second time.

The probability of drawing a ten the first time and a diamond the second time is ___________.
(Type an integer or a simplified fraction.)

ID: 11.3.56

---

57. You draw one card from a 52-card deck. Then the card is replaced in the deck and the deck is shuffled, and you draw again. Find the probability of drawing a heart each time.

The probability of drawing a heart each time is ___________.
(Type an integer or a simplified fraction.)

ID: 11.3.57

---

58. You draw one card from a 52-card deck. Then the card is replaced in the deck, the deck is shuffled, and you draw again. Find the probability of drawing a diamond each time.

The probability is ___________.
(Type an integer or a simplified fraction.)

ID: 11.3.58

---

59. What is the probability of obtaining six tails in a row when flipping a coin?

The probability of obtaining six tails in a row when flipping a coin is ___________.
(Type an integer or a simplified fraction.)

ID: 11.3.59

---

60. A coin is tossed and a die is rolled. Find the probability of getting a head and a number greater than 5.

__________ (Type an integer or a simplified fraction.)

ID: 11.3.60

---

61. The probability that a certain state will be hit by a major tornado (category F4 or F5) in any single year is $\frac{1}{19}$. Use this information to answer the questions below.

(A) What is the probability that the state will be hit by a major tornado two years in a row?

__________ (Simplify your answer. Round to five decimal places as needed.)

(B) What is the probability that the state will be hit by a major tornado in three consecutive years?

__________ (Simplify your answer. Round to five decimal places as needed.)

(C) What is the probability that the state will not be hit by a major tornado in the next ten years?

__________ (Round to three decimal places as needed.)

(D) What is the probability that the state will be hit by a major tornado at least once in the next ten years?

__________ (Round to three decimal places as needed.)

ID: 11.3.61

---

62. The accompanying graph shows that adults dependent on tobacco have a greater probability of suffering from some ailments than the general adult population. When making two or more selections from populations with large numbers, such as the general adult population or the population dependent on tobacco, we assume that each selection is independent of every other selection. If two adults are randomly selected from the general population, what is the probability that they both suffer from severe pain?
[2] Click the icon for a graph of adults suffering from various ailments.

The probability that both adults suffer from severe pain is __________.
(Round to four decimal places as needed.)

2: Probability that Adults Suffer from Various Ailments

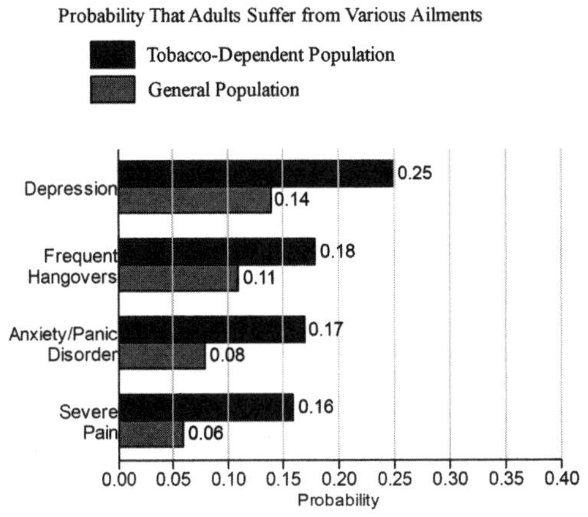

Probability That Adults Suffer from Various Ailments

	Tobacco-Dependent Population	General Population
Depression	0.25	0.14
Frequent Hangovers	0.18	0.11
Anxiety/Panic Disorder	0.17	0.08
Severe Pain	0.16	0.06

Probability axis: 0.00 0.05 0.10 0.15 0.20 0.25 0.30 0.35 0.40

ID: 11.3.62

---

63. The accompanying graph shows that adults dependent on tobacco have a greater probability of suffering from some ailments than the general adult population. When making two or more selections from populations with large numbers, such as the general adult population or the population dependent on tobacco, we assume that each selection is independent of every other selection. If two adults are randomly selected from the general population, what is the probability that they both suffer from severe pain?
[3] Click the icon for a graph of adults suffering from various ailments.

The probability that both adults suffer from severe pain is __________.
(Round to four decimal places as needed.)

3: Probability that Adults Suffer from Various Ailments

Probability That Adults Suffer from Various Ailments

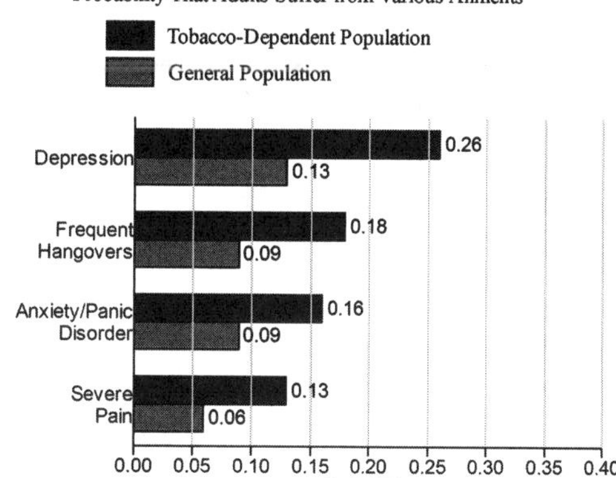

ID: 11.3.63

64. The graph below shows that adults dependent on tobacco have a greater probability of suffering from some ailments than the general adult population. When making two or more selections from populations with large numbers, such as the general adult population or the population dependent on tobacco, we assume that each selection is independent of every other selection. If three adults are randomly selected from the population of cigarette smokers, what is the probability that at least one person suffers from anxiety / panic disorder?
[4] Click the icon for a graph of adults suffering from various ailments.

The probability that at least one person of the three selected from the population of cigarette smokers suffers from anxiety / panic disorder is __________.
(Round to four decimal places as needed.)

4: Probability that Adults Suffer from Various Ailments

Probability That Adults Suffer from Various Ailments

Tobacco-Dependent Population
General Population

Depression 0.28 0.14
Frequent Hangovers 0.21 0.11
Anxiety/Panic Disorder 0.19 0.08
Severe Pain 0.12 0.06

0.00 0.05 0.10 0.15 0.20 0.25 0.30 0.35 0.40
Probability

ID: 11.3.64

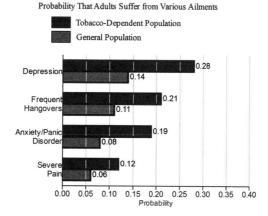

65. If one person is selected from the population described in the table, find the probability that the person is not married.

Marital Status of the U.S. Population, Ages 18 or Older, in Millions

	Never Married	Married	Widowed	Divorced	Total
Male	28.1	63.5	2.3	8.5	102.4
Female	22.5	62.8	13.0	12.4	110.7
Total	50.6	126.3	15.3	20.9	213.1

P(not married) ≈ __________
(Round to three decimal places as needed.)

ID: 11.3.65

66. If one person is selected from the population described in the table, find the probability that the person is divorced or is married.

Marital Status of the U.S. Population, Ages 18 or Older, in Millions

	Never Married	Married	Widowed	Divorced	Total
Male	28.6	62.1	2.7	9.6	103.0
Female	23.3	63.6	10.7	13.0	110.6
Total	51.9	125.7	13.4	22.6	213.6

P(divorced or married) ≈ ___________
(Round to three decimal places as needed.)

ID: 11.3.66

67. If one person is selected from the population described in the table, find the probability that the person is male or is married.

Marital Status of a Certain Population, Ages 18 or Older, in Millions

	Never Married	Married	Widowed	Divorced	Total
Male	42	62	3	7	114
Female	34	62	13	11	120
Total	76	124	16	18	234

The probability that the person is male or is married is ___________.
(Round to three decimal places as needed.)

ID: 11.3.67

* 68. If the probability of being hospitalized during a year is 0.15, find the probability that no one in a family of three will be hospitalized in a year.

The probability is ___________. (Round to five decimal places as needed.)

ID: 11.3.68

69. If a single die is rolled six times, what is the probability it lands on 6 on the second, third and fourth rolls, but not on any of the other rolls?

The probability is ___________. (Type an integer or a simplified fraction.)

ID: 11.3.69

70. A single die is rolled twice. Find the probability of rolling an even number and a number greater than 1 in either order.

The probability of rolling an even number and a number greater than 1 is ___________.
(Type an integer or a simplified fraction.)

ID: 11.3.70

71. Determine whether the following individual events are overlapping or non-overlapping. Then find the probability of the combined event.

Getting a sum of either 4, 6, or 8 on a roll of two dice

Choose the correct answer below and, if necessary, fill in the answer box to complete your choice.
(Type an integer or a simplified fraction.)

○ **A.** The individual events are non-overlapping. The probability of the combined event is ___________.

○ **B.** The individual events are overlapping. The probability of the combined event is ___________.

ID: 11.4.1

72. Determine whether the following individual events are overlapping or non-overlapping. Then find the probability of the combined event.

Drawing either a black eight or a black king on one draw from a regular deck of cards

Choose the correct answer below and, if necessary, fill in the answer box to complete your choice.
(Type an integer or a simplified fraction.)

○ **A.** The individual events are non-overlapping. The probability of the combined event is ___________.

○ **B.** The individual events are overlapping. The probability of the combined event is ___________.

ID: 11.4.2

73. Determine whether the following individual events are overlapping or non-overlapping. Then find the probability of the combined event.

Drawing either a heart or a diamond from a regular deck of cards

The individual events are (1) ____________

The probability of drawing either a heart or a diamond from a regular deck of cards is ____________.
(Type an integer or a simplified fraction.)

(1) ○ overlapping.
○ non-overlapping.

ID: 11.4.3

---

74. Determine whether the following individual events are independent or dependent. Then find the probability of the combined event.

Selecting 3 fully charged batteries in a row from a large batch in which 4% of the batteries are dead

Choose the correct answer below and, if necessary, fill in the answer box to complete your choice.
(Type an integer or decimal rounded to three decimal places as needed.)

○ **A.** Since 3 different batteries are being chosen, the individual events are independent. The probability of the combined event is approximately ____________.

○ **B.** While the individual events are technically dependent, since there are a large number of batteries, the probability of the combined event can be calculated as though the events are independent. The probability of the combined event is approximately ____________.

ID: 11.4.4

---

* 75. You randomly select one card from a 52-card deck. Find the probability of selecting a three or a four.

The probability is ____________. (Type an integer or a fraction. Simplify your answer.)

ID: 11.4.5

---

76. You randomly select one card from a 52-card deck. Find the probability of selecting a black six or a red jack.

The probability is ____________. (Type an integer or a fraction. Simplify your answer.)

ID: 11.4.6

---

77. You randomly select one card from a 52-card deck. Find the probability of selecting the jack of diamonds or the nine of clubs.

The probabilitiy is ____________. (Type an integer or a fraction. Simplify your answer.)

ID: 11.4.7

---

78. The mathematics faculty at a college consists of 9 professors, 6 associate professors, 4 assistant professors, and 11 instructors. If one faculty member is randomly selected, find the probability of choosing a professor or an instructor.

The probability is ____________. (Type an integer or a fraction. Simplify your answer.)

ID: 11.4.8

---

* 79. A single die is rolled. Find the probability of rolling an odd number or a number less than 5.

The probability is ____________. (Type an integer or a fraction. Simplify your answer.)

ID: 11.4.9

---

80. You are dealt one card from a 52-card deck. Find the probability that you are dealt a nine or a red card.

The probability is ________. (Type an integer or a fraction. Simplify your answer.)

ID: 11.4.10

---

81. You are dealt one card from a 52-card deck. Find the probability that you are dealt a club or a picture card.

The probability is ________.
(Type an integer or a simplified fraction.)

ID: 11.4.11

---

* 82. It is equally probable that the pointer on the spinner shown will land on any one of the eight regions, numbered 1 through 8. If the pointer lands on a borderline, spin again. Find the probability that the pointer will stop on an odd number or a number less than 7.

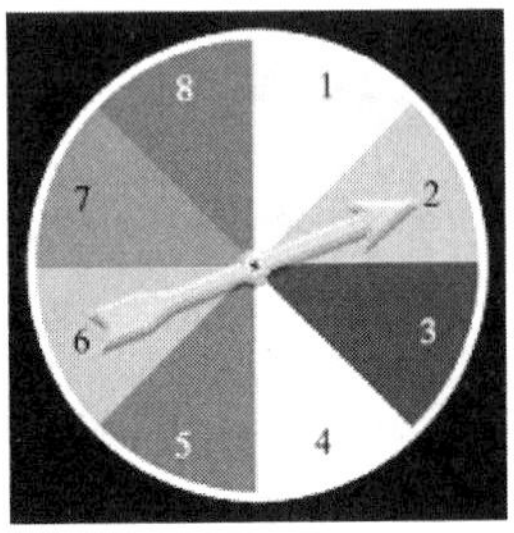

The probability is ________. (Type an integer or a fraction. Simplify your answer.)

ID: 11.4.12

---

83. It is equally probable that the pointer on the spinner shown will land on any one of the eight regions, numbered 1 through 8. If the pointer lands on a borderline, spin again. Find the probability that the pointer will stop on an even number or a number greater than 6.

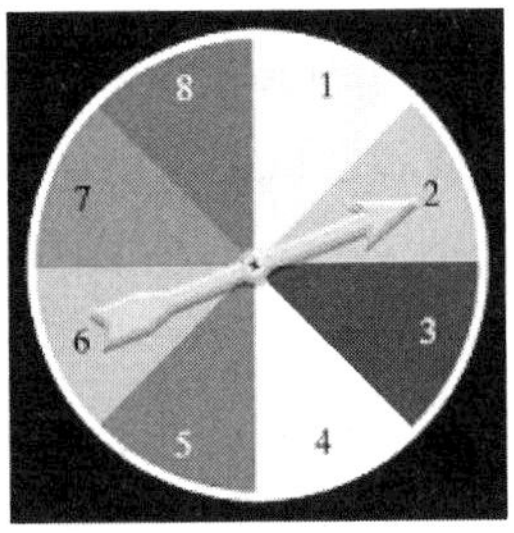

The probability is ________. (Type an integer or a fraction. Simplify your answer.)

ID: 11.4.13

---

84. The mathematics department of a college has 12 male professors, 7 female professors, 5 male teaching assistants, and 6 female teaching assistants. If a person is selected at random from the group, find the probability that the selected person is a professor or a male.

The probability is ________. (Type an integer or a fraction. Simplify your answer.)

ID: 11.4.14

---

85. The mathematics department of a college has 7 male professors, 14 female professors, 15 male teaching assistants, and 8 female teaching assistants. If a person is selected at random from the group, find the probability that the selected person is a teaching assistant or a female.

The probability is ________. (Type an integer or a fraction. Simplify your answer.)

ID: 11.4.15

---

86. In a class of 60 students, 42 are Democrats, 8 are business majors, and 7 of the business majors are Democrats. If one student is randomly selected from the class, find the probability of choosing a Democrat or a business major.

P(Democrat or business major) = ________
(Simplify your answer. Type an integer or a simplified fraction.)

ID: 11.4.16

---

87. The table shows the educational attainment of the population of a country, ages 25 and over, expressed in millions. Find the probability that a randomly selected person, age 25 or over, has completed four years of high school only or some college, but less than four years.

	Years of High School		Years of College		
	Less than 4	4 only	Some (less than 4)	4 or more	Total
Male	16	28	19	20	83
Female	12	24	19	17	72
Total	28	52	38	37	155

The probability is ________.
(Type an integer or a simplified fraction.)

ID: 11.4.17

* 88. The table shows the educational attainment of the population of Mars, ages 25 and over, expressed in millions. Find the probability that a randomly selected martian, aged 25 and over has completed four years of high school only or is a male.

	Years of High School		Years of College		
	Less than 4	4 only	Some (less than 4)	4 or more	Total
Male	11	24	20	25	80
Female	12	27	20	25	84
Total	23	51	40	50	164

The probability is ________. (Type an integer or a simplified fraction.)

ID: 11.4.18

89. If one person is randomly selected from the population represented in the bar graph, find the probability that the person is in the Navy or is a woman.

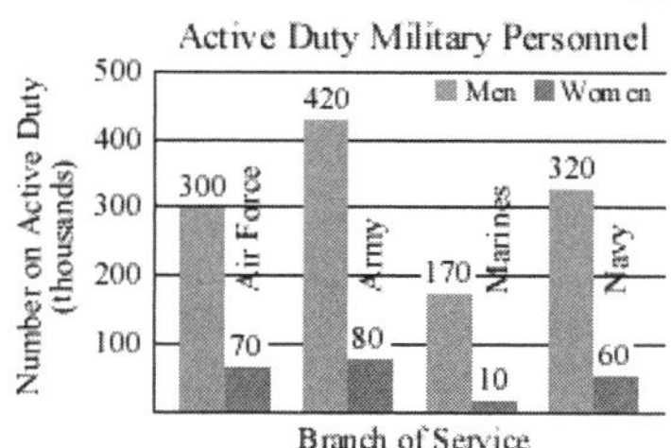

The probability is ________. (Type an integer or a simplified fraction.)

ID: 11.4.19

90. If one person is randomly selected from the population represented in the bar graph, find the probability that the person is in the Army or the Navy.

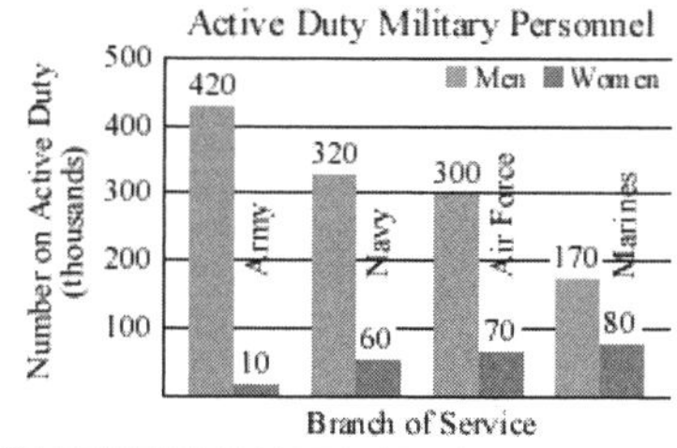

The probability is ________. (Type an integer or a simplified fraction.)

ID: 11.4.20

!* 91. You estimate there is a 0.7% chance of hitting a hole in one (hitting the ball in the hole on your first shot on a par 3).
(a) What is the probability of hitting at least one hole in one after playing 30 such holes?
(b) What is the probability of hitting at least one hole in one after playing 65 such holes?
(c) What is the probability of hitting at least one hole in one after playing 160 such holes?
(d) How many such holes do you have to play for the probability of hitting at least one hole in one to be over 83%?

(a) The probability is ________%.
(Type an integer or decimal rounded to the nearest tenth as needed.)

(b) The probability is ________%.
(Type an integer or decimal rounded to the nearest tenth as needed.)

(c) The probability is ________%.
(Type an integer or decimal rounded to the nearest tenth as needed.)

(d) You would have to play ________ holes.
(Type a whole number.)

ID: 11.4.21

* 92. Determine the probability of the given opposite event.

What is the probability of rolling a fair die and not getting an outcome less than 2?

The probability of rolling a fair die and not getting an outcome less than 2 is ___________.
(Type an integer or a simplified fraction.)

ID: 11.4.22

---

93. Determine the probability of the given opposite event.

What is the probability that a 42% free-throw shooter will miss her next free throw?

The probability that a 42% freethrow shooter will miss her next free throw is ___________.
(Type an integer or a decimal.)

ID: 11.4.23

---

94. Use the "at least once" rule to find the probabilities of the following events.

Getting at least one tail when tossing three fair coins

The probability is ___________.
(Type an integer or a simplified fraction.)

ID: 11.4.24

---

95. Use the "at least once" rule to find the probability of the following event.

Getting rain at least once in 8 days if the probability of rain on each single day is 0.5

The probability is ___________.
(Round to three decimal places as needed.)

ID: 11.4.25

---

96. Use the "at least once" rule to find the probability of the following event.

Purchasing at least one winning lottery ticket out of 5 tickets when the probability of winning is 0.05 on a single ticket

The probability is ___________.
(Round to four decimal places as needed.)

ID: 11.4.26

---

97. Determine the following probability.

Rolling six fair dice and getting an even number on all six dice

The probability is ___________.
(Simplify your answer.)

ID: 11.4.27

---

98. Determine the probability of rolling a 3 or a red number on a die on which the odd numbers are red and the even numbers are black.

The probability is ___________.
(Type an integer or a simplified fraction.)

ID: 11.4.28

---

99. Use the "at least once" rule to find the probability of getting at least one 5 in three rolls of a single fair die.

The probability is ___________.
(Round to three decimal places as needed.)

ID: 11.4.29

---

100. You draw one card from a 52-card deck. Then the card is replaced in the deck and the deck is shuffled, and you draw again. Find the probability of drawing a club each time.

The probability of drawing a club each time is ________.
(Type an integer or a simplified fraction.)

ID: 11.4.30

---

101. You randomly select one card from a 52-card deck. Find the probability of selecting a jack or a seven.

The probability is ________. (Type an integer or a fraction. Simplify your answer.)

ID: 11.4.31

---

102. Use the method of your choice to determine the following probability.

Drawing three aces in a row from a standard deck of cards when the drawn card is not returned to the deck each time

The probability of drawing three aces is ________.
(Type an integer or a simplified fraction.)

ID: 11.4.32

---

103. Use the *at least once* rule to find the probability of the event.

Drawing at least one ten when you draw a card from a standard deck 2 times (replacing the card each time you draw, so there are always 52 cards in the deck)

The probability is ________.
(Round to the nearest thousandth as needed.)

ID: 11.4.33

---

104. Use the method of your choice to determine the following probability.

Purchasing 2 winning lottery tickets in a row when each ticket has a 1 in 10 chance of being a winner

The probability of purchasing 2 winning lottery tickets is ________.
(Type an integer or a simplified fraction.)

ID: 11.4.34

---

105. Determine the following probability.

Meeting at least one left-handed person in six random encounters on campus when the incidence rate is 19% (19 in 100 people are left-handed)

The probability is ________.
(Round to three decimal places as needed.)

ID: 11.4.35

---

106. The mathematics department of a college has 6 male professors, 15 female professors, 10 male teaching assistants, and 14 female teaching assistants. If a person is selected at random from the group, find the probability that the selected person is a teaching assistant or a female.

The probability is ________. (Type an integer or a fraction. Simplify your answer.)

ID: 11.4.36

---

107. Determine the following probability.

Randomly selecting a three child family with either zero or two girl children

The probability is ________.
(Type an integer or a simplified fraction.)

ID: 11.4.37

---

108. Determine the following probability.

Meeting at least one person with the flu in nine random encounters on campus when the infection rate is 7% (7 in 100 people have the flu)

The probability is ____________.
(Round to three decimal places as needed.)

ID: 11.4.38

---

109. The data in the following table shows the outcomes of guilty and not-guilty pleas in 1065 criminal court cases. Complete parts (a) and (b) below.

	Guilty plea	Not-guilty plea
Sent to prison	395	56
Not sent to prison	588	26

a. What is the probability that a randomly selected defendant either pled not guilty or was sent to prison?

____________ (Round to three decimal places as needed.)

b. What is the probability that a randomly selected defendent either pled guilty or was not sent to prison?

____________ (Round to three decimal places as needed.)

ID: 11.4.39

---

* 110. An allergy drug is tested by giving 120 people the drug and 100 people a placebo. A control group consists of 70 people who were given no treatment. The number of people in each group who showed improvement appears in the table.
[5] Click the icon to view the table.

a. What is the probability that a randomly selected person in the study was given either the drug or the placebo?

The probability is ____________. (Round to the nearest thousandth as needed.)

b. What is the probability that a randomly selected person either improved or did not improve?

The probability is ____________. (Round to the nearest thousandth as needed.)

c. What is the probability that a randomly selected person either was given the drug or improved?

The probability is ____________. (Round to the nearest thousandth as needed.)

d. What is the probability that a randomly selected person was given the drug and improved?

The probability is ____________. (Round to the nearest thousandth as needed.)

5: Data Table

	Allergy drug	Placebo	Control	Total
Improvement	65	32	41	138
No improvement	55	68	29	152
Total	120	100	70	290

ID: 11.4.40

---

* 111. Suppose that the Chevalier de Mère had bet that he could roll a double-6 in 25 rolls, rather than 24. In that case, what would have been his probability of winning? Had he made this bet, would he still have lost over time? Explain.

In this case, what would have been his probability of winning?

P(at least one double-6 in 25 rolls) = ____________
(Type an integer or decimal rounded to three decimal places as needed.)

Had he made this bet, would he still have lost over time? Explain. Choose the correct answer below.

○ **A.** He would win more over time, because his probability of winning is greater than even odds.

○ **B.** He would win more over time, because his probability of winning is equal to $\frac{25}{36}$.

○ **C.** He would lose more over time, because his probability of winning is less than even odds.

○ **D.** He would lose more over time, because he needs more rolls to get a double-6.

ID: 11.4.41

---

*112. Studies show that, historically, a certain city is hit by a tornado about every 10 years.

a. Based on the historical record, what is the empirical probability that the city will be hit by a tornado next year?
b. What is the probability that the city will be hit by a tornado in two consecutive years?
c. What is the probability that the city will be hit by at least one tornado in the next 11 years?

a. The empirical probability that the city will be hit by a tornado next year is __________.
(Simplify your answer.)

b. The probability that the city will be hit by a tornado in two consecutive years is __________.
(Simplify your answer.)

c. The probability that the city will be hit by at least one tornado in the next 11 years is __________.
(Round to four decimal places as needed.)

ID: 11.4.42

113. You are dealt one card from a 52-card deck. Find the probability that you are not dealt a seven.

The probability is __________. (Type an integer or a fraction. Simplify your answer.)

ID: 11.4.43

114. You are dealt one card from a 52-card deck. Find the probability that you are not dealt a diamond.

The probability is __________. (Type an integer or a fraction. Simplify your answer.)

ID: 11.4.44

115. You are dealt one card from a 52-card deck. Find the probability that you are not dealt an even card.

The probability is __________.
(Type an integer or a simplified fraction.)

ID: 11.4.45

116. The graph shows the probability of cardiovascular disease by age and gender. Use the graph to find the probability that a randomly selected man between the ages of 35 and 44

a. has cardiovascular disease.

b. does not have cardiovascular disease.

a. Use the graph to estimate the probability that a randomly selected man between the ages of 35 and 44 has cardiovascular disease. This probability is approximately __________.
(Type a decimal to two places.)

b. Use the graph to estimate the probability that a randomly selected man between the ages of 35 and 44 does not have cardiovascular disease. This probability is approximately __________.
(Type a decimal to two places.)

ID: 11.4.46

*117. The table shows the distribution, by age, of a random sample of 3800 moviegoers ages 12-74. If one moviegoer is randomly selected from this population, find the probability, expressed as a simplified fraction, that the moviegoer is not in the 65-74 age range.

Age Distribution of Moviegoers

Ages	Number
12-24	1210
25-44	1070
45-64	750
65-74	770

The probability is __________.
(Type an integer or a simplified fraction.)

ID: 11.4.47

118. The table shows the distribution, by age, of a random sample of 2800 moviegoers ages 12-74. If one moviegoer is randomly selected from this population, find the probability, expressed as a simplified fraction, that the moviegoer's age is at least 25.

Age Distribution of Moviegoers

Ages	Number
12-24	890
25-44	860
45-64	780
65-74	270

The probability is ________.
(Type an integer or a simplified fraction.)

ID: 11.4.48

119. The table shows the educational attainment of the population of Mars, ages 25 and over, expressed in millions. Find the probability that a randomly selected martian, aged 25 and over has not completed four years (or more) of college.

	Years of High School		Years of College		
	Less than 4	4 only	Some (less than 4)	4 or more	Total
Male	13	31	19	19	82
Female	14	30	23	23	90
Total	27	61	42	42	172

The probability is ________. (Type an integer or a simplified fraction.)

ID: 11.4.49

120. If one person is randomly selected from the population represented in the bar graph, find the probability that the person is not in the Marines.

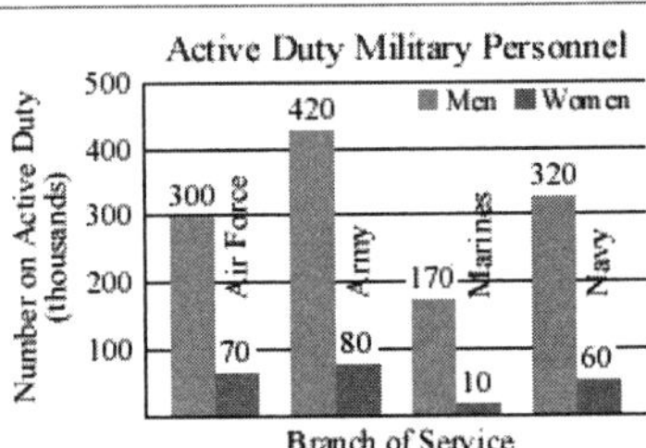

The probability is ________. (Type an integer or a simplified fraction.)

ID: 11.4.50

!* 1. Assume that you go to the beach 25% of the time it is sunny and 5% of the time it is not sunny. It is sunny 65% of the time. Fill in the Bayes table. Complete parts (a) through (f) below.

[1] Click the icon to view the empty Bayes table.

(a) What is the probability it is not sunny?

Hypotheses (H_i)	Priors $P(H_i)$	Likelihoods $P(D\|H_i)$	Products $P(H_i) \cdot P(D\|H_i)$	Posteriors $P(H_i\|D)$
Sunny				
Not Sunny	________%			
Totals				

(b) What is the likelihood you go to the beach given it is sunny?

Hypotheses (H_i)	Priors $P(H_i)$	Likelihoods $P(D\|H_i)$	Products $P(H_i) \cdot P(D\|H_i)$	Posteriors $P(H_i\|D)$
Sunny		________%		
Not Sunny				
Totals				

(c) What is the likelihood you go to the beach given it is not sunny?

Hypotheses (H_i)	Priors $P(H_i)$	Likelihoods $P(D\|H_i)$	Products $P(H_i) \cdot P(D\|H_i)$	Posteriors $P(H_i\|D)$
Sunny				
Not Sunny		________%		
Totals				

!* 1. (cont.) **(d)** Ignoring the percent symbols, multiply the priors and likelihoods and sum the products.

Hypotheses (H_i)	Priors $P(H_i)$	Likelihoods $P(D\|H_i)$	Products $P(H_i) \cdot P(D\|H_i)$	Posteriors $P(H_i\|D)$
Sunny			____	
Not Sunny			____	
Totals			____	

(e) What is the probability it is sunny given you are at the beach?

Hypotheses (H_i)	Priors $P(H_i)$	Likelihoods $P(D\|H_i)$	Products $P(H_i) \cdot P(D\|H_i)$	Posteriors $P(H_i\|D)$
Sunny				____ %
Not Sunny				
Totals				

(Round to two decimal places as needed.)

(f) What is the probability it is not sunny given you are at the beach?

Hypotheses (H_i)	Priors $P(H_i)$	Likelihoods $P(D\|H_i)$	Products $P(H_i) \cdot P(D\|H_i)$	Posteriors $P(H_i\|D)$
Sunny				
Not Sunny				____ %
Totals				

(Round to two decimal places as needed.)

1: Bayes table

Hypotheses (H_i)	Priors $P(H_i)$	Likelihoods $P(D\|H_i)$	Products $P(H_i) \cdot P(D\|H_i)$	Posteriors $P(H_i\|D)$
Sunny				
Not Sunny				
Totals				

ID: 11.5.1

!* 2. Assume that you eat popcorn 85% of the days you go to the movies and 20% of the days you do not go to the movies. You go to the movies about 1 in every 14 days. Fill in the Bayes table. Complete parts (a) through (g) below.

[2] Click the icon to view the empty Bayes table.

(a) What is the probability you go to the movies?

Hypotheses (H_i)	Priors $P(H_i)$	Likelihoods $P(D\|H_i)$	Products $P(H_i) \cdot P(D\|H_i)$	Posteriors $P(H_i\|D)$
Go to movie	____			
Do not go to movie				
Totals				

(Type an integer or a fraction.)

(b) What is the probability you do not go to the movies?

Hypotheses (H_i)	Priors $P(H_i)$	Likelihoods $P(D\|H_i)$	Products $P(H_i) \cdot P(D\|H_i)$	Posteriors $P(H_i\|D)$
Go to movie				
Do not go to movie	____			
Totals				

(Type an integer or a fraction.)

(c) What is the likelihood you eat popcorn given you go to the movies?

Hypotheses (H_i)	Priors $P(H_i)$	Likelihoods $P(D\|H_i)$	Products $P(H_i) \cdot P(D\|H_i)$	Posteriors $P(H_i\|D)$
Go to movie		$\frac{\_\_\_\_}{100}$		
Do not go to movie				
Totals				

(Type a whole number.)

!* 2. (cont.) **(d)** What is the likelihood you eat popcorn given you do not go to the movies?

Hypotheses (H_i)	Priors $P(H_i)$	Likelihoods $P(D\|H_i)$	Products $P(H_i) \cdot P(D\|H_i)$	Posteriors $P(H_i\|D)$
Go to movie				
Do not go to movie		____ / 100		
Totals				

(Type a whole number.)

(e) Multiply the priors and likelihoods and sum the products.

Hypotheses (H_i)	Priors $P(H_i)$	Likelihoods $P(D\|H_i)$	Products $P(H_i) \cdot P(D\|H_i)$	Posteriors $P(H_i\|D)$
Go to movie			____ / 1400	
Do not go to movie			____ / 1400	
Totals			____ / 1400	

(Type whole numbers.)

(f) What is the probability you went to the movies given you ate popcorn?

Hypotheses (H_i)	Priors $P(H_i)$	Likelihoods $P(D\|H_i)$	Products $P(H_i) \cdot P(D\|H_i)$	Posteriors $P(H_i\|D)$
Go to movie				____ %
Do not go to movie				
Totals				

(Round to two decimal places as needed.)

(g) What is the probability you did not go to the movies given you ate popcorn?

Hypotheses (H_i)	Priors $P(H_i)$	Likelihoods $P(D\|H_i)$	Products $P(H_i) \cdot P(D\|H_i)$	Posteriors $P(H_i\|D)$
Go to movie				
Do not go to movie				____ %
Totals				

(Round to two decimal places as needed.)

2: Bayes table

Hypotheses (H_i)	Priors $P(H_i)$	Likelihoods $P(D\|H_i)$	Products $P(H_i) \cdot P(D\|H_i)$	Posteriors $P(H_i\|D)$
Go to movie				
Do not go to movie				
Totals				

ID: 11.5.2

!* 3. Three siblings, Galen, Mei, and Beau are all equally likely to have eaten an apple. Galen leaves the core on the counter 30% of the time, Mei, leaves the core 65% of the time, and Beau leaves the core 90% of the time. Fill in the Bayes table assuming a core was left on the counter. Complete parts (a) through (f) below.
[3] Click the icon to view the empty Bayes table.

(a) What are the priors?

Hypotheses (H_i)	Priors $P(H_i)$	Likelihoods $P(D\|H_i)$	Products $P(H_i) \cdot P(D\|H_i)$	Posteriors $P(H_i\|D)$
Galen ate an apple	____			
Mei ate an apple	____			
Beau ate an apple	____			
Totals				

(Type integers or fractions.)

!* 3. (cont.) **(b)** What is the likelihood each sibling left the core on the counter given they ate the apple?

Hypotheses (H_i)	Priors $P(H_i)$	Likelihoods $P(D\|H_i)$	Products $P(H_i) \cdot P(D\|H_i)$	Posteriors $P(H_i\|D)$
Galen ate an apple		____ / 100		
Mei ate an apple		____ / 100		
Beau ate an apple		____ / 100		
Totals				

(Type whole numbers.)

(c) Multiply the priors and the likelihoods and sum the products.

Hypotheses (H_i)	Priors $P(H_i)$	Likelihoods $P(D\|H_i)$	Products $P(H_i) \cdot P(D\|H_i)$	Posteriors $P(H_i\|D)$
Galen ate an apple			____ / 300	
Mei ate an apple			____ / 300	
Beau ate an apple			____ / 300	
Totals			____ / 300	

(Type whole numbers.)

(d) What is the probability Galen ate the apple given a core was left on the counter?

Hypotheses (H_i)	Priors $P(H_i)$	Likelihoods $P(D\|H_i)$	Products $P(H_i) \cdot P(D\|H_i)$	Posteriors $P(H_i\|D)$
Galen ate an apple				____ %
Mei ate an apple				
Beau ate an apple				
Totals				

(Round to two decimal places as needed.)

(e) What is the probability Mei ate the apple given a core was left on the counter?

Hypotheses (H_i)	Priors $P(H_i)$	Likelihoods $P(D\|H_i)$	Products $P(H_i) \cdot P(D\|H_i)$	Posteriors $P(H_i\|D)$
Galen ate an apple				
Mei ate an apple				____ %
Beau ate an apple				
Totals				

(Round to two decimal places as needed.)

(f) What is the probability Beau ate the apple given a core was left on the counter?

Hypotheses (H_i)	Priors $P(H_i)$	Likelihoods $P(D\|H_i)$	Products $P(H_i) \cdot P(D\|H_i)$	Posteriors $P(H_i\|D)$
Galen ate an apple				
Mei ate an apple				
Beau ate an apple				____ %
Totals				

(Round to two decimal places as needed.)

3: Bayes Table

Hypotheses (H_i)	Priors $P(H_i)$	Likelihoods $P(D\|H_i)$	Products $P(H_i) \cdot P(D\|H_i)$	Posteriors $P(H_i\|D)$
Galen ate an apple				
Mei ate an apple				
Beau ate an apple				
Totals				

ID: 11.5.3

!* 4. Another version of the Monty Hall problem is that there are 4 doors, one of them has a car behind it (equally likely), and you select door A. The game show host, Monty Hall then opens door B showing you there is no car there and asks if you would like to switch to door C or D. Should you switch? Fill in the Bayes table assuming you chose door A and Monty opens door B. Complete parts (a) through (k) below.

[4] Click the icon to view the empty Bayes table.

(a) What are the priors?

Hypotheses (H_i)	**Priors** $P(H_i)$	**Likelihoods** $P(D \mid H_i)$	**Products** $P(H_i) \cdot P(D \mid H_i)$	**Posteriors** $P(H_i \mid D)$
Car behind door A	____			
Car behind door B	____			
Car behind door C	____			
Car behind door D	____			
Totals				

(Type integers or simplified fractions.)

(b) What is the likelihood of Monty opening door B given you chose door A and the car is behind door A?

Hypotheses (H_i)	**Priors** $P(H_i)$	**Likelihoods** $P(D \mid H_i)$	**Products** $P(H_i) \cdot P(D \mid H_i)$	**Posteriors** $P(H_i \mid D)$
Car behind door A		____		
Car behind door B				
Car behind door C				
Car behind door D				
Totals				

(Type an integer or a simplified fraction.)

(c) What is the likelihood of Monty opening door B given you chose door A and the car is behind door B?

Hypotheses (H_i)	**Priors** $P(H_i)$	**Likelihoods** $P(D \mid H_i)$	**Products** $P(H_i) \cdot P(D \mid H_i)$	**Posteriors** $P(H_i \mid D)$
Car behind door A				
Car behind door B		____		
Car behind door C				
Car behind door D				
Totals				

(Type an integer or a simplified fraction.)

(d) What is the likelihood of Monty opening door B given you chose door A and the car is behind door C?

Hypotheses (H_i)	**Priors** $P(H_i)$	**Likelihoods** $P(D \mid H_i)$	**Products** $P(H_i) \cdot P(D \mid H_i)$	**Posteriors** $P(H_i \mid D)$
Car behind door A				
Car behind door B				
Car behind door C		____		
Car behind door D				
Totals				

(Type an integer or a simplified fraction.)

(e) What is the likelihood of Monty opening door B given you chose door A and the car is behind door D?

Hypotheses (H_i)	**Priors** $P(H_i)$	**Likelihoods** $P(D \mid H_i)$	**Products** $P(H_i) \cdot P(D \mid H_i)$	**Posteriors** $P(H_i \mid D)$
Car behind door A				
Car behind door B				
Car behind door C				
Car behind door D		____		
Totals				

(Type an integer or a simplified fraction.)

!* 4. (cont.)

(f) Multiply the priors and likelihoods and sum the products.

Hypotheses (H_i)	Priors $P(H_i)$	Likelihoods $P(D\|H_i)$	Products $P(H_i) \cdot P(D\|H_i)$	Posteriors $P(H_i\|D)$
Car behind door A			$\frac{\quad}{24}$	
Car behind door B			$\frac{\quad}{24}$	
Car behind door C			$\frac{\quad}{24}$	
Car behind door D			$\frac{\quad}{24}$	
Totals			$\frac{\quad}{24}$	

(Type whole numbers.)

(g) What is the probability the car is behind door A given you chose door A and Monty opened door B?

Hypotheses (H_i)	Priors $P(H_i)$	Likelihoods $P(D\|H_i)$	Products $P(H_i) \cdot P(D\|H_i)$	Posteriors $P(H_i\|D)$
Car behind door A				$\frac{\quad}{8}$
Car behind door B				
Car behind door C				
Car behind door D				
Totals				

(Type a whole number.)

(h) What is the probability the car is behind door B given you chose door A and Monty opened door B?

Hypotheses (H_i)	Priors $P(H_i)$	Likelihoods $P(D\|H_i)$	Products $P(H_i) \cdot P(D\|H_i)$	Posteriors $P(H_i\|D)$
Car behind door A				
Car behind door B				$\frac{\quad}{8}$
Car behind door C				
Car behind door D				
Totals				

(Type a whole number.)

(i) What is the probability the car is behind door C given you chose door A and Monty opened door B?

Hypotheses (H_i)	Priors $P(H_i)$	Likelihoods $P(D\|H_i)$	Products $P(H_i) \cdot P(D\|H_i)$	Posteriors $P(H_i\|D)$
Car behind door A				
Car behind door B				
Car behind door C				$\frac{\quad}{8}$
Car behind door D				
Totals				

(Type a whole number.)

(j) What is the probability the car is behind door D given you chose door A and Monty opened door B?

Hypotheses (H_i)	Priors $P(H_i)$	Likelihoods $P(D\|H_i)$	Products $P(H_i) \cdot P(D\|H_i)$	Posteriors $P(H_i\|D)$
Car behind door A				
Car behind door B				
Car behind door C				
Car behind door D				$\frac{\quad}{8}$
Totals				

(Type a whole number.)

!* 4. (cont.)

(k) Should you switch?

Since the probability of winning is (1) __________ if you switch, you (2) __________ switch.

4: Bayes table

Hypotheses (H_i)	Priors $P(H_i)$	Likelihoods $P(D\|H_i)$	Products $P(H_i) \cdot P(D\|H_i)$	Posteriors $P(H_i\|D)$
Car behind door A				
Car behind door B				
Car behind door C				
Car behind door D				
Totals				

(1) ○ less
○ greater

(2) ○ should
○ should not

ID: 11.5.4

5. Write the following expression as a quotient of integers, reduced to lowest terms.

$$\frac{\frac{1}{7}}{\frac{1}{7}+\frac{1}{3}}$$

The expression is reduced to __________. (Type an integer or a simplified fraction.)

ID: 11.5.5

6. Write the expression as a quotient of integers, reduced to lowest terms.

$$\frac{\frac{7}{5}\cdot\frac{4}{7}}{\frac{7}{5}\cdot\frac{4}{7}+\frac{1}{5}\cdot\frac{1}{4}}$$

The expression is reduced to __________. (Type an integer or a simplified fraction.)

ID: 11.5.6

7. Find the probability by referring to the tree diagram on the right.

$P(M \cap B) = P(M)P(B|M)$

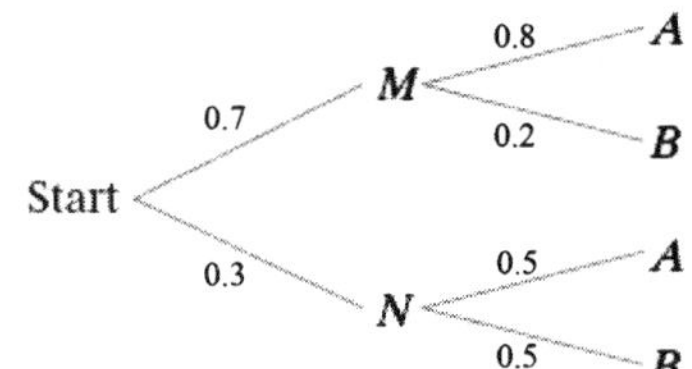

The probability is __________. (Type an integer or a decimal.)

ID: 11.5.7

8. Find the probability by referring to the tree diagram on the right.

$P(B) = P(M \cap B) + P(N \cap B)$

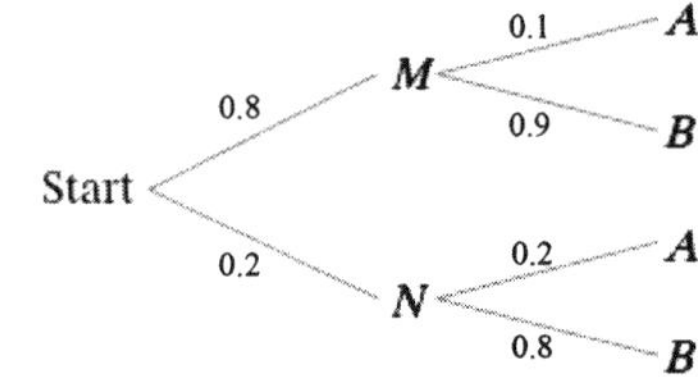

The probability is __________. (Type an integer or a decimal.)

ID: 11.5.8

9. Find the probability by referring to the tree diagram on the right.

$$P(M|A) = \frac{P(M \cap A)}{P(M \cap A) + P(N \cap A)}$$

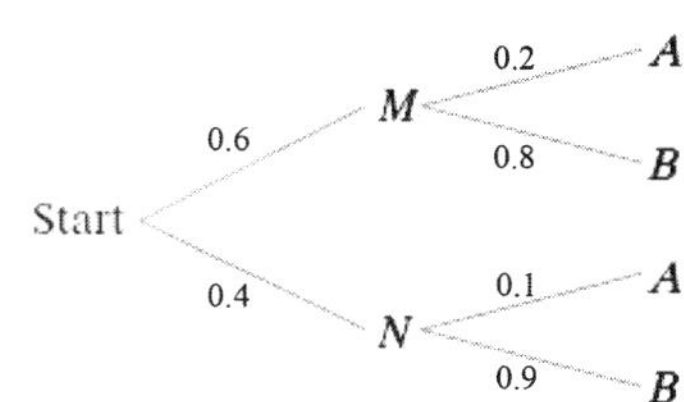

The probability is ______.
(Type an integer or a decimal. Round to the nearest hundredth as needed.)

ID: 11.5.9

---

10. Find $P(U_1|R)$ by referring to the following Venn diagram and using Bayes' formula (assume the simple events in S are equally likely).

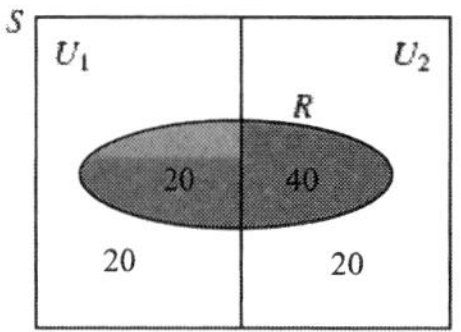

$P(U_1|R) =$ ______ (Type a decimal. Round to three decimal places if needed.)

ID: 11.5.10

---

* 11. Find P(W|C) by referring to the tree diagram and using Bayes' formula.

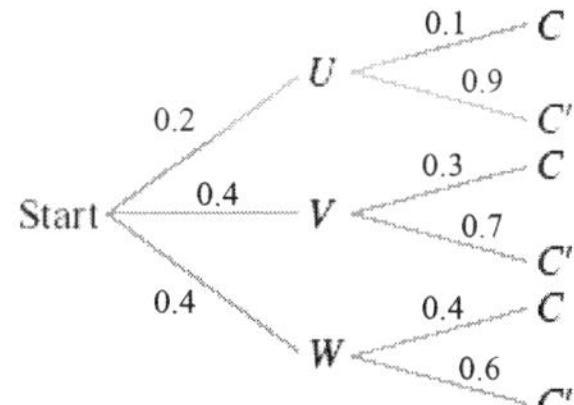

$P(W|C) \approx$ ______ (Type a decimal. Round to three decimal places if needed.)

ID: 11.5.11

---

12. Find P(W|C) by referring to the tree diagram and using Bayes' formula.

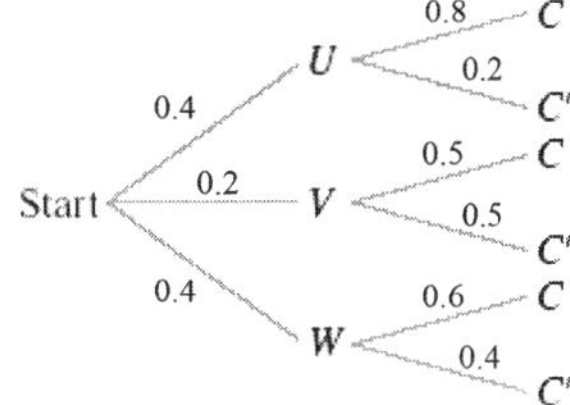

$P(W|C) \approx$ ______ (Type a decimal. Round to three decimal places if needed.)

ID: 11.5.12

---

13. Find $P(W|C')$ by referring to the tree diagram and using Bayes' formula.

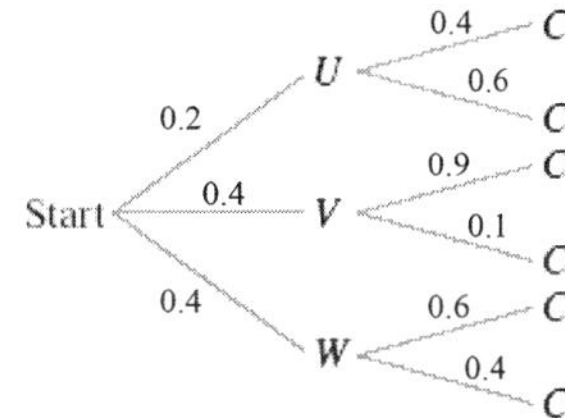

$P(W|C') =$ ______ (Type a decimal. Round to three decimal places if needed.)

ID: 11.5.13

---

14. Find $P(U_1|R)$ by referring to the Venn diagram and using Bayes' formula (assume that the simple events in S are equally likely).

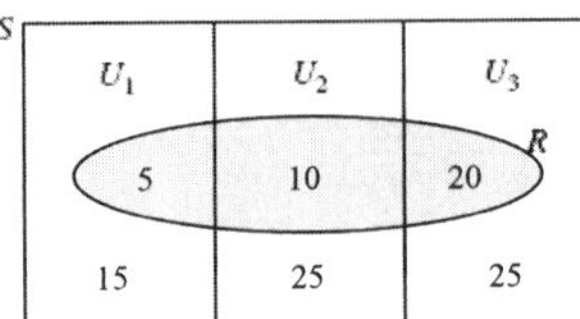

$P(U_1|R) =$ __________ (Round to three decimal places as needed.)

ID: 11.5.14

15. Find $P(U_3|R)$ by referring to the Venn diagram and using Bayes' formula (assume that the simple events in S are equally likely).

S	U_1	U_2	U_3
R	5	10	20
	15	25	25

$P(U_3|R) =$ __________ (Type a decimal. Round to three decimal places if needed.)

ID: 11.5.15

16. Find $P(U_1|R)$ by referring to the Venn diagram and using Bayes' formula (assume that the simple events in S are equally likely).

S	U_1	U_2	U_3
R	10	15	15
	10	20	30

$P(U_1|R) =$ __________ (Round to three decimal places as needed.)

ID: 11.5.16

17. One of two urns is chosen at random with one as likely to be chosen as the other. Then a ball is withdrawn from the chosen urn. Urn 1 contains 1 white and 3 red balls, and urn 2 has 2 white and 2 red balls. If a white ball is drawn, what is the probability that it came from urn 2?

Probability = __________ (Type a fraction. Simplify your answer.)

ID: 11.5.17

18. An urn contains 7 red and 5 white balls. Two balls are drawn in succession without replacement. If the second ball is white, what is the probability that the first ball was white?

Probability = __________ (Type a fraction. Simplify your answer.)

ID: 11.5.18

19. Urn 1 contains 2 red and 8 white balls. Urn 2 contains 4 red and 5 white balls. A ball is drawn from urn 1 and placed in urn 2. Then a ball is drawn from urn 2.

If the ball drawn from urn 2 is red, what is the probability that the ball drawn from urn 1 was red?

The probability is __________.
(Type an integer or decimal rounded to three decimal places as needed.)

ID: 11.5.19

20. A box contains 17 balls numbered 1 through 17. Two balls are drawn in succession without replacement. If the second ball has the number 4 on it, what is the probability that the first ball had a smaller number on it? An even number on it?

The probability that the first ball had a smaller number is __________.
(Type a fraction. Simplify your answer.)

The probability that the first ball had an even number is __________.
(Type a fraction. Simplify your answer.)

ID: 11.5.20

21. A 4-card hand is dealt from a standard 52-card deck, and then one of the 4 cards is chosen at random. If only one of the cards in the hand is a 6, what is the probability that the chosen card is a 6?

The probability that the chosen card is a 6 is ___________.
(Simplify your answer. Type an integer or a fraction.)

ID: 11.5.21

---

22. A 3-card hand is dealt from a standard 52-card deck, and then one of the 3 cards is chosen at random. If the chosen card is a diamond, what is the probability that it is the only diamond among the 3 cards?

The probability is approximately ___________. (Round to the nearest thousandth.)

ID: 11.5.22

---

23. A manufacturer obtains clock-radios from three different subcontractors: 40% from A, 10% from B, and 50% from C. The defective rates for these subcontractors are 1%, 2%, and 3% respectively. If a defective clock-radio is returned by a customer, what is the probability that it came from subcontractor A? From B? From C?

The probability that it came from subcontractor A is ___________.
(Type a decimal. Round to three decimal places if needed.)

The probability that it came from subcontractor B is ___________.
(Type a decimal. Round to three decimal places if needed.)

The probability that it came from subcontractor C is ___________.
(Type a decimal. Round to three decimal places if needed.)

ID: 11.5.23

---

24. A computer store sells three types of microcomputers, brand A, brand B, and brand C. Of the computers they sell, 65% are brand A, 20% are brand B, and 15% are brand C. They have found that 25% of the brand A computers, 15% of the brand B computers, and 5% of brand C computers are returned for service during the warranty period. If a computer is returned for service during the warranty period, what is the probability that it is a brand A computer? A brand B computer? A brand C computer?

The probability that it is a brand A computer is ___________.
(Type a decimal. Round to three decimal places if needed.)

The probability that it is a brand B computer is ___________.
(Type a decimal. Round to three decimal places if needed.)

The probability that it is a brand C computer is ___________.
(Type a decimal. Round to three decimal places if needed.)

ID: 11.5.24

---

25. A new, simple test has been developed to detect a particular type of cancer. The test must be evaluated before it is put into use. A medical researcher selects a random sample of 2,000 adults and finds (by other means) that 3% have this type of cancer. Each of the 2,000 adults is given the test, and it is found that the test indicates cancer in 98% of those who have it and in 1% of those who do not. Based on these results, what is the probability of a randomly chosen person having cancer given that the test indicates cancer? Of a person having cancer given that the test does not indicate cancer?

Based on these results, what is the probability of a randomly chosen person having cancer given that the test indicates cancer?

____
(Round to three decimal places as needed.)

What is the probability of a person having cancer given that the test does not indicate cancer?

____
(Round to six decimal places as needed.)

ID: 11.5.25

---

26. A new lie-detector test has been devised and must be tested before it is put into use. Three hundred people are selected at random, and each person draws and keeps a card from a box of 300 cards. Half the cards instruct the person to lie and the others instruct the person to tell the truth. Of those who lied, 85% fail the new lie-detector test (that is the test indicated lying). Of those who told the truth, 5% failed the test. What is the probability that a randomly chosen subject will have lied given that the subject failed the test? That the subject will not have lied given that the subject failed the test?

What is the probability that a randomly chosen subject will have lied given that the subject failed the test?

____

(Round to four decimal places as needed.)

What is the probability that the subject will not have lied given that the subject failed the test?

____

(Round to four decimal places as needed.)

ID: 11.5.26

27. In a given county, records show that of the registered voters, 45% are Democrats, 30% are Republicans, and 25% are Independents. In an election, 80% of the Democrats, 40% of the Republicans, and 90% of the Independents voted in favor of a parks and recreation bond proposal. If a registered voter chosen at random is found to have voted in favor of the bond, what is the probability that the voter is a Republican? An Independent? A Democrat?

The probability that the voter is a Republican is __________.
(Type a decimal. Round to three decimal places if needed.)

The probability that the voter is an independent is __________.
(Type a decimal. Round to three decimal places if needed.)

The probability that the voter is a Democrat is __________.
(Type a decimal. Round to three decimal places if needed.)

ID: 11.5.27

!* 28. A certain disease occurs in 3 out of 500 people. A test has a false positive rate of 8% and a false negative rate of 5%. What is the probability that a person who tests positive actually has the disease, P(Sick|+)? Fill in the Bayes table given a person tests positive (Data = positive). Complete parts (a) through (f) below.

[5] Click the icon to view the empty Bayes table.

(a) What are the priors that someone is sick or well?

Hypotheses (H_i)	Priors $P(H_i)$	Likelihoods $P(D\|H_i)$	Products $P(H_i) \cdot P(D\|H_i)$	Posteriors $P(H_i\|D)$
Sick	$\frac{\_\_\_}{500}$			
Well	$\frac{\_\_\_}{500}$			
Totals				

(Type whole numbers.)

(b) What is the likelihood of testing positive given that you are sick?

Hypotheses (H_i)	Priors $P(H_i)$	Likelihoods $P(D\|H_i)$	Products $P(H_i) \cdot P(D\|H_i)$	Posteriors $P(H_i\|D)$
Sick		$\frac{\_\_\_}{100}$		
Well				
Totals				

(Type a whole number.)

(c) What is the likelihood of testing positive given that you are well?

Hypotheses (H_i)	Priors $P(H_i)$	Likelihoods $P(D\|H_i)$	Products $P(H_i) \cdot P(D\|H_i)$	Posteriors $P(H_i\|D)$
Sick				
Well		$\frac{\_\_\_}{100}$		
Totals				

(Type a whole number.)

!* 28. (cont.) **(d)** Multiply the priors and likelihoods and sum the products.

Hypotheses (H_i)	Priors $P(H_i)$	Likelihoods $P(D\|H_i)$	Products $P(H_i) \cdot P(D\|H_i)$	Posteriors $P(H_i\|D)$
Sick			______ / 50,000	
Well			______ / 50,000	
Totals			______ / 50,000	

(Type whole numbers.)

(e) What is the probability of being sick given a positive test result?

Hypotheses (H_i)	Priors $P(H_i)$	Likelihoods $P(D\|H_i)$	Products $P(H_i) \cdot P(D\|H_i)$	Posteriors $P(H_i\|D)$
Sick				______ %
Well				
Totals				

(Round to one decimal place as needed.)

(f) What is the probability of being well given a positive test result?

Hypotheses (H_i)	Priors $P(H_i)$	Likelihoods $P(D\|H_i)$	Products $P(H_i) \cdot P(D\|H_i)$	Posteriors $P(H_i\|D)$
Sick				
Well				______ %
Totals				

(Round to one decimal place as needed.)

5: Bayes table

Hypotheses (H_i)	Priors $P(H_i)$	Likelihoods $P(+\|H_i)$	Products $P(H_i) \cdot P(+\|H_i)$	Posteriors $P(H_i\|+)$
Sick				
Well				
Totals				

ID: 11.5.28

!* 29. A certain disease occurs in 6 out of 5,000 people. A test has a false positive rate of 0.5% and a false negative rate of 5%. What is the probability that a person who tests positive actually has the disease, P(Sick|+)? Fill in the Bayes table given a person tests positive (Data = positive). Complete parts (a) through (f) below.

[6] Click the icon to view the empty Bayes table.

(a) What are the priors that someone is sick or well?

Hypotheses (H_i)	Priors $P(H_i)$	Likelihoods $P(D\|H_i)$	Products $P(H_i) \cdot P(D\|H_i)$	Posteriors $P(H_i\|D)$
Sick	______ / 5,000			
Well	______ / 5,000			
Totals				

(Type whole numbers.)

(b) What is the likelihood of testing positive given that you are sick?

Hypotheses (H_i)	Priors $P(H_i)$	Likelihoods $P(D\|H_i)$	Products $P(H_i) \cdot P(D\|H_i)$	Posteriors $P(H_i\|D)$
Sick		______ / 100		
Well				
Totals				

(Type a whole number.)

!* 29. (cont.) **(c)** What is the likelihood of testing positive given that you are well?

Hypotheses (H_i)	Priors $P(H_i)$	Likelihoods $P(D\|H_i)$	Products $P(H_i) \cdot P(D\|H_i)$	Posteriors $P(H_i\|D)$
Sick				
Well		____ / 100		
Totals				

(Type a whole number.)

(d) Multiply the priors and likelihoods and sum the products.

Hypotheses (H_i)	Priors $P(H_i)$	Likelihoods $P(D\|H_i)$	Products $P(H_i) \cdot P(D\|H_i)$	Posteriors $P(H_i\|D)$
Sick			____ / 500,000	
Well			____ / 500,000	
Totals			____ / 500,000	

(Type whole numbers.)

(e) What is the probability of being sick given a positive test result?

Hypotheses (H_i)	Priors $P(H_i)$	Likelihoods $P(D\|H_i)$	Products $P(H_i) \cdot P(D\|H_i)$	Posteriors $P(H_i\|D)$
Sick				____ %
Well				
Totals				

(Round to one decimal place as needed.)

(f) What is the probability of being well given a positive test result?

Hypotheses (H_i)	Priors $P(H_i)$	Likelihoods $P(D\|H_i)$	Products $P(H_i) \cdot P(D\|H_i)$	Posteriors $P(H_i\|D)$
Sick				
Well				____ %
Totals				

(Round to one decimal place as needed.)

6: Bayes table

Hypotheses (H_i)	Priors $P(H_i)$	Likelihoods $P(+\|H_i)$	Products $P(H_i) \cdot P(+\|H_i)$	Posteriors $P(H_i\|+)$
Sick				
Well				
Totals				

ID: 11.5.29

30. A table on audit status and income is available below. Show how to find the probability of:
a. Being audited, given that the taxpayer is in the lowest income category.
b. Being in the lowest income category, given that the taxpayer is audited.
[7] Click the icon to view the table.

a. P(being audited given in lowest income category) = (1) / (2)

= ____

(Round to four decimal places as needed.)

b. P(in lowest income category given being audited) = (3) / (4)

= ____

(Round to four decimal places as needed.)

30. (cont.) 7: Contingency Table on Audit Status and Income

Income	Audited No	Audited Yes
< $200,000	0.9388	0.0096
$200,000 – $1mil	0.0485	0.0007
> $1mil	0.0023	0.0001

(1) ○ 0.9388 + 0.0485 + 0.0023 ○ 0.0485 + 0.0007 ○ 0.0023
○ 0.0001 ○ 0.9388 + 0.0096 ○ 0.0485
○ 0.0023 + 0.0001 ○ 0.0096 ○ 0.9388
○ 0.0007 ○ 0.0096 + 0.0007 + 0.0001

(2) ○ 0.0485 + 0.0007 ○ 0.0096 ○ 0.0096 + 0.0007 + 0.0001
○ 0.0001 ○ 0.0485 ○ 0.9388
○ 0.9388 + 0.0096 ○ 0.0023 + 0.0001 ○ 0.9388 + 0.0485 + 0.0023
○ 0.0023 ○ 0.0007

(3) ○ 0.0023 ○ 0.0485 + 0.0007 ○ 0.0096
○ 0.0485 ○ 0.0007 ○ 0.9388 + 0.0096
○ 0.0023 + 0.0001 ○ 0.0001 ○ 0.9388 + 0.0485 + 0.0023
○ 0.9388 ○ 0.0096 + 0.0007 + 0.0001

(4) ○ 0.9388 + 0.0096 ○ 0.0096 ○ 0.9388
○ 0.0023 ○ 0.0023 + 0.0001 ○ 0.0485
○ 0.0485 + 0.0007 ○ 0.0096 + 0.0007 + 0.0001 ○ 0.0001
○ 0.0007 ○ 0.9388 + 0.0485 + 0.0023

ID: 11.5.30

31. A census reported the given table for how workers 16 years and over commute to work. **a.** What is the probability that a randomly selected person carpooled to work or walked to work?
b. Given that a person carpooled to work or walked to work, what is the probability that the person carpooled to work?

Method Used To Commute	Frequency
Drove alone	97,186,266
Carpooled	15,624,079
Public transportation	6,048,100
Walked	3,736,978
Other means	1,535,792
Worked at home	4,136,333
Total	128,267,548

a. P(carpooled to work or walked to work) = ________
(Round to three decimal places as needed.)

b. P(carpooled|carpooled or walked) = ________
(Round to three decimal places as needed.)

ID: 11.5.31

32. One pro basketball player was known for being a good shooter. In games during 1980-1982, when he missed his first free throw, 51 out of 58 times he made the second one, and when he made his first free throw, 244 out of 280 times he made the second one. Complete parts (a) through (c).

a. Form a contingency table that cross tabulates the outcome of the first free throw (made or missed) in the rows and the outcome of the second free throw (made or missed) in the columns.

	2nd free throw made	2nd free throw missed	Total
1st free throw made	________	________	________
1st free throw missed	________	________	________
Total	________	________	________

b. For a given pair of free throws, estimate the probability that the player made the first free throw. (Hint: Use counts in the row margin.)

The probability is ________. (Round to the nearest hundredth as needed.)

For a given pair of free throws, estimate the probability that the player made the second free throw. (Hint: Use counts in the column margin.)

The probability is ________. (Round to the nearest hundredth as needed.)

32. (cont.) **c.** Estimate the probability that the player made the second free throw, given that he made the first one.

The probability is __________. (Round to the nearest hundredth as needed.)

Does it seem as if his success on the second shot depends strongly on whether he made the first?

- ○ No
- ○ Yes

ID: 11.5.32

---

33. An article about evaluating e-mail filters that are designed to detect spam described a test of an Anti-Spam Program (ASP). In the test, there were 7888 spam messages, of which ASP caught 7000. Of the 7048 messages that ASP identified as spam, they were correct in all but 48 cases. Complete parts a through c below.

a. Set up a contingency table that cross classifies the actual spam status (with the rows "spam" and "not spam") by the ASP filter prediction (with the columns "predict message is spam" and "predict message is not spam"). Using the information given, enter counts in given cells.

	Predict message is spam	Predict message is not spam	Total
Spam	__________	__________	__________
Not Spam	__________		
Total	__________		

(Type integers or decimals.)

b. For this test, given that a message is truly spam, estimate the probability that ASP correctly detects it.

__________ (Round to four decimal places as needed.)

c. Given that ASP identifies a message as spam, estimate the probability that the message truly was spam.

__________ (Round to four decimal places as needed.)

ID: 11.5.33

---

34. According to an article in a magazine, a government agency is experimenting with installing devices for detecting radiation at bridges, tunnels, roadways, and waterways leading into a city. That city's police department has expressed concerns that the system would generate too many false alarms. Complete parts a through c below.

a. Form a contingency table that cross classifies whether a vehicle entering the city contains radioactive material and whether the device detects radiation. Identify the cell that corresponds to the false alarms the police department fears.

Complete the contingency table below.

	(1) __________	
(2) __________	(3) __________	(4) __________
(5) __________	a	b
(6) __________	c	d

The cell that contains (7) __________ corresponds to false alarms.

b. Let A be the event that a vehicle entering the city contains radioactive material. Let B be the event that the device detects radiation. Sketch a Venn diagram for which each event has similar (not the same) probability but the probability of a false alarm equals 0.

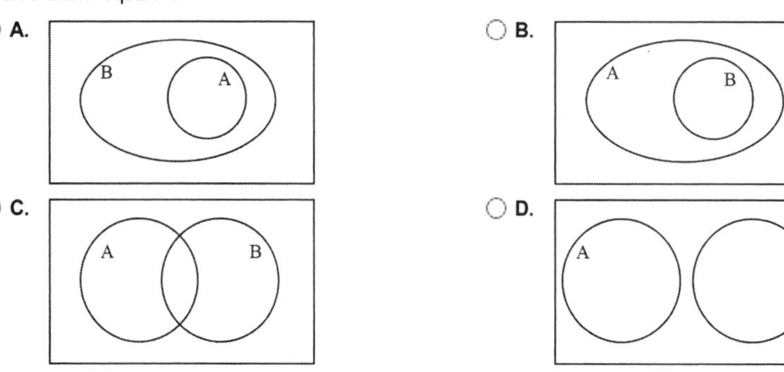

34.. (cont.) **c.** For the diagram you sketched in part b, explain why P(A|B) = 1, but P(B|A) < 1.

Since (8) ____________ P(A|B) = 1. Since (9) ____________ P(B|A) < 1.

(1) ○ **No** ○ **Radioactive Material**

(2) ○ **Detected by Device** ○ **Yes**

(3) ○ **Yes** ○ **Detected by Device**

(4) ○ **No** ○ **Radioactive Material**

(5) ○ **Detected by Device** ○ **Yes**

(6) ○ **Radioactive Material** ○ **No**

(7) ○ a ○ b ○ d ○ c

(8) ○ A contains B, ○ A is a subset of B, ○ B contains A, ○ A and B intersect, ○ A and B are disjoint, ○ B is a subset of A,

(9) ○ A contains B, ○ B is a subset of A, ○ A is a subset of B, ○ A and B are disjoint, ○ A and B intersect, ○ B contains A,

ID: 11.5.34

---

*35. 4969 pregnant women were tested to see if their babies had Down syndrome (D). The results of the test are given in the table. Use the values in the table to answer parts **a-c.**

	Blood Test		
Down	POS	NEG	Total
D	41	11	52
D^c	1147	3770	4917
Total	1188	3781	4969

a. Given that a test result is negative (NEG), what is the probability that the fetus actually has Down syndrome?

P(D|NEG) = ____________

(Do not round until the final answer. Then round to four decimal places as needed.)

b. Given that the fetus has Down syndrome, what is the probability that the test result is negative?

P(NEG|D) = ____________

(Do not round until the final answer. Then round to four decimal places as needed.)

c. Is P(D|NEG) equal to P(NEG|D)?

○ **A.** No, because P(NEG|D) deals with a much larger pool of fetuses than P(D|NEG).

○ **B.** No, because P(NEG|D) deals with a much smaller pool of fetuses than P(D|NEG).

○ **C.** Yes, because P(NEG|D) deals with a much smaller pool of fetuses than P(D|NEG).

○ **D.** Yes, because P(NEG|D) deals with a much larger pool of fetuses than P(D|NEG).

ID: 11.5.35

---

36. Workers specified as actively disengaged are those who are emotionally disconnected from their work and workplace. A poll surveyed individuals who were either unemployed or who were actively disengaged in their current position. Individuals were asked to classify themselves as thriving or struggling. The poll reported that 50% of the actively disengaged group claimed to be thriving, compared to 43% of the unemployed group. Complete parts a through c below.

a. Are these percentages (probabilities) ordinary or conditional? Explain, by specifying events to which the probabilities refer.

○ **A.** Ordinary, because the statement gives the probability of one independent event occurring.

○ **B.** Conditional, because the statement gives the probability of one event occurring, given that another event has occurred.

○ **C.** Conditional, because the statement gives the probability of one independent event occurring.

○ **D.** Ordinary, because the statement gives the probability of one event occurring, given that another event has occurred.

Express the statement "50% of the actively disengaged group claimed to be thriving" as a probability.

○ **A.** P(respondent claimed to be thriving) = 0.50

○ **B.** P(respondent claimed to be thriving|respondent is actively disengaged) = 0.50

○ **C.** P(respondent is actively disengaged|respondent claimed to be thriving) = 0.50

○ **D.** P(respondent is actively disengaged) = 0.50

36. (cont.) Express the statement "43% of the unemployed group claimed to be thriving" as a probability.

- A. P(respondent is unemployed) = 0.43
- B. P(respondent claimed to be thriving|respondent is unemployed) = 0.43
- C. P(respondent claimed to be thriving) = 0.43
- D. P(respondent is unemployed|respondent claimed to be thriving) = 0.43

b. Of the individuals polled, 1252 were unemployed and 500 were actively disengaged. Create a contingency table showing counts for job status and self-classification.

	Thriving	Struggling	Total
Actively disengaged	____	____	500
Unemployed	____	____	1252

(Round to the nearest whole number as needed.)

c. Create a tree diagram such that the first branching represents job status and the second branching represents self-classification. Fill in the blanks to complete the tree diagram.

(2) ________ — 71% — 43% (1) ________; 57% (3) ________

____

(4) ________ — 29% — 50% (5) ________; 50% (6) ________

(1) ○ Actively disengaged ○ Thriving ○ Struggling ○ Unemployed

(2) ○ Unemployed ○ Thriving ○ Actively disengaged ○ Struggling

(3) ○ Actively disengaged ○ Unemployed ○ Thriving ○ Struggling

(4) ○ Unemployed ○ Struggling ○ Actively disengaged ○ Thriving

(5) ○ Struggling ○ Actively disengaged ○ Unemployed ○ Thriving

(6) ○ Actively disengaged ○ Thriving ○ Unemployed ○ Struggling

ID: 11.5.36

---

37. In a women's tennis tournament, the winner of the event played in seven matches. For the seven matches she played, her total number of first serves was 382, total number of good first serves was 259, and total number of double faults was 19. Complete parts a through c below.

a. Find the probability that her first serve is good.

________ (Round to three decimal places as needed.)

b. Find the conditional probability of double faulting, given that her first serve resulted in a fault.

________ (Round to three decimal places as needed.)

c. On what percentage of her service points does she double fault?

________% (Round to two decimal places as needed.)

ID: 11.5.37

---

38. For the use of a test for a certain disease, the sensitivity is 0.95, the specificity is 0.95, and the prevalence is 0.003.
a. Given that a test is positive, find the probability that a random patient has the disease.
b. Draw a tree diagram for a typical sample of 1000 patients.
c. Of the cases that are positive, explain why the proportion in error is larger if the prevalence is lower.

a. The probability is approximately ________.
(Round to four decimal places as needed.)

38. (cont.) **b.** Fill in the numbers in the tree diagram.
(Round to the nearest integer as needed.)

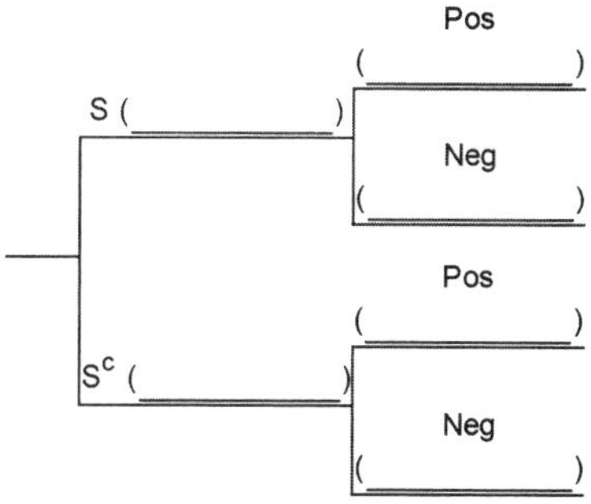

S (______)
Pos (______)
Neg (______)

S^c (______)
Pos (______)
Neg (______)

c. Choose the correct answer below.

○ **A.** The number of false positives is very affected by the prevalence, while the number of true positives is not.
○ **B.** The number of false positives and the number of true positives are both very affected by the prevalence.
○ **C.** The number of false positives is not affected by the prevalence, while the number of true positives is.

ID: 11.5.38

---

*39. Bob was bitten by an animal. He claims since 47 of 100,000 pet owners are bitten by their pet each year, the probability that it was his dog is $P(\text{bitten by own pet} \mid \text{owns a pet}) = \frac{47}{100{,}000}$. It is estimated that each year, of every 100,000 pet owners, of those that are bitten, 5 are bitten by pets that are not their own. Complete parts a through c below.

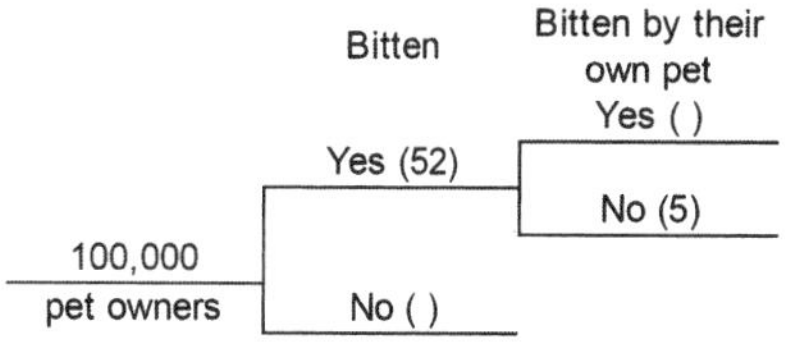

100,000 pet owners
- Bitten: Yes (52)
  - Bitten by their own pet: Yes ( )
  - No (5)
- Bitten: No ( )

a. Based on the results stated, explain why the numbers 52 and 5 are entered as shown on two of the branches.

The number 52 is the number of (1) ________

The number 5 is the number of (2) ________

b. Complete the tree diagram.

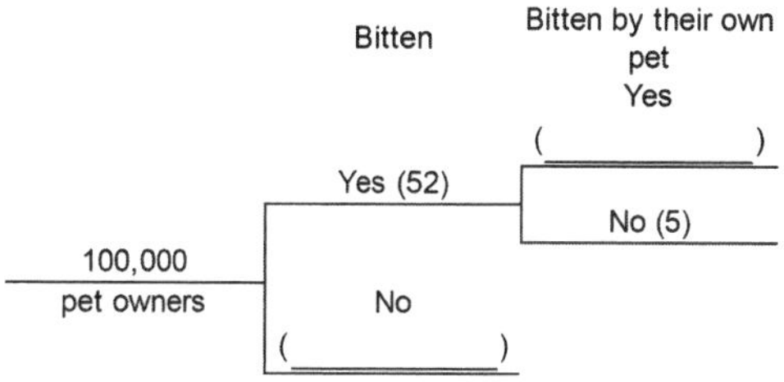

100,000 pet owners
- Bitten: Yes (52)
  - Bitten by their own pet: Yes (______)
  - No (5)
- Bitten: No (______)

c. Conditional on owning a pet and being bitten (by some animal), explain why the probability the owner was bitten by his or her own pet is $\frac{47}{52}$. Why is this so dramatically different from $P(\text{bitten by own pet} \mid \text{owns a pet}) = \frac{47}{100{,}000}$?

The probability is (3) ________. Using the definition of conditional probability this is the (4) ________ of (5) ________ and (6) ________

Why are the two probabilities so different?

○ **A.** The denominator for one is the total number of pet owners, which is large, while the denominator for the other is the total number of owners bitten, which is small.
○ **B.** The denominator for one is the total number of owners not bitten, which is large, while the denominator for the other is the total number of owners bitten, which is small.
○ **C.** The numerator for one is the total number of owners not bitten, which is large, while the numerator for the other is the total number of owners bitten, which is small.
○ **D.** The numerator for one is the total number of pet owners, which is large, while the numerator for the other is the total number of owners bitten, which is small.

(1) ○ pet owners not bitten.
○ pet owners bitten by any pet.
○ pet owners bitten by their own pet.
○ pet owners bitten, but not by their own pet.

(2) ○ pet owners bitten by their own pet.
○ pet owners bitten by any pet.
○ pet owners bitten, but not by their own pet.
○ pet owners not bitten.

(3) ○ P(bitten by own pet)
○ P(bitten by other pet | bitten)
○ P(bitten | bitten by own pet)
○ P(bitten by own pet | bitten)

(4) ○ product
○ ratio

(5) ○ P(not bitten)
○ P(bitten by own pet and bitten)
○ P(bitten)
○ P(bitten by other pet and bitten)

(6) ○ P(bitten by own pet and bitten).
○ P(not bitten).
○ P(bitten).
○ P(bitten by other pet and bitten).

ID: 11.5.39

40. In a criminal trial in the United States, it must be proven that a defendant is guilty beyond a reasonable doubt. In a civil trial, it must only be proven by a preponderance of the evidence that a defendant is guilty. Complete parts a through c below.

a. In a criminal trial by jury, suppose the probability the defendant is convicted, given guilt, is 0.84, and the probability the defendant is acquitted, given innocence, is 0.84. Suppose that 87% of all defendants truly are guilty. Given that the defendant is convicted, find the probability he or she was actually innocent.

The probability is __________.
(Type an integer or a decimal. Round to the nearest thousandth as needed.)

b. Repeat part a, but under the assumption that 50% of all defendants truly are guilty.

The probability is __________.
(Type an integer or a decimal. Round to the nearest thousandth as needed.)

c. In a civil trial, suppose the probability the defendant is convicted, given guilt, is 0.98, and the probability the defendant is acquitted, given innocence, is 0.76. Suppose that 85% of all defendants truly are guilty. Given that the defendant is convicted, find the probability he or she was actually innocent.

The probability is __________.
(Type an integer or a decimal. Round to the nearest thousandth as needed.)

ID: 11.5.40

* 41. Given that a person is innocent, suppose that the probability of his or her DNA matching that found at the crime scene is only 0.000001, one in a million. Further, given that a person is guilty, suppose that the probability of his or her DNA matching that found at the crime scene is 0.99. Jane Doe's DNA matches that found at the crime scene. Complete parts a through c below.

a. Find the probability that Jane Doe is actually innocent, if absolutely her probability of innocence is 0.55. Interpret this probability. Show your solution by introducing notation for events, specifying probabilities that are given, and using a tree diagram to find your answer.

Innocent (__________)
- Match (__________)
- No Match (__________)

Guilty (__________)
- Match (__________)
- No Match (__________)

(Type integers or decimals. Do not round.)

The probability is (1) __________ = __________.
(Round to eight decimal places as needed.)

b. Repeat part a if the unconditional probability of innocence is 0.94. Compare results.

The probability becomes __________.
(Round to eight decimal places as needed.)

c. Explain why it is very important for a defense lawyer to explain the difference between P(match | innocent) and P(innocent | match).

When the absolute probability of innocence is large and P(match | innocent) is (2) __________ the probability P(innocent | match) can be significantly (3) __________ than P(match | innocent).

(1)
- ○ P(innocent | match)
- ○ P(match | innocent)
- ○ P(innocent)
- ○ P(match and innocent)

(2)
- ○ small,
- ○ large,

(3)
- ○ larger
- ○ smaller

ID: 11.5.41

42. The results for a blood test for a certain disease are shown.
a. Estimate the probability that the sickness occurs.
b. Find the estimated (i) sensitivity, (ii) specificity.
c. Find the estimated (i) P(Yes|POS), (ii) P(No|NEG).
d. Explain how the probabilities in parts b and c give four ways of describing the probability that a diagnostic test makes a correct decision.

	Blood Test		
Sick	**POS**	**NEG**	**Total**
Yes	46	6	**52**
No	1285	3765	**5050**
Total	**1331**	**3771**	**5102**

a. The probability is approximately ___________.
(Round to four decimal places as needed.)

b. (i) The sensitivity is approximately ___________.
(Round to four decimal places as needed.)

(ii) The specificity is approximately ___________.
(Round to four decimal places as needed.)

c. (i) P(Yes|POS) = ___________ (Round to four decimal places as needed.)

(ii) P(No|NEG) = ___________ (Round to four decimal places as needed.)

d. Describe the probabilities below.

The probability in b-i is that (1) ___________

The probability in b-ii is that (2) ___________

The probability in c-i is that (3) ___________

The probability in c-ii is that (4) ___________

(1)
- ○ one would have the disease if the test is positive.
- ○ the test would be negative if one does not have the disease.
- ○ one would not have the disease if the test is negative.
- ○ the test would be positive if one has the disease.

(2)
- ○ one would not have the disease if the test is negative.
- ○ the test would be negative if one does not have the disease.
- ○ the test would be positive if one has the disease.
- ○ one would have the disease if the test is positive.

(3)
- ○ one would not have the disease if the test is negative.
- ○ the test would be positive if one has the disease.
- ○ one would have the disease if the test is positive.
- ○ the test would be negative if one does not have the disease.

(4)
- ○ one would have the disease if the test is positive.
- ○ the test would be negative if one does not have the disease.
- ○ the test would be positive if one has the disease.
- ○ one would not have the disease if the test is negative.

ID: 11.5.42

Chapter 1: An Excel-lent Approach to Relationships

Absolute cell reference

A cell reference used in a formula with both the row and column fixed, indicated with $ signs in front of the row number and column letter (e.g., **$C$3**). This cell reference will not change when the formula is filled.

Amortized loan

A loan that has a set length of time to payback and a set schedule for when fixed regular payments are to be made.

Annual percentage rate (*APR*)

The interest rate for a period of 1 year.

Annual percentage yield (*APY*)

The ratio of the total interest charged for the year to the original principal, or the *effective interest rate* charged.

Balance

What you owe at the end of each period, factoring in any interest and payments made on a loan.

Bin

A range or category into which data values from a data set may fall.

Category x-axis labels

The term used for the labels associated to the x-axis of a chart (usually a column chart).

Cell reference

The address for a cell in Excel, given by column heading then row number. So **C3** indicates the cell in column C and row 3.

Constant function

A function for which the output is the same, or constant, for all inputs; there is only one output!

Count

The number of values (usually referred to as N) in a data set.

Dependent variable

Outputs that depend on inputs; a dependent variable is typically represented with the letter y.

Descriptive statistics

The eight basic statistics we can compute for a given data set: mean, median, mode, standard deviation, max, min, range, and count.

Distribution

An arrangement of data values that shows the frequency of occurrence.

Domain

The set, or collection, of all allowable, valid inputs; it is the realm in which a function operates (e.g. not every U.S. citizen is part of the domain of senator/state function, but they all are part of the domain of the citizen/S.S.# function).

Frequency

The number of times a data value occurs in a data set or the number of times a data value appears in a given bin related to a histogram.

Function

A relationship between quantities referred to as inputs and outputs, in which every input is paired up with one and only one output.

Histogram

A column chart showing the counts or frequencies of data values in a data set. The counts are either of individual data values or of the data values that fall into each bin.

Independent variable

Inputs that are independently chosen; an independent variable is typically represented with the letter x.

Input

A value that is plugged into a function; the function then returns the associated value (output) paired with the input.

Interest

The money or fee a lender charges you for borrowing money.

Max

The largest value in a data set.

Mean

The arithmetic average of a data set.

Median

The middle of an ordered data set (half above, half below, 50th percentile).

Min

The smallest value in a data set.

Mixed cell reference

A cell reference used in a formula with only one $ sign, indicating either the row is fixed (e.g., **C$3**) or the column is fixed (**$C3**) when the formula is filled.

Mode

The most frequently occurring value in a data set.

One-to-one function

A function for which every input has a different output; every output has one and only one input (kind of the opposite of a constant function).

Order of operations

An agreed-upon procedure for determining in what order to perform calculations:

1. **Parentheses:** Everything entered in parentheses will be computed first. When in doubt use parentheses, especially for the numerator and denominator of fractions.
2. **Exponents:** Exponents are next; use the ^ symbol above the number 6. Complicated exponents need parentheses: = 2^(1/3).
3. **Multiplication and Division:** These have the same rank; Excel will compute from left to right.
4. **Addition and Subtraction:** These are also of equal rank and will be computed from left to right.

Output

The value a function returns when an input is plugged into the function.

Payment

Money sent to the lender of a loan to pay off all or a portion of the balance owed.

Period

The length of time before your next payment is due and interest is charged; typically 1 month for most loans.

Periodic rate

The interest rate for a period other than 1 year; it is the APR divided by the number of periods in a year: APR/n. A 6% APR computed monthly will give a 6%/12 = 0.5% periodic rate.

Principal

The amount of money borrowed from a lender (for a loan) or the original amount of money invested (for investments).

Range

The set, or collection, of all outputs over which a function ranges.

Range

The difference between the largest and smallest data values (Max – Min).

Relative cell reference

A cell reference used in a formula with no **$** signs (e.g., **C3**), indicating the row number or column letter will change when the formula is filled up/down or left/right respectively.

Select Data

A menu in Excel that allows us to see and manipulate the data highlighted for a given chart.

Standard Deviation

The "average distance" of data values in a data set from the mean.

Statistic

A number you compute related to a data set, which gives you information about the data set. The word comes from "statists," the name given to 18th-century mathematicians who studied demographic data in Europe and analyzed it for the state.

Term

The length of time to pay back an amortized loan.

Variable

Inputs/outputs that *vary*; the input is independently chosen and then determines the output.

Arithmetic average

The mean of a data set, computed by summing the data values and dividing by the number of data values.

Bell-shaped curve

A distribution of data values with most values clustered about the median and fewer values farther from the middle. The histogram looks like a bell:

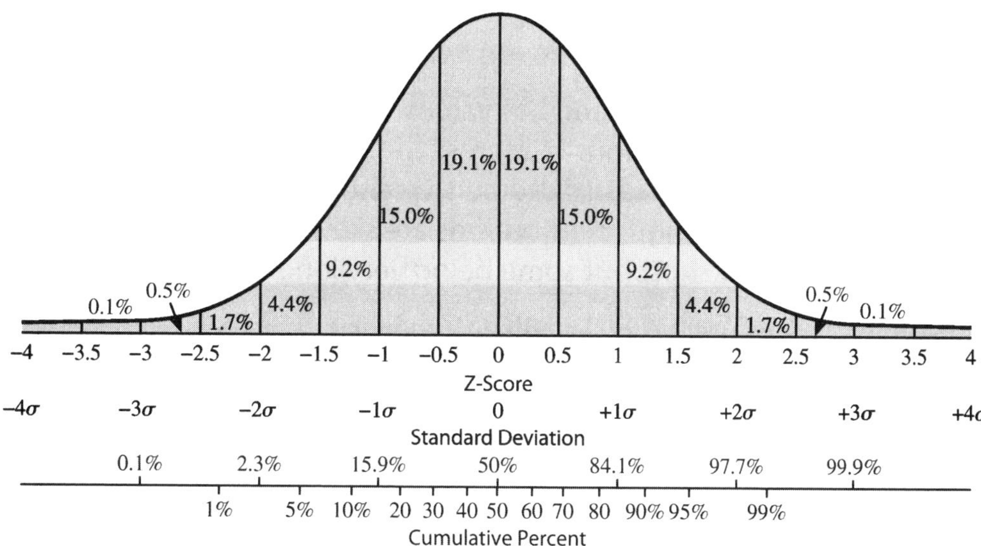

Constant of proportionality

Given two proportional quantities, the decimal equivalent of the constant ratio. It is also referred to as the *scaling factor*, or the *conversion factor*, and can be computed by scaling one of the quantities to 1. Thus there are two possible constants! The relationship between proportional quantities can be represented by the equation $y = k \cdot x$, where k is either of the constants of proportionality.

Consumer Price Index (CPI)

A measure of the average change over time in the prices paid by urban consumers for a market basket of consumer goods and services.

Dividends

Money a company pays out to its shareholders due to earning profit. The dividend is reported as so much money per share or as a percentage of the current share price (and then called the *dividend yield*).

Earnings

How much money a company has made over a fixed period of time (often one quarter or one year) after paying all its bills. Also known as *profit*. (Revenue is the amount of money the company took in before paying its bills.)

Earnings per share

The ratio of the earnings for a given period of time (often one quarter or one year) to the number of shares.

Fat tail

A distribution of data values that is skewed and has values "far" from the mean, as measured in standard deviations (*z*-scores). In the U.S., the income distribution has a fat tail because extremely wealthy people are far from the mean. Word length distributions are skewed to the right, with most words being short but some being very long.

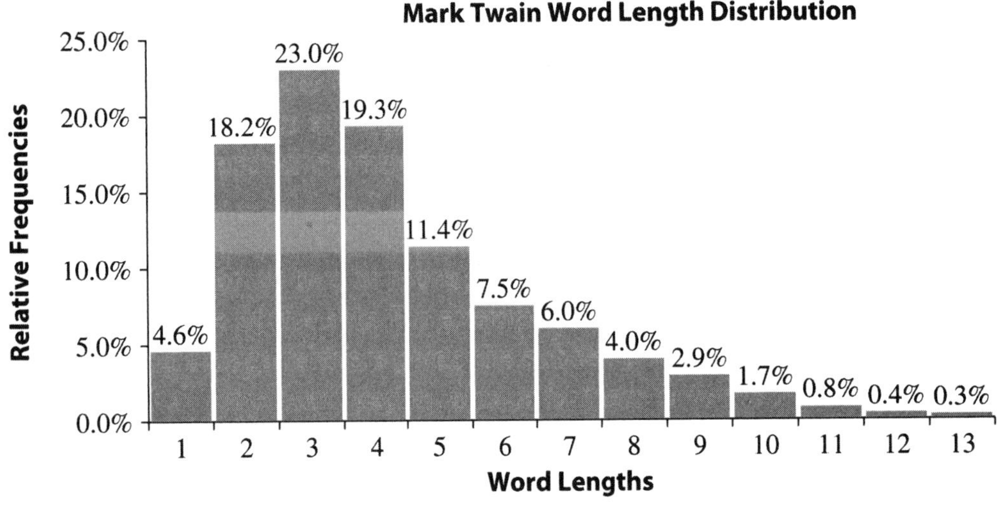

Inflation

In economics, a persistent increase in the general price of goods and services in an economy over a period of time.

Normal distribution (normal curve)

A distribution that has a bell shaped curve, and the following properties:

- Mean = Median
- *z*-scores on the horizontal axis correspond to number of standard deviations above and below the mean.
- The percentage of data values above/below any *z*-value have been compiled in tables; we can use an Excel function, **NORMDIST**, which computes the percentage of data values below any *z*-value.

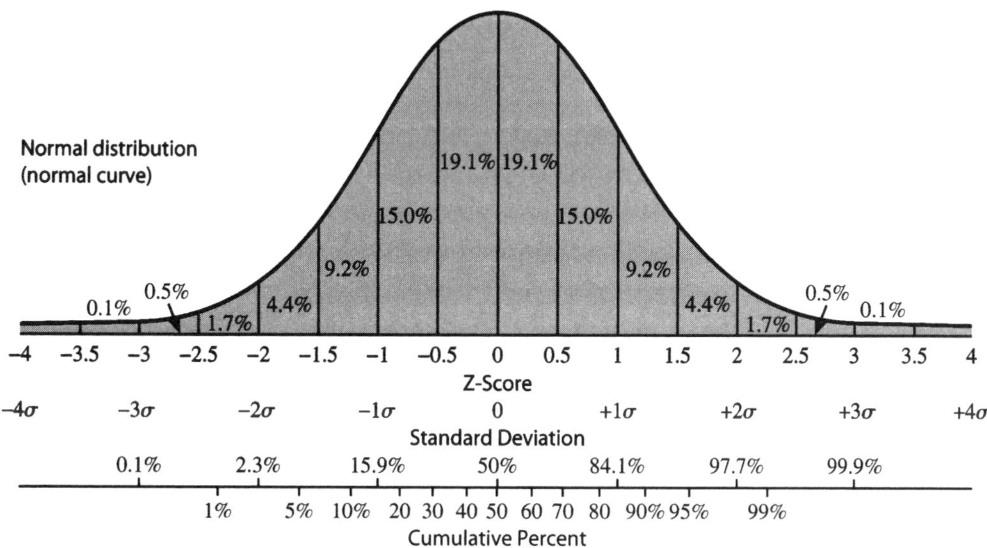

Part-to-part ratio

A ratio that compares two quantities that are parts of a whole, such as tuition and fees to room and board expenses.

Part-to-whole ratio

A ratio that compares one part of a whole to the total, such as tuition and fees to the total cost of going to college.

PE ratio

The price-to-earnings ratio, the ratio of the price per share to the earnings per share of stock in a company.

Price per share

The price of one share of stock in a company.

Profit

How much money a company has made over a fixed period of time (often one quarter or one year) after paying all its bills. Also known as *earnings*. (Revenue is the amount of money the company took in before paying its bills.)

Proportion

An equality of two ratios. Setting two ratios equal to each other is called *setting up a proportion*, and solving by multiplying denominators and numerators on opposite sides of the equal sign is called *cross multiplying*.

Proportional or in proportion

Having a constant ratio, in a multiplicative sense: doubling one doubles the other, tripling one triples the other, etc.

There is a special relationship between proportional quantities; changing one necessitates a precise quantifiable change in the other:

$$na : nb = \frac{na}{nb} = \frac{a}{b} = a : b$$

Quarter

A basic unit of time in the world of finance, equal to three months. Each quarter, companies report their profits (or earnings) for the quarter.

Rate

A ratio between quantities with different units, with the second quantity scaled to a meaningful standard and read using the word *per*. Rates will have *compound units* like meters per second (m/s), miles per gallon (mi/gal), or deaths per 100,000 people.

Ratio

A comparison of the *relative* sizes of two or more quantities. If the ratio of quantity A to quantity B is 2 to 5, or 2 : 5, then for every 2 units of quantity A, there are 5 units of quantity B. The comparison is *multiplicative*, meaning the fraction $\frac{a}{b} = \frac{2}{5}$ for a units of quantity A and b units of quantity B.

Ratio table

A table that allows one to compare various quantities by listing the quantities involved in columns and the proportional amounts of the quantities in rows.

Retirement plan

A plan for saving/investing money for your retirement after working. This money you save/invest is what you will live on when you stop earning a paycheck.

Share

The unit used to denote owning a part of a company.

Stock

A portion of a company that an investor can purchase to take an ownership (equity) stake in the company. The parts are measured in units of *shares*.

Stock quote

The current price of one share of stock in a company; often the stock quote will include other pertinent information, such as number of shares, PE ratio, high price for the day, etc.

Units

The choice of measurement system in measuring a quantity. There are two distinct types of units:

1. **Units of observation:** Units that pertain to a quality or category such as nationality: American, Indian, Mexican etc. A data value or observation either belongs to a category or it does not.
2. **Units of measurement:** Units that pertain to a quantity such as length, using an agreed upon standard: feet, cm, miles etc. A data value for a given quantity can be measured using any associated unit of measurement, each of which can be converted to the other units of measurement.
    a. **Ratio units:** Units that have the property that doubling them doubles the underlying quantity (and hence any units used). Examples are units of length (e.g., feet, cm) and units of money (e.g., euros and dollars).
    b. **Interval units:** Units that do not have the property that doubling them doubles the underlying quantity because there is not a well-defined zero point (where zero denotes the absence of something).

Weighted average

Given a sequence of values, x_k, occurring with different weights, weight_k, the ratio of the sum of the products, $\text{weight}_k \cdot x_k$, to the sum of the weights:

$$\text{Weighted average} = \frac{\Sigma(\text{weight}_k \cdot x_k)}{\Sigma\text{weight}_k}.$$

z-score

The ratio of the distance of a data value, x, from the mean, $\overline{X}$, to the average distance from the mean (standard deviation, or SD):

$$z = \frac{x - \overline{X}}{\text{SD}} = \text{number of standard deviations from the mean}$$

Chapter 3: Units, Conversions, Scales, and Rates

Center

One of the three essential characteristics of variability, which refers to the middle of the data in a data set and is measured by the mean, median, and mode.

Compound units

Units for rates involving more than one measurement system, as in meters per second (m/s), miles per gallon (mi/gal), or deaths per 100,000 people.

Concentration

The ratio of the amount of one substance mixed with the amount of another substance; typically a weight to volume ratio but can also be weight to weight.

Conversion

A ratio used to compare two different systems of measurement. A conversion indicates a change in units of measurement, which are typically proportional to one another.

Conversion factor

The constant of proportionality for a ratio, used to compare two different systems of measurement.

Density

The ratio of an object's weight to the volume it occupies.

Dimensional analysis

A technique to convert units that involves multiplying by conversion factors to cancel units.

Distribution of sample means

A new data set consisting of means from samples (of the same size) repeatedly drawn (randomly) from an original data set.

Dosage

The ratio of the amount of a medication to the weight of a patient.

Interval unit

A unit that does not have the property that doubling it doubles the underlying quantity because there is not a well-defined zero point (where zero denotes the absence of something). Temperature units like Celsius and Fahrenheit are good examples of interval units: 18°F is not twice as hot as 9°F since the equivalent temperatures in Celsius (–7.8°C and –12.8°C) are not double each other. In this case, zero is an arbitrary value—the freezing point of a brine solution for Fahrenheit and the freezing point of water for Celsius.

Measurement scale

A system of ordered marks used as a reference standard, such as rulers and thermometers. These can be *ratio scales* or *interval scales*, depending on whether the units are ratio units or interval units.

Model scale

A ratio used to determine the relationship between a model and that which it represents. A model scale indicates a change in size or magnitude. A model scale is typically given with the first quantity scaled to 1 and always between proportional quantities, with the constant of proportionality called the *scaling factor*.

Percentile

A value below which a certain percentage of ordered data fall. Certain groups of percentiles are given special names associated to how many equal subintervals the data are divided into (tenths, fourths, fifths, etc.).
Deciles: 10th, 20th, . . ., 100th
Quintiles: 20th, 40th, 60th, 80th, 100th
Quartiles: 25th, 50th, 75th, 100th

Ratio unit

A unit that has the property that doubling it doubles the underlying quantity (and hence any units used) because there is a well-defined zero point (where zero denotes the absence of something). Examples are units of length (e.g., feet, centimeters) and units of money (e.g., euros and dollars). Kelvin is a ratio unit of temperature because zero Kelvin represents the absence of thermal motion.

Sample mean

The mean of a sample of data.

Scale

A reference standard used for purposes of measurement, either a system of ordered marks or a ratio indicating proportionate size.

Scaling factor

The constant of proportionality for a ratio, used to determine the relationship between a model and that which it represents.

Spread

One of the three essential characteristics of variability, which refers to how spread out or dispersed the data in a data set are and is measured by the range, max, min, count, and standard deviation.

Standard error of the mean

The standard deviation of the distribution of sample means. The standard error can be estimated using a standard deviation from a sample, $\mathrm{SE} \approx \frac{\mathrm{SD}}{\sqrt{N}}$, where N is the number of values in the sample.

Statistics

The discipline that deals with collecting, organizing, analyzing, and displaying data and the study of the variability inherent in such data. Also a number you compute related to a data set, which gives you information about that data set. The word comes from "statists", the name given to mathematicians in the 18th century who studied demographic data in Europe and analyzed it for the state.

Three essences of variability

The three essential characteristics of statistics, the study of variability:

1. The shape of the distribution (bell shape, skewed, etc.)
2. The center of the distribution (mean, median, mode)
3. The spread of the distribution (standard deviation, range, count, max, min)

True population mean

The mean of an entire population, which usually can only be estimated from a sample mean.

Two types of variability

Two types of variability in statistics are: natural variability (e.g., heights, IQ scores) and sampling variability (e.g., distribution of sample means).

Units of measurement

Units that pertain to a quantity such as length, using an agreed-upon standard: feet, cm, miles etc. A data value for a given quantity can be measured using any associated unit of measurement, each of which can be converted to the other units of measurement.

Units of observation

Units that pertain to a quality or category such as nationality: American, Indian, Mexican, etc. A data value or observation either belongs to a category or it does not.

Unit-less scale

A model scale in which both quantities have the same units; any units can be used for both quantities.

Unit-less ratio

A ratio between two quantities with identical units; the units cancel, and the ratio is typically given without units.

Chapter 4: Percentages

Annuity

A type of retirement account that allows you to invest money without paying income tax on the deposit. This money can then be withdrawn after retirement. A traditional annuity is a contract that guarantees a distribution of income over time, based on premiums paid into the annuity.

Base

The second quantity in a ratio which is represented as a percentage.

Categorical variable

A quantity with units of observation, such as gender or political affiliation.

Cumulative frequency

The sum of relative frequencies in a distribution up to and including a certain data value or bin.

Cumulative frequency polygon

A line chart of the cumulative frequencies.

Dilution

The act of diluting a solution by adding water to reduce the concentration.

Growth/decay factor

Given a **growth/decay rate** of $x\,\%$, the number given by $1 \pm x\,\%$:

Using the **growth/decay factor** $1 \pm x\,\%$, we can say that:

$$\text{New} = \text{Original} \cdot (1 \pm x\,\%)$$

Growth/decay rate

Given a percent change of $x\,\%$, the rate at which a quantity increased **(growth rate)** or decreased **(decay rate)**:

Using the **growth/decay rate** $x\,\%$, we can say that:

$$\text{New} = \text{Original} \pm x\,\% \cdot \text{Original}$$

Interest rate

The ratio of interest charged to the amount owed, typically represented as a percentage, which is a rate per 100. An interest rate of 6 % means you will be charged \$6 for every \$100 you owe.

Percent change

The relative quantity change in value from an original value to a new value:

Percent (Relative) **change** = (Total Change)/Original

The percent change is a ratio of total change to the original value and is read as a percentage of the original. We say, "The new value is x % more (or less) than the original."

Percent difference

The relative difference in size between two quantities:

Percent (Relative) **difference** = (Total Difference)/(1st Quantity)

The percent difference is a ratio of total difference to the 1st Quantity and is read as a percentage of the first quantity. We say, "The second quantity is x % more (or less) than the first quantity."

Percentage

A ratio where the second quantity has been scaled to 100 (e.g., $x : 100$). The first quantity is then said to be x percent (x %) of the second. The second quantity is referred to as the *base*. Percentages are sometimes referred to as *rates* because they are per 100, with interest rates and rates of return being the two most common examples of this, comparing interest to the starting balance. The word *percent* originally was two words, *per cent*, meaning "per one hundred." The symbol % contains a line and two zeros, like the numeral 100.

Percentage points

The unit (pp) in which the total change between two percentages is given.

Rate of return

The interest rate associated with an investment. It is a ratio of the interest gained to the amount invested and is represented as a percentage.

Relative frequency

The frequency of a data value divided by the number of data values in the data set.

Relative frequency polygon

A line chart of the relative frequencies.

Total change

The absolute quantity change in value from an original value to a new value:

Total (Absolute) **change** = New – Original.

Total difference

The absolute difference in size between two quantities:

Total (Absolute) **difference** = 2nd Quantity – 1st Quantity

Two-way table

A table organizing two categorical variables by row and column—for example, gender by row and political affiliation by column. The numbers in the table represent how many data values have units of observation for both that row and column.

Average change

The constant rate of total change between the input and output quantities as given by:

$$m = \frac{y_2 - y_1}{x_2 - x_1} = \frac{\Delta y}{\Delta x} = \frac{\text{Rise}}{\text{Run}},$$

where (x_1, y_1) and (x_2, y_2) are points in the coordinate plane such that $x_1 \neq x_2$.

Extrapolation

The process of making a prediction using a trendline outside the domain of inputs for a scatterplot.

Interpolation

The process of making a prediction using a trendline within the domain of inputs for a scatterplot.

Linear equation

An equation of the form

$$y = m \cdot x + b,$$

where m and b can be any real numbers, m is the slope of the linear function, and b is the y-intercept of the equation.

Linear function

A function that can be represented with an equation of the form

$$y = m \cdot x + b,$$

where m and b can be any real numbers. The constant m is the *slope* of the linear function; the constant b is the y-intercept. This equation is called the slope-intercept form of a linear equation.

Linear trendline

Given a scatterplot of data points, an estimated line through the data that captures the overall trend. This line can be estimated in various ways:

- We can simply draw by hand a line that seems to run through the *middle* of the data points.
- We can select two data points that seem to capture the trend and use the line between them.
- We can use a computer program, like Excel, which will compute the *best-fit* line, also called the *least-squares* line or *regression* line.

Slope

A ratio of the total change in the output to the total change in the input, which has two interpretations:

1. The steepness of the line connecting the two points. A negative slope indicates that the line slants down, moving from left to right.
2. The constant rate of total change between the input and output quantities. If the line goes through the origin, this is the constant of proportionality. This rate of total change is also referred to as the *average change*, *difference quotient*, or *rate of change*

If (x_1, y_1) and (x_2, y_2) are points in the coordinate plane such that $x_1 \neq x_2$, the slope of the straight line that passes through these two points is given by:

$$m = \frac{y_2 - y_1}{x_2 - x_1} = \frac{\Delta y}{\Delta x} = \frac{\text{Rise}}{\text{Run}}$$

Slope-intercept form

A linear function of the form

$$y = m \cdot x + b.$$

y-intercept

In any straight nonvertical line, the y-value of the point where the line crosses the y-axis—that is, where the x-coordinate is zero. The y-intercept has two interpretations:

1. The location of the line in the x-y coordinate system—that is, where it hits the y-axis.
2. The *initial value* of the output variable when the input variable is time. The y-intercept has an x-coordinate of zero, so if the input variable is time, the y-intercept is referred to as the starting value.

Chapter 6: Exponential Functions

Arithmetic mean

Given n numbers, $a_1, a_2, \cdots, a_n$, the average obtained by adding them and dividing by n,

$$\frac{a_1 + a_2 + \cdots + a_n}{n}$$

Average Percent Change

Given any two data points, (x_1, y_1) and (x_2, y_2), the rate of percent change of output unit per input unit obtained by the formula:

$$r = \left(\frac{y_2}{y_1}\right)^{\left(\frac{1}{x_2 - x_1}\right)} - 1$$

Average Total Change

Given any two data points, (x_1, y_1) and (x_2, y_2), the rate of total change of output unit per input unit obtained by the formula:

$$r = \frac{y_2 - y_1}{x_2 - x_1}$$

Closed Formula

Given a sequence of values $P_1, P_2, \ldots, P_n$ (e.g., the ending yearly balance for an investment), a formula that calculates P_n from n.

Continuous growth/decay rate

The average percentage change over an interval so small the change appears continuous. Quantities in nature appear to change continuously and their growth or decay can be modeled with the exponential equation:

$$y = a \cdot e^{k \cdot x}$$

where a is the initial value, e is Euler's number, and k is the continuous growth rate ($k > 0$) or continuous decay rate ($k < 0$).

Exponential Function

A function with an equation of the form

$$y = a \cdot b^x$$

The constant a is called the *initial value*, and the constant b is called the *growth/decay factor*, or the *base*. Compound interest is a standard example of an exponential function, in which the equation is written using P for principle (P_0 is its initial value), r for the *growth/decay rate*, $1 + r$ for the *growth/decay factor*, and t for time:

$$P = P_0 \cdot (1 + r)^t$$

A negative growth rate, r, results in a decay factor.

Quantities in nature change continuously (not just once or 12 times a year), and thus scientists prefer to use the following representation of the equation:

$$y = a \cdot e^{k \cdot x}$$

where e is Euler's number, and k is the *continuous growth rate* ($k > 0$) or *continuous decay rate* ($k < 0$).

Geometric mean

Given n numbers, $a_1, a_2, \cdots, a_n$, the average obtained by multiplying them and taking the nth root,

$$\sqrt[n]{a_1 \cdot a_2 \cdot \ldots \cdot a_n}$$

Harmonic mean

Given n numbers, $a_1, a_2, \cdots, a_n$, the average obtained by substituting into the following equation,

$$\frac{n}{\frac{1}{a_1} + \frac{1}{a_2} + \cdots + \frac{1}{a_n}}$$

Initial value

The output associated to an input of zero for an exponential function.

Recursive Formula

Given a sequence of values $P_1, P_2, \cdots, P_n$ (e.g., the ending yearly balance for an investment), a formula that requires the computation of all preceding values in order to calculate P_n.

Chapter 7: Logical Arithmetic

Common logarithm

A logarithm of x to the base, $\log_b x$, where the base, $b = 10$, is not written:

$$y = \log x \underset{\textit{is equivalent to}}{\Longleftrightarrow} y = \log_{10} x$$

Doubling time

Given a quantity that grows or decays exponentially, $P = P_0 \cdot (1 + r)^t$, the length of time before the quantity doubles ($r > 0$):

$$\textit{Doubling time}: t = \frac{\log 2}{\log(1 + r)}$$

Effective interest rate

The *yield* or *annual percentage yield* (*APY*) of an investment, which represents the total amount of interest generated over the course of one year.

Euler's number

(Euler is pronounced "oiler.") The limit of the process:

$$e = \lim_{N \to \infty}\left(1 + \frac{1}{N}\right)^N = 2.718281828459$$

Half-life

Given a quantity that grows or decays exponentially, $P = P_0 \cdot (1 + r)^t$, the length of time before the quantity is cut in half ($r < 0$):

$$\textit{Half-life}: t = \frac{\log (1/2)}{\log(1 + r)}$$

Inverse operations

An operation that reverses, or undoes, the effect of another operation; for example, subtraction undoes addition, taking a square root undoes squaring, and taking the logarithm undoes raising to a power.

Linear scale

A measurement scale that displays equally spaced intervals.

Logarithm

A function which outputs the exponent to which a given base must be raised to equal the input. The logarithm of x to the base b, $\log_b x$, is the *power* of b equal to x. Taking a logarithm to the base b is the inverse operation of raising the base to a power, b^y, just as taking the nth root of a number is the inverse operation of raising that number to the nth power:

$$y = \sqrt[n]{x} \underset{\textit{is equivalent to}}{\Longleftrightarrow} x = y^n$$

$$y = \log_b x \underset{\textit{is equivalent to}}{\Longleftrightarrow} x = b^y$$

The number, b, is called the *base* of the logarithm (also the base of the exponential on the right).

Logarithmic scale (log scale)

A measurement scale that displays intervals measured by order of magnitude (e.g., powers of 10), rather than equally spaced intervals as in a linear scale. A semi-log plot is a scatterplot where one axis uses a logarithmic scale and the other a linear scale. A log-log plot refers to a scatterplot where both axes use logarithmic scales.

Log-log plot

A scatterplot where both axes use logarithmic scales.

Natural logarithm

A logarithm of x to the base, $\log_b x$, where $b = e$ (Euler's number), written as follows:

$$y = \ln x \underset{\textit{is equivalent to}}{\Longleftrightarrow} y = \log_e x$$

Periodic compounding form

An exponential equation that can be written in the form:

$$P = P_0 \cdot \left(1 + \frac{\text{APR}}{n}\right)^{n \cdot t}$$

where P_0 = the initial value, t = years, and n = the number of periods in one year.

Power-law distribution

An arrangement of data values where the frequency of an event is a function of a ranking of the event having a power-law equation of the form:

$$y = k \cdot x^{-a}$$

Power-law equation

An equation that represents a power-law distribution and has the form:

$$y = k \cdot x^{-a}$$

Semi-log plot

A scatterplot where one axis uses a logarithmic scale and the other a linear scale.

Chapter 8: Curve Fitting and Correlation

Best-fit line (line of best fit)

The linear function that *best fits* bivariate data in the sense that it makes the sum of the *squared deviations* from the line as small as possible. This line is also called the *least-squares line*, or the *regression line.*

Bivariate data

Data of two variables, such as X = gas prices and Y = oil prices.

Body mass index

The ratio of a person's weight in kilograms to his or her height in meters squared.

Causation

A *causal relationship* between bivariate data in which the change in one variable is directly attributed to the change in the other. For example, there is a causal relationship between electricity usage and the temperature; extremely high or low temperatures cause people to stay indoors and use more electricity to heat or cool their homes. *Reverse causation* refers to mixing up which variable causes the other. For example, high use of electricity does not cause extreme temperature events (in the short term!).

Coefficient of linear determination, R^2

A measure of the proportion of variability of one variable in bivariate data that can be attributed to variability in the other variable—that is, a ratio of explained variability to total variability. This coefficient can be interpreted as a percentage, using the following sentence:

$R^2 \cdot 100\%$ *of the variability in the output can be attributed to variability in the input.*

Confounding factors

Hidden variables that are the real *causal agents* behind the correlation of bivariate data. For example, the CDC mistakenly attributed 400,000 deaths to obesity, when the true causal agent behind most of these deaths was old age. Mistaken attribution is said to be *spurious*.

Correlation

A relationship between bivariate data in which the two variables are co-related, meaning they both increase together (*positive correlation*) or one decreases while the other increases (*negative correlation*). There is *perfect correlation* if one variable is a linear function of the other.

Correlation coefficient, R

A measure of the strength and direction of the linear relationship for bivariate data. The *correlation coefficient* is defined by the formula $R = \frac{\text{Covar}}{\text{SD}_x \cdot \text{SD}_y}$ and will lie between -1 and 1. Squaring the correlation coefficient gives the *coefficient of linear determination*, R^2.

Covariance

For sample bivariate data, a measure of how correlated the two variables are and given by an equation similar to the variance $\text{Covar} = \frac{\Sigma(x_i - \overline{X})\cdot(y_i - \overline{Y})}{N-1}$.

Least-squares line

The linear function that *best fits* bivariate data in the sense that it makes the sum of the *squared deviations* from the line as small as possible. This line is also called the *line of best fit* or the *regression line.*

Obesity

Having a body mass index greater than 30.

Univariate data

Data of a single variable, such as X = women's heights.

Variance

For sample univariate data, the standard deviation squared:

$$\text{Var} = \frac{\Sigma(x_i - \overline{X})^2}{N-1} = \text{SD}^2$$

Chapter 9: Financial Health

401(k)

A retirement plan that employers can offer their employees, based on a pension law passed in 1978, subsection 401(k) of the Internal Revenue Code. Employers can offer a retirement plan with a defined annual contribution to your retirement account which is deducted from your paycheck before taxes (up to $17,500 in 2014). Employers can also offer to match a fraction of your contribution. Typically employers offer to match 50 cents for every dollar you contribute, up to 6% of your salary.

Amortization schedule

A table detailing each month's payments and interest for an amortized loan.

Bonds

Loans to either the federal government (*Treasuries*), local governments or municipalities (*munis*), or companies (*corporate bonds*). Bonds are rated by independent agencies based on the bond issuer's ability to pay back the loan, in just the same way people are given credit scores. Bonds are rated from best (AAA) to worst (C, or junk bonds). Bondholders thus have a lender/creditor stake.

Certificate of deposit (CD)

A conservative investment that requires you to invest your cash for a fixed period of time and gives a fixed APY.

Checking/savings/money market accounts

Ultra-safe investments that offer correspondingly low rates of return. With them, you may withdraw your money at any time with no penalty.

Closing costs

Fees charged to the borrower by the bank and attorney for approving a mortgage, including costs to appraise and inspect the home.

Corporate bonds

Bonds that are loans to companies.

Coupon rate

The fixed annual rate for a bond.

Discount rate

The rate set by the Federal Open Market Committee (the Fed) eight times a year. This is the rate banks are charged for borrowing from the Fed.

Expense fee

The fee a mutual fund charges (a percentage of your investment each year) for investing your money for you.

Federal funds rate

A rate that banks set, which they charge each other for overnight loans.

Front end load

An up-front fee or a deferred fee (called a deferred load) for allowing you to invest your money with a financial planner offering investment products such as mutual funds.

Index fund

A mutual fund managed by a computer program that simply tracks an index, like the S&P 500 Index or the Russell 2000 Index of "small cap" companies.

Market capitalization

For a company, its share price multiplied by the number of shares that can be traded.

Medicare

A federal social insurance program that provides guaranteed health care for U.S. citizens 65 and over who have paid into the system.

Mortgage

A loan to buy a house.

Munis

Bonds that are loans to local governments or municipalities.

Mutual fund

A pool of money from many investors that is invested for them by a manager who charges a fee for this service.

Net asset value (NAV)

A measure of a fund's value that allows us to track its performance over time.

Prime rate

The rate banks charge their best customers, which then affects credit card rates, typically a fixed value plus the prime rate.

RATE/NPER/PMT/PV/FV

Excel's five built-in financial functions. The arguments for each function are the other four financial functions, in order. Thus the mnemonic device RNPPF is helpful to remember this order:

Rover Needs Poopy Paper Fast.

=**RATE**(nper, pmt, pv, fv): Calculates the *periodic* rate required to achieve some financial goal.

=**NPER**(rate, pmt, pv, fv): Calculates the number of periods required to achieve some financial goal.

=**PMT**(rate, nper, pv, fv): Calculates the payment required to achieve some financial goal.

=**PV**(rate, nper, pmt, fv): Calculates the present value required to achieve some financial goal.

=**FV**(rate, nper, pmt, pv): Calculates the future value required to achieve some financial goal.

Savings bonds

Bonds that have a similar rate of return as savings accounts and CDs. The difference is that with savings bonds, you are in effect lending money to the federal government to pay its bills. In return, the government will give you interest on the amount you loan (i.e., the value of the bond). There are two types of savings bonds: I bonds, which have an interest rate that varies with inflation (1.38% composite rate in April 2014), and EE bonds, which come with a fixed rate (0.10% in April 2014).

Securities

Investments that make you feel secure, knowing you have money available for retirement or other life choices.

Social security

A federal social welfare/insurance program that provides money for the old and disabled (insurance) and also for the dependent survivors of deceased wage earners (welfare). It is funded through a payroll tax; that is, current wage earners are taxed to pay for the benefits of the retired and disabled. As the U.S. population continues to age, meaning a higher percentage of senior citizens, the current Social Security program will become underfunded.

S&P 500

An index that consists of 500 of the largest U.S. companies (weighted by market capitalization), which span many different industries and account for about three-fourths of the U.S. stock market's value.

Ticker symbol

The lettered symbol for a company with publicly traded stock, such as GM for General Motors and AAPL for Apple.

Treasuries

Bonds that are loans to the federal government.

Treasury bills (T-bills)

Treasuries issued in terms of 4 weeks, 13 weeks, 26 weeks, and 52 weeks. They are sold at a discount to their face value and are redeemed for the full face value at the end of the term. For example, if you buy a $1,000 T-bill at a price per $100 of $99.986111, then you pay $999.86 ($\$1{,}000 \cdot 0.99986111 = \$999.86111$). When the bill matures, you will be paid its face value, $1,000.

Treasury bonds (T-bonds)

Treasuries issued in terms of 30 years that pay simple interest every 6 months until they mature. When a Treasury bond matures, the bearer is paid its face value.

Treasury notes (T-notes)

Treasuries issued in terms of 2, 3, 5, 7, and 10 years that pay the bearer simple interest every 6 months until maturity. When a Treasury note matures, the bearer is repaid its face value.

Chapter 10: Logically!

Biconditional statement

A conditional statement and its converse, which are either both true or both false. A biconditional statement *P if and only if Q* is actually two conditional statements: *If P then Q* and *If Q then P.*

Conditional statement (If-Then)

An *If-Then statement,* which may be true or false, that connects a hypothesis to a conclusion. The hypothesis may also be true or false. If the conditional statement and hypothesis are both true, then the conclusion must necessarily be true also. Given the conditional statement, *If P then Q,* we can form four associated logical statements:

1. Converse: *If Q then P.*

2. Contrapositive: *If not Q then not P.*

3. Inverse: *If not P then not Q.*

4. Negation: *P and not Q.*

The conditional is logically equivalent to the contrapositive.

Contrapositive statement

Given the conditional statement *If P then Q,* the associated logical statement *If not Q then not P*. The contrapositive is logically equivalent to the conditional.

Converse error

The error made when one mistakenly assumes that the converse is logically equivalent to the original conditional.

Converse statement

Given the conditional statement *If P then Q,* the associated logical statement *If Q then P.* The converse is logically equivalent to the inverse.

Inverse statement

Given the conditional statement *If P then Q,* the associated logical statement *If not P then not Q*. The inverse is logically equivalent to the converse.

Logically equivalent

Saying the same thing. For example, *If it is sunny then we will go to the beach* is logically equivalent to *If we do not go to the beach then it is not sunny.*

Negation

A statement that has the opposite truth value of the original statement. The negation of a conditional statement *If P then Q* is *P and not Q.*

Piecewise function

A function in which the output is determined by two (or more) possible functions, depending on a criterion.

Chapter 11: Chance, Risk, and Likelihood

1st Law of Probability

The **1st Law of Probability** says that the probability of event A and event B both occurring is:

$$\mathbf{P}(A \textbf{ AND } B) = \mathbf{P}(A) \cdot \mathbf{P}(B|A)$$

If A and B are *independent* events then $\mathbf{P}(B|A) = \mathbf{P}(B)$ and the formula is: $\mathbf{P}(A \textbf{ AND } B) = \mathbf{P}(A) \cdot \mathbf{P}(B)$

Flipping two coins are *independent* events, the probability of the second flip does not depend on the first. Choosing two committee members are *dependent* events, the probability of choosing the second member depends on the first choice.

2nd Law of Probability

The **2nd Law of Probability** says that the probability of event A or event B occurring is:

$$\mathbf{P}(A \textbf{ OR } B) = \mathbf{P}(A) + \mathbf{P}(B) - \mathbf{P}(A \textbf{ AND } B)$$
$$\mathbf{P}(A \cup B) = \mathbf{P}(A) + \mathbf{P}(B) - \mathbf{P}(A \cap B)$$

If A and B are *disjoint* events then $\mathbf{P}(A \textbf{ AND } B) = \mathbf{0}$ and the formula is: $\mathbf{P}(A \textbf{ OR } B) = \mathbf{P}(A) + \mathbf{P}(B)$.

The probability of event A or event B occurring means A or B or both, and is the same as the probability of *at least one* of event A or event B occurring.

3rd Law of Probability

The **3rd Law of Probability** says that the probability of event A is one minus the probability of its complement, **NOT** A:

$$\mathbf{P}(A) = 1 - \mathbf{P}(\text{NOT } A)$$
$$\mathbf{P}(A \textbf{ OR } B) = 1 - \mathbf{P}(\text{NOT } A \textbf{ AND } \text{NOT } B)$$

For *independent* events we can apply the **1st Law** to the last formula and get the *Golden Rule of Probability*:

$$\mathbf{P}(\textit{At Least One Independent Event } (A, B, C, \ldots) \textit{ Occuring}) =$$
$$1 - \mathbf{P}(\text{NOT } A) \times \mathbf{P}(\text{NOT } B) \times \mathbf{P}(\text{NOT } C) \times \ldots$$

Bayes' Formula

Bayes' formula allows us to update a starting probability (the *prior*), given new information (the *data*), to a new probability (the *posterior*) using the *likelihoods* of the data occurring given different hypotheses. The likelihoods are the conditional probabilities $\mathbf{P}(D|H_i)$ which are multiplied by the priors in the numerator and denominator of the formula. We wish to compute $\mathbf{P}(H_i|D)$. The denominator in the formula is the sum of the products:

$$\mathbf{P}(H_i|D) = \frac{\mathbf{P}(H_i) \cdot \mathbf{P}(D|H_i)}{\Sigma_i \, \mathbf{P}(D|H_i) \cdot \mathbf{P}(H_i)}$$

Certainty

The **certainty**, *chance, risk*, or *likelihood* of an event occurring is the probability of the event occurring using either past data or data from simulations. It will rain tomorrow with 20% certainty implies that past data with similar conditions resulted in rain on the next day 20% of the time, or that 20% of the simulations modeling these conditions resulted in rain 20% of the time.

Chance

The *certainty*, **chance**, *risk*, or *likelihood* of an event occurring is the probability of the event occurring using either past data or data from simulations. It will rain tomorrow with 20% certainty implies that past data with similar conditions resulted in rain on the next day 20% of the time, or that 20% of the simulations modeling these conditions resulted in rain 20% of the time.

Combination

A **combination** is a selection of r items from a group of n, with no item being selected twice and the order items are selected is NOT counted differently (*abc* is the same combination as *bca*). The total number of combinations is given by:

$$_nC_r = \binom{n}{r} = \frac{_nP_r}{r!} = \frac{n!}{(n-r)! \cdot r!}$$

For combinations think number of ways to choose a committee, order does not matter.

Complement

The **complement** of a subset is the collection of elements belonging to the larger set but not itself. Note it only makes sense to think of the complement of a *subset* because we get everything outside of the subset but constrained to the larger set under consideration.

Conditional probability

The **conditional probability** of A *given* B is written $\mathbf{P}(A|B)$ and is the ratio of the number of outcomes occurring in both events A and B (the intersection), to the number of total outcomes in B. The conditional probability of A *given* B can be computed as follows:

$$\mathbf{P}(A|B) = \frac{\mathbf{P}(A \textbf{ AND } B)}{\mathbf{P}(B)} = \frac{\mathbf{P}(A \cap B)}{\mathbf{P}(B)}$$

Dependent

Dependent events have probabilities influenced or affected by each other. Flipping two coins are *independent* events, the probability of the second flip does not depend on the first. Choosing two committee members are *dependent* events, the probability of choosing the second member depends on the first choice.

Disjoint

Disjoint sets have no elements in common, their intersection is empty.

Event

The *probability* of an **event** occurring, **P***(event)*, is the ratio of the number of ways this event can occur to the total number of *outcomes* possible. The collection of all possible outcomes is called the *sample space*, and the event is considered to be a subset of the sample space. Thus the probability ratio can always be represented as a fraction/decimal between zero and one.

For example, to compute the probability of the event: getting at least one head when flipping two coins, we must determine the outcomes in the sample space: {**HH, HT, TH,** TT}, and the outcomes in the event: {**HH, HT, TH**} which are a subset of the sample space.
Thus $\mathbf{P}(1H) = 3/4 = 75\%$.

False negative

A **false negative** is someone or something that is incorrectly identified as NOT satisfying a definition (having a disease, being bullied, etc.). A narrow definition (Bullying must result in physical harm) will result in more false negatives than a broad definition (Bullying is any action intended to inflict physical or emotional harm.)

False positive

A **false positive** is someone or something that is incorrectly identified as satisfying a definition (having a disease, being overweight, etc.). A broad definition (Body Mass Index > 25 is obese) will result in more false positives than a narrow definition (Body Mass Index > 35 is obese).

Fundamental Principle of Counting

Given a series of k choices to be made, each with a different number of options: $n_1, n_2, \ldots, n_k$, then the total number of possible ways to choose one option from each of the k choices is the product: $n_1 \times n_2 \times \ldots \times n_k$. This is called the **Fundamental Principle of Counting**.

Golden Rule of Probability

The **Golden Rule of Probability**:

$$\mathbf{P}(\textit{At Least One Independent Event } (A, B, C, \ldots) \textit{ Occuring}) =$$
$$1 - \mathbf{P}(\text{NOT } A) \times \mathbf{P}(\text{NOT } B) \times \mathbf{P}(\text{NOT } C) \times \ldots$$

Moral of the Golden Rule of Probability: Even against long odds keep trying and you will succeed. Persistence and determination trump luck every time; it's the law!

Independent

Independent events have probabilities not influenced or affected by each other. Flipping two coins are *independent* events, the probability of the second flip does not depend on the first. Choosing two committee members are *dependent* events, the probability of choosing the second member depends on the first choice.

Intersection

The **intersection** of two or more sets consists of the elements belonging to each one of the sets. For example, the intersection of Americans, vegans, and alpaca farmers gives the subset of these three sets that consists of all American, vegan, alpaca farmers (a very small eclectic bunch to be sure!).

Likelihood

The *certainty, chance, risk*, or **likelihood** of an event occurring is the probability of the event occurring using either past data or data from simulations. It will rain tomorrow with 20% certainty implies that past data with similar conditions resulted in rain on the next day 20% of the time, or that 20% of the simulations modeling these conditions resulted in rain 20% of the time.

In a Bayes table the **likelihoods** are the conditional probabilities of the data given a certain hypothesis, $\mathbf{P}(D|H_i)$.

Odds

The **odds in favor** of an event occurring are the ratio of the probability of the event occurring to the probability it does not occur (In gambling situations the odds are typically given as the ratio of amount won to the amount bet). Odds in favor of $2 : 1$ imply $2/3$ chance of the event occurring and $1/3$ chance of it not occurring.

Outcome

The *probability* of an *event* occurring, **P***(event)*, is the ratio of the number of ways this event can occur to the total number of **outcomes** possible. The collection of all possible outcomes is called the *sample space*, and the event is considered to be a subset of the sample space. Thus the probability ratio can always be represented as a fraction/decimal between zero and one.

For example, to compute the probability of the event: getting at least one head, when flipping two coins, we must determine the outcomes in the sample space: {**HH, HT, TH,** TT}, and the outcomes in the event: {**HH, HT, TH**} which are a subset of the sample space.
Thus **P**$(1H) = ¾ = 75\%$.

Permutation

A **permutation** is a selection of r items from a group of n, with no item being selected twice and the order items are selected is counted differently (*abc* is a different permutation than *bca*). The total number of permutations is given by:

$$_nP_r = n \times (n-1) \times (n-2) \times \cdots \times (n-r+1) = \frac{n!}{(n-r)!}$$

For permutations think number of ways to finish a race, order matters.

Posteriors

Bayes' formula allows us to update a starting probability (the *prior*), given new information (the *data*), to a new probability (the **posterior**) using the *likelihoods* of the data occurring given different hypotheses.

Priors

Bayes' formula allows us to update a starting probability (the **prior**), given new information (the *data*), to a new probability (the *posterior*) using the *likelihoods* of the data occurring given different hypotheses.

Probability

The **probability** of an *event* occurring, **P***(event)*, is the ratio of the number of ways this event can occur to the total number of *outcomes* possible. The collection of all possible outcomes is called the *sample space*, and the event is considered to be a subset of the sample space. Thus the probability ratio can always be represented as a fraction/decimal between zero and one.

- $0 \leq$ **P***(Event)* ≤ 1
- **P***(Event)* $= 0$ implies it will not occur, zero chance.
- **P***(Event)* $= 1$ implies it will occur, guaranteed 100% certain.

For example, to compute the probability of the event: getting at least one head, when flipping two coins; we must determine the outcomes in the sample space: {**HH, HT, TH,** TT}, and the outcomes in the event: {**HH, HT, TH**} which are a subset of the sample space.
Thus **P**$(1H) = ¾ = 75\%$.

Risk

The *certainty*, *chance*, **risk**, or *likelihood* of an event occurring is the probability of the event occurring using either past data or data from simulations. It will rain tomorrow with 20% certainty implies that past data with similar conditions resulted in rain on the next day 20% of the time, or that 20% of the simulations modeling these conditions resulted in rain 20% of the time.

Sample space

The *probability* of an *event* occurring, **P***(event)*, is the ratio of the number of ways this event can occur to the total number of *outcomes* possible. The collection of all possible outcomes is called the **sample space**, and the event is considered to be a subset of the sample space. Thus the probability ratio can always be represented as a fraction/decimal between zero and one.

For example, to compute the probability of the event: getting at least one head, when flipping two coins, we must determine the outcomes in the sample space: {**HH, HT, TH,** TT}, and the outcomes in the event: {**HH, HT, TH**} which are a subset of the sample space.
Thus **P**$(1H) = ¾ = 75\%$.

Set

A **set** is a collections of objects, often referred to as *elements* of the set. A *subset* is a collection of objects all drawn from a larger set.

Subset

A **subset** is a collection of objects all drawn from a larger set.

Union

The **union** of two or more sets consists of the elements belonging to at least one of the sets. For example, the union of Americans, vegans, and alpaca farmers gives the larger set containing anyone who is American, vegan, or an alpaca farmer.

Venn diagram

A **Venn diagram** is a visual graphic showing unions and intersections of sets typically as overlapping circles. Two-way tables can always be represented as a Venn diagram.

Appendix

Active cell

The cell in a spreadsheet that has been clicked on and is currently highlighted and ready to have information typed into it. Note that if you highlight a region or regions, the first cell you clicked on will be active.

Argument

The inputs for a built-in function in Excel.

Built-in function

A command in Excel to perform a function, such as **SUM** or **AVERAGE**. Every built-in function must be typed in starting with an equal sign, then the function name, followed by the arguments, or inputs, in parentheses: ***=function_name***(*input1, input2, ...*).

Chart

A visual display of quantitative information. Common types of charts are bar charts, column charts, pie charts, and x-y scatter plots. Some people refer to a table of numbers as a chart, but this is not the usage for Excel. In Excel, a chart is a graph or picture of the numbers from a table.

Constant

A number or an input that is fixed for a formula, such as the sales tax rate for a state or the density of water.

Fill

In Excel, the action of filling a formula up/down or left/right. Filling a formula up/down changes the row numbers of all relative cell references in the formula, while filling left/right changes all the column letters of relative cell references.

Fill handle

The box in the lower-right corner of a highlighted cell or region in Excel. Clicking on the fill handle and dragging will fill the formula or cell contents.

Formula

An equation that is used to compute a desired quantity. In Excel, we refer to anything we type into a cell that begins with an equal sign as a *formula*. So to compute the cost of soda in cell E3 of our hotdog stand example, we entered the formula:
= C3 * D3.

Formula bar

The space located right above the column headings in a spreadsheet that shows the formula that is typed into a cell. You can enter formulas by typing directly in the cell itself or by typing in the formula bar.

Model

A spreadsheet built to analyze a real-world situation, such as retirement, with assumptions that can be changed (as parameters), allowing for "what-if" analysis.

Name box

The space above cell **A1**, which displays the cell address of the active cell. Clicking in the name box allows you to name a cell. Named cells are absolute cell references in formulas.

Parameter

A number or an input that is in between a variable and constant. A parameter is usually held fixed for a specific use of the formula but may change, given different circumstances. The price you charge for an item is a good example of a parameter.

Syntax

The grammar and punctuation required when typing in built-in functions.

Template

A spreadsheet with blank input cells and formulas entered into the output cells. When a user types in input, the output cells display answers.